COMMON ELEMENTS

Name	Symbol	Approx. at. wt.	Common ox. nos.	Name	Symbol	Approx. at. wt.	Common ox. nos.
aluminum	Al	27.0	+3	magnesium	Mg	24.3	+2
antimony	Sb	121.8	+3,+5	manganese	Mn	54.9	+2,+4,+7
arsenic	As	74.9	+3,+5	mercury	Hg	200.6	+1,+2
barium	Ba	137.3	+2	nickel	Ni	58.7	+2
bismuth	Bi	209.0	+3	nitrogen	N	14.0	−3,+3,+5
bromine	Br	79.9	−1,+5	oxygen	O	16.0	−2
calcium	Ca	40.1	+2	phosphorus	P	31.0	+3,+5
carbon	C	12.0	+2,+4	platinum	Pt	195.1	+2,+4
chlorine	Cl	35.5	−1,+5,+7	potassium	K	39.1	+1
chromium	Cr	52.0	+2,+3,+6	silicon	Si	28.1	+4
cobalt	Co	58.9	+2,+3	silver	Ag	107.9	+1
copper	Cu	63.5	+1,+2	sodium	Na	23.0	+1
fluorine	F	19.0	−1	strontium	Sr	87.6	+2
gold	Au	197.0	+1,+3	sulfur	S	32.1	−2,+4,+6
hydrogen	H	1.0	−1,+1	tin	Sn	118.7	+2,+4
iodine	I	126.9	−1,+5	titanium	Ti	47.9	+3,+4
iron	Fe	55.8	+2,+3	tungsten	W	183.8	+6
lead	Pb	207.2	+2,+4	zinc	Zn	65.4	+2

COMMON IONS AND THEIR CHARGES

Name	Symbol	Charge	Name	Symbol	Charge
aluminum	Al^{+++}	+3	lead(II)	Pb^{++}	+2
ammonium	NH_4^+	+1	magnesium	Mg^{++}	+2
barium	Ba^{++}	+2	mercury(I)	Hg_2^{++}	+2
calcium	Ca^{++}	+2	mercury(II)	Hg^{++}	+2
chromium(III)	Cr^{+++}	+3	nickel(II)	Ni^{++}	+2
cobalt(II)	Co^{++}	+2	potassium	K^+	+1
copper(I)	Cu^+	+1	silver	Ag^+	+1
copper(II)	Cu^{++}	+2	sodium	Na^+	+1
hydronium	H_3O^+	+1	tin(II)	Sn^{++}	+2
iron(II)	Fe^{++}	+2	tin(IV)	Sn^{++++}	+4
iron(III)	Fe^{+++}	+3	zinc	Zn^{++}	+2
acetate	$C_2H_3O_2^-$	−1	hydrogen sulfate	HSO_4^-	−1
bromide	Br^-	−1	hydroxide	OH^-	−1
carbonate	CO_3^{--}	−2	hypochlorite	ClO^-	−1
chlorate	ClO_3^-	−1	iodide	I^-	−1
chloride	Cl^-	−1	nitrate	NO_3^-	−1
chlorite	ClO_2^-	−1	nitrite	NO_2^-	−1
chromate	CrO_4^{--}	−2	oxide	O^{--}	−2
cyanide	CN^-	−1	perchlorate	ClO_4^-	−1
dichromate	$Cr_2O_7^{--}$	−2	permanganate	MnO_4^-	−1
fluoride	F^-	−1	peroxide	O_2^{--}	−2
hexacyanoferrate(II)	$Fe(CN)_6^{----}$	−4	phosphate	PO_4^{---}	−3
hexacyanoferrate(III)	$Fe(CN)_6^{---}$	−3	sulfate	SO_4^{--}	−2
hydride	H^-	−1	sulfide	S^{--}	−2
hydrogen carbonate	HCO_3^-	−1	sulfite	SO_3^{--}	−2

Modern Chemistry

Teacher's Edition

H. Clark Metcalfe
John E. Williams
Joseph F. Castka

The Holt Modern Chemistry Program
Metcalfe, Williams, and Castka

Modern Chemistry (Student Text)
Modern Chemistry (Teacher's Edition)
Laboratory Experiments in Modern Chemistry
Exercises and Experiments in Modern Chemistry
Tests in Modern Chemistry (Duplicating Masters)

HOLT, RINEHART AND WINSTON, PUBLISHERS
New York • London • Toronto • Sydney

ISBN: 0-03-057991-0
3456 032 9876543

Contents

Introduction

The *Modern Chemistry Program* is designed to help you achieve your teaching objectives. The program consists of six components that may be used appropriately to implement your teaching strategy. Each component contains more material than is ordinarily included in a first year chemistry course so that you can select optional topics to fit the needs of your students and community. The *Modern Chemistry Program* by Metcalfe, Williams, and Castka consists of the following items:

Modern Chemistry (student text)

Modern Chemistry Teacher's Edition

Laboratory Experiments in Chemistry

Exercises and Experiments in Chemistry

Exercises and Experiments in Chemistry Teacher's Edition

Tests in Chemistry (test masters)

The student text offers features that can help you increase your effectiveness. Most study systems or systems designed to improve reading comprehension include a "preview" or "survey" step. Taking time in class to preview the visual material, the chapter-opener paragraph, the vocabulary words, and the photo essays in an assigned section may help spark curiosity. Students may find it helpful to read the Summary at the end of the chapter and the sequence of topics indicated by the section heads in the chapter before they read the assigned sections. Calling attention to the marginal notes, which include references to other parts of the book and refresher definitions of terms and phrases, may help students retain and recall what they have read. Additional features of the student edition that you may incorporate into your teaching strategy are described in the *Preface* of the student text.

The *Teacher's Edition* offers you aid in using the complete program. It consists of the following parts:

Part 1, An Overview of the Teaching of Chemistry. This section contains a brief review of research relevant to the teaching of chemistry, specific details for adapting *Modern Chemistry* to a minimal, average, and enriched course, and a discussion of laboratory safety.

Part 2, Teacher Notes, includes suggested activities, demonstrations, films, transparencies, displays, and laboratory exercises that are appropriate to each section of the student text. Also included is a suggested schedule for treatment of each chapter.

Part 3, Key to Suppliers, includes a listing and the key (code) used in the *Teacher Notes* section when referring to these sources.

Part 4, Answers to Questions and Problems, includes answers to the questions and solutions to the problems in the *student text*.

The experiments in *Laboratory Experiments in Chemistry* fit into one of the following categories:

1. Descriptive-observational, in which students observe, summarize, and draw conclusions.

2. Qualitative, in which students record observations in data tables and draw conclusions based upon qualitative interpretation of the data.

3. Quantitative, in which students measure various quantities and make computations based upon these quantitative observations.

The laboratory experiments in *Exercises and Experiments in Chemistry* are the same as those in *Laboratory Experiments in Chemistry*. The difference between these two publications is that *Exercises and Experiments in Chemistry* is designed to be written in by the students. Spaces are provided for students to record their observations and answer the questions. The exercises in *Exercises and Experiments in Chemistry* may be used in a variety of ways as instructional aids. They may be assigned for completion after the student has read the chapter, or assigned as a self-test or review before a test. The items in each exercise parallel the text in sequence so that the conscientious student can easily locate the answer in the text. The exercises also serve as instructional complements to the questions and problems in the text.

The *Teacher's Edition* to *Exercises and Experiments in Chemistry* includes answers and other useful details for the laboratory section of the program.

Tests in Chemistry is published as a book of duplicating masters. Most of the tests are based upon specific chapters in the student text. The final examination includes material from the entire textbook. As with other components, sufficient questions are provided so that teachers can choose test items that coincide with the material taught. Answers to each test item are printed on the master sheet in a contrasting color and do not print on the students' copies.

PART

1

An Overview of the Teaching of Chemistry

"It is in fact nothing short of a miracle that the modern methods of instruction have not yet entirely strangled the holy curiosity of inquiry."[1]

This quotation defines a basic problem in science teaching today, and at the same time establishes the main objective of chemistry teaching for the 1980's. "The terms *inquiry* and *discovery* refer to the technique of allowing and encouraging students to learn by personal discovery through experimentation."[2] All chemistry teachers subscribe, in theory, to the ideal; however, their results all too frequently fall far from the goal.

An article by Hansrote, "A Decade of Change: A Survey of New Approaches to and Ideas for the Teaching of Chemistry Courses,"[3] is a result of a search of over one hundred articles that appeared in the *Journal of Chemical Education* from 1968 to 1978. After studying the modified course offerings and methods of teaching chemistry that were developed in response to the challenges of the past decade, Hansrote concluded that no clear answer to the question "Where do chemists turn in the 'eighties' in designing a new course for effectively teaching chemistry?" could be found. The *Holt Modern Chemistry Program 1982* attempts to provide an answer to that question.

The article "Searching for Meaning in Science Education" by Berkheimer and McLeod[4] concerns itself with the proliferation of science courses, including chemistry courses. The attempt to produce content *relevance* (environmental education, energy education, career education) has resulted in the creation of new courses or the inclusion of relevant topics in standard courses. An accompanying tendency on the part of students to gravitate toward the easier courses has been noted. Another result has been the deterioration of traditional disciplines as relevant topics have been included in such standard courses as academic chemistry. The authors conclude, "We believe that the increasingly vocal requests to get back to the basics constitute a message more profound than teaching reading, writing, and arithmetic. That message is to get back to the disciplines and make sure that students *know the content of the disciplines* before they attempt to apply them. . . . Science is especially important because it teaches students to think, to resolve problems, and to learn the science concepts necessary to cope with problems in everyday life . . ."

It is important to note, however, the motivational value of brief consideration of relevant topics where appropriate. Inclusion of such information in introductions, summaries, or supplementary features does promote student awareness of the relationship between science and everyday living. The **Teacher Notes** in this *Teacher's Edition* of *Modern Chemistry 1982* include specific suggestions for implementing this strategy.

Obviously, chemistry curricula will show diversity when such variables as geographic location, size of school population, academic level of student population, and teacher ability and interest are considered. However, any chemistry course should contain a solid core of fundamental concepts designed for students who wish to qualify for and pass some type of standardized examination. The *Modern Chemistry 1982* program is designed to meet the requirements of students taking the College Entrance Examination, a state-mandated examination, and/or a local terminal examination.

It is difficult to determine the "common denominator" for the content of high school chemistry courses. Increasing pressure for student and teacher "accountability" has resulted in the standardization of curriculum in many states. Student awareness of chemistry-related problems, such as smog, pollution, or energy, has resulted in the inclusion of relevant topics in the curriculum. However, the primary emphasis should continue to be on chemistry content and concepts.

Modern Chemistry 1982 provides the basic facts and concepts of chemistry presented in a framework of laboratory experiments, textual material, and review and evaluation techniques.

A large number and variety of newer "tools" for teaching chemistry are presently available. Suggestions for their use are detailed in the **Teacher Notes** in this book. Teaching the course therefore requires a realignment of many of the "old" demonstrations, techniques, and resources with the "new."

The **Teacher Notes** for each chapter or sections selected may be used continuously as a basic reference for activities. demonstrations, teaching aids, exercises, and tests. The suggested assignments for experiments are in the Teacher's Edition of *Exercises and Experiments in Chemistry*, 1982 edition. Representative items may be selected from *Tests in Chemistry*. These tests generally contain 40 multiple-choice questions from which the selection may be made.

The *Modern Chemistry Program* provides sufficient diversity to meet the needs of students of varying abilities and interests. The first half of the text is devoted to the important fundamental concepts, principles, and processes of chemistry, as well as a discussion of the role of chemistry in today's world. The latter half of the text deals with descriptive chemistry and chemical technology.

Reading ability is vital to student success in chemistry. The article "How Can We Help Kids Read Science Textbooks?"[5]

discusses the difficulties implied in the title. Some of the valuable suggestions offered in this article are:

1. Since the language of chemistry and chemistry texts are loaded with concept-bearing words, the essential terms in a lesson should be taught experientially by using familiar words. This procedure will ultimately lead to a grasp of the abstract concept words.

2. To learn chemistry is to learn the language of chemistry. The objective is to expand the students' vocabulary. You should identify the students' level of language and manipulate the content of chemistry so that the students experience language expansion. Eventually, the students begin to *think* chemistry.

3. Break complex sentences into simple phrases.

4. Point out that chemistry is problem-oriented, not chronology-oriented, as is social studies.

5. Preview with the class the material to be read by scanning the table of contents or the subsections of the chapter. After such previewing, have the students pose questions based on the material surveyed by asking *where, what, when, how,* and *why.* Then have individual students read the assigned passage, recite the highlights, and review the passage.

6. Make a variety of reading materials in chemistry and related topics available to students. A classroom or departmental library may consist of copies of reference texts, *Science Digest, SciQuest* (formerly *Chemistry*), *Chemistry* reprints, *Scientific American* and its offprints, *Reader's Digest, National Geographic, Journal of Chemical Education, The Science Teacher.*

7. Occasionally read aloud from the text or from reference materials. Encourage students to do likewise. Student difficulties with vocabulary and pronunciation can be identified and corrected in this way. This procedure may be particularly useful at the beginning of the course when instruction in using the text and locating information (Appendix, Glossary, Index) is being given.

8. Train students to refer to the illustrations, graphs, and tables in the text. Provide supplemental visual representations of information that appears in written form.

9. Divide the class into working groups of about six students. Structure the groups to include at least one very bright student and one slower student. Listen to the language that the students use. Can they talk chemistry? Are they incorporating recently acquired vocabulary into their thinking?

10. Encourage students to examine the advertisements of merchandise that is chemical in nature. Ask them to read the chemical ingredients (including safety and antidote directions) on the labels of household, pharmaceutical, and food items. Correlate the facts of chemistry with the students' everyday lives.

11. In conclusion, reading aloud, providing visual illustrations, listening closely to the students' use of chemical language, and organizing the class into small groups promise to foster a greater degree of "languaging" chemistry.

Additional valuable suggestions can be found in the articles "New Approach to Reading Difficulties,"[6] and "Enhance Reading through Science,"[7] both by Wright.

The spectrum of interests, objectives, ability, and background of our high school chemistry population is broad. To cope with this diversity the *Modern Chemistry Teacher's Edition* outlines the content, sequence, and methods that may be used at three levels: (1) Minimal Course for the general student; (2) Average Course for the college preparatory student; (3) Enriched Course for the science-oriented student.

Courses based on the suggestions for the Minimal Course vary considerably in content and sequence. Such courses often are labeled as General Chemistry or Applied Chemistry. A fine outline for such a course, *General Chemistry, 1970 Edition,* may be obtained from the Bureau of Science Education, The University of the State of New York, Albany, NY 12224. This course is for nonscience majors whose interests and goals may be different from those who take the average course or the enriched college preparatory course. The areas in the course that are dealt with in more detail than that suggested in the Minimal Course include Chemistry in the Home, Environmental Pollution, and Qualitative Analysis. Obviously, this General Chemistry Course offers some preparation for students who may be interested in careers as chemical or medical technicians, in food preparation, in practical nursing, and in environmentally related jobs. *Modern Chemistry* may be used as the basic text for this course.

The average course includes the units and chapters that correspond to such statewide required syllabi as that of the New York State Chemistry Regents Syllabus, and to the coverage described in the "About the Achievement Tests—Chemistry," *College Entrance Examination Board,* for the Achievement Test in Chemistry. The subject areas are (1) kinetic-molecular theory and the three states of matter; (2) atomic structure and the periodic table; (3) quantitative relations as applied to chemical formulas and equations; (4) chemical bonding and molecular structure and their relations to properties with some of the illustrations selected from organic chemistry; (5) the nature of chemical reactions, including acid-base reactions, oxidation-reduction reactions, ionic reactions, and other chemical changes occurring in solutions; (6) energy changes accompanying chemical reactions; (7) interpretation of chemical equilibria and reaction rates; (8) solution phenomena; (9) electrochemistry; (10) nuclear chemistry and radioactivity; (11) physical and chemical properties of the more familiar metals, transition elements, and nonmetals, and of the more familiar compounds; (12) understanding and interpreting laboratory procedures and observations.

The enriched course includes the remaining units and chapters which, in effect, permits coverage of the entire text. Although the enriched course for above-average students requires a faster pace and hence greater textual coverage, there are many variations of such a procedure. In some instances, the enrichment may involve more laboratory experience; more individualization in outside reading; independent laboratory investigations; participation in fairs and contests; excursions; and projects. The **Teacher Notes,** Part 2, contain many references and suggestions for enrichment activities.

The Minimal Course

Students should be directed to and taught how to use such features of the text as the chapter objectives, vocabulary, marginal notes, figures, and tables. Have them refer to pages vi and vii of the text, "How to Use This Book." Complementary instructional aids are the Worksheets (for drill) and the *Exercises*. Generally questions should be assigned from Group A Questions. Reading the selected sections of the text in class is recommended to strengthen reading skills and the ability to master details and concepts independently. Obviously there will be less emphasis on the mathematics of chemistry and related problem solution. Sample Problem solution should be illustrated and followed by use of the Practice Problems. This pacing guide lists the sections that *should be omitted or given minor emphasis for mastery*.

Chapter 1. Section 1.16. Omit material related to joules; Section 1.17. Omit absolute deviation; Sections 1.19 and 1.20. Students probably will need training in the use of the metric units, the factor-label method (dimensional analysis), and proportions.

Chapter 2. Section 2.14. At this point Chapter 9, *Two Important Gases: Oxygen and Hydrogen*, provides interesting descriptive chemistry. Use word equations. Omit details of O_2 and O_3 molecular structure (Sections 9.5 and 9.12).

Chapter 3. Sections 3.13 and 3.14. Exposure to theory but not necessary to dwell on mathematical details. Use Bohr atom-shell model.

Chapter 4. Sections 4.2–4.5. Omit details. Concentrate on structure and electron-dot symbols for atomic numbers 1–20. Sections 4.8–4.10 may be omitted completely.

Chapter 5. Emphasize classification of elements based on atom-shell models (atomic numbers 1–20). In Section 5.5, omit periods 5–7. In Sections 5.7–5.9, ionization energy and electron affinity should be omitted or only briefly explored. General emphasis on variation in properties of elements by group and period.

Chapter 6. Omit Section 6.17 and Section 6.22. Deal with energy changes in bonding. Sections 6.4 and 6.13 should be treated descriptively. Illustrate oxidation number rules. Use models and discuss properties of types of compounds. Teach formulas: ionic, structural, electron-dot. Illustrations of percentage of ionic character and electronegativity difference should be used.

Chapter 7. Omit Sections 7.12 and 7.13 on determination of empirical and molecular formulas. Emphasize the mole concept. Use problems on formula weight and percentage composition.

Chapter 8. Emphasize writing of equations and solution of simple mass-mass problems. Details of Sections 8.5 and 8.6 may be omitted, although Section 8.6 should be related to Activity Series (Section 8.8). Also emphasize mole relationships in equations and the factor-cancel operations in problem solving.

Chapter 10. Emphasize kinetic theory and properties of gases. If gas laws are treated mathematically, problem work should be minimal. Discuss Kelvin temperature and STP. Omit Section 10.12 on combined gas laws.

Chapter 11. Do Sections 11.1–11.5 and Section 11.8. Use gas-volume–gas-volume problems, possibly including volume of air. The rest of the chapter should be omitted.

Chapter 12. Omit Section 12.8, Critical Temperature, and Section 12.13, except for definition and concept of crystals, omitting details of crystalline systems.

Chapter 13. Omit problems in Sections 13.11–13.14.

Treatment of freezing-point depression and boiling-point elevation should be minimal. Use demonstrations for heat of solution. At this point you may wish to provide a break in the largely theoretical-conceptual topics and select from more factual-descriptive chapters such as Chapter 30, *The Halogen Family*, or Chapter 24 *The Metals of Group I*, both of which deal with group relationships, or Chapter 23, *The Elements of Period Three*.

Chapter 14. Concentrate on the writing of equations: dissociation, ionization, hydrated ions, and net ionic equations. Brief treatment of Sections 14.9 and 14.10.

Chapter 15. Emphasize the operational (factual) definitions of acids, bases, and salts. Use Arrhenius' definitions and equations as the basis for developing the more comprehensive Brønsted concepts and equations, using models extensively. Do Section 15.12. Relative strengths of acids and bases may be too difficult. In salt production emphasize neutralization.

Chapter 16. Emphasize molarity, omitting chemical equivalents and normality (Sections 16.2–16.5 and 16.13). Titration techniques and the pH scale should be taught merely as practical procedures and scale for determination of acid-base properties of solutions. Omit problems dealing with pH (Sections 16.6–16.10). Demonstrate use of pH meter, pH paper, and choice of indicator.

Chapter 17. Omit resonance structures of CO_2 (Section 17.17) and CO (Section 17.22).

Chapter 18. In conjunction with parts of Chapter 17 and Chapter 19, problems of pollution, ecology, energy, and the uses of organic compounds should be considered extensively. Omit Section 18.21 on details of synthetics, and possibly Section 18.22.

Chapter 19. Omit Sections 19.7–19.9.

Chapter 20. Omit most of the details of this chapter using brief, simplified treatment of exothermic and endothermic reactions, stability and heat of formation, rates of chemical reaction, reaction pathways, and concept of activation energy. Definitely omit free energy (Section 20.7) and reaction rate law (Section 20.13).

Chapter 21. Omit chapter contents except Sections 21.1, 21.2, and 21.4 (apply Le Chatelier's principle to a single example, the Haber process). Do Section 21.5 (detailed treatment). For Section 21.9 use simple equations for hydrolysis.

Chapter 22. Omit Sections 22.3 and 22.5. Use the Table of Relative Strengths of Oxidizing and Reducing Agents in replacement reactions (Section 21.4).

Chapter 23. Omit the hydride reactions except for H_2S and HCl.

Chapters 24 and 25. Select either Chapter 24 or 25 for family relationships of the active metals.

Chapter 26. Omit Section 26.5 and the complicated equations in Section 26.16. The detailed equations in Section 26.11, Steel Production, may also be omitted.

Chapter 30. The chapter may have been used much earlier in the course, as suggested, after Chapter 12 or 13.

Chapter 31. Omit Sections 31.9 and 31.10. Some courses omit all except the descriptive details of radioactivity and the relationship of radioactivity to atomic structure and atomic theory (Chapter 4). Some go a bit further to writing nuclear equations such as those for transmutations (Section 31.7). Applications of radioactivity and the uses of radioisotopes may be discussed. Sections 31.18–31.21 on fission and fusion are important, particularly in light of the many important problems related to nuclear energy, radioactive waste disposal, nuclear reactors and safety, atomic weapons, and so on.

The Average Course

Chapters 1–22	All sections except those in Chapter 16 dealing with chemical equivalents, normality, and titration with normal solutions.
Chapter 23	Sections 23.1–23.3.
Chapter 24	Sections 24.1 and 24.2, and the sections on spectroscopy.
Chapter 25	Section 25.1.
Chapter 26	Sections 26.1–26.8 and 26.17.
Chapter 27	Sections 27.1, 27.2, 27.9, and 27.13.
Chapter 28	Sections 28.3, 28.4, and 28.6.
Chapter 29	Sections 29.3–29.5.
Chapter 30	Sections 30.1, 30.9, and 30.11.
Chapter 31	Possible omission of Sections 31.9 and 31.14.

The Enriched Course

Chapters 1–22	All sections should be studied. In Chapter 15, introduce Lewis acid-base concepts. For Chapter 16, include chemical equivalents and normality calculations and titrations and all types of pH calculations.
Chapters 23–31	Complete as much as possible of each of these chapters beyond what is recommended for the Average Course.

Safety in the School Laboratory

Laboratory experience is a necessary part of any chemistry program. In order to facilitate student performance and maximize learning opportunities in the laboratory, students should be familiar with *safe, efficient,* and *effective* laboratory procedures. The rules for laboratory safety found in *Laboratory Experiments in Chemistry* and *Exercises and Experiments in Chemistry* should be reviewed thoroughly by the students.

1. *Responsibilities of the Instructor* Teachers must know the local and state policies and laws regarding laboratory safety and teacher liability. Specific laboratory responsibilities necessary to prevent accidents and avoid danger include:
a. Teach safety at all times, not just during the first laboratory session.
b. Circulate among the students during the laboratory period.
c. Stay in the laboratory.
d. Emphasize precautions that are specific to each laboratory experiment.
e. Plan and/or check the physical facilities to insure that they are in proper working condition and afford maximum safety.
f. Personally supervise the amounts of hazardous chemicals (Na, K, Mg ribbon, red P, white P, Na_2O_2, etc.)

obtained by students for experimentation. Also restrict use of burners when flammable liquids are being used. Have students remove jewelry when Hg and/or its compounds are being used.
2. *Physical Facilities for the Safe Laboratory*
a. Adequate first aid equipment backed up by a knowledge of what to do in the event of injury.
b. Appropriate fire extinguishers.
c. Fire protection for flammable chemicals.
d. Two exits from the laboratory, as far apart as possible.
e. Properly designed ventilation systems.
f. Adequate space for both storage and laboratory work.
g. Safe methods for the disposal of dangerous waste chemicals and materials.
h. Deluge showers, if deemed necessary.
i. All electrical equipment checked against shock and arcing hazards.
3. *Obligations of the Student*
a. Follow instructions, printed and verbal.
b. Plan the laboratory experiments to minimize the possibility of accidents.
c. Attempt no experiments beyond the directed ones.
d. Become familiar with the health and safety hazards of all equipment and chemicals used.
e. Record and investigate with the teacher any accidents or unplanned events that occur.
f. Wear goggles at all times for maximum eye protection.
4. *Types of Avoidable Accidents*
a. The most common injury is cuts, caused by broken glass tubing, other broken glassware, and sharp hand tools.
b. Chemical spills and uncontrolled reactions.
c. Splashing hot liquids.
d. Careless pipetting.
e. Exposure to vapors or gases.
f. Foreign bodies in the eye.
g. Electrical shocks.
h. Careless handling of mechanical equipment.
i. Falls.
5. *Explosion Hazards* Avoid the following combinations of chemicals commonly found in the high school laboratory:
a. Sodium or potassium with water.
b. Ammonium nitrate, zinc powder, and a small amount of water.
c. Potassium nitrate with sodium acetate.
d. Nitrate and an ester.
e. Peroxides with magnesium, zinc, or aluminum.
f. Chlorate and sulfuric acid.
g. Nitric acid with zinc, magnesium, or other metals.
h. Halogen and ammonia.
i. Phosphorus with nitric acid, a nitrate, or a chlorate.
j. Mercury(II) oxide with sulfur.
6. *Possible Fire Hazards* The table included in the *Teacher's Edition* of *Exercises and Experiments in Chemistry* indicates chemical combinations that could result in a hazardous reaction.

7. *Safe Use of Radioisotopes* The National Science Teachers Association offers an excellent 16-page booklet *How to Handle Radioisotopes Safely* ($1).

The student should be presented with safety information in all forms. Safety wall charts may be purchased from Science Related Materials, Inc., P. O. Box 1422, Janesville, WI 53545, or as a set of 12 chemical laboratory safety posters ($3.50 per set) from Manufacturing Chemists Association, 1825 Connecticut Ave., NW, Washington, DC 20009. Two excellent references dealing with science safety are "Safety in the Secondary Science Classroom," NSTA Publications, 1742 Connecticut Ave., NW, Washington, DC 20009, and "STOP: SAFETY First in Science Teaching," Division of Science Education, State Department of Public Instruction, Raleigh, NC 27611, a publication distributed with the compliments of Holt, Rinehart and Winston. A recent article in *Journal of Chemical Education* on laboratory safety is "Lab Safety and Safety Rules."[8] A copy of these rules may be obtained from the author, R. J. Friesen, Department of Chemistry, University of Waterloo, Waterloo, Ontario, Canada N2L3G1. Also, the booklet "Safety in Handling Hazardous Materials" is available from the Matheson Scientific Company, 1850 Greenleaf Ave., Elk Grove, IL 60007.

A set of symbols has been prepared for this edition of *Modern Chemistry* to alert students of potentially dangerous situations in the laboratory. They are explained fully to the student in *Laboratory Experiments in Chemistry* and in *Exercises and Experiments in Chemistry*. These symbols will tell the student at the beginning of each experiment what protective gear is to be used or what precautions are necessary for that particular experiment. The symbol will be repeated at the appropriate place in the *Procedure* section in order to keep the student continually conscious of safety in the lab. A special session with these symbols should be part of your introductory lessons on how to use chemicals and chemistry apparatus. An occasional check will insure that all students recognize and pay attention to the warning conveyed wherever encountered.

Literature Cited

1. "Einstein and Chemical Thought," from an announcement of a symposium celebrating the centenary of Einstein's birth, Sept. 11, 1979, *Journal of Chemical Education,* 56(6), 408 (1979).
2. Wiseman, F. L., Jr., *Journal of Chemical Education,* 56(4), 233 (1979).
3. Hansrote, C. J., Jr., *Journal of Chemical Education,* 56(4), 232 (1979).
4. Berkheimer, G. D., and McLeod, R. J., *The Science Teacher,* 46(4), 38 (1979).
5. Gage, T., *The Science Teacher,* 41(9), 37 (1974).
6. Hosker, G. W., *The Science Teacher,* 41(6), 42 (1974).
7. Wright, J. D., and Hounshell, P. B., *The Science Teacher,* 45(7), 34 (1978).
8. Friesen, R. J., *Journal of Chemical Education,* 53(6), 373 (1976).

Teacher Notes

PART 2

Introduction: The suggestions in the **Teacher Notes** cover activities, demonstrations, audiovisual aids, and references. These items are generally organized to correspond with individual sections of the student text. On several occasions, several obviously related sections are linked together. The suggestions complement and supplement the textbook treatment. It is understood that, in general, the demonstrations described in the text and represented by accompanying figures will be selectively performed and representative equations then developed. Sequences for the establishment of generalizations and concepts are described. The appropriate exercises from *Exercises and Experiments in Chemistry,* along with text questions and problems that are appropriate to sections or groups of sections, are frequently mentioned. Refer to the Teacher Commentary section of the Teachers Edition to *Exercises and Experiments in Chemistry* for a complete correlation of the laboratory experiments with the chapters of the text. Refer to the Key to Suppliers (Part 3, p. T-93) of Films, Filmstrips, Film Loops, Cassettes, Transparencies, and Slides for the key letters that identify the suppliers of these aids.

Teacher Notes
Chapter 1

Chapter Note

The objectives of this chapter are:

1. To develop an appreciation of the significance of chemistry and an understanding of its scope.
2. To indicate the career opportunities in chemistry.
3. To develop an understanding of the historical evolution of the modern era of chemistry.
4. To develop an understanding of the characteristics of the scientific method and the related characteristics of scientists.
5. To develop understandings of the nature of matter and energy and the law that relates their relationship.
6. To develop fundamental skills in making accurate measurements, using measurement units, and performing related mathematical operations.
7. To develop an understanding of the manipulation of measurements in problem solving.
8. To develop mastery of fundamental skills in the manipulation of significant figures and numbers expressed exponentially.

The chapter requires six periods. One possible arrangement is:

Lesson 1 Sections 1.1–1.4: Chemistry, Scientific Method
Lesson 2 Sections 1.5–1.11: Matter and Energy
Lesson 3 Sections 1.12–1.16: Measurement, Metric System, Temperature, Heat
Lesson 4 Sections 1.17–1.18: Uncertainty, Significant Figures
Lesson 5 Sections 1.19–1.20: Significant Figures and Operations with Them
Lesson 6 Sections 1.21–1.22: Operation with Units, Proportions

Section 1.1 To arouse student interest and tie together the content of this section and the introduction to this chapter, start with a "spectacular." A small cone of a mixture of zinc dust and flowers of sulfur on a ceramic plate is ignited and produces an impressive mushroom-shaped white cloud. Add colorless solutions in acid-base-acid sequence to a tall cylinder having an almost invisible quantity of phenolphthalein solution. A "wine-to-water-to-milk" demonstration, using successive solutions of $KMnO_4$, $NaHSO_3$ or H_2SO_3, then $BaCl_2$ is another alternative. Encourage students to ask questions or suggest explanations (although detailed answers and discussion of questions should be deferred until much later). As examples of the chemist's concern with the composition and structure of materials, exhibit ball-and-stick models of H, H_2, O_2, H_2O, CO_2, C_2H_5OH, and C_8H_{18}. Students have had previous scientific exposure to these substances and may be able to furnish several formulas. To indicate the scope of chemistry, exhibit several household chemicals, a variety of plastics and fibers, medicinals, and vitamins. These demonstrations and exhibits should be made the basis of the development of the definition of chemistry and lead to some discussion of its importance in life. Exhibit a variety of texts whose titles are representative of the main branches of chemistry.

Section 1.2 To emphasize the relevance of chemistry, have students discuss reasons for studying chemistry: its importance in daily life, in industry, and in related ecological situations (air and water pollution, radioactive wastes, etc.). Discuss the role of chemistry in preparation for possible careers in chemistry and for other careers that require the study of chemistry such as medicine, dentistry, pharmacy, forestry, etc. Refer to Figures 1-2, 1-3, and 1-4. Useful audiovisual aids are: **Films:** GE: *Man-made Diamond* (16mm, 12 min., s, c); SE: *The Modern Chemist–Diamond Synthesis* (16mm, 13 min., s, c), **Sound Filmstrips:** PH: WCC 688 *Chemistry Career Challenges* (2 sound cassettes, c) ACS: 30835 *Baseline: The*

Chemist; Bell Laboratories, 600 Mountain Ave., Murray Hill, N.J. 07974, *A Fundamental Scientist* (25 min.); EBE: 2943 *Patterns of Scientific Investigation* (22 min.). **Teacher References:** Molitor, T. E., ''Career Education Toward a Larger View,'' *The Science Teacher*, 47(5), 28 (1980). Solomon, P. G., ''Does Career Education Make a Difference?'' *The Science Teacher*, 47(5), 32 (1980). Hultgren, C., ''Chemistry But I want to be a . . .'', *Journal of Chemical Education*, 57(5), 365 (1980). National Science Teachers Association. *Keys to Careers in Science and Technology*, Washington, D.C.; 1973. Refer to Careers in Chemistry, Part I of this Teacher Edition for some of the source booklets available for student use.

Section 1.3 Perform demonstrations related to the phlogiston theory. Burn a piece of paper and ask relevant questions. Counterpoise a candle on a balance and have students note the loss of weight as it burns. Balance a piece of steel wool on a platform balance. Burn it and have students note the gain in weight. A wad of thin copper turnings also gives good results on a sensitive balance. Discuss the replacement of the phlogiston theory and the work of Lavoisier to show how science uses experimental evidence. Use the **Film,** EBE: S-81567 *Decomposition of Mercuric Oxide* (3 min. c, s) and discuss its relationship to the discovery of oxygen (Priestley), the reversibility of the reaction (Lavoisier: the chemical elements and the modern theory of combustion). In the past, teachers demonstrated the thermal decomposition of HgO but due to the hazardous properties of mercury, this experiment should be avoided. **Loop:** MH: 101195-1 *Combustion 1—Burning Candle* (8mm, 4 min., s). If possible, exhibit photos of important chemists from the past. Refer to the biographical sketches in the textbook such as Arrhenius, Figure 14-2. Students may be referred to Chapter 1 of *Foundations of Chemistry*, Toon and Ellis, for details of the contributions of Lavoisier and Dalton. This text also includes many biographical sketches of famous chemists, which could be shown to the classroom (Lavoisier, p. 10; Dalton, p. 76; and many Nobel prize winners). Show the **Filmstrip** *Chemistry and the Nobel Prize*, I 67157. Have students select several American Nobelists of interest. Mention that students interested in possibly making reports on famous chemists should consult the Subject Index of the December issues of the *Journal of Chemical Education* under such subheadings as Biography or History of Chemistry. **Films:** CF: *Alfred Nobel—The Merchant of Death* (26 min., c); CF: *Marie Curie—A Love Story* (32 min., c).

Section 1.4. You may wish to precede or follow up the discussion of the scientific method with a demonstration series. Burn Mg ribbon in air. Heat steel wool or a strip of Cu in air. To get more spectacular results, heat the metals (held in tongs) and then insert them into a bottle of O_2. An appropriate series of questions should cover the following: observing, generalizing, explaining-theorizing, testing. Have students predict the behavior of a heated platinum wire both in air and in oxygen. Follow up by performing the demonstration. **Filmstrip:** IFB: N 81050 *Scientists Work Together*. **Films:** IBF: *Scientific Method in Action* (19 min., c); EBF: 702 *The Scientific Method* (16mm, 12 min., c or b/w); CHEM: 4160 *A Research Problem: Inert(?) Gas Compounds* (19 min., c); MH: 2943 *Patterns of Scientific Investigation* (22 min.).

Section 1.5. Exhibit a variety of objects and materials to help students realize that matter is recognized through the senses. **Demonstrations:** Balance an evacuated 500 mL flask with a one-hole rubber stopper and clamp or valve attachment on a simple balance such as a horn-pan balance. Open the valve and have students note the change in mass. This demonstrates that air has mass and occupies space. Half-fill a wide-mouth bottle with water. Stopper the bottle with a one-hole rubber stopper containing a funnel tube. The bottom of the funnel tube should reach well below the surface of the water in the bottle. Have a student attempt to pour more water into the bottle through the funnel tube. For inertia, refer to student experiences when a bus or automobile starts or stops suddenly. **Loop:** MH: 101195-1 *Air Occupies Space; Air Has Weight* (8mm, 4 min., s).

Section 1.6. Demonstration: Perform a mass determination similar to that in Figure 1-10. Discuss the mass-weight relationship (distinction) by referring to astronauts on the moon.

Section 1.7. Use Figure 1-11 as an exhibit or a demonstration. **Demonstration:** Find the density of a cube of metal by measuring dimensions, calculating volume, and measuring mass; find the density of an irregularly shaped solid heavier than water such as a lead sinker by measuring volume of displaced water; find the density of a liquid by measuring the mass and volume (alcohol versus water). To demonstrate that density is a specific property, use a larger sinker and compare density calculated for smaller and larger sinkers.

Section 1.8. Exhibit ice, water, and boiling water, and moisten the chalkboard with a small quantity of water to show phase changes. Change positions of a solid in a battery jar. Change the position and/or use a variety of different-shaped vessels for an equal volume of water or colored water. Tie the simple experiments together by the idea that matter occupies space in all phases. **Demonstrations:** Open a bottle of colored gas to show diffusion of gasses. Pour a liquid from one container into another to demonstrate fluidity, or use the diffusion of a colored gas into air. ''Magically'' extinguish a candle burning in a battery jar by pouring invisible CO_2 into the battery jar. **Films:** EBF: *The Physical States of Matter;* YF: 238 *Phase Demonstration* (Three Phases of Naphthalene); EBF: 1675 *Explaining Matter—Molecules in Motion* (11 min., c). **Loop:** MH: *Change of State* (8mm, 4 min., s).

Section 1.9. Demonstrate that a single specific property will not necessarily serve to identify a substance: Students observe the color and odor of water and ethanol or water and white vinegar. Use a variety of substances pinpointing physical properties such as NH_3 for odor, NO_2 for color, NaCl and clay for solubility. Ask how physical properties are determined. For chemical property demonstrations use such experiments as: **(a)** Attempt to burn a square of a ceramic board (Ceram-fab Duraboard). **CAUTION.** In the hood ignite a piece of yellow phosphorus on a ceramic board with a heated glass rod; duplicate with sulfur. **(b)** Put a piece of Mg and one of Cu into separate test tubes containing hydrochloric acid. **(c)** Add a very small piece of Na or Ca to water in an evaporating dish **(CAUTION)**; repeat, using a piece of Fe or steel wool instead. **(d)** Add a solution of NaCl first to a solution of KNO_3, then to a solution of $AgNO_3$. In all instances give the names of substances and have students read name labels. Have students report observations and indications, if any, of changes in identity. This procedure trains powers of observation and stresses the importance of noting a change as well as recognizing that no perceptible change has occurred. Therefore students will not *always* expect something to happen.

Section 1.10. This section involves difficult physical concepts that in a course in physics would require at least one day for development. The teacher may choose to present the material rather than try to develop it wholly or in part according to the suggested plan. **(a)** Chemical energy: **Question:** Why is the chemist so interested in whether or not things burn? What accompanies the process of burning? Discuss heat resulting from burning in connection with fuels: home, auto, rocket, etc. **Demonstration:** Heat a stoppered test tube containing a small amount of water until the stopper is shot out. **Question:** How is heat utilized? (production of motion-mechanical energy) Where did the heat come from? Explain how the heat caused the stopper to be shot out. **(b)** Mechanical energy: **Demonstration:** Use a single fixed pulley over which two unequal weights are strung. Have the lighter weight on the floor and the other on the table top. Release the weight from the table top. **Question:** What is done when a weight is lifted? (This question should lead to the concept of work as a force resulting in motion. It may be used in connection with the "cannon" experiment above to give the idea that work is done on the stopper since a force produces motion. It may be necessary for the teacher to explain briefly that work is done whenever something is moved, that is, a force results in motion. It may also be expedient for the teacher to define energy.) Where did the energy involved in raising the weight come from? How much more energy does the heavier weight have? (Discussion may lead to the idea that if the weight fell a greater distance to the floor below, it could do more work.) What kind of energy did the weight have on the table top? On the floor? (Potential.) What kind of energy did it possess as it fell? (Kinetic.) What happened to the potential energy? To the kinetic energy? (Transformation.) How much energy does the smaller weight have? How could this be demonstrated? **Demonstration:** Replace the heavier weight (now on the floor) with one smaller than the weight which was raised and which you now place on the table. Repeat the demonstration by releasing the weight that is on the table. (Class discussion may arise about losses of energy, as by friction.) **(c)** Other forms of energy: energy transformations. Have the class trace back the source of light for the classroom. Turn on the light switch. **Question:** What happens to the light and heat energy of the bulb? Where does the energy propelling the Polaris submarines come from? **(d)** Conservation of energy: Some attempt should be made to have the law of conservation of energy (in non-nuclear processes) stated or recognized. Discuss forms of radiant energy, fossil fuels, and energy transformations of chemical energy of gasoline, as in text. **Film:** CORF: *The Nature of Energy*. **Loops:** E: 80-3445/1 *Conservation of Energy (pendulums and pile drivers);* E: 80-2769/1 *Conservation of Energy (potential to kinetic);* E: 80-3427/1 *Energy Conversion.* Use Figure 1-13 to trace energy transformations. Refer interested students to Section 1.14 *Modern Physics*, 1980.

Section 1.11 **(a)** Conservation of mass: Weigh a photoflash bulb before and after flashing. **(b)** Balance a flask containing two test tubes, one containing a solution of lead nitrate and the other a solution of potassium chromate. Invert the stoppered flask and replace it on the balance. **Question:** What did you observe? (Appearance?) Mass? (Weight?) How do you interpret the results? Tell the students that repeated experiments *always* give this result. Why is this statement (interpretation) called a law? What does a law tell us? **(c)** Conservation of mass and energy. **Question:** Where does the energy resulting in the explosion of an atomic bomb or hydrogen bomb come from? Student report on Section 1.11 in the text. **Question:** If this law is true, where does the energy of ordinary chemical reactions come from? **Films:** W-PSSC: 0313 *Conservation of Energy* (27 min.); CORF: C1710 *Matter and Energy* (12 min.); MH: *Energy* (27 min.); CORF: *Conservation of Energy and Matter.* **Loop:** MH: 641721 *Conservation of Matter* (4 min.).

Section 1.12. Exhibit food packages, pharmaceuticals, bottles of soft drinks, photos of highway signs, etc., that have both metric and English units (equivalents). Have students examine meter sticks and small rulers for metric units of length. Exhibit liter block ($1000 \ cm^3$). Remove smaller portions ($1 cm^3$, $10 cm^3$). Exhibit graduates and flasks of various capacities. Exhibit set of weights (masses) and have students read the gram markings. Refer to text figures and tables with appropriate discussion. Discuss the uses, advantages, and disadvantages of the English and metric systems. **Film:** MH: *The Metric System* (13 min.). **Transparency:** V: 15-2376-0 *The Metric System.* **Filmstrips** (with slides and cassettes): PH: WCC 8122 *How to Use the Metric System of Length, Volume, and Mass Measurements;* PH: WCC 821 *Metric System of Linear Measurement;* PH: WCC 822 *Metric System of Measurement: Volume and Mass.*

Section 1.13. Define physical quantity; illustrate, and explain the necessity for description of its magnitude by both a number and a unit. List the important fundamental quantities (5) in chemistry. Define derived quantities and illustrate for volume and density. Have students measure the length and width of the textbook front cover and then calculate its area. **Demonstration:** Find the density of a cube of metal by measuring dimensions, calculating volume, and measuring mass; find the density of an irregularly shaped solid heavier than water, such as a lead sinker, by measuring the volume of displaced water; find the density of a liquid by measuring the mass and volume (alcohol versus water). To demonstrate that density is an intensive property, use a larger sinker and compare density calculated for smaller and larger sinkers. You may wish to differentiate between extensive and intensive properties. The measurement of an extensive property (mass, length, volume) depends on *how much* matter is being considered. The value of an intensive property (density, temperature) *does not depend* on how much matter is being considered. **Films:** W-PSSC: 0105, *Measurement;* CORF: *Measurement in Physical Science* (13 min.). **Filmstrip:** (slides and cassette) PH: WCC 824 *Density and Specific Gravity.*

Section 1.14. Have students perform the experiments described in the second paragraph and report the results to the class. To show heat transfer, insert a metal U-shaped yolk into hot and cold water samples in plastic cups. Have a student touch the metal yolk. Check the thermometers in each beaker after a time lapse sufficient to reach thermal equilibrium. Define temperature and heat. **Films:** CORF: *The Nature of Heat* (11 min.); EBF: *Heat—Its Nature and Transfer* (11 min.). **Transparency:** EYE: 008 *Heat.* **Loop:** ICF: 13130 *Heat Is Produced in Different Ways.* **Filmstrips:** I: 67247 *Heat and Temperature;* EYE: TF-2-6 *Heat and Cold,* (6 filmstrips, 3 cassettes).

Section 1.15. Take the temperatures of melting ice and boiling water (steam point) on both the Fahrenheit and the Celsius scales. Refer to Figure 1-19. **Film:** EBF: 2068 *Thermometers and How They Work* (11 min.). **Filmstrip:** I: 67245 *How We Measure Heat.*

Section 1.16. If the experiment on *Measuring Temperature and Heat* has not been performed by students, use different masses of water and perform it as a demonstration. Have students make the observations, record data, and make the calculations. Define a calorie in terms of the joule. Have students illustrate conversions of calories to joules and of joules to calories. Emphasize the cancellation of unit (factor-cancel) in making the calculations. Refer to Table 1-5, kilocalories and kilojoules, and compare the relative magnitudes of some of the common foods. **Film:** CORF: *The Nature of Heat* (11 min.). Selections from the short films or loops mentioned in the Teacher Edition of the *Exercises and Experiments* may be used either before or after the experiment.

Section 1.17. Either by individual student experiment or by teacher demonstration with student aid, have a series of measurements made with devices of different degrees of precision. For example, a length may be measured first by meter stick and then by caliper or micrometer, or a mass measured by using balances of differing degrees of precision. By comparing measurements reported by several students and measurements reported by the same student but with different instruments, students can be led to the idea that the degree of accuracy of any measurement depends on one's ability to use the instrument properly and on the precision of the device. Exhibit a duplicate (chalkboard or large cardboard) of Figure 2-6, p. 27 of *Modern Physics*, 1980 edition, and use the observed results to have students distinguish between accuracy and precision. Have students attempt definitions of accuracy and precision. Use the text example to demonstrate the calculation of experimental and relative (percentage) errors. Refer to Figure 1-20 and Figure 1-21. **Filmstrip:** PH: WCC 803B *Precision and Accuracy* (also slides and cassette). **Films:** EBF: *Weighing—The Analytical Balance* (35 min.); *Weighing with the Analytical Balance* (18 min.); *The Top-Loading Balance* (21 min.); *The Modern Balance* (16 min.), on free loan from the Mettler Instrument Corporation, 20 Nassau St., Princeton, N.J. 08540. This company provides a number of filmstrips and transparencies including some dealing with analytical balance theory and sources of weighing errors.

Section 1.18. Use Figure 1-22 or a chalkboard duplicate of the figure to have students recognize the uncertain figure in the measurement(s). Define significant figures. Have a student measure the sides of a metal block and record the results on the chalkboard. Have the class perform computations of area and volume as in this text section to establish the procedure and reason for rounding off to the correct number of significant figures in each step. If possible have some students use pocket calculators and compare the results with others obtained. Some students may round off the area computation before computing volume while others may not. **References:** Satek, L. C., "Calculators and Significant Figures," *Journal of Chemical Education*, 54(3), 177(1977); Benfey, T., "The New Abaci and Significant Figures," *Chemistry*, 49(9), 2(1976). Use examples such as those in Table 1-7 to establish the rules concerning zeros in a measurement expression. Use the Practice Problem

for both the odd and even numbered examples. **Transparency:** V: 15-3127-6 *Rounding Off and Approximation;* C: *Significant Figures; Significant Figures, Order of Magnitude.* **Filmstrip:** PH: WCC 906 *Approximation.* You may wish to explain the rules for addition and subtraction of significant figures (Section 1.20) in addition to those for multiplication (and division) already established. For other examples, refer to p. 28, *Modern Physics*, 1980.

Section 1.19. Write some of the extremely large numbers in the text on the chalkboard and discuss the reasons for the use of scientific (exponential) notation. Since the mole was mentioned in Section 1.13 and since it appears in the Practice Problem, include the Avogadro number among these extremely large numbers. Explain and write the expression representing scientific notation on the chalkboard. Illustrate its use and apply this expression to several of the unusually large numbers. After having applied the two rules, have students use Practice Problems 1 and 2 to round off to three significant figures. Refer to Table 1-8. For very small numbers, such as those for the mass of an electron, a proton, and a neutron, use the ordinary notation for such numbers and convert to exponential notation (Table 3-1). **Filmstrip:** (slides and cassette) PH: WCC 801 *Converting Numbers to Exponential Notation.* **Transparency:** C: *Exponents.*

Section 1.20. Illustrate the addition and subtraction of significant figures. State and illustrate addition and subtraction using scientific notation. Review Section 1.18 for multiplication and division of significant figures. If desirable, perform multiplication and division by slide rule and calculator for the examples in the text. Then illustrate the rounding off to two and three significant figures. Refer to Table 1-9. Then illustrate multiplication and division operations with measurements expressed in scientific notation. Explain and illustrate that the use of pure numbers has no influence on the number of significant figures in the result. **Filmstrips:** PH: SCC 802 *Addition, Subtraction, Multiplication and Division of Exponential Numbers* (with slides and cassette); PH: WCC 803A *Determining Significant Figures*, (slides and cassette). **Transparency:** C: *Significant Figures—Orders of Magnitude.*

Section 1.21. Discuss speed as a derived unit, and its expression. As another example use a highway sign (mph). Illustrate the arithmetical manipulations for the density expression in the text and show that both sides of an equation must have the same dimensions. In the process, show the cancellation of dimensional units and why only identical units may be cancelled. Then indicate how conversion units may be used to establish identical units. Identify the key step in the problem-solving technique as *dimensional analysis* or the factor-label method. Illustrate it, on the chalkboard, as the first step in the solution of the Sample Problems and in the subsequent, more efficient, solution setup for the problem. For the Practice Problems you may wish to demonstrate a representative concentration problem. For homework, assign selected problems from the Group A and/or Group B problems, depending on the abilities of the class. **Filmstrips:** PH: WCC 907 *Problem-Solving: Units and Dimensionless Quantities* (slides and cassette); PH: WCC 722 *The Factor-Unit Method* (slides and cassette).

Section 1.22. Use the figures in Table 1-10 on the chalkboard to demonstrate the construction of a graph. Have students compute the density of water at 4°C from the tabular data. Question students about the relationships involved and the proportionality sign, and develop the concept of proportionality constant. Develop the definition of direct proportion and the two forms of the generalized equations, and relate to the linear character of the graph for a direct proportion (Figure 1-23). Repeat the construction of the graph (Figure 1-24) from the data in Table 1-11. Have students compute the distance (constant) from the data. Develop the specific formulas for the data and then the generalized formulas for an inverse proportion. Have students attempt a definition and then recognize the shape (hyperbola) of the representative graph. **Filmstrips:** PH: WCC 806 *Collecting and Plotting Data: Linear Graphs* (slides and cassette); PH: WCC 800 *Collecting and Plotting Data: Non-Linear Graphs* (slides and cassette). **Transparency:** V: 15-2563-3 *Analyzing Graphs and Charts*. **Teacher References:** Furth, R., "The Limits of Measurement," *Scientific American Offprint,* 255, July 1950; *Chemistry* (SciQuest Reprints): 23, Livingstone, H. K., "Techniques in the Chem. Lab." 80, Schaar, B., "Chance Favors the Prepared Mind" (stories of 13 scientific discoveries made by accident, including dynamite). 103, Alexander, G., "A Chemist in Industry." 111, Paul, M. A., "International System of Units." 117, Alexander, G., and Fernelius, W. C., "A Day in the Life of a Research Director." Dence, J. B., "Mathematical Techniques in Chemistry," John Wiley & Sons. New York, 1975; Calder, Richie, Lord, "Conversion to the Metric System," *Scientific American*, July 1970; Munn, R. J., "Measurement Errors—A Lecture Demonstration," *Journal of Chemical Education* 56(4), 267 (1979). **Additional Audiovisual Aids: Loops:** BFA: 82-0043/1 *Density of Liquids;* BFA: 82-0142/1 *Liquids;* BFA: 80-3262/1 *Identifying Solids by Density;* BFA: 80-3270/1 *Identifying Liquids by Density;* BFA: 80-3254/1 *Conservation of Mass;* ISBN-0-03-080162/1 *Inertia I;* ISBN-0-03-080163-X *Inertia II;* BFA: 80-3437/1 *Energy Conversion;* BFA: 89-3503/1 *Introducing Liquids and Solids* (5 loops). **Sound Filmstrips** (with cassettes or records): BFA: 3J2000 *Investigations in Science: Energy and Motion-Work; Energy; Acceleration; Inertia* (4 filmstrips); BFA: 3H9000 *Investigations in Science: Properties of Matter—Is Air Matter?; Pressure; What is Temperature?; Solid, Liquid, Gas; Water* and *Heat* (5 filmstrips). EYE: TF2-8 *Heat and Cold* (6 filmstrips). **Filmstrips:** I: 67739 *Scientific Attitude and Method;* I: 67150 *Significant Figures in Science;* AGA: N81050 *Scientists Work Together*. **Films:** BFA: 10258 *Accuracy in Measurement* (9+ min.); BFA: 10860 *Meter, Liter, and Gram* (13 min.). **Filmstrip and Audio Cassette:** W(Ward's) Solo-Learn System (for individuals or small groups) 78 W 0480 *Using Units of Measurements;* 78 W 0460 *Measurement and Scientific Notation;* 78 W 0470 *Introduction to Significant Figures*. **Transparencies:** EYE: 008 *Heat* (10 transparencies); EYE: 014 *Nature of Matter* (8 transparencies). **Individualized Programmed Instruction:** PH: WCC 801 *Converting Numbers to Exponential Notation;* PH: WC 802 *Addition, Subtraction, Multiplication, and Division of Exponential Numbers;* PH: WCC 803A *Determining Significant Figures;* PH: WCC 803B *Precision and Accuracy;* PH: WCC 806 *Collecting and Plotting Data: Linear Graphs;* PH: WCC 807 *Collecting and Plotting Data: Non-Linear Graphs;* PH: WCC 722 *The Factor-Unit Method;* PH: Chem-Review (microfiche) WCF 1001 *Scientific Notation and Significant Figure;* WCF 1002 *Dimensional Analysis;* WCF 1003

Logarithms. **References:** Anderlik, B., "Whatever Became of Significant Figures? The Trend Toward Numerical Illiteracy," *Journal of Chemical Education* 57(8), 591 (1980); Wittcoff, H., and Fernelius, W. C., "The Chemical Industry: What Is It?" *Journal of Chemical Education* 56(4), 253 (1979). **Audio-Tutorial:** HM: 3-49504, *Definition of Chemistry, Chemical Classification;* HM: 3-49503, *Metric System, Signed Numbers and Solving Simple Equations.*

Teacher Notes
Chapter 2

Chapter Note

The chapter development requires at least three periods (lessons). One pattern for reading assignments is:

Lesson 1 Sections 2.1–2.5: Classes of Matter
Lesson 2 Sections 2.6–2.10: Symbols, Compounds, Mixtures, Law of Definite Composition
Lesson 3 Sections 2.11–2.15: Changes in Matter

Corresponding sections of Exercise 2 from *Exercises and Experiments in Chemistry* and appropriate textbook questions and problems complement the reading assignments.

Section 2.1. Activities and demonstrations: Classification. Two different approaches may be employed. One is the textbook approach, in which matter is subdivided into categories of materials and further analytic exposition and demonstration are carried on as indicated by Figure 2-1. Develop Figure 2-2 on the chalkboard. Develop the figure continually as sections after 2.1 are demonstrated and discussed. The development proceeds either downward to the left-hand corner (mixtures) or upward and sideways from the right-hand corner (elements). Later, the kinds of elements (metals, nonmetals, metalloids, and noble gases) may be placed under the category of elements. A different approach may be termed the synthetic one, in which the reverse procedure is employed. Elements that the student meets in everyday experiences are identified, and concepts pertaining to the more complex classes of matter are developed. In either approach, extensive use of exhibit materials should be made. For example, after examination of granite with a hand lens, separate large specimens of mica, feldspar, and quartz should be exhibited. Later, samples of the elements comprising these three materials should be shown.

Section 2.2. Exhibit: granite, quartz, feldspar, mica. **Demonstrations:** Prepare a sugar solution. Students taste portions of the solution with warning that unknown substances should not be tasted and known substances *tasted only by instructor direction*. Divide the solution into halves. Add water to one half and sugar to the other half. Prepare a solution of table salt. Have students taste the solution and use portions for evaporation and distillation. **Film:** EBE: S-81553 *Solution, Evaporation, and Crystallization* (4 min.). **Demonstrations:** Figure 2-2(A) (use sand and small lead or copper pellets); Figure 2-2(B) (use mixture of $CuSO_4 \cdot 5H_2O$ and MnO_2). Burn a splint in O_2 and air. Expose a watch glass with limewater solution to air and have students note white crust deposit with lapse of time. **Film:** EBE: 5-81568 *Distillation from Liquid Air* (4 min.). **Demonstrations:** Zn, Cu, and brass filings in separate test tubes containing hydrochloric acid.

Section 2.3. Demonstration: Thermal decomposition of sugar (write the formula for sucrose on the chalkboard to indicate chemical composition). **Films:** EBE: 5-81569 *Electrolysis of Water* (4 min.); EBE: 5-81567 *Decomposition of Mercuric Oxide* (3 min.).

Section 2.4. A good summary or introduction is to play the song, "The Elements," from *An Evening with Tom Lehrer* (Reprise Records). This features the names of most of the elements to the tune of Gilbert and Sullivan's "Pirates of Penzance." It may also be used with Chapter 5, "The Periodic Law." Exhibit samples of common elements and the periodic table chart. Use the Project Physics transparency T 35 *Periodic Table* (overlays include Mendeleev elements and transuranium elements) or the HM: 2-10521 Transparency *The Periodic Table*. Student reports may be based on the following references from *Chemistry*, 47 (1974): "Anonymous Elements 104 and 105," March; 43 (1970): "From Mendeleev to Mendelevium and Beyond," Jan.; "Predicted Properties of Elements 113 and 114," Nov.; "Discovery of Element 105," June; 42 (1969): "Element 104," May; "A New Element, Eka-platinum?" Feb.; "Henry Cavendish, Discoverer of Hydrogen," Nov. See references to *Handbook of Chemistry and Physics* and *Discovery of the Elements* at the end of this chapter. Another useful reference is *Chemistry Profiles*, a 92-page book consisting of 25 articles reprinted by *Chemistry* (now *SciQuest*). **Films:** AEC: *The Alchemist's Dream;* AEC: *The Atom in Physical Science;* W: CHEM 140-4178 *Transuranium Elements* (23 min.). **Filmstrip:** I: 67107 *Evolution of the Elements.* Use the examples in the text and Table 2-1 to illustrate the use of the systematic nomenclature for the elements numbered over 100. **Teacher Reference:** "Recommendations for the Naming of Elements of Atomic Numbers Greater Than 100," *Pure and Applied Chemistry,* Feb. 1977.

Section 2.5. Activities: Exhibit representative samples of metals and nonmetals, including noble gases (tubes) and metalloids. Such samples may include sheet metals: Cu, Zn, Pb, Al (including foil) to show malleability. Hammer a Pb sheet to show malleability of Pb. Exhibit wire of various metals to show ductility; aluminum pot or pan to show heat conductivity; coated Cu wire to show electrical conductivity. You may wish to use more elaborate demonstrations of heat and electrical conductivity (Welch 1653 Conductometer, six-rod form) or some form of lamp, electrodes, dry-cell electric setup. Powder rhombic (roll) sulfur in a mortar. Exhibit chunks of antimony and crush in a mortar. Refer students to Figures 2-5 and 2-6. **Exhibit** Hg and mention the dangers and precautions necessary because of its high volatility. If a sample of gallium is available, demonstrate its low melting point. In summary refer to Figure 5-3, "Sublevel Blocks of the Periodic Table." **Film:** EBE: 2950, *Metals and Nonmetals* (10 min.). **Transparencies:** See Section 2.4 for Periodic Table.

Section 2.6. Use the chalkboard to illustrate alchemical symbols and those of Dalton and Berzelius (Figure 2-7). **Reference:** Bernheim, R. A., "Chemistry in 1876: The Way It Was," *Chemical and Engineering News,* p. 38, Apr. 1976. **Activities:** Have students examine a picture of chemical symbols, particularly the symbols of Dalton and Berzelius. A comparison of different symbols appeared in the article by Robert A. Bernheim cited above. Contrast the earlier types of symbols, the concern for secrecy, and the resulting difficulties in communication with modern symbols which constitute a sort of international language. Display representative sets of the elements —C, Cl, Cr, Co, Ca—and discuss the use of two letters in symbols. Discuss the derivation of certain symbols from the Latin names and give examples. Refer to the *Handbook of Physics and Chemistry.* Discuss the quantitative significance of a chemical symbol. Illustrate the use of coefficients and subfigures (in formulas) indicating numbers of atoms.

Section 2.7. Exhibit samples of the most abundant elements and discuss details of Table 2-3. Refer to Figure 2-8 for regions and dimensions of the interior of the earth. Discuss details of Tables 2-4 and 2-5. **References:** Wylie, P. J., "The Earth's Mantle," *Scientific American,* 232(3), 50 (1975); Pacer, R. A., and Ehrman, W. D., "The Apollo Missions and the Chemistry of the Moon," *Journal of Chemical Education,* 52(6), 363 (1975). **Filmstrip:** I: 67151 *Probing the Interior of the Earth.*

Sections 2.8 and 2.9. Activities: Exhibit samples of common mixtures and compounds. Make up mixtures of varying proportions of salt and pepper, salt and sand, etc. Summarize differences in chalkboard replica of Table 2-5 as they become evident. **Demonstration:** Using the periodic table have students find the atomic weights of Fe and S and solve the problem: Why is a 7:4 ratio used in forming the compound? On this basis have students attempt to write the formula, since the 1:1 atom ratio will then be clear. In addition, a qualitative approach to the law of definite proportions may be used. Try three different mixtures of Zn and S: 1 g of Zn to 1 g of S, 2 g of Zn to 1 g of S, 3 g of Zn to 1 g of S, igniting one after another under the hood with the flame of the burner held at arm's length. Note which of the above ratios burns the best and has the least free Zn or S in the product. **Films:** UA: *Elements, Compounds and Mixtures* (30 min.); EBE: S-81568, *Properties of Mixtures and Compounds* (4 min.); W: 140-0111, *Compounds and Mixtures* (32 min.); W: 140-0110, *Definite and Multiple Proportions* (30 min.); CORF: *Elements, Compounds, Mixtures.* **Loops:** BFA: 84-0165 1 *Definite Proportions: Electrolysis of Water;* MH: 641721-2 *Mixtures and Compounds.* **Filmstrips:** EYE: X 200-C *Definite Composition;* EYE: X 200-D *Conservation of Matter.*

Section 2.10. Exhibit mixtures and compounds in text. **Demonstration:** Na burning in Cl_2 (Alyea, p. 201). Write formulas for such compounds of C, H, and O as ethanol, acetic acid, and formaldehyde.

Sections 2.11 and 2.12. Demonstrations: Perform text examples. In addition, powder sulfur and antimony (mortar and pestle); bend glass. Heat paradichlorobenzene and have students recognize phase changes as sublimed solid solidifies on upper part of tube. Pour the liquid on a cold surface (table top). Have students cite types of energy change (exothermic, endothermic) involved in phase changes. Dissolve solid NH_4Cl or KNO_3 and pellets of NaOH in H_2O with inserted thermometers or have students feel outside of test tubes. For chemical changes refer to previous demonstrations or experiments: FeS formation, burning H_2, synthesis of water, electrolysis of water, decomposition of sugar. Assign selected questions from text. **Films:** UA: *Physical and Chemical Changes* (28 min.); MH: *A Look at Chemical Change* (15 min.), or video-cassette; BFA: 10217 *Combustion, An Introduction to Chemical Change* (16 min.); EBE: *Explaining Matter—Chemical Change* (11 min.).

Loops: MH: Series 641721-2: *Chemical Change vs. Physical Change; Dissolving: A Physical Change; Chemical Change; Slow Oxidation; Rapid Oxidation.* **Transparency:** EYE: 003-1 *Physical vs. Chemical Change.*

Section 2.13. Endothermic Demonstrations: Go-stop-go electrolysis of water; Thermal decomposition of sugar; Go-stop-go decomposition of HgO with splint tests. Or use **Loop:** EBE: S-81567 *Decomposition of Mercuric Oxide.* **Exothermic Demonstrations:** Ignite burner and paper with match. Ignite S and P in ceramic-lined deflagrating spoons. Flash a photoflash lamp. Use a flashlight cell in a flashlight or to ring a bell. **Demonstrate:** gas production by HCl on $CaCO_3$; precipitation by reaction between solutions of NaCl and $AgNO_3$; H_2O to baking powder; MnO_2 to H_2O_2 (3% solution). Have students summarize the various agents used to initiate chemical reactions or control those already started. **Film:** BFA: 10942 *Energy: A First Film* (8 min.).

Section 2.14. Demonstration: Show ice cubes melting in beaker. Review boiling and evaporation of water. Develop a chalkboard replica of Figure 2-13. Demonstrate evaporation of H_2O from moistened cotton wad attached to thermometer bulb to show how higher entropy overcomes unfavorable higher energy. Refer to production of ice cubes in refrigerator where the energy-change factor overcomes the entropy-change factor. Open a bottle of soda water and discuss entropy change. To illustrate disorder-entropy, shuffle a stacked deck of cards, reverse the shuffle. Stir layered colored marbles in a beaker or battery jar. Stir in reverse direction. **Film:** ROB: *Entropy;* ROB: *The Second Law.* **Filmstrip:** I: 67738, *Energy and Entropy: Driving Force of a Chemical Reaction.* **References:** Stevenson, K. L., ''Brief Introduction to the Three Laws of Thermodynamics,'' *Journal of Chemical Education,* 52(5), 330 (1975); Porter, G., ''The Laws of Disorder,'' *Chemistry,* Reprint No. 85; Toon, E. R., and Ellis, G. L., *Foundations of Chemistry,* 1973 ed., pp. 347–350, 429–431. **Chapter References:** (Note: The sources for these references are given in the bibliography at the end of the Teacher Notes section.) *Handbook of Chemistry and Physics* (consult Index under ''Elements, derivation of names, description, discoverers, occurence''); Kieffer, W. F., ''The Elementary Composition of the Earth,'' *Selected Readings in General Chemistry;* Weeks, M. E., and Leicester, H. M., ''Discovery of the Elements''; Seaborg, C. T., and Evans, G., ''Elements of the Universe,'' Dutton; ''Lunar Samples and Transuranium Elements'' (March) and ''Alchemical Symbols'' (Oct.), *Chemistry,* 44 (1971).

Section 2.15. Define nuclear change and contrast with chemical change. Refer students to Figure 31-6 or use a previously prepared chart of this figure. Pinpoint radium in this figure. Identify some of the daughter elements and the final element, Pb. **Film:** BFA: 10849, *Conservation of Mass* (14 min.). **Additional Audiovisual Aids:** EBE: Series of 6 loops on physical and chemical changes: S-81553 *Solution, Evaporation, and Crystallization* (S in CS_2); S-81554 *Slow Reaction (Iron and Oxygen);* S-81555 *Fast Reaction (Mercury and Silver Nitrate);* S-81556 *Fast Reaction (Ammonium Dichromate Volcano);* S-81557 *Phase Demonstration (Melting, Volatilization and Condensation of Naphthalene);* S-81558 *Compounds and Mixtures (Iron and Sulfur).* **EBE Filmstrips:** Series 9080: *Classification of Matter; Molecules, Atoms, and Simple Reac-*

tions; Series 6917 (with discs or cassettes): *Substances; Elements; Chemical Properties; Chemical Reaction.* **Individualized Programmed Instruction:** W: 78 W 0430 *Elements, Compounds, Mixtures;* W: 78 W 0450 *Introduction to the Laws of Chemistry.*

Teacher Notes
Chapter 3

Chapter Note

Two recommended sources for student reports for Chapters 3 and 4 are *Project Physics Text,* Chapters 17–20, and *Foundations of Chemistry,* 1973 edition, Chapters 1, 5, and 6. A film such as IFB: *Conquest of the Atom* (22 min.) or USDE: *A Is for Atom* (15 min.) may be used to introduce the chapter or as a summary. Some examples of student reports that may be preassigned from *Foundations of Chemistry,* 1973 edition, are History of Atomic Theory: Sections 1.6 and 1.7; The Electron: Section 5.5 (cathode rays), Section 5.6 (J. J. Thomson), Section 5.7 (Millikan); The Proton: Section 5.8; The Neutron: Section 5.11; X Rays and Atomic Number: Sections 5.9 and 5.10. This chapter requires four or five periods (lessons) dependent on the more or less extensive use of student reports and audiovisual aids. One arrangement is:

Lesson 1   Sections 3.1 and 3.2: Atomic Theory (use of film or filmstrip)

Lesson 2   Sections 3.3–3.7: Atomic Structure, Atomic Number, Mass Number

Lesson 3   Sections 3.8–3.12: Atomic Structure Through the Third Series (Worksheet 1)

Lesson 4   Sections 3.13–3.15: Atomic Mass, Avogadro Number and the Mole, Atomic Weight (Problems)

Section 3.1. Demonstrations: The particulate nature of matter: sugar and gas as described in text. Drop a crystal of $KMnO_4$ into a large cylinder of water to show diffusion. Other suitable demonstrations are in Alyea, *Tested Demonstrations,* p. 63, 5-10-s, p. 152, p. 180.

Section 3.2. Review: Sections 2.6–2.9. Student reports or teacher discussion of history of atomic theory through Dalton. **Reference:** The *Project Physics* text, Unit 5, pp. 1–15. Present Dalton's postulates from this source. Discuss their use in explaining the laws of conservation of mass and definite composition as outgrowths of experiments about the ways and proportions in which substances react with one another. Help the class ''discover'' significant differences between Dalton's ideas and the five text statements about atoms and their properties. This leads to questions as to why and how Dalton's ideas were revised, i.e., statements 3 and 4 of Series 1–5, Section 3.2. **Demonstrations:** This series of demonstrations helps students understand details of atomic structure before considering Rutherford's scattering experiment.

(a) Charge ebonite and glass or plastic rods by friction. Mount rods in metal saddles and show attraction of unlike charges and repulsion of like charges.

(b) Touch torn paper strips with the charged rubber rod.

(c) Use a suspended pith ball to show attraction, contact, and final repulsion.

(d) Place a charged rubber rod in a box of sawdust or puffed rice. Remove the rod with attached particles and note subsequent repulsion and ejection from the rod.

(e) Charge an electroscope (Braun) by contact and induction. With the aid of a chalkboard diagram, have students attempt explanations in terms of the two kinds of electric charges and the mobility of negative charges and/or particles.

(f) Show charged balloons sticking to a wall or to a student's back.

Transparencies: EYE: 003-3 *History of the Atom;* EYE: 003-4 *Proof of the Existence of Atoms;* EYE: 003-5 *Why Atoms Have Remained Invisible;* W: 167-W 1020 *Atomic Structure.*

Section 3.3. Demonstrations: Show that atoms are not indivisible particles by using a radioactive source and a Geiger counter. Have students report on Becquerel's discovery, Section 31.1, *Modern Chemistry* or Section 5.9, *Foundations of Chemistry,* 1973 ed. To show the complex nature of radioactivity, use a chalkboard diagram of Figure 31-5. Then substitute charged plates for the magnet so that students can explain the charges on the rays and the amount of deflection. **Transparencies:** PP: T-40 *Separation of α, β, γ Rays;* EYE: 003-36 *Types of Radiation;* EYE: 003-37 *Radioactive Decay.* Rutherford's scattering experiment can be described with the aid of a chalkboard diagram (Figure 3-4). Students should understand that the gold foil is composed of atoms. They should explain the relative numbers of undeflected and deflected particles in terms of the nature of the atom, dimensions of the atom and the nucleus, and the structure of the nuclear atom. The results of the experiment may be interpreted to indicate the type of charge of the nucleus and electrons, the mass of the nucleus, and, later on, the nuclear components. The super-8 filmloops HRW: 087793-8 *Rutherford Scattering* and HRW: 087792-x *Thomson Model of the Atom* may be used to complete the presentation, as well as another possible atom model. The film W: 140-0416 *Rutherford Atom* may also be used. See *Project Physics Handbook,* pp. 306–308, for simulated demonstration of atom models using magnets and steel balls. **Transparency:** EYE: 003-38 *Rutherford Scattering.* Refer interested students to Section 4.3 of *Modern Chemistry* for more experimental evidence of electrons and their location and motion within the atom; and to pp. 224–229, "Probability," *Fundamentals of Chemistry,* for the idea of electron cloud. Additional audiovisual aids for this section are: **Film:** IBF: *The Discovery of Radioactivity* (15 min.); IBF: *Conquest of the Atom* (22 min.). **Filmstrip:** I: 67249, *Radioactivity.* **Loop:** BFA: 80-3346/1, *Radioactivity.*

Section 3.4. Activities: Use a variety of Crookes tubes activated by a tesla coil to show that cathode rays travel in straight lines (Maltese cross) and that they possess momentum and energy (kinetic energy effect tube), and use deflection by a magnet to show that the rays have a negative charge (deflection effect tube). Interesting effects may be obtained by bringing a bar magnet toward the shadow of the Maltese cross, toward the patterns on an oscilloscope tube, and toward pictures on a television tube. **Films:** 2936 *Crookes Tubes,* (9 min.); EBE: 2938 *Millikan's Oil Drop Experiment* (7 min.); EBE: 2948 *E/M Demonstration* (4 min.); W: 140-0413 PSSC *Mass of the Electron* (18 min.); W: 140-0404 *Millikan Experiment* (30 min.); W: 140-0412 *Electrons in a Uniform Magnetic Field* (11 min.); PH: WCC810 *Measuring Electron Charge and Mass.*

Section 3.5. Activities: Use a chalkboard diagram of a gas tube with a perforated cathode (*Foundations of Chemistry,*

Figure 5-8) for experimental investigation of "positive rays," and the proton, which was first investigated by E. Goldstein and J. J. Thomson. For the discovery of the neutron, refer students to Section 31.13. As a summary, reproduce Table 3-1 on the chalkboard or as a transparency. Add representative symbols for the electron (e, −, $-_{-1}^{0}e$), proton (p, +, $_{1}^{1}H$), and neutron (n, $_{0}^{1}n$). **Filmstrips:** I: 67115 *Atomic Structure and Chemistry;* I: 67252 *What's in the Atom?;* I: 67253 *What Is a Neutron?*

Sections 3.6 and 3.7. Activities: Chalkboard diagrams. Shown below are types of chalkboard models that may be

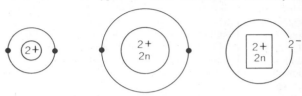

used. Have students construct similar models for the hydrogen isotopes. Use the models to develop the concepts of atomic number, isotopes, nuclide, and mass number. You may also wish to use the symbols for the hydrogen isotopes: $_{1}^{1}H$, $_{1}^{2}H$, $_{1}^{3}H$. **Audio tape:** HM: 3-49505 *Sub-atomic Structures of the Atom—Isotopes.* **Student Reports:** *Foundations of Chemistry* —Section 5.10 (Atomic number, Moseley), Section 5.12 (Isotopes).

Section 3.8. Activity: Exhibit a wall chart of the periodic table. Use **(a)** the Periodic Table of the Elements and **(b)** Sublevel Blocks of the Periodic Table in Chapter 5. The latter is especially useful since it uses the atomic number with each symbol. **Transparencies:** HRW: PP T35 *Periodic Table;* HM: 2-10521 *The Periodic Table;* HRW: PP T39 *Energy Levels —Bohr Theory;* HM: 2-10525 *Electron Energy Levels;* W: 167-W 0120 *Periodic Chart.*

Sections 3.9–3.12. Activity: Have students construct chalkboard diagrams for helium-3, lithium-6, and lithium-7. For each of the other elements in the second and third series, list the symbol of the element with its atomic number and the mass number of its most common nuclide, e.g., $_{11}^{23}Na$. Have students construct models for each of these elements. This activity leads logically to the idea of energy levels and shells. Also develop the answer to the table in question 26. You may wish to use Worksheet I: Atomic Models for Some Elements in the Periodic Table from the set in the Test Sampler. These may be used for elements with atomic numbers 1–20 and later for selected elements with atomic numbers 21–31. Use Table 3-2 for details about the naturally occurring nuclides in the first and second series.

Section 3.13. Definitions: Emphasize the definition of atomic mass and the basis of the scheme, i.e., carbon-12 = exactly 12. Use Table 3-2 as an aid to definition of mass number as the integer closest to the atomic mass and the total number of protons and neutrons in the atom nucleus. Mention the atomic masses of electron, proton, neutron, and relate to the placement of the mass number in their representative symbols. **Demonstration:** Exhibit a container of one dozen pencils and a box containing one gross to aid concept of *relative* scale. Use a balance to measure the mass of a nickel and then of a quarter. Have students calculate the relative mass of a quarter to a nickel. Measure the mass of *X* number of nickels and the same number of quarters in small plastic bags. Then have students count and find that X is the same for both coins. Define and illustrate *atomic mass units* and the abbreviation *u*.

Section 3.14. Use the chalkboard to perform the text calculations of the Avogadro number for carbon-12, hydrogen-1. Have the students perform calculation for oxygen-16. Define the mole. Mention such units as a dozen used by the grocer (egg carton) and a ream used in purchasing paper to illustrate that different types of activities use different unit quantities. State that the mole is the chemist's unit, indicating that it has an experimental basis. Use the introductory frames of the **Filmstrip** I: 67130 *The Mole Concept*. Use simple arithmetic questions: How many atoms are there in (a) 2 moles, (b) 0.5 mole of carbon-12? How much of a mole of carbon-12 has a mass of 6.00 g? Refer to Table 3-3. For more detailed examples see Section 7.11, *Modern Chemistry*.

Section 3.15. Define and illustrate: Gram-atomic weight and atomic weight. Refer to periodic table chart or transparency. Duplicate the text examples for hydrogen and carbon. Refer students to Tables 4 and 5 in the Appendix. Solve the Sample Problems. In each case assign half the class to solve Practice Problems 1 and 2 with students at the board. Exhibit or weigh out one mole (gram-atomic weight) of Zn (powder), S (powder), and examples from Figure 3-7 (C, Cu, Pb). Use textbook questions 20, 21, 27, 28, 30, 31, 32. **Student Report References:** Kieffer, W. F., "The Mole Concept in Chemistry," pp. 1–10; Young, J. A., and Malik, J. G., "Chemical Queries," *Journal of Chemical Education*, 48, 271 (1971); "The Mole Concept," *Journal of Chemical Education*, 52(11), 725 (1975). **Filmstrip:** EBE: Series 9080 *The Composition of Atoms, Atomic and Molecular Weights; The Mole Concept.* **Individualized Instruction:** These materials may also be used for class use: PH: WCC *Electron-Configurations and Orbital Diagrams;* PH: WCC 852, *Atomic Structure and the Periodic Table* (filmstrip or slides, audio cassette, student workbook). Ward's Solo-Learn (filmstrip, cassette, student review sheets, manual): W: 78 W 0390 *Introduction to Atomic Structure;* W: 78 W 0440 *Atoms and Molecules;* W: 78 W 0420 *Introduction to Electrostatics.* **Audio-Tutorial:** HM: 3-49505, *Sub-Atomic Structures of the Atom, Isotopes.* **References:** Kolb, D., "What if Atoms Are So Tiny . . . ," *Journal of Chemical Education* 54(8), 543 (1977); Kolb, D., "What Is an Element?," *Journal of Chemical Education* 54(11), 696 (1977). **Additional References:** Herron, J. D., "Rutherford and the Nuclear Atom," *Journal of Chemical Education*, 54(8) 499 (1977); Kragh, H., "Chemical Aspects of Bohr's Theory," *Journal of Chemical Education* 54(4), 208 (1977); Morwick, J. J., "What Is the Electron, Really?" *Journal of Chemical Education* 55(10), 662 (1978); Krisch, A. D., "The Spin of the Proton," *Scientific American* 240(5), 69 (1979); Jacob, M., and Landshoff, P., "The Inner Structure of the Proton," *Scientific American* 242(3), 66 (1980); Rutherford, K. L., "Avogadro's Number," *Journal of Chemical Education* 55(5), 334 (1978); Kolb, D., "The Mole," *Journal of Chemical Education* 55(11), 728 (1978); Zare, R. N., "Laser Separation of Isotopes," *Scientific American* 236(2), 86 (1977); "The Reality of Quarks," *Scientific American* 241(3), 82 (1979); Johnson, K. A., "The Bag Model of Quark Confinement," *Scientific American* 241(1), 112 (1979); "Quark Glue," *Scientific American* 241(5), 84 (1979); "Vanishing Point," *Scientific American*

242(3), 82 (1979); Ainslie, D. S., "Electrostatic Pendulum," *The Science Teacher*, 47(4), 42 (1980); Ekstrom, P., and Wineland, D., "The Isolated Electron," *Scientific American* 243(2), 104 (1980).

Teacher Notes
Chapter 4

Chapter Note

Student mastery of the details of the arrangement of electrons in atoms requires that they play an active role, particularly in the methodical, element-by-element evolutions of the various schematics on the chalkboard and at the desk. Once basic concepts such as electron-pair, octet stability, Hund's rule, and the Pauli exclusion principle have been developed, the students should be able to apply the rules to electron arrangements. Students should use an element's atomic number and their knowledge of electron configuration from Chapter 3. Students should realize that the Aufbau process of building electron structures of atoms as atomic numbers increase is a *mental process*. Models and schematics of the electron arrangement of atoms in the ground state are the result of this process. Students may not fully understand that they are dealing with the wave-mechanical model of the atom, but any demonstrations or activities that afford them some confidence in the model enhance the eventual usefulness of the model. Some teachers complement the experimental spectral data by use of experimental ionization energies. Although ionization energies are not dealt with until Chapter 5 of this text, tables such as Table 5-1 in this text and Tables 6-1 and 6-5 in *Foundations of Chemistry* provide the mathematical data for successive ionization energies for many elements. Based on the numerical values of such successive ionization energies, students can successfully make inferences about the electron arrangements in levels, sublevels, and orbitals. Such numerical values provide a degree of reality that supports the varieties of electron notations developed in this chapter.

	ev	kcal/mole
n = 1	−13.6	−313.6
n = 2	− 3.40	− 78.4
n = 3	− 1.51	− 34.8
n = 4	− 0.85	− 19.6
n = 5	− 0.54	− 12.5
n = 6	− 0.4	− 9.7

Teachers may wish to use these energy values, which relate to the transitions in Figure 4-6, or transparency set: PP T39.

This chapter probably requires four periods. A possible arrangement of lessons is:

Lesson 1 Sections 4.1–4.3: Evidence for Electron Energy Levels

Lesson 2 Sections 4.4 and 4.5: Wave Mechanics and Quantum Numbers

Lessons 3 and 4 Sections 4.6–4.10: Electron Configuration Schematics

Note

Refer to Section 3.4 for audiovisuals that may also be used in this chapter.

Section 4.1 Demonstrate again or **Review:** Electrostatic attraction and repulsion. Frame questions as to how this behavior does and does not satisfactorily explain the structure of atoms and their failure to collapse. Review electron configurations by lettered shells. Use models as needed. **Transparencies:** HRW: PP T39 *Energy Levels—Bohr Theory;* HM: 2-10525 *Electron Energy Levels.* **Films:** INDU: FS-357 *What Makes Atoms Stick Together?;* INDU: FS-358 *Why Are Atoms Unpredictable?;* IBF: *Conquest of the Atom* (22 min.).

Section 4.2 Activity: Make a chalkboard diagram similar to Figure 4-1 and use it to develop the concept of waves and the relationship between frequency and wavelength. In using the formula for electromagnetic radiation, emphasize the inverse proportionality of λ to f. Demonstrate the photoelectric effect to show that only photons of a certain frequency and hence a certain energy will be absorbed and produce the discharge of a charged electroscope. A freshly polished zinc plate is attached to an electroscope. The electroscope is charged negatively. Show that the negatively charged electroscope is not discharged by a tungsten light but is discharged by a black-light source. Use this demonstration to develop $E = hf$. Refer interested students to Experiment 43, "Photoelectric Effect," in *Project Physics Handbook*. Use a chalkboard replica of Figure 4-2 to develop the concept that when an excited atom with energy E_2 returns to E_1, it gives off a photon having energy $E_2 - E_1 = E = hf$. **Films:** IBF: *Wave-Particle Duality* (22 min.); IBF: *A New Reality* (51 min.); W: 140-423m *Matter Waves* (28 min.); CORF: 1281 *Light: Wave and Quantum Theories* (13 min.). **Loops:** W: 140-0470 *Photoemissions of Electrons;* BFA: ISBN 0-03-080153-2 *The Interaction of Radiation and Matter.* **Filmstrip:** I: 67234 *Photons and Electrons.*

Section 4.3. Demonstrations: (a) continuous spectrum using a slide projector, a mounted slit, and either a prism or diffraction grating; **(b)** representative flame tests; **(c)** activated gas tubes (H, Ne, Ar); **(b)** and **(c)** represent radiation from excited atoms. Demonstrate triboluminescence (emission of light that occurs as the result of excitation of a solid by mechanical stress). In a dark room, grind sugar or candy in a glass jar with a metal spoon or crush a wintergreen Life Saver suddenly between the jaws of a pair of pliers. **Reference:** Angeles, Zink, and Hardy, "Triboluminescence Spectroscopy of Common Candies," *Journal of Chemical Education*, 56(6), 413 (1979). **References:** *Modern Physics*, 1980, Sections 12.5–12.11; *Foundations of Chemistry*, Chapters 5 and 6; Christoudouleas, N. D., "Particles, Waves, and the Interpretation of Quantum Mechanics," 52, 573 (1975); Davis, J. C., Jr., "Introduction to Spectroscopy, Part I: The Nature of Spectra," *Chemistry* 47(9), 6 (1974), and "Introduction to Spectroscopy, Part II: Emission Spectroscopy," *Chemistry*, 48(11), 5 (1975). **Transparencies:** W: 167 W 0100 *Spectrum;* EYE: 012-1 *The Electromagnetic Spectrum;* HRW: PP T39 *Bohr Theory* (deals with the hydrogen spectrum). **Films:** W: 140-4207 *Spectroscopy;* W: 140-4148 *The Hydrogen Atom—As Viewed by Quantum Mechanics* (13 min.) (The advanced version is 140-4149.); CORF: 1281 *Light: Wave and Quantum Theories* (13 min.); CORF: 1646 *Radiant Energy and the Electromagnetic Spectrum.* **Loops:** W: 168 W 1038 T *Atomic Hydrogen;* BFA: ISBN 0-03-0810149-4 *The Nature of Spectra;* BFA: ISBN 0-03-080152-4 *Light and the Electromagnetic*

Spectrum; BFA: ISBN 0-03-080154-0 *Emission Spectroscopy;* EBE: S80708 *The Spectrum of the Hydrogen Atom.* **Demonstrations:** Line Spectra: Students examine the light from a mounted neon tube through a slit and diffraction grating and establish that the emitted radiation consists of definite lines and energy level transitions. Base the development of textbook Sections 4.2 and 4.3 on the suggested demonstrations in order to explain the wave nature of light, relationships between wavelength and frequency, a photon as a quantum (unit) of electromagnetic radiation energy, and the wave-particle duality of light. Discuss details of Figures 4-4, 4-5, 4-6 in explaining the hydrogen spectrum and the possible energy-level transitions.

Section 4.4. Activity: Develop the concept of a space orbital in terms of probability. Discuss electron cloud (use Figure 4-7) and its role in giving size and shape to the atom and preventing two free atoms from occupying the same space. **Transparencies:** EYE: 003-8 *Hydrogen Atom Orbitals;* EYE: 003-7 *Stabilizing Forces of Orbits.* **References:** *Foundations of Chemistry*, Sections 6.9–6.11 and Section 4.5; Morwik, J. J., "Should Orbitals Be Taught in High School?" *Journal of Chemical Education*, 54(4), 262 (1979).

Section 4.5. Activities: Define quantum numbers in terms of what each indicates. Use the Pauli exclusion principle to explain why no electron may have the same four quantum numbers. You may wish to employ an analog that compares the electron's quantum number "address" with the details of a student's address such as state, city, street, and street number. Refer to zip code number as a kind of U.S. "quantum number" pinpointing a location in a certain geographical area. Students should realize that the letters s, p, d, and f are subdesignations for the orbital quantum numbers. **Exhibit:** Models of s and p orbitals (use Figures 4-7 and 4-8). One source of models is set KC9001, Klinger Scientific Co. Develop a chalkboard chart for Table 4-1. **References:** Krupsaw, M., "Electron Configuration Diagram," *Journal of Chemical Education*, 49, 443 (1972); Grotz, L. C., and Gauerke, E., "Orbital Memory Devices," *Chemistry*, 45 (1972); Luder, W. F., "Atomic Structure Without Quantum Theory," *Chemistry*, 48(6), 6 (1975); *Foundations of Chemistry*, Sections 6.12–6.17. **Transparencies:** EYE: 003-9 *Directed Orbitals;* EYE: 003-11 *Energy Level Diagram;* HM: 2-10524 *Electron Orbitals;* HM: 2-10525 *Electron Energy Levels.* **Filmstrips:** I: 67118 *Orbitals—Atomic and Molecular* (frames 3–15); Welch: Chart 4837 *Electron Energy Levels* (similar to Figure 4-9).

Sections 4.6–4.10. Activity: Develop the variety of electron notations in Table 4-2 through student activity. Use Worksheet II: Electron Configurations and Notations or a suitably arranged student notebook. Discuss one element at a time. Write the results on the chalkboard at the same time the students are filling in their notebooks. The information given is the symbol and atomic number of the element. Deal with the first twenty elements to get the pattern of filling in orbitals. (Some teachers go as far as $_{30}Zn$ in the tabulation. This introduction increases student understanding through student performances related to part of Table 4-3 and Section 4.7.) Work with the principal quantum numbers and electron configuration notation. The generalized formula nl^x is developed from the electron notations for H and He. The letter n represents the principal quantum number, l represents the letter subdesignations (s, p, d, f) for orbital quantum number, and x represents the electron population of each orbital. If you just use the textbook model, x represents the electron population of the sublevel. If you choose to use the more detailed model, which is more directly related to the orbital notation and electron-dot notation, the equivalent for $_7N$ is $1s^2 2s^2 2p_x{}^1 2p_y{}^1 2p_z{}^1$ instead of $1s^2 2s^2 2p^3$. This activity may take one complete period. Some teachers develop the more detailed electron-configuration notation after the orbital notation equivalents are developed. Emphasize concepts involving the electron-pair and the octet rule for the outermost electron shells in developing student understanding and mastery of the various notation schemes. Some teachers use the term valence electrons (Section 6.2) for the outer-shell electrons. The orbital notation portion of Table 4-2 is developed next. The first problem arises with $_6C$, which is resolved on the basis of electron repulsion of electrons with parallel spins. Hund's rule of maximum multiplicity may be developed and stated, if desired, as: Additional electrons singly occupy equivalent orbitals of the same sublevel before beginning to pair up. The first pairing of p electrons occurs with $_8O$.

Electron-dot notation: Use a chalkboard replica of Figure 4-10 to explain the general procedure for placement of the dots. Develop the electron-dot notation through atomic number 20. Explain the placement of single electrons and electron-pairs about the chemical symbol in the electron-dot notation as representative of the arrangement of the outer-shell (valence) electrons in the orbital notation. Then have the students fill in the electron-dot notations in the last column of the table. Because of multiple valence of the transition elements, electron-dot symbols are used infrequently. Have students write electron-dot symbols for the nontransition elements of the fourth and succeeding series. Have students use the data in Tables 4-3, 4-4, and 4-5 in writing these electron-dot symbols. One scheme that students may use to help them in determining the order of energy levels of subshells appears in *Foundations of Chemistry*, Fig. 6-5. If the transition elements are included in the classroom table, as it develops, the various configurations are developed showing that though additional electrons are present *after* Ca (4th series), they are in the $3d$ sublevel after $4s$ (Aufbau buildup), as shown in Figure 4-12. However, in the atom in its ground state, the $3d$ electrons are below the $4s$ electrons (Table 4-3) for Sc-Zn. The orbital notations for Cr and Cu may be used to develop the concepts of extra stability of half-filled (Cr) or completely filled (Cu) orbitals (sublevels). The completion of the $4p$ orbitals after completion of the $3d$ orbitals is illustrated by reference to Table 4-3. The arrangement of the $4f$ orbitals after the $6s$ orbitals are filled is followed by the completion of the $5d$ sublevel (Table 4-5). Refer students to Figure 5-5, Sublevel Blocks of the Periodic Table, to show how elements may be arranged according to their atomic structure. Compare the electron-dot notations for the elements in each group of Groups I, II, III-VII elements. Refer to Tables 4-3, 4-4, and 4-6. Review previous treatment of arrangements of d and f electrons and the schematics for placement. Use questions 18–20 and select from questions 21–28. **Programmed Instruction:** PH: WCC-851 *Electron Configurations and Orbital Diagrams;* Ward's Solo-Learn: 78 W 0400 *Introduction to the Electronic Structure of Atoms.* **References:** "The Newest Element: 106," *Science News,* 106(11), 164 (1974); "Element 107: U. S. Group Skeptical," *Science News,*

110(15), 229 (1976); Davis, J. C., Jr., in *Chemistry:* "The Nature of Spectra," 47, 6 (Oct. 1974); "Interaction of Light and Matter," 48, 15 (July–Aug. 1974); "Light and the Electromagnetic Spectrum," 48, 19 (May 1975); "Emission Spectroscopy," 45, 5 (Dec. 1975); "The Spectrometer," 48, 11 (Jan.–Feb. 1975); "Introduction to Spectroscopy," 49, 18 (Nov. 1976); "Electrons Fill Subshells," *Journal of Chemical Education,* 53(10), 645 (1976). Cavagnoim, R., and Barnett, T., "Simple Models For Tough Concepts," *Journal of Chemical Education,* 53(10), 643 (1976). The list of references for model construction is excellent: Kaufman, G. B., "Electrostatic Molecular Models," *Chemistry,* 52, 6 (Oct. 1975); Roberts, R. M., and Traynham, J. G., "Molecular Geometry: As Easy as Blowing Up Balloons," *Journal of Chemical Education* 53(4), 233 (1976); Rioux, F., "The Stability of the Hydrogen Atom," *Journal of Chemical Education,* 50, 550 (1973); Pilar, F. L., "4s is Always above 3d!" *Journal of Chemical Education,* 55(1), 2 (1978), and "Letters," *Journal of Chemical Education,* 56(11), 767 (1979); Hansh, T. W., Schawlow, A. L., and Series, G. W., "The Spectrum of Atomic Hydrogen," *Scientific American* 240(3), 94 (1979); Morwick, J. J., "Should Orbitals Be Taught in High School?" *Journal of Chemical Education* 56(4), 262 (1979).

Teacher Notes
Chapter 5

Chapter Note

The primary objective of this chapter is to help students develop demonstrable appreciations and skills concerning both the sequence of experimentally discovered facts about atomic structure and the organization of these facts into a major scientific concept. Related aspects of the scientific method include: **(a)** the inductive processes of observation, experimentation, correlation, and inference in the formulation of concepts and **(b)** the deductive process and prediction based on the use of scientific law and theory as a tool. The extensive use of data organized into tables or graphs correlated with previously developed models of atomic structure (Chapters 3 and 4) unifies and simplifies the study of chemistry. The development of the chapter requires a minimum of three periods and one possible arrangement is:

Lesson 1   Sections 5.1–5.4: Development of the Periodic Law

Lesson 2   Section 5.5: Modern Periodic Table: Periods, Groups, Transition and Rare Earth Elements, Metalloids. This lesson may require two periods. Items 6–18 in the related Exercise 5 may require considerable class time.

Lesson 3   Sections 5.6–5.10: Periodic Properties: Atomic Radii, Ionization Energy, Electron Affinity

Section 5.1. As a prelude to the discussion of combining weights (Berzelius) and atomic weight determination (Stas), describe Dalton's assignment of hydrogen atomic mass (weight) of 1 and oxygen's relative atomic mass of 8 (actually its combining weight, based on the analysis of water in which 8 g of oxygen is combined with 1 g of hydrogen). **Reference:** *Foundations of Chemistry,* Section 2.13 and Sections 2.15–

2.17 (Gay-Lussac, Avogadro, Cannizzaro). Discuss the attempts at classification: Dobereiner's triads and Newland's law of octaves. Exhibit wall chart of periodic table with covers over noble gases and Sc, Ga, and Ge. **Transparency Set:** HRW: PP T35 *The Periodic Table* (A, B, C, D, E, F, G)—use selected portions. **Demonstrations:** Similarities in properties: **(a)** Li, Na, K on H_2O **(CAUTION); (b)** powdered Sb (cold) into Cl_2, Sb (heated) into Br_2 (vapor), Sb (heated) into hot I_2. **Activities:** Students compute atomic weight of Br as approximately one-half of sum of atomic weights of Cl and I. Students count off number of elements before demonstrated property (and electronic structures). Items 6 through 18 in the related Exercise 5 may require considerable class time. **Slides:** I: 69101 *Historical Development of the Periodic Table.* **Transparencies:** EYE: 003-12 *Historical Development of the Periodic Law;* PH: WCC 741 *The Periodic Table of Elements, Introduction.*

Section 5.2. Have students note that the alkali metals Group I and the halogens Group VII, respectively, occur in Figure 5-1 (Mendeleev's original periodic table) in the same horizontal positions. Have students count off the number of elements (7) for Li-Na-K before similar property recurs. Repeat for F-Cl. Mendeleev found that there were 17 elements in the third and fourth series before properties reoccurred, i.e., Cl-Br and Br-I). The above emphasizes that similar chemical properties occur at definite intervals, and are in periodic dependence on their atomic weights. Have students discover discrepancy in placement of Te (128) and I (127). Remove the cover from Ge and compare Mendeleev prediction with actual values. See Table 5-1 and Table 7-1 in *Foundations of Chemistry.* Also uncover Sc and Ga, which were discovered after Mendeleev's prediction. **Reference:** *Project Physics Text,* Sections 17.3–17.7 and Section 5.3. Use the **Film:** IFB: *The Discovery of the Inert Gases* (19 min.). Remove the covers over these gases in the periodic chart. **Filmstrip:** I: 67108 *The Noble Gases.* Have students explain how atomic number correctly places Ar, K, Te and I, indicating that atomic numbers are a more fundamental property than atomic weights. Give examples of missing elements according to Moseley and the discovery of 43 (Tc), 61 (Pm), and 75 (Re). **Transparency:** HRW: PP T45 *Mass Spectrometer.* Emphasize the use of "new" apparatus in the discovery of facts that lead to new ideas. Mention the mass spectrograph (*Foundations of Chemistry,* Section 5.10, Figure 5-16). **References:** Hogg, J. T., "Moseley at Oxford," *Journal of Chemical Education* 52(5), 325 (1975); Mazurs, E. G., *Graphic Representations of the Periodic System During One Hundred Years,* University of Alabama Press, Birmingham, Alabama, 1974; Hyde, J. F., "A Newly Arranged Periodic Chart," *Chemistry,* 49(7), 15 (1976); Research Reporter, "The Growing Periodic Table," *Chemistry,* 49(7), 26 (1976) (Superheavies, Elements 116, 124, 126); Research Reporter, "Growing Periodic Table," *Chemistry,* 47(11), 22 (1974); Trimble, R. F., "What Happened to Alabamine, Virginium, and Illinium?" *Journal of Chemical Education,* 52(9), 585 (1976); Bunting, R. K., "Element Number 61," *Chemistry* 50(5), 16 (1977); Pett, V. B., "Whole Numbers and Atomic Theory," *Chemistry* 51(1), 16 (1978); vanSpronsen, J. W., "Atomic Numbers before Moseley," *Journal of Chemical Education* 56(2), 106 (1979); Kragh, H., and Robertson, P., "On the Discovery of Element

72," *Journal of Chemical Education* 56(7), 456 (1979); Seaborg, G. T., "The Periodic Table," *Chemistry & Engineering* Apr. 16, 1979, p. 46; Kolb, D., "What Is an Element?" *Journal Chemical Education* 54(11) 696 (1979); "A Legacy from Sweden," *Journal of Chemical Education* 56(11), 669 (1979).

Section 5.4. Have the Periodic Law stated and discuss occurrence of elements of similar properties at certain intervals; discuss how properties of successive elements go through a pattern of change (i.e., across a period: metal → metalloid → nonmetal → noble gas).

Section 5.5. Exhibits and **Transparencies:** Make a chalkboard replica of Figure 5-3 to identify details in a block in the periodic table. Display a wall chart of the periodic table, or one of the previously mentioned transparencies, in conjunction with the text table and have students locate atomic number and weight. Have them also note the electron energy levels and electron population. Period and group are defined and the representative numbers identified and located on the table. Have students identify the main types of elements labeled in the table. It is useful at this point to concentrate on the first 20 elements. Exhibit samples of elements of Period 3 (Figure 5-4, A and B) and as many of the other elements as possible. Review the electron configuration of elements 1-20 using either chalkboard diagrams of the main shell structures or electron-dot symbols to point out similarities in the outermost shell population among members of the same groups (I–VIII). Use Worksheet I: Atomic Models for Some Elements in the Periodic Table. It consists of boxed outlines for the first twenty elements and affords space for inclusion of the electron configuration notation. The given data is the symbol with the atomic number and the mass number of the most abundant isotope. Have students draw models and fill in boxes complemented by chalkboard development. Use Figure 5-5, Sublevel Blocks of the Periodic Table. Have students put in the zigzag lines on their worksheet. **Demonstrations:** Select demonstrations from the ones listed below to help provide actual experiences in identifying physical and chemical properties and to help maintain student interest in the descriptive details that appear in Section 5.4.

(1) *Metallic luster:* Na, Mg, Al, K, Ca.

(2) *Toughness of metals versus brittleness of solid nonmetals:* Cut Na, K, Mg ribbon, sheet Al; beat Al or Mg with a hammer, attempt to cut S; hit crystal of rhombic (roll) S and powder in mortar.

(3) *Electric conductivity:* Use two dry cells in series with a flashlight bulb and place samples across open terminals. By replacing the bulb with a lecture table ammeter and by using the appropriate range with a suitable resistor in series, it is possible to show decrease in conductivity for elements of Period 3. A conductivity tester (Welch) may also be used with 120-v ac and a 25-w bulb.

(4) *Reaction with O_2 (air):* Have students observe storage of Na in hydrocarbon and P in water, rapid tarnishing of freshly cut Na, burning Mg ribbon, burning Na in deflagrating spoon, Al powder in burner flame, "smoking" of white P, burning of S and red P in deflagrating spoon.

(5) *Reactions with H_2O:* Test Na, Mg, Ca, K, C, S, Si. Use **Loop:** W: 168-1003(T) *Alkali Metal Reactions with Chlorine and Water.*

(6) *Reactions with dilute HCl:* Mg, Al, S, C, Si, P.

(7) *Reactions with dilute NaOH:* Test Mg versus Al, nonmetals.

(8) *Identify He, Ne, Ar:* Use gas tubes with Tesla coil.

(9) *Oxides with H_2O and effect on litmus:* Use CaO, SO_2, or P_4O_{10}. The oxides produced by burning S or red P in a deflagrating spoon in a bottle of air may be used along with solid CaO.

Films: EBE: 2950 *Metals and Nonmetals* (10 min.); CORF: *Metals and Nonmetals.* **Activities:** The variation in properties across a period is established as follows: Metals of decreasing activity (e.g., Na versus Mg) → metalloids → nonmetals of increasing reactivity → noble gases (inert for He, Ne, Ar). Correlation of class of element with outer-shell electron population is established by comparing representative worksheet models and with element properties. Metals are recognized as having a few electrons—one, two, and sometimes three (Al)— in outermost shell, while the most active nonmetals have an almost complete octet and usually many electrons—five, six, or seven. The inertness of the first three noble gases is related to the stability of an electron pair (He) and of the octet (Ne and Ar). Show the **Film:** W: 140-4112 *Chemical Families,* and use it in connection with group properties and variations in properties. It emphasizes the relation of the most active metals and nonmetals as having, respectively, one more and one fewer outer-shell electrons than related noble (inert) gases, which have an octet. The film also demonstrates the reaction between xenon and fluorine. On the basis of demonstrations such as the reaction of Ca versus Mg with H_2O, Na on H_2O, and K releasing H_2 from ice, the relative activity of metals in a family is established as increasing with increasing atomic number. Use the reactions of Sb with Cl_2 and Br_2 to establish that chlorine is more active than bromine and, by analogy, to have students predict that fluorine is the most active. Have students generalize that nonmetallic reactivity decreases with an increase in atomic number. The filmstrip I: 67105 *The Noble Gases* presents evidence of the inertness of He, Ne, and Ar, and of compound formation by Xe and Kr. Student reports may be based on such articles as: Stein, L., "Noble Gas Compounds," *Chemistry,* 47(9), 15 (1974); Selig, H., Malm, J. G., and Classen, H., "The Chemistry of the Noble Gases," *Scientific American,* 210(5), 66 (1964). Identify and discuss the transition elements of Periods 4 and 5 and review the electron configurations involving the 3*d* and 4*d* orbitals. Exhibit some of the more common and recognizable metals: Fe, Cr, Cu, etc. Have students explain why the transition elements are metals, emphasizing the electron populations of the outermost *s* sublevel. The first ten frames of the I: 67112 Filmstrip 633 *The Transition Elements* may be used for an introduction to transition metals. You may also refer students to Table 7 in the Appendix or to the first few pages of Chapter 26 of this text. The electron configurations of the Lanthanide and Actinide series are established as involving incomplete 4*f* and 5*f* orbitals respectively. Point out the similarity of the two outer shells of the rare earth elements in explaining why these elements have almost identical chemical properties. Discuss the significance of the zigzag line separating metal from metalloid in the periodic table. Identify and define metalloids. Discuss the change in properties of Groups IV and V: nonmetal →

metalloid → metal. The students probably are most acquainted with the Group IV elements, such as C (nonmetal in some forms), Si (metalloid), Sn and Pb (metals). Note that for Groups I–VII, as the atomic number increases, chemical reactivity as a metal increases while chemical reactivity as a nonmetal decreases. Items 1–9 and 19–23 in Exercise 5 of *Exercises and Experiments in Chemistry* may be used as a summary of Section 5.5. **Transparencies:** EYE: 003-13 *Periodic Functions;* W: 167 W 0120 *Periodic Chart.* **Loops:** EBE: 2954 *Atomic Structure and the Periodic Table* (11 min.); EBE: 2950 *Metals and Nonmetals* (10 min.). **Slides:** I: 69105 *Metals, Nonmetals, Transition Elements;* I: 69106 *The Periodic Table and Chemical Behavior.* **Filmstrips:** PH: WCC 742 *The Group Relationships;* PH: WCC 852 *Atomic Structure and the Periodic Chart: An Introduction.* **Reference:** Lipeles, E., "Rediscovered Elements," *Chemistry* 51(10), 17 (1978).

Section 5.6. Activity: Have students examine the tabular and graphic data (Figure 5-5, Figure 5-6) for size of atoms. Students should be challenged and helped to recognize and state generalizations (conclusions 1 and 2 in text) on the basis of these data and their relationship to atomic structure and periodicity of properties. **Chart:** Welch: 4844 *Relative Sizes of Atoms and Ions in the Periodic Table.* **Slides:** I: 69102 *Periodicity: Physical Appearance, Atomic Size.* **References:** *Fundamentals of Chemistry,* Section 7.7; "The Correct Size of the Noble Gas Atoms," *Journal of Chemical Education* 45, 791 (1968).

Section 5.7. Start the lesson with one or more of the following: **Film:** W: 140-4151 *Ionization Energy* (22 min.). **Loop:** W: 168 W 1041(T) *Ionization Energy of Sodium.* **Slides:** I: 69104 *Ionization Energy, Electron Affinity, Electronegativity;* EBE: 2947 *Demonstrations of Electronegativity* (4 min.). **Filmstrip:** I: 67131 *Ionization Potential and Electronegativity.* **Transparency Set:** W: 75 W 8020 *Trends in Periodic Table.* The attraction between nucleus and electrons leads to the problem: How can the electron(s) be totally removed from an atom? The CHEM film shows students how ionization energy is experimentally determined. On the basis of this film and Figures 5-8 and 5-9, develop the series of generalizations pertaining to the first ionization energies. Develop functional concepts related to ionization energy for noble gas, metal, nonmetal, and metalloid. The noble gas data furnish evidence for the stability of the octet, and for He of the electron-pair. The general decrease in ionization energy for a group with increasing atomic number is explained by the increase in radius. The general but irregular increase in ionization energy in a period (Groups I–VIII) is identified as another periodic property. Present the explanations in Section 5.7 for the decreases between Groups I and II and Groups V and VI as they relate to the electron population of sublevels. Another viewpoint is to consider the ionization energies for Be and N (Period 2) and for Mg and P (Period 3) as being unexpectedly larger than they would be if there were a regular, instead of an irregular, increase in ionization energies. From this viewpoint, the stability of the electron-pair and the extra stability of the half-completed sublevel may be developed. **Review:** Electron configuration notations or orbital notations for the elements. Have students explain how the experimental data presented throughout Section 5.7 reinforce the models developed on the basis of wave mechanics. Have students locate an unusually large decrease in ionization energies of successive elements in Periods 4, 5, and 6. Have them explain this decrease in terms of the population of the $(n-1)d$ sublevel of np orbitals.

Section 5.8. **Discussion:** Figure 5-9, Table 5-2. Have students explain the differences in the values for removal of successive electrons for Na, Mg, and Al in terms of the electron configuration and orbital designation for the electrons undergoing removal. Have students attempt to answer question 29. Some teachers present the ionization energy experiments and data while they are developing the concepts of energy level, sublevels, and orbitals in Chapter 4. Students can, and do, understand the numbers indicating experimental measurements more easily than abstractions of wave mechanics. **Reference:** Liebman, J. F., "Regularities and Relations among Ionization Potentials of Nontransition Elements," *Journal of Chemical Education,* 50(12), 831 (1973).

Section 5.9. **Filmstrip** PH: SCC 854 *Classification of the Elements: Metals, Nonmetals, Metalloids* defines and uses the concepts of electron affinity and ionization potential. The slide series I: 69104 *Ionization Energy, Electron Affinity, Electronegativity* includes a number of useful slides on electronegativity. **Activity:** Define electron affinity and develop the equation representing the exothermic and endothermic changes. In each case, the stability of ion versus atom should be discussed. Have students examine the data in Figures 5-11 and 5-10. Have them discover which groups (II and VIII) and which subfamily (zinc subfamily) have zero or negative electron affinities. Have students refer to the electron configurations of these elements and arrive at the appropriate explanation (filled outermost s or p sublevels and stable inner energy levels). Develop the generalizations regarding variations in electron affinities and the explanations for regularities and irregularities as in the text. **References:** Chen, E. C. M., and Wentworth, W. F., "The Experimental Values of Atomic Electron Affinities: Their Selection and Periodic Behavior," *Journal of Chemical Education,* 52(8), 486 (1975); Brooks, D. W., Meyers, E. A., Sicillio, F., and Nearing, J. C., "Electron Affinity: The Zeroth Ionization Potential," *Journal of Chemical Education,* 50, 487 (1973)—Assign questions 17, 18, 30, 31.

Section 5.10. **Activity:** You may wish to demonstrate the burning of Na in Cl_2 to set the stage for the next chapter and challenge students to attempt to use the concepts of ionization energy, electron affinity, and octet completion in explaining the formation of NaCl. **Activity and Programmed Instruction:** The ideas developed throughout this chapter may be reinforced by using Exercise 5, The Periodic Law, and the programmed instructional references at the end of this chapter. **Summary:** You may wish to lighten the treatment of this chapter by (1) playing "The Elements," from *An Evening Wasted with Tom Lehrer* (Reprise Records); or (2) having students locate the answers to the following by finding the names from the atomic numbers in the periodic table: A doctor can do two things for patients, 2 (heal-um) or 96 (cure-em). Failing that, the doctor will have to 56 (bury-em). The only element without a stomach is 102 (no-belly-um). **General References:** *Chemistry Handbook,* New York State Education Department, Albany, N. Y. (sixty-four generalizations based on the periodic table and suggested activities, pp. 68–76); *Project Physics Handbook,* Chapter 17; Sisler, H., *Electron*

Structure, Properties, and the Periodic Table, Chapter 1: "Electronic Structures of Atoms and the Periodic Law." **Programmed Instruction:** PH: WCC 852 *Atomic Structure and the Periodic Chart: An Introduction;* PH: WCC 853 *Electrical Forces Within Atoms;* PH: WCC 854 *Classification of the Elements: Metals, Nonmetals, Metalloids;* Ward's Solo-Learn: 78 W 0680 *Electronic Structure and the Periodic Chart.*

Teacher Notes
Chapter 6

Chapter Note

The objectives of this chapter are the development of the concepts and mastery of the skills involved in chemical bonding. The concepts are (a) Chemical bonding: ionic, covalent, empirical, and molecular formulas; (b) Particles of matter: elements and compounds; (c) Oxidation and reduction: oxidation number (oxidation state), oxidizing and reducing agents; (d) Electronegativity: bond types and electronegativity difference, ions, polar and nonpolar molecules, polyatomic ions; (e) Energy changes in bonding. The fundamental skills are (1) Using notation systems in chemical bond formation and formulas; (2) Writing representative equations for energy changes involved in bond formation; (3) Using the concept of electronegativity and electronegativity difference as an aid in the determination of bond formation, bond type, molecular and polyatomic structure; (4) Applying oxidation rules and concepts.

This chapter requires a minimum of six lessons.

Lesson 1   Sections 6.1–6.4: Compounds, Ionic Bonding
Lesson 2   Sections 6.5–6.8: Oxidation Number, Ionic Bonding
Lesson 3   Sections 6.9–6.12: Covalent Bonding, Bond Energy
Lesson 4   Sections 6.13–6.18: Covalent Bonds: Unlike Atoms, Hybridization, Molecule Size
Lesson 5   Sections 6.19–6.21: Electronegativity, Chemical Bonding, Molecular Polarity
Lesson 6   Sections 6.22–6.25: Resonance, Polyatomic Ions, Particles of Matter, Oxidation-Number Rules

Section 6.1. **Activity:** List the formulas in this section on the chalkboard and have students recognize and pose the problem: Why are there differences in the number of H (and Cl) atoms per atom of the other elements? Students may be able to suggest a mode of attack based on their knowledge of atomic structure and electron configuration of the atoms. They may recognize that five of the compounds consist of two nonmetals and three of the compounds consist of a metal combined with a nonmetal. Exhibit samples and models of the compounds. **Films** related to previous chapters are: NAVC: 696340-HH *Solid State Principles* (26 min.); CORF: 1404 *Chemical Bond and Atomic Structure;* MG: S 100-08 B *Periodic Table, the Ionic and Covalent Compounds.* Selected portions may be used now or the showing deferred until later in the chapter development.

Section 6.2. **Activities:** Have students make chalkboard shell diagrams and write electron-dot symbols for the elements appearing in the list of compounds. Review the models and electron-dot symbols for Ne, He, and Ar and have students explain the chemical stability and high ionization energies of these elements. Have students explain how the other elements *could* attain more stable electron structures (a stable outer shell having a noble-gas configuration) by electron transfer—loss and gain, or sharing. Define and identify the valence electrons. Refer to the kernel and electron dots of the electron-dot symbols. Have students use the periodic table to recognize that the group number of Groups I–VII is related to the number of valence electrons. **Demonstrations:** Burn Mg ribbon in air; drop powdered Sb into Cl_2; lower a burning H_2 jet into Cl_2, show H_2O formation by placing the burning H_2 jet under an inverted beaker. These demonstrations are used to show that energy changes occur during compound formation.

Section 6.3. Demonstration: (CAUTION) Burn Na in a bottle of Cl_2. See also Alyea, pp. 201, 212, or duplicate demonstration in Figure 6-2. **Exhibits:** A crystal of halite, crystals of NaCl (hand lens), and both ball-stick (Klinger KC80604) and close-packed (Science Related Materials 7027). Also see Ealing's *Atomic Model Reference Library.* Pose the question: How can the formula NaCl represent the compound and the combined atoms (ions)? Define empirical formula. Use the orbital configurations for Na, Cl, and NaCl in Section 6.3. Use Table 6-1 and the electron-dot formula for NaCl. Complement these with the atom-shell chalkboard diagrams with the half-reaction equations, the energies involved, and the labeling of the half-reactions as oxidation and reduction. Use the chalkboard first for developing the atom-shell model at the top of the page to show how NaCl forms by electron transfer resulting in ions having outer octets. The space underneath the model may be used subsequently to write the equations and identification of the process as oxidation or reduction, as energies and processes are discussed later. This model is also useful in counting the protons and electrons in corresponding ions and thus helping students appreciate how ion charge originates. Have students make chalkboard atom-shell diagrams for the Na^+ and Cl^- ions, each of which has attained the noble gas configuration. **Film:** W: 140-4112 *Chemical Families* (22 min.). **Loops:** W: 168 W 1003(T) *Alkali Metal Reactions with Chlorine and Water;* LCG: E-65A *The Structure of an Ionic Crystal;* LCG: E-65 *The Properties of an Ionic Compound.* **Filmstrips:** I: 67144 *The Ionic Bond;* PH: WCC 862 *Bonding Between Atoms of Different Elements: Metals and Nonmetals: The Ionic Bond.* **Transparency:** EYE: 003-15 *Covalent and Ionic Bonds.* **Demonstration:** Conductivity of fused sodium chloride to show students that ions exist: An electrode-bulb conductivity assembly using closely placed iron rod electrodes is used in the demonstration. First a knife blade is held across the electrode gap to light the lamp and show conductivity. A small porcelain crucible into which the electrodes may be completely introduced is strongly preheated, preferably with a Fisher burner. A small amount of NaCl (no more than ½ teaspoonful) is then placed in the crucible and the heating continued. Melting will take place almost immediately. The crucible is then raised or the electrode assembly lowered so that the electrodes are in the melt. The bulb lights, showing existence of charged particles (ions). Other salts such as sodium or potassium nitrate or silver nitrate melt much more readily but the NaCl is recommended because of the direct relation to the lesson content. A small amount of KCl mixed with the NaCl will cause the NaCl to melt more readily.

The properties of ionic (electrovalent) compounds may be thus summarized: Crystalline solids, of high melting points, which do not conduct electricity in the solid state but do conduct it when molten or when dissolved in water. It may also be demonstrated that the solid halite crystal or a mass of salt crystals in the crucible does not conduct and that a salt solution will conduct electricity. You may wish to introduce the concept of dissociation and free-moving ions in the liquid phase and in aqueous solution.

$$NaCl(s) + energy \rightarrow Na^+ + Cl^-$$
$$\text{(bound ions)} \qquad \text{(free-moving ions)}$$

$$NaCl(s) + water \rightarrow Na^+(aq) + Cl^-(aq)$$
$$\text{(free-moving ions)}$$

Section 6.4. Activities: Develop the text equations with the energies involved on the chalkboard. In summation, arrive at the exothermic nature of the net process. **Reference:** *Foundations of Chemistry,* "Born-Haber cycle," pp. 371–375.

Section 6.5. Develop: The three rules for oxidation numbers as they apply to the formation of NaCl. If you used the chalkboard atom-shell models suggested above, label half-reaction equations. Also define oxidizing agent and reducing agent and label Cl and Na respectively. **Demonstrations:** Using atom-shell models, show the formation of MgO and relate the demonstration to burning Mg ribbon, which students readily recognize and label as the process of oxidation. **Demonstrate:** The burning of Mg in Cl_2 (**CAUTION:** use goggles and glass shield). **Activities:** Show the formation of $MgCl_2$ using atom-shell models on the chalkboard. Have students recognize the

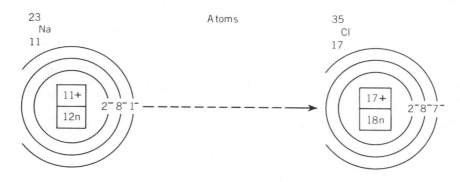

similarity for the half-reaction: $Mg - 2e^- \rightarrow Mg^{++}$ for both formation of MgO and $MgCl_2$. This permits the framing of the definition of oxidation as electron loss. The gain of electrons by both the O and the Cl is labeled reduction (some teachers also use deoxidation). Expand Rule 1: Elements whose atoms are not combined with atoms of a different element have an oxidation number of zero. As examples use metals (Na, Mg, Zn) and nonmetals as they occur in the elementary molecular condition: He, Ne (monatomic molecules); H_2, O_2, N_2, Cl_2 (diatomic molecules); O_3, P_4, S_8 (more complex molecules). Exhibit samples or models of these and then place a zero above each of the symbols or formulas on the chalkboard. Develop Rule 3 by placing the oxidation numbers in the formulas of compounds:

$$\overset{+1}{Na}\,\overset{-1}{Cl}, \quad \overset{+1}{Na^+}\,\overset{-1}{Cl^-}; \quad \overset{+2}{Mg}\,\overset{-2}{O}, \quad \overset{+2}{Mg^{++}}\,\overset{-2}{O^{--}}$$

Repeat for $MgCl_2$, Al_2O_3. On the chalkboard, demonstrate that multiplying the oxidation number of each element by its subscript results in the numerical equivalence of the total positive and total negative oxidation numbers. **Transparencies:** EYE: 003-30 *Oxidation Numbers;* EYE: 003-31 *Principle of Oxidation-Reduction Numbers.* (These may be used later for the other oxidation number rules.)

Section 6.6. Activities: The preceding activities readily lead to the details in the formula:

$$\overset{+2}{Mg^{++}}\,\overset{-1}{Br_2^-}$$

which appears in the final paragraph of Section 6.6. Develop the orbital model representing the electron transfer in the formation of $MgBr_2$. Use Table 6-2, developing details on the chalkboard. Refer students to Figures 6-5 and 6-6. Use the chalkboard to develop the electron-dot and ionic formulas for $MgBr_2$. Write the oxidation and reduction equations and label oxidizing and reducing agents. Reemphasize that all formulas for ionic compounds are empirical formulas. You may have students construct atom-shell diagrams or electron-dot formulas for $CaCl_2$ and Al_2O_3. By questions, have students arrive at the ideas that (a) the element oxidized attains a more positive oxidation number, and (b) the element reduced attains a more negative oxidation number. Show the **Film** MH: 612007 *Oxidation-Reduction.* Use such questions as: Which groups of elements would tend to have oxidation numbers of +1 or +2? Use Al as an example of a metal with an oxidation number of +3. Which groups of elements could have oxidation numbers of −1 or −2? Lead to the general idea that ionic compounds are generally formed by the metals of Groups I and II and Al of Group III with the nonmetals of Groups VI and VII. The teacher may supplement with the additional information that some metallic hydrides and some metallic nitrides are also ionic. Have the students solve the Practice Problem for Li_2O.

Section 6.7. Activities: Exhibit samples of the compounds shown in Figure 6-7. Write the formulas for $FeCl_2$ and $FeCl_3$. Have students decide on the oxidation number of Fe in each compound using the oxidation number of the chloride ion (−1) as the basis. Students may recognize that, unlike the metals of Groups I and II and Al, the transition metals (Figure 5-5, "Sublevel Blocks of the Periodic Table") generally have several oxidation states. Your wall chart of the periodic table may show the several oxidation states of various elements (Sargent-Welch 4854, Sargent-Welch student chart S-18806). For Fe, you may wish to develop the orbital notation and use the ionization energies per mole: 1st = 182 kcal, 2nd = 375 kcal, 3rd = 708 kcal. The wall chart may also show that nonmetals generally have several oxidation numbers. Refer students to Appendix Table 5, which also appears on the front page of this text, for elements with several oxidation numbers.

Section 6.8. Have students use Table 6-3 for the framing of generalizations and explanations pertaining to these generalizations, including variations within a group and a period. Define cation and anion using atomic-shell chalkboard diagrams to illustrate the effects of unbalanced charges. Exhibit crystal models of NaCl and other ionic compounds. **Film:** BFA: 10785 *Considering Crystals* (15 min.). **Filmstrip:** I: 67116 *Crystals and Their Properties.* **Loops:** EBE: Series 9190 *Relative Sizes of Atoms; Relative Sizes of Ions; Packing of Atoms in Crystals; Construction of Molecular Models;* EBE: Series 9080 *Electron Arrangement and Chemical Bonds; Ionic and Covalent Bonds.*

Sections 6.9–6.12. In developing the concept of covalence and of covalent bonding of like atoms for H_2, Cl_2, O_2, and N_2, use atomic-shell chalkboard diagrams such as the one for the F_2 molecule shown. Focus attention on the inter-

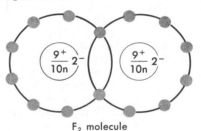

F_2 molecule

mediate placement of the electron pair in the combination of identical atoms—i.e., X:X and its equal attraction for each atomic kernel. Have students count the numbers of protons and electrons in the molecule. The two electrons in the shared electron pair(s) are counted as part of the octets for both atoms. For O_2 and N_2 shell diagrams, place the binding electrons along the ellipse of the overlapping shells. Ball-and-stick as well as spatial models of each molecule should be displayed. For each molecular formula, develop chalkboard equivalents for text models: electron configuration, electron-dot, structural, and orbital. Use Worksheet III: Molecules and Ions. Define molecule, molecular formula, structural formula, and bond energy. Show the **Film** W: 140-4157, *Chemical Bonding,* which deals primarily with the electric interactions that cause exothermic bonding in the hydrogen molecule and nonbonding of helium atoms. Use **Transparency** HM: 2-10527 *Formation of the Hydrogen Molecule.* Define bond energy and write the equations for the bond energies for each of the molecules. Refer to Table 6-4. **Filmstrips:** PH: WCC 861 *Bonding Between Atoms of the Same Element: Metals and Nonmetals;* PH: WCC 862 *Bonding Between Atoms of the Same Element: Nonmetals and the Covalent Bond.* **Transparencies:** HM: 2-10528 *The Fluorine Molecule;* EYE: 003-15 *Covalent and Ionic Bonds.* **Loops:** EBE: Series 9190 *Sizes and Shapes of Molecules; Shapes and Properties of Molecules; Construction of Molecu-*

lar Models. You may wish to use the electron-dot formula for O_2 as $:\ddot{O}:\ddot{O}:$ for the O_2 molecule in the liquid state, in which O_2 can experimentally be shown to be paramagnetic (indication of unpaired electrons). **Demonstration:** Bond energies: A heated glass rod is first thrust into a test tube of HCl(g) and then, after reheating, into a test tube of HI(g). The violet color of I_2 produced indicates the smaller bond strength of the H—I bond. HCl shows no evidence of decomposition. Similarly, HBr is not decomposed by the heated rod, although continuous external heating results in the production of red-brown Br_2. **Reference:** Amador, A., "Bond Free Energies," *Journal of Chemical Education*, 56(7), 453 (1979).

Sections 6.13–6.16. Activities: Assemble and exhibit ball-and-stick and spatial models for HCl, H_2O, NH_3, CH_4, and H_2O_2. Use the chalkboard for representative orbital configurations, electron-dot, and structural formulas. Have students describe the shapes of the assembled models. Start with models of the elementary molecules and take (pull) them apart to represent bond-breaking. Then assemble to represent bond-making. Relate bond-breaking to bond energy. Refer to the results of the previous demonstration of bond energies of HI and HCl. Use Worksheet III: Molecules and Ions. See Fowles, *Lecture Experiments in Chemistry*, pp. 270–272, for preparation of HI and decomposition by heat. A hot iron rod may cause an explosion when thrust into HI. Develop the equation series for HCl as in Section 6.13. Refer to Table 6-4 for bond energy data. State rules 4 and 5. Discuss the oxidation state of oxygen in H_2O_2. Assemble models of the compounds in Table 6-5; discuss the several oxidation numbers of nitrogen and carbon. Use Worksheet III: Molecules and Ions. In the electron-dot formulas of compounds, the bonding electron pair(s) may be placed closer to the central atom than to other atoms such as hydrogen atoms, i.e., $H:\ddot{Cl}:$. Students can explain this on the basis of the larger nuclear charges of Cl, O, and N. This treatment provides the basis for the later development of bond polarity, dipoles, and electronegativity. It also helps in developing oxidation number rules 4 and 5. **Transparencies:** HM: 2-10530 *The Hydrogen Peroxide Molecule;* HM: 2-10532 *The Water Molecule—Simple.* **Filmstrips:** I: 67117 *Covalent Bonds—Covalent Structures;* I: 67145 *The Covalent Bond: Molecular Orbitals;* PH: WCC 864 *Bonding Between Atoms of Different Elements: Nonmetals and Covalent Compounds.* Have students solve the Practice Problem.

Section 6.17. Activities: Have a student write the electron-dot symbol and the electron-configuration for carbon in the ground state. Indicate that the experimental evidence shows that the bond angles (Figure 6-11) and bond lengths in the compound CH_4 are equal. Exhibit the ball-stick model, a model of a tetrahedron in clear plastic (Welch 7579), and have students construct a cardboard or soda-straw tetrahedron model at home. This approach poses the problem of how carbon can have four equivalent bonds and four equivalent bonding orbitals. Use the series of orbital notations for C in the ground state and then in the sp^3 hybrid state. **Activity:** Challenge students to write an electron-dot linear structure for H_2O. Draw the *p* orbitals for O on the three axes and show how the overlap of the *s* orbitals of H with the two $3p$ orbitals of oxygen results in a bent (theoretically 90°) shape for H_2O. Relate to Figure 6-13 and discuss the effect of the unshared electron pair repulsion.

Discuss the shapes of NH_3 and H_2O from the point of view of four imaginary tetrahedral orbitals. **Transparencies:** HM: 2-10529 *Hybrid Orbitals;* HM: 2-10533 *The Water Molecule Hybridized;* HM: 2-10535 *The Methane Molecule, CH_4;* HM: 2-10536 *The Ammonia Molecule—Hybridized.* **Loops:** EBE: S 80709 *The Properties of a Covalent Bonded Compound;* EBE: S 80710 *The Structure of a Covalent Molecule (CCl_4);* EBE: S 80707 *The Properties of an Ionic Compound;* EBE: S 80708 *The Structure of the Ionic Crystal.* **Demonstrations:** Mix 1 part red paint with 3 parts white paint to represent sp^3 hybridization. Mix 1 part red paint with 2 parts white paint for sp^2. Mix 1 part red paint with 1 part white for *sp* hybridization. **References:** Salem, L., "A Faithful Couple: The Electron Pair," *Journal of Chemical Education*, 5(6), 344 (1978); Mickey, C. D., "Molecular Geometry," *Journal of Chemical Education*, 57(3), 210 (1980).

Section 6.18. Discussion: Cite and write out numbers representing molecular sizes. Refer to Figure 6-13. For experimental determination of molecules, refer students to Experiment 34: "The Size of a Molecule," Lehrman, *Scientific Experiments in Physics*, Holt, Rinehart and Winston, Publishers, 1968; or to Experiment 2-3: "Estimation of Avogadro Number," Toon and Ellis, *Laboratory Experiments for Foundations of Chemistry*, Holt, Rinehart and Winston, Publishers, 1973.

Section 6.19. Activity: Refer to atom-shell models of H_2 and F_2 and write the electron-dot formulas with the bonding electron pair equidistant from each symbol. Ask: Which nucleus has the greater attraction for the bonding electron pair? Define pure (nonpolar) covalent bond. Write the electron pair in HCl nearer the Cl. Have students explain that Cl has the greater attraction. Define polar covalent bond. Redefine ionization energy and electron affinity. **References:** For electronegativity scales: Pauling, L., *The Nature of the Chemical Bond*, pp. 63–72; Gould, *Inorganic Reactions and Structure*, pp. 139–141; Sisler, *Electronic Structure and Properties and the Periodic Law*, Table 2.6: "Electron Affinities"; *Foundations of Chemistry*, Tables 7.20 and 7.21. Develop generalizations for electronegativities from data in Figure 6-14.

Refer to Gould, *Inorganic Reactions and Structure*, pp. 139–141, for discussion of Pauling and Millikan (both Nobel Prize winners) electronegativity scales. Gould points out that, for the Millikan scale, when ionization potential and electron affinity are expressed in electron volts, the electronegativity = ½ (IP − EA) and that the Millikan units are about 3.2 times the Pauling units. You may also wish to refer to Pauling, *Nature of the Chemical Bond*, pp. 63–72, for formulation of his electronegativity scale and idea of the partial ionic character of bonds. **Filmstrips:** I: 67131 *Ionization Potential and Electronegativity;* PH: WCC 865 *Electronegativity, Polar Covalent Bonds, Polar Molecules.*

Section 6.20. Activities: Use Table 6-6 and electronegativity data in Figure 6-14 for calculations of electronegativity difference and identification of bond type for text examples and those in question 34. The Welch student chart of the periodic table has data for Table 6-6. Develop oxidation rule 6 by referring to the polar bond in HCl. Use the electronegativity difference to establish the ionic nature of NaH. Pose the problem of bonds in F_2O. Using examples, develop the generalizations: **(a)** Bonding essentially ionic between metals of Group I and II and oxygen or the halogens. **(b)** Bonding between two nonmetals, and between nonmetals and metalloids, is essentially covalent. If you wish to briefly explore metallic bonding use **Filmstrip** I: 67136 *Metals and the Metallic Bond.*

Section 6.21. Demonstration: To test for the polarity of water, show deflection of a thin stream from a buret or from the faucet by a charged rod. The stream is deflected by either a negatively or a positively charged rod. A stream of nonpolar liquid is not deflected. The streams of nonpolar liquids CCl_4, benzene, and toluene are not deflected but their use is proscribed because of their poisonous nature. Try a stream of medicinal mineral oil. The demonstration is included in the **Film** W: 140-4154 *Shapes and Polarities of Molecules* (18 min.) and the **Loop** W: 168 W 1040 T *Polar and Nonpolar Molecules.* Establish possible polarities of molecules having **(a)** nonpolar bonds only, **(b)** polar bonds. Refer to shapes of molecules and the effect of the arrangement (symmetry) of polar bond arrangements as in CH_4 and CCl_4; H_2O and CO_2. Refer back to atom-shell models of H_2 and F_2 and write the electron-dot formulas with the bonding electron pair equidistant from each symbol. Ask the question: Which nucleus has the greater attraction for the electrons or electron pair? Why? Define pure (nonpolar) covalent bond. Write the electron-dot formula for HCl but place the electron pair nearer the Cl. Have students explain why the Cl has the greater attraction. Students may use the electron affinities in the explanation. Refer to Figure 5-11, "Periodic Table of Electron Affinities." On the basis of the unequal sharing, have students define polar covalent bonds. One scheme for representing a polar bond consists of an arrow with a plus sign at the tail end, the arrowhead representing the negative end of the bond.

$$H \! : \! \overset{\cdot\cdot}{\underset{\cdot\cdot}{Cl}} \! : \; + \rightarrow$$

Use of this vector type of symbol aids students in understanding how a nonpolar molecule (substance) may have polar bonds. Refer to *Foundations of Chemistry,* Figures 8-45 and 8-46, which illustrate the use of such vector representations (BeF_2, H_2O, NH_3). Place the unshared electron pair on top of the N in the spatial structural formula of NH_3 in Section 6.17 to help

H_2O polar bonds

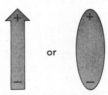

or

H_2O polar molecule
(a dipole)

students realize its role in molecular polarity. **Film:** MH: 611999 *The Structure of Water.* **Loop:** LCG: E-66A *The Structure of the Covalent Molecule, CCl_4.* **Filmstrips:** I: 67117 *Covalent Bonds—Covalent Substances;* I: 67145 *The Covalent Bond: Molecular Orbitals;* PH: SCC 865 *Electronegativity; Polar Covalent Bonds, Hydrogen Bonds and Coordinate Covalent Bonds.*

Section 6.22. Explain resonance (as in Section 16.22 for SO_2) and define the term. You may wish to circle the coordinate covalent bond and indicate that the bonding electron pair is from one atom only, i.e., S. A structural formula (dash

bond), which may be used to represent the coordinate covalent bond, is:

$$S \overset{\nearrow O}{\underset{\diagdown\!\!\diagdown O}{}}$$

The arrow represents the coordinate covalent bond, the electron pair being donated by the S.

Section 6.23. Exhibit models for Figure 6-17. Write the electron-dot representations of these polyatomic ions on the chalkboard. Have students locate and circle the coordinate covalent bonds. Then write the dash and arrow (coordinate covalent bond) equivalents. Illustrate oxidation rule 7 for $[NH_4]^+$:

$$\left[\begin{array}{c} H \\ \uparrow \\ H\!-\!N\!-\!H \\ | \\ H \end{array} \right]^+$$

Use Worksheet V: Oxidation Numbers, Covalent Molecules, Polyatomic Ions. This worksheet may be deferred until Section 6.25 has been completed. Some teachers use the following demonstrations for an early introduction to acids and bases (protolysis) by employing the coordinate covalent bond as a device for establishing the production of such ions as H_3O^+, OH^-, and NH_4^+, as well as showing that polar compounds may form ions by dissolving in polar water with the solution electrical conductivity. Since the demonstrations involve the use of benzene or toluene as solvents, they should be proscribed. **Loop:** W: 168 W 1041 (T) *HCl in Water and Benzene* may be used instead of the demonstrations. Prepare a solution of dry HCl in either benzene or toluene. The dry HCl is produced by passing concentrated HCl into concentrated H_2SO_4 through a dropping funnel whose tube reaches below the H_2SO_4 in the generator flask. The delivery tube reaches to the bottom of an almost full bottle of solvent. A solution of dry NH_3 is produced by dropping concentrated NH_3(aq) into a generator flask containing pellets of solid NaOH. The NH_3 is dissolved in the same manner as the HCl. These solutions do not keep for any length of time and should be tightly stoppered when not in use. Make a litmus-paper test for water solutions of common mineral acids to identify a common species representative of acids. Use the conductivity apparatus to test conductivity of the benzene or toluene solution of HCl. Add water and stir. Note a marked increase in conductivity. Insert a piece of blue litmus paper through the benzene and water layers. Explain the formation of the H_3O^+ ion using the equation and model shown in Figure 15-2. The litmus test is repeated with aqueous bases. Writing the formulas of the bases enables students to identify a common factor, i.e., OH^- radical.

Use the conductivity apparatus (25-w bulb) with the NH_3 solution. Then add water to the sample, stir, and note that the solution becomes conductive. Previous experience with NaCl solution allows students to realize that ions are being liberated. Litmus paper indicates the presence of OH^-. Develop the equation below. Circle the coordinate covalent bond in NH_4^+.

$$H\!\overset{\circ\circ}{:}\!N\!\overset{\circ\circ}{:}\!H + H\!\overset{\cdot\cdot}{:}\!\overset{\cdot\cdot}{\underset{\cdot\cdot}{O}}\!: \;\rightleftharpoons\; H\!\overset{\circ\circ}{:}\!\overset{H^+}{N}\!\overset{\circ\circ}{:}\!H + :\!\overset{\cdot\cdot}{\underset{\cdot\cdot}{O}}\!:^-$$
$$\quad\;\; H \qquad\qquad H \qquad\qquad\; H \qquad\;\; H$$

$$NH_3 + H_2O \rightleftharpoons NH_4^+ + OH^-$$

Section 6.24. Exhibit: Samples of monatomic, diatomic, and more complicated substances and write their formulas (symbols for the noble gases). Refer to Figure 23-3 for P_4 and to Figure 23-4 for S_8. A model of P_4 may be made from 4 plastic spheres arranged into a tetrahedron. A model of S_8 may be made from 8 C atoms in the Welch ball-stick models by using only two of the holes in each sphere for connection by sticks. Write various symbols and formulas with coefficients and have students explain what each means. As examples use O, $2O$, O_2, $2O_2$, $3H_2O$, etc. Complement by using corresponding numbers of models of atoms or molecules. Further examples: $5H_2O$ represents 5 molecules of water, which contain a total of 10 atoms of H and 5 atoms of O. NaCl represents one formula unit of sodium chloride. 5 NaCl represents 5 formula units of NaCl, which contain a total of 5 sodium ions and 5 chloride ions. Use questions 22, 24, 25.

Section 6.25. Summarize the oxidation-number rules. Assign questions 21, 35–38. Use Worksheet V; reuse **Transparencies:** EYE: 003-30 *Oxidation Numbers* and 003-31 *Principles of Oxidation—Reduction Numbers.* **Filmstrip:** L: 67125 *Oxidation-Reduction.* You may wish to use the CHEM **Film** W: 140-4157 *Chemical Bonding* (16 min.) as the chapter summary. **Summary:** Contrast the properties of covalent molecules with those of ionic compounds: They are nonconductors of electricity in any state—solid, liquid, or gas. Test liquids benzene and toluene, solid paradichlorobenzene; then melt. Ionic crystals do conduct when liquefied. Polar covalent molecules may be dissolved in water to demonstrate conductivity (ionization of HCl and NH_3 was previously demonstrated). Liquids often have low boiling points and solids have low melting points. (Boil water or ethanol.) Liquids do exist as molecules. **Demonstrate** diffusion of colored gas or vapor (NO_2, Br_2). Solubility: Like dissolves like—polar liquids readily dissolve in each other (acetic acid and water); nonpolar liquids dissolve in each other (benzene, carbon tetrachloride, and toluene). Some polar liquids dissolve when mixed with nonpolar liquids (benzene and ethanol). **Loops:** W: 168 W 0996(T) *Molecular Structure Determines the Properties of Substances;* LB: 15 *Symmetry in Molecules.* **Programmed Instruction:** Barrow, G. M., *Understanding Chemistry II Chemical Bonding,* W. A. Benjamin, 1967 (pp. 43–78: Lewis diagrams; pp. 79–120: structure of molecules). Dawson, C., *Chemistry, A Basic Systems Program—Atomic Structure and Bonding,* Appleton-Century Crofts, Lyons and Carnahan, 1962 (pp. 534, 624: Electronegativity; pp. 625–700: Oxidation Numbers; pp. 701–781: Covalent Bonds; pp. 781–804: Polarity of Molecules); Kass, G. A., *Individual Study Program in Chemistry, Vol. II; The Chemical Bond,* W. A. Benjamin, 1969 (pp. 1–42: Covalent Bonds; pp. 68–89: Polarity and Shape; pp. 104–110: Coordinate Covalent Bond; pp. 122–140: Bond Type Summary).

PH: WCC Series
860 Chemical Bonding
861 Bonding Between Atoms of the Same Element: Metals and the Metallic Bond
862 Bonding Between Atoms of the Same Element: Nonmetals and the Covalent Bond
863 Bonding Between Atoms of Different Elements: Metals and Nonmetals—The Ionic Bond

864 Bonding Between Atoms of Different Elements—Nonmetals and Covalent Compounds
865 Electronegativity, Polar Covalent Bonds, Polar Molecules, Hydrogen Bonds, and Coordinate Covalent Bonds
Ward's Solo-Learn: W: 78 W 0360 *Introduction to Chemical Bonding;* W: 78 W 0370 *Polar Covalence;* W: 78 W 0380 *Bond Types and Properties of Matter.*

References

Chemistry Reprints:
126 Valence-Shell Electron-Pair Repulsion Theory
119 What is Bond Polarity and What Difference Does It Make?
109 Weak Intermolecular Interactions
108 Do-It-Yourself Molecular Models
101 Water
91 Ionic Bonding in Solids
65 Geometry and Chemical Bonding
59 Framework Molecular Models
49 The Significant Structure Theory of Water
21 Water—H_2O or $H_{180}O_{90}$?
11 Molecular Architecture
Ramsay, O. B., "Molecules in Three Dimensions, Part I," *Chemistry,* 47(1), 6 (1974); "Molecules in Three Dimensions, Part II," *Chemistry,* 47(2), 6 (1974). Meyers, R. T., "Electronegativity, Bond Energy, and Reactivity," *Journal of Chemical Education,* 56(11), 711 (1979); Sisler, H. H., and Vanderwerf, C. A., "Oxidation-Reduction," *Journal of Chemical Education,* 57(1), 42 (1980); Robinson, E. A., and Gillespie, R. J., "Bent Bonds and Multiple Bonds," *Journal of Chemical Education,* 57(7), 329 (1980); Halpern, M., "A Simple Inexpensive Model for Student Discovery of VSEPR," *Journal of Chemical Education,* 56(8), 531 (1979); Sanderson, R. T., "Understanding Chemistry, Current and Possible," *Journal of Chemical Education,* 53(11), 675 (1976); Fitzgerald, R., and Kieffer, W. F., *Supplementary Readings for the Chemical Bond Approach,* pp. 3–6, 43–47, 104–108, 184–201, models 203–206; Mickey, C. D., "Molecular Geometry," *Journal of Chemical Education,* 57(3), 210 (1980); Kolb, D., "Chemical Formula, Part I: Development," *Journal of Chemical Education,* 55(1), 44 (1978); "Chemical Formula, Part II: Determination," *Journal of Chemical Education,* 55(2), 109 (1978); Companion, A. L., *Chemical Bonding,* McGraw-Hill, 1979; Holleran, E. M., and Jespersen, N. D., "Elementary Oxidation-Number Rules," *Journal of Chemical Education,* 57(9), 670 (1980).

Teacher Notes
Chapter 7

Chapter Note

The primary aim of this chapter is to develop fundamental skills in formula writing. The suggested procedural sequence is to develop understanding of the rules and of the necessity for memorizing the tables (Tables 7-1 and 7-2). Use Worksheet IV: Formula Writing; Worksheet V: Oxidation Number, Covalent Molecules, Polyatomic Ions; Worksheet VI: Quizzes on Formula Writing, Ions and Their Charge(s). These help to develop skills by an application, drill, and testing (daily quizzes)—a scheme that works for students who are having trouble. Permit them to take a retest (quiz) at their request when they think they have mastered the memory task and/or the writing of formulas. Thus, initial difficulty does not penalize the student who might otherwise feel defeated throughout the chemistry course. Quizzes may be marked by having students exchange papers immediately after the quiz. Correct answers should be written on the chalkboard. In this way sources of error are apparent, and reteaching of correct procedures and application can follow immediately.

This chapter requires five or six periods. One possible arrangement is:

Lesson 1 Sections 7.1–7.4: Chemical Formulas and Nomenclature. The development and drill may require two periods.

Lesson 2 Section 7.5–7.7: Significance of Chemical Formulas, Formula and Molecular Weights

Lesson 3 Sections 7.8–7.10: Percentage Composition of a Compound, Laws: Definite Composition, Multiple Proportions

Lesson 4 Sections 7.11 and 7.12: Mole Concept, Empirical Formula.

Lesson 5 Section 7.13: Molecular Formula, Problem Reviews.

Section 7.1. Review the electron configurations, valence electrons, and significant successive ionization energies of the metals of Groups I and II. Also refer to the periodic table to establish the ionic charges on their monatomic ions. Review the electron configurations and the high positive electron affinities of the Group VII nonmetals to establish the ionic charge on their monatomic ions. Later, review the electron configurations and the ionic charges of polyatomic ions (Section 6.23). A recommended procedure to introduce the problem of writing formulas is to divide the class into several groups and send one student from each group to the chalkboard to draw an atom-shell diagram for the formation of a compound such as NaCl, $CaCl_2$, $AlCl_3$, AlF_3, and possibly Al_2O_3. In each case the student should draw the atoms, show the electron transfer(s) necessary to achieve the noble-gas configuration (octet) using the appropriate number of atoms, draw the ion models, and finally write the ionic formula—for example, $Ca^{++}Cl_2^-$. Have students realize that if they know the ion name, symbol, and charge, they can readily write formulas without the laborious process of drawing atom-shell diagrams or using equivalent electron configurations or orbital models.

This demonstrates the need to memorize the contents of Tables 7-1 and 7-2. Have students pick out examples of polyatomic ions from Table 7-1. Have students write the electron configurations for Fe, Fe^{++}, and Fe^{+++}. State or have students state the appropriate names (old and new systems) for these ions. Refer to Table 7-2.

Explain that to help them learn the names and charges for selected ions on Worksheet IV, the first task will be to derive the charge(s) on the ions of opposite charge(s) using the correct formulas for compounds of sodium and the series of chlorides that are given. Start with NaCl. Place the $^+$ above Na and the $^-$ above Cl. Then, for the horizontal row of the sodium compound, have students place a $^+$ sign above each Na. Then, from the number of positive-charged sodium ions, place the appropriate number of negative charges above the anions. Use a chalkboard replica of the Worksheet to guide student activity. Then have them place these charges on the named ions in the horizontal row above the row of sodium compounds. Have students proceed in similar fashion for the vertical lists of chlorides, placing a minus sign above each Cl. Have them derive the charges on the metallic ions. Write the formula NaH on the board and have students determine the charge on the hydride ion. Schedule the first quiz on the 25 ions whose charge(s) are determined on Worksheet VI (first 25 items).

Section 7.2. Activities: Tell students that the next task is to write the formulas and to derive and learn the principles (rules) for writing formulas from the ions of known charge(s). Have them write the formulas in appropriate spaces for sodium bromide, calcium bromide, and aluminum bromide. You may wish to use the following illustration for developing the first ion-charge rule for writing the empirical formula. The ion charges cross over to get the appropriate subscript.

$$Mg^{++} \diagdown \, Br^- \qquad \text{(The subscript ``one''}$$
$$\diagup \qquad \qquad \text{is not written.)}$$

The resultant formula is $MgBr_2$. Repeat for writing the formula of Fe_2O_3.

Section 7.3. Activities: Have students write a series of oxide formulas: sodium oxide, calcium oxide, aluminum oxide. From CaO, they get the idea that where ionic charges are equal and opposite no matter what their magnitude, no subscripts are needed. Have them fill in the formula for lead(II) sulfate. Then let them attempt the formula for magnesium hydroxide and have them derive the rule for use of parentheses. Have them fill in the formulas for lead(II) nitrate, ammonium sulfate, and iron(III) carbonate. Have a student read the last paragraph in this section. Assign the completion of Worksheet IV up to phosphate, as homework. Have students write the formulas for such compounds as lead(II) acetate, ammonium sulfate, and tin(IV) chromate. Summarize the procedures on the ion-charge method and its limitations.

Section 7.4. Activities: This section may be used as part of the first or second day's activities. Sections 7.1–7.3 frequently require an entire period. During the next day there is the scheduled Quiz 1, which is then corrected in class. Afterward, students should be assigned to the chalkboard to complete one vertical column of Worksheet IV. While this is in progress, the class should work out the charges on the horizontal list of sodium compounds from F to CrO_4 on Worksheet IV. Quiz 1 is then corrected. The additional ions on Worksheet IV are checked. Students are assigned to complete Worksheet IV as homework. Quiz 1(b) is scheduled for the next day. You may wish to add other anions to those listed. This provides an opportunity for testing student mastery of memorized ion names, composition, and charges. Time permitting, the term *binary compounds* is defined and illustrated for the ionic compounds appearing in Section 7.4. Covalent compounds: Students may be confused by the problems of naming and writing formulas of covalent compounds. If this is the case, take the opportunity for reviewing and applying the rules for oxidation numbers in Chapter 6, particularly as they apply to covalent compounds and polyatomic ions. Before dealing with this section, the second quiz on Tables 7-1 and 7-2 is given and corrected. Worksheet V is also completed at the chalkboard, and students correct their own homework. **Note:** This Worksheet and Worksheet IV provide space for the later development of the relationships of acids, their formulas, and names of their anions. Use of this portion of the Worksheet is a matter of teacher choice. Schedule Quiz 2 on formulas. A second quiz on formulas may be scheduled later. **Exhibit:** Ball-and-stick and spatial models of SO_2, SO_3, SO_4^{--}, CO, and CO_2, and the oxides of nitrogen. Refer to Table 7-3 or duplicate the table on the chalkboard. Discuss the rules for naming binary compounds. Worksheet VI on oxidation states and formulas is used. Its use may extend to another class period. Exhibit models of CH_4, NH_3, CCl_4. Have students name $SbCl_3$, As_2S_3, P_4O_{10}. Have the students state the steps used in naming covalent binary compounds. **Filmstrips:** WCC: 731 *Naming Chemical Compounds: Elements and Binary Compounds;* WCC: 732 *Naming Chemical Compounds: Ionic Compounds;* WCC: 841 *Metal–Nonmetal Compounds;* WCC: 842 *Nonmetal–Nonmetal Compounds;* WCC: 843 *Coordination Compounds and Other Special Topics: Radicals —Polyatomic Ions.* **Note:** All the above PH (Prentice Hall) filmstrips are part of programs that may be used by individual students for additional or correctional training. Use the Practice Problems.

Section 7.5. Activities: Exhibit models of molecules of the elementary gases (H_2, O_2, N_2, F_2, Cl_2) and of covalent compounds (H_2O, H_2O_2, HCl, H_2S, NH_3, CH_4, C_2H_6, CCl_4, etc.). Write the formulas for these and define molecular formula. Have students state what each formula represents. You may wish to write coefficients in front of several of these formulas and again have students state what these represent. Use the formula of H_2S as in text for number of atoms and formula weight. Use other examples and then have formula weight defined. Write the formula for NaCl and several other ionic compounds. Have the empirical formula redefined. Have students state the simple guidelines for determination of molecular and ionic compounds. Designate that the empirical formula represents one formula unit and have students calculate the formula weight for one formula of NaCl and any other ionic compound that you may be using. You may also wish to use coefficients with the ionic formulas and have students state the numbers of formula units, formula weights, and numbers of atoms of each element in the ionic compounds. Assign Problems 1–7.

Section 7.6. Activities: Define and illustrate molecular weight. Have students explain why formula weight is preferred in chemical usage. **Film:** CORF: *Molecular Weight of Oxygen.*

Section 7.7. Activity: Illustrate the calculations of the formula weights for the compounds in this section. Have students try a more complicated example, $Cr_2(SO_4)_3$. Review the concepts of gram-atomic weight and atomic weight, Section 3.14.

Section 7.8. Filmstrips: EYE: X226F *The Percentage of Oxygen in Potassium Chlorate;* PH: WCC 832 *Formulas and Composition Calculations.* **Activity:** Develop the steps used in finding the percentage composition of the compounds in the text, Fe_2O_3 and $Na_2CO_3 \cdot 10H_2O$. Use Problems 8–13. **Demonstrations:** Heat $CuSO_4 \cdot 5H_2O$, $KClO_3$, HgO, or use **Films:** EBE: S–81566 *Catalytic Decomposition of Potassium Chlorate;* EBE: S–81567 *Decomposition of Mercuric Oxide;* EBE: S–81569 *Electrolysis of Water.* You may wish to use the $AgNO_3$ test for Cl^- ion in $KClO_3$ and KCl to complement the $KClO_3$ demonstration.

Section 7.9. Activities: Have students state the law of definite composition (Section 2.9). Have the law stated in terms of the percentage composition of the compound. Discuss the constancy of atomic weight as being basic to the atomic theory (Section 3.2, Section 3.14). Redefine atomic weight and illustrate, if needed, the calculation of atomic weight from percentage of isotopes in naturally occurring atoms (Cl, H, O). Use ball-and-stick models or chalkboard diagrams of HCl (H_2O, CH_4, etc.). Relate the diagrams to the number of electrons shared, or transferred. Perform calculation for HCl as in text. Refer to the articles: Suchow, L., ''Failings of the Law of Definite Proportion,'' *Journal of Chemical Education,* 52(6), 367 (1975); Wilhelm, D. L., ''The Law of Definite Proportions,'' *Journal of Chemical Education,* 50, 436 (1973).

Section 7.10. Activity: Develop the law of multiple proportions as in the text. You may also wish to use parts by weight (atomic weights for H_2O and H_2O_2—2:16 and 2:32 parts by weight respectively). **Film:** W: 140-0110 *Definite and Multiple Proportions.* Review the electron-dot formulas for H_2O and H_2O_2. Use problem 35. **Demonstrations:** Weigh out two 6.35-g amounts of iodine. To 10 g of mercury (**CAUTION**) in a mortar, add one of the iodine samples, a little at a time, thoroughly grinding the mixture after each addition. Green powder, mercury(I) iodide is left. To the green powder, add the second weighed sample of iodine, a little at a time, and grind well. A reddish-yellow powder of mercury(II) iodide is produced. Wolf, W. A., ''Chem Ed Compacts,'' *Journal of Chemical Education,* 52(8), 519 (1975). Decompose $CuBr_2$ to CuBr and Br_2 thermally, leading Br_2 into $Na_2S_2O_3$ solution. **Suggestion:** Then add H_2SO_4 to CuBr and heat to drive off the residual Br in CuBr. **References:** Giguere, P. A., ''Physical Properties of Pure Hydrogen Peroxide,'' *Journal of Chemical Education,* 51(7), 470 (1974); ''Addition Compounds,'' *Journal of Chemical Education,* 53(6), 354 (1976). Use the Practice Problems.

Section 7.11. Activities: Review and illustrate the four quantitative definitions from Sections 3.15 and 3.14: Avogadro number, mole, gram-atomic weight, atomic weight. Discuss the details of Tables 7-4 and 7-5. Exhibit in separate beakers one mole of the following: Hg (201 g), Zn (65 g clean, mossy Zn), S (256 g broken roll S), H_2O (18 g), $C_{12}H_{22}O_{11}$ (342 g), C_2H_5OH (46 g), NaCl (58 g). Have gram-molecular weight defined and illustrate it for diatomic gases and covalent compounds. Define and illustrate formula weight as representative for nonmolecular (ionic) compounds (as well as molecular compounds). Indicate that, for ionic compounds, the formula weight represents the mass of one mole, the Avogadro number of one mole of *formula units* of the ionic compound, and the relevant number of moles of ions. Discuss Figure 7-7. Ask students why the level of liquids indicated in the beakers appears higher than it actually is. **Answer:** Parallax. Ask why the beaker containing 32.0 g of methanol actually reads 40.5 mL. **Answer:** The density of methanol is 0.79 g/mL. Use Worksheet VII for drill on mole relationships and quantities. Use Problems 14–17. **Filmstrips:** I: 67130 *The Mole Concept;* I: 67149 *The Avogadro Number;* PH: WCC 831 *Atomic Weights, Molecular Weights, Mole Concept.* **References:**

Kolb, D., "The Mole," *Journal of Chemical Education,* 55(11), 728 (1978); Kolb, D., "The Chemical Formula, Part I: Development," *Journal of Chemical Education,* 55(1), 44 (1978); Kolb, D., "The Chemical Formula, Part II: Determination," *Journal of Chemical Education,* 55(2), 109 (1978); Hauck, E. M., "Conservation of Mass-Mole Relationship," Lab Bench, *Chemistry,* 50(5), 25 (1977); Herron, J. D., High School Forum: "The Mole Concept," *Journal of Chemical Education,* November (1975); Slade, R., and Freidman, F., "Mole Concept Tips," *Journal of Chemical Education,* 53(12), 781 (1976).

Section 7.12. Define empirical formula. Use the text treatment for the calculation of the simplest mole ratio and simplest formula for water by both methods, i.e., from percentage composition data and relative mass data. Solve the Sample Problems. Have the students solve the Practice Problems. Assign selected problems from Problems 21–31. **Filmstrip:** PH: WCC 833 *Formulas from Analysis of Composition of Compounds.*

Section 7.13. Film: MH: 612008 *Determination of a Molecular Formula.* **Filmstrip:** EYE: X226C *Determining the Molecular Weight of a Gas.* Develop the concept that for molecular substances: (empirical formula)$_x$ = (molecular formula), and (empirical formula weight)$_x$ = (molecular weight). Solve the Sample Problem and assign Problems 32–34. **Programmed Individualized Instruction:** Use the PH: WCC programs for the filmstrips mentioned throughout the chapter; Ward's Solo-Learn 78 W 0490 *Introduction to the Mole Concept.* **Audio Tape Programs:** HM: 3-49507 *Writing Formulas for Ionic Compounds—Calculating Formula Weight and Percentage Composition;* HM: 3-49508 *The Mole Concept—Balancing a Chemical Equation;* HM: 3-49509 *Calculation of the Simplest Formula for a Compound—Weight-Weight Problems.*

Teacher Notes
Chapter 8

Chapter Note

Since this chapter deals with many chemical reactions, it is necessary to provide a maximum of demonstrations, student experiments, and/or teaching aids that provide vicarious experience. Assigned homework equations and problems should be complemented by classroom reviews. The realism of demonstrations and experiments helps maintain student interest, but ample provision for gradual development, drill, and written quizzes must be made if students are to develop mastery of the necessary skills. Gradual development of skills and understandings require carefully programmed use of the questions and problems in the chapter and complementary use of Exercise 8.

Most students have had some previous experience with word and formula equations in elementary science. In Chapters 5 and 6 students have used equations related to ionization energy, electron affinity, oxidation-reduction, and bond energy. Practically all of these have had mathematical interpretation in terms of mole quantities. These experiences and their mathematical background may be appropriately integrated with the concept of an equality and the principle of conservation of mass (conservation of atoms).

This chapter requires five periods. One possible arrangement is:

Lesson 1   Sections 8.1–8.3: Writing Formula Equations
Lesson 1A (Optional)   Review and Drill (with possible quiz in equation writing)
Lesson 2   Sections 8.4–8.6: Types of Chemical Reactions
Lesson 3   Sections 8.7 and 8.8: Reversible Reactions, Activity Series, Review of Lesson 2
Lesson 4   Sections 8.9–8.11: Stoichiometry, The Mole and Mass–Mass Problems

Section 8.1. Perform the demonstration represented by Figure 8-1. Have students state any observation(s) indicating that a chemical reaction has occurred upon the addition of water. Exhibit a sample of zinc iodide. Related questions should deal with the significance of the violet vapor produced and the role of water in the reaction. Have a word equation for the reaction written on the chalkboard. Later, after completing the demonstration and activities for the combustion of hydrogen (below), duplicate the details of Figure 8-2 on the chalkboard for the zinc-iodine reaction. **Demonstration:** Electrolysis of water. **Loops:** EBE: S-81569 *Preparation of Oxygen: Separation through Electrolysis of Water;* BFA: 84-0173 1 *Combining Volumes: Synthesis of Water;* BFA: 80-3254 1 *Conservation of Mass.* Cite an example of an invalid equation (text) for a reaction that does not occur and hence is contrary to known facts.

Stress the differences between word equations and formula equations. In stepwise fashion, using appropriate questions, develop the series of Figure 8-2 on the chalkboard. Have the equivalent Statements 1–4 framed by students as Figure 8-2 is reproduced on the chalkboard. Use the data $4g + 32g \rightarrow 36g$ (line 4) and have students arrive at the relative masses as $1:8:9$. This leads to framing of Statement 5. Ask students to write the equation for the decomposition of water. Add this to the replica of Figure 8-2 on the chalkboard. Then have students arrive at Statement 6. Add this to the Figure 8-2 on the chalkboard. Then write the statement appearing at the end of Statement 5: $x + y = z$ and $z = x + y$. Have students frame a definition for a chemical equation (Caption for Figure 8-2, first paragraph in this section). **References:** Hauck, E., "Conservation of Mass and Mole Relationships," *Chemistry,* June 1977, p. 25; Whitaker, R. D., "An Historical Note on the Conservation of Mass," *Journal of Chemical Education,* 52(10), 658 (1975).

Section 8.2. Refer back to the word and formula equation for the production of gold(III) oxide (Section 8.1) to arrive at *Factor* 1 in writing balanced chemical equations. Exhibit models and use a chalkboard replica of Table 8-1 for elements with diatomic molecules. It may be necessary to review Sections 7.5–7.8 on chemical formulas to lead to the statement of *Factor* 2. Ask students why the formula equation $H_2 + O_2 \rightarrow H_2O$ is not a correct chemical equation. This should result in the statement of *Factor* 3 with the suggestion for use of coefficients.

Section 8.3. Refer to Marginal Note (summary of factors for a balanced equation). Apply the three factors to the text equation for the electrolysis of water. Use the abbreviations for the physical phases of reactants and products in the electrolysis of water equation and utilize where significant (volatility and precipitation) in subsequent equations. Define oxide. Review bonding and electronegativity related to oxides. **Demonstrations:** Burn sulfur in air (or oxygen), decomposition of mercury(II) oxide, zinc and hydrochloric acid, and aluminum sulfate and calcium hydroxide solutions. **Demonstrate:** Decomposition of HgO or use **Loop** S-81567 *Decomposition of Mercuric Oxide;* Zn + HCl (H_2 test): $Al_2(SO_4)_3$ + $Ca(OH)_2$ (observe precipitate). Refer students to Appendix Table 12: Solubility Chart. Develop the equations for the demonstrations as in the text to train students in the use of the steps in equation writing. Have students summarize the five statements at the end of Section 8.3. Have students summarize the five procedures for writing chemical equations correctly. Use the Practice Problems. **Transparency:** EYE: 003-29 *Balancing Equations by Inspection.* **Filmstrips:** PH: WCC 712 *Balancing Chemical Equations;* W: Solo-Learn 78 W 0670 *Chemical Equations and the Mole Concept.* **Audio cassette:** HM: 3-49507 *The Mole Concept, Balancing a Chemical Equation.* **References:** Kolb, D., "The Chemical Equation, Simple Reactions," *Journal of Chemical Education,* 55(3), 184 (1978); Kolb, D., "The Mole," *Journal of Chemical Education,* 55(11) 728 (1978); Silver, J., and Silver, L., "Learning about the Mole," *The Science Teacher* 44(5), 45 (1977).

Section 8.4. Demonstration: Have students identify and label gaseous product (g) by using Appendix Table 11, "Solubilities of Gases in Water." They should be able to treat precipitates in a similar manner by using Table 12. Use these as an introduction to the idea of reactions going almost to completion. As a possible reason that an ionic reaction occurs, indicate the formation of a molecular species, i.e., H_2O, by demonstrating the solution of precipitated $Al(OH)_3$ in HCl, and follow by writing the equation. Demonstrate as many of the reactions as possible before developing the balanced equations. Identify as many as possible of the products of the reactions by physical or chemical properties: i.e., litmus for CO_2, NH_3, SO_2; limewater for CO_2; odor (waft) test NH_3, SO_2; $KMnO_4$ solution for SO_2, glowing splint test for O_2. **Audio cassette:** HM: 3-49513 *Double Replacement Reactions, Neutralization.*

Section 8.5. Activity: Demonstrate as many of the text reactions as possible. Try heating $CuCO_3$, which gives a perceptible color change. Heat soda water for production of CO_2 from H_2CO_3. **References:** Lemay, H. E., Jr., and Kemp, K. C., "Writing Chemical Equations," *Journal of Chemical Education,* 52(2), 121 (1975); Preer, J. R., "A General Chemistry Experiment on the Identification of Reaction Products," *Journal of Chemical Education,* 52(6), 389 (1975). **Film:** UA: *Synthesis of a Compound* (Cu_2S) (16 min.).

Section 8.6. Demonstration: Demonstrate as many of the text examples as possible. In the replacement of a metal in a compound (aqueous salt solutions), use a variety of metals with various salt solutions to establish relative positions of representative metals in activity series of metals (Table 8-2). Establish controls, i.e., Cu + $ZnSO_4$. Also use a variety of metals with water and acids. Use some that do not "work." To demonstrate that magnesium does react with hot water, heat Mg turnings in water or refer to Alyea, p. 142, "Magnesium Burning in Steam." To show that iron reacts with steam, place a moistened piece of asbestos sheet in the bottom

of a Pyrex test tube supported horizontally. Iron filings are placed in the middle part of the tube and kept in place by either glass or steel wool. Place in the generating tube a one-hole stopper that has a delivery tube leading to a test tube for gas collection by water displacement. The filings are heated by one burner and then a second burner heats the asbestos sheet, converting the water to steam. Hydrogen is collected and identified by the "bark" test. Control experiments and "shake-out" solvents (CCl_4, CS_2, perchloroethylene which is replacing CCl_4) are used with the halogen replacement series. **Chart:** Welch-Sargent: 4851 *Electromotive Series.* **Reference:** Mickey, C. D., "Artifacts and the Electromotive Series," *Journal of Chemical Education,* 57(4), 275 (1980).

Section 8.7. Demonstration: Reduction of Fe_2O_3 (rather than Fe_3O_4) may be demonstrated to complement the replacement of hydrogen in water (steam) by hot iron. The Fe product may be identified by its magnetic property and different color. Refer to burning H_2 and electrolysis of water as another example of reversibility.

You may wish to demonstrate other examples of reversibility. Pass dry NH_3 over heated iron catalyst and collect gases. Test for H_2 in the gases collected by water displacement. Plunge a heated glass rod into gaseous HI and note violet color of iodine.

Section 8.8. Activities: See activities for Section 8.6 (above). **Demonstrate:** Exothermic aspect of metal replacement. Have students feel the outside of the test tube in which Zn reacts with $CuSO_4$ solution or iron filings react with $CuSO_4$ solution. Use half-reactions and net-reaction as in the text for the Zn + $CuSO_4$ reaction. Relate contents of Table 8-2 to summary statements at the end of this section. Mention that *Generalization 1* applies to both the metals and nonmetals and that *Generalizations 9 and 10* only apply to metals listed, not to the nonmetals.

Section 8.9. Activities: Review the quantitative aspects of mole relationships as they apply to formulas, percentage composition of compounds, and empirical formulas in Chapter 7. Define stoichiometry. **Reference:** Ozsogomonyan, A., "An Application of Gagne's Principles of Instructional Design: Teaching the Limiting Reactant Problem," *Journal of Chemical Education,* 56 (12, 799 (1979). **Filmstrips:** PH: WCF 1004 *Chem Review: Stoichiometry;* PH: WCC 721 *Stoichiometric Concepts;* I: 67130 *The Mole Concept.* **References:** Kolb, D., "The Mole," *Journal of Chemical Education,* 55 (11), 728 (1978).

Section 8.10. Review the quantitative interpretations of the mole relationships in a chemical equation. Use the CO_2 text example that provides the basis for Section 8.11. **Filmstrip:** Wards: Solo-Learn 78 W 0490 *Introduction to the Mole Concept.*

Section 8.11. After establishing and illustrating the four steps in setting up the text mass-mass problem, illustrate the four operations leading to the final solution. Emphasize the cancellation of units and formulas in the solution operations. Use the Practice Problems. **Problems:** Solve the Sample Problems, noting that in Sample Problem 2, Part b does require the number of moles rather than the number of grams. Problems 1–5 deal with moles. Problems 6–10 are mass-mass problems. **References:** Strong, L. E., "Balancing Chemical Equations," *Chemistry,* 47 (1), 13 (1974) (see references at end of this article); Bowman, L. H., and Shull, C. M., "Mysterious Stoichiometry," *Journal of Chemical Education,* 52 (3), 186 (1975); Vipond, D., "Stoichiometry and Chemical Equations," *The Science Teacher,"* 43 (5), 48 (1976). **Filmstrips:** PH: WCC 834 *Calculations Involving Equations;* PH: WCC 723 *The Limiting Reagent Concept;* PH: WCC 722 *The Factor-Unit Method.* **Audio cassette:** HM: 3-49509 *Calculation of the Simplest Formula for a Compound, Weight-Weight Problems.* **Individualized and Programmed Instruction:** These are listed in the appropriate sections as the PH filmstrip programs, Wards Solo-Learn, and audio cassettes (HM). **Microfiche:** PH: WCF 1004 *Chem Review,* Stoichiometry.

Teacher Notes
Chapter 9

Chapter Note

This chapter, largely on descriptive chemistry, provides an interlude between the theoretical and conceptual preceding and following chapters. Students have had laboratory experiences with oxygen in the earlier laboratory experiments.

The chapter requires three or four periods. A suggested lesson schedule is:

Lesson 1   Sections 9.1–9.8: Occurrence, Preparations, and Properties of Oxygen

Lesson 2   Sections 9.9–9.14: Completion and Review of Lesson 1, Ozone

Lesson 3   Sections 9.15–9.21: Hydrogen: Occurrence, Preparations, Properties, and Uses

Lesson 4   Section 9.22: Deuterium, Completion of Lesson 3

Sections 9.1 and 9.2. **Activities:** Review the structure of the oxygen atom and molecule by using the chalkboard and having students at their desks diagram the atom-shell models, electron configuration notations, orbital notations, and electron-dot symbol and formula. Exhibit models. Review pertinent facts about the occurrence of oxygen in Section 2.7 and the related tables. Have students calculate the mass percentage of oxygen in H_2O, SiO_2, and $CaCO_3$. **Demonstration:** To show percentage of oxygen in air, ignite a small quantity of red phosphorus on cork floating in water. Cover with a graduated cylinder or hydrometer jar. Have students observe how much the water rises in the cylinder. Cover with a glass plate under water, invert, and test the residual air with a burning splint. See also Experiment 14, "Percentage of Oxygen in Air," *Exercises and Experiments in Chemistry,* 1974 edition.

Section 9.3. **Demonstrations:** Demonstrate Scheele's discovery of oxygen as in text. Use the chalkboard for balancing the equation and have students determine the changes in the oxidation numbers of the Mn and O_2 in the MnO_2. **Reference:** Cassebaum, H., and Schufle, J. A., "Scheele's Priority for the Discovery of Oxygen," *Journal of Chemical Education,* 42(7), 442 (1975). Use the **Film** EBE: S-81567 *Decomposition of Mercuric Oxide* as a safe alternative to actually demonstrating Priestley's preparation of oxygen. If you choose to perform the actual demonstration, heat mercuric oxide in a test tube. Have students note production of the mercury mirror above the heated mercuric oxide. Thrust a glowing splint into the upper part of the test tube. Contrast use

of the burner with Priestley's use of a lens. Discuss the details of Figure 9-3. Have the equation written and the changes in the oxidation numbers of Hg and O determined. Briefly discuss the phlogiston theory. Describe Lavoisier's bell jar experiment, using chalkboard diagrams of the beginning and end of the experiment. Have students attempt conclusions about oxygen in the air, the fall of the phlogiston theory, the formation of the modern theory of combustion, the naming of oxygen, and its recognition as an element. Mention that Lavoisier thought that oxygen was present in all acid and that the name meant "acid-former." Refer students to Figure 9-4. **Film:** SUTH: *Combustion.* **Loops:** MH: 669026 *Combustion I—Burning a Candle;* MH: 669027 *Combustion II—Burning Phosphorus.* **References:** *Chemistry* Reprint, "Element Profiles," Weeks and Leicester, *Discovery of the Elements* (7th ed.), American Chemical Society; Woodhouse, J., and Beer, J. J., "Answer to Dr. Priestley's Considerations on the Doctrine of Phlogiston," *Journal of Chemical Education,* 53(7), 414 (1976).

Section 9.4. **Demonstrations:** Preparations of oxygen: (1) Decomposition of hydrogen peroxide: Collect five or more bottles of oxygen by displacement of water (Figure 9-5) and use them for demonstrating the properties of oxygen. Test the first and second bottles with a glowing splint to show that the first sample is largely displaced air. Write the equation. **Film:** EBE: S-81565 *Catalytic Decomposition of Hydrogen Peroxide.* (2) Addition of water to sodium peroxide: To establish the identity of the NaOH produced, first test a labeled sample of NaOH with red and blue litmus, then duplicate the litmus tests with the residual NaOH in the generator. Stress the dangerous caustic nature of the solution. Write the equation. (3) Heating potassium chlorate: To establish the source of the oxygen and the role of MnO_2 as the catalyst, first heat the MnO_2 and perform the glowing splint tests. The potassium chlorate must be heated strongly until it melts, after which it is possible to perform the glowing splint test. After performing this test, permit the potassium chlorate to cool so that it is no longer possible to perform the glowing splint test. Drop in a very small amount of the manganese dioxide, which results in the observable evolution of gas and gives the positive test with the glowing splint. You may wish to demonstrate the dangerous nature of potassium chlorate with dramatic pyrotechnics: (a) drop a wood splint into the heated sample of $KClO_3$; or (b) carefully mix a small quantity of $KClO_3$ with sugar ($C_{12}H_{22}O_{11}$) in a beaker and add a few drops of H_2SO_4. Both of these demonstrations should be pretested and performed with caution. Refer to Figure 9-6 and write the equation. You may wish to use the **Film** EBE: S-81566 *Catalytic Decomposition of Potassium Chlorate.* Other catalysts, such as pure Fe_2SO_3, may be used. (4) By electrolysis of water: Demonstrate or use the **Film** EBE: S-81569 *Electrolysis of Water.* Refer to Figure 9-7 and write the equation. (5) From liquid air: **Film:** EBE: 5-81568 *Distillation from Liquid Air.* (6) Other preparations: Decomposition of mercuric oxide in Section 9.3. Thermal decomposition of BaO_2, KNO_3, HNO_3, and $KMnO_4$. **Filmstrips:** I: 67102 *Preparing Oxygen—the Life-Giving Gas;* I: 67120 *Oxidation.* **Loops:** MH: 657294-3 *Preparation and Collection of Oxygen;* MH: 641721-2 *Electrolysis of Water.* **Transparency:** W: 75 W 8020 *Laboratory Preparations: Oxygen.* **Loop:** BFA: 80-2041/1 *Paramagnetism of Liquid Oxygen.*

Section 9.6. **Activities:** Refer students to Figure 6-15: Periodic Table of Electronegativities, to establish the high electronegativity of oxygen as second to fluorine. Exhibit metallic oxides (MgO, CaO) and nonmetallic oxides (CO_2, H_2O, SiO_2). Write the formulas, determine the oxidation number of oxygen, and define oxides. Have students determine electronegativity differences between metals of Groups I and II with oxygen and decide on the types of compounds. Discuss details and conditions of production of these oxides and peroxides, writing the representative equations. To indicate ease of reaction with oxygen, exhibit samples of Na and K under liquid hydrocarbons and cut the samples to reveal the shiny metals beneath the surface oxides. Also exhibit calcium turnings that have been exposed to air. **Demonstration:** Add samples of oxidized calcium turnings and fresh turnings to water to show the effect of the oxide formation. Burn magnesium ribbon in air and plunge it into a bottle of oxygen. Heat copper foil in air and plunge it into a bottle of oxygen. Heat a copper strip and have students note the formation of surface black oxide. Moisten sample of steel wool and insert it into the bottom of a test tube equipped with a one-hole rubber stopper and a long piece of glass tubing. Place the other end of the tubing in a beaker of colored water, and have students note how the liquid rises (slow oxidation) and Fe_2O_2 is produced. Iron filings may be mixed with the steel wool, and it may be necessary first to clean the steel wool by placing it into acetic acid. Plunge a very hot ball of steel wool into a bottle of oxygen, noting the vigorous reaction and the production of Fe_3O_4. An alternate demonstration is to drop or blow iron filings into the flame of a Bunsen burner. Write the equations. Amalgamate a sample of aluminum foil by gently rubbing it with cotton soaked in a solution of mercury(I) nitrate. **CAUTION:** Use gloves. Students can note production of Al_2O_3 flakes, which drop off. Having a student feel the back of the aluminum foil will reveal that oxidation is exothermic, since considerable heat results. Have students determine electronegativity differences between other metals in this section and oxygen. For the nonmetals, demonstrate the burning of carbon (charcoal stick), sulfur, and phosphorus (deflagrating spoons) in oxygen. Write the representative equations. Calculate electronegativity differences in the oxides formed and establish their covalent nature. **Films:** BFA: 10217 *Combustion, An Introduction to Chemical Change;* SUTH: *Combustion.* **Loops:** MH: 641721-2 *Slow Oxidation, Rapid Oxidation;* MH: 669027 *Combustion II—Burning Phosphorus;* BFA: E 84-0173 1 *Combining Volumes: Synthesis of Water.*

Section 9.7. This test has been demonstrated in preceding sections and chapters.

Section 9.8. **Demonstrations:** Have students blow through limewater to establish use of oxygen in breathing and production of carbon dioxide. Demonstrate production of water from laboratory burner. Close the collar and demonstrate difference in the temperature of the flame with collar closed and opened by placing a piece of glass tubing first in yellow flame and then in blue flame. Refer to Figure 9-9 and Marginal Notes 11 and 12. Refer to Figures 9-10 and 9-11 for other uses. Discuss other uses, i.e., production of chemicals, rocket propulsion. **References:** "Oxygen Therapy" *Science News,* 110(16), 254 (1976); Cook, G. A., "The Real World of Industrial Chemistry: The Use of Oxygen in the Treatment of Sewage," *Journal of Chemical Education,* 57(2), 137 (1980); Shakhashirir, B. Z., Direen, G. E., and Williams, L. G., "Paramagnetism and Color of Liquid Oxygen. A Lecture Demonstration," *Journal of Chemical Education,* 57(5), 373 (1980).

Sections 9.9 and 9.10. **Demonstration:** Produce ozone using the apparatus shown in Figure 9-13. Consult Alyea: pp. 57, 127 for ozone preparation. A piece of filter paper moistened with a solution of potassium iodide turns brown as the ozone produced oxidizes the iodine ion. Discuss the occurrence of ozone and its importance in the upper atmosphere. Discuss the potential danger to the ozone layer from fluorocarbon propellants. See *Foundations of Chemistry,* pp. 140, 141, 397, 398. Write the equations for production of ozone and discuss the energy factor.

Sections 9.11 and 9.12. **Activities:** Exhibit examples of allotropy (i.e., red and yellow phosphorus), diamond and graphite, forms of sulfur. Define allotropy and allotropes. Rewrite formulas for O_2 and O_3. Then write electron-dot formulas for ozone. Discuss the bond energies in O_2 and O_3: their length and strength.

Sections 9.13 and 9.14. Refer to Table 9-2. Relate vigorous oxidizing action to bond energy (Sections 6.9 and 6.11) and bond length. Discuss uses as they relate to its oxidizing action. **Reference:** Research Reporter, "Ozone Damage Overestimated?" *Chemistry,* 49(5), 24 (1976).

Section 9.15. **Activities:** Discuss the occurrence of hydrogen (as in text) by weight in earth's surface environment (Table 2-2), number of atoms in the universe, quantity in the sun and stars, number of hydrogen compounds. Exhibit acids, hydroxides, gypsum, and fuels as representative of the presence of hydrogen in combined form. Write formulas for some acids, hydroxides, rock (gypsum).

Section 9.16. **Activities:** Discuss history as in text. Refer to Scott, A. F., "Beginning Chemistry in America," *Chemistry,* 49(6), 8 (1976), for brief review of chemical history from 1754 to 1789. **Demonstration:** Place sulfuric acid and iron filings in a test tube and use the "bark test" for the hydrogen produced.

Section 9.17. **Demonstrate:** Methods of preparing hydrogen. **(1)** From acids by replacement: Demonstrate production by using a variety of metals and acids. Identify hydrogen by the "bark test." Also use Cu with HCl and H_2SO_4, and Zn with HNO_3 to show that not all metals react. Write the equations. **Loop:** EBE: S-81549 *Hydrogen Generator.* **(2)** From water by replacement: Place a small piece of sodium on water in a large beaker and have students observe its movement around the surface of the water until it is finally consumed. Test the residual solution for NaOH with red and blue litmus. If the piece of sodium is placed on top of a piece of filter floating on water, the sodium will burst into yellow flame. Place a small piece of potassium on top of the water and have students note it bursting into violet flame. Place another piece of potassium on top of a chunk of ice and have students observe results. Drop a fresh calcium turning into a test tube containing water. Stopper with thumb and perform the "bark test." Have students note production of calcium hydroxide (white solid) and test with litmus papers. Boil cleaned magnesium ribbon in water and test for hydrogen with burning splint and for the hydroxide with litmus papers. To demonstrate action of steam with iron, place a small piece of moistened ceramic paper in the bottom of a Pyrex test tube. Support the test tube in horizontal position and insert a loose wad of steel wool halfway down the tube. Insert a one-hole rubber stopper with glass tube assembly and prepare to collect a test tube of hydrogen by water displacement. Using two burners, heat the steel wool first and then start heating the moistened ceramic sheet. Test the gas collected for hydrogen. Write equations for reactions of Na, K, and Ca with H_2O. **Audiovisual: Loop:** W: 168 W 1003(T) *Alkali Metal Reactions with Chlorine and with Water.* **(3)** From water by electrolysis: Redemonstrate if necessary or show **Film** EBE: S-81569 *Electrolysis of Water.* **(4)** From hydrocarbons: Write the equation for reaction of methane and steam. Discuss removal of carbon monoxide. **(5)** From water by hot carbon: Use the same apparatus as that for iron and steam (Demonstration 2 above), substituting charcoal or coke. Write the equations for the reaction and follow with the equation for passing the water gas with additional steam to produce more hydrogen. **(6)** Others: Heat solution of NaOH with Al or Zn. **Film:** UA: *Preparation and Properties of Hydrogen* (19 min.). **Filmstrip:** I: 67103 *Hydrogen—The Fundamental Atom.* **References:** Reilly, J. J., and Sandrock, G. D., "Hydrogen Storage in Metal Hydrides," *Scientific American*, 242(2), 118 (1980); Bamberger, C. E., Braunstein, J., and Richardson, D. M., "Thermochemical Production of Hydrogen from Water," *Journal of Chemical Education*, 55(9), 561 (1978); "Hydrogen Advocates Focus on Practical Goals," *Chemical and Engineering News*, Aug. 14, 1978, p. 28.

Section 9.18. Demonstrations: Density: **(a)** Open a bottle of hydrogen with mouth of bottle upward. Have a student hold another bottle mouth downward with cover removed. After one to two minutes, use flaming splint and "bark test" for hydrogen in each bottle; **(b)** Place a bottle of air (mouth downward) over a bottle of hydrogen (mouth upward). Remove the cover plate. After one minute bring each bottle to the burner flame; **(c)** Hold a bottle of air mouth downward. Bring a bottle of hydrogen in the horizontal position toward the mouth of the bottle of air. Remove the cover plate. After one minute test both bottles for hydrogen by bringing to the burner flame; **(d)** Inflate a balloon with hydrogen. A convenient method for doing this is to attach the balloon mouth to the sidearm of a suction flask that is used as the generator. Replacing the thistle tube assembly with a tight-fitting solid stopper once the acid has been added, create enough pressure to inflate the balloon. After the balloon is inflated, close and tie the opening. If inflated enough, the balloon will rise to the ceiling. Refer to the Hindenberg disaster. Now or later bring a lighted candle attached to a long pole (for example, a window pole) toward the balloon. This results in an impressive flash. For a demonstration of hydrogen diffusion, see Figure 10-6. **Loop:** EBE: S-81563 *Hydrogen Fountain.* **Demonstration:** To demonstrate adsorption, drop activated charcoal pellets into a bottle of Br_2 vapor or NO_2 gas. Cover with plate and shake. Discuss hydrogen adsorption and define adsorption. **Reference:** "Soviets Produce Metallic Hydrogen," *Science News*, 110(16), 254 (1976).

Section 9.19. Demonstrations: To show that hydrogen burns but does not support combustion, hold a bottle of hydrogen mouth downward. Slowly insert a lighted candle tied to a rod such as a deflagrating spoon. The flame goes out inside the bottle. Slowly withdraw the candle, which will re-ignite from the almost colorless flame of the burning hydrogen at the mouth of the bottle. This demonstration may be repeated several times. For variation, repeat the demonstration with a burning wooden splint. Inside the bottle, the flame is extinguished. The middle of the splint, in the mouth of the bottle, catches fire from the almost colorless hydrogen flame. See Figure 9-18. Ignite the hydrogen jet (see **CAUTION** in Section 9.6 above) and hold it beneath a large inverted beaker or bell jar. Note the formation of water (Figure 9-17). Hydrogen and air or hydrogen and oxygen form an explosive mixture. Make a hydrogen gun from a small can with a narrow opening, firmly attached to a long handle (see diagram below) and fill it with hydrogen by air displacement. Bring the opening at the top of the gun to the burner so that the escaping hydrogen is ignited. Walk around the classroom to permit students to see the almost colorless hydrogen flame at close range. When sufficient air has entered and mixed with the remaining hydrogen to form an explosive mixture, an impressive explosion occurs. Have students explain the "happening."

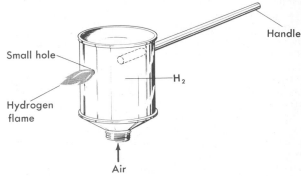

Hydrogen "gun"

Demonstrate: The burning of hydrogen jet in chlorine. Write the equations for the production of water, hydrogen chloride, and ammonia. Discuss reactions with metals and hydrides as in the text.

Section 9.20. Demonstrate the "bark test" for elemental hydrogen. The nearly colorless flame has been demonstrated in the burning of H_2 in Cl_2. The burning jet impinging on a cold surface produces H_2O.

Section 9.21. Activities: List the compounds commercially produced from hydrogen and discuss their uses. Exhibit some hydrogenated products such as shortening, margarine, peanut butter, etc. **Demonstrate:** The reduction of copper oxide by hydrogen (see the following diagram). The wire form of copper oxide may be used, and the hydrogen should be permitted to continue flowing over the copper oxide when it has perceptibly changed to copper, after the removal of the flame. Water will drop from the mouth of the test tube. You may wish to start with a strip of copper. Heat in burner flame until covered by black oxide. Reduce this in the apparatus instead of using the wire form of CuO. Write the equation for reaction. Analyze in terms of electron transfer. Redefine reducing agent (Section 6.5). Discuss use of reducing atmosphere. Discuss uses as a fuel either as an element or part of other fuels. Refer to Figure 9-17.

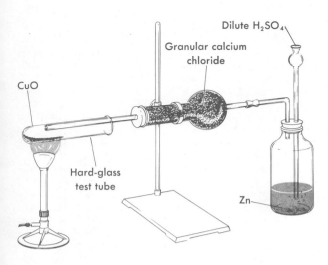

Dilute H₂SO₄

Granular calcium chloride

CuO

Hard-glass test tube

Zn

Section 9.22. Activities: Use Table 9-4 for comparison of protium and deuterium. Use chalkboard to draw atom-shell models. Stress the great mass difference between these hydrogen isotopes and that between the isotopes of other elements such as chlorine-35 and chlorine-37 by explaining that heavy water does not behave the same as natural water in biological systems. Discuss heavy water (Section 12.21) and the ways in which chemical properties of the compounds of protium and deuterium differ. **Reference:** Pasachoff, J. M., and Fowler, W. A., "Deuterium in the Universe," *Scientific American,* 230(5), 108 (1974). **Chapter References:** Letheridge, J. W., and Davies, M. B., "The Paramagnetism of Liquid Oxygen," *Journal of Chemical Education,* 50, 656 (1973), refer to 50, 217 (1973); Schultz, C. W., "Properties of Air—A Freshman Chemistry Demonstration," *Journal of Chemical Education,* 51(11), 751 (1974) (condensation of air by liquid N₂); Medeiros, R. W., "Air Pollution: Could It Change the World's Climate?" *Chemistry,* 47(6), 18 (1974); Leh, F., "Ozone, Properties, Toxicity, and Applications," *Journal of Chemical Education,* 50, 404 (1973); Research Reporter, "Metal Hydrides Conserve Energy," "New Hydrogen Ion," and "Hydrogen Bond Model," *Chemistry,* 49(7), 27–28 (1976); "The Gases of Life," *Journal of Chemical Education,* 56(11), 748 (1979); French, S. J., "The du Ponts and the Lavoisiers," *Journal of Chemical Education,* 56(12), 791 (1979).

Teacher Notes
Chapter 10

Chapter Note

Activities and Demonstrations: One or more of these devices may be used to introduce and explain the kinetic theory. They may also be used at more specific sections in the text. **(a)** Drinking Duck (Edmund Scientific Co.), **(b)** Cartesian Diver (Welch Scientific Co.), **(c)** Simple Air Thermometer (glass air-thermometer tube, Cenco). Construct by heating the bulb slightly and inserting the open end of the tube into a beaker containing colored liquid. To demonstrate the effect of temperature changes on the air thermometer: **(1)** apparently squeeze the bulb, **(2)** wet the bulb with alcohol or water and observe result of evaporation, **(3)** apply a piece of ice to the bulb. **(d)** Molecular Vibration Tube (Welch Scientific Co.); Molecular Demonstration Tube (Cenco). Heat the mounted tube, which contains mercury under reduced pressure and colored glass chips floating on it. Students may construct their own air thermometers or divers. A small pill bottle or vial for litmus paper may be made into a diver. Put it into a graduated cylinder and use either rubber sheeting or a stopper to close the cylinder. **Demonstration Sources:** Alyea, 5-14s-5-19s, pp. 63, 65, 145, 156, 160, 180, 195; *Physics Handbook,* N. Y. State Education Department, 1970, pp. 68–73. **Reference:** Wiseman, F. L., "An Experiment-Oriented Approach to Teaching the Kinetic Molecular Theory," *Journal of Chemical Education,* 56(4), 233 (1979). This chapter requires four or five periods because of the need for drill on problems. One arrangement is:

Lesson 1   Sections 10.1–10.4: Kinetic Theory, Properties of Gases
Lesson 2   Sections 10.5–10.8: Standard Temperature and Pressure, Boyle's Law
Lesson 3   Sections 10.9 and 10.11: Kelvin Scale, Charles' Law
Lesson 4   Sections 10.12–10.15: Combined Gas Laws, Gas Collection by Displacement, Real Gases

Section 10.1. Review previous experiences indicating the particulate nature of matter (Section 3.1), for Assumption 1. For Assumption 2, use the air thermometer demonstrations. For Assumption 3, let 2 balls collide. You may use one or more of the following or defer their use to later sections in this chapter. In many instances, the title indicates the chapter section to which the aid fits. **Films:** W: 148-4115 *Molecular Motions* (13 min.); W: 140-4119 *Vibration of Molecules* (12 min.); W: 140-4106 *Gas Pressure and Molecular Collisions* (21 min.); MH: *The States of Matter* (18 min.); EBE: 2227 *The Molecular Theory of Matter* (2nd ed.) (11 min.); MH: *The Nature of Matter;* MH: 612006 *Kinetic-Molecular Theory.* **Loops:** BFA: 80-3361/1 *Motion of a Molecule;* BFA: 80-3379/1 *Gas Diffusion Rates;* BFA: 80-2926/1 *Random Walk and Brownian Movement;* BFA: 80-2751/1 *Conservation of Momentum-Elastic Collisions;* LBF: 15A *A Model of Kinetic-Molecular Theory;* HR: *Molecular Motion;* MH: 101195-1, *Property of Air Series* (demonstrations of simple kinetic theory, inverted tumbler, suction cup, collapse of an evacuated can, the Madgeberg hemispheres). **Demonstration Apparatus:** Molecular Motion Demonstrator, Educational Materials and Equipment Co.; Cenco, Kinetic Theory Apparatus.

Section 10.2. Demonstrations: Fuel gas collected by water displacement is opened. Odor is detected. Do waft test for opened bottle of household ammonia. Bring together moistened stoppers from HCl and NH₃(aq). Note colored gases (NO₂, Br₂) escaping from opened container. Heat flask of air with attached balloon or manometer. Hold partially inflated balloon over hot steam radiator or hot plate. Heat Hg in molecular vibration tube (Welch). Heat iodine diffusion tubes (Welch). Fill Brownian movement apparatus (Welch) with smoke and view through microscope. Place a beaker containing H₂O and phenolphthalein and another containing concentrated NH₃(aq) in a bell jar. Refer to Figure 10-2. **Audiovisual:** W: 140-0115 *Behavior of Gases.* **Loops:** ICF: 13220 *Brownian Movement;* ICF: 13210 *Diffusion Explained.*

Section 10.3. Demonstrations: Drop a very small piece of dry ice into a flask with a balloon attached (molecular movement, volume and density of gas). Into one end of a wide glass tube in a horizontal position, insert cotton moistened with HCl. Into the other end, simultaneously insert cotton moistened with NH_3(aq). The location of NH_4Cl indicates different rates of gas diffusion. Use the arrangement (Figure 10-5) with hydrogen or table fuel gas in the beaker above the porous cup to demonstrate rate of diffusion. Demonstrate hydrogen diffusion experiments for Figures 10-4 and 10-5. Heat a 500- or 1000-mL flask, to which a balloon is attached. Before the heating, ask a student to read the volume etched on the flask. Then ask, "What is the volume of the air in the flask?" The same question follows the heating. If the teacher desires, the flask may be heated by hot water enclosed in a large beaker. Several one-hole stoppered test tubes each with a long glass tube containing liquid such as water, mercury, and alcohol may also be heated by hot water so that the expansion of liquids and gases can be compared. The air in a stoppered can is heated so that the stopper is ejected, to show the effect of temperature on pressure. A compressed-air popgun may be made from a foot-long section of a glass or plastic tube. One end is stoppered and a piston that fits the tube bore is inserted in the other end. Pushing down the piston causes the ejection of the cork. This shows the effect of decreased volume on pressure. A large bell jar, with a suitable base through which air may be withdrawn by means of a vacuum pump, may be used to show two effects of decreased pressure on volume. First, a rubber diaphragm attached to the open end of the bell jar is pushed down into the jar as the pressure is decreased. (Call attention to the decreased air content inside the bell jar.) Second, when the pressure is decreased by the pump, the stopper on a bottle inside the bell jar is ejected because the air within the bottle is pushing against less pressure.

These demonstrations are on the general-science level, but they do help the student resolve the problem of why the expression "one liter of air" means "small." The student realizes the need for selecting a standard temperature and pressure for gas-volume measurements.

Activities: Explain gas pressure by referring to Figure 10-3. Write the formula for E_k on the chalkboard after making a chalkboard replica of Figure 10-6. Use this figure to help students reach the conclusions relating to the average kinetic energy. In using this figure, help students realize that the area under each of the two curves is the same and hence represents the same number of gas molecules. **Films:** W: 140 4106 *Gas Pressure and Molecular Collisions;* EBE: S-81563 *The Hydrogen Fountain;* MH: 612006 *Kinetic-Molecular Theory.* **Loops:** BFA: 80-3379/1 *Diffusion Rates;* ICF: 13250 *Diffusion Velocities.* **Transparency:** HM: 2-10542 *Molecular Distribution of Kinetic Energy.* **Reference:** Rice, B., and Raw, C. J. G., "The Assumption of Elastic Collisions in Elementary Gas Kinetic Theory," *Journal of Chemical Education*, 51 (2), 139 (1974).

Section 10.4. Activities: Exhibit a scrambled set of models and samples of the substances in Table 10-1. Have students classify each by type of substance. Have students explain the condensation of water vapor on the outside of a vessel containing ice. Define condensation temperature. Discuss the two types of van der Waals forces and the factors

upon which their strengths depend. Have students calculate the molecular weights of CCl_4, CH_4, C_6H_6. Also have students calculate the molecular weight of Ne (condensation temperature: $-246°C$). Compare with the molecular weights and condensation temperatures of H_2O and NH_3 to establish effect of molecular polarity (dipole-dipole attraction). Repeat for CH_4. Refer to the demonstration (Chapter 6) in which a thin stream of water is deflected by a charged rod. **Filmstrip:** I: 67148 *van der Waals Forces.* **References:** "Measuring van der Waals Forces," *The Science Teacher*, 41 (2), 13 (1974); "Weak Molecular Interactions," *Chemistry*, Reprint 109.

Sections 10.5 and 10.6. Exhibit and Demonstrate: The operation of barometer, manometer (J and U tube types), and pressure gauges. Connects a U-type manometer to a thistle tube with a rubber diaphragm to show pressure effects. A mercury barometer inside the tall-form bell jar (Welch) on a pump plate is used to show the effect of reducing pressure. Heat a flask containing air and connected to a manometer (effect of temperature on volume and pressure of a gas). Exhibit a laboratory barometer. Have a student read the pressure. Use a thermometer in melting ice to establish standard temperature. Define standard pressure and standard temperature. Refer to Figures 10-7, 10-8, and 10-9. **Note:** The pressure units, millimeters of mercury, torr, and atmosphere are to be abandoned eventually; and the SI pressure unit, pascal (newton per square centimeter), used exclusively according to the recommendations of the General Conference on Weights and Measures and the National Bureau of Standards. Because the authors do not wish to use the unit "pascal" until it is more generally accepted by chemists, we are continuing to use millimeter of mercury because of its convenient association with barometric readings. **Films:** EBF: *Gas Laws and Their Application;* W: 140-4101 *Gas Pressure and Molecular Collisions.*

Sections 10.7 and 10.8. A form of Boyle's law apparatus (Welch, J-form or adjustable form) may be used in the classroom. *Project Physics Handbook*, Experiment 29, "Behavior of Gases," describes the use of elasticity-of-gas apparatus (Cambosco) that may be used in the demonstration with several books or bricks to show variation of gas volume with pressure. Have students graph representative data from the table

Pressure	Volume
200 mm	2000 mL
250	1600
333	1200
400	1000
500	800
800	500
1000	400
1200	333
1600	250
2000	200

shown. Have students identify the parabola as representative of an inverse proportionality. **Problems:** Solve the text Sample and Practice Problems (Section 10.8). In solving problems, have students use the reasoning process in approximating answers and the factor-label-cancellation process. **Films:** EBF: 779 *Gas Laws and Their Applications;* CORF: *Laws of*

Gases; CORF: *Demonstrating the Gas Laws;* MLA: *Behavior of Gases;* UA: *Demonstrating the Gas Laws* (21 min.). **Loops:** BFA: 80-3387 1 *Boyle's Law;* W: 168 W 1007 (T) *Gas Pressure.* **Filmstrips:** EYE: X 200A *Boyle's Law;* PH: SCC 891 *Boyle's Law, Charles' Law, and Gay-Lussac's Law.* **Transparency:** MH: 2-10518 *Boyle's Law—Ideal Gas.* **Overhead Projectuals:** *Boyle's Law/Absolute Zero Unit,* Educational Material and Equipment Co. **References:** Hawthorne, R. M., ''Boyle's/Hooke's/Townsley and Power's/ Mariotte's Law,'' *Journal of Chemical Education,* 56(11), 741 (1979); Davenport, D. A., ''Tested Demonstrations: Boyle's Law,'' *Journal of Chemical Education,* 56(6), 322 (1979).

Sections 10.9, 10.10, and 10.11. **Activities:** Review previous demonstrations of temperature effects on gas volume. **Film:** EBE: 2942 *Determination of the Triple-Point of Water.* **Demonstrations:** A simple air thermometer is used to show the effects of heating and cooling the enclosed gas volume by placing a hand on the bulb and then placing a piece of ice on the bulb. A demonstration of Charles' law that you may wish to use is described in the D. T. Haworth article on Charles' law, *Journal of Chemical Education,* 44, 353 (1967). State Fact 1 in Section 10.9. Use the data table below to derive

Volume	Celsius	Kelvin
373 mL	100°	373°
323 mL	50°	323°
273 mL	0°	273°
223 mL	−50°	223°
173 mL	−100°	173°

Fact 2 in Section 10.9. The Kelvin scale should be based on the results of the data table (above). The Absolute Zero Demonstrator (Welch) may be used to complement a redemonstration of a simple air thermometer and the effects of cooling and heating an enclosed air volume. This apparatus, also called the Charles' law apparatus (Cenco), shows the effect of increased temperature on the pressure of a gas having constant volume and mass (a variation of Charles' law). It may be used according to directions for Experiment 5-2: ''Determination of Absolute Zero,'' *Laboratory Experiments for Foundations of Chemistry.* Solve the Practice Problems, Section 10.11, preceding this activity by using Kelvin temperature conversion examples (see Table 10-2). **Problems:** Numbers 5–9. **Film:** YF: 233 *Triple Point Determination.* **Loops:** BFA: 80-3393/1 *Finding Absolute Zero;* W: 168 W 1001 (T) *Absolute Zero;* BFA: 80-3312/1, *Thermal Expansion of Gases.* **Filmstrip:** EYE: X 200B *Charles' Law.* **Transparency:** HM: 2-10519 *Charles' Law.* **References:** Markow, P. G., ''A Charles' Law Demonstration, Rehatched,'' *Journal of Chemical Education,* 57(4), 307 (1980) (A hardboiled egg into and then out of a glass milk bottle); Woods, F., ''The Kinetic Theory of Gases and the Gas Laws,'' *Journal of Chemical Education,* 55(6), 395 (1978).

Section 10.12. **Activities:** Derive the relationship for the combined gas laws. Solve the Sample and Practice Problems. Assign Problems 10–14. **Filmstrips:** PH: SCC 892 *General Gas Law and Dalton's Law of Partial Pressure.* **Programmed Instruction:** Barrow, G. M., *et al., Understand-*

ing Chemistry, Benjamin, W. A., I—Chemical Quantities, pp. 41–80.

Sections 10.13 and 10.14. **Demonstrate:** Collection of an insoluble or slightly soluble gas by displacement of water. Attempt to collect a soluble gas such as NH_3 by displacement of water. Then collect a sample by displacement of Hg (use a test tube). Exhibit a eudiometer. Simulate the three situations in Figure 10-13 by collecting an insoluble gas by displacement of water. Stopper collectors (2) and (3). Unstopper each successively in a tall cylinder of water. Manipulate each until the water levels inside and outside are equal (atmospheric pressure) and note the effects on the enclosed gas volume. To demonstrate the corrections needed when gases are collected by water displacement, insert a droplet of water through the mercury into the bottom of a Torricelli barometer and have students note the fall of the mercury. **Activity:** Discuss the procedures for correction of volume. **Problems:** Use the Sample Problems. Solve selected problems from 15–20. **Audiovisuals:** EBE: S-81573 *Handling Gases;* EBE: 2953 *Vapor Pressure* (8 min.).

Section 10.15. **Activity:** Discuss the conditions under which real gases conform closely to ideal gas behavior and those under which they do not. **Reference:** Deal, W. J., ''Ideal Gas Laws,'' *Journal of Chemical Education,* 52(6), 405 (1975). **Individualized and Programmed Instruction:** Ward's: Solo-Learn: 78 W 0730 *Introduction to Behavior of Gases;* 78 W 0740 *Gaseous Mixtures;* 78 W 0750 *Kinetic Molecular Theory of Gases;* PH: WCC 894 *Generalized Gas Equation: PV = nRt.* **Loops:** Kinetic Theory: BFA: 80-2918 1 *Maxwellian Speed Distribution;* BFA: 80-2926 1 *Random Walk and Brownian Movement;* BFA: 80-2934 1 *Equipartition of Energy;* BFA: 80-2959 1 *Diffusion;* BFA: 80-2967 1 *Properties of Gases.*

Teacher Notes
Chapter 11

Chapter Note

The primary chapter objective is the development of student skills in solving the variety of volume-related problems. The basic concepts include gas density, molar volume, the gas constant, and the mole concept (Avogadro number). Various aspects of the scientific method involved include: **(a)** the formulation of a law (Gay-Lussac) based on previous experimental results, **(b)** the emergent problem: inconsistency of Dalton's theory and Gay-Lussac's Law, **(c)** resolution of the problem by Avogadro's explanation, **(d)** application of Avogadro's Principle: determination of molecular and atomic weights and scientific conservatism; the time lapse 1811–1860 before Cannizzaro established the Avogadro principle.

The chapter requires four or five periods. One possible arrangement is:

Lesson 1 Sections 11.1–11.4: Gay-Lussac's Law, Avogadro's Principle, Diatomic and Monatomic Molecules

Lesson 2 Sections 11.5 and 11.6: Molar Volume, Molecular Weight

Lesson 3 Sections 11.7–11.9: Problems: Gas Volume-Gas Volume, Mass-Gas Volume

Lesson 4 Sections 11.10–11.13: Problems—STP, Water Displacement, Gas Constant, Real and Ideal Gases

Section 11.1. Review the gas laws and the similarities in the physical behavior of gases. Pose the question, "Is there any evidence that gases exhibit similarities in chemical behavior?" The **Film** W: 140-4103 *Gases and How They Combine* (22 min.) provides the data for Gay-Lussac's law (combining volumes of NH_3 and HCl; H_2 and O_2; NO and O_2; H_2 and Cl_2). As an alternative, use the **Loop** BFA: 84 0173/1 *Combining Volumes: Synthesis of Water.* **Demonstration:** (CAUTION: Use a safety shield.) The electrolysis of water is performed with the two electrodes in a thick, wide-mouth bottle wrapped in a wire shield. The collected mixture of H_2 and O_2 is then exploded. Eudiometers may be used in the synthesis, with the gases being collected by water displacement. Platinum electrodes sealed in the closed end of a eudiometer produce the spark for igniting the mixture. The excess unexploded gas may be identified by using a flaming splint and/or a glowing splint. Use models for reactions in Figure 11-1, 11-2, and 11-3.

Section 11.2. Refer to the **Loop,** W: 168 W 1007 (T) *Gas Pressure* (used in Chapter 10), in which the principles of gas pressure are related to Avogadro's principle. Write the word equations for the combining volumes and then the corresponding number of molecules underneath for each of the examples. Have students attempt explanation (Avogadro's) of the simple molecules of hydrogen, oxygen, chlorine, hydrogen chloride, water, and ammonia. Use molecular models to simulate reactions producing HCl. Have students use Avogadro's explanation for resolution of the Dalton-Gay-Lussac inconsistency. Discuss why Avogadro's explanation is not known as Avogadro's principle.

Section 11.3. Activities: Develop the supporting evidence for the diatomic composition of molecules of active gaseous elements showing that the simplest formulas must be checked by calculation of the molecular weights of gases from experimentally determined gas densities. Now write the formula equations underneath the sets of word equations for Section 11.2. Establish the significance of the coefficients and the relative volumes. Use models for Figures 11-1, 11-2, and 11-3.

Section 11.4. Activity: Establish the monatomic nature of the noble gases. Use electron-dot symbols and the stability of the electron-pair (He) and octet (Ne, Ar) and the low condensation temperatures (Appendix Table 16: Properties of Common Elements).

Section 11.5. If you do not let your students use $KClO_3$, an alternate experiment is described in *Chemistry*, 43 (1970), Jan., "Lab Bench–Molar Volume: A Safe Method." This experiment uses Dry Ice. Review the concepts of mole and Avogadro number and tabulate the related facts for molecular substances. Exhibit a 22.4-liter box. Some teachers have the formulas and gram-molecular weights of selected gases written on different sides of the box (Figure 11-4) and state that the data has been experimentally determined. This leads to the definition of molar volume and the related generalization pertaining to the molar volume of all gases. Define gas density as the mass in grams per liter at STP and have students calculate the molar volumes of various gases (H_2, O_2, and others) from the gas densities. Exhibit a volumetric 1-liter flask. Focus attention on the functional relationships:

$$D \text{ (of a gas)} = \frac{\text{g-mol wt}}{22.4 \text{ L}}$$

$$\text{g-mol wt} = D \times 22.4 \text{ L}$$

Activities: Use the chalkboard to calculate the density of SO_2. Have the class do the Practice Problems. **Loop:** BFA: 80-3288/1, *Identifying Gases by Density.* **Filmstrips:** PH: SCC 893 *Gay-Lussac's Law of Combining Volumes, Avogadro's Law, Molar Volume, and Molecular Weights;* I: 67130 *The Mole Concept;* EYE: X226D *The Molar Volume of a Gas.*

Section 11.6. Filmstrip: EYE: X226C *Determining the Molecular Weight of a Gas.* **Exhibit:** One of the variety of glass bulbs (Welch Balloon, Gas-Density-Dumas; Welch Glass Balloon with Stop-cock) used in determining the density of gases. **Problems:** Solve the Sample Problem, reviewing concepts of partial pressure and correction of measured volume to STP. Students find the following to be a functional aid:

$$D(g) = \frac{g}{mL} \times \frac{1000 \text{ mL}}{L}$$

which is followed by the use of g-mol wt = $D \times 22.4$ L. Solve the second Sample Problem dealing with conditions other than STP.

Illustrate the successive procedures: Correction for water vapor pressure (refer students to Table 8 in the Appendix), conversion of Celsius temperature to Kelvin temperature, and correction for pressure and temperature changes. Use the PH: WCC program 892, *General Gas Law & Dalton's Law of Partial Pressures.*

Sections 11.7 and 11.8. Activity: Review the use of the equation for coefficient-mole relationships in gas reactions and its use in solving gas volume-gas volume problems. Apply the problem setup of mass-mass problems for the text (Section 8.11) problem for H_2. **Problem:** Solve the Sample Problems, including the procedure for calculating the volume of air.

Section 11.9. Problems: For the mass-gas volume problems (gas volumes given or required at STP), have the students suggest the two possibilities, i.e., volume given, mass required; mass given, volume required. Emphasize the mole relationships in the equation (Section 11.9) and the use of molar volume (22.4 liters) to determine the number of moles given in the typical problem before the use of operations 2–4 of mass-mass problems. A good technique is to use the results of the text problem, 17.9 g of $CaCO_3$, to have students devise the solution of mass–gas volume problem with the mass given and the volume at STP (in this case, the volume of CO_2) required. The reverse problem may be stated as: "How many liters of carbon dioxide at STP are produced by the decomposition of 17.9 grams of calcium carbonate?"

$$X = \frac{17.9 \text{ g CaCO}_3}{100 \text{ g/mole}} \times \frac{1 \text{ mole CO}_2}{1 \text{ mole CaCO}_3} \times 22.4 \text{ L/mole}$$

$$= 4.00 \text{ L CO}_2 \text{ at STP}$$

In this type of problem, operations 1 and 2 of the mass-mass problem procedure are followed by multiplying the resultant expression (number of moles required) by 22.4 L/mole. Follow up by assigning representative Problems 18 and 19. Refer to marginal note on the four operations in solving mass-mass problems.

Section 11.10. Develop the procedures for gases not measured at STP for **(a)** gas reactants and **(b)** gas products. Use Problems 30 and 31. In part **(b)** of Problem 30, the gas volume calculated at STP from a given mass is converted to nonstandard conditions. In Problem 31, the mass is required and the gas volume is given at nonstandard conditions.

Section 11.11. Problems: For mass-gas volume problems where the gases are collected by displacement of water, first review Section 10.14, Pressure of a gas collected by displacement of water, and apply to conversion of a gas volume at STP to nonstandard conditions involving collection by displacement of water. Solve the Sample Problem.

Section 11.12. Activity: Review the reasons for differences in the behavior of real gases versus ideal gas and the conditions for making measurements under which ideal gas behavior is approximated (Section 9.15). Derive the equation: $pV = nRT$ as in Section 11.12 by applying Avogadro's principle, Boyle's law, and Charles' law. Show how the units for the gas constant R are determined, i.e., dimensions of R being liter $\times$ atm per mole $\times$ °K (L atm/mole °K). **Demonstrate:** Derive the numerical value of the gas constant, $R = 0.082057$ L atm/mole °K for one mole of an ideal gas at exactly 1 atm and 273.15°K. Apply the ideal-gas equation to the text problem dealing with the determination of the molecular weight of a gas from gas density measurements, nonstandard conditions. Use Problems 41, 42, and 43 for applications of the ideal-gas equation. You may wish to illustrate how the ideal-gas equation simplifies the solution of **(a)** mass-to-gas-volume problems and **(b)** a gas-volume-to-mass problem. For **(a),** Problem 30 is restated as: "What volume does the sulfur dioxide gas occupy at 25°C and 745mm pressure when 50 grams of sulfur are burned?" For **(b)** use Problem 31. Compare the answers obtained previously. Assign the Practice Problems. **Filmstrip:** PH: WCC 894 *Generalized Gas Equation:* pV = nRT. **Transparency:** W: 75 W 8025 *pVT Surface for Ideal Gas.*

Section 11.13. Discuss: The factors that contribute to the deviation of real gases from the perfect behavior of an ideal gas. List the molar volumes of ammonia, chlorine, oxygen, and nitrogen measured at normal conditions and their condensation temperatures: $NH_3(-33°C)$, $Cl_2(-34.6°C)$, $O_2(-183°C)$, $N_2(-195.8°C)$. Have students correlate molar volume deviations and condensation points. Review the related factors (see Section 10.4, Attractive forces between gas molecules). **Filmstrip:** I: 67148 *van der Waals Forces.* **Individualized and Programmed Instruction:** Audio-Tutorial: HM: 3-49510 *Kinetic Molecular Theory of Matter and the Gas Laws/General Gas Law Equation;* HM: 3-41911 *Volume-Volume and Weight-Volume Problems/Density of a Gas at STP;* Ward's Solo-Learn: 78 W 0450 *Introduction to the Laws of Chemistry;* PH: WCC 890 Series: *Gas Laws* (891, 892, 893, 894); PH: WCC 834 *Calculations Involving Equations.* **References:** Goldwhite, H., "Gay-Lussac after 200 Years," *Journal of Chemical Education,* 55(6), 366 (1978); Vaitkunas, J. J., "The Problem: 'Derivation of the Ideal Gas Law,'" *Journal of Chemical Education,* 56(8), 530 (1979); Herron, J. D., ed., "The Solution: 'Derivation of the Ideal Gas Law,'" *Journal of Chemical Education,* 57(3), 201 (1980); Alexander, M. D., "Verification of Avogadro's Law," *Journal of Chemical Education,* 51(11), 708 (1974); Toon and Ellis, *Foundations of Chemistry,* pp. 53–61.

Teacher Notes
Chapter 12

Chapter Note

Introduce the chapter by showing a **Film** such as MH: *The States of Matter* (18 min.) or a simpler one such as EBE: 1675 *Explaining Matter—Molecules in Motion* (11 min.).

The role of a theory as a part of the scientific method is exemplified by its use in describing and explaining the liquid and solid states of matter. The principle of Le Chatelier is used in explaining phase changes. The role of binding forces in the various types of substances serves to explain such physical properties as vapor pressure, melting and boiling points, and critical temperatures and critical pressures. Binding forces also are used in consideration of the nature of amorphous and crystalline solids and the types of lattice structure in crystals.

Water, as the most abundant and essential liquid, is of paramount importance. Its physical properties are considered in the light of its polarity and hydrogen bonds. Its chemical properties involve such concepts as anhydride, efflorescence, and deliquescence. The properties of water are contrasted with those of deuterium oxide and hydrogen peroxide.

The chapter requires five or six periods. One arrangement is:

Lesson 1   Sections 12.1–12.4: Liquids, Kinetic Theory, Dynamic Equilibrium, Vapor Pressure

Lesson 2   Sections 12.5–12.8: Le Chatelier's Principle, Phase Changes, Critical Temperature

Lesson 3   Sections 12.9–12.14: Solids, Kinetic Theory, Phase Changes, Amorphous Solids, Crystals

Lesson 4   Sections 12.15–12.17: Water, Physical Properties, Structure-Polarity, Hydrogen Bonds, Phase Changes

Lesson 5   Sections 12.18–12.20: Chemical Behavior of Water, Deuterium Oxide

Lesson 6   Section 12.21: Hydrogen Peroxide

Section 12.1. Demonstrations: *Definite volume*—pour a measured volume of water (from a graduated cylinder) into a variety of containers, returning eventually to the graduated cylinder. This also shows fluidity, free surface, and variability of shape. *Diffusion*—layer alcohol over water or water over glycerine in a graduate by lowering a deflagrating spoon just to the level of the denser liquid and pouring the second liquid into the bowl of the spoon through a thistle tube. Layers are visible because of differences in optical density. Liquids may be observed over several days. *Evaporation*—moisten chalkboard with several liquids (water, ethanol, ether, perchloroethylene, and a liquid Freon) simultaneously. Note different rates of evaporation.

Section 12.2. Activities: Review the assumptions of the kinetic theory (Section 10.1), density data for gases and liquids (Section 10.2), and van der Waal's forces (Section 10.4). Use the data in Table 12-1 as the basis of establishing the nature and strength of attractive forces existent in various types of substances: Have students establish the type of substance (metallic) in which the liquid range is greatest (in general). Use the data to have students calculate the molecular weights of water, methane, and benzene. **Demonstrations:** *Density:* Have students (carefully) lift bottled samples of various liquids of the same volume. *Brownian Movement:* Have students view carmine suspension through microscope (Figure 12-2). *Miscibility:* Water and ethanol, water and glycerol, water and mineral oil, mineral oil and gasoline. *Odor:* Waft test on various liquids: ethanol, acetic acid or vinegar. *Evaporation:* See prior Section 12.1 and Figure 12-3. **Loops:** BFA: 82-0043/1 *Density of Liquids;* BFA: 82-0088/1 *Convection in Liquids;* BFA: 80-3304/1 *Thermal Expansion of Liquids;* BFA: 80-3270/1 *Identifying Liquids by Density;* BFA: 80-2926/1 *Random Walk and Brownian Movement;* ICF: *Brownian Movement;* ICF: *Liquids Evaporate;* ICF: *Heat Expands Liquids.* **Filmstrips:** I: 67148 *van der Waal's Forces;* I: 67117 *Metals and the Metallic Bond.* **Transparency:** W: 75 W 8020 *Trends in Melting Point.* **References:** Thomsen, D. E., "The Tie That Binds Molecules," *Science News,* 104(22), 344 (1973); Kerker, M., "Brownian Movement and Molecular Reality Prior to 1900," *Journal of Chemical Education,* 51(12), 764 (1974). Explain the use of the word *vapor.*

Section 12.3. **Activity:** Develop the concept of physical equilibrium, according to the text treatment, to derive its definition. Use the chalkboard for the three-word equations representing **(a)** evaporation process, **(b)** condensation process, and **(c)** state of dynamic equilibrium. **Transparency:** EYE: 033-20 *Physical Equilibrium.*

Sections 12.4 and 12.5. **Demonstrations:** Dynamic equilibrium and vapor pressure. Insert several drops of liquids (water, ethyl alcohol, diethyl ether) into separate Torricelli barometers. Use a Florence flask connected to a manometer (colored liquid). Add several drops of ethanol or ether. Warm bottom of flask with hand or cautiously with a match, then cool with an ice cube to demonstrate the factors involved in evaporation and condensation as well as the energy factors in displacement of equilibrium and establishment of a new equilibrium state. Define equilibrium vapor pressure and discuss the factors on which the amount depends. Based on the demonstrations and the results in vapor pressure changes, develop Le Chatelier's principle and have students state it. Then discuss the effects of volume changes. Use Figure 12-4. **Film:** EBE: 2953 *Vapor Pressure/Demonstrations.* **Loops:** ICF: *Evaporation Causes Cooling;* ICF: *Gases Condense as They Cool;* W: 168 W 1009 (T) *Molecular Motion in Condensed Phases.* **Filmstrip:** I: 67140 *Le Chatelier's Principle.* **Slide Sequences:** I: 69134 *Le Chatelier's Principle.* **Transparency:** I: 68745 *Le Chatelier's Principle* (4 transparencies, 8 overlays. The first two transparencies deal with physical equilibrium). **Reference:** Trepton, R. S., "Le Chatelier's Principle," *Journal of Chemical Education,* 56(4), 253 (1979).

Section 12.6. **Demonstrations:** Have water boiling in a beaker with thermometer inserted. Assign a student to record initial reading and readings at time intervals as boiling proceeds. Increase boiling rate. Keep temperature constant. To demonstrate water boiling at reduced pressure, stopper a flask of boiling water (a thermometer may be inserted into the liquid). Invert the flask and permit the water to cool. Produce boiling at a lower temperature by cooling the flask in running cold water. Entrance of air bubbles as the stopper is loosened shows reduced pressure. An alternate demonstration is to use either water at room temperature or heated to some temperature below the boiling point in a beaker placed in a bell jar that can be partially evacuated by using suction. **Activities:** Define boiling point and standard boiling point. Use replica of Figure 12-6 in

developing these definitions. Use Figure 12-7 as a source of data for student statements of the boiling points of the liquids, their boiling points at pressures below and above 760 mm pressure. **Reference and Experiment:** Refer students to Williams, *Modern Physics* (1980), pp. 185 and 186, for determination of heat of vaporization of water and to the related laboratory experiment for the determination of standard molar heat of vaporization. Refer students to Figure 2-13, "Changes of Phase." **Loops:** BFA: 803403/1 *Boiling Point and Pressure* (HR 3403); ICF: *Boiling Points of Water;* EBE: S-81552 *Le Chatelier's Principle.*

Section 12.7. **Demonstration:** To demonstrate the liquefaction of gases such as ammonia or sulfur dioxide, cool the collecting tube in Dry Ice-acetone mixture. The heating effect of compression may be demonstrated by having a student use a hand pump to inflate a football or basketball. **Activity:** Relate liquefaction to kinetic theory and attractive forces. Use Figure 12-8. Define critical temperature and critical pressure. Refer to Table 12-2 data as basis for developing understanding of the two conditions necessary to liquefy a gas. Refer students to Section 9.4(5) for production of liquid air. **Film:** EBE: S-81568 *Distillation from Liquid Air—Condensation of Oxygen from Air.* Define *vapor.*

Section 12.8. **Activity:** Use models and electron-dot formulas for the substances listed in Table 12-2 to review the nature of the attractive forces in water versus those in the gases listed. Then have students calculate the molecular weights of the nonpolar molecules. **Loops:** BFA: 80-2058/1 *Critical Temperature;* LBF: #16 *The Critical Point.* **Film:** EBE: 2942 *Determination of the Triple-Point of Water* (25 min.).

Section 12.9. **Activities:** Change the position of a book on a table top or of a chalkboard eraser in a bell jar and contrast with the changing shape of a liquid in a container. Discuss the other properties of solids as listed in this section. **Demonstration:** Formation of crystalline sulfur: *rhombic* by evaporation from solution of sulfur in CS_2, *monoclinic* by pouring molten sulfur into a folded filter paper, breaking top crust and pouring out the residual molten sulfur, *amorphous* by pouring boiling sulfur into cold water, removing the mass, and showing its somewhat elastic property.

Section 12.10. **Activity:** Refer to Figure 12-10 in discussion of vibratory motions of particles in solids.

Sections 12.11 and 12.12. **Exhibit:** Display a beaker of melting ice cubes with inserted thermometer and take temperature at intervals. Heat a beaker of ice cubes (thermometer inserted) with the burner and note constant temperature. **Demonstrations:** *Sublimation.* Heat a few crystals of I_2 in an evaporating dish and collect recrystallized I_2 in the bottom of a water-cooled watch glass; expose a piece of Dry Ice (sublimation) or put a piece of it into a cylinder of water. Insert a small piece of naphthalene or paradichlorobenzene into the mercury column of a Torricelli barometer to show vapor pressure of a solid. To show softening property of amorphous solids: exhibit paraffin, heat it until melting, taking the temperature at intervals; heat a soft glass tube or rod until it softens and bends under its own weight (gradual softening instead of the sharply defined melting point of pure substances). Discuss metallic glass: production, properties, and uses. **Demonstrate:** Iodine Diffusion Tubes (Welch), Cryophorus (freezing by evaporation) (Welch); freeze the mercury in the Molecular

Vibration Tube (Welch). **Film:** YF: 238 *Phase Demonstration* (Naphthalene). **Reference, Experiment, and Demonstration:** Refer students to Williams, *Modern Physics* (1980), pp. 181–183, for determination of heat of fusion of ice (molar heat of fusion) and the related laboratory experiment.

You may wish to demonstrate this use of the method of mixtures by using ice in hot water with appropriate temperature readings and calculations. You may also wish to show how the molar heat of fusion in calories per mole may be calculated from the usual 79.9 cal/g. **Loops:** BFA: 80-3411/1 *Heat of Crystallization;* BFA: 80-3429/1 *Heat of Fusion;* ICF: *Most Solids Melt.*

Section 12.13. Student or Class Project. References: Kershnar, L., and Goodstein, M. P., "The Poor Chemist's Rotary Crystallizer," *Chemistry,* 50(2), 25 (1977). **Activity:** Exhibit halite crystal, and have students examine salt crystals with hand lens or microscope. Also have them examine large alum crystal or chrome alum crystal and small crystals with hand lens, if necessary. Exhibit laboratory or homegrown $CuSO_4 \cdot 5H_2O$ crystals and samples of quartz garnet, and other crystals. Exhibit models of NaCl, Mg, Cu, diamond, and graphite—commercial or constructed. Exhibit models of unit cells (Welch) and of basic crystal systems (Figure 12-15). **Demonstrate:** Methods of crystal formation not previously demonstrated, i.e., cooling a hot, saturated solution of NH_4Cl. **Loops:** W: 168 W 1005 (T) *Crystals and X-ray Diffraction;* W: 168 W 1012(T) *A Problem in Diffraction;* PH: WCT 568 *Crystals: Growth in Solution;* PH: WCT 569 *Crystals, Growth from a Melt;* PH: WCT 570 *Crystals, Optical Properties;* PH: WCT 571 *Crystals, Physical Properties.* **Filmstrips:** EBE: Series 9190 *Crystals and Their Deformations: Packing of Atoms in Crystals Construction of Molecular Models.* **Sound Filmstrips** (discs or cassette): EBE: Series 6917 *Crystals.* **Reference:** Suchow, L., "Other Views of Unit Cells," *Journal of Chemical Education,* 53(4), 226 (1976). **Demonstration Equipment:** The Universal Crystal Model and the complementary student sets are available from Dyna-Slide Co., 1566 Sherman Ave., Evanston, Ill. 60201. Similar kits are available from other suppliers, such as Science-Related Materials. **Films:** BFA: 10785 *Considering Crystals* (15+ min.); CH: *Crystallization;* free films from Bell Laboratories, 600 Mountain Ave., Murray Hill, N. J. 07974: *Crystals —An Introduction* (25 min.), *Crystal Growing Morphologies* (17 min.); MG: S24-S25-02 B, *Determination of Molecular Geometry II: Diffraction Methods.*

Section 12.14. Activities: Exhibit samples and models of the five types of substances listed in Table 12-3. Discuss and review the properties of each type of crystal lattice and the nature and magnitude of the binding forces. Mention or describe crystal-growing experiments in Skylab. **Films:** W: 140-4139 *Crystals and Their Structure* (4039 Teacher Training for 4139); W: 140-0114 *Crystals;* Bell System (local source); *Crystals, An Introduction;* STER: KRYSTALLOS; STER: *Quartz Crystal Growing.* **Loops:** BFA: 84-0116/1 *Bubble Model of a Crystal;* LBF: *Crystal Structure of Metals;* HR: 04-96331 *Close-packing of Spheres;* HR: 04-96299 *Crystal Growth.* **Filmstrip:** I: 67116 *Crystals and Their Properties.*

Section 12.15. Activities: Discuss the occurrence of water on earth and recent discoveries of water on Mars and Jupiter. Refer to Figure 12-17. Introduce and briefly discuss social and economic problems related to water pollution, water supply and population explosion, purification and recovery, desalination plants (including nuclear plants); drought, floods, etc. **References:** Geer, I. W., "Water in the Geosystem," *The Science Teacher,* 41(5), 39 (1974); "Water in Jupiter's Atmosphere," *Science News,* 107(7), 102 (1975); Boyd, T. A., "The Wonders of Water," *Chemistry,* 47(6), 6 (1974); Sheehan, J. C., "A Review of Recent Studies on the Association of Water," *Chemistry,* 47(4), 19 (1974). **Films:** BFA: 10177 *Physics and Chemistry of Water* (21 min.); MH: 612024 *The Structure of Water* (14 min.).

Section 12.16. Discuss the physical properties of water. Refer to phase changes in liquids (Sections 12.3–12.7). **Demonstrations:** Ice cubes floating in water (density); water purification by distillation or ion exchange (Alyea, pp. 33, 87, 132, 219; *New York State Chemistry Handbook,* pp. 123–129). Refer back to demonstrations of water boiling at temperatures below standard boiling point under reduced pressure. Exhibit a pressure cooker. **Demonstration:** Squeeze two ice cubes together until they stick or perform regelation experiment using a weighted U-shaped wire and ice. **Film:** EBE: S-81552 *Le Chatelier's Principle.*

Section 12.17. Recall or redemonstrate the polarity of water by deflecting a stream from a burette with an electrostatically charged rod. In conjunction with Table 12-4, use Figures 8-7 and 8-8 from Williams, *Modern Physics* (1980) (density-temperature and volume-temperature changes for water). Explain the unusual properties of water in terms of molecular structure and hydrogen bonds using models and chalkboard diagrams. **Transparencies:** HM: 2-10533 *The Water Molecule Hybridized.* **Filmstrip:** PH: SCC 865 *Electronegativity, Polar Covalent Bonds, Polar Molecules, Hydrogen Bonds, and Coordinate Covalent Bonds.* **Film:** MH: *The Structure of Water* (14 min.).

Section 12.18. Demonstration: For efflorescence, place samples of sodium carbonate decahydrate and sodium sulfate decahydrate in separate watch glasses and have students examine several times during the period. Use a sample of $CuSO_4 \cdot 5H_2O$ and discuss differences in vapor pressure. Samples may also be balanced on the pan of a balance and loss in weight observed. The sodium sulfate decahydrate crystals are readily prepared from a saturated solution by evaporation. Its long white crystals should be stored in airtight bottles before use. Insert a small solid sample of sodium carbonate decahydrate into the mercury column of a Torricelli barometer or place into the equivalent vapor pressure setup of a flask connected to a manometer.

Section 12.19. Demonstration: For deliquescence, expose samples of calcium chloride and pellets of sodium hydroxide on watch glasses early in the period. Have students observe and report at intervals. A balance setup may also be used to observe changes in mass. For vapor pressure use the flask-manometer setup with insertion of several granules of calcium chloride. Define and discuss: *hygroscopic.* **Film:** SUTH: *Chemistry of Water.* Student reports on water may be based on Reprints from **(a)** *Chemistry* (Now *SciQuest*): 110: "What is Bond Polarity and What Difference Does It Make?" 101: "Water," 21: "Water—H_2O or $H_{180}O_{90}$?" 91: "Ionic Bonding in Solids," 31: "Crystal Growth as Chemical Research;'' **(b)** *Scientific American* Offprints: 262: ''Water,'' 249: ''The Nature of Solids.''

Section 12.21. Discuss the laboratory and commercial preparations of H_2O_2. Review its structure (Sections 6.15 and 7.10). Discuss and contrast properties of H_2O and H_2O_2 (Table 12-5). For autooxidation try the equation:

$$\overset{-1}{H_2O_2} + \overset{-1}{H_2O_2} \rightarrow \overset{-2}{2H_2O} + \overset{0}{O_2}$$

Discuss the uses of H_2O_2 and exhibit the 3% antiseptic as well as the 6% hair bleach. **Demonstrations: (1)** Precipitate black PbS by mixing solutions of $Pb(NO_3)_2$ and H_2S or $(NH_4)_2S$. Then stir in 6% H_2O_2—the black PbS is oxidized to white $PbSO_4$. **(2)** Mix solutions of H_2S and H_2P_2 to precipitate ''milk'' of sulfur. **(3)** Addition of H_2O_2 to fresh animal blood results in frothing evolution of O_2. **Reference:** ''Hydrogen Peroxide Gets Spate of New Capacity,'' *Chemistry and Engineering News,* Dec. 10, 1979, p. 16. **Chapter References:** Candy, T. Y., ''Our Most Precious Resource: Water,'' *National Geographic* 158(2), 144 (1980); Arvidson, R. E., Binder, A. B., and Jones, K. L., ''The Surface of Mars,'' *Scientific American,* 238(3), 76 (1978); Soderblom, L. A., ''The Galilean Moons of Jupiter,'' *Scientific American,* 242(1), 88 (1980); ''Metallic Glass,'' *Scientific American,* 238(4), 86 (1978); Chaudhari, P., Giessen, B. C., and Turnbull, D., ''Metallic Glasses,'' *Scientific American* 242(4), 98 (1980); Liu, C. F., O'Donnell, T. J., Gelder, J. I., and Jones, L. L., ''A 3-dimensional Animated Videocassette on the Unit Cell,'' *Journal of Chemical Education,* 57(8), 590 (1980); Brock, C. P., and Lingafelter, E. C., ''Common Misconceptions about Crystal Lattices and Crystal Symmetry,'' *Journal of Chemical Education,* 57(8), 552 (1980); Wells, A. F., ''Some Structural Principles for Introductory Chemistry,'' *Journal of Chemical Education,* 54(5), 273 (1977); Fackler, J. P., Jr., ''Symmetry in Molecular Structure—Facts, Fiction and Fun,'' *Journal of Chemical Education,* 55(2), 79 (1978); Myers, R. T., ''Physical and Chemical Properties and Bonding of Metallic Elements,'' *Journal of Chemical Education,* 56(11), 712 (1979); Baisley, D., ''Boiling at Reduced Pressure,'' *The Science Teacher,* 47(5), 45 (1980); Keller, E., ''What is Happening to Our Drinking Water?'' *Chemistry,* 48(2), 16 (1975); Talesnick, I., ''Vapor Pressure,'' Idea Bank, *The Science Teacher,* 42(1), 36 (1975); Sheehan, J. C., ''A Review of Recent Studies on the Association of Water,'' *Chemistry,* 47(4), 19 (1974); Shavitz, R., ''Phase Changes of Hexachloroethane,'' *Journal of Chemical Education,* 52(4) 231 (1975); Wood, E. A., ''Homegrown Crystals,'' *Chemistry,* 47(2), 49 (1974); *Crystals—A Handbook for School Teachers,* Polycrystals Book Service, P. O. Box 11576, Pittsburgh, Pa. 15428 (1972; paper, $2); Davies, D., and Vance, R., ''Determination of Dissolved Oxygen,'' Lab Bench, *Chemistry,* 48(2), 25 (1975); Twiddy, C., ''Ether Vapor Water Gun,'' Idea Bank, *The Science Teacher,* 43(4), 38 (1976); ''The Water You Drink: How Safe Is It?'' League of Women Voters Education Fund, 1730 M St., N.W., Washington, D.C. 20036. **Programmed Instruction:** Kass, G., *Individual Study Program in Chemistry,* Benjamin, 1968, pp. 57–67, 90–91, 102, 120–134. Ward's Solo-Learn: 78-W-0380 *Bond Type and Properties of Matter;* 78 W 710 *Introduction to Equilibrium Concepts;* PH: WCC 865 *Electronegativity, Polar Covalent Bonds, Polar Molecules,*

Hydrogen Bonds and Coordinate Covalent Bonds. **Additional Audiovisual Aids: Film:** *Crystal Gazing* (14 min.), Moody Institute of Science, 12000 E. Washington Blvd., Whittier, CA 90606. **Loops:** W: 168 W 0996(T) *Molecular Structure Determines the Properties of Substances;* W: 168 W 0997(T) *Crystal Structures of Metals I;* W: 168 W 0998(T) *Crystal Structures of Metals II;* W: 168 W 0999(T) *Crystal Structures of Metals III.* **Films** (free): Association Films, 600 Grand Ave., Ridgefield, N.J. 07657: *Critical Phenomena in Carbon Dioxide* (phase transitions) (8 min.); *Crystal Structures at High Pressures* (40 min.). **Videocassette:** ''A 3-dimensional Animated Videocassette on the Unit Cell (7.5 min.), contact J. I. Gelder, Oklahoma State University, Stillwater, OK 74074.

Teacher Notes
Chapter 13

Chapter Note

The chapter affords many opportunities for the application and extension of many of the concepts previously developed: bonding, phase changes, Le Chatelier's principle, Dalton's law of partial pressures, reaction tendencies, energy and entropy. Effective use may therefore be made of models previously exhibited, as well as demonstrations, experiments, and other instructional aids that have been employed.

This chapter requires five periods. One possible arrangement is:

Lesson 1 Sections 13.1–13.4: Solutions and Suspensions, Types of Solutions, Solvent Selectivity, Hydrogen Bonds

Lesson 2 Sections 13.5–13.8: Solution Equilibrium, Influence of Pressure and Temperature, Rate of Dissolving

Lesson 3 Sections 13.9 and 13.10: Dissolving Mechanisms, Heat of Solution

Lesson 4 Sections 13.11 and 13.12: Concentration of Solutions, Freezing-Point Depression of Solvents

Lesson 5 Sections 13.13 and 13.14: Boiling-Point Elevation of Solvents, Molecular Weights of Solutes

Section 13.1. Exhibit: A variety of materials that emphasize the importance of solutions and suspensions: household ammonia, vinegar, and bleaches indicate percent of chemical; pancake syrup (sugar solution); tincture of iodine (solvent other than water). Samples of salad dressings and medicines (labeled ''Shake well before using'') represent suspensions. Samples of water-base paints and India ink are colloidal suspensions that may be diluted with water. **Demonstrations:** Make a sugar solution, dialysis of starch, glue, sugar, salt as in Section 13.1. Use demonstrations involving NaCl, $KMnO_4$ (visibility), MgO powder, clay, etc., so that students can recognize and state differences between solutions and suspensions, e.g., clarity, settling, filtration, homogeneity. Filter diluted India ink, then coagulate filtrate with acetic acid and refilter. Produce colloidal sulfur by adding HCl to a sodium thiosulfate solution in a tall cylinder. Use the beam from a flashlight (in a darkened room, if you wish), as the colloid forms from the thiosulfate solution, to illustrate the Tyndall effect (Figure 13-1). Coagulate milk with acid. Demonstrations of dialysis (Figure 13-2) and colloid phenomena: Alyea, pp. 49, 113, 146; Alyea, TOPS Demonstration 259–267. Develop definitions in Sections 13.1. **Demonstrations:** Demonstrate conductivity apparatus with water, salt and sugar solution, glacial acetic acid, and diluted acetic acid. **Films:** EBE: 201 *Colloids;* CORF: *The Colloidal State;* ICF: short films 13220 or 13225 *Brownian Movement;* BFA: 10981 *Colloids* (14+ min.); BFA: 10315 *Solutions* (12+ min.); CORF: 1225 *Solutions* (16 min.). **Filmstrips:** I: 67135 *Colloids;* EBE: 6917 Series *Solutions;* EBE: 9080 *Ionization and Dissociation in Solution.* **Transparency:** EYE: 003-22 *Solutions (General Principles);* Note that these audiovisual aids may be used in conjunction with later sections of this chapter. **Reference:** Sarquis, J., "Chem. 1 Supplement: Colloidal Systems," *Journal of Chemical Education,* 57(8), 602 (1980).

Section 13.2. Exhibit selected samples from Table 13-1. **Demonstrations:** *Adsorption:* Drop pellets of activated charcoal into a bottle containing NO_2. Cover and shake. Exhibit a gas mask. Exhibit alloys such as brass or bronze. *Miscibility:* Demonstrate the examples in the text, kerosene and mineral oil. For immiscibility use oils and water, kerosene and water. Use Figure 13-4 or produce replica with polystyrene balls.

Section 13.3. Use models and chalkboard diagrams to review bonding and polarity of H_2O, CCl_4, CH_4 and other hydrocarbons including C_6H_6. You may redemonstrate polarity tests by deflection of a thin stream of liquid by electrostatically charged rods of ebonite, glass, or plastic. **Loop:** W: 168 W 1040(T) *Polar and Nonpolar Molecules* (water, acetone, carbon disulfide, and benzene). **Films:** W: 140-4154 *Shapes and Polarities of Molecules* (18 min.); LCG: short films E-66 and E-66A deal with the structure and shape of CCl_4. **Demonstration: CAUTION:** Dissolve nonpolar I_2 in CCl_4 and oil in CCl_4. Construct a ball-and-stick model of ethanol, discuss polarity of bonds and molecule. Perform the polarity deflection test for ethanol. Use Figure 13-5. Other films are MH: 612002 or 612014 *Liquids in Solution;* CORF: *Properties of Solutions.*

Section 13.4. **Activity:** Review hydrogen bonds (Section 12.16). Relate to abnormally high boiling point and melting point (ice). See Figure 13-6. Relate to solubility of ethanol in water. Use chalkboard formulas for H_2O: Long dashes for covalent bonds and a series of dots representing hydrogen bonds between molecules. See Figure 9-20, Toon and Ellis, *Foundations of Chemistry.* **Demonstration:** "Hydrogen Bonding in Liquids," Alyea, p. 143. Mix equal volumes of H_2O and C_2H_5OH in burette, shake, and note decrease in total volume. **Films:** FAC: *Physics and Chemistry of Water;* MH: 611999 or 612024 *The Structure of Water.* **Filmstrips:** I: 67310 *Water —A Most Unusual Substance;* PH: WCC 865 *Electronegativity, Polar Covalent Bonds, Polar Molecules, Hydrogen Bonds and Coordinate Covalent Bonds.*

Section 13.5. **Activities:** Start with a very small amount of a very soluble substance (NH_4Cl, KNO_3), and gradually add more and more solute until a saturated solution results. Define saturated solution and solution equilibrium. Exhibit equivalent of Figure 13-7. Although some of these terms do not appear until Section 13.11, students can identify the solutions produced as dilute, concentrated, and eventually saturated. Have them identify the first two terms as also being unsaturated and attempt pairings such as dilute-unsaturated, concentrated-unsaturated, concentrated-saturated. Make up a saturated solution of boric acid in cold water as an example of a dilute-saturated solution. Shake up a few iodine crystals with water and heat to show increase in solubility upon heating and evidence of a dilute-saturated solution. Save the saturated solution of NH_4Cl for later use in demonstrating the effect of temperature changes on solubility. Add H_2O to a saturated solution of sugar, shake, and note effect on amount of undissolved solid. Decant a portion of the liquid (saturated solution) and have students explain how they could experimentally distinguish between this solution and an unsaturated solution. Use Figure 13-8 and weigh out the solutes as shown. **Film:** MH: 612005 *Dynamics of Solution.* You may wish to set up a saturated solution of NaCl (small crystals) in a stoppered vessel and eventually large cubic crystals will grow as the surface area minimizes. A quantitative project for student(s) may be to determine the initial mass of undissolved NaCl and, after a sufficient time lapse, the final mass of the larger crystals (both at the same room temperature).

Section 13.6. Demonstrations: To demonstrate the relationship between the pressure of a gas and its solubility, uncap a bottle of carbonated beverage. Pour it into a beaker. Students note and explain effervescence. Place a sample in an open container on the base of a vacuum table, cover with a bell jar, and reduce the pressure. A water aspirator may be used instead of the vacuum table and vacuum. Test (with limewater) a sample of soda water that has been standing exposed to air for some time and a sample that has stopped effervescing. Demonstrate an NH_3 or HCl fountain (Alyea, p. 13) as an example of compound formation. State Henry's law. **Activities:** Discuss pressure changes and solubility in terms of Le Chatelier's principle. Review Dalton's law of partial pressures (Section 10.14). Discuss Henry's law and its nonapplicability to the soluble gases (see Appendix Table 11). Demonstrate the effect of reduced pressure (vacuum aspirator) on the solubility of the gases (largely oxygen). **Transparencies:** HM: 2-10545, 2-10546 *Aqueous Solubilities.*

Section 13.7. Demonstrations: Let a tall cylinder of cold tap water stand from the beginning of the period. Have students note gas bubbles as the solution warms. Hold a test tube containing tap water almost horizontally; heat slowly and gently. Have students note gas bubbles that appear well before boiling starts. Use the data in Appendix Table 11 for the effect of temperature on the solubility of gases. Warm the saturated solution of NH_4Cl and discuss equilibrium disturbance. After solution of the undissolved solute is complete, cool the hot concentrated solution under the tap. Have students note crystallization. **Activities:** Use Figures 13-9, 13-11, 13-12, and Table 13-2 to have students arrive at generalizations about the effect of temperature on the solubility of solids in liquids. Have them identify substances that do not conform to the generalization. **Demonstration:** To show the decrease in solubility with increase in temperature, use a saturated solution of calcium acetate (8 g of solid in 25 mL of H_2O). The salt precipitates upon heating (see *Journal of Chemical Education,* 47, 275 (1970); and Alyea, p. 189, "The Effect of Temperature on Solubility," which involves the formation and changes in solubility of various hydrates of $MnSO_4$). For demonstrations of supersaturation, see Alyea, pp. 14, 21. Discuss generalizations for solution of solids in liquids and of liquids in liquids in terms of phase changes and energies involved. For an interesting experiment involving temperature effect on solubility of two liquids, see *Journal of Chemical Education,* 48, 668 (1971). A crystal of malachite green is dissolved in 50 mL of anhydrous methanol. This solution is then shaken with 50 mL of pentane, producing a uniformly green-colored solution. Cooling this for two minutes in a mixture of Dry Ice and acetone causes it to separate into a colorless upper layer of pentane and a green lower layer of methanol. Shaking after the solutions have warmed to room temperature again produces a uniform green solution. A simple explanation involves the kinetic energy at higher temperature which overcomes the attractive forces between identical molecules of the two liquids. You may wish to have students draw solubility curves such as Figure 13-11 for substances listed in Table 13-2. **Filmstrip:** EYE: X226B *Solubility Curves.* **Transparencies:** HM: *Aqueous Solubilities I & II; C Solubilities of Various Substances.* **Films:** MH: *Liquids in Solution;* CORF: *Solutions;* CORF: *Properties of Solutions;* W: 140-4205 *Solution of Salts; The Variation of Solubility with Temperature* (12 min.). **Reference:** Hiegel, G. A., "Crystallization of Sodium Acetate," *Journal of Chemical Education,* 57(2), 152 (1980).

Section 13.8. Demonstrations: Demonstrate effects of stirring, powdering, and heating for $CuSO_4 \cdot 5H_2O$; use equal masses of cube, granulated, and powdered sugar to study rate of solution and surface area.

Sections 13.9 and 13.10. Demonstrations: Dissolve NH_4Cl, KNO_3, $NaOH$, and H_2SO_4 separately in water and have students note temperature changes by touch and thermometer readings. Dissolve a gas (air-cooled) such as NH_3 or HCl in water at room temperature. Take the temperature of the resultant solution. Relate the findings of these demonstrations to Table 13-3. **Activities:** Use (a) a plastic-ball model (Figure 13-13), and (b) a lattice or crystal model of NaCl and ball-stick models of H_2O to develop the three important actions that occur during the solution process (Section 13.9). For (b), simulate the solution of Na^+ by attachment of the negative ends of the polar H_2O molecules, of Cl^- by the positive ends of H_2O molecules. Discuss the nature of the energy changes for the three actions, the entropy changes, and the final demonstrated solubility. This discussion should be in terms of the net energy change versus entropy change for (a) solids, (b) gases. Use Question 25. Use the general and specific equations in Section 13.10. Discuss the meaning of the positive and negative values for heats of solutions (Table 13-3). Explain the effect of temperature changes on the solubility of solids, gases, and liquids. The explanations should be made as applications of Le Chatelier's principle. Relate data in Tables 13-2 and 13-3. **Optional Demonstrations:** Dehydrate Epsom salts. Insert a thermometer into the dry $MgSO_4$ and add water, several drops at a time. Smith, W. L., "Thermochemistry and First Aid," *Chemistry,* 45, (Apr. 1972), utilizes instant hot packs and cold packs. The demonstration is relevant. It has value in showing relationships of heat (enthalpy) of solution and heat (enthalpy) of hydration, as well as applying Le Chatelier's principle to solubilities of salts during temperature changes. The cold pack contains the dry chemical NH_4NO_3 and a pouch of water. The hot pack contains dry calcium chloride and a pouch of water. Striking the packs causes the pouch to break. The pertinent data are: NH_4NO_3: solubility at 20°C is 192 g per 100 mL of water,

$$\Delta H_{soln} = +77 \text{ cal per gram}$$

$CaCl_2$: Solubility at 20°C is 74.5 g per 100 mL H_2O.

$$\Delta H_{soln} = -178 \text{ cal per gram}$$

Perform the demonstration for Figure 13-14. **Film:** MH: *Dynamics of Solution;* MH: *How Things Dissolve;* **Filmstrips:** I: 67134 *The Solution Process;* portion of I: 67140 *Le Chatelier's Principle.* **Transparency:** I: 68745 *Le Chatelier's Principle.* **Loop:** MH: 641721-2 *Dissolving, A Physical Change.*

Section 13.11. Review or Redemonstrate: Qualitative concentration terms. Demonstrate dilution by addition of water, and concentration by evaporation or addition of solute. Exhibit or weigh out masses representing one mole of selected solutes. Prepare representative solutions of varying molalities. Label. Relate to details in Figure 13-12. Use the Sample and Practice Problems. Assign Problems 1–9. Refer to Table 13-4.

Section 13.12. Demonstration and Activities: Recall or redemonstrate vapor pressure of water (and effect of temperature change) using a Torricelli barometer or equivalent apparatus. Insert a drop of salt solution into another barometer tube. Use Figure 13-15 to explore details of effect of solute on vapor pressure and later on freezing and boiling points. Discuss the uses of antifreeze and coolants in automobiles. Have students inquire at local service stations and garages about the amounts of these substances recommended for different automobiles (varying radiator capacities). Exhibit and use the hydrometer used for testing concentration of antifreezes. Note effect of temperature on recommended concentration (amount of antifreeze). Compare melting rates of ice cubes or crushed ice with and without addition of solid NaCl (rock salt). Base the development of K_f on Section 13.12 and the related data in Table 13-5. Solve the Sample Problems. Use the Practice Problems and Problems 10–14 and 18. **Filmstrips of Individualized Programs:** PH: WCC 814 *Preparing Solutions;* PH: WCC 895 *Mole Fraction and Molal Concentration: Boiling Point Elevation and Freezing Point Depression.* **Microfiche:** PH: WCF 1005 *Chem-Review 5, Solution Preparation.*

Section 13.13. Activity: Use Figure 13-15 for boiling point elevation for nonvolatile, nonelectrolyte solutes. **Demonstrate:** Elevation of boiling point by taking temperature of boiling solutions of sugar and salt. Refer to Table 13-5. Do Problems 11–14.

Section 13.14. Develop the mathematical relationships needed for the solution of the Sample Problem. Have students solve the Practice Problems and Problems 15–17. A student project for determination of the molecular weight of urea: Use 8 g of urea in 40 mL of water in a salt-ice mixture and measure freezing point depression. Refer to *Journal of Chemical Education,* 47, 275 (1970). **Films:** UA: *Molecular Weight of Solutes.* As a chapter summary, show a film such as CORF: *Solutions;* UA: *Properties of Solutions.* **Programmed Instruction:** Barrow, G. M., *et al., Understanding Chemistry—Chemical Systems* (V), Benjamin, 1967, "Colligative Properties," pp. 101–149; Kass, G. A., *Individual Study Program in Chemistry,* Benjamin, vol. II, pp. 114–134, vol. III, pp. 88–92, 162–165. **Reference:** Olsen, J. O., "Freezing Ice Cream and Making Caramel Topping," Chemical Principles Exemplified, *Journal of Chemical Education,* 53(1), 49 (1976) [freezing and boiling point effects].

Teacher Notes
Chapter 14

Chapter Note

Activities and Demonstrations: Many of the demonstrations in this chapter may be repeats of those used in previous chapters (Chapters 6 and 13). The emphasis is different. Where demonstrations of conductivity of molten electrovalent compounds and of solutions were used previously to establish some reality upon which bonding concepts were based, in this chapter bonding concepts are used to explain the demonstrated reality. Again extensive use is made of models to complement the demonstrations and help develop equation writing skills.

The chapter furnishes an excellent opportunity for the development and understanding of scientific methods and scientific attitudes. One good approach is to start a teacher demonstration of conductivity similar to the text description. The experiment as described lends itself to almost infinite variation. The experimental approach should allow the class to recognize phenomena that call for explanation. First, students should be challenged to offer their explanations of why electrolytes conduct and nonelectrolytes do not. Student theories should be explored. For example, students may offer the Faraday explanation. This may be examined in the light of other evidence such as freezing point and boiling point phenomena, in which electrical potential (the student may say electricity or electric current or electric voltage) plays no part. Some students may offer explanations similar to the Arrhenius theory. These should be checked against previously developed concepts of bonding and structure. Some students undoubtedly will observe that in the demonstration some solutions caused a bright light and others caused a dim light. The story of the initial reception of the Arrhenius theory by his chemistry professor should be told at an appropriate point. An attempt to evaluate the professor's reaction should also be made. According to one version of the story, Arrhenius came to his conclusion during the night of May 17, 1883, after two years of ceaseless toil. The next morning he rushed to his chemistry professor and said, "I have a new theory of electrical conductivity." The professor looked at Arrhenius rather disdainfully and replied, "How interesting. Goodby." The class then may be asked to evaluate the professor's reaction as a scientific attitude. According to one version, the professor explained his reason for failing to listen. He had heard many theories of ionization, all of which were soon proved wrong or inadequate. He reasoned that this was merely another unacceptable student theory. **Activity:** Use Worksheet VIII: Ionization and Dissociation of Acids, Bases, Salts.

This chapter requires four periods. One possible arrangement is:

Lesson 1 Sections 14.1–14.3: Conductivity of Solutions, Electrolyte Behavior, Theory of Ionization

Lesson 2 Sections 14.4 and 14.5: Hydration of Ions: Ionic Compounds, Dissociation, Ionic Equations, Net Ionic Equations

Lesson 3 Sections 14.6–14.8: Ionization: Covalent Compounds, Strength of Electrolytes, Ionization of Water

Lesson 4 Sections 14.9 and 14.10: Electrolytes: Freezing and Boiling Points of Solvents, Apparent Degree of Ionization; Debye-Hückel Theory

Section 14.1. Review the related details pertaining to electrolytes and nonelectrolytes in Section 13.1. **Demonstrations:** Use Alyea, p. 15, demonstrations 6-1, 6-2, "Conductivity of Solutions"; also Alyea, pp. 74–75, 6-1s to 6-7s. Conductivity of Solutions: Start with observation by the class of a simplified, plug-in conductivity apparatus. Draw the diagram on the chalkboard. After asking students to explain why the lamp does not light (use an inserted switch and close it), first put the wooden handle of a knife, then the blade across the gap between the electrodes. Students realize that some solids (metals) are conductors and others are not conductors. Generally they will explain metallic conductivity as being due to movement of electrons (emphasize that they are *charged particles*) through the solid conductor. Put a large halite crystal across the gap to show that a solid salt does not conduct. Exhibit a crystal model of NaCl, review electrovalent compounds, have students identify the ions and write the formula $Na^+Cl^-(s)$. Have students explain that conduction does not occur because there are no free electrons and that the ions are fixed in the NaCl lattice and cannot move. At this point you may wish to insert an ice cube (held in rubber gloves or rubber-tipped tongs) across the electrode gap to show that solid water is also a nonconductor. Granular NaCl in a beaker or crucible is similarly tested. Fuse the NaCl by preheating a crucible with a high-temperature burner and dropping in half a teaspoon of granular NaCl. Have students recall the general high melting point of electrovalent compounds (salts). After fusion, drop in successive small portions of NaCl until the melted salt covers the bottom of the crucible. Insert the electrodes and have students explain conductivity in terms of *free-moving* ions. Distilled water is tested for conductivity. It is added to NaCl(s) in a beaker, stirred, and the solution is tested for conductivity. The question as to which substance, NaCl or H_2O, is conducting is raised and resolved. The conclusion reached is that the ions of NaCl become free-moving in water solution. Two representative equations for dissociation of electrovalent compounds are written:

$$Na^+Cl^-(s) \rightarrow Na^+ + Cl^-$$
$$\text{(fixed in lattice)} \qquad \text{(free moving)}$$

$$Na^+Cl^-(s) + H_2O \rightarrow Na^+(aq) + Cl^-(aq)$$
$$\text{(fixed in lattice)} \qquad \text{(free moving)}$$

Either use the data collected as a result of the student experiment or repeat conductivity tests for a variety of acids, bases, and salts, as well as solutions of sugar, alcohol, glycerine, and so on. Have students attempt to arrange the electrolytes under headings: Acids, Bases (hydroxides), and Salts. Have them also note which electrolytes are poorer conductors than the obviously good conductors [e.g., $Ca(OH)_2$, $HC_2H_3O_2$, $NH_3(aq)$]. Raise the question: What happens to the charged particles as they conduct? Use the electrolysis of fused (melted) NaCl as an example. Help students understand that positively charged ions migrate to the negative electrode and vice versa. Also write equations for oxidation: $2Cl^- - 2e^- \rightarrow Cl_2(g)$ and reduction: $Na^+ + e^- \rightarrow Na$ taking place at the respective electrodes.

Section 14.2. Use the chalkboard to list data from Table 14-1 for freezing-point depression for 0.1-*m* solutions of ionic solvents. Have them compare with the freezing-point depression for a 0.1-*m* solution of sugar. Have them attempt to frame the related generalization. Discuss boiling-point elevation. Have students realize that the freezing-point depressions and boiling-point elevations are not exactly two, three, or more times as much as those for nonelectrolytes of the same molalities. A possible demonstration is determining the boiling-point elevation of 1-m solutions of NaCl, $CaCl_2$, $C_{12}H_{22}O_{11}$ using a Beckman thermometer (Welch 5698).

Section 14.3. **Activities:** Have students evaluate Faraday's explanation in the light of freezing and boiling point data. Use the caption for Figure 14-2 or the Arrhenius anecdote in the introductory suggestions. Have student state Arrhenius' explanation and evaluate it in terms of present-day knowledge of crystalline electrovalent compounds and the polar nature of water. Summarize the three assumptions of the modern theory of ionization. To make the last assumption dramatic, stress the fact that this beaker of salt solution contains billions and billions of electrically charged particles (ions). Then call for a "brave" volunteer to stick his or her finger into the beaker to find out which, if any, of the charged ions are in excess. **Films:** CORF *Principles of Ionization;* UA *Principles of Ionization* (14 min.); UA *Ionic Equilibrium* (16 min.); Indu *Ionization and Ionic Equilibrium.*

Section 14.4. **Activities:** Review the structure and properties of electrovalent compounds (crystalline solids, high melting point, *do not* conduct in solid phase, *do* conduct in liquid phase), identify as salts. Exhibit models of NaCl (Figures 14-3, 14-4, 14-5). Stress differences in properties and structure of atoms versus ions—electronic configurations and electron-dot symbols.

Section 14.5. **Activity:** Have students at the board and in their seats write the dissociation equations for the electrovalent electrolytes. Use examples besides those in this section to train students in writing dissociation equations emphasizing the oxidation numbers of the ions and *Assumption 3,* that the total positive ionic charge equals the total negative ionic charge (Na_2SO_4, $CaCl_2$, AlF_3, Na_3PO_4, $Al_2(SO_4)_3$, etc.). Demonstrate hydration of ions during solution by using water models with a model of the NaCl crystal as in Figure 14-6. Emphasize the negative end of the water molecules attracted to the Na^+ ion and the positive hydrogen ends of the dipole attracted to the Cl^- ion. Make a saturated solution of NaCl (40 g) in 100 mL of H_2O; write the equation using $\leftrightarrows$ for the ionic equilibrium. Weigh out 80 g of $NaNO_3$ and dissolve to emphasize the difference in solubility. Add more $NaNO_3$ to saturation and write the equilibrium equation. Add a very small amount of $BaSO_4$ to water and stir to emphasize practical insolubility. Precipitate AgCl (KCl + $AgNO_3$) and have students identify the precipitate by using Table 12 in Appendix, Solubility Chart. Write the empirical, ionic, and net ionic equations. Define precipitation. **Demonstration:** To show that the hydroxides of Group I and Group II metals are largely ionic, carefully melt solid NaOH in a metal crucible and demonstrate its conductivity. Write the dissociation equations for NaOH, KOH, $Ca(OH)_2$, and $Ba(OH)_2$.

Section 14.6. **Activity:** Exhibit a bottle of glacial acetic acid and have students predict conductivity. Test for conductivity, dilute, and retest for conductivity of the aqueous solution. Have ionization defined. Using models, reestablish the polar nature of HCl and H_2O. Have students explain how ions can be produced by ionization due to dipole-dipole attraction

and hydrogen bonding. Since the use of benzene solutions is hazardous, use the **Film loop** W: 168 W1041(T) *HCl in Water and Benzene* or the **Film:** W: 140-4154 *Shapes and Polarities of Molecules.* You may wish to point out that adding water to the benzene-HCl solution causes the HCl to dissolve in the benzene, producing a water solution that is an electrolyte. Furthermore, addition of $AgNO_3$ to the water solution of HCl produces a precipitate, indicating that the chloride ion is present in the solution. You may also wish to describe the non-conductivity of benzene-NH_3 solution, and the result of mixing this solution with water. Identify the hydronium ion (Figure 14-7) using models and the equation and test with blue litmus paper. Write ionization equations for $HC_2H_3O_2$, H_2SO_4, HNO_3, H_3PO_4, resulting in hydronium ion production. Contrast these equations with the Arrhenius-type equations, that is, $HCl \rightarrow H^+ + Cl^-$. Write the equation for the ionization of NH_3 and contrast with dissociation equations for metallic hydroxides [NaOH, $Ca(OH)_2$, $Ba(OH)_2$]. **Transparency:** EYE: 003-27 *Ionization of Acids, Bases, Salts.* **Filmstrip:** EBE: Series 9080 *Ionization and Dissociation in Solution; Ionic and Covalent Bonds; Electron Arrangement and Chemical Bonds.* **Loop:** MH *Electrolytes.* **References:** Giguere, F. A., "The Great Fallacy of the H^+ ion and the True Nature of H_3O^+," *Journal of Chemical Education,* 56(9), 571 (1979); Deck, J. C., "Strong and Weak Acids and Bases," *Journal of Chemical Education,* 56(12), 814 (1979). Display a model of Al_2Cl_6 and discuss its molecular nature and that of other aluminum halides. Explain its conductivity, liquid phase, and solution. Explain its ionization and the role of hydration. Write the ionization equation.

Section 14.7. **Demonstration:** Redemonstrate the intensity of the light bulb for HCl versus acetic and boric acids; NaOH versus $NH_3(aq)$. Try the series NaOH, $Ca(OH)_2$, $Ba(OH)_2$, and $Mg(OH)_2$, using filtered solutions of the last three. Lecture-table meters may be used to show that solutions that have little, if any, effect on the light bulb, do have perceptible conductivity. Salts that dissociate to only a slight extent by conductivity are $HgCl_2$, $CdSO_4$. Discuss strong electrolytes (ionic compounds and hydrogen halides with the exception of HF). Demonstrate conductivity of solutions of HCl and HF. Review Table 6-4, Bond Energies. **Exhibit:** Models of the hydrohalogens. On the relative strengths and degree of ionization of these refer to Pauling, L., "The Strength of Hydrohalogenic Acids," *Journal of Chemical Education,* 53(12), 762 (1976); Meyers, T. R., "The Strength of Hydrohalic Acids," *ibid.,* 53(1), 17 (1976); letter by Myers, *ibid.,* 53(12), 802 (1976); Lesley, S. D., and Ragsdale, R. O., "Trends in the Acidity of Some Binary Hydrides in Aqueous Solution," *ibid.,* 53(1), 19 (1976). Refer to Table 6-4 for data on bond energies. Write the equation for the ionization of $HC_2H_3O_2$ and discuss the effect of dilution on its degree of ionization. Write the equation for the ionization of NH_3 and illustrate with models. Discuss ammonia-water solution versus ammonium hydroxide. Establish the meanings of strong and weak versus dilute and concentrated. **Reference:** Ladd, M. F. C., "Dissociation of a Weak Acid," *Journal of Chemical Education,* 57(9), 669 (1980).

Section 14.8. **Demonstration:** First test the conductivity of water with a 25-watt bulb. Then use either a neon or an argon lamp. Have students suggest a mechanism for ionization (autoionization) of water. Discuss the role of hydrogen bonds in water and their role in autoionization. Add red and blue litmus to water to establish equivalency of the hydronium and hydroxide ion concentrations and the consequent neutrality of water. Use models for Figure 14-11 and write the equation. Discuss the use of H^+ and $H^+(aq)$, water of hydration, and hydrated ions in water solution.

Section 14.9   Activity: Refer to Section 13.11 and Figure 14-12. Discuss freezing point and boiling point effects for non-electrolytes versus electrolytes using the data in Table 14-1. Have students discover the effect of dilution by using the data in this table. Review the ionization equations for H_2SO_4 and $CaCl_2$ as in this section. Have students make predictions about conductivity and hence colligative effects for 1-m solution of H_3PO_4. Demonstrate its low conductivity, leading to stepwise explanation of ionization.

Section 14.10. Use the chalkboard for writing the numbers in the section representing the freezing point for a 0.1-m solution of NaCl and its actual freezing point. Have students attempt an explanation. The discussion should involve the Debye-Hückel theory of interionic attraction as it relates to the apparent degree of ionization being less than the actual ion concentration, and the dilution effect on the freezing point depression. Use Figure 14-14 and Tables 14-1 and 14-2. A useful table from *Handbook of Chemistry and Physics* is:

**Approximate Degree of Ionization
for Active Salts (0.1-N solution)**

Type $R^+ R^-$ (e.g., KCl)	0.86
Type $R^{++} (R^-)_2$ (e.g., $BaCl_2$)	0.72
Type $(R^+)_2 R^{--}$ (e.g., K_2SO_4)	0.72
Type $R^{++} R^{--}$ (e.g., $CuSO_4$)	0:45

Teacher Notes
Chapter 15

Chapter Note

The chapter treatment calls for the application of concepts of bonding (Chapter 6) and ionization (Chapter 13). It provides opportunities for the review and strengthening of these concepts through the use of electron-dot formulas, models, oxidation states, and electronegativity. Equations of various types are written. Some of these relate to Table 8-2, Activity Series of the Elements. Operational definitions of acids, bases, and salts are formulated and provide the basis for the conceptual models and definitions. An excellent series of articles by Jensen, W. B., ''Acid-Base Theory,'' *Chemistry* Reprint 123, is recommended for use by both students and instructors. It summarizes and evaluates the theories through HSAB, Hard and Soft Acids and Bases. Other useful references are Toon and Ellis, *Foundations of Chemistry,* ''Lewis Theory,'' pp. 505–507; and Castka, J. F. ''High School Chemistry Demonstrations: Acid-Base Theory; Bond Strength,'' *Journal of Chemical Education,* 52(6), 394 (1975). Use Worksheet IX: Names and Formulas of Acids and Salts; and Worksheet X: Solution Concentrations. Another excellent reference for both students and teachers is Kolb, D., ''Chemical Principles Revisited: Acids and Bases, *Journal of Chemical Education,* 55(7), 459 (1978).

This chapter requires five periods. One possible arrangement is:

Lesson 1   Sections 15.1–15.4: Acids: Nature, Industrial, Aqueous, Modern Definitions
Lesson 2   Sections 15.4–15.7: Acids: Properties, Naming, Anhydrides
Lesson 3   Sections 15.8–15.11: Bases (Hydroxides): Nature, Properties, Anhydrides, Periodic Trends
Lesson 4   Section 15.12: Relative Strengths of Acids and Bases
Lesson 5   Sections 15.13–15.15: Salts: Nature, Production Reactions, Naming

Section 15.1. Redefine electrolyte and have students recall or exhibit representatives of the three classes of electrolytes. Write a representative ionization equation for a base (NaOH), a salt (NaCl), and dissociation equation for an acid (HCl). Exhibit fruits, foods, and acids mentioned in this section. Perform the litmus and taste test. (Warn students not to taste anything in the lab except when instructed.) Redemonstrate acid conductivity and demonstrate properties 4, 6, and 7 (Section 15.5) to provide basis for an operational definition of an acid. Exhibit model of acetic acid and write equation for its ionization (simple as in Table 15-1), also using model to show that the hydrogen atom of the carboxyl group is the one ionized. Use models to illustrate hydration of hydrogen ion to become the H_3O^+ ion. List the names and formulas of the four mineral acids. Explain aqueous acids.

Section 15.2. Exhibit large labeled bottles of the industrial acids. Discuss their importance, uses, and compositions. **Demonstration:** Prepare dilute acids as in text. To demonstrate the density of sulfuric acid, have a student lift a laboratory bottle of the acid **(CAUTION)** and a similar bottle filled with water. Have students describe, from observing your procedures, the dilution of acids by pouring acids into water. **Transparency:** EYE: 003–27 *Ionization of Acids, Bases, Salts.* **Filmstrip:** EBE: 9080 *Ionization and Dissociation in Solution.*

Section 15.3. Write simple equations for Arrhenius' ionization, that is $HCl \rightleftarrows H^+ + Cl^-$, for acids as in Table 15-1. Use the electron-dot formula and a model of HCl to illustrate covalent structure. If necessary, redemonstrate the conductivity and litmus tests for glacial and diluted acetic acid. Describe the similar tests for HCl-benzene, HCl-benzene-water in the **Film loop** W: 168 W 1041(T) *HCl in Water and Benezene.* Review the polar nature of water and write the equations for hydronium ion production. You may wish to show that HSO_4^- is an acid (ion) by litmus test of solution of $NaHSO_4$. Retest or discuss conductivity of acetic and carbonic acids, identifying these as weak acids and defining weak and strong acids. Use litmus paper reactions as well. Demonstrate slight conductivity of boric acid, phosphoric acid, and selected organic acids such as citric, tartaric, and so on. Define strong and weak acids and refer to Table 15-1.

Section 15.4. Cite evidence for the existence of the hydronium ion as in text. Exhibit models of H_3O^+ and $H_9O_4^+$ (Figure 15-1). Spatial models may be constructed from plastic spheres held together by a variety of connectors such as toothpicks, pipe cleaners, magnets, magnetic strips, and so on. Recall previous demonstration on conductivity tests for HCl in nonpolar solvent, result on addition of water, litmus tests (make sure that the litmus paper was dried previously). Write the formula equation, electron-dot equation for the HCl-H_2O reaction. Simulate the proton donation with models. Circle the electron pair representing the coordinate covalent bond in H_3O^+. Repeat with the NH_3 + HCl reaction. Use Figures 15-2, 15-3, 15-4. Repeat for the NH_3 + H_2O reaction. Describe and discuss the results of the following experiment series: conductivity and litmus tests for NH_3 in benzol and NH_3 + benzol + water. Hold bottles (or their stoppers) of NH_3(aq) and HCl (concentrated) mouth to mouth. This may also be performed with bottles of the dried gases. (A cloud of NH_4Cl forms when toluol or benzol solutions of HCl and NH_3 are mixed.) Permit the material to settle (this takes time in a stoppered bottle). Observe the deposited solid, NH_4Cl. This may be removed by filtration and tests performed to establish its identity. Develop the Brønsted definition of an acid on the basis of these activities and demonstrations. In the reaction between NH_3 and H_2O, identify the H_2O as the acid. Throughout utilize the concept of hydrogen bonding as in Figures 14-7 and 14-11. Space and time permitting, write the Brønsted equations next to the Arrhenius equations (Figure 15-1). **Filmstrip:** I: 67124 *Acid-Base Theories;* PH: WCC 820 *Protons in Chemical Change.* **References:** Giguere, P. A., "The Great Fallacy of the H$^+$ Ion: and True Nature of H_3O^+," *Journal of Chemical Education,* 56(9), 571 (1979); MCA Staff, "An Acid Can Be Basic," *Journal of Chemical Education,* 56(8), 529 (1979).

Section 15.5. Demonstrate the properties of aqueous acids that have not been performed previously, that is, 5, 7, 8. Include the reactions of oxidizing acids, H_2SO_4 and HNO_3 with metals. Develop the formula, ionic, and net ionic equations including those for the successive ionizations of polyprotic acids. Use models to simulate Figure 15-6 for neutralization. **Reference:** Driscoll, D. R., "Calcite-Acid Reaction," *Journal of Chemical Education,* 57(10), 672 (1979).

Section 15.6. List representative selection of formulas of binary acids (Table 15-2) and oxyacids (Table 15-3). Have students recognize that binary acids contain only two elements. You may wish to use the term ternary with the oxyacids since they contain three elements, one of which is oxygen. Use the chalkboard for reproduction of Figure 15-8, electron-dot formulas of the oxyacids of chlorine. Arrange the oxidation states, formulas, and names of the five chlorine acids at the left of a table. At the right, have students write the formulas of the sodium compounds of each acid that could be formed by reaction with (a) sodium, (b) sodium hydroxide. Later the names of these salts are filled in (Section 15.15). Drill the formula and the name of the acids listed. Emphasize the formulas of the *ous* and *ic* acid pair in Table 15-3.

Section 15.7. Demonstrate the formation of a binary acid by direct union, burning H_2 in Cl_2. Use moist blue litmus, first in the Cl_2, then in the product. **Reference:** Corso, C. R., and DeOlivieros, J. E., "Acid-Base Reactions in the Gaseous State (An Illustrative Experiment)," *Journal of Chemical Education,* 55(4), 244 (1978).

Section 15.8. Activities: Exhibit the common household bases. Have students read the labels and the antidotes for household ammonia and lye. Test these as well as $Ca(OH)_2$, KOH, and $Ba(OH)_2$ solutions with litmus; test milk of magnesia with litmus. In reverse pattern, use the electron-dot equation and

model for Figure 14-11 (autoionization of water and hydrogen bond role) for investigating the mechanism of neutralization between hydronium and hydroxide ion. After establishing the hydroxide ion as the most common basic ion in aqueous solutions, develop the Brønsted definition of a base. Identify the acids and bases in the reactions in this section. Use the general format for these reactions:

$$\text{acid} + \text{base} \rightarrow \text{acid} + \text{base}$$

or its useful equivalent

$$A_1 + B_2 \rightarrow A_2 + B_1$$

In the HCl + H_2O equation, identify the weaker acid and base. Demonstrate the reaction between HCl and NH_3 by bringing the moistened stoppers from bottles of saturated ammonia-water solution and concentrated hydrochloric acid together. Use models and the electron-dot formulas for the equation. Refer to the article in Section 15.7. Depending upon the abilities of the class, discuss the Lewis acid-base theory. Refer to Castka, J. F., "Demonstrations for High School Chemistry: Acid-Base Theories," *Journal of Chemical Education,* 52(6), 394 (1975); Toon and Ellis, *Foundations of Chemistry,* pp. 505–507. **Transparencies:** RH (Reinhold): 21748 *Neutralization;* 21750 *Proton Exchange Reactions.*

Section 15.9. Demonstrate: The conductivites for various hydroxides to compare strengths. Use indicators, phenolphthalein and methyl orange. See Table 15-4. Have students detect slippery feeling of soap, which is tested with litmus. Use CO_2 + $Ca(OH)_2$ as demonstration reaction for Section 15.9(6). Produce a precipitate of $Fe(OH)_3$ from either NaOH or NH_3(aq) and $FeCl_3$. Demonstrate that it is not amphoteric. Write equations to illustrate that water and ammonia both are amphoteric. **Reference:** Law, O. W., "A Lecture Demonstration, the Precipitation of Ferrous Hydroxide," *Journal of Chemical Education,* 56(7), 474 (1979).

Section 15.10. Review basic anhydrides from Section 12.18(3) and acidic anhydrides from Sections 15.7 and 12.18(4). **Reference:** Toon, *Foundations of Chemistry,* Table 15-1, for placement of O^{--} (O^{2-}) ion in the table of Relative Strengths of Acids and Bases.

Section 15.11. Discuss the O—H bond, its ease of breaking, amphoterism, and acidic behavior as it relates to the oxidation states, and the high electronegativity of the central atom. Write the two equations for $HClO_4$. Give examples and draw conclusions about behavior of ionic oxides and molecular oxides (hydroxyl groups). See Section 15.7 and use chalkboard equivalent of Figure 15-13 as developed in Section 15.11.

Section 15.12. Develop the concept and define conjugate acid, conjugate base, and conjugate acid-base pair by writing equations and organizing or identifying by the scheme:

$$A_1 + B_2 \rightarrow A_2 + B_1.$$

For selected acids, develop part of Table 15-5 using formulas to complement the equations, that is,

Equation

A_1	B_2	A_2	B_1
HCl	+ H_2O	→ H_3O^+	+ Cl^-
Acid			Conjugate base

Conductivity tests have established that strong acids are ionized completely and weak acids are ionized incompletely. In the developing table, place the strong acids above H_3O^+ and the weaker acids below. Mention the leveling effect of water on strong acids (refer to Vander Werf, *Acids, Bases, and the Chemistry of the Covalent Bond*, pp. 22–25, for details and representative diagrams). **Demonstration:** A strong acid like H_2SO_4 reacts practically completely with ions like $C_2H_3O_2^-$, CO_3^{--}, HCO_3^-, HS^{--}, to yield the weaker acids and the weaker base HSO_4^- or SO_4^{--}. This serves to establish the statement that protolytic reactions favor the production of the weaker acid and the weaker base. **Transparencies and Chart:** RH: 21759 *Chart of Acid and Base Strengths;* or the Welch chart 4839 *Chart of Relative Strengths of Acids and Bases.* Apply the text statement to the hydronium ion-hydroxide ion neutralization. **Reference and Demonstrations:** Below are two schematics that can be used with Table 15-5. The first schematic represents stronger acid + stronger base, which react almost completely to form the weaker acid and weaker base.

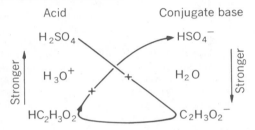

A weaker acid and a weaker base react to a slight extent to form the stronger species.

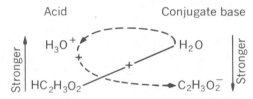

Note: The dashes indicate that the reaction proceeds only to a slight extent, that is acetic acid is a slightly ionized, weak acid.

The Welch wall chart 4839 *Chart of Relative Strengths of Acids and Bases* may be used instead of the transparencies. Have students explain why the neutralization of a strong acid and a strong base is practically complete. You may wish to test a solution of NaCl (established as a product of strong acid-strong base neutralization with litmus). Then test a solution of sodium acetate or sodium carbonate with red litmus and challenge the students to explain the result. The second schematic deals with reactions between weaker acid and weaker base, reactions which proceed to only a slight extent to form the stronger species. The example deals with the ionization of acetic acid, which has been shown to be a weak acid, that is, the ionization takes place to a very limited extent. Test a solution of sodium acetate or sodium carbonate with litmus and challenge the students to explain the results. **References:** Deck, J. C., "Strong and Weak Acids and Bases,"

Journal of Chemical Education, 56(12), 814 (1979); Atkinson, G. F., "Acid-Base Half-Reactions—A Useful Formalism for Review Lessons," *Journal of Chemical Education,* 56(4), 238 (1979); Pauling, L., "The Strength of the Hydrohalogenic Acids," *Journal of Chemical Education,* 53(12), 762 (1976).

Section 15.13. Review the series of equations in this section representing neutralization and leading to the definition of a salt. **Demonstrations:** You may wish to demonstrate neutralization by mixing 50 mL of solutions of NaOH and HCl of equal molarity and evaporating to dryness. See Alyea, pp. 146, 201, 212 for methods for demonstrating production of NaCl by direct union. Refer to Table 15-6 for precipitates (salt solubility generalizations), Tables 11 and 12 in the Appendix.

Section 15.14. Demonstrate: Several ways of forming salts. In addition, for Method 1 drop Sb into Cl_2, or heated copper foil into Cl_2. For Method 2 evaporate to show $ZnCl_2$ produced. Additionally, add Cu to HNO_3 (concentrated) (hood for NO_2), add water to develop blue color of $Cu(NO_3)_2$. For Method 3 add hydrochloric acid to milk of magnesia. For Method 4 the sequence of the CO_2 reactions first with $Ca(OH)_2$ and then with excess CO_2 with the dissolution of $CaCO_3$ and the production of soluble $Ca(HCO_3)_2$. Demonstrate precipitation of $BaSO_4$ for Method 6 and write the formula and the net ionic equation. For Method 7 use Na_2CO_3 and HCl and evaporate. Test a solution of the residue with $AgNO_3$ to identify NaCl as a product. Write equations for Method 8. Add water to a sample of air-slaked lime (no evident reaction). Carefully add a drop of HCl to the air-slaked lime to identify the $CaCO_3$. **Transparency:** W: 75 W 8015 *Preparation of Salts.*

Section 15.15. You may wish to use Worksheet IX: Names and Formulas of Acids and Salts. To establish rules for naming salts of the oxyacids, complete the table of the acids (and salts) of chlorine. Have students name the salts they recognize; for example, they may be able to name $NaClO_3$ from previous experience with $KClO_3$. Have them suggest a name for $NaClO_4$, since its acid name also ends in *ic*. Have a student read the label on a bottle of a bleach that mentions sodium hypochlorite. This is used in changing the *ous* ending of acids to the *ite* ending for the salts. Refer to Table 15-7 for Stock system and use Table 15-8. **Films and filmstrips:** As a summary, CORF: 1227 *Properties of Acids, Bases, and Salts* (21 min.); UA: *Properties of Acids, Bases, and Salts* (28 min.). **Loop:** W: 168 W 1002(T) *Acid-Base Indicators;* or the longer film W: 140-4130 *Acid-Base Indicators* (19 min.). **Individualized and Programmed Instruction:** Ward's Solo-Learn: 78-0690 *Introduction to Acid-Base Theory;* Audio: HM: 3-49512 *Definition of Electrolytes, Acids, Bases and Salts, Single Replacement;* HM: 3-49513 *Double Replacement Reactions, Neutralization;* Barrow, G. M., et al., *Understanding Chemistry III: Chemical Reactions*, Benjamin, 1967; Brønsted acids and bases: theory and reaction stoichiometry, pp. 1–40; *Understanding Chemistry IV: Chemical Equilibria*, Benjamin, 1967, pp. 89–120: equilibrium calculations: the ionizations of acids and bases; Kass, G. A., *Individual Study Program in Chemistry, Volume V: Acid-Base Chemistry*, Benjamin, 1969; pp. 1–116: the Brønsted model; pp. 117–128: the Lewis acid-base theory; pp. 129–158: optional. *Chemistry Reprint 89*, "Dilute Solutions of Strong Acids—Effect of

Water on pH,'' originally appeared 42(11), 1969; ''Brønsted-Lowry Acid-Base Theory,'' 43(3), 1970; reprint 100, ''Stress, Collisions, and Constants,'' originally appeared 44(4), (5), (6), 1971.

Teacher Notes
Chapter 16

Chapter Note

Although the chapter calls for a great deal of problem work, the mathematics is relatively simple and the use of logarithms is a matter of choice. It affords ample opportunity to review the mole concept and its application to the preparation of solutions, use of equations, and development of the concepts of chemical equivalents and normal solutions. Exhibits of various mole quantities, fractional and multiple, show the facts on which the mathematics depend. The large number and variety of student experiments and audiovisual aids provide real or vicarious experience. The graphs of experimental results (titration) and various tables (indicators) provide the basis for related demonstrations and also may be used as the basis on which students can apply the concepts in this chapter. Worksheet X: Solution Concentrations: I Molality, II Molarity, III Equivalents, IV Normality, V Normality and Molality.

This chapter requires six periods. One possible arrangement is:

Lesson 1 Sections 16.1 and 16.2: Molar Solutions, Chemical Equivalents of Acids and Bases
Lesson 2 Sections 16.3–16.5: Chemical Equivalents of Elements, Salts, Normal Solutions
Lesson 3 Sections 16.6 and 16.7: Ion Concentration in Water, pH of a Solution
Lesson 4 Sections 16.8 and 16.9: Calculations of (a) pH and (b) H_3O^+
Lesson 5 Sections 16.10–16.12: Neutralization, Acid-base Titration, Titration with Molar Solutions
Lesson 6 Sections 16. 13–16.15: Titration with Normal Solutions, Indicators in Titration, pH Measurements

Section 16.1. Review the mole concept. **Demonstrations:** The molality and makeup of 1-m solutions of NaCl, $C_{12}H_{22}O_{11}$, C_2H_5OH. Measure the resultant volumes of the sucrose and ethanol solutions. Discuss the number of solute molecules per kg of H_2O versus the number per liter of solution. Make up 1-M solutions of sucrose and ethanol using a volumetric flask. Pour out 100 mL of each of these 1-M solutions. Discuss the number of solute molecules in the 100 mL. Make up 1-M solutions of NaCl and KCl. Discuss the number of ions: K^+, Cl^-, and Na^+ in each solution. Weigh out 0.5 and 2.0 moles of NaCl and make up 0.5-M and 2.0-M solutions. Display volumetric flasks of different capacities; use to make representative volumes of desired molarity. Demonstrate preparation of solutions of fractional molarities by dilution. Use the equation $M_1V_1 = M_2V_2$ to illustrate how either the new molarity or new volume may be calculated. Discuss the K_2CrO_4 example in Section 16.1. Another relationship which is similar is:

$$\text{Molarity} = \frac{\text{moles}}{\text{liters}}$$ and therefore Moles = Molarity × liters.

Assignments: Question 1; Problems 1–7 and 16. **Filmstrips:** B #111: *Molarity of Solutions*—1. *Understanding Molarity,*

2. *Molarity Calculations: Learning by Practice,* 3. *Changing Concentrations* (with cassettes, each 14–19 min.); PH: WCC 896 *Introduction: Preparing Percent, Molar and Normal Solutions.* **Review:** PH: 898 *Mole Fraction and Molal Concentration: Freezing Point Depression and Boiling Point Elevation.*

Section 16.2. **Activities:** Develop the definitions of one equivalent of an acid and one equivalent of a base (in proton transfer reactions) using the examples for neutralization in Section 15.2. Use the same procedure for HNO_3 and $HC_2H_3O_2$ to develop the fact that one equivalent of a monoprotic acid is the same as one mole of the acid. Then consider the meaning of one equivalent of diprotic and triprotic acid in *complete* neutralization in terms of the number of H_3O^+ ions that one mole of the respective acids (H_2SO_4 and H_3PO_4) can supply. Repeat the activities above for the bases NaOH, KOH, $Ca(OH)_2$. Treat the topic of incomplete neutralization of diprotic and triprotic acids as in Section 16.2 to establish the concept: Equivalents (equivalent weights) are not constants; they are a function of the nature of the reaction.

Section 16.3. **Activities:** Display 1 mole of Na, Ca, Al (or others, e.g., Mg, Zn). For Ca display 20 g; for Al, 9 g. Have students write the equations for electron loss and develop the mole and mass relationships for each equation. Use these activities to lead to the determination of one equivalent of an element by dividing the mass of one mole by the *change in oxidation state* these atoms undergo in a chemical reaction. For balance, repeat with nonmetals such as Cl_2 and S. To show that equivalents may differ, depending on the particular reaction, try: $H_2 + S \rightarrow H_2S$ and $S + O_2 \rightarrow SO_2$.

Section 16.4. **Activities:** As a lead-in to the consideration of salts, have the students reconsider the previous equations for Na, Ca, and Al and the number of moles of Ca^{++} and Al^{+++} ions (and their masses) that are equivalent to one mole of Na^+ ions. Starting with NaCl, have the students write dissociation equations for Na_2SO_4, Na_3PO_4, $Al_2(SO_4)_3$. Using the Na^+ ion equivalent as the foundation, illustrate the calculation of one equivalent successively of NaCl, $CaCl_2$, Na_2SO_4, empirical $AlCl_3$, Na_3PO_4, $Ca_3(PO_4)_2$. These activities may be used to formulate the rule for calculating the equivalent of a salt. For some students it is more strategic simply to state the rule and have the students apply it. For application, apply the rule to $Al_2(SO_4)_3$, $Ca_3(PO_4)_2$. **Assignment:** Questions 2–5, Problem 8. Worksheet X: III Equivalents. Ward's Solo-Learn: 78-0700 *Introduction to Chemical Equivalents.*

Section 16.5. **Activities:** If the determination of salt equivalents has immediately preceded the introduction of normality, use volumetric flasks to make up solutions of salts containing a variety of equivalents of the salts in one liter of solution. Measure out various volumes of these solutions: that is, 100 mL, 250 mL, 500 mL of NaCl. Have students calculate the number of equivalents in each sample of solution, developing the relationships: $\text{normality} = \dfrac{\text{equiv}}{\text{liter}}$, $N = \dfrac{\text{equiv}}{V(\text{liters})}$, equiv = $N \times V(\text{liters})$. Have students calculate the mass of solute in each solution. **Activities:** Illustrate dilution operations for preparing smaller normalities from a 1-N solution of one or more salts. Develop the relationship: $N_1V_1 = N_2V_2$. Illustrate that mL may be used instead of liters (L) if both V_1 and V_2 are in milliliters. Have students read the data (percent HCl and density) on the label of the concentrated acid (Figure 16-2). Also have them refer to Table 16-2. Have them calculate the mass of HCl in each milliliter of the concentrated acid. Develop the relationships between molarity and normality for acid solutions (i.e., 1-M HC1 = 1-N, 1-M H_2SO_4 = 2-N, 1-M H_3PO_4 = 3-N) and illustrate for solutions other than 1-M. Refer to Table 16-1 for summary and comparison of methods of expressing concentration of solutions and to Table 16-2. **Assignment:** Questions 17–20; Problems 9, 10, 12, 18, 19. Discuss the preparation of solutions of a hydrate, for example $CuSO_4 \cdot 5H_2O$, as in text. **Audiovisuals:** PH: WCC 896 *Introduction: Preparing Percent, Molar and Normal Solutions;* PH: WCC 814 *Preparing Solutions.* Worksheet X: IV Normality, V Normality and Molarity.

Section 16.6. Demonstrations: Test for the conductivity of water first by using a 25-watt bulb (water is a nonelectrolyte) and then a Ne or Ar lamp (autoprotolysis). Insert red and blue litmus to show the neutrality of water and the equal concentrations of H_3O^+ and OH^- ions. Write the equation for autoprotolysis (Section 14.8 and Section 15.9(7) for amphoterism). Use models for Figure 16-3. Using the chalkboard, go through the calculations in the text. Illustrate the use of square brackets to represent concentration in moles per liter, mole/L: $[H_3O^+] = [OH^-] = 10^{-7}$ mole/L. Cite examples of H_3O^+ concentration representing an acid solution and of OH^- representing a basic solution. Use the chalkboard to show calculation of the ion product constant K_w for water. Cite values of it at $0°C$, $25°C$, and $60°C$ and have students state conclusion about the effect of increased temperature on the ionization of water.

Section 16.7. Activities: Illustrate the use of the ion constant product of water to calculate H_3O^+ concentration in a solution of a base, and of the K_w OH^- concentration in the solution of an acid, for which the molarities of the solutions are known (Sample Problem). Illustrate how the value of the exponent for the hydronium-ion concentration can be used to indicate an acid (smaller negative exponent than -7) or a base (larger negative exponent than -7). Discuss the convenience of using the logarithmic function of the concentration. Define pH and use the equation pH $= \cdot \log(1/[H_3O^+])$ to calculate the pH of pure water. Discuss the magnitude of the number of pH of acidic and basic solutions.

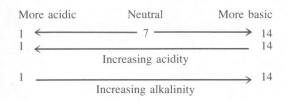

Refer to Table 16-3. Use pH paper or universal indicator for representative examples: HCl, lemon, vinegar, $NaHCO_3$, Na_2CO_3, NaOH in concentrations in the in the table. **Reference:** Kolb, D., "The pH Concept," *Journal of Chemical Education,* 56(1), 49 (1979).

Section 16.8. Develop the useful form of the pH equation, pH $= - \log [H_3O^+]$ as in text. Solve the Sample Problems in which the hydronium-ion concentrations are integral powers of ten. For advanced classes, do the Sample Problem in which the hydronium-ion concentration is not an integral power of ten. Use Figure 16-4 for the relationship between the pH and the $[H_3O^+]$ concentration. Have students locate the answer on Figure 16-4 for the Sample Problem. This scale for Figure 16-4 can be used by students to help them check their answers to problems. Use Problems 13, 23, 24. Review the meaning and use of logarithms and refer students to the Appendix Table 17 before doing the Sample Problem. **Filmstrip:** PH:WCC 804A *Using Simple Logarithms, Logs and Antilogs;* PH:WCC 804B *Using Simple Logarithms, Multiplication and Division.*

Section 16.9. Activities: Use the chalkboard to convert the equation pH $= - \log [H_3O^+]$ to the form $[H_3O^+] =$ antilog$(-pH) = 10^{-pH}$. Solve the Sample and Practice Problems. Use Problem 22. Discuss the hydronium-ion concentrations of dilute solutions of strong (HCl) and weak $(HC_2H_3O_2)$ acids as in text. For additional problems see Toon and Ellis, *Foundations of Chemistry,* p. 509, problems 1, 7, and 8.

Section 16.10. Activities: Review and apply the ion-product of water concept as in the introductory paragraphs of Section 16.7. Demonstrate the addition of 0.1 mole of solid NaOH to a liter of 0.1-M HCl or use 0.01 mole of the NaOH with 100 mL of the acid. Use phenolphthalein as the indicator. The complementary demonstration using solutions and burettes may also be used, possibly as a lead-in to the framing of the definition of titration in which the HCl concentration is theoretically unknown. Use models for Figure 16-5.

Section 16.11. Demonstrate: Titration of dilute solution of HCl with a solution of NaOH of the same molarity, using phenolphthalein indicator. Have students make observations of color change as drops are added near the equivalence point. Define end point (or equivalence point) and titration. Discuss primary standard and standardizing procedure. **Films:** UA *Standard Solutions and Titrations* (21 min.); W: 140-4130 *Acid-Base Indicators* (19 min.). **Loops:** BFA: 4B0665 *Use of Burette-Titration;* LBF: 3 *Titration Curves I;* 4, *Titration Curves II;* 5 *Titration Curves, Potentiometric;* MH: *Titrating;* EBE: S 80458 *Titrating with Phenolphthalein.* **Filmstrips:** PH: WCC 813A *Titration Techniques, Part I;* PH: WCC 897 *Dilution and Titration Problems.*

Section 16.12. Activities: Go through the calculations in the text for the determination of the molarity of the NaOH solution first for HCl and then for the H_2SO_4 titrations. Summarize the steps involved in determining the molarity of an acid or base of unknown concentration. Solve the Sample Problem for HCl and $Ba(OH)_2$. An interesting demonstration is that for titration of $Ba(OH)_2$ with H_2SO_4 using phenolphthalein and a conductivity apparatus. At the equivalence point the conductivity drops to zero with the production of water and the $BaSO_4$ precipitate (see Alyea, p. 16, E-6-14). **Film:** EBE: 2944 *Ion Removal by Metathesis* (5 min.) deals with this reaction. Solve the Practice Problems.

Section 16.13. Activity: Develop the relationship $V_aN_a = V_bN_b$ on the basis of the equality: equiv. of acid = equiv. of base, since solutions of the same normality are always chemically equivalent. **Demonstration:** Before dealing with the strong base-weak acid neutralization, demonstrate the basic character of a solution of sodium acetate (litmus, phenolphthalein, pH paper). Refer to Figure 16-7 for titration curves, or furnish data to students and have them attempt to plot the curves. **Filmstrip:** EYE: X226A *The Percentage of Acetic Acid in Vinegar.* Assign problems 14, 15, 20, 21.

Section 16.14. Exhibit as many actual examples as possible of Figure 16-10 and Table 16-5; illustrate and define transition interval. Illustrate the four types of acid-base combinations and the choice of indicator. **Films:** UA *Indicators and pH* (28 min.); W: 140-4130 *Acid-Base Indicators* (19 min.). **Loop:** W: 168 W 1002(T) *Acid-Base Indicators.* **References:** Schultz, C. W., and Spannuth, S. I., "Comparison of Strong and Weak Acid Titration Curves," *Journal of Chemical Education*, 56(3), 194 (1979); Forster, M., "Plant Pigments as Acid-Base Indicators," *Journal of Chemical Education*, 55(2), 107 (1978).

Section 16.15. Demonstrate the use of short range pH paper such as Hydrion D(11-13) with solutions of $Mg(OH)_2$, $Ca(OH)_2$, and $Ba(OH)_2$. Then check with a pH meter. The **Film** W: 140-4130, *Acid-Base Indicators* determines the equilibrium constant for four indicators that are arranged in order of decreasing acid strength. **Film:** UA: *Indicators and pH* (28 min.). **Loop:** HR: 04-96356 *pH Meter.* **Filmstrips:** PH: WCC 866 *Tritration Curves and Indicators;* PH: WCC 815 *pH Measurements;* B #115: *Working in the Laboratory— Part Three:* 4. *pH and Its Measurement,* 5. *How to Perform an Acid-Base Titration—Part 1,* 6. *How to Perform an Acid-Base Titration, Part 2.* **Reference:** Lott, J. A., "Hydrogen Ions in the Blood," *Journal of Chemical Education*, 54(1), 6 (1978). **Individualized and Programmed Instruction:** In addition to the PH: WCC filmstrips mentioned in the above sections (all with cassettes) use PH: WCC 883 *pH, pOH and Buffers;* the PH *Chemical Review* microfiches: WCF: 1005 *Solution Preparation* and WCF: 1007 *Acid-Base Equilibria and pH;* Ward's Solo-Learn: 78 W 0700 *Introduction to Chemical Equivalence;* HM audio: HM 3-49513 *Double Replacement Reactions, Neutralization.* **Programmed Instruction:** Barrow, G. M., et al., *Understanding Chemistry: I Chemical Quantities,* Benjamin, 1967, pp. 95–121; *III Chemical Reactions,* Benjamin, 1967, pp. 1–40; Kass, G. A., *Individual Study Program in Chemistry, Volume V; Acid-Base Chemistry,* Benjamin, 1969, pp. 40–96, 129–158.

Teacher Notes
Chapter 17

Chapter Note

The chapter affords the students a brief introduction to organic chemistry. It applies concepts of bonding to the allotropes of carbon and the resonance hybrids of carbon dioxide and carbon monoxide. Also involved are concepts of hybridization and allotropism.

The chapter requires four or five periods. One possible arrangement is:

Lesson 1   Sections 17.1–17.6: Carbon-Allotropy, Diamond, Graphite
Lesson 2   Sections 17.7–17.13: Coal, Destructive Distillation, Other Forms of Carbon
Lesson 3   Sections 17.14–17.19: Carbon Dioxide
Lesson 4   Sections 17.20–17.25: Carbon Monoxide

Section 17.1. Activities: Discuss abundance, occurrence, and importance of carbon. Exhibit forms of carbon, coal (Figure 17-1, Table 17-1) petroleum, limestone, common organic chemicals, medicinals, and synthetics. The latter are representative of the large number of carbon compounds and lead to the definition of organic chemistry. Exhibit varieties of CO_2 extinguishers and Dry Ice.

Section 17.2. Activities: Exhibit periodic table and locate C. Review the electron-dot symbol for C in the ground state and in the hybrid sp^3 state. Exhibit models or samples of carbon in the bonded state: tetrahedron (Figure 17-2), CH_4, CCl_4, $CHCl_3$, CO_2. Discuss tetravalency and covalent bonds. Review schematic for sp^3 hybridization (Sections 6.17 and Chapter 6 in Teacher Edition). To indicate varieties of ways in which carbon atoms can link together, exhibit ball-and-stick models of diamond, graphite, simple hydrocarbons, benzene, and crystal models of diamond and graphite. These structures should not be examined in detail at the present time, but merely used to point out the ways of combination and hence the large number of carbon compounds in existence. **Transparencies:** HM: 2-10529 *Hybrid Orbitals;* HM: 2-10535 *Methane Molecule,* CH_4.

Section 17.3. Activities: Review allotropy of oxygen (Section 9.11) and Marginal Note. Exhibit diamond model and graphite model, as well as samples of these two carbon allotropes. Exhibit samples of amorphous forms and discuss structure as in text.

Section 17.4. Activities: Exhibit diamond model, tetrahedron (Figure 17-3), phonograph needle. Discuss network structure of diamond and relate properties—density, hardness, melting point, nonconductivity of electricity, heat conductivity. Discuss uses. Use diamond phonograph needle to scratch glass, mention MOH scale of hardness. **Film:** SUTH: *The Modern Chemist—Diamond Synthesis;* GE: *Manmade Diamond* (12 min.). Discuss production of synthetic diamonds. Discuss experiments on burning diamond (Lavoisier and Tennant). **Reference:** Diamond and graphite structure: *Foundations of Chemistry,* Toon and Ellis, pp. 315, 316. **Student and Teacher References:** Ward, F., "The Incredible Crystal, Diamond," *National Geographic,* 155(1), 85 (1979); Cox, K. C., "Kimberlite Pipes," *Scientific American,* 238(4), 120 (1978); "Even a Diamond Has to Give Sometime," *Science News,* 113(23) 374 (1978).

Sections 17.5 and 17.6. Activities: Exhibit samples of graphite—chunk, powdered, lubricant, model (Figure 17-4). **Demonstrations:** Make a light mark on paper with a graphite-chunk, erase; duplicate with pencil. Exhibit graphite greases and lubricants, crucibles, electrodes, and discuss properties and uses of each. Include use as moderator in atomic reactor (Chapter 31). **Discuss:** Properties and structure layer and weak interaction forces, sp^2–sp^2 bonding. Discuss properties and relate to structure (distances with a layer and between layers), softness, greasy feeling, electrical conductivity, melting point. **Exhibit:** Articles made of carbon fibers: graphite tennis racquet, Figure 17-5.

Section 17.7. Exhibit: Various types of coal (Table 17-1). Discuss the processes of their formation and occurrence (Figures 17-6 and 17-7). The large number of references, listed below, indicate the increasing concern for coal as our most plentiful source of energy. **References:** Chemistry Education

Staff, "Energy from Coal," *Journal of Chemical Education,* 56(3), 186 (1979); "Clean Coal," *Scientific American,* 241(4), 76 (1979); "Continuous Coal," *Scientific American,* 241(2), 74 (1979); Griffith, E. D., and Clark, A. W., "World Coal Production," *Scientific American,* 241(1), 38 (1979); "Coal Prospects and Problems," *Scientific American,* 241(1), 72 (1979); "The Coal Option," *Scientific American,* 238(1), 64 (1978); "Coal and the Coming(?) Superinterglacial," *Science News,* 111(23), 356 (1977); "Coal and Climate: A Yellow Light on CO_2," *Science News,* 112(5), 62 (1977); Chemical Education Staff, "Solar Energy," *Journal of Chemical Education,* 56(5), 264 (1979); "Underground Coal Gasification: A Crucial Test," *Chemical and Engineering News,* Dec. 3, 1979, p. 19; "Underground Coal Gasification Tests Successful," *Chemical and Engineering News,* Apr. 21, 1980, p. 33. **Films:** USDE: 525 *Taking the Lumps Out* (5 min.); USDE: 526 *Coal: The Other Energy* (15 min.); USDE: 527 *Energy Update* (28+ min.).

Section 17.8. Activities: The definition of destructive distillation should be developed in conjunction with the demonstrations in following sections for the production (preparation) of charcoal, coke, and boneblack.

Sections 17.9–17.11. Activities: Exhibit samples of forms of amorphous carbon and representative uses—charcoal chunks and brickets, dry-cell electrode, petroleum coke, coke, portions of a tire, ink, paints, carbon paper, phonograph records, etc. **Demonstration:** Destructive distillation— charcoal and coke. **Demonstrations:** The following sequence of demonstrations may be used to develop understanding of the process of destructive distillation. A wooden splint held in an open flame and the same splint heated in a test tube challenges student interest. Three or four splints broken in half may be heated strongly with the mouth of the test tube held downward over a watch crystal. As the vapor is liberated it is ignited. Blue litmus paper is used to indicate the acid nature of the distillate. The resultant charcoal strips are removed from the test tube and the manner of burning compared with the manner of a wooden splint. The porosity of the charcoal may be used to explain the steady glow of the charcoal splint. The definition of destructive distillation is developed with emphasis on decomposition by heat in the absence of air, followed by condensation and collection of volatile materials. More complex setups may also be used, such as collecting the condensate in a bottle and burning the volatile material at another outlet from the bottle.

The production of coke by destructive distillation may also be demonstrated. If the soft coal is powdered and heated with a Fisher burner, good results are obtained after a brief heating. The coal tar collects in the bottle and the coal gas may be ignited at the bottle outlet (see Figure 17-8). A piece of moist red litmus paper suspended from the cork inside the bottle turns blue, indicating the production of ammonia. The ammonia is generally liberated toward the end of the process rather than at the beginning. Some teachers dramatize this by strongly heating the open test tube and permitting the vapor to reach a foot-square piece of moistened red litmus paper, which turns blue. The properties of coke as a fuel and as a reducing agent should be compared with charcoal. The reduction of CuO may be redemonstrated if desired and the production of CO_2 shown by the use of $Ca(OH)_2$. The three main forms produced by

destructive distillation should then be briefly reviewed. Soot may be produced by deposit from a candle flame, and carbon black by deposit from a yellow Bunsen flame. The importance of the latter in automobile tires should be emphasized. **Demonstration:** Carbon black production—hold a test tube in the yellow burner flame and note carbon deposit. Discuss uses of charcoal, coke, and boneblack. At this point you may wish to discuss coal in general and related problems of pollution. **References:** *Chemistry* Reprint 55, "Coal"; Bailey, M. F., "The Chemistry of Coal and Its Constituents," *Journal of Chemical Education,* 51(7), 453 (1974); Young, G., "Will Coal Be Tomorrow's 'Black Gold'?" *National Geographic,* 148 (2), 234 (1975). **Films:** DUART: MIS 676 *Control of Air Pollution;* DUART: MIS 677 *Sources of Air Pollution;* DUART: MIS 678 *Effects of Air Pollution.* For demonstration on making water gas, see Alyea, pp. 9 and 97.

Section 17.12. Demonstrations: Collect a test tube of dry NH_3 by displacement of Hg **(CAUTION).** Introduce pellets of activated charcoal through the Hg into the gas and observe result. Add pellets of activated charcoal to a bottle of Br_2 vapor **(CAUTION),** stopper and shake and observe the result. Remove the pellets of charcoal and heat in a test tube **(CAUTION: Br_2 vapor).** Fill a test tube one-half full of very dilute hydrogen sulfide solution. Cautiously note its odor. **CAUTION:** *Hydrogen sulfide is very poisonous.* As a chemical test for its presence add 3 drops of the solution to 2 mL of a solution of lead acetate. Add 5 pellets of activated charcoal to the test tube and shake vigorously at intervals for several minutes. Decant and note the odor of the decantage. Drop 3 drops of the decantate into 2 mL of lead acetate solution. Test the relatively colorless filtrate with Fehling's or Benedict's solution for glucose. Use Figures 17–9 and 17–10.

Section 17.13. Demonstrations: Put the bottom of an evaporating dish into a candle flame. Black carbon deposit will result. Also, put the luminous Bunsen flame on a test tube. (This black deposit may be burned off by the oxidizing blue flame.) **Exhibit:** Lamp chimney with soot, tires, printer's ink, carbon paper, phonograph records, electrodes, and dry cells (petroleum coke to graphite).

Section 17.14. Discuss the problem of CO_2 buildup in the atmosphere. **References:** "CO_2 Buildup's Effect on Climate Explored," *Chemical and Engineering News,* Aug. 1, 1977, p. 18; Woodwell, "The Carbon Dioxide Question," *Scientific American,* 238(1), 34 (1978); "The Gases of Life," *Journal of Chemical Education,* 56(11), 748 (1979); "Coal and Climate: A Yellow Light on CO_2," *Science News,* 112(5), 68 (1977); "Making the Most of the CO_2 Problem," *Science News,* 115(15), 244 (1979); Leovy, C. B., "The Atmosphere of Mars," *Scientific American,* 237(1), 34 (1977); "Ambiguities of Mars," *Scientific American,* 236(2), 48 (1977); Horowitz, N. H., "The Search for Life on Mars," *Scientific American,* 237(5), 52 (1977). **Demonstrations:** Expose limewater to the air in a watch glass on the table top and have students observe the formation of the crust of $CaCO_3$ on the upper surface. Burn a splint in a bottle of air and test result with limewater. Have students blow breath through a straw into limewater in a test tube. Discuss CO_2 in atmospheres of Venus and Mars.

Section 17.15. A good introductory demonstration consists of Dry Ice pellets bubbling in water in a large vessel that may contain litmus or another indicator. **Demonstrations:** The topic of carbon dioxide provides an excellent opportunity for the use of a series of fire-extinguishing demonstrations (Section 17.19) that may well be used before dealing with its preparations and properties. Carbonates that may be heated to yield CO_2 are $MnCO_3$, $CuCO_3$ or $CuCO_3 \cdot Cu(OH)_2$. The easiest demonstration is the thermal decomposition of $NaHCO_3$. Chunk limestone may be heated on the grid of a high-temperature burner. After cooling, H_2O is added to the CaO produced and the litmus test for $Ca(OH)_2$ performed. The laboratory process for the production of carbon dioxide may be generalized by using a variety of carbonates or hydrogen carbonates and acids. Add HCl to marble, seashells, and limestone for observable gas production. Ask students how they would produce CO_2 by using materials in the home—vinegar or lemon juice with baking soda, adding water to baking powder, fermentation using dry yeast. Develop board equations representative of various methods of preparation. **Transparency:** W: 75 W 8000 *Carbon Dioxide*. **Film:** Association Films (600 Grand Ave., Ridgefield, N.J. 07657): *Critical Phenomena in Carbon Dioxide*.

Section 17.16. **Activity:** Exhibit a ball-and-stick model of CO_2 and have students explain the nonpolarity of the molecule. Develop the electron-dot formula(s) and the electronic formulas for the resonance hybrids. **Transparency:** HM: 2-10537 *Carbon Dioxide Structure*.

Section 17.17. **Demonstrations of Physical Properties:** Use a Kipp generator as a source of CO_2 for large-scale demonstrations. Set up a very large battery jar with a staircase arrangement of burning candles, as in Figure 17-9. Extinguish them in succession by pouring CO_2 (previously collected by displacement of air in a large cylinder). CO_2 fills the jar from bottom to top. Exhibit the contents of a disassembled soda-acid extinguisher. Use a laboratory model to extinguish a newspaper fire in the sink. Demonstrate that a soda-acid extinguisher does extinguish an oil (benzol or benzene—**CAUTION**) fire. Use a small-scale foam extinguisher to extinguish an oil fire, directing the foam nozzle against the side of the vessel rather than directly at the burning oil. A benzol fire in a large tray is dramatically extinguished by using the liquid CO_2 extinguisher. The production of Dry Ice may be shown by permitting the CO_2 from the liquid CO_2 extinguisher to fill a paper bag. Shake out the contents of the inverted bag. Relate the laboratory preparation of CO_2 to the soda-acid and foam extinguisher reactions.

Section 17.18. **Demonstrations of Chemical Properties:** Plunge a burning splint into a bottle of CO_2. Follow up by inserting a burning Mg ribbon (use tongs and **CAUTION**) into another bottle of CO_2. Have students note both the black and white deposits on the bottle and explain the burning. Heat a sample of soda water. Test with litmus before and after heating. Pass CO_2 into limewater. Do this until a precipitate forms and redissolves. **Activities:** Develop formula and ionic equations. Discuss effects of increasing CO_2 concentration in air.

Section 17.19. **Activities:** Discuss other uses of carbon dioxide besides firefighting. Show one or more **Films** on photosynthesis: CHUR: *The Photosynthesis and Respiration Cycle;* EBE: 2530 *Photosynthesis* (2nd ed.) (24 min.); EBE: 2136 *Photosynthesis* (24 min.); USDE: 459 *Controlled Photosynthesis* (24 min.); USDE: 324 *The Riddle of Photosynthesis*

(14+ min.). **Loops:** BFA: 81-5639/1 *Measuring the Rate of Photosynthesis;* BFA: 81-5118/1 *Photosynthetic Fixation of Carbon Dioxide* (Part I); BFA: 81-5126/1 *Photosynthetic Fixation of Carbon Dioxide* (Part II); PH: WCT 610 *Fermentation;* PH: WCT 604 *Photosynthesis*. **Filmstrips:** EYE: X223B *Photosynthesis;* I: 67020 *Chlorophyll—Capturing the Sun's Energy*. **Slide Carousel:** I: 68679-M *Understanding Photosynthesis;* I: 68982-M *The Biochemistry of Photosynthesis*. **Slides:** *Photosynthesis Slide Sequence,* I: 69141, 69142, 69143, 69144. **Transparencies:** I: 68730 *Photosynthesis* (set of 8 with 15 overlays); EYE: 002-16 *Photosynthesis and Respiration*. Write the simplified equation for photosynthesis. **Exhibit:** Carbonated beverages, baking powder (read labels for composition). Add dried yeast to mixture of warm water with a little sugar and starch added. Students will see bubbles and swelling of mass in a few minutes. The yeast mixture can be placed in a test tube and tested for gas evolved. Add water to baking powder, test for CO_2 evolved. Repeat using an Alka-Seltzer tablet. **Reference:** Fernelius, W. C., "CO_2 Snow," *Journal of Chemical Education,* 50(7), 466 (1973).

Section 17.20 (and 17.25). **Discussion:** Introduce carbon monoxide by pointing out that both carbon dioxide and carbon monoxide may cause asphyxiation, and lead into an explanation of the differences between their physiological actions. **Reference:** Newton, C., and Morse, L. R., "Portable Apparatus for Determining Atmospheric Carbon Monoxide," Lab Bench, *Chemistry,* 47(6), 27 (1974), Discuss its occurrence as in text. Gordon, M. A., and Burton, W. B., "Carbon Monoxide in the Galaxy," *Scientific American,* 240(5), 54 (1979); Zoller, U., "Smoking and Cigarette Smoke," *Journal of Chemical Education,* 56(8), 54 (1979).

Section 17.21. **Demonstrations:** Water gas preparation (Alyea, pp. 9, 97). Refer to burning of gaseous product of destructive distillation (wood and soft coal)—**Demonstrations** (Section 17.9). Use a diagram of a coal furnace or an old-fashioned pot-belly stove showing flames burning at the top of the coal layer. Develop a series of equations and place on the diagram: (**1**) burning of coal on bottom grate; (**2**) reduction of CO_2 by C as it passes through the hot coal; and (**3**) burning the CO at the top of the coal layer. The first two equations may be combined into a single equation that represents the incomplete combustion of coal or coke. Closing the air entrance at the side of the stove leaves CO, representative of the manufacture of producer gas. Alternate closing of the draft to the chimney shows how a furnace may produce CO that could leak into the home. Have students write equations representing incomplete combustion of octane. If the laboratory preparation is demonstrated, emphasize the precautions necessary when using hot H_2SO_4 and collecting the poisonous and combustible CO. See Alyea, pp. 36, 16–9. **Transparency:** W: 75 W 8000 *Carbon Monoxide*.

Section 17.22. Use Figure 17-17. Develop chalkboard structures for the resonance hybrid of the four structures. Discuss the stability and slight polarity of the molecule.

Sections 17.23 and 17.24. List the physical and chemical properties of carbon monoxide. Refer to Figure 17-16 (solubility and method of collection) and Figure 17-1 (poisonous nature and explanation of breathing apparatus). **Exhibit** such equipment and/or a gas mask. Use equations for combustion, reduction, and synthesis of methanol. **Activi-**

ies: Discuss details of physiological action of CO and its dangers. **Reference:** Mancott, A., "Chemical Relevance—A Heuristic Approach, Part III: Carbon Monoxide," *Chemistry,* 50(2), 24 (1977) [answers in 50(3), (1977)]. **Summary Film:** CORF: *Carbon and Its Compounds;* EBF: 1954 *Carbon 14.* **Filmstrip:** I: 67109 *The Chemistry of Carbon and Silicon.* **References:** Bundy, F. P., "Superhard Materials," *Scientific American,* 231(2), 62 (1974); Derjaguin, B. V., and Fedoseev, D. B., "The Synthesis of Diamond at Low Pressure," *Scientific American,* 233(5), 102 (1975); Huntress, W. T., Jr., "The Chemistry of Planetary Atmospheres," *Journal of Chemical Education,* 53(4), 204 (1976); "CO Levels High in American Blood," *Science News,* 106(10), 148 (1974); Arehart-Treichel, ., "Will Dirty Air Do You In?" *Science News,* 104(18) 280 1973); Wilbraham, A. G., "Fire Safety and Fire Control in he Chemistry Laboratory," *Journal of Chemical Education,* 56(10), 311A (1979) (diagrams and details of the various types of fire extinguishers).

Teacher Notes
Chapter 18

Chapter Note

Activities and Demonstrations: Many of the generalizations in this chapter—such as reasons for the abundance of carbon compounds, homologous series, general formulas, isomers, and properties of organic versus inorganic compounds—are developed best by the use of samples, transparencies, models, formulas, tables such as Table 18-2, and demonstrations (or student experiment results). The inductive development is accompanied by the step-by-step accumulation of data on the chalkboard, which students record in notebooks. Separate recording of generalizations are written on the board and recorded by students as they emerge from discussion. Some examples are given below. The gradual presentation and accumulation of facts leading to pertinent generalizations help students' mastery of organic chemistry. You may wish to demonstrate the "Reversion of the Synthesis of Urea," Alyea, pp. 152, 209 in conjunction with the vital-force theory. In this demonstration, a solution of urea is tested for electrical conductivity and precipitation with $AgNO_3$ solution. Another solution of urea is boiled for several minutes, and the conductivity and precipitation tests are performed. The boiling produces ammonium and cyanate ions (NH_4^+, CNO^-). Another reagent that can be used is iron(III) chloride, which produces a red color with the solution that has been boiled. Try cooling the boiled solution in ice and retesting. Details of the Wöhler synthesis are described in Lucas, H. W., and Pressman, D., *Principles and Practice of Organic Chemistry,* Wiley, 1949, p. 310. An interested student may wish to attempt this experiment as a project. **Reference:** Kaufman, G. B., and Choolijian, S. H., "Wöhler's Synthesis of Artificial Urea: A Modern Version of a Classic Experiment," *Journal of Chemical Education,* 56(3), 197 (1979).

The contents of the chapter afford many opportunities for the use of student reports.

The chapter requires six or seven periods. One possible arrangement is:

Section 18.1. **Activities:** Redefine organic chemistry (Section 17.1). The **Film,** CORF: 3105 *Carbon and Its Compounds* (2nd ed.) (16 min.) may be used as an introduction. **Exhibit** substances that indicate multiplicity and variety of carbon compounds: sugar, alcohol, vinegar and acetic acid, medicine (aspirin), saccharin, burner gas (natural gas), gasoline, petroleum, polyethylene, laboratory apparatus of plastic, rubber, etc. Have students propose a question about the existence of the great number of carbon compounds (3,000,000 + 100,000 new ones per year). To show that carbon is not among the ten most abundant elements, refer to the tables in Chapter 2. Review details of tetravalency of carbon covalent bonding and hybridization developed in Chapter 17. Use the chalkboard for the electron-dot formulas for the isomers of octane developed in conjunction with display of ball-and-stick models of them. Exhibit ball-and-stick model of *n*-butane and have students attempt construction of model of isobutane: 2-methylpropane (branched-chain concept). Review double-bond structure of CO_2 and display model. Defer discussion of triple bonds and rings until the representative series are considered. One possible listing on the chalkboard of reasons for the abundance of carbon compounds is: (1) Tetravalency of carbon, hybridization; (2) Carbon atoms can combine with each other in (a) chains—straight and branched, (b) networks (diamond), (c) rings (benzene); (3) Carbon atoms combine by (a) single bonds, (b) double and triple bonds; (4) Isomers (define); (5) Combination with other elements (substitution, addition). Display carbon tetrachloride, perchloroethylene, Teflon, and Freon for reason 5 above. **Transparencies:** HM: 2-10535 *The Methane Molecule;* HM: 2-10538 *Structure of C_2H_4.* **Loop:** EBE: 5-81574 *Examples of Isomerism.*

Section 18.2. **Activities:** Write structural formula for methane. Redefine structural formula. Write structural formula for octane and have students attempt structural formulas for its three branched-chain isomers. **Transparency:** EYE: 003-44 *Isomerism.*

Section 18.3. **Activities:** Review calculation of empirical formula from data in Section 18.3. Construct, or have students construct, models of two different substances. Have students make the waft-odor test with samples of each substance. Write the structural formulas. You may wish to demonstrate the action of sodium on ethanol and exhibit the reagent phosphorus trichloride and ethyl chloride. Develop resolution of the problem as in Section 18.3. **Transparency:** EYE: 003-42, *Nomenclature—Organic Chemistry.*

Section 18.4. **Demonstrate:** The differences with the text-suggested substances or equivalents: (1) *Solubility:* NaCl, NH_4Cl, KNO_3 in water and mineral oil; naphthalene in H_2O; kerosene or gasoline in mineral oil. (2) *Decomposition:* heat sugar, NaCl. **(3)** *Rate:* a precipitation contrasted with fermentation (Chapter 17) and later on with esterification and saponification. **(4)** *Reaction conditions:* review burning wood splints versus destructive distillation (Chapter 17); mention temperature, pressure, catalyst. **(5)** *Molecular structure:* review conductivity tests: molten NaCl and wax, solutions of NaCl and C_2H_5OH, etc., for covalence versus ionic bonding. Discuss **CAUTION** with examples: aerosol sprays, CCl_4, C_6H_6 (see Marginal Note 11). **References:** Carter, D. E., and Fernando, O., ''Chemical Toxicology, Part I: Organic Compounds,'' *Journal of Chemical Education,* 56(5), 284 (1979); Fung, B. M., ''Aerosol Sprays,'' *Journal of Chemical Education,* 56(7), in 446 (1979); ''Health Effects of Halogenated Hydrocarbons,'' *Chemistry,* 51(8), 20 (1978).

Section 18.5. Discuss the composition, occurrence, and formation of natural gas and petroleum. Refer to past and present costs of gasoline, fuel oil, and gas and to the search for new sources of substitutes (Section 18.24). A large number of related teaching aids can be obtained from the American Petroleum Institute, 2101 L St., N.W., Washington, D.C. 20037, and from Education Services, American Gas Association, 1515 Wilson Blvd., Arlington, Va. 22209. Booklets from the latter include: *The Story of Natural Gas Energy* #N00480, *History of Natural Gas* #N00430, *Gas-Centered Projects for Science Fairs* #N00470, *Properties of Gas and Heat Energy Experiments* #N0085. Free classroom materials (packets) on energy are available from U. S. Dept. of Energy, P. O. Box 62, Oak Ridge, Tenn. 37830—e.g., #23 *Energy for the Future,* #20 *Bioconversion.* **Film:** *Living with Energy* (1979 documentary), Standard Oil Co., P. O. Box 5910-A, Chicago, Il. 60680. **References:** Hodgson, B., ''Natural Gas: The Search Goes On,'' *National Geographic,* 154(5), 632 (1979); Drake, E., and Reid, R. C., ''The Importation of Liquified Natural Gas,'' *Scientific American,* 236(4), 22 (1977). Flower, A. R., ''World Oil Production,'' *Scientific American,* 238(3), 42 (1978); Kolb, D., and Kolb, K. E., ''Petroleum Chemistry,'' *Journal of Chemical Education,* 56(7), 465 (1979); Moseley, C. G., ''Chemistry and the First Great Gasoline Shortage,'' *Journal of Chemical Education,* 57(4), 288 (1980). Coppa, G., ''Methane: A Neglected Resource,'' *Chemistry* 48(11), 12 (1975); Grove, N., and Kristof, E., ''Oil, the Dwindling Treasure,'' *National Geographic,* 145(6), 792 (1974).

Section 18.6. Activities: Discuss processing of natural gas as in text. Display models of propane and butane and a butane lighter. Display picture of bottled gas, possibly attached to a trailer or mobile home. Have fractional distillation redefined (Sections 9.4 and 9.5).

Section 18.7. Activities: Exhibit the wall chart (American Petroleum Institute) of distillation apparatus or reproduce Figure 18-4. Discuss structure and operation of pipe still and fractionating column. Contrast fractional distillation (physical change) with destructive distillation (chemical change). Use Table 18-1 as a summary. Demonstrate fractional distillation of a mixture of alcohol and water. See Alyea, p. 105, for demonstration of the distillation of petroleum. **Loops:** BFA: ISBN 0-03-086084-9 *Distillation;* ISBN 0-03-086085-7 *Fractional Distillation, Part 1.* **Booklets** from American Petroleum Institute: *Facts About Oil; The Why and How of Undersea Drilling;* **Catalog:** *Movies About Oil.* **Filmstrip:** PH: WCC 9173 *Distillation: Simple and Fractional.*

Section 18.8. Define hydrocarbons. Exhibit models of each of the five series and discuss bonding in each group.

Section 18.9. Activity: Develop the concept of homologous series and general formula for the alkanes and reinforce with later series. **Exhibit:** Paraffin, butane-fueled cigarette lighter. Light the laboratory burner and mention that natural gas is composed largely of methane. Now or later exhibit a set of hydrocarbon products from petroleum. Develop the details of the outline table.

Name of Series:
General Formula:

Names	Molecular Formula	Electron-dot Formula	Structural Formula	Phase

Develop the idea of series from name endings and recognition of CH_2 increment, and challenge students to produce a general formula for the first four alkanes. Use the data in Table 18-2 to generalize increase in melting and boiling points for the normal alkanes with increasing molecular complexity. **Film:** CORF: 1405 *Hydrocarbons and Their Structure* (13+ min.).

Section 18.10. Activities: Use models and ''discover'' isomers of butane. Then use systematic names for pentane and beyond by use of general formula. Construct isomers of pentane. Illustrate naming procedure and identify different alkyl groups. Write the formula for common isooctane and have students name it according to nomenclature procedure. Provide groundwork for understanding saturation from inspection of formulas and bonds. Discuss low chemical reactivity and stability. Use R as representative of alkyl groups and have students identify R—H as a formula for the alkanes. You may wish to review sp^3 hybridization (Section 17.2). Identify sp^3–sp^3 bonds and use models to show that a straight chain is a continuous chain but not a ''straight'' chain because of the directional nature of sp^3–sp^3 tetrahedral arrangement.

Section 18.11. Activities: Prepare and collect methane according to Figure 18-8. You may also wish to show its collection by downward displacement of air. From the two methods of collection, the students infer several physical properties. Refer to Table 18-2 for data on melting and boiling point of ethane versus methane. Discuss occurrence in atmosphere of various planets.

Section 18.12. Demonstrations: Ignite a collected sample of methane. Light the laboratory burner. Write equations for combustion of CH_4 and C_2H_6. For substitution, use white mineral oil or paraffin with Br_2 in perchloroethylene (instead of CCl_4). Ligroin (a mixture of C_6 and C_7 compounds) or *n*-heptane (both from Arthur H. Thomas Co.) may be tested with bromine water. Try bringing an ultraviolet lamp across the mouth of the bottle and then blow breath across the mouth of the bottle to detect fuming HBr. (Also test with moist blue litmus paper at bottle mouth). Addition of $KMnO_4$ solution with an alkane produces no perceptible change. Write equations for substitution process for Br_2. For chlorine, use successive substitution equations; use common and systematic names for CH_3Cl, CH_2Cl_2, $CHCl_3$, CCl_4. Exhibit samples and models of these. Exhibit Teflon samples and Freon. For formulas and details, refer to Section 19.3. Write the equation for reaction of propane with steam and compare with reactions in Sections 9.17(4) and 17.14(2).

Sections 18.13 and 18.14. Activities: Exhibit ball-and-stick models of ethene and propene. Develop a chalkboard table for ethene and propene similar to that for alkanes and establish general formula. **Exhibit and Activities:** Polyethylene and propylene laboratory beakers, etc. Write the molecular formulas for ethane and ethene, and challenge students to write a structural formula for C_2H_4. Ask why both compound names start with *eth*. **Demonstrations:** Preparation of ethene and testing with Br_2 and $KMnO_4$ solutions (Fowles, Exps. 138a, 142, 143; Alyea, pp. 47, 174). *Cracking:* pretest white mineral oil with Br_2 solution. Heat a sample of the mineral oil in a test tube with steel wool and repeat Br_2 test. On a larger scale, the vapor from boiling mineral oil is passed over steel wool heated in a connected glass tube. Collect the gases produced by displacement of water. Define cracking, thermal cracking, and catalytic cracking. Write equations for thermal cracking of C_3H_8. Dehydration of ethanol demonstration. Fowles, Exp. 138a: Sulfuric Acid and Exp. 138b: Phosphoric Acid. Write an equation for the dehydration of ethanol. **References:** Wiseman, P., "Ethylene by Naphtha Cracking," *Journal of Chemical Education*, 54(3), 154 (1977); Fernelius, W. C., Whittcoff, H., and Varnerin, R. E., "Ethylene: The Organic Chemical Industry's Most Important Building Block," *Journal of Chemical Education*, 56(6), 385 (1979); "Ethylene Technology Moves to Liquid Feeds," *Chemical and Engineering News*, May 28, 1979, p. 32.

Section 18.15. Demonstration: Demonstrate addition by shaking bromine water or Br_2 in perchloroethylene with collected sample of gas from thermal cracking of white mineral oil. Amylene or 1-pentene may also be used to demonstrate addition. Use ball-and-stick models for addition reactions with H_2 hydrogenation, Br_2 (isomers of dibromoethane), HBr, and polymerization. Write the representative equations, structural formulas, and names of products. Illustrate by use of models the alkylation reaction for isobutene and isobutane and the resultant 2, 2, 4-trimethyl-pentane (used in gasoline). Repeat use of models and write equation for combustion of ethene. Exhibit objects made of polyethylene. **Reference:** "Ethylene in Plants," *Chemistry*, 48(3), 25 (1975). **Film:** NAVC: 003053/HH *The Poetry of Polymers.* **Filmstrip:** I: 67746 *Synthetic Giant Molecules.*

Sections 18.16 and 18.17. Activities: Develop a table for ethyne and propyne similar to the previous tables. **Demonstrations:** Drop 1 or 2 chunks of CaC_2 into a test tube half filled with H_2O. Ignite the gas at the test tube mouth. Test the remaining contents with litmus or phenolphthalein. Exhibit an acetylene lamp. Describe flame color of oxyacetylene torch. Discuss the results in terms of completeness of combustion. Discuss and write equations as in Section 18.17–1, 2.

Section 18.18. Activities: Treat equations for Section 18.18 as above. Models may be used to illustrate complete combustion of C_2H_2. Use models, write equations, name products of halogen addition and dimerization of ethyne. Identify the vinyl group. Discuss vinylacetylene and its use in the production of neoprene. You may wish to illustrate this further by using models to show formation of chloroprene by addition of HCl and the neoprene unit for catalytic polymerization of chloroprene. Exhibit sample of neoprene hose and its use in delivering gasoline. **Demonstrate:** Addition of bromine to sample of ethyne collected by displacement of water.

Section 18.19. Activities: Exhibit a ball-and-stick model of 1, 3-butadiene. Write its molecular and structural formula. You may wish to use models and develop a chalkboard formula for the polymerization of butadiene and styrene (Section 18.22) resulting in the *SBR* structural unit (Section 18.28). Exhibit a sample of *SBR* rubber.

Section 18.20. Activities: Exhibit models of benzene, toluene, and xylene. Write molecular formulas and develop a table similar to those for the preceding hydrocarbon classes of hydrocarbon, including a general formula. Discuss and illustrate resonance hybrids of benzene and its relationship to saturation in benzene and other aromatics versus unsaturation of alkenes. Write the benzene ring structure symbol and that for the phenyl group. Discuss commercial production of benzene, coal tar, and petroleum as sources of the aromatic hydrocarbons. Benzene's odor is readily detectible. (**CAUTION:** Benzene is poisonous.) Discuss its uses and exhibit samples of products manufactured from it. Demonstrate destructive distillation of bituminous coal using a test tube, collecting bottle, and jet assembly, and ignite the coal gas at the jet exit. Use a high-temperature burner to speed decomposition. Coal tar collects in the bottle. **References:** Vanderbilt, B. M., "Kekulé's Whirling Snake: Fact or Fiction?" *Journal of Chemical Education*, 52(11), 709 (1975); Smith, R. M., "Benzene, A Familiar Hazard," *Journal of Chemical Education*, 57(3), A85 (1980); Kolb, D., "The Aromatic Ring," *Journal of Chemical Education*, 56(5), 334 (1979). **Transparency:** EYE: 003-43 *Aromatics.*

Section 18.21. Use models to show halogenation reactions, starting with the production of bromobenzene and ending with hexabromobenzene. Write equations for substitution, nitration, sulfonation, and Friedel-Crafts reaction. **Filmstrips:** PH: WCC 9175 *Preparation of Nitrobenzene;* PH: WCC 9181 *Friedel-Crafts Preparation of 4-Acetylbiphenyl.* **Reference:** Doheny, A. J., and Loudon, G. M., "The Effect of Free Radical Stability on the Rate of Bromination of Hydrocarbons," *Journal of Chemical Education*, 57(7), 507 (1980).

Section 18.22. Activities: Exhibit toluene and xylene samples and models. Discuss their uses. Write equations for production of ethyl benzene and styrene. Exhibit styrofoam or articles of polystyrene. Ignite a sample that burns with a characteristic odor. Solid polystyrene objects give a metallic ring when dropped on a hard surface. Exhibit naphthalene. Write its formula and that of anthracene and discuss their production and uses. Use the hexagonal representations as well as their molecular formulas. See Figure 18-12.

Section 18.23. Activities: Have students examine octane ratings of various grades of gasoline posted on gasoline pumps. Discuss engine knock, its causes and prevention, the octane rating scale, and the antiknock properties of various components in terms of branched hydrocarbons and tetraethyl lead. Discuss the automobile-related problems of pollution, control devices in automobiles, and effects on the type of gasoline, its composition, and the costs. **References:** Kolb, D., and Kolb, K. E., "Petroleum Chemistry," *Journal of Chemical Education*, 56(7), 465 (1979); "Walrus: Be Sure You Understand Octane Numbers," *Chemistry*, 47(1), 3 (1974); Research Reporter, "Cars—Robbing Peter to Pay Paul," 48(3), 26 (1975); Research Reporter, "Catalytic Converters and Sulfuric Acid," 47(4), 23 (1974); Wildeman, T. R., "The Automobile and Air Pollution: A Chemical Review of the Problem," *Journal of Chemical Education,* 51(5), 290 (1974); Pierce, J. R., "The Fuel Consumption of Automobiles," *Scientific American,* 232(1), 34 (1975); Walters, E. A., and Wewerka, E. M., "An Overview of the Energy Crisis," *Journal of Chemical Education,* 52(11), 709 (1975).

Section 18.24. Activity: Discuss the problems and alternative petroleum substitutes: conversion of coal to fuel gases and petroleum-like liquids, oil shale, fission. Discuss details of Bergius and Fischer-Tropsch processes. Mention other possible energy sources: underground steam, sun, ocean water, fusion, and biomass. Students may report on various aspects of the problems. **References:** "Energy Review," *Journal of Chemical Education,* 55(4), 263 (1978); "Coal to Oil to KWH," *Scientific American,* 240(1), 74 (1979); "Energy from Coal," *Journal of Chemical Education,* 56(3), 186 (1979); "Synfuels: Uncertain and Costly Fuel Option," *Chemical and Engineering News,* Aug. 27, 1979, p. 20; "South Africa Commits to Oil-from-Coal Process," *Chemical and Engineering News,* Sept. 17, 1979, p. 13; "Process Upgrades Shale Oil to Usable Crude," *Chemical and Engineering News,* Jan. 9, 1978, p. 33; Navickis, R., "Biomass," *Science News,* 113(16), 258 (1978); Raloff, J., "Crude Yet Unconventional," *Science News,* 116(3), 42 (1979); Mosely, C. G., "The Capitalist, the Chemist, and Lima Sour Crude Oil," *Journal of Chemical Education,* 56(10), 657 (1979); "Cloud Nine," *Scientific American,* 240(6), 99 (1979); Bozak, R. E., and Garcia, M., "Chemistry in the Oil Shales," *Journal of Chemical Education,* 53(3), 154 (1976); Research Reporter, "Methanol-Solution for the Energy Crisis," *Chemistry,* 47(4), 24 (1974); Cochran, N. P., "Oil and Gas from Coal," *Scientific American,* 234(5), 24 (1976); American Petroleum Institute, *Supplementary Energy Sources* (pamphlet). **Films:** USDE: 508 *Challenge of the Future* (29 min.); USDE: 526 *Coal, the Other Energy* (15 min.); USDE: 527 *Energy Update* (28+ min.); USDE: 519 *Geothermal, Nature's Boiler* (27 min.); USDE: 513 *Look to the Sun* (12 min.); USDE: 501 *Power from the Earth* (12+ min.). **Filmstrip:** "New Sources of Energy," J. L. Ruhle & Associates, P.O. Box 4301, Fullerton, CA 92631. **Slides:** *Geothermal Energy; Oil Production in the Los Angeles Basin; New Sources of Methane* (all from Ruhle and Associates).

Sections 18.25 and 18.26. Activities: Exhibit rubber latex, unvulcanized (if available) and vulcanized rubber, sulfur, carbon black, tires, and rubber objects. **Demonstration:** Add acetic acid to rubber latex to produce coagulation. Squeeze into a ball and bounce. A salt solution will also produce coagulation. See Alyea, p. 101, "Vulcanization with Sulfur"; p. 114, "Electrodeposition of Rubber"; p. 157, "Coagulation of Rubber Latex." Construct a ball-and-stick model of isoprene.

Sections 18.27 and 18.28. Activities: Exhibit gloves and tubing made of neoprene. Use models and equations for the reactions involved in its manufacture. Compare the structure of the neoprene unit with that of the C_5H_8 unit of natural rubber. Discuss details of manufacture and unit structure of *SBR* rubber as in Section 17.28. Exhibit tires. **Demonstration:** "Production of Thiokol Rubber," Alyea, p. 110 (22-48s), (22-52s); Experiment 20-3: Synthetic Rubber. *Laboratory Experiments for Foundations of Chemistry* is based on Alyea,

22-52s, for production and coagulation of Thiokol latex. The Thiokol is a condensation polymer that splits off NaCl when $C_2H_4Cl_2$ reacts with sodium polysulfide. The sulfur atoms provide linkage, and the production illustrates the role sulfur plays in vulcanization of natural rubber.

As a chapter summary use the **Filmstrip** I: 67121, *Organic Chemistry.* **General References:** "Plastics: Utilizing the Properties of String-like Molecules," *Journal of Chemical Education,* 56(1), 42 (1979); Ensley, E. K., Plancher, H., Robertson, R. E., and Peterson, J. C., "Asphalt—We Hardly Know You," *Journal of Chemical Education,* 55(10), 656 (1978); "Report Touts Expanded Use of Coal," *Chemical and Engineering News,* May 19, 1980, p. 6; "Coal Conversion, New Processes from Old," *Chemical and Engineering News,* Sept. 5, 1977, p. 24; "Coal: Energy Bridge to the 21st Century," *Science News,* 117 (21), 325 (1980); "Coal Mixers for Oily Thirsts," *Science News,* 117(10), 152 (1980). **Students' References:** *SciQuest* Reprints: #17, *Benzene— The Story of the Formulas;* #29, *The Structural Theory of Organic Chemistry, Parts I, II, III—A Short Summer Course in Carbon Chemistry;* #43, *Design and Formation of Long-Chain Polymers;* #54, *The Tetrahedral Atoms, Parts I, II.* *Scientific American* Offprint: 3033 *World Coal Production.* **Sources of Instructional Materials:** American Petroleum Institute, 2101 L St., N. W., Washington, D. C. 20037; American Gas Association, 1515 Wilson Blvd., Arlington, Va. 22209; Allied Chemical Corporation, 40 Rector St., New York, N. Y. 10006; B. F. Goodrich Co., 227 Park Ave., New York, N. Y. 10017; The Goodyear Tire and Rubber Co., 50 Rockefeller Plaza, New York, N. Y. 10020. **Individualized Programmed Instruction:** HR: WCC 9102, *Nomenclature in Organic Chemistry, Introduction.*

Teacher Notes
Chapter 19

Chapter Note

Activities and Demonstrations: General formulas and characteristic-distinguishing (functional) groups can be arrived at by use of exhibited samples, models, and molecular and structural formulas for the main types of compounds. Discussion of pesticides, polyvinyl chloride, ketene, Freon propellants, and detergents as they relate to ecology and safety may be based on student reports from articles appearing in *Chemistry, Scientific American,* and *Science News.* Specific references are listed at various sections where such discussion is useful. Enrichment experiments may be selected from Weaver, E. C., *Experiments in Environmental Pollution, II,* Holt, Rinehart and Winston, and *Experiments in the Chemistry of Foods,* Manufacturing Chemists Association, 1974. Some review of the molecular, electron-dot, and structural formulas of representative alkanes, alkenes, and alkynes will probably be required, particularly those of the first four alkanes. This provides the basis for most of the chapter and for understanding of the relationship of the various types of compounds in this chapter. Exhibit samples of the halogen substitution products, including those with which the student may have had environmental contact. These may include Teflon and Teflon-coated pots, ethyl chloride, aerosol dispensers, and iodoform.

The chapter requires four periods. One possible arrangement is:

Lesson 1   Sections 19.1–19.3: Alkyl Halides
Lesson 2   Sections 19.4–19.6: Alcohols
Lesson 3   Sections 19.7–19.10: Ethers, Aldehydes, Ketones
Lesson 4   Sections 19.11–19.14: Carboxylic Acids, Esters

Section 19.1. In the classroom, ball-and-stick models can be manipulated to illustrate the preparation and properties of hydrocarbon compounds. The use of these models complements exhibited samples, actual experiments or demonstrations, writing molecular and structural formulas, and equations. Useful models are Ealing Demonstration-size sets: Molecular Orbital Models and Space-Filling Molecular Models. **Activities:** Write the molecular and structural formula equations for the progressive chlorination of CH_4. List the names: monochloromethane (methyl chloride), dichloromethane, trichloromethane (chloroform), tetrachloromethane (carbon tetrachloride). Review demonstrations for substitution (Section 18.12) and addition (Sections 18.15 and 18.18). **Demonstrations:** Allow octane or petroleum ether to react with bromine water. Illuminate the reaction with a sunlamp or 150-watt projection lamp for evidence of substitution. Write general equations using X_2 for halogen and develop general formula for alkyl halides (RX). Write the equation for alcohol + hydrogen halide. Prepare iodoform by shaking dilute I_2 (aq) with ethanol and a pellet of KOH (Alyea, p. 106). **Transparency:** EYE: 103-45 *Typical Organic Reactions.*

Section 19.2. Activities: Write the ionic equation for reaction of alkyl halides with water solution of strong hydroxide (OH^-). Review Friedal-Crafts reaction. (Section 18.21[4])

Section 19.3. Activities: Exhibit CCl_4 (pyrene fire extinguisher, if available), $CHCl_3$, CCl_2F_2 (spray can), Teflon-coated pots. Write equations in Section 19.3. Use models. Write the structural formula for C_2F_4 and the related monomer unit for Teflon. Discuss uses and properties of alkyl halides, mentioning ethyl chloride (local anesthetic). Other exhibit materials of which the following are representative are: Fuller Brush Co. Spot Remover Spray (label includes statement "Does not contain carbon tetrachloride" but does contain perchloroethylene). Texize K2r also includes perchloroethylene. Exhibit paradichlorobenzene pellets in package container and Fuller Brush Co. Moth Proofer can. Contents label mentions paradichlorobenzene as well as diethyl diphenyl dichloroethane. Exhibit some pump-type dispensers and discuss replacement of spray-type dispensers. It may be worthwhile to devote an entire lesson to the Freon–ozone problem and controversy. The series of *Science News* and other articles that follows gives a current illustration of the scientific method(s): Theorizing, searching for evidence, changing the theory in light of new evidence, degree of uncertainty of predictions, restrictive actions taken by governmental bodies, etc. Part of the lesson may also be devoted to discussion of vinyl chloride and ketene. **References:** Moore, J. W., and Moore, E. A., "Science–Society Case Study: PVC: Proliferating Polymer," *The Science Teacher*, 42(10), 23 (1975); "Ketene, Expensive Lesson," *Research Reporter, Chemistry*, 49(6) 24 (1976). Exhibit samples of polyvinyl products. Fernelius, W. C., Witcoff, H., and Varnerin, R. E., "Ethylene: The Organic Industry's Most Important Building Block," *Journal of Chemical Education*, 56(6), 385 (1979); Moseley, C. G., "The Discovery of the

Anesthetic Properties of Chloroform," *Journal of Chemical Education*, 55(9), 596 (1978); Bassow, H., "The Great Spray Can Debate," *Journal of Chemical Education* 54(6), 371 (1977); Ferguson, L. N., "Organic Chemicals: Angels or Goblins?" *Journal of Chemical Education*, 55(9), 553 (1978); Carter, D. E., and Fernando, Q., "Chemical Toxicology, Part I: Organic Compounds," *Journal of Chemical Education*, 56(5), 284 (1979); "Ozone destruction exceeds predictions," *Science News* 114(24), 407 (1978); "Ozone depletion: Double the trouble," *Science News*, 116 (20), 340 (1979); "Ozone: Worldwide, many-faceted problem," *Science News*, 117(1), 5 (1980); Fox, J. L., "Atmospheric ozone issue looms again," *Chemical and Engineering News*, Oct. 15, 1979, p. 25; "High in the Sky," *Scientific American*, 231(6), 66 (1974); Lieber, C. S., "The Metabolism of Alcohol," *Scientific American*, 234(3), 25 (1976); "Freon Refrigerants," *Journal of Chemical Education*, 52(6), 413 (1975); "Freon: Destroying the ozone layer?" *Science News*, 106(12), 180 (1974); "Fluorocarbons and Ozone: New Predictions Ominous," *Science News*, 106(14), 212 (1974); "NAS Launches Study on Fluorocarbons," *Science News*, 106(22), 340 (1974); "Task Force to Study Ozone Problem," *Science News*, 107(7), 100 (1975); Weinberg, J. H., "Ozone Verdict: On Faith or Fact?" *Science News*, 107(20), 322 (1975); "High Altitude Data Confirm Ozone Theory," *Science News*, 108(6), 84 (1975); "Fine-tuning of Fluorocarbons," *Science News*, 108(10), 152 (1975); "Ozone Drop Supports Depletion Theory," *Science News*, 109(3), 38 (1976); "To Ban or Not to Ban: Data for the Ozone Question," *Science News*, 109(12), 180 (1976); "Rumor and Confusion Follow Ozone Theory Revision," *Science News*, 109(19), 292 (1976); "Aerosols, Ozone and the NAS: Delay Urged," *Science News*, 110(12), 180 (1976); "Agencies to Ban Fluorocarbon Sprays," *Science News*, 110(17), 262 (1976).

Sections 19.4 and 19.5. Activities: Exhibit samples of methanol, ethanol, denatured alcohol, ethylene glycol (antifreeze), glycerol, isopropyl alcohol. Have students use common names, i.e., wood and grain alcohol and glycerine. Light alcohol lamp and Sterno can. Develop a chalkboard table showing the relationship of the primary alcohol to the alkanes using structural formulas and names and leading to the concept: An alcohol is the hydroxyl substitution product of the hydrocarbon and may be represented as ROH. Complement by ball-and-stick models. Also use models for propanol and isopropanol and respective names as 1-propanol, 2-propanol. Use models to develop isomeric butanols and give example of naming, e.g., tert-butyl alcohol as 2-methyl-2 propanol. You may distinguish between primary, secondary, and tertiary alcohols by the number of carbon atoms bonded to the COH group or use alternate:

$$-CH_2OH \text{ (primary)} \quad -CHOH \text{ (secondary)} \quad -\overset{\textstyle |}{\underset{\textstyle |}{C}}-OH$$

(tertiary)

Attempt separation of ethanol by fractional distillation from fermentation experiment. Discuss methods for preparing alcohols in Section 19.4 by using equations, models, structural formulas. Refer to Section 19.14 for production of glycerol by saponification. Discuss uses and properties of specific alcohols. Display samples of sugarless chewing gum. Write formulas and names of alcohols used instead of sugar as sweeteners. **References:** O'Sullivan, D. A., "UN workshop urges wider use of ethanol," *Chemical and Engineering News*, Apr. 23, 1979, p. 11; "Gasohol takes to the road," *Science News*, 112(18), 280 (1977); Navickis, R., "Biomass," *Science News*, 113(16), 258 (1978); Anderson, E. V., "Gasohol: energy mountain or molehill?" *Chemical and Engineering News*, July 31, 1978, p. 8; O'Sullivan, D. A., "Biotechnology gains brighten resource outlook," *Chemical and Engineering News*, Sept. 17, 1979, p. 27; Stinson, S. C., "New plants, processes set for octane booster," *Chemical and Engineering News*, June 25, 1979, p. 35; "Mobil proves gasoline-from-methanol process," *Chemical and Engineering News*, Jan. 30, 1978, p. 26; Stinson, S. C., "Methanol primed for future energy role," *Chemical and Engineering News*, Apr. 7, 1980, p. 37; "The Sobering effect of alcoholism," *Science News*, 114(18), 293 (1978); Shorey, R. L., "Effects of Ethanol on Nutrition," *Journal of Chemical Education*, 56(8), 532 (1979); Miller, J. A., "Hot Bug for Energy," *Science News*, 116(18), 317 (1979).

Section 19.6. Activities: Light alcohol lamp and Sterno if not used previously. Have students write equations for complete combustion of methanol and ethanol. Test various alcohols and their water solutions with litmus to show they do not ionize to yield hydroxide ion. React a small piece of Na with ethanol to show relationship to H_2O. Fowles (pp. 120–122) describes demonstrations for dehydration of ethanol using H_2SO_4 or H_3PO_4. Demonstrate formaldehyde production from methanol by oxidation with CuO. Preparation of "solid" alcohol: Add 60 mL of denatured alcohol to 10 mL of saturated solution of calcium acetate. Sample is ignited on ceramic sheet. Chemical tests distinguishing primary, secondary, tertiary alcohols: reaction with Na **(CAUTION)**—1-butanol, 2-butanol, 2-methyl—2-propanol yields progressively fewer bubbles with production of white solids for last two.

Write equations for reactions in this section. Exhibit cleaning agent containing sodium lauryl sulfonate. Exhibit other commercial cleaners and detergents. **References:** "The Chemistry of Cleaning," *Journal of Chemical Education*, 56(9), 611 (1979); McLean, C. E., "Detergents—Soaps and Syndets," *Chemistry*, 49(7), 6 (1976); "Household Soaps and Detergents," *Journal of Chemical Education*, 55(9), 596 (1978). As a possible activity, have students look up the boiling points of primary alcohols (they may also do this for alkyl halides) and graph the boiling point against the number of carbon atoms.

Section 19.7. Illustrate the methods of production of ethers by use of equations and models. Use the general formula ROR′ and define as an organic oxide. Exhibit container of diethyl ether. Demonstrate its volatility by rapid evaporation on chalkboard. Discuss use of ether and of $(CH_3)_3CO(CH_3)$.

Sections 19.8 and 19.9. Exhibit aldehydes: formaldehyde, formalin, paraformaldehyde, acetaldehyde, and paraldehyde. Test for odors by waft test **(CAUTION)**. Acetaldehyde has a pear-like odor. Refer to demonstration in Section 19.6 for formaldehyde preparation. Discuss use of formaldehyde and preparation and uses of acetaldehyde. **Demonstrations:** (1) Fehling's test, production of a silver mirror. (2) *Oxidation of an aldehyde:* Dissolve 1 g $K_2Cr_2O_7$ in 5 mL of 3-M H_2SO_4. To this add a few drops of ethanol. Observe dichrome color change. Detect pear-like odor of acetaldehyde. Heat contents of tube gently and test vapors with moist blue litmus paper for acetic acid. Its odor is also apparent. (3) *Condensation:* plastic production—mix equal volumes of aniline hydrochloride and formalin in a beaker, stirring results in a stiff, colored gel which eventually turns black. See Alyea, p. 48 (22–18), for dramatic production of a phenol-formaldehyde plastic. You may wish to display some plastics and adhesives made from or with formaldehyde. **References:** Wilson, A., and Peterson, V. R., "The Bakelite Demonstration, A Safer Procedure," *Journal of Chemical Education*, 55(10), 652 (1978); Kelly, M. W., "Adhesive Bonding," *Chemistry*, 49(6), 14 (1976). Other references on polymerization are from the Symposium: Learning Chemistry from the Macromolecule, *Journal of Chemical Education*, 50 (1973); Mark, H., "The Early Days of Polymer Science," 757; Morton, M., "Polymerization as a Model Chain Reaction," 740; Rodriquez, F., "Demonstrating Rubber Elasticity," and Morton, M., "Polymers—Ten Years Later," *Chemistry*, 47(9), 11 (1974).

Section 19.10. Activities: Display acetone and note odor. **Demonstrations: (1)** Careful heating of calcium or barium acetate with a luminous flame. **(2)** Methyl ethyl ketone is produced by addition of sodium dichromate solution to a mixture of 6-M H_2SO_4 and 2-butanol in a reaction flask in an ice bath **(CAUTION)**. The temperature is kept between 20° and 40°C, as recorded by an inserted thermometer. **(3)** Dissolve a sample of cellulose acetate (cleaned safety film) in acetone. Pour some of the solution on a glass plate to obtain a film of the acetate by evaporation (use hood). **(4)** Separate Fehling solution tests with acetone and acetaldehyde; no reaction with acetone. Write the equation for production of acetone from 2-propanol and use models. You may wish to develop the idea that oxidation of a primary alcohol produces an aldehyde and then an acid, whereas the initial oxidation of a secondary alcohol produces a ketone. Write the general formula for ketones.

Section 19.11. Activities: Exhibit samples of vinegar, lactic, citric, tartaric, oxalic, and other carboxylic acids. Test vitamin C tablets and fruit (lemons, grapefruit, oranges) with litmus paper. On occasion, a bottle of cider vinegar contains a gelatinous mass (mother of vinegar bacteria); review details of fermentation of glucose yielding ethanol. Test an unrefrigerated sample of wine, left standing for a long time, for acid with litmus paper; write equations for preparation of acetic acid and formic acid. Exhibit models of acetic acid and formic acid, identifying carboxyl group and writing general formula.

Section 19.12. Activities: Perform conductivity tests with glacial acetic and lactic acid. Test these with litmus. Breathe on litmus or moisten with water. Dilute acids and repeat conductivity test. Write equations for ionization of acetic and formic acids. Stir an aspirin in water and test with litmus (refer to TV commercials). Test aspirin and Bufferin tablets dissolved in water with pH paper, e.g., Hydrion paper A. **References:** Brown, D. B., and Friedman, L. B., "The Aspirin Project," *Journal of Chemical Education*, 50, 214 (1973); Plumb, R. C., "Stomach Upset Caused by Aspirin," *Ibid.*, 50, 212 (1973). **Film:** W: 140-4163 *Synthesis of an Organic Compound* (22 min.); W: 140-4160 *Mechanism of an Organic Reaction* (20 min.). **Loop:** W: 168 W 1011(T), *An Organic Mechanism*.

Section 19.13. Demonstrate: The production of methyl salicylate using a beaker for mixing salicylic acid and methanol. Add a few drops of H_2SO_4. Heat gently. Hold the beaker with tongs, walk around the classroom and have students recognize the oil of wintergreen odor. Prepare other esters. Exhibit these esters and have students note characteristic odors. Review mechanism of esterification in Section 19.12. Discuss reversibility (hydrolysis). Develop the general formula,

$$R—\overset{\overset{\displaystyle O}{\|}}{C}—O—R'$$

for esters of carboxylic acids. Write other equations such as production of glyceryl trinitrate.

Section 19.14. Activities: Exhibit various long-chain acids, e.g., stearic, oleic, palmitic, and write the representative formulas. Exhibit various samples of fats and oils. Develop the formula for glyceryl tristearate and then the formula representing the general structure of a fat or oil. Exhibit Crisco solid and oil. (Label reads: "High in Polyunsaturates.") Discuss catalytic hydrogenation of vegetable oils. Test a light-colored cooking or salad oil with Br_2 in CCl_4 or in perchloroethylene for unsaturation evidence. Define saponification and write a representative equation. Demonstrate "salting out" by adding NaCl to a soap solution. Discuss soap production. Write the equation for hydrolysis of fats. Discuss the neutralization of the resultant long-chain carboxylic acids and varieties of soap. As chapter summary, use the **Filmstrip** I: 67121 *Functional Organic Groups*. For review of Chapters 17, 18, 19 use the **Filmstrips:** I: 76121 *Organic Chemistry*, and I: 67746 *Synthetic Giant Molecules*. **General References:** Kaufman, G. B., Choolijian, S. H., "Wöhler's Synthesis of Artificial Urea: A Modern Version of a Classic Experiment," *Journal of Chemical Education*, 56(3), 197 (1979); Sears, J. A., "Polymer Pioneers," *Chemistry*, 50(7), 6 (1977); Bieber, T. L., "Improving the Nylon Rope Trick," *Journal of Chemical Education*, 56(6), 409 (1979); McLoan, C. E., "Fibers Natural and Synthetic," *Chemistry*, 51(3), 8 (1978); Connick, W. J., "Flame Retardant Cotton Textiles," *Chemistry*, 51(3), 13 (1978); Raloff, J., "Keeping That Tiger in Your Tank," *Science News*, 117(15), 234 (1980); "Gasohol holds key to ethanol outlook," *Chemical and Engineering News*, May 19, 1980, p. 21; "Medical History of Aspirin and Related Drugs," *Journal of Chemical Education*, 56(5), 331 (1979). **Individualized Programmed Instruction:** PH: WCC 9103 *Identification and Naming Compounds with One or More Functional Groups;* PH: WCC 9104 *Nomenclature of the Functional Groups and Heterocyclic Compounds.*

Teacher Notes
Chapter 20

Chapter Note

Because of the multiplicity of available demonstrations, experiments, references, and audiovisual aids, it is improbable that all of the suggestions can be utilized. The matter of strategic choice depends on local course requirements and the general caliber of students of particular classes. As an introductory overview, a **Film** such as W: 140-4121 *Introduction to Reaction Kinetics* or a **Film Loop** such as HR: 04-96455 *Reaction Kinetics* or BFA: E 84-0231/1 *Reaction Rates* may be shown.

Students should be encouraged to consult the classroom reference library. See list of texts (mostly paperbacks) at the end of this chapter. Several copies of the *Chemistry* Reprint 85, *The Laws of Disorder*, which is written at the students' level, should be made available. **Teacher Reference:** Batt, R. H., "A Piagetian Learning Cycle for Introductory Chemical Kinetics," *Journal of Chemical Education*, 57(9), 634 (1980); Collins, M. P. S., "A Popular Approach to Reaction Kinetics," *Journal of Chemical Education*, 56(10), 653 (1979).

This chapter requires five periods. One possible arrangement is:

Lesson 1 Sections 20.1–20.4: Heat of Reaction, Heat of Formation

Lesson 2 Sections 20.4–20.6: Stability and Heat of Formation, Heat of Combustion, Bond Energy and Reaction Heat

Lesson 3 Section 20.7: Factors that Drive Reactions

Lesson 4 Sections 20.8–20.11: Reaction Pathways, Collision Theory, Activation Energy, Activated Complex

Lesson 5 Sections 20.12–20.13: Rate Influencing Factors, Reaction Rate Law

Section 20.1. Activities: Use models (ball-and-stick or spatial) for the HI reaction. This raises the problem: "How could this reaction take place?" Have students manipulate the models to represent bond breaking and bond making. This may lead to the realization that energy is required to break existent bonds and consequently that energy may be evolved during the making of new bonds. Demonstration of reaction rates: **(a)** $NaCl + AgNO_3$ solutions (instantaneous precipitate); **(b)** HCl to $Na_2S_2O_3$ solution produces sulfur (perceptible time lapse); **(c)** rusting of moistened steel wool in test tube with one-hole stopper and long glass tube inverted into colored water (slow reaction). Selected clock reaction: Alyea, pp. 19, 85, 130, 149, 179, 220 for a sequence of steps or pathways. **Films:** EBE: S 81554 *Slow Reaction—Iron and Oxygen;* EBE: S 81555 *Fast Reaction—Mercury and Silver Nitrate;* EBE: S 81556 *Very Fast Reaction—Ammonium Dichromate.* Define chemical kinetics. As an introduction to thermochemistry: Add Zn to HCl and let students feel the outside of the test tube for temperature change. Discuss decomposition of HgO by heating. **Film:** EBE: S 81567 *Decomposition of Mercuric Oxide.*

Section 20.2. Demonstrations: Ask: "What happens when hydrogen and oxygen are mixed?" Students may state that an explosion occurs with the formation of water. Place labeled bottles of H_2 and O_2, previously collected, mouth to mouth. Remove cover plates. Result? Remove one bottle and ignite with flame. A mixture made by collection of 20 mL of H_2 and 10 mL of O_2 may also be made in a eudiometer and then sparked. To illustrate further the idea of mechanisms or pathways, exhibit and have students manipulate models of H_2, O_2, and H_2O. During the discussion, introduce and review concepts of bond breaking, bond making, the related energies. (See Sections 6.9–6.12 for bond energies.) Discuss the exothermic nature of the reaction. Write the set of equations in Section 20.2 sequentially. Use them to define thermochemistry and heat of reaction. Define enthalpy. Emphasize reference temperature as 25 °C. Discuss the representative standard state phase symbols, and the expression of heat of reaction stated first, in kcal for $2H_2(g) + O_2(g)$ and then conventionally in kcal/mole. Make sure that students understand the use of $\frac{1}{2}O_2$ and the reason for its use. Develop the curve for Figure 20-2(A) on the chalkboard. Write the related equation using the ΔH notation (mention *change* in heat content—enthalpy). Explain the negative sign for exothermic reactions. Refer students to Appendix Table 14 for the exothermic equation and rate for $H_2O(g)$ to emphasize use of state symbols in thermochemical equations. For endothermic reaction, write the two forms of thermochemical equations for the decomposition of H_2O. Develop Figure 20-2(B) on the chalkboard and discuss H as being positive. **Film:** EBE: 2934 *The Bomb Calorimeter* (10 min.). Discuss Figure 20-1. **Transparencies:** HM: 2-10540 *Heat of Reactions—Enthalpy Change;* I: 68744 *Thermochemistry* (6 transparencies and 12 overlays).

Section 20.3. **Activities:** Use the previous activities for the reaction of $H_2 + O_2$ for developing the definition of heat of formation. Have students attempt to interpret the relationship between heat of formation magnitude, sign, and stability. This hypothesis will be evaluated in the next section. Have students discover that each element in its standard state is assigned a heat content of zero by using Appendix Table 14 for carbon (graphite), hydrogen, oxygen, and iodine. Also have them look up data for element in nonstandard state, for example, carbon (diamond), ozone, iodine (g). Use the notation ΔH_f in writing some values on the chalkboard. By further use of data in Table 20-1 and Appendix Table 14, have students discover relationship between sign of heat of formation and type of reaction (exothermic or endothermic), and that few compounds have positive heats of formation.

Section 20.4. **Demonstrations:** To show stability, boil water and show that it is not decomposed by using burning splint. Plunge a heated glass rod into $HI(g)$ and have students observe release of violet iodine vapor. Pass hydrogen sulfide over heated glass wool in a reaction tube at the jet end of which H_2S is ignited. (See diagram.) The H_2S passing over

the heated glass wool decomposes and a sulfur mirror may be observed on the glass beyond the heated glass wool. Pass dry ammonia over heated steel wool in a reaction glass tube. The decomposition products are collected by water displacement. The ammonia, of course, dissolves in the water, and the collected gas mixture contains enough H_2 to give a positive "bark test." You may wish to demonstrate that nitrogen triiodide will explode when the solid is "tickled" with a feather or touched by a glass rod (**EXTREME CAUTION**). See Alyea, pp. 37, 98, for NI_3 demonstration. As a result of the demonstrations and use of the data in the two heat of formation tables, have students arrive at the three generalizations relating stability to heat of formation. **Filmstrip:** I: 69133 *Thermochemistry.*

Section 20.5. **Demonstration:** (a) Burn a charcoal stick in a bottle of O_2 and test for CO_2 with limewater. Use as lead-in to heat of combustion (formation of CO_2) of C (graphite). Write the equation using ΔH, define heat of combustion, and use ΔH_c. Ask students why the heat of formation of carbon dioxide is the same as the heat of combustion of carbon. (b) Burn CO and identify CO_2 product. Show how the heat of formation of CO is calculated. This leads to the concept of conservation of the energy of a system during chemical activity (additivity of heats of reaction). Write the thermochemical equations for the two preceding demonstrations. Have students recall that carbon is a reducing agent to suggest the problem of direct measurement of the heat of formation of CO. Have them suggest a method for its calculation from the data. Use the equation series in Section 20.5 sequentially and arrive at the principle for a substance that cannot be formed directly from its elements. Initially this principle may be used with the series of equations for calculating the heat of formation of CH_4. Show how the heat of formation of CO_2 may be calculated from the heat of formation of CO and the heat of combustion of CO, using the equation series in Section 20.5. This example illustrates the principle of additivity of heats of reaction. Use Figure 20-3 on the chalkboard to illustrate the additivity principle. (Hess's law: the heat of a given overall reaction is the same regardless of the intermediate steps involved.) Use the series of equations for the calculation of ΔH_f for CO. A useful schematic is:

$$C + O_2 \longrightarrow CO_2$$
$$\Delta H_1$$

$$C + \tfrac{1}{2}O_2 \to CO \qquad \Delta H_2 \qquad \Delta H_3 \qquad CO + \tfrac{1}{2}O_2 \to CO_2$$

$$H_1 = H_f\,CO_2$$
$$H_2 = H_f\,CO$$
$$H_3 = H_c\,CO$$

Illustrate the use of the principle of additivity for the series of equations dealing with (a) thermochemical equations for water, (b) the formation of water gas and its combustion.

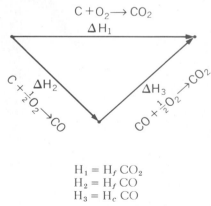

Burning H$_2$S

Glass wool

H$_2$S from generator

Yellow sulfur forms here

Demonstration or student experiments that may be used to illustrate the additivity principle are Exp. 11-1: "Additivity of Heat of Reaction," *Laboratory Experiments for Foundations of Chemistry*. The measurements include: (1) Heat of solution of NaOH(s); (2) Heat of reaction of NaOH(s) with HCl(aq); (3) Heat of neutralization of HCl(aq) and NaOH(aq). Another experiment or demonstration is the calculation of the heat of formation of MgO by using the reactions between Mg and HCl(aq) and MgO + HCl(aq). A suitable experiment for a student project is Bigelow, M. J., "Thermochemistry of Hypochlorite Oxidation," *Journal of Chemical Education, 46, 378 (1969).* **Reference for Demonstration:** Banks, R. C., Carter, L., and Peterson, E. R., "Heat of Combustion of Zirconium," *Journal of Chemical Education, 52(4), 235 (1975)* (uses Flashbulb—G. E. AG1—Mass of Zi in bulbs 0.0223g). Selections from the following set of **Filmstrips** may be used as a medial summary: B #112: *Chemistry: The Ins and Outs of Energy:* 1. *Energy: Kinetic and Potential;* 2. *Potential and Kinetic Energy of Chemical Systems;* 3. *The Meaning of ΔH;* 4. *Energy and Mole Calculations;* 7. *Predicting ΔH: Adding Up Heats of Reaction;* 8. *Adding up Reaction Heats: Learning by Practice.* **Reference:** Lloyd, W. G., and Davenport, D. A., "Applying Thermodynamics to Fossil Fuels," *Journal of Chemical Education, 57(1), 56 (1980).*

Section 20.6. Activities: Develop the details in Figure 20-4 progressively at the chalkboard with the aid of models. Emphasize bond-breaking and bond-making energies. In the final step, add the *H*'s and compare the bond energy calculated with the experimental value. **Questions:** 1–3, 5, 14. **Problems:** 1–6. **References:** Amador, A., "Bond-Free Energies," *Journal of Chemical Education, 56(7), 453 (1979);* Cater, E. D., Letters: On the Validity of Bond-Free Energies," *Journal of Chemical Education, 57(4), 325 (1980)* (relates to the Amador article—with answer by Amador on the same page); DeRose, J. V., "To See for Yourself," (Hess's law experiment or demonstration), *Journal of Chemical Education, 57(1), 70 (1980).* **Filmstrips:** B #112: 5. *Bond Energies and Heat of Reaction,* 6. *Bond Energy Calculations: Learning by Practice.*"

Section 20.7. Activities: Review the concepts in Section 2.14, Figure 2-13, "Changes of Phase." A class introductory participation experiment on entropy and energy consists of each student having a rubber band (in which the structural units are relatively disordered): (1) Hold the rubber band to the lips and stretch it (stretching produces a more ordered arrangement); (2) Let the stretched band contract while in contact with the lips; (3) Attach a paper clip to an unstretched rubber band. Hold the rubber band along the side of a lighted electric light bulb. A more elaborate arrangment is to have the band stretched with a weight. In each case the band contracts as it heats up. **References** (rubber band): Laswick, P. H., "Entropy in a Rubber Band," *Journal of Chemical Education, 49, 469 (1972);* Craig, N. C., *ibid.,* 47, 342 (1970); Dole, N., "Lecture Table Experimental Demonstration of Entropy," *Journal of Chemical Education, 54(12), 754 (1977);* Dezube, B., "A Freshman Chemistry Thermodynamics Experiment," *Journal of Chemical Education, 56(6), 313 (1979).* **Demonstrations (optional):** From Chapter 2 on energy-entropy relationships as they relate to physical changes and spontaneous processes: evaporation of volatile liquids, "disappearance" of Dry Ice,

using the Hg-glass molecular vibration tube (Welch, 1924). **Demonstrations:** The following leads to the lesson problem of spontaneous endothermic water gas reaction: **(a)** Tendency to lowest possible energy state: (1) Zn + HCl (note exothermic nature by feeling outside of test tube or reading inserted thermometer); (2) Mix H_2O and coke, pass steam over coke, demonstrate water gas production (Alyea, pp. 9, 97; p. 142 apparatus for burning magnesium in steam may be adapted substituting and preheating coke). Fowles, pp. 113, 503, 571. **(b)** Tendency to highest possible entropy state: (1) Simulate Figure 20-5 using a colored gas (NO_2, Br_2) in one vessel and air in the other. Open connecting valve. Note result. Keep demonstration setup displayed for a considerable time. Note that gases do not reorder themselves. For free-energy change, define free-energy change as net driving force. Write the equation, identifying each symbol in the equation. Develop the principle: A chemical change tends to proceed spontaneously in the direction of diminished free energy content (ΔG is negative). Write the thermochemical equation for the water gas reaction and have students attempt to explain the spontaneity of the reaction at elevated temperature. Perform the calculations determining the ΔG for the water gas reaction at 25 °C. Repeat for 900 °C at which the free energy change becomes negative.

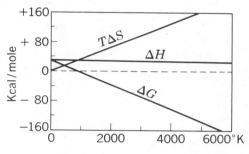

"JANAF Thermochemical Tables" The Dow Chemical Co. Midland, MI, 1961.

It helps to explain the spontaneity of the water-gas reaction at the higher temperature by showing the variations of ΔG and $T\Delta S$ with temperature. **Reference:** See Toon and Ellis, *Foundations of Chemistry,* pp. 427–428, for summation of the thermal effects on *H* and *S* and spontaneity of reactions. **Filmstrip:** I: 67738 *Energy and Entropy: Driving Force of a Chemical Reaction;* PH: WCC 821 *Energy and Entropy in Chemical Reactions* (2 filmstrips with records or cassettes). (2) Spontaneous endothermic reactions: Matthews, G. W. J., *Journal of Chemical Education,* 43, 476 (1966). Measurable temperature decrease and color changes as 1 g of a transition metal hydrated chloride such as $CoCl_2 \cdot 6H_2O$ reacts with 3–5 mL of thienyl chloride. Increase in entropy as large volumes of gases are released. $MCl_2 \cdot 6H_2O + 6SOCl_2 \rightarrow MCl_2 + 12HCl(g) + 6SO_2(g)$. Webber, H. D., "Spontaneity of Chemical Reaction," *CHEM 13 News,* 8 (May 1976). This article describes mixing $Ba(OH)_2 \cdot 8H_2O(s)$ and $NH_4NCS(s)$ in a beaker placed upon a film of water on a wood block. The ΔH of the reaction is positive and the products of the reaction are $Ba(OH)_2 \cdot 8H_2O(s) + 2NH_4NCS(s) \rightarrow Ba(NCS)_2(aq) + 2NH_3(g) + 10 H_2O(l)$. It also discusses the solution of NH_4NO_3 in water for which the ΔH is positive: $NH_4NO_3(s) + H_2O(l) \rightarrow NH_4^+(aq) +$

NO_3^- (aq). It also recommends three 8 mm film loops, from Technicolor Limited, Longman Group Limited, Pinnacles, Harlow, Essex, England: *Energetics I—Heat Energy Changes; Energetics II—Entropy Changes; Energetics III—Spontaneous Changes*. (3) Free energy: Alyea, pp. 221–223. Eberhardt, W. H., "Concerning Equilibrium, Free Energy Changes, Le Chatelier's Principle, I, II, III. For the equilibria:

I. $Cu^{++} + 2I^- = CuI + \frac{1}{2}I_2$
II. $CoCl_4^{--} + 6H_2O \rightleftarrows Co(H_2O)_6^{++} + 4Cl^-$
III. Halite-Halate Equilibria

(A) KI and KIO_3 (C) KBr and $KBrO_3$
(B) KI and $KBrO_3$ (D) KBr and KIO_3
(E) $5Br^- + BrO_3^- + 6H^+ \rightarrow 3Br_2 + 3H_2O$

(4) Enthalpy decrease versus entropy decrease: Mix concentrated solutions of $AgNO_3$ and either HCl or NaCl at room temperature. Inserted thermometer registers temperature increase. Precipitation of AgCl indicates entropy decrease. Difference between $\Delta H = -15.7$ kcal/mole and $\Delta G = -13.2$ kcal/mole is the "organization" energy required for the ordering of the crystalline AgCl. (5) Probability and entropy. **Recommended references** for teachers and for interested students include: Young, J. A., *Chemistry: Reflections of Another Teacher*, Silver Burdett, 1965; Ford, K. W., "Probability and Entropy in Thermodynamics," *The Physics Teacher*, 5, 77 (1967). **Film:** *You Can't Go Back* (Topic—Energy Transformations and Second Law of Thermodynamics), Elementary Penguin Productions, 043-3 South Westmoreland, Los Angeles, CA 90006 (16 mm, color, sound; super-8 silent, color; video cassette). **References:** Vamvakism, S. N., and Schmukler, U. S., "Teaching about 'Why Do Chemical Reactions Occur?'" *Journal of Chemical Education*, 54(12), 757 (1977); Riley, G. F., and Eberhardt, W. H., "Thermodynamics and Solubilities of Salts of Dipositive Ions," *Journal of Chemical Education*, 56(3), 206 (1979); Stevenson, L. K., Brief Introduction to the Laws of Thermodynamics," *Journal of Chemical Education*, 52(5), 330 (1975); Rogers, D. W., "An Informal History of the First Law of Thermodynamics," *Chemistry*, 49(10), 11 (1976); Smith, W. L., "Thermodynamics, Folk Culture, and Poetry," *Journal of Chemical Education*, 52(2), 97 (1975); Spencer, J. N., Gordon, D., and Schreiber, H. D., "Entropy and Chemical Reaction," *Chemistry*, 47(11), 10 (1974). Questions 4, 6, 7, 15–18.

Section 20.8. Activity: Use colored polystyrene spheres held together by magnets to simulate the pathways or possible pathways and the representative equations for the HBr and HI reactions. **Student references:** on flash photolysis, "Flash Photolysis," *Chemistry*, 40 (Sept. 1967); "Bewhiskered Theory Disproved" (the HI reaction), *ibid.*, 40 (Apr. 1967); "The Chemical Effects of Light," *Scientific American*, 219 (Sept. 1968) (flash photolysis and the photolytic reaction for HCl). **Demonstration:** (a) Photochemical Reaction of Hydrogen and Chlorine, Alyea, p. 154. Plastic pharmaceutical vials or "baggies" may be substituted for the balloons mentioned in the reference. Clock reactions: Alyea, pp. 19, 85, 130, 147, 149, 179, 220. Clock reactions are interpreted in terms of the steps involved. **(b)** Chen, P. S., *Journal of Chemical Education*, 47, A784 (1970): A reaction between 100 mL of 1-*M* solution of $FeCl_3$ mixed with 100 mL

of 1-*M* $Na_2S_2O_3$ results in three color changes which are explained in the reference. Clock reactions: Huber, H., "Simulation of the Old Nassau Reaction," *Journal of Chemical Education*, 56(5), 320 (1979)—based on article by Alyea, H. N., *Journal of Chemical Education*, 54(3), 167 (1977); Shigematsu, E., "A Few Chemical Magic Tricks Based on the Clock Reaction," *Journal of Chemical Education*, 56(3), 184 (1979); Moss, A., "The Landolt 'Old Nassau' and Variant Reactions," *Journal of Chemical Education*, 55(4), 244 (1978); Brice, L. K., "Rossini, William Tell and the Iodine Clock Reaction," *Journal of Chemical Education*, 57(2), 152 (1980). **Transparencies:** EYE: 003-18 *Reaction Mechanism:* I: 68743 *Chemical Kinetics* (7 transparencies, 14 overlays). **Filmstrips:** I: 67138 *Chemical Kinetics;* B #116: 5. *Understanding Potential Energy Diagrams*—Part 1, 6. *Understanding Potential Energy Diagrams*—Part 2, 7. *Mechanisms of Reactions: A Step-by-Step Look*. **Slide Sequences:** I: 69131 *Chemical Reactions: Reaction Mechanisms*.

Section 20.9. Activities: Construct a duplicate of Figure 20-7 on the chalkboard. Have students attempt to discover the relationship between rise in temperature, the average kinetic energy, and the proportion or percentage of the molecules that reach activation energy. The latter may be done by drawing a vertical line, possibly at the point at which the label "Higher Temperature" starts. Students easily can see that a larger proportion of the molecules reaches the desired higher energy (activation energy). Use models to simulate collision patterns in Figure 20-8 (A), (B), (C), emphasizing the necessary violence (energy) and orientation in terms of activation energy, bond breaking, bond making, and electron cloud interpenetration. Toon and Ellis, *Foundations of Chemistry*, Figure 12-7 and p. 385, show how the number of possible collisions (collision frequency) depends on the number of molecules present. Use the term "collision effectiveness" with reference to sufficient energy and orientation.

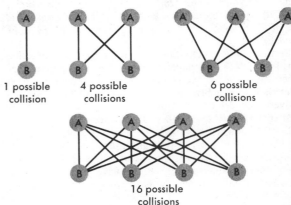

1 possible collision 4 possible collisions 6 possible collisions

16 possible collisions

Section 20.10. Activities: Discuss the problem of the failure of H_2 and O_2 to react at room temperature. Have students use models to simulate bond breaking and bond making (Figure 20-9). Define activation energy. You may wish to demonstrate the explosion of a mixture of H_2 and O_2 or H_2 and air, or ignite a small sample of white phosphorus with a heated glass rod. Reproduce Figures 20-10 and 20-11 on the chalkboard. Then, for Figure 20-12, have students discover the magnitudes of the activation energies for endothermic versus exothermic reactions and the change in internal energy for reversible reactions.

Section 20.11. **Activities:** Use the conversion of kinetic energy into potential energy concept at the beginning of this section. Refer to the chalkboard diagram of Figure 20-7. This shows how the increase in the number of molecules reaching the required activation energy increases the number of collisions as well as the increase in the efficiency of the collisions, with the larger portion of molecules having reached the required energy. Discuss Figure 20-14, details of HI decomposition. **Films:** W: 140-4121 *Introduction to Reaction Kinetics;* W: 140-4166 *Mechanism of an Organic Reaction;* MH: *Energy and Reaction.* **Loop:** W: 168 W 1012, or W: 168 W 1031 *An Organic Mechanism.* **Filmstrips:** HR: C4-96455 *Reaction Kinetics;* see Section 20.10. **References:** Short, B. G., "The Activated Complex," *The Science Teacher,* 43(5), 48 (1976), which relates to an earlier article by Deroo, J., *The Science Teacher,* 44 (Jan. 1944). Also consult the article by Yohe, G. R., "Dominoes and Activation Energy," *Chemistry,* 49(8) 8 (1976).

To complement the concept of the activated complex, you may wish to introduce the concept of a free radical as a type of reaction mechanism. Use the electron-dot equivalent of $HI + HI \rightarrow H_2 + 2I$ to show that a free radical has an unshared electron. The 2I atoms are free radicals and have more energy than the combined atoms in I_2. You may wish to use the following equation sets for the photoinitiated HCl synthesis series. In this series, the atoms marked with the (*) are examples of free radicals. The chain reaction is:

$$Cl_2 + h\nu \rightarrow Cl^* + Cl^*$$
$$H_2 + Cl^* \rightarrow HCl + H^*$$
$$Cl_2 + H^* \rightarrow HCl + Cl^*$$

For a demonstration of this $H_2 + Cl_2$ reaction, see Alyea, p. 154. **References:** Toon and Ellis, *Foundations of Chemistry,* pp. 392, 393; *Scientific American* Offprint 263: "Frozen Free Radical." The change of brown NO_2 to the colorless dimer N_2O_4 may be demonstrated by cooling the NO_2. It has an unshared electron on the N atom, $:\ddot{O}:\ddot{N}::\ddot{O}:$. In effect, the molecule is a free radical and the combination of two molecules of NO_2 to form the dimer results in the formation of an electron pair consisting of the two unshared electrons in the two NO_2 molecules.

Section 20.12. **Demonstrations:** Pose the problem by starting with a series of reactions in which (1) reactions take place very quickly, (2) reactions are perceptible but of slow velocity, (3) reactions are very slow, and (4) reactions do not occur. Refer to demonstrations and films for Sections 20.1. A very slow reaction is the precipitation of calcium oxalate using solutions of magnesium nitrate and sodium oxalate. The reactants show no change on mixing but by the next day precipitation is evident. A series using Alka-Seltzer tablets stimulates student attention and suggests some of the factors affecting reaction rates. Fill small Erlenmeyer flasks with 50 mL of tap water, 50 mL of colder water, and 50 mL of hot water. The one-hole stoppers for the flasks should each have a small glass tube with a balloon attached. Three students simultaneously drop one tablet into each of the flasks and insert the stoppers. The rate of inflation is observed by the class. In another flask use a powdered tablet in 50 mL of tap water, and compare the rate of inflation with that caused by the solid tablet (amount of surface for a heterogeneous reaction). Students will also observe that the balloons become equally full, after sufficient time lapse, whatever the variables. A demonstration that suggests the reaction rate may be determined by measuring the volume of reactant consumed per unit of time is the rusting of iron. Moistened steel wool is placed in the bottom of a test tube with a long glass tube inserted into the stopper. The end of the tube is inserted in a beaker of colored water. At intervals, students measure the distance the colored water has risen in the tube.

For factors that influence reaction rate:

(1) *Nature of reactants:* Expose the freshly cut surface of Na. Use a metal + acid series (Zn, Mg, Cu + HCl and Cu + HNO_3). Drop Na or Ca and Mg into H_2O; expose red and yellow phosphorus to air. Discuss bond breaking and bond making. Mix solids $Pb(NO_3)_2$ and $K_2Cr_2O_7$ in mortar, then mix the solutions.

(2) *Amount of surface.* Hold an iron file in the burner flame. Sprinkle iron filings through the flame; repeat with aluminum foil and powder. Attempt to ignite a pile of lycopodium powder, then drop into flame from a vertical distance of three feet. Cut a wood or plastic cube into nine smaller cubes and have students measure respective surface areas. Dissolve equal masses of chunk and powdered $CuSO_4 \cdot 5H_2O$ in water by stirring and discuss heterogeneous and homogeneous systems and reactions.

(3) *Concentration:* Perform demonstration for Figure 20-14. Discuss effect of pressure on concentrations of gases, pure solids, and pure liquids. For concentration effects in homogeneous reaction systems, demonstrate a clock reaction (Alyea, p. 19) for iodine clock, which is used as Experiment 12 in *Laboratory Experiments for Foundations of Chemistry.* This reaction demonstrates that the reaction between HSO_3^- and IO_3^- is the slow, rate-determining step. Demonstrate that the reaction $IO_3^-(aq) + 5I^-(aq) + 6H^+(aq) \rightarrow 3I_2(s) + 3H_2O$ is practically instantaneous. This rate of reaction is shown by the color change to I_2 or that of the starch previously added to the solution. For iodide-iodate reaction, see Alyea, p. 233. Emphasize the necessity for measured experimental determination of the effect of concentration, and the lack of information furnished by the balanced equation.

(4) *Temperature:* Use a chalkboard replica of Figure 20-7 to show the effect on average kinetic energy and the effect of activation energy on a portion of molecules. Explain the general rate increase for a 10-degree rise above room temperature in terms of the increase of collision frequency and particularly of collision energy that increases the formation of the activated complex.

(5) *Catalysts:* Rub cigarette ash into the edge of a sugar cube. This is readily ignited with a match flame. One explanation is that the metallic oxides in the ash are catalytic. **Films:** EBE: 5-81565 *Catalytic Decomposition of Hydrogen Peroxide;* EBE: 5-81566 *Catalytic Decomposition of Potassium Chlorate.* For autocatalysis demonstration: Mix solutions of potassium permanganate ($KMnO_4$), H_2SO_4, and oxalic acid. There is no evident change until a crystal of $MnSO_4$ or other Mn^{++} salt is added, then it becomes colorless Mn^{++}. Develop

Figure 20-16 on the chalkboard or review previous use. **Films:** W: 140-4127 *Catalysis* (and related teacher training film); FAC *Chemical Change and Temperature;* FAC Speed of Chemical Change; EBE: 253 *Velocity of Chemical Reactions;* W: 140-4021 *Introduction to Reaction Kinetics* (teacher training film) which uses the oxygen-dextrose-methylene blue reaction. **Loop:** BFA: E 84-0231/1 *Reaction Rates.* **Filmstrips:** B #116: 1. *Reaction Rates: Meaning and Methods,* 2. *What Changes the Rate? Part 1,* 3. *What Changes the Rate? Part 2,* 4. *What Changes the Rate? Part 3,* 8. *Speeding Up with Catalysts,* 9. *Catalysts in Your Life;* I 67122, *Catalysts at Work.* **Slide Sequences:** I 69132, *Chemical Reactions: Reaction Rates.* **Loops:** BFA: 470004 *Temperature and Activation Energy;* BFA: 470002 *Particle Size and Speed of Chemical Change;* MH: *Evidences of Chemical Reactions.* **Films:** BFA: 10253 *Speed of Chemical Change* (14⁺ min.); BFA: 10268 *Chemical Change and Temperature* (14⁺ min.). UA: *Rate of Reaction* (28 min.). **Transparency:** EYE: 003-19 *Factors Affecting the Rate of Reaction.* **References:** Mickey, C. D., "Chemical Kinetics: Reaction Rates," *Journal of Chemical Education,* 57(9), 659 (1980); Kolb, D., "Catalysis," *Journal of Chemical Education,* 56(11), 743 (1979); Felice, M. S., and Freilich, M. B., "Chemical Kinetics: The Effect of Area on Reaction Rate," *Journal of Chemical Education,* 55(1), 34 (1978); Ruda, P. T., A Versatile Kinetic Demonstration," *Journal of Chemical Education,* 55(10), 652 (1978) (catalysis, activated complex, temperature); White, J. M., and Campbell, C. T., "Surface Chemistry in Heterogeneous Catalysis: An Emerging Discipline," *Journal of Chemical Education,* 57(7), 671 (1980); McNaught, I. J., "Thermodynamic versus Kinetic Control: A Lecture Demonstration," *Journal of Chemical Education,* 55(11), 722 (1978).

Section 20.13. Teacher Reference: Perkins, R. S., Rate Laws for Elementary Chemical Reactions," *Journal of Chemical Education,* 51(4), 254 (1974). Develop for the H_2 + NO reaction as in text. For more detail, refer to Toon and Ellis, *Foundations of Chemistry,* pp. 392–395. Table 12-1 from this source may be used to show experimentally that the rate of reaction is proportional to **(a)** the square of the concentration of NO and **(b)** the concentration of H_2. Discuss the value of k as the temperature increases. Develop the rate laws for the reaction A + B → 2C and relate to the H_2 + NO reaction as in text to illustrate that the rate law is dependent on the slowest rate-determining step and hence cannot be written from the balanced equation for the net reaction. This leads to the general rate law and to the statement of the law of mass action. **References:** Nechamkin, H., Keller, E., and Goodkin, J., "Reaction Rates for a Homogeneously Catalyzed Reaction," *Journal of Chemical Education,* 54(12), 775 (1977); Gilbert, H. F., "The 'Rule of Thumb' for Deriving Steady State Rate Equations," *Journal of Chemical Education,* 54(8), 492 (1977); Smoot, P., Ragan, S., and Burkett, A. R., "A Demonstration of the Relationship between Rate Constants and Equilibrium Constants," *Journal of Chemical Education,* 55(12) 790 (1978). **Programmed Instruction:** Barrow, G. M., et al., *Understanding Chemistry V: Chemical Systems,* Benjamin, 1976, pp. 1–38: Thermochemistry; pp. 39–82: Rates of chemical reactions; Kass, G. A., *Individual Study Program*

in Chemistry, Vol. IV: *Kinetics and Equilibrium,* Benjamin, 1969, pp. 1–54: Kinetics; Vol. III: *The Forces That Drive Chemical Reactions,* pp. 1–25; Enthalpy change; pp. 26–39: Heat of reaction—heat of formation; pp. 40–50: Additivity of enthalpy changes—Hess's law; pp. 51–68: Bond energy and heat of chemical reaction; pp. 75–92: Entropy. Questions 20–25, Problems 7 and 10.

Teacher Notes
Chapter 21

Chapter Note

Review Sections 12.3–12.5 (Physical Equilibrium: Dynamic Equilibrium, Equilibrium Vapor Pressure, Le Chatelier's Principle) and Section 13.5 (Solution Equilibrium). Use the **Film** W: 140-4124 *Equilibrium* (24 min.). Review the role of free energy change and the spontaneity of a reaction for the water gas reaction (Section 20.7). You may wish to use the data in that section for ΔS and ΔH and have the students calculate the temperature at which such a closed system would reach equilibrium (about 980°K).

This chapter requires five periods. One possible arrangement is:

Lesson 1 Sections 21.1–21.3: Reversible Reactions, Equilibrium, Equilibrium Constant
Lesson 2 Sections 21.4 and 21.5: Factors That Disturb Equilibrium, Reactions That Run to Completion
Lesson 3 Sections 21.6–21.8: Common Ion Effect, Ionization Constants of (a) Weak Acid, (b) Water
Lesson 4 Sections 21.9–21.11: Hydrolysis, Basic Anion Hydrolysis, Acid Cation Hydrolysis
Lesson 5 Sections 21.12–21.14: Solubility Product, Calculating Solubilities, Precipitation Calculations

Section 21.1. Use the **Film** EBE: S 81567 *Decomposition of Mercuric Oxide* and have students write the formula equation. Discuss Lavoisier's bell-jar experiment and have students write the equation for this experiment and for equilibrium. Define chemical equilibrium and discuss the balance of the driving force of energy change and the driving force of entropy change. **Demonstrations:** Demonstrate one or both of the reactions of Figure 21-1. To demonstrate hydrogen production, place a piece of ceramic paper saturated with H_2O into the bottom of a test tube. A wad of steel wool, positioned in the middle of the horizontal test tube, is preheated. The delivery tube from the reaction test tube is connected to a test tube arranged for water displacement. Heat the bottom of the test tube to vaporize the water and simultaneously heat the steel wool. Identify the collected H_2 by the "bark test." To demonstrate reduction use Fe_2O_3 instead of Fe_3O_4 since the former undergoes a perceptible color change and the iron produced is magnetic while the iron oxide (Fe_2O_3) is not. **Reversibility Demonstration:** By heating, convert hydrated copper(II) sulfate, $CuSO_4 \cdot 5H_2O$, crystal to white anhydrous powder, $CuSO_4$. Add the powder to water. Add a few drops of water to the powder.

Section 21.2. Demonstration: Repeat equilibrium vapor pressure demonstrations from Chapter 12 to review physical equilibrium and its dynamic nature. **Discussion** of equilibrium vapor pressure (and saturated solutions) reveals that for a given closed system, the particular equilibrium state depends upon temperature and, for systems involving gases, also depends on the pressure. See Section 12.4, Figure 12-4. Use **Film** EBE: 2953 *Vapor Pressure*. **Demonstrations:** Demonstrate saturated solutions of NaCl and sugar. To indicate that an equilibrium state may be recognized by observation of a macroscopic property, drop a crystal of NaCl (rock salt) into a filtered portion of the saturated solution that was prepared before the class. Write ionic equations representative of ionic equilibria for NaCl(s) and $HC_2H_3O_2$. Repeat conductivity test of glacial acetic acid. Test after several successive dilutions. This shows that concentration is a factor in equilibrium states. To show reversibility of this reaction, add H_2SO_4 to solid $NaC_2H_3O_2$. Have students detect the odor of acetic acid or test for its release by moistened blue litmus paper in the upper part of the test tube. **Transparencies:** EYE: 033-20 *Physical Equilibrium*, 033-21 *Chemical Equilibrium*. Discuss the ionization of diluted acetic acid as an example of a reaction reaching equilibrium far to the left since acetic acid is a weak acid (test with pH paper if necessary). Discuss the dissociation of NaCl or the ionization of HCl as reactions that go far to the right. Discuss the chemist's problem of producing desirable products in terms of the ammonia synthesis. Have students restate the five factors that determine the rate of chemical reaction. **Films:** ROB: *Equilibrium—The Limit of Disorder;* INDU: *Ionization and Ionic Equilibrium.* **Loops:** E: 84-0215/1 *Equilibrium Solutions and Precipitates.* These may be used now or later on as desired.

Section 21.3. Develop Figure 21-2 on the board, starting with zero concentrations of **C** and **D**. Discuss the changes in rates as concentrations change. Define the equilibrium constant. Write the representative equation and the equilibrium constant. Write the representative equation and the equilibrium constant expression for $A + B \rightleftarrows C + D$ and for its more general form. Use the terms chemical equilibrium law and mass action expression. Have students apply these terms to the equation $3A + B \rightleftarrows 2C + 3D$ or variations of this equation. Derive the expression for the HI reaction. Discuss constancy of color of this system as a macroscopic method of detecting equilibri-

um. **Problem:** Solve the Sample Problem for Section 21.3. Divide the class into four sections and have each section calculate the K from separate experimental data listed in Table 21-1. Follow through the sequences of equations and related expressions for the rate laws that lead to K. This should lead to the conclusion that the expression for K is the same whether calculated from the balanced chemical equation or from the rate law treatment. **Demonstrations:** Martin, D. F., "A Mechanical Demonstration and Approach to Equilibrium," *Journal of Chemical Education* 53, 634 (1976); Smoot, F., Ragan, S., and Burkett, A. R., "A Demonstration of the Relationship between Rate Constants and Equilibrium Constants," *Journal of Chemical Education* 55(12), 790 (1978). Both of these references simulate and accumulate data by using exchanges of water into larger receptacles. Students or demonstrators use beakers of different capacities to pour water into the two opposed receptacles until equilibrium is reached. Volumes are measured after each cycle and a graph similar to Figure 21-4 may be drawn from the data accumulated. A simpler and effective demonstration that could be adapted as a laboratory experiment is described in the article by Cunningham, P., "Time Dependence of Reactions," *The Science Teacher,* 52(10), 35 (1979). A simple analogy makes the connection between reaction rates and equilibrium concentration. The teacher engages in a "game" with a student. Beginning with $1 (100 pennies) in the teacher's hand, and no money in the student's hand, transactions are made according to an established rate. For example, at each transaction the teacher may give the student half the money in his hand, and the student may give the teacher one-fourth the money in his hand. The rate of exchange will continuously change until the "forward" rate (teacher to student) equals the "reverse" rate (student to teacher). This is the "equilibrium condition," though the amounts in each person's hand will be different. Sample results are shown in the table. The table may be converted into two graphs showing the time dependence of both rate and concentration. **Filmstrip:** PH: WCC 881 *Chemical Equilibrium Molecular and Ionic, Problems Involving K_{eq} and K_i.*

Transaction Number	Teacher Concentration $T_{IN} - \frac{1}{2}T_{IN} + \frac{1}{4}S_{IN}$ (Reactants)	Forward Rate $T \rightarrow S$ $\frac{1}{2}T_{IN}$	Reverse Rate $S \rightarrow T$ $\frac{1}{4}S_{IN}$	Student Concentration $S_{IN} - \frac{1}{4}S_{IN} + \frac{1}{2}T_{IN}$ (Products)
1	$100 - 50 = 50$	50	0	$0 + 50 = 50$
2	$50 - 25 + 13 = 38$	25	13	$50 - 13 + 25 = 62$
3	$38 - 19 + 16 = 35$	19	16	$62 - 16 + 19 = 65$
4	$35 - 18 + 16 = 33$	18	16	$65 - 16 + 18 = 67$
5	$33 - 17 + 17 = 33$	17	17	$67 - 17 + 17 = 67$
6	$33 - 17 + 17 = 33$	17	17	$67 - 17 + 17 = 67$

Section 21.4. Raise the problem of how chemists may displace an equilibrium in order to increase desired production. Review and restate Le Chatelier's principle (Section 12.5) and the demonstrations relating to physical changes such as regelation (demonstrated by squeezing two ice cubes together) and use the film *Le Chatelier's Principle*. Also use *Vapor Pressure*. These films reveal that pressure and temperature changes affect

equilibrium. **Reference:** A recommended reference is Morris, D. L., "Stress, Collisions and Constants," *Chemistry*, 44(4), (1971), which is Part I in the Reprint 100. This article complements the text by treating various factors from the viewpoint of Le Chatelier's principle, collision theory, and the equilibrium constant. Burke, B. A., "Tested Demonstrations—Chemical Equilibrium," *Journal of Chemical Education,* 54(1), 29

(1977). This demonstration is designed for use on an overhead projector and is based on the equilibrium:

$$CuSO_4(aq) + 4KBr(aq) \rightleftarrows K_2(CuBr_4)(aq) + K_2SO_4(aq)$$
$$\text{blue} \qquad \text{colorless} \qquad \text{green} \qquad \text{colorless}$$

(a) Change in concentration: Some of these demonstrations obviously also fit Section 21.6, Common Ion Effect, and Section 21.12, Solubility Product. Some of the demonstrations suggested for those sections may be substituted here. Consult "Effect of pH on Chemical Equilibrium of K_2CrO_4—$K_2Cr_2O_7$—H_2O Systems," *Chemistry,* 37, July (1964). **Demonstrate:** Addition of concentrated HCl to a saturated solution of $CoCl_2$. Also refer to *Journal of Chemical Education,* 47, A438 (1970), demonstrations 787, 788, 790. **Activity:** Summarize results of selected demonstrations by using the text development [Section 21.4(1)] with the generalized equation and the effect of concentration changes on *K*. **Reference:** Campbell, J. A., *Journal of Chemical Education,* 47, 276 (1970) "Sealed Tube Experiments," Exp. 35, describes the rapid compression of NO_2 in a piston. Use a plastic syringe. This demonstration should probably be used after the temperature effects for the $2NO_2 \rightleftarrows N_2O_4$ are demonstrated. The initial results of the compression should be posed as a problem before the expected fading of color finally occurs. (1) Homogeneous systems: Discuss the Haber process with aid of Figure 21-3. Consider the effects of continuous removal of NH_3 by condensation. Discuss the effect of pressure on the CO(g) + $H_2O(g) \rightleftarrows CO_2(g) + H_2(g)$ system. (2) Heterogeneous systems: Develop the *K* for the decomposition of $CaCO_3$ and discuss the treatment of pure solids (and liquids) in the expression for *K* and the effect of pressure changes on *K*.

(b) Temperature changes: Discuss the effects of temperature increase on the rates of both reactions, the favoring of the endothermic reaction according to Le Chatelier's principle, and the effect on the equilibrium constant. Apply to the commercial production of ammonia. Use data in Table 13-1, Toon and Ellis, *Foundations of Chemistry.* Show the effects of temperature changes on the $2NO_2(g) \rightleftarrows N_2O_4(g)$ $\Delta H = 14.1$ kcal/ system (Welch #4226 Temperature Equilibrium Tubes.) Sealed test tubes may be homemade. See "Making Tubes for NO_2–N_2O_4 Equilibrium Reaction," *Chemistry,* 45, Jan. (1972). These demonstrations may be performed so that students decide on the thermal aspects of the reaction before using the thermochemical equation. The production of N_2O_4 is practically complete in Dry Ice-acetone.

Use the data for the Haber process in Table 21-2 to show that the value of equilibrium constants changes with temperature. Also refer to the data on HI for temperature variations of *K*. Use other data as basis for discussion of the composition of equilibrium mixtures when *K* is (a) large and (b) very small. You may demonstrate the Ag^+ + Cu replacement to illustrate a reaction with a large *K* and a precipitation reaction (Table 21-4, Solubility-Product Constants), i.e., precipitate AgCl to demonstrate slight solubility of AgCl in a saturated solution. Complement by using TOPS Dem 787: Equilibrium AgOAc, *Journal of Chemical Education,* 47, A437 (1970).

(c) Catalysts: To show that the catalyst accelerates both forward and reverse reactions (and does not affect the value of *K*) demonstrate the decomposition of dry NH_3 by passing over heated steel wool, collecting the H_2 and N_2 mixture by water displacement, and obtaining a positive test for H_2. Consult the references to Alyea in the listed references for other demonstrations, particularly "Introduction to Le Chatelier's Principle," p. 194. This demonstration shows that the solution of dry HCl in H_2O is exothermic and hence heating concentrated hydrochloric acid reverses the solubility. **Loop:** BFA: E 84-0223/1 *Equilibrium: Le Chatelier's Principle.* **Filmstrips:** I: 67133 *Equilibrium Constant;* I: 67140 *Le Chatelier's Principle.* **Transparencies:** I: 68745 *Le Chatelier's Principle* (4 transparencies, 8 overlays); HR: 2-10544 *Factors Affecting Chemical Equilibrium.* **Questions:** 5–7, 13–16, 20, 22. **Loop:** MH: *Shifting Chemical Equilibrium.*

Section 21.5. Demonstrations: The simplest approach is to demonstrate, in sequence, the three possible situations that permit students to predict whether or not a given reaction will run to completion. Many teachers prefer to start with neutralization reactions, then proceed to volatility, and finally to precipitation. This emphasizes the analytic procedure in which the student first examines the reactants to see whether they are acid or base. Volatility is then looked for in terms of a gaseous product. Finally a precipitate is sought through the use of solubility rules and/or tables. Writing the formula equation first is frequently desirable. The formula equation is then converted into ionic form and then into net ionic form where this is desirable. Use selected demonstrations beyond those in text to emphasize equation balancing, i.e., $Ca(OH)_2$ and HNO_3. After the three principles have been developed, propose situations such as mixing solutions of $CuSO_4$ and NaCl or NaCl and KNO_3. The reaction between $Ba(OH)_2$ and H_2SO_4 is another one that should be explored. This may be done by first measuring the conductivity during neutralization of NaOH by HCl and then performing the $Ba(OH)_2$ and H_2SO_4 neutralization using indicator and conductivity apparatus (titrate, using burets). **Film:** EBE: 2944 *Ion Removal by Metathesis,* uses the barium hydroxide neutralization. This demonstration is also described in Alyea, p. 163: "Removal of Ions by Metathesis." Other related demonstrations include: (1) In the bottom of a small beaker place 50 mL of a 0.1-*N* solution of sodium sulfate. Arrange two platinum electrodes to reach into this solution. Let a thin layer of paraffin harden over the sulfate solution. Take a galvanometer reading. Pour 50 mL of 0.1-*N* barium chloride on top of the paraffin and take another reading. Break the paraffin and mix the solutions. Take another reading. (2) As a variation, use solutions of $MgSO_4$ and $Ba(OH)_2$. Use **Questions:** 8, 9, 17. **Loops:** MG: S/100 11B and S 100/12B *Chemical Reactions I & II.* **Filmstrip:** I: 67141 and transparency set 68746 *Reversible Reactions and Reactions to Completion.*

Section 21.6. Demonstrations: If not previously demonstrated, use the demonstrations described in this section. Use methyl red (violet to red) or methyl orange (pink-red to yellow) for the acetic acid-sodium acetate demonstration. Common ion demonstrations in Alyea are p. 19: NH_4Cl to NH_3(aq), phenolphthalein; pp. 86–87 (18.8), 198, 200: foam produced by reaction between acetic acid and $CaCO_3$ versus that using acetic acid, sodium acetate, and $CaCO_3$; p. 210: balloon filling with Mg and acetic acid versus Mg + acetic acid + sodium acetate. **Loop:** EBE: S-81560 *Solubility: Common Ion Effect.* **Filmstrip:** PH: WCC 882 *Common Ion Effect Principle, Ion Product Constant of Water and Introduction to pH.* **Film:** UA: *Ionic Equilibrium—Common Ion Effect* (16 min.).

Section 21.7. **Activities:** Have students recall or use a redemonstration of the conductivity of acetic acid (glacial) and the effect of water addition. Use the textbook development for the derivation of K and K_a for acetic acid. Have students use the data in Table 21-3 to compute the K_a for acetic acid. Solve the related problem using the pH data. Derive the generalized form for K_a of a weak acid. Discuss the effect of the addition of a common ion on the hydronium ion concentration and the effect of temperature increase on K_a according to Le Chatelier's principle.

Demonstrate buffering action by adding a small quantity of NaOH solution to a solution of acetic acid and sodium acetate using methyl red or methyl orange indicator. Also demonstrate the effect of addition of an acid to the buffered solution. Explain according to text. Refer to Morris, D. L., "Stress Collisions and Constants, Part II: Buffers," *Chemistry,* 44, May (1971). Reprint 100. This article describes a titration experiment-demonstration, using a pH meter or thymol blue indicator, for 0.1 M acetic acid by (a) 0.1 M NaOH and (b) 0.1 M sodium acetate. Calculations for the titrations and K_a of acetic acid are made. It also includes an extensive discussion of the carbon dioxide–bicarbonate ion buffering action in the blood, which may be the subject of a student report. A pertinent demonstration is to test the pH of aspirin and Bufferin with pH paper. For additional demonstrations, see Alyea, pp. 62, 155. To test student understanding of the value (magnitude) of K_a, its relationship to acid strength and pH, refer to Table 15-2 in Toon and Ellis, *Foundations of Chemistry,* and to text Table 15-5, Relative Strengths of Acids and Bases, and Table 16-3, Approximate pH of Some Common Substances. **Filmstrip:** PH: WCC 883 *pH, pOH and Buffers.* **References:** Lott, J. A., "Hydrogen Ions in the Blood," *Chemistry,* 51(4), 6 (1978); Wiger, G. R., and de la Camp, U., "Conjugate Acid-Base Mixtures in General Chemistry Laboratory: A Comprehensive Buffer Experiment," *Journal of Chemical Education,* 55(6), 401 (1978).

Section 21.8. Repeat demonstrations (Chapter 16) testing for water conductivity with 25-watt lamp and then with a neon or argon bulb. Derive the expression for K and K_w for water. Define ion-product constant for water. Review previous treatment in Section 16.6 and of pH in Section 16.7 and Section 16.8. Recall the changes of K_w with temperature change, e.g., values at $0°C$ and $60°C$. Exp. 40 in Campbell, J. A., *Journal of Chemical Education,* 47, 274 (1970), describes the change in color of bromthymol blue in very pure water upon heating, as related to the value of K_w. **Filmstrip:** PH: WCC 882 *Common Ion Effect Principle, Ion Product Constant of Water, and Introduction to pH.* **Questions:** 19, 23; **Problems:** 1–7.

Section 21.9. Define hydrolysis and discuss the two general types of hydrolysis reactions. Demonstrate reactions of solutions of $NaC_2H_3O_2$ and NH_4Cl with litmus and other indicators. List the ions that do not hydrolyze in aqueous solution (marginal note). **Filmstrip:** PH: WCC 884 *Hydrolysis of Salts* may be used now or after Section 21.11.

Section 21.10. **Exhibit** pharmaceutical box of $NaHCO_3$ and commerical box of $Na_2CO_3 \cdot 10H_2O$. Ask students why baking soda may be safely ingested as an antacid while the Na_2CO_3 cannot. In front of class, test separate solutions of $NaHCO_3$ and Na_2CO_3 made from solids by inserting and quickly withdrawing red litmus paper (the $NaHCO_3$ gives a much lighter blue than the Na_2CO_3). Follow up with Hydrion pH paper tests. Ask why washing soda is widely used as a cleaning agent and refer to pH table of common substances (Chapter 16). Write ionic equations for acetate, carbonate, and hydrogen carbonate ions with water. Then write the net pattern reaction for the basic anion B^- with water. Develop the expression for K_h as in the text. Identify the B^- ion as a Brønsted base. Discuss how equilibrium is reached, how the pH is greater than 7. Have students generalize about the hydrolysis of salts formed from weak acids and strong hydroxide.

Section 21.11. Write the ionic equations for ammonium and the hydrated cations of aluminum and copper(II) salts reacting with water. Test solutions with indicators. Write equation for secondary hydrolysis of $Cu(H_2O)_2OH^-$. Identify the ions as Brønsted acids. Develop the generalization about the hydrolysis of salts formed from strong acids and weak hydroxides based on the results of the demonstrations and student experiment. Relate the hydrolysis of salts to reasoning why the end point of a neutralization may occur at a pH other than 7 (Section 16.4). **Demonstrate:** Hydrolysis of Al_2S_3. Write the equation and discuss extent of hydrolysis. Demonstrate pH of ammonium acetate and ammonium carbonate, and discuss the results in terms of salts of a weak acid and a weak base. **Additional Demonstrations:** (a) Hydrolysis of $AsCl_3$ and $BiCl_3$: the solid chlorides dissolve in HCl and, when water is added, form precipitates such as BiOCl, which redissolve in acid. (b) Make solution of $NaHSO_4$ or $KHSO_4$ and test with litmus. Contrast the demonstrated result with that of basic anion hydrolysis of HCO_3^-. Refer to Table 15-5: Relative Strengths of Acids and Bases. (See Alyea, pp. 40, 44, 85, 120.) (c) Campbell, J. A., *Journal of Chemical Education,* 47, 276 (1970). **Filmstrip:** PH: WCC 886 *Titration Curves and Indicators;* Reference: Hentz, F. C., Jr., "Synthesis, Properties, and Hydrolysis of Antimony Trichloride, *Journal of Chemical Education,* 52, 189 (1975).

Section 21.12. **Discussion:** Open the discussion with a question pertaining to saturated solutions and their qualitative descriptions. Refer students to Appendix Table 13, Solubility Chart, for examples of substances whose saturated solution would be (1) concentrated or (2) dilute. **Demonstration:** Add solid $CaSO_4$ to water. Test the filtrate with the flame test for calcium and the test for sulfate ion. Review terms associated with solubility: soluble, slightly soluble, partly soluble, sparingly soluble, and insoluble. Select example of soluble, insoluble, and slightly soluble from Appendix Table 12. Precipitate $CaSO_4$ by mixing solutions of $CaCl_2$ and Na_2SO_4. Use the text examples (AgCl and CaF_2) for deriving the K and K_{sp} for the systems and define solubility product constant. Go through the calculations of K_{sp} for each of these salts. Have students refer to Appendix Table 13, for AgCl used in the calculation of its K_{sp}. Solve the Practice Exercises. **Demonstration:** The article by Morris, D. L., in *Chemistry,* 44, Apr. (1971), "Stress, Collisions, and Constants, Part I, Solutions," suggests a method for using NaCl in dealing with K_{sp} and the related calculations. **Film:** EBE: S-81559 *Solubility: Effect of Concentration.* **Loop:** BFA: E 84-0215/1 *Equilibrium: Solutions and Precipitates.* **Filmstrips:** I: 67133 *Equilibrium Constant;* PH: WCC 885 *Polyprotic Acids and Solubility Product Principle.* **Films:** EBE: 2945 *Demonstration for Solubility Product Calculations* (8 min.). **Loop:** EBE: S-81560 *Solubility: Common Ion Effect.*

Sections 21.13 and 21.14. Activities: Use the text example and emphasize the resultant ion concentrations. As an application have students solve the reversed CaF_2 problem in Section 21.12. In Section 21.14, Precipitation Calculations, reemphasize the concept that K_{sp} is an equilibrium constant and that therefore varying ion concentrations may result in exceeding the K_{sp}. Solve Problem in Section 21.13. Use the portion of the I: 67140 filmstrip, *Le Chatelier's Principle*, that deals with the equilibrium states of $BaSO_4$. Also use the portion of the related transparency set I: 68745, which covers the $BaSO_4 K_{sp}$.

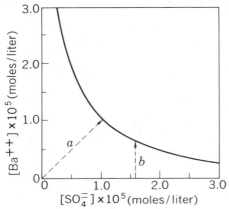

Bruce H. Mahan, UNIVERSITY CHEMISTRY, SECOND EDITION, 1969, Addison-Wesley, Reading, Mass.

The diagram represents the equilibrium states of the $BaSO_4$–H_2O system. The equilibrium states of the system lie on a rectangular hyperbola. The broken line *a* represents the equal increase in concentration of both Ba^{++} and SO_4^{--} as $BaSO_4$ dissolves. The broken line *b* represents the increase in concentration of Ba^{++}, if small amounts of $BaCl_2$ are added to a solution of H_2SO_4. At the point where *b* intersects the hyperbola, the first $BaSO_4$ precipitates. As more Ba^{++} is added, more $BaSO_4$ precipitates and the $[SO_4^{--}]$ decreases. As this process continues, the point representing the system follows the curved line toward decreasing $[SO_4^{--}]$. Thus, any point on the curved line represents one of the many possible equilibrium states of the system. Solve the Practice Exercises. Use Questions 9 and 10, and Problems 8, 9, 10. For additional problems, see Toon and Ellis, *Foundations of Chemistry*, Chapters 13 and 16. Use the references for programmed instruction at the end of the TE chapter for students who can profit from such activity. **Individualized and Programmed Instruction:** The filmstrips identified as PH: WCC in the prior sections are parts of modules that can be used for individualized instruction. Each module consists of the filmstrip, a duplicate set of 35-mm slides, an audiocassette, and a student workbook or study guide. In addition to those listed: 881, 882, 883, 884, 885, 888, *Solubility and Partition* is also useful. In addition, the microfiche Chem Review PH: WCF 1008 *Chemical Equilibrium, Le Chatelier's Principle* may be used. Ward's Solo-Learn: 78-0710 *Introduction to Equilibrium Concepts*. Barrow, G. M., et al., *Understanding Chemistry IV Chemical Equilibria*. Benjamin, 1967,

pp. 1–56: Equilibrium Calculations: Homogeneous Gas Reactions; pp. 57–88: Solubility Product; pp. 89–120: The Ionization of Acids and Bases. Kass, G. A., *Individual Study Program in Chemistry, Volume IV: Kinetics and Equilibrium*, Benjamin, 1969, pp. 55–116: Chemical Equilibrium; pp. 117–156: Quantitative Aspects of Equilibrium; *Volume V: Acid-Base Chemistry*, Benjamin, 1969, pp. 129–158: Quantitative Aspects; *Volume III: The Forces That Drive Chemical Reactions*, Benjamin, 1968, pp. 93–110: Free Energy and Equilibrium. **References:** Mickey, C. S., ''Chemical Equilibrium,'' *Journal of Chemical Education*, 57(11), 801 (1980); Bodner, G. M., ''On the Misuse of Le Chatelier's Principle for the Prediction of the Temperature Dependence of the Solubility of Salts,'' *Journal of Chemical Education*, 57(2), 117 (1980); Ackerman, M. N., ''Determination of the Equilibrium Constant for Triiodide Formation: Use of a Less Toxic Solvent,'' *Journal of Chemical Education*, 55(12), 797 (1978). (Use of n-hexane or mixture of isomers for CCl_4) Friedman, F., ''Le Chatelier's Principle: A Laboratory Exercise,'' *Journal of Chemical Education*, 54(4), 236 (1977); Driscoll, D. R., ''Invitation to Inquiry: The Fe^{3+} CNS^- Equilibrium, *Journal of Chemical Education*, 56(9), 603 (1979). *Chemistry*, 50, 549 (1973). *Chemistry* Reprints: 62: ''Mercury(II) Nitrate-Potassium Iodide-Water System,'' 100. ''Stress, Collisions, and Constants.'' ''Making Tubes for NO_2—N_2O_4 Equilibrium Reaction,'' 45(1), (1972) and ''Chemistry and Metallurgy,'' 45(10), (1972). (H_2 gas at high temperature and pressure can precipitate metals from solution.) Shakhashiri, B. Z., Direen, G. E., and Juergens, F., ''Solubility and Complex Ion Equilibria of Silver (1) Species in Aqueous Solution,'' *Journal of Chemical Education*, 57(11), 813 (1980).

Teacher Notes
Chapter 22

Chapter Note

Students should perform as many of the experiments related to oxidation-reduction as possible. The rules for determining oxidation numbers are reviewed and used extensively in balancing redox equations. The demonstrations suggested and the numerous audiovisual aids available provide for a choice of those activities that are best suited to the abilities of your students and the requirements of your course. A film that can be used as an introduction or a summary is IFB: 393 *The Development of Electrochemistry*.

This chapter requires five periods. One possible arrangement is:

Lesson 1 Sections 22.1 and 22.2: Oxidation-reduction Processes. Oxidation and Reduction Occur Simultaneously.

Lesson 2 Section 22.3: Balancing Oxidation-reduction Equations: Oxidation-number Change, Ion-electron Method

Lesson 3 Sections 22.4 and 22.5: Oxidizing and Reducing Agents and Their Chemical Equivalents

Lesson 4 Sections 22.6–22.9: Electrochemical Reaction, Electrolysis of Water, Electrolysis of Salt Solutions, Electroplating

Lesson 5 Sections 22.7–22.11: Lead Storage Battery, Electrode Potentials

Section 22.1. **Demonstrations:** If necessary, repeat previous demonstrations relating to oxidation and reduction primarily in Chapter 6. Sequentially these are (a) *Oxidation-reduction involving oxygen:* oxidize a strip of copper and reduce copper(II) oxide (strip or pellets) with H_2 and with carbon; (b) *Oxidation-reduction involving electron shift:* burn Na in Cl_2 (Alyea, pp. 146, 201, 212). Burn Mg in air and in Cl_2 **(CAUTION).** Use oxidation electronic equations in the form $Na \rightarrow Na^+ + e^-$ for half-reactions. Burn steel wool in air and Cl_2. Sprinkle antimony into Cl_2; (c) *Oxidation-reduction for covalent species:* Burn H_2 in Cl_2. **Activities:** Define oxidation and reduction. Explain their simultaneous occurrence. Apply oxidation rules to text examples. **Questions:** 6 and 7. By using text examples and equation series, emphasize that oxidation results in algebraic increase in oxidation number of a species while the reverse is true in reduction. **Questions:** 1–3 and 4. (Find oxidation-reduction reactions from among a list of equations.)

Section 22.2. **Activity:** By applying the rules for assigning oxidation numbers (Table 22-1) to the half-reactions for redox equations, develop the principle that oxidation and reduction occur simultaneously. Provide opportunity also for preliminary activities leading to the balancing of oxidation-reduction equations (Section 22.3). The formula equations for the reactions (a) $Na + Cl_2$ and (b) $Na + Al^{+++}$ are developed from the representative half reactions. In effect, this may be used to establish Step 4 in Section 22.3. You may wish to state that the reaction between Na and Al^{+++} represents the first commercial process developed for the production of aluminum. **Demonstrations:** (a) Place Cu strip in a solution of a Zn salt and a strip of Zn in a copper salt solution. Exhibit a setup of the latter, prepared previously, in which the blue color of the Cu^{++} ion has disappeared. Both results of oxidation-reduction are observable. (b) Use the "Methylene Blue Reduction and Oxidation," Alyea, p. 187. Use 4g of dextrose, 4g of KOH, and a few drops of methylene blue to 150 mL of H_2O in a 250 mL or larger flask. Stopper the flask. The color of the mixture is blue at first because an activated complex is formed between the oxygen dissolved in the water and methylene blue. The oxygen in the complex is reduced by the glucose, which is oxidized. When all the oxygen is removed, the solution becomes colorless. Shake the flask. Oxygen from the air in the flask mixes with the solution and the flask contents turn blue. After standing, the solution again becomes colorless. The sequence of shaking and standing is repeated until all the oxygen in the flask has been exhausted. Remove the stopper for a short time, replace the stopper, and resume the sequence. The methylene blue acts as a catalyst in the oxidation of dextrose. The effect may be compared to the taking up of oxygen by the hemoglobin of the blood and its eventual release to oxidize food in the body cell. CHEM Study, **Teacher Training Film:** *Introduction to "Reaction Kinetics,"* W: 140-4021. **Transparencies:** ETE: 003-30, *Oxidation Numbers;* 003-31, *Principle of Oxidation-Reduction Numbers.* **Loops:** MH: *Redox-Metals; Redox-Nonmetals.* **Filmstrips:** PH: WCC 712 *Oxidation and Reduction Reactions;* I: 67120 *Oxidation;* I: 67125 *Oxidation-Reduction.* **Demonstrate:** Reactions such as precipitation of AgCl or neutralization. Use analysis of ionic equation by use of oxidation numbers to show that the reaction (ion-exchange) is not an oxidation-reduction. Reuse Worksheet V, if necessary.

Section 22.3. State and illustrate the rules for the oxidation number method using examples from the text and the Sample and Practice Problem. Establish the steps for using the ion-electron method in the text and solve the Practice Problems. You may wish to demonstrate the reaction involved. **Transparency:** EYE: 003-32 *Balancing Equations by the Oxidation-Reduction Method.* **Filmstrips:** I: 67125, *Oxidation-Reduction* (illustrates various methods of balancing redox equations); PH: WCC 713, *Balancing Redox Equations: Ion-Electron Method;* PH: WCC 714 *Balancing Redox Equations: Change in Oxidation Number Method;* PH: WCC 820 *Electrons and Protons in Chemical Change;* PH: WCF 1007 *Chem-Review 8: Balancing Redox Equations* (a microfiche); Ward Solo-Learn: 78 W 0720, *Introduction to Oxidation-Reduction Chemistry.* **References:** Kolb, D., "Chemical Equations, Part II: Oxidation-Reduction Reactions," *Journal of Chemical Education,* 55(5), 326 (1978); Kolb, D., "More on Balancing Redox Reactions," *Journal of Chemical Education,* 56(3) 181 (1979); Journal of Chemical Education Staff, "Everyday Examples of Oxidation-Reduction Processes," *Journal of Chemical Education,* 55(5), 332 (1978); Sisler, H. H., and Vanderwerf, C., "Oxidation-Reduction: An Example of Chemical Sophistry," *Journal of Chemical Education,* 57(1), 42 (1980).

Section 22.4. Refer to Section 6.5. Define oxidizing and reducing agents. Develop the relationships in Table 22-2 on the chalkboard. Discuss Group I elements as reducing agents and Group VII elements as oxidizing agents. Develop the marginal notes in Section 22.4. **Demonstrations:** Use the previous replacement of Cu^{++} by Zn (or equivalent) and of Br^- by Cl_2 to identify the respective half-reactions as oxidation or reduction. **Loop:** BFA: 84-0140/1 *Oxidation-Reduction: the Halogens;* **Films:** W: 140 4112 *Chemical Families;* CORF: *The Sodium Family.* Relate the demonstration reaction to Table 22-3. Some teachers use the generalization that a reducing agent will react spontaneously with any oxidizing agent below it to yield the weaker reducing agent and the weaker oxidizing agent (i.e., stronger + stronger → weaker + weaker). **Demonstrations:** (a) $HCl + KMnO_4$, $HCl + K_2Cr_2O_7$; identify oxidizing and reducing agents and write equations. (b) Hydrogen peroxide + catalyst (manganese dioxide, activated charcoal). Define autooxidation and write the equation (Section 22.4). **Additional Demonstrations:** (1) Changing a penny into a dime by amalgamating a penny in a mercury(I) nitrate solution **(CAUTION)** and rubbing it with cotton. (2) Display a large-scale series of metal replacements (metal strips) in cylinders of salt solutions. Metal trees form, i.e., Cu in $AgNO_3$, Zn in $Pb(NO_3)_2$. Have students relate the replacement of hydrogen in acids by the active metals and its non-replacement by metals below it to Table 22-3. **References:** *Supplementary Readings for Chemical Bond Approach:* "The Activity Series of Metals," "Oxidation-Reduction: A Re-evaluation," "A Lecture Demonstration of Oxidation-Reduction"; Hill, S. W., Foss, D. L., and Scott, L. W., "A Copper Mirror, Electro-less Plating of Copper," *Journal of Chemical Education,* 56(11), 752 (1979); Carmody, W. R., and Weirsma, J. J., "A Study of the Silver Tree Experiment," *Journal of Chemical Education,* 41(7), 417 (1967); Walker, N., "Synthesis and Decomposition of ZnI_2," *Journal of Chemical Education,* 57(10), 738 (1980); Mickey, C. D., Artifacts and the Electromotive Series," *Journal of Chemical Education,* 57(4), 275 (1980).

Section 22.5. Define chemical equivalent in terms of the Avogadro number of electrons (a mole of electrons). **Demonstrations:** For iron to iron(II) ion use Fe + HCl. For iron to iron(III) ion burn steel wool in Cl_2. Students do calculations. **Transparency:** EYE: 003-28 *Equivalent Weight.*

Section 22.6. **Introductory Demonstrations:** (a) ''Spit and Eleven Cents.'' A silver dime (if available) and a penny are separated by a piece of blotting paper that is moistened with salt solution (some people use the title electrolyte). The leads from a lecture table galvanometer are touched to the coins. A piece of sterling silver may be substituted for the dime or try the existent devalued dime. (b) Use two dry cells in series to light a flashlight or use two beaker Zn-Cu-H_2SO_4 cells in which chemical action is evident. (c) Dry cell equivalent: zinc strip, carbon rod or plates, blotting paper moistened with ammonium chloride or demonstration kit Welch 2242. Exhibit a dry cell cut in half. Precede Section 22.6 dry cell treatment by demonstrating: (1) testing the temperature of the Zn + $CuSO_4$ or Fe (steel wool is good) + $CuSO_4$ test tube reaction; (2) electron transfer in external circuit of the equivalent cell (Zn-Cu-$CuSO_4$) by meter or deflection of a compass placed beneath or over the wire. **Reference:** Baca, G., and Lewis, D. A., ''Electrochemistry in a Nutshell,'' *Journal of Chemical Education,* 55(12), 804 (1978). **Demonstrations:** Electrolytic Cells. (1) To demonstrate that electrolysis is a nonspontaneous or driven reaction, demonstrate that copper reacts spontaneously with silver(I) ion in an electrolytic cell; demonstrate that copper may by plated out on a silver electrode by supplying electric energy. The silver cathode is where the copper(II) ions plate out from a solution of copper(II) nitrate. Demonstrate that silver does not spontaneously replace copper in a solution containing copper(II) ions. (2) Use Figure 22-5 or show W: 140-4109 *Electric Interactions in Chemistry.* To illustrate the equivalent of ion migration in an electrolytic cell use electrolysis of a dilute (blue) solution of copper(II) bromide. As copper plates out on the cathode, there is a lightening of the blue color. At the same time bromine is liberated at the anode and the blue color turns a dark green. Extract a sample of this greenish solution. Shake it with carbon tetrachloride or another solvent (liquid Freon). The characteristic orange-red color of bromine is produced. **Teacher Note:** *We may define the cathode as the electron-rich electrode and the anode as the electron-poor electrode. Reduction occurs at the cathode and oxidation occurs at the anode in electrolytic (driven) cells. In electrochemical (spontaneous) cells the opposite reactions occur at the respective electrodes. This convention is reasonable since the direction of the current is reversed in the latter cells. In the storage or other rechargeable cells, the same electrode always has the same name whether the cell is on charge or discharge cycle. With redox definitions, the names cathode and anode are usually dropped in the case of rechargeable cells because the names must change going from charge to discharge, and vice versa.*

Section 22.7. **Demonstration:** Redemonstrate electrolysis of water. Explain in terms of equations and type of reaction at each electrode, the net cell equation, and changes in oxidation states. **Films:** BFA: 84-0165 *Definite Proportions: Electrolysis of Water;* EBE: S-81561 *Electrolysis of an Aqueous Salt Solution.* Note: In a demonstration using either Na_2SO_4 or Na_2CO_3 as electrolyte, litmus will show the production of H_3O^+ and OH^- ions at the electrodes. **Transparency:** EYE:

003-39 *Reduction of Electropositive Metals by Electrolysis;* W: 75 W 8015 *Electrolysis: Electrochemical Series;* EYE: 003-25 *Electrolysis of Water Solutions of Salts.*

Section 22.8. **Demonstrate:** Electrolysis of NaCl solution using a U-tube with carbon electrodes. Provide a vent tube for the collection of H_2 at cathode and test for H_2 by using ''bark test.'' Insert blue and red litmus papers in the solution at both electrodes. Hold them in place by the stoppers. Note the litmus changes at each electrode and have students explain. Have a student perform the waft test for Cl_2 by removing stopper at anode. Write the electrode equations. Identify the process. Write the net equation.

Section 22.9. **Demonstrations:** Refer back to any previous demonstrations of electroplating, i.e., copper on carbon electrode in copper(II) bromide. Demonstration series for Cu plating: (a) pass a low current (6v) through $CuSO_4$ using carbon electrodes until copper has plated. (Compare the adhesion of copper on the carbon rods to the deposit of copper in the reaction of zinc + copper sulfate.) Reverse the electrode polarity to remove the deposited copper. (b) Electroplate copper onto a cleaned iron file by connecting the file with a copper electrode wire. Use no battery. Have students explain. (c) Use copper anode and carbon cathode. Reverse polarity after copper deposits out. (d) Use two copper electrodes and write electrode equations. Review discussion for naming electrodes. **Demonstrate:** Silver plating. Contrast nature of deposit with that for test tube reaction (Cu + $AgNO_3$). Electrolyze a solution of HCl(2:1) using carbon electrodes and rather loose stoppers. Stop the electrolysis and immediately connect electrodes to a galvanometer. This procedure demonstrates the H_2-Cl_2 electrochemical cell. See Alyea, pp. 193, 213, 158. **Filmstrip:** I: 67142 *Electrochemical and Electrolytic Cells.* **Transparency:** EYE: 003-26 *Electricity by Chemical Action;* W: 75 W 8015 *Electrolysis.* **Film:** W: 140-4133 *Electrochemical Cells.*

Section 22.10. **Demonstrations:** Start with two lead plates in H_2SO_4 solution. Produce the storage cells by passing d.c. current through the setup until the production of brown deposit of PbO_2 is evident at the anode. Use the ''charged'' cell to ring a bell. Test for voltage of this cell with voltmeter. Use Figure 22-9 as the equations are developed. Display a storage cell and demonstrate the use of a battery testing hydrometer. **Loops:** ICF: 10100 *Lead-Acid Storage Battery;* BFA: 84 0181/1 *Hydrogen-Oxygen Battery and Fuel Cells.* **Filmstrip:** I: 67142 *Electrochemical and Electrolytic Cells.* **Films:** W: 140-4133 *Electrochemical Cells* (22 min.); NAVC: 741750 *Theory of the Lead-Acid Storage Battery* (25 min.). **References:** ''Batteries and Fuel Cells,'' *Journal of Chemical Education,* 55(6), 399 (1978); Gilbert, G. L., ''Electrical Energy from Cells—A Corridor Demonstration,'' *Journal of Chemical Education,* 57(3), 216 (1980); Weissman, E. Y., ''Batteries: the Workhorses of Chemical Energy,'' *Chemistry,* 45, Oct. (1972). ''Fuel Cells,'' *Chemistry,* 40, July–Aug. (1967); ''Electrochemical Principles in a Fuel Cell,'' *Journal of Chemical Education,* 47, 680 (1970); Plumb, R. C., ''Racing Car Batteries,'' *Journal of Chemical Education,* 50(12), 857 (1973) (Silverzinc alkaline battery is more efficient than the lead storage battery); McCullough, T., ''A Semimicro Salt Bridge,'' (Use of capillary U-tubes from 5–6mm glass tubing), *Journal of Chemical Education,* 50, 781 (1973). **Filmstrip:** I: 677152 *Fuel Cells;* I: 67123 *Electrochemistry, Linking of Two Sciences.*

Section 22.11. Activity: Review Section 22.6 for processes occurring at each electrode in an electrochemical cell. Set up the Zn-Cu cell (Figure 22-10). Demonstrate voltage measurement for this cell and establish half-cell equations. Define electrode potential. Exhibit a hydrogen electrode (Figure 22-11); see Alyea, p. 141, "Electrode Potentials—Hydrogen Electrode" for construction. **Demonstration:** Use a Sn rod as a reference electrode in a solution of $K_2Cr_2O_7 + H_2SO_4$. Readings are taken on a lecture table zero-centered voltmeter using rods or strips of other metals and carbon. These readings may be used in conjunction with Tables 8-1 and 22-4. State the rule for the values of the standard electrode potential, E^0. Illustrate its use with equations and details for the $Zn-H_2$ and $Cu-H_2$ cells as in the text. Illustrate the calculation of the cell potential for the Zn-Cu cell. Use other illustrations and Questions 24 and 25. Explain Table 22-4 and discuss the relationship between the magnitude of the electrode potential and the tendency of the half-reaction, as written, to occur. **Films:** W: 140-0430 EMF; W: 140-0431 *Electrical Potential Energy and Potential Difference;* MH: 612013 *The Electromotive Force Series.* **Loops:** CHEM STUDY: 168W-1004(T) *A Copper-Silver Electrode Cell;* 168W-1006(T), *An Electrochemical Cell* (animated mechanism); 168W-1013(T), *Silver-Hydrogen Electrochemical Cell.* **Problem:** For enrichment, challenge the students to explain how the standard electrode potential for $Fe^{+++} + 3e^-$ $\rightarrow$ Fe may be calculated from the standard electrode potentials for $Fe^{++} + 2e^- \rightarrow$ Fe and $Fe^{+++} + e^- \rightarrow Fe^{++}$. For the answer, refer to Young, J. A., and Malik, J. G., "Chemical Queries," *Journal of Chemical Education,* 45, 477 (1968). **References:** Parker, G. A., "Stoichiometry of Redox Reactions," *Journal of Chemical Education,* 57(10), 721 (1980). Baruch, G. (ed.), "50-Minute Experiment, An Appropriate Determination of the Avogadro Constant," *Journal of Chemical Education,* 57(10), 735 (1980). (Note: Uses electrolysis of water); Blatt, R. G., "Anodizing Aluminum, An Electrolytic Oxidation Experiment for General Chemistry," *Journal of Chemical Education,* 56(4), 268 (1979); "Corrosion: A Waste of Energy," *Journal of Chemical Education,* 56(10), 673 (1979); Stevenson, L. S., "Oxidation-Reduction Potentials and Hess's Law," *Journal of Chemical Education,* 53(7), 453 (1976). On corrosion as an electrochemical process: Smith, W. L., "Corrosion, Part III: Electrochemical Aspects and Control," *Chemistry,* 49(8), 10 (1976). Also by same author, Corrosion, Part I," *Chemistry,* 49(1), 14 (1976); "Corrosion, Part II: Passivity and Mechanism," *Chemistry,* 49(5), 7 (1976); Slabaugh, W. H., "Corrosion," *Journal of Chemical Education,* 51, 218 (1974). **Individualized Enrichment Programs** (filmstrip, cassette, workbook): PH: WCC 871 *Electrical Units, Definitions, Faraday's Laws of Electrolysis;* PH: WCC 872 *Classification of Electrodes, The Hydrogen Electrode and Standard Potentials;* PH: WCC 873 *The Nerst Equation and Related Problems;* PH: WCC 874 *Electrochemical Measurements: The Glass Electrode and other Specific Ion Electrodes, Potentiometric Titrations.*

Teacher Notes
Chapter 23

Chapter Note
Many of the demonstrations and other instructional aids may have been used in previous chapters. Their re-use here does not detract from their instructional utility because they motivate and do maintain student interest. The chapter focuses on variations within a period, providing a balance for preceding Chapters 21 and 22 as well as for the groups treated in subsequent chapters.

The chapter requires three periods:

Lessons 1, 2 Sections 23.1–23.3: Appearance, Physical Properties, Electron Configurations, Ionization Energies, Oxidation States
Lesson 3 Sections 23.4 and 23.5: Oxides and Hydrides

Section 23.1. Exhibit samples of the elements arranged horizontally and refer to exhibited chart of periodic table. Cut sodium with a knife **(CAUTION)** exposing silvery surface. Scratch magnesium and aluminum. Attempt to make a mark on paper with silicon (recall graphite and diamond). Cut white (yellow) phosphorus under water. Exhibit red phosphorus. Crush roll sulfur. Use a Tesla coil to activate argon tube. Use details of Table 23-1.

Section 23.2. Exhibit metal crystal models: sodium (body-centered cubic), magnesium (hexagonal), aluminum (face-centered cubic close packing). Discuss lattice structure of metals (metallic ions and "gas" of valence electrons). Relate properties to nature of the binding force and resultant properties (Table 23-1). Exhibit silicon crystal models (Klinger) or diamond model as representative (Figure 17-3). Discuss silicon electron configuration and compare with carbon and aluminum. Identify silicon as a metalloid (Sections 27.1 and 27.13). Exhibit models of P_4, S_8, and Cl_2 and discuss nature of binding forces and properties. Have students write electron configuration of argon and recognize its monatomic condition. **Loops:** W: 168, W: 0997(T) *Crystal Structures of Metals (I);* W: 168, W: 0998(T) *Crystal Structures of Metals (II);* W: 168, W:0999(T) *Crystal Structures of Metals (III).* Refer to Table 23-1 for differences in melting and boiling points. **Films:** EBE: 2935 *Melting Points—Determination and Trends* (11 min.); EBE: 2960 *Melting Points (Relation to Periodic Table—Summary)* (4 min.); EBE: 2950 *Metals and Nonmetals* (10 min.); EBE: 2952 *Sulfur, Its Physical States and Properties* (9 min.).

Section 23.3. List the eight elements with their atomic numbers in a vertical column on the chalkboard. Have students record in notebooks and write the electronic configurations. To the chalkboard table add the ionization energies (Section 5.7). Have students explain the variations in ionization energies as they relate to the electron configurations. Discuss the variation in atomic radii across the period. Refer to Section 6.8 for ionic radii. Use the electron-dot symbols for the elements for explanation of their oxidation states (Section 5.8). **Film:** W: 140-4151 *Ionization Energy.* **Loop:** W: 168 W 1042(T), *Ionization Energy of Sodium.* **Transparency:** HM: 2-10526, *Trends in Ionization Energies.*

Section 23.4. Demonstrations: CAUTION: Burn a very small piece of sodium in a deflagrating spoon. Hold a length of magnesium ribbon with tongs and ignite it. Add water to Na_2O_2 and test solution with litmus. Write equations for this reaction and that of Na_2O. Add water to the MgO produced and test with litmus. It may be necessary to heat the $MgO + H_2O$ and test with phenolphthalein or pH paper. Demonstrate the amphoteric behavior of aluminum hydroxide. See Alyea, p. 205, "Aluminum: Oxidation, Reduction," in which amalgamated aluminum reacts with H_2O, liberating H_2. Also see Alyea, p. 142, "Burning Magnesium in Steam." Use electronegativity differences to explain the kind of bonds in the metallic oxides and then those of Si and the nonmetals. Exhibit quartz and sand and a model of the $SiO_4{}^{----}$ structure. Demonstrate insolubility of sand in water. You may wish to etch glass with HF as representative of the reaction of SiO_2 with HF. Expose a small piece of yellow phosphorus to air. Have students note the result. It may be ignited with a hot glass rod. Perform this on a ceramic plate. Ignite a small sample of red phosphorus in a deflagrating spoon and insert the burning phosphorus into a gas collecting bottle whose mouth is partially covered by a glass plate. Extinguish the phosphorus by plunging the deflagrating spoon into a basin of water. Add water to the P_4O_{10} in the bottle, cover with the glass plate, shake the contents, and test with litmus. Write the equation. Ignite a small sample of sulfur in another deflagrating spoon and repeat the operations performed with the burning phosphorus, testing the solution of SO_2 with litmus. Write the equations for the preparation of Cl_2O, its reaction with water, and the ionization of HClO. Compare the magnitudes of the equilibrium constants for H_3PO_4, H_2SO_3, and HCl. You may wish to write the reaction of SO_3 with H_2O and compare the strength of H_2SO_4 with that of H_2SO_3. **Films:** CORF: *Phosphorus* (16 min.); CORF: *Sulfur and Its Compounds* (16 min.); SUTH: *Chlorine—A Representative Halogen* (15 min.). **Loop:** MH: 669027 *Combustion II—Burning Phosphorus*. **Filmstrip:** I: 67743 *Hydrides and Oxides*.

Section 23.5. Discuss the nature of the metallic hydrides, their preparation, and reaction with water. List the formulas for the silanes (silicon hydrides). Compare with the alkane formulas and explain the greater reactivity of the silicon hydrides. Write equations for the preparation of monosilane and its reaction with water. For preparation of phosphine, see Alyea, p. 172, "Reactions of metals with phosphorus for production of magnesium phosphide, Mg_3P_2, and of phosphine, PH_3." Other phosphine demonstrations are in Fowles, pp. 296–298. Silane demonstrations are in Fowles, pp. 287, 288. Exhibit models of PH_3 and SiH_4. Prepare H_2S from FeS and HCl **(under the hood)** and test its water solution with litmus. Burn a hydrogen jet in a bottle of Cl_2. Insert moist litmus paper into the product after noting the change in color of the contents of the bottle. Prepare and collect a bottle of HCl(g) by displacement of air using NaCl and H_2SO_4 as reagents. Test the relative strengths of the solutions of H_2S and HCl using pH paper. **Films:** EBE: S-81551 *Phosphorus Smoke Rings;* CORF: *Silicon and Its Compounds* (13+ min.); CORF: *Sulfur and Its Compounds* (13+ min.); CORF: *Sulfur and Hydrogen Sulfide* (13+ min.); CORF: *Phosphorus* (18+ min.); CORF: *Chemical Properties of Water* (13+ min.). As a summary use the **Filmstrip:** I: 67110 *Chemistry of Period 3*.

Teacher Notes
Chapter 24

Chapter Note

The primary emphasis is on the group properties with more detailed consideration of sodium and potassium and important industrial processes. Some of the demonstrations, activities, and experiments undoubtedly have been used during earlier parts of the course: reactions of sodium and potassium with water, metallic hydroxide, hydrolysis, periodic table, spectroscopy, etc. Repeating some of these demonstrations is useful. An important article on which students may report is, Young, G., "The Essence of Life: Salt," *National Geographic*, 152(3), 183 (1977).

This chapter requires three periods. One possible arrangement is:

Lesson 1 Sections 24.1–24.5: Group Structure and Properties, Chemical Activity, Sodium: Occurrence, Preparation, Properties and Uses
Lesson 2 Sections 21.6–21.8: Sodium Chloride, Sodium Hydroxide, Solvay Process
Lesson 3 Sections 21.9–21.12: Potassium, Potassium Compounds, Spectroscopy

Section 24.1. Activities: Exhibit samples of the metals Na and K in chunk form and in smaller pieces under liquid hydrocarbon. Cut samples to expose silvery luster and softness. Exhibit Li samples (not necessarily kept under hydrocarbon) and small sealed ampules of Cs and Rb. (One source is Kawecki Perylco Industries, Inc., 220 E. 42 St., New York, NY 10017.) Samples of lithium and literature on lithium and its compounds may be obtained from the Foote Minerals Co., Exton, Pennsylvania. Discuss safe storage as it relates to chemical activity and have students note rapid surface oxidation of cut samples. Exhibit a model of body-centered cubic lattice. Discuss structure of the lattice (mobility of free electrons and related properties). Contrast the low melting points, densities, and softness of these metals with that of the more familiar metals (Table 24-1 and Appendix Table 16, for such metals as Cu, Zn, Fe, Ag, etc.), relating to the lattice structure of the Group I metals. Have students explain the long liquid temperature range (melting point to boiling point) of these metals as indicative of the strength of the metallic bond. Gradually develop data for Table 24-1 on the chalkboard, having students supply details of electronic configuration. Have them discover or rediscover that the Group I ions have stable electron configurations of the preceding Group VIII noble gases. A homemade replica or transparency of Table 24-1 is desirable. Discuss metallic and ionic radii. Review electron configurations of the metals of the Copper Family. Discuss the similarities (+1 oxidation state) and differences (other oxidation states) and the related structure (+1 ions do not have electron configuration of noble gases and the other oxidation states as they involve energy of *d* electrons). Discuss the electron configuration of negative ions such as Na^-, and the oxidation state of the anions. **References:** Dye, J. L., "Anions of the Alkali Metals," *Scientific American,* 237(1), 92 (1977); Davidson, S., "Display of Sodium as a Shiny Metal," *Journal of Chemical Education,* 54(1) 29 (1977) [sodium in kerosene with a few drops of diisobutylcarbinol].

Section 24.2. Activities: Use Table 24-2 as basis for discussion of variation in ionization energies with atom size. Refer to Table 22-3: Relative Strengths of Oxidizing and Reducing Agents, Table 22-4: Standard Oxidizing Potentials, and Table 22-2 to raise the problem of lithium position and its relatively high ionization energy. Explain the problem in terms of the small ion size of lithium, the consequent high charge density and hydration energy. Expose samples of NaCl and LiCl on separate watch glasses to the air and have students note the hydration of LiCl. Write the generalized equation for the electrode reaction. **Demonstrate:** Flame tests by using platinum or nichrome wire. Discuss energy acquisition and emission. As a variation, spray solutions from squeeze bottles through the blue burner flame. Another variation of flame tests for class demonstration: Place the carbonates of sodium, potassium, and lithium in watch glasses or evaporating dishes. Add HCl. The burner is placed with the collar openings immediately above the reacting substance (**CAUTION**). This results in a colored burner flame that is not as fleeting as the flame using the wire. **Safety:** Discuss the safe storage of potassium and sodium. Use the article by Lehrfeld, J., "A Convenient and Easily Handled Source of Sodium," *Journal of Chemical Education*, 48, 279 (1971). It suggests the use of a granular sodium-lead alloy, "dry-Na," a product of J. T. Baker Chemical Co., Phillipsburg, NJ. **Reference:** Rosenberg, P. L., "Flame Tests Minus Platinum," *The Science Teacher*, 43(2), 37 (1976) (presoaked wood splints dipped into solid salts). **Film:** CORF: *The Sodium Family;* **Loops:** W: 168 W 1042(T) *Ionization Energy of Sodium;* 4112 *Chemical Families;* W: 168 W 1003(T) *Alkali Metal Reactions with Chlorine and Water;* HR: *Group IA Elements: Chemical Properties.* **Filmstrip:** I: 67136 *Metals and the Metallic Bond.* (Selected materials from those listed may be used now or later in the chapter.) Another Film previously used is W: 140-4151, *Ionization Energy.* **Transparency** W: 75 W 8020 *Trends in Ionization Energy.* **Reference:** Myers, R. T., "Physical and Chemical Properties and Bonding of Metallic Elements," *Journal of Chemical Education*, 56(11), 712 (1979).

Section 24.3. **Activities:** Exhibit samples of compounds mentioned. Demonstrate their solubility and refer students to Appendix Table 13, "Solubility of Compounds." Discuss occurrence and production of NaCl (Section 13.6) now or later. **Reference:** Booklet, *Salt,* from Morton-Norwich Products, Inc., 110 North Wacker Drive, Chicago, IL 60606.

Section 24.4. **Reference:** *Historical production of sodium:* Alyea, p. 178, "Electrolysis of Solid Sodium Hydroxide," **Loop:** BFA: E 80 3940/1 *Production of Sodium-Electrolysis.* **References:** Pearce, W. L., "Humphrey Davy," *Scientific American,* June 1960. *Commercial production:* Fowles, G., *Science Master's Book Series IV, Part 2: Chemistry,* pp. 143–144: "Down's process of Na." **Demonstration:** Melt NaCl in graphite crucible with iron rods as electrodes. Cathode has a glass tube sleeve (7.6 cm) at the end to be inserted into the melt. This jacketed electrode results in the production of a sodium mirror on the inside of the glass. Cool the hot electrode in salt, crush the glass tube, add pieces to H_2O in test tube, and test for hydrogen and for NaOH with indicator. The crucible is mounted inside an insulating metal can, cement-lined jacket and heated with a high temperature burner. See Alyea, pp. 133, 214, for demonstrations of formations of sodium mirror in an incandescent light bulb. Develop the diagram for the Down cell (Figure 24-3) and the equations for the process. Lithium may also be prepared by the electrolysis of fused LiCl using an iron anode and a platinum (loop) wire as cathode.

Section 24.5. **Activities:** The physical properties have been demonstrated and discussed previously. Discuss reaction with air, Na_2O_2 and Na_2O (include equation for NaOH + Na). **Demonstrate ions:** $Na_2O_2 + H_2O$, burning sodium in chlo-

rine. (Alyea, pp. 146, 201, 212). **Loop:** W: 168 W 1003(T) *Alkali Metal Reactions with Chlorine and with Water.* **Activities:** Discuss the uses of sodium. Explain production of tetraethyl lead from ethyl chloride and a sodium-lead alloy. Display and operate a sodium lamp. Discuss the uses of sodium as a heat transfer agent in exhaust valves of engines and atomic reactors. **Questions:** 1–3, 11, 15, 21.

Section 24.6. **Activities:** Display rock salt, table salt, iodized salt, salt tablets, halite crystal. Examine NaCl crystals with a hand lens and exhibit a model of NaCl face-centered cubic structure. Have students report on the Morton Salt Co. booklet, *Salt* (history, methods of production, uses). Mention the location of industrial chemical plants near available sources of NaCl such as in upper New York State near Syracuse. Refer students to Block, M. R., "The Social Influence of Salt," *Scientific American,* July 1963.

Section 24.7. **Demonstrate:** The electrolysis of brine using a large U-tube, carbon electrodes, and vent for hydrogen collection at the cathode. Insert red and blue litmus papers at each electrode. Test for hydrogen collected in a test tube by air displacement. Identify chlorine by waft test and the bleaching of both litmus papers. Identify NaOH by litmus change. The Hoffman apparatus may be used with carbon electrodes. **References:** Fowles, *Lecture Experiments in Chemistry,* p. 431 and pp. 125 and 126, Exp. 151, for the preparation of NaOH from soda; and Fowles, *Science Master's Book Series IV, Part 2: Chemistry,* p. 98, NaOH in the Hg-brine cell. **Activities:** Exhibit forms of NaOH—flake, stick, pellet, along with containers of commercial lye. Have students read the labels on the can of lye that provide valuable instructions about the preparation of solutions, the uses of NaOH, and the antidotes. Some labels indicate that lye should not be used with aluminum utensils. Demonstrate the reaction between Al and NaOH solution. Exhibit a can of any product used to clear clogged drains that contains NaOH in excess of 50 percent. For details, refer to Breedlove, C. H., "Chemical Basis for a Common Type of Drain Cleaner," *Chemistry,* 44, Sept. (1971). This article explains the overall reaction, the cleaning action, and the reason for the inclusion of $NaNO_3$ in the commercial product. You may wish to demonstrate that the solution of NaOH is exothermic. Exhibit containers of oven cleaners. Have students read labels. Explain why oven cleaners can be used on porcelain or stainless steel pots and ovens but not on aluminum. **Films:** PPG: *Commercial Production of Caustic Soda* (7+ min); EBE: S-81561 *Electrolysis of an Aqueous Salt Solution.* MG: S 100 09B *Ionic Reactions* (Castner Cell).

Section 24.8. **Demonstration:** Pass CO_2 through a wash bottle to remove excess HCl. Then pass it into a 28% solution NH_3(aq) saturated with NaCl. If a Kipp generator is not used, Dry Ice pellets may be dropped into the NH_3–NaCl solution. Start early to allow time for $NaHCO_3$ to precipitate. During this time, exhibit commercial samples of washing and baking soda. Write equations for the Kipp and commercial methods for CO_2 production. Demonstrate the laboratory preparation, collection of NH_3. Write formula and ionic equation. Identify the $NaHCO_3$ precipitate by filtering, heating, and identifying the CO_2, and adding HCl to the cooled residual Na_2CO_3 again identifying the CO_2 by limewater test. **Activities:** Develop chalkboard replica of Figure 24-6 and write appropriate equations. Refer to Alyea, p. 217, and Fowles, *Science Master's Book Series IV, Part 2: Chemistry*, p. 142, for other Solvay demonstrations. **Film:** PPG: *Commercial Production of Caustic Soda* (free loan). **Exhibit** commercial varieties of baking soda and washing soda. **References:** Schofield, M., "First Soda Makers," *Chemistry*, 47(6), 16–17 (1974); Kirksey, H. G., "The Solvay Synthesis of Sodium Hydrogen Carbonate, An Undergraduate Laboratory Experiment," *Journal of Chemical Education*, 55(4), 272 (1978); Peck, L., and O'Connor, R., "The Bicarbonate in Alka-Seltzer," *Journal of Chemical Education*, 57(7), 517 (1980); Hill, J. C., "Johann Glauber's Discovery of Sodium Sulfate," *Journal of Chemical Education*, 56(9), 593 (1979). Display samples of representative sodium compounds, Table 24-3 and discuss uses. **Reference:** Wedig, L. A., "The Kitchen Wonder Chemical," *Chemistry*, 51(9), 31 (1978).

Sections 24.9 and 24.10. Activities: Refer to "Discovery of Potassium," *Chemistry*, 37, Aug. (1964). **Demonstrate:** The flame test for potassium. Use Figure 24-8. Production of KNO_3: To 25 mL of H_2O add 12 g $NaNO_3$ and 10 g KCl. Heat to complete solution and evaporate to one-half volume. Let the solution cool. Filter out crystals. Examine with hand lens and compare with NaCl crystals. Evaporate filtrate further until a second crop of crystals forms. Filter and examine these with the lens or under microscope. **Activity:** Discuss crystallization procedures and products as in text. Exhibit samples of compounds in Table 24-4 and discuss uses. **Reference:** May, I., "Chemistry in Colonial America," *Chemistry*, 49, 6 (1976); Wagner, W., "Saltpeter and Colonial Chemistry," *Chemistry*, 47, 29 (1976). Discuss substitution of sodium compounds for potassium compounds except in chemical fertilizers. Exhibit a fertilizer such as 10-6-4 and discuss the meaning of each number. Use **Questions** 8–11 and 21.

Sections 24-11 and 24-12. Activities: Exhibit a prism spectroscope and explain structure. Have students come up and view the line spectrum of a tube of neon, mercury, sodium. Refer to Figure 24-9 and the Welch chart 4856A. Students may use the inexpensive Macalaster Hand Spectroscope (tube and diffraction grating) to examine flames of flame tests or the operating tubes. Discuss the origin of spectral lines. **Film:** W: 140-4112 *Chemical Families.* **Filmstrip:** I: 67111 *Metals of Group IA and IIA.*

Teacher Notes
Chapter 25

Chapter Note

Compare and contrast the properties of Group II and Group I metals. Also contrast the properties of Group II metals with those transition metals that also have two outer-shell electrons.

This chapter requires three periods. One possible arrangement is:

Lesson 1 Section 25.1: Calcium Family and Group I Metals (Sections 24.1 and 24.2)
Lesson 2 Sections 25.2–25.5: Magnesium
Lesson 3 Sections 25.6–25.13: Calcium, Calcium Compounds, Hard Water

Section 25.1. Exhibit available samples of metals of Group II and some of Group I. Also exhibit samples of their natural compounds and demonstrate insolubility of $CaCO_3$ and slight solubility of gypsum. Develop a chalkboard and student notebook table in which the symbols and atomic numbers of Group II are listed. From the atomic numbers have the students state and record the electron configuration and oxidation number. For data on radii (atomic, metallic, and ionic), refer to Tables 5-6, 5-8, and 6-3. Have students discover and attempt to explain variations between members of Group I and between members of Group II and Group I in the same period. Discuss differences between Group II and Group I in density, hardness, melting and boiling points, and the explanations. Discuss stability of M^{++} ion using data on successive ionization energies from Table 25-2. Fill in details of chalkboard table comparable to Table 25-1. Also refer to Table 22-3, Strengths of Oxidizing and Reducing Agents, and Table 22-4, Standard Oxidation Potentials, for discussion of relative chemical activities of Group II elements. Exhibit oxides and hydroxides of Ca, Mg, and Ba ($Ba(OH)_2$). Test solutions with litmus and solubility of hydroxides (Table 15-4). Write formulas of hydrides and discuss covalent structures of BeH_2 and the amphoteric nature of BeO and $Be(OH)_2$. **Filmstrip:** I: 67111, Metals of Groups IA and IIA.

Section 25.2. Exhibit magnesium ribbon, turnings, and crystal solid. Exhibit dolomite, carnallite, asbestos, and talc, and discuss their uses. Also exhibit articles made from asbestos and demonstrate its noncombustibility. You may also wish to discuss safety as it relates to inhalation of asbestos fibers. Demonstrate how asbestos fibers may be torn from a larger sample.

Section 25.3. Demonstrate: The precipitation of $Mg(OH)_2$ by addition of $Ca(OH)_2$ solution to solution of $MgCl_2$. This represents the removal of Mg from seawater. See Fowles, pp. 434–435, for demonstration of preparation of magnesium (and calcium) by electrolysis. It is possible to obtain magnesium by electrolysis of molten $MgCl_2$. However, students who have tackled this as a project have found it almost impossible to obtain the molten $MgCl_2$ unless HCl is carefully and continuously added to the melt that forms initially from the hydrate due to extensive conversion to the hydroxide-oxide by heat. **Exhibit** samples of crystalline magnesium and *Dowmetal* and articles made from magnesium alloys. Discuss the details of Figure 25-3, the magnesium extraction process, and write the important equations.

Section 25.4. Demonstrations: Remove the tarnish from magnesium ribbon with steel wool and discuss it as a self-protective metal. Refer to use of magnesium alloys in ladders and outdoor furniture. Burn magnesium ribbon in CO_2 and note the solid deposits (white MgO and black carbon) on the sides of the bottle. Write the equation for this combustion.

Burn magnesium ribbon in a crucible. After flame has subsided, carefully add a few drops of water to the hot mix. A piece of moist red litmus paper held above the crucible turns blue, and the odor of ammonia (due to reaction of Mg_3N_2 with H_2O) is perceptible. Place some of the residual MgO in a beaker, add water and heat. The slight solubility of the MgO will produce enough $Mg(OH)_2$ in solution to give a positive red litmus paper test. **Demonstrations:** The reaction of Mg with steam: Fowles, pp. 43–47; Alyea, p. 142 (very dramatic demonstration). A burning Mg ribbon held with forceps will continue to burn in the steam from boiling water in an Erlenmeyer flask while a burning match is extinguished. Demonstrate reaction of Mg with acid solution; test for H_2.

Section 25.5. **Activities:** Exhibit samples of magnalium and *Dowmetal* and articles made from magnesium alloys: outdoor furniture, ladders, typewriter parts, etc.

Section 25.6. **Activities:** Exhibit limestone, calcite, marble, seashells, coral, coquina, and chalk. Add HCl to samples and have students note effervescence. Other $CaCO_3$ deposits, i.e., stalactite, stalagmite, boiler scale, hardened lime mortar may also be similarly tested. Exhibit gypsum. A crystal of selenite may be heated to show that the natural hydrate contains water of hydration. Exhibit plaster of Paris. Exhibit samples of fluorite and apatite. Refer to Fowles, pp. 434, 435, for preparation of calcium by electrolysis. Write the equation as well as the one for reduction of CaO by Al. Discuss why this reaction occurs. Have students find boiling point data for Al and Ca in Appendix Table 16.

Section 25.7. **Demonstrations:** Demonstrate the action of tarnished calcium turnings with those of a fresh sample with H_2O. Have students note the formation of some solid $Ca(OH)_2$ and test with phenolphthalein. Compare the activity of fresh calcium with that of sodium upon addition to H_2O. Have students "notice" that calcium is above sodium in both Table 22-3 and Table 22-4. Compare the ionic radii and explain the apparent anomaly in terms of the greater charge of the doubly charged calcium ion. Demonstrate the calcium flame test. Discuss uses of calcium. Discuss uses of Ca as reducing agent and deoxidizer. Exhibit lead storage battery plates.

Section 25.8. **Exhibit** the various forms of calcium carbonate. Test sample with hydrochloric acid and have students note effervescence. The vapors, admitted to the burner through the portholes, will produce the characteristic flame test for calcium. Demonstrate the preparation of precipitated chalk and write the equation. Discuss cement. **References:** Dandy, A. J., "Chemistry of Cement," *Chemistry,* 51(2), 13 (1978); Double, D. D., and Hallawell, A., "The Solidification of Cement," *Scientific American,* 237(1), 82 (1977); Goreau, T. F., Goreau, N. I., and Goreau, T. J., "Corals and Coral Reefs," *Scientific American,* 241(2), 82 (1977).

Sections 25.9 and 25.10. **Hard Water Demonstrations:** Add liquid soap to distilled water, tap water, and hard water (equation). Simulated natural production: (a) $Ca(HCO_3)_2$—have CO_2 continuously bubbling through a tall, water-filled cylinder containing limestone or marble chips. Pass CO_2 through $Ca(OH)_2$ solution until the initial precipitate dissolves; (b) $CaSO_4$—pass CO_2 through another cylinder containing broken chunks of gypsum. Samples from (a) and (b) should be tested with soap solution. Boil samples of both temporary and permanent hardness and retest with soap. Have students note evolution of CO_2 bubbles from heated $Ca(HCO_3)_2$ long before actual boiling starts. Write the equation for softening water of temporary hardness. Demonstrate softening by precipitation of $CaCO_3$ or $MgCO_3$ by addition of Na_2CO_3 to both kinds of hardness samples (write equations). Demonstrate softening by $NH_3(aq)$ or limewater addition to temporary hard water and write equations. Try borax and sodium phosphate as softening agents. Demonstrate softening by zeolite column (Welch 5756). Demonstrate cation exchange, anion exchange,

and mixed bed resin exchangers. See Castka, J., and Crane J., "Demonstrations of Ion-Exchange Resins," *Journal of Chemical Education,* 27, 673 (1950). Details of this article are also described in the *N.Y.S. Chemistry Handbook,* pp. 127–129, and in Alyea, p. 87 (8.20). In Alyea also refer to p. 219; p. 94 (13.3s, Calgon demonstrations); p. 48 (22–24). **Films:** UA: *Hard Water* (28 min.); *The Water Below,* Modern Talking Picture Service, Inc., 2323 New Hyde Park, NY 11040; *Operation and Maintenance of the Ion Exhcanger,* NAVC: 003053-HH, videocassette (25 min.). **Loop:** W: 168 W 1008(T) *Ion Exchange.* **Reference:** Ebmier, H., "Determination of Water Hardness, Acidity and Alkalinity," *Chemistry,* May (1978), p. 27.

Section 25.11. **Demonstrations:** Place a small piece of limestone directly on the grid of a high-temperature burner. Permit it to cool after heating 15 minutes. Add H_2O to residue in a beaker and test with phenolphthalein. To a large chunk of fresh CaO in a beaker, add H_2O. Note evolution of steam and swelling of the chunk to form a mound of powder. Test with indicator. Refer to the reactions and equations of the Solvay process (Section 24.10). Relate to this demonstration. Add a chunk of "old" and probably air-slaked lime to H_2O. Add acid (**CAUTION**) to another chunk of the air-slaked lime.

Section 25.12. Exhibit solid $Ca(OH)_2$, whitewash, and limewater. Test with litmus paper, phenolphthalein, and pH paper. Heat a mixture of $Ca(OH)_2$ and NH_4Cl and relate to Solvay process. Test a sample of hardened lime mortar with HCl. Discuss hardening of mortar and write equation. Discuss uses of $Ca(OH)_2$. **Reference:** Hall, C., "On the History of Portland Cement," *Journal of Chemical Education,* 53(4), 222 (1976); "Chemistry of Fossilization," *ibid.,* 53(5), 270 (1976).

Section 25.13. **Demonstrations:** Heat *selenite.* Mix plaster of Paris with water and make a mold or casting. Have students note the rapidity of the initial setting; write the reversible equation. **Exhibit** castings, wall board, rock lath, statuary, and other examples of the use of plaster of Paris.

Teacher Notes
Chapter 26

Chapter Note

This chapter deals with many of the world's functional metals with emphasis on the iron and copper families. The socioeconomic aspects—such as depletion of natural resources, competition among nations for available ore supplies, technological advances, and attempts by industry and society to solve ecological aspects—are relevant to the chapter. The **Filmstrip** I: 67112 *The Transition Elements* may be used as an introduction or summary.

This chapter requires five periods. One possible arrangement is:

Lesson 1 Sections   26.1–26.4: General Properties, Subgroups, Oxidation States, Color
Lesson 2 Sections 26.5–26.7: Complex Ion Formation, Paramagnetism, Transition Metal Similarities
Lesson 3 Sections 26.8–26.11: Iron Family, Occurrence of Iron, Blast Furnace, Steel Production

Section 26.1. **Exhibit** a periodic table and refer to Figure 26-1. Discuss or review changes in properties of first three periods (short periods), going horizontally across the period, and similarities in properties, going down each main group. Have students identify the section for periods 4–7 for the transition elements. For period 4, exhibit the elements and have students state the electron population of the outermost shell and the build-up of the electron population in the next-to-outermost shell. (They should read data from exhibited periodic table.) Have them explain why the transition elements are metals. Describe the difference between the transition metals' physical properties and those of Group I and Group II metals. Refer students to the last column of Table 26-2 and discover the variable oxidation states of the transition metals. Have students attempt an explanation for the +3 oxidation state of scandium. List the other properties mentioned in the last paragraph of this section for discussion later on.

Have students compare the melting points from Appendix Table 16. Refer to marginal note about the melting points of gallium and cesium.

Section 26.2. Have students note the pattern of change in electron population of period 4 transition elements noting regularities and irregularities. Then follow through period 4 for atomic numbers 31–36 and build-up of the $4p$ electrons. Discuss irregularities at Cr and Cu and relate to extra stability of half-filled and completely filled sublevels. Repeat for elements of period 5, after developing chalkboard replica of Table 26-1. Refer students to Appendix Table 7 for data in discussion of lanthanide and actinide series. Refer to Section 5.5 for description of the lanthanide and actinide series. Discuss the $6d$ build-up and subgroup placement of elements 103–107.

Section 26.3. Redemonstrate some quick color changes from Alyea, pp. 42 (19-17), 45–46 (21-15, 21-21, 103-105, 171, 175, 182). These are indicative of variable oxidation states and the comparative ease of transition (energies of d and s electrons do not differ greatly). **Demonstration:** Add HCl to steel wool or iron filings to show that iron(II) chloride rather than iron(III) chloride is produced. This reaction indicates that the s electrons are generally lost before d electron(s). Burn ignited steel wool in chlorine to show production of $FeCl_3$ (higher oxidation state produced with chlorine, which is a stronger oxidizing agent than H_3O^+—refer to Table 22-3). Use details of Table 26-2 and have students write electron populations for titanium in its various oxidation states. **Film:** W: 140-4172 *Vanadium—A Transition Metal* (22 min.). **Loops:** BFA: 4B0057 *Oxidation States of Manganese* (experiments); BFA: 4B0059 *Reaction of Chromium in Aqueous Solution* (experiments). **Reference:** Cornelium, R., "Ion Exchange Separation of the Oxidation States of Vanadium," *Journal of Chemical Education*, 57(4), 316 (1980); Hentz, F. G. and Long, G. G., "Oxidation State Determinations for Some Reduction Products of Vanadium (V)," *Journal of Chemical Education*, 55(1), 55 (1978).

Section 26.4. **Exhibit** samples of the various colored compounds in Table 26-3 and Figure 26-3. Point out instances where color is related to oxidation state, i.e., Fe^{++}—Fe^{+++}, and of the anion with which the metal is combined. Discuss color (d electrons) as in Section 26.4. **Demonstrate** white light on opaque surfaces—white, red, blue (complement of light removed). Show that red light on red surface is reflected and that red light on blue surface makes the surface look black. Heat blue vitriol crystal to form anhydrous $CuSO_4$. Discuss hydrated Cu^{++} ion. **Reference:** Leybold, P. G., "Color in Nature," *Chemistry*, 49(9), 7 (1976).

Section 26.5. Discuss structure of polyatomic ions and that of complex ions using examples and models. Compare relative stabilities of polyatomic versus complex ions. Discuss coordination numbers. Use examples. Refer to Table 26-4, illustrating how complex ions get their final charge. Use text discussion of complex ions of silver and the equilibrium constants (refer to Table 26-5).

Section 26.6. **Activity:** Define paramagnetism. **Loop:** E: 80 2041/1 *Paramagnetism of Liquid Oxygen* (discuss related electron-dot formula for O_2). **Demonstration References:** Campbell, J. A., "Sealed Tube Experiments" (Exp. 58), *Journal of Chemical Education*, 47, 273 (1970); Alyea: diamagnetism, p. 100; paramagnetism, pp. 208, 215; *Journal of Chemical Education*, 40, A407 (1963); "A Qualitative Test for the Presence of Paramagnetic Species," *ibid.*, 41, 450 (1964); "Paramagnetism," *ibid.*, 48, 5 (1971). **Student Project:** Use a soda-straw balance developed for PSSC physics (as Guoy balance), a strong U-shaped magnet, and small pharmaceutical gelatine capsules containing equivalent minimole(s) of substances to be tested ($MnSO_4$, $FeSO_4$, $CoSO_4$, and $ZnSO_4$). Try MnO_2, $KMnO_4$, and Mn. Develop schematic for manganese similar to that for titanium in Section 25.3. **Films:** Bell Laboratories: *Ferromagnetic Domains* (22 min.); *The Formation of Ferromagnetic Domains* (25 min.); *Domains and Hysteresis in Ferromagnetic Domains* (38 min.); CVF(GE): *Magnetism at Work* (11+ min.). **Loop:** BFA: 82-0118/1 *Magnet Patterns.* **References:** Shakhashiri, B. Z., Dureen, G. F., and Williams, L. G., "Paramagnetism and Color of Liquid Oxygen; A Lecture Demonstration," *Journal of Chemical Education*, 57(5), 373 (1980); Viswanadham, P., "An Inexpensive Guoy Balance for Magnetic Susceptibility Determination," *Journal of Chemical Education*, 55(1) 54 (1978).

Section 26.7. Review the similarities in structure and properties, particularly the horizontal similarities as in the text, systematically first for first five subgroups; then for the 6th, 7th, and 8th; and finally for 9th and 10th subgroups.

Section 26.8. **Exhibit** samples of the three metals of the iron family and their alloys (alnico, stainless steel, permalloy, etc.). Develop Tables 26-6 and 26-7 at the chalkboard. Students may locate data for Table 26-6 in Appendix Table 16. Discuss ferromagnetism and the domain explanation (Figure 26-5). **Loop:** BFA: E-80-2033/1 *Ferromagnetic Domain Wall Motion.* Also use films and loop from Section 26.6.

Section 26.9. Discuss the abundance of iron. **Exhibit** samples of hematite, magnetite, taconite, iron pyrites, and other iron minerals or ores. Discuss the reasons for the use of taconite and the details for its preparation for use in the blast furnace. Samples of pulverized taconite and sintered pellets are tested with a magnet. Discuss why pyrite is not an iron ore. Discuss details of Figure 26-6. **References:** Maddin, R., Muhly, J. D., and Wheeler, T. S., "How the Iron Age

Began," *Scientific American,* 237(4), 122 (1977); Bonatti, E., The Origin of Metal Deposits in the Oceanic Lithosphere," *Scientific American,* 238(2), 54 (1978); "Sea-floor Ore," *Scientific American,* 240(5), 95 (1979)

Section 26.10. Transparency: EYE: 003-40 *The Blast Furnace Process.* Use Figure 26-7. Develop the equations for reduction and slag formation as the structural and functional aspects of the blast furnace and its operation are considered. **Filmstrip:** From American Iron and Steel Institute, 150 West 42nd St., New York, NY 10017. One copy free to each school system: Chemistry of Iron, Raw Materials, and Steel. **Reference:** "Direct Reduction of Iron Ore," *Scientific American,* July (1976). **Exhibit** iron ore, coke, slag.

Section 26.11. Emphasize steel production as a process in which impurities in blast furnace iron are removed by oxidation. The sources of oxygen are the elemental gas or the oxygen in the iron ore. Develop the equations for the oxidation process. Also develop the equations for slag formation. Discuss the use of scrap iron in recycling. Refer students to Figures 26-8(A) and 26-8(B). **Reference:** Sellers, N., "The Chemistry of Steel Making," *Journal of Chemical Education,* 57(2), 139 (1980).

Section 26.12. Demonstrations: Steel wool, iron filings, nails + (a) HCl, (b) NaOH. *Rusting:* Moistened steel wool in bottom of test tube (one-hole stopper, long glass tube) inverted in beaker of colored H_2O. *Corrosion:* Alyea, pp. 46, 51, 89, 104, 125, 162, 171; Fowles, pp. 73–79; *N.Y.S. Chemistry Handbook,* pp. 301–307 (p. 306); *Journal of Chemical Education,* 47, A387 (1970). **Loop:** MH: 669028 *The Rusting of Iron.* **References:** "Corrosion: A Waste of Energy," *Journal of Chemical Education,* 56(10), 673 (1979); Smith, W. L., Part I: "Corrosion," *Chemistry,* 49(1), 14 (1976); Part II: "Passivity and Mechanism, *ibid.,* 49(5), 7 (1976); Part III: "Electrochemical Aspects and Control," *ibid.,* 49(8), 10 (1976); Slabaugh, W. H., "Corrosion," *Journal of Chemical Education,* 51(4), 218 (1974); *Scientific American,* "Mechanical Alloying," July (1976), p. 68; Lauren, P. M., "Sir Humphrey Davy's Battle with the Sea," *Chemistry,* 50(7), 14 (1977); Lauren, P. M., Investigating the Corrosion of Iron," *Chemistry,* 50(7), 25 (1977).

Section 26.13. Exhibit the oxides of iron. Discuss their formulas and uses.

Section 26.14. Exhibit $FeSO_4 \cdot 7H_2O$. Discuss its uses and preparation. Write the equation for its oxidation and explain how the addition of sulfuric acid and pieces of iron keep the Fe^{++} ion in the reduced state. Exhibit $Fe(NH_4)_2$ $(SO_4)_2 \cdot 6H_2O$ and discuss its stability in air and use as a good source of Fe^{++} ions. Demonstrate the addition of hydrochloric acid to steel wool. Exhibit a previously prepared sample of $FeCl_2$ solution that has the iron in the Fe^{++} state by the inclusion of either excess steel wool or iron nails. Write the equation for the oxidation of $Fe(NO_3)_2$.

Section 26.15. Exhibit hydrate iron(III) chloride. Discuss its uses. Write the equations for the hydrolysis of Fe^{+++} ion. Test a solution of the chloride with litmus paper. Demonstrate the production of colloidal iron(III) hydroxide (see details in Section 26.16).

Section 26.16. Demonstration: Hydroxides: Add either $NH_3(aq)$ or $NaOH(aq)$ to a solution of Fe^{+++} ions and write the equation for the production of the red-brown jelly-like pre-

cipitate of $Fe(OH)_3$. Repeat with solution of either $FeSO_4$ or $FeCl_2$. $FeSO_4(aq)$ or $FeCl_2(aq)$ + $NH_3(aq)$ → $Fe(OH)_3(s)$ white changing to blue-green. $FeCl_3(aq)$ + $NH_3(aq)$ → $Fe(OH)_3(s)$ red-brown. Shake the $Fe(OH)_2(s)$ so that the test tube contents moisten the upper part of the test tube and the $Fe(OH)_2$ adhering rapidly changes to the red-brown of $Fe(OH)_3$. This change illustrates the change of $Fe(OH)_2$ to $Fe(OH)_3$ in the process of electrolytic corrosion. Aqueous sodium hydroxide produces the same results and addition of excess NaOH shows that the hydroxides are not amphoteric. *Colloidal Iron(III) hydroxide:* To 200 mL of boiling distilled water add 1 mL of $1M$ $FeCl_3$ drop by drop to develop the deep red colloid. Compare the color with the $FeCl_3$ solution color. Demonstrate the production of the complex $FeSCN^{++}$ ion. Add a solution of $AgNO_3$ to the blood-red solution. The color disappears due to the formation of AgSCN complex, which has a smaller K_i than the $FeSCN^{++}$ ion.

Section 26.17. Develop the chalkboard and student notebook table duplicate of Table 26-8. Have students compare the details of Table 26-8 with the similar table for Group I metals, Table 24-1. Also refer to Tables 22-3 and 22-4 for data on metals of Group I as reducing agents contrasted with metals of the copper family (oxidation states, oxidation potentials). **Exhibit** samples of native copper, silver- and gold-bearing ore. Gold leaf may be exhibited now or later. **Reference:** "The Color of Metals," *Journal of Chemical Education,* 48, 270 (1971).

Section 26.18. Activities: Exhibit available copper ores. **Demonstration:** Flotation, Alyea, p. 25, Exp. 51. See Figures 26-10 and 26-11. Discuss steps in copper metallurgy and write equations. Exhibit samples of calcine, matter, blister copper.

Section 26.19. Demonstrate copper plating using copper as anode, graphite as cathode and a solution of $CuSO_4$. Reversing the polarity of the electrodes after the deposition of copper has been observed will result in the removal of the copper from the graphite electrode. Refer to Figure 26-12. Discuss the production of the silver-gold sludge and the use of low voltage. Explain why only the Cu^{++} ions are reduced at the cathode. Write the equations involved.

Sections 26.20 and 26.21. Demonstrate heating Cu in air; production of $Cu(OH)_2$ using $NH_3(aq)$ and then add excess $NH_3(aq)$ producing the complex $Cu(NH_3)_4^{++}$ and reprecipitation of the hydroxide upon addition of acid; hydrolysis of Cu^{++} ion; reaction of Cu with acids; heating Cu in sulfur vapor, flame and borax bead tests; and precipitation of $Cu_2Fe(CN)_6$. **Transparency:** EYE: 003-41 *Alloys.* Exhibit copper wire, tubing, sheet, and electrical equipment. This establishes its physical properties and its uses in the home in plumbing, heating, gutters, and leaders. Display alloys, brass devices, bronze statue, etc. Direct student attention to condition of weathered bronze statues in park and copper-roofed buildings to indicate corrosion. **References:** Alyea, p. 158 (decomposition of cupric ion by white phosphorus), p. 165 (synthesis of Cu(I) sulfide); *Journal of Chemical Education,* "Determination of Copper Colorimetrically," 47, A484 (1970); Wilhelm, D. L., "The Law of Definite Proportion," *ibid.,* 50, 436 (1973) uses the synthesis of copper(I) iodide as a laboratory experiment. Demonstrate the tests for Cu^{++} ion. Discuss uses of copper and its compounds. **Film:** BFI: *Copper Mining.* **Loop:** HR: *Group IB Elements: Copper.* **Chapter References:** Arvidson, R. E., Binder, A. B., and Jones, K. L., "The Surface of Mars," *Scientific American,* 238(3), 76 (1978); Chaudhari, P., Giessen, B. C., and Turnbull, D., "Metallic Glasses," *Scientific American,* 242(4), 98 (1980); Tarbell, D. S., and Tarbell, A. T., "Murray Raney of Chattanooga and Nickel Catalysts," *Journal of Chemical Education,* 54(1), 26 (1977); Mellon, E. K., "Alfred E. Stock and the Insidious 'Quecksilbervergiftung'," *Journal of Chemical Education,* 54(4), 211 (1977); Treptow, R. S., "Amalgam Dental Fillings Part I, Their Sometimes Outrageous History," *Chemistry,* 51(3), 17 (1978); Treptow, R. S., "Amalgam Dental Fillings Part II, Their Chemistry and a Few Problems," *Chemistry,* 51(4), 15 (1978); Jovanovic, B., The Origins of Copper Mining in Europe," *Scientific American,* 242(5), 152 (1980); Carter, D. E., and Fernando, Q., "Metal Toxicity," *Journal of Chemical Education,* 56(8), 490 (1979).

Teacher Notes
Chapter 27

Chapter Note

The importance of aluminum as an industrial metal and the importance of solid state devices (semiconductors, transistors) should highlight the activities and demonstrations program. There are many opportunities for student reports based on such articles as Garrett, A. B., "The Flash of Genius—Discovery of the Transistor, W. Chockley, J. Bardeen and W. Brattain," *Journal of Chemical Education,* 40, 302 (1963) and "Synthetic Borane Chemistry—Challenge to Chemical Theory," *Chemistry,* 41, Nov. (1968, reprint 8). References indicate how students may do related projects. Free or inexpensive material can be obtained from Educational Services, The Aluminum Association, 818 Connecticut Ave., NW, Washington, DC 20006. These include Wall Charts—*Aluminum, Aluminum and Health, Aluminum and the Environment, Energy Conservation and the Aluminum Industry, The Story of Aluminum, Uses of Aluminum, Teachers' Resource Guide, The Aluminum Film Catalog* (motion pictures and filmstrips). Recent films are Dow Corning *Wondering about Things* and PPG *Glass for the Seventies.*

This chapter requires three periods. One possible arrangement is:

Lesson 1 Sections 27.1–27.3: Metalloids, Aluminum, Aluminum Recovery
Lesson 2 Sections 27.4–27.7: Properties of Aluminum, Thermite Reaction, Uses of Aluminum Oxide, Alums
Lesson 3 Section 27.8–27.15: Boron; Occurrence and Compounds, Borax Bead Tests; Silicon, Silicones, Arsenic, Antimony

Section 27.1. **Exhibit** aluminum and the metalloids. Define metalloid and have students identify them in Figure 27-1 and their location relative to the zigzag line in the figure. In stepwise fashion, develop a chalkboard and student notebook replica of Table 27-1. Furnish the symbols and atomic numbers and have students state and write in the electron configurations that can be developed in greater detail for the valence electrons, i.e., Al: 2, 8, $3s^2 3p^1$. Have them locate data for form, melting points, appearance, boiling points, density, and oxidation states from Appendix Table 16. Have them locate data for atomic

radii (Figure 5-6) and first ionization energies (Figure 5-8). Have them find out from the data on melting and boiling points which element (B) has the smallest temperature range for the liquid phase. Discuss the implications of this fact about the nonmetallic behavior of boron. Discuss other pertinent facts and generalizations in this section, such as variations from metallic to more nonmetallic in a period from left to right (Ge vs. As) and increase in metallic properties going down a group (Te vs. Se). Mention characteristics of the hydroxide, oxide, and hydride of Al.

Section 27.2. Identify aluminum as a metal by its physical properties, exhibiting foil, wire, pots, etc. Mention and exhibit its alloys. Discuss the abundance of Al. **Exhibit** clay and bauxite. Discuss the nonmetallic and metalloidal behavior of boron with reference to its small atomic size, covalence of its compounds, high ionization energy (compared to Al), high electronegativity, and increasing electrical conductivity as its temperature increases.

Section 27.3. You may wish to have students report on the history and discovery of aluminum and the "coincidence" of the Hall-Heroult discovery. Exhibit a set of charts and exhibit materials such as bauxite, refined alumina, clay, cryolite, carbon electrode. These may be obtained from the Aluminum Company of America. Develop a chalkboard outline diagram of an electrolytic cell and write the electrode equations. Discuss the energy requirements for refining aluminum and contrast it with recycling aluminum scrap. For a classroom demonstration see Castka, J. F., "Demonstration of the Electrolytic Extraction of Aluminum," *Journal of Chemical Education,* 18(4), 193 (1941); Alyea, p. 91, 14-1s. Write the electrode equations summarizing the oxidation-reduction processes in the cell.

Section 27.4. **Demonstrations:** Al + HCl, Al + NaOH. Write the textbook equations. Demonstrate Al + HNO_3. Sn + HNO_3 (use Al and Sn foil); amalgamation with solution of mercury(I) nitrate. (**CAUTION: Mercury compounds should be used with care.**) In amalgamating Al foil, students note rapid formation of white powder of aluminum oxide on amalgamated side and feel increased temperature on the other side of the foil. For related demonstrations see Castka, J. F., "Aluminum: Oxidation-Reduction," *Journal of Chemical Education,* 39(6), A505 (1962), Alyea, p. 205. Flash an aluminum foil photoflash bulb. Discuss physical properties of Al. Demonstrate the hydrolysis of $Al_2(SO_4)_3$, then add H_2O to a mixture of solid $NaHCO_3$ and $Al_2(SO_4)_3$. **Exhibit** can of *Drano.* Have students read the label and detect many pieces of Al in the solid mix. Remove the Al from a small sample (**CAUTION**) and test the residue with litmus to show OH^- ion. Add a sample of the *Drano* to H_2O and note the vigorous gas production but a negative test for hydrogen. Refer to Breedlove, C. H., "Chemical Basis for a Common Type of Drain Cleaner," *Chemistry,* 44, Sept. (1971) for complete description of reactants and reactions. Students expected hydrogen because of Al + NaOH reaction. *Drano* contains $NaNO_3$ and the net equation is as follows.

$$8Al(s) + 5OH^-(aq) + 2H_2O(l) + 3NO_3^-(aq)$$
$$\rightarrow 3NH_3(g) + 8AlO_2^-(aq) + heat$$

The NH_3 odor is masked by the pleasant odor of inert ingredients. Demonstrate electrolytic cleaning of tarnished silverware (Alyea, p. 31).

Section 27.5. **Demonstration:** Perform the thermite reaction according to Figure 27-6. A variation uses a mounted small porcelain crucible, which is destroyed. After cooling, the pellets in the sand may be broken up with a hammer to reveal the iron pellets that are attracted by a magnet. **Activity:** Discuss uses of the thermite reaction and write equations. For other variations see Alyea, p. 17, 7-3; p. 168. **Reference:** Bozzelli, J. W., and Barat, R. B., "The Thermite Lecture Demonstration," *Journal of Chemical Education,* 56(10) 675 (1979).

Section 27.6. **Exhibit** various forms of bauxite, corundum, emery, synthetic ruby, and sapphire. See Figures 27-7 and 27-8. Discuss fiber composites and exhibit if available. Exhibit articles to indicate uses: emery cloth and boards, grinding wheels, Alundum laboratory articles, jewels in watches.

Section 27.7. **Exhibit** samples of alums, including chrome alum. Develop general formula from specific formulas. See Alyea, p. 31 (14-13) for growing alum crystals. Test an alum solution for hydrolysis and precipitate aluminum hydroxide from an alum solution. **Loops:** LB: loop 16 *Filiform Corrosion of Aluminum; BFA: loop 497002 Vaporizing Aluminum.* **Filmstrip:** I: 67113 *Boron and Aluminum* (This may be used as a summary of aluminum and an introduction to boron.) **Reference:** Ganby, T. Y., and Amos, J. L., "Aluminum the Magic Metal," *National Geographic,* 154(2), 186 (1978). A reprint ($1) may be purchased from The Aluminum Association; Blatt, R. G., "Anodizing Aluminum," *Journal of Chemical Education,* 56(4), 268 (1979).

Section 27.8. Discuss properties of boron, including those mentioned in the above for Section 27.2.

Section 27.9. Discuss preparation of boron by reduction of boron trichloride by hydrogen and its use in filament and fiber materials. **Exhibit** Colemanite, kernite, elemental boron, borax, and boric acid.

Section 27.10. Discuss Norbide and Borazone production, properties, and uses. **Demonstrations:** Preparation of boric acid (Alyea, p. 73, 15-2); flame tests, Figure 27-11 (Alyea, p. 33, 15-4); boric acid as a weak acid (pH and conductivity); hydrolysis of borax. Also see Alyea, p. 95, 15s, and Alyea *TOPS,* topic 15. Discuss uses of borax. **Exhibit** borosilicate glass. **Reference:** Brown, W. H., "A Simple Method of Distinguishing Borosilicate and Soda-lime Glass," *Journal of Chemical Education,* 56(10), 692 (1979).

Section 27.11. Demonstrate the borax bead test.

Section 27.12. **Films:** IFB: *The World of Semiconductors* (38 min.); Bell Laboratories: *Genesis of the Transistor* (15 min.); *Brattain on Semiconductor Physics* (30 min.); NAVC: 696340-HH *Solid State Principles* (26 min.). **Loop:** BFA: 408021 *Silicate Minerals.* **References:** Adler, D., "Chemistry and Physics of Amorphous Semiconductors," *Journal of Chemical Education,* 57(8), 560 (1980). "A Fundamental Advance in Solid-state Technology," *The Science Teacher,* 46(1), 11 (1979). **Filmstrip:** I: 67109 *The Chemistry of Carbon and Silicon.* Exhibit model of diamond. Discuss and compare properties of carbon atom versus silicon atom. Compare the silicon-silicon bond with the silicon-hydrogen and silicon-oxygen bonds. List the data for silicon as was done for boron, which establishes it as a metalloid. Refer to interchangeability of silicon and boron in glass (compare atomic radii). **Demonstrations:** Alyea, p. 95, 14-3s, silicon by thermite; *N.Y.S. Chemistry Handbook,* p. 185, reaction of silicon and

steam. **References:** Holden, A., *Conductors and Semiconductors;* Myers, S. S., *Experimenting with Conductors and Semiconductors,* Bell Telephone Laboratories.

Section 27.13. The Dow Corning Corporation, P.O. Box 1767, Dept. No. 01-58. Midland, MI 48640, has an organosilicon chemistry course (slides, cassette, chart, etc.) available for $20, that can be used for this section. Discuss the structure, properties and uses of silicones. **Demonstrations:** Silicones (structure and properties)—A number of demonstrations may be performed with the silicones. For example, pieces of Silastic and natural rubber may be burned. The products of combustion form a deposit on the bottom of a test tube. Or, filter paper can be immersed into a mixture composed of 5 parts of Dow Corning 104 Emulsion, 1 part of Dow Corning catalyst No. XE21 and 4 parts of water. The filter paper may be air dried or dried in an oven. A mixture of toluene and water colored with red ink is shaken and poured on to the treated paper and on to some untreated filter paper. The water goes through the untreated paper and the colorless toluene through the treated paper. This demonstration indicates water repellancy. Demonstrate "silly putty." **Reference:** West, R., and Barton, T. J., "Organosilicon Chemistry, Part I," *Journal of Chemical Education,* 57(3) 165 (1980), Part II, 57(5), 341 (1980).

Section 27.14. Discuss the properties and uses of arsenic and its compounds. **Exhibit** lead shot and insecticides. **Reference:** Sarquis, A. M., "Arsenic, Old Myths," *Journal of Chemical Education,* 56(12), 815 (1979).

Section 27.15. **Exhibit** type metal, antifriction alloys, and storage battery plates. Display tartar emetic and potassium antimonyl tartarte. **Additional Chapter References:** Kolb, D., and Kolb K. E., "Chemistry of Glass," *Journal of Chemical Education,* 56(9), 604 (1979); Millot, G., "Clay," *Scientific American,* 240(4), 108 (1979).

Teacher Notes
Chapter 28

Chapter Note

The central theme of this chapter may be the Haber process, discussed as a contributory cause of World War I. Most students are acquainted with the names of conventional explosives and, from such names, realize that nitric acid is necessary to their manufacture. The process was worked out commercially by 1913. The significance of Germany's previous dependence on Chilean nitrate for fertilizers and nitric acid and the Allied control of the sea may be discussed. This can involve consideration of natural resources, stockpiling, and the effect of chemical discoveries on a changing world economic, industrial, and political situation. This type of approach leads to appreciation of the importance of nitrogen in fertilizer, in feeding underdeveloped nations, and in explosives; the problems of the air as a source of nitrogen; and the processes of oxygen and nitrogen fixation. Related ecological problems involving nitrogen compounds include water supply, smog, and pollution. Consideration of the steady addition of ammoniacal wastes and the excessive growth of blue-green algae as well as the presence of excessive nitrates in water supplies brings into focus problems of sewage disposal and water purification processes. Also discuss oxides of nitrogen produced in automobile engines as a source of pollution. These problems should be considered at appropriate times during the chapter development.

This chapter requires three periods. One possible arrangement is:

Lesson 1 Sections 28.1–28.6: Nitrogen, Nitrogen Fixation
Lesson 2 Sections 28.7–28.10: Ammonia
Lesson 3 Sections 28.11–28.14: Nitric Acid

Section 28.1. Discuss the occurrence of nitrogen (elemental and combined). **Demonstrations:** Prepare a sample of oxygen-free air by igniting a small sample of red phosphorus on a cork floating in water. The cork must be small enough so that covering it and the burning phosphorus with a graduated cylinder permits the floated cork to rise with the water as the oxygen is depleted. The water rises approximately 20% of the length of the cylinder. The oxygen-free air is then tested with a flaming splint. See Alyea, p. 23 [10-4(c)], for an alternate version of this demonstration. Oxygen-free air may also be prepared by passing air over heated copper or by the oxidation of moistened steel wool (or iron filings), as in Alyea, p. 23 [10-4(a)]. The presence of elemental nitrogen in air can be demonstrated by igniting cut-up Mg ribbon in a small crucible **(CAUTION).** When the Mg is completely burned, cautiously add a drop or two of water to the contents. The small amount of Mg_3N_2 produced reacts with the water to produce NH_3. Its odor is detected by the waft test, and a piece of moistened red litmus paper held above the crucible contents, when the water is added, turns blue.

Section 28.2. Review Section 12.7. Show the EBE loop S 81568, *Preparation of Oxygen: Distillation from Liquid Air—Condensation of Oxygen from Air*. Discuss the marginal notes. You may wish to demonstrate the laboratory preparation of nitrogen. This utilizes the gentle heating of a mixture of ammonium chloride and sodium nitrite solutions. The dissolved ammonium and nitrite ions form ammonium nitrite, which then decomposes and yields nitrogen: $NH_4NO_2(aq) \rightarrow N_2(g) + 2H_2O(l)$. The nitrogen is collected by displacement of water. **Transparency:** W: 75-8000, *Nitrogen*.

Section 28.3. Have students examine sample of the gas collected (either oxygen-free air or nitrogen produced in laboratory preparation). For solubility refer to method of collection of N_2 or to evidence from demonstrations on oxygen-free air. List the physical properties. You may wish to discuss diving and the "bends."

Section 28.4. To compare chemical activity of nitrogen versus phosphorus: Expose white phosphorus to air and have students note occurrence of oxidation; ignite white phosphorus with a heated glass rod; burn red phosphorus in a deflagrating spoon. Contrast chemical activities of first elements of Groups VI and VII (O_2 and S_8, F_2 and Cl_2) with relative inactivity of N_2 and P_4. Review bonding in P_4 (Figure 23-1); exhibit model. Exhibit model of N_2; review electronic configuration of N, its electron-dot symbol, and electron-dot formula of N_2. Review and discuss bond energies (Table 6-4). Discuss nitrides, drawing electron-dot symbol for nitride ion. A possible demonstration for the production of oxides of nitrogen in an electric arc utilizes a large flask with two metal electrodes that are subjected to sparking by a Tesla coil. The brown NO_2 is eventually produced from the NO formed and from the residual oxygen in the air. (See Alyea, 17-15s). For details of smog

formation, see Toon and Ellis, *Foundations of Chemistry* (1973), pp. 396—399. **References:** Huntress, W. T., Jr., "The Chemistry of Planetary Atmospheres," *Journal of Chemical Education*, 53(4), 204 (1976); "Smog Formation Simplified," *Chemistry*, Jan. 1972, Reprint 104. "Nitrogen Oxides in Polluted Air," *Science News*, 113(13), 199 (1978).

Section 28.5. Discuss the uses of nitrogen. Emphasize the manufacture of ammonia and its importance (uses of NH_3, Section 28.10). Display a "burned out" tungsten filament bulb, calling attention to the gray deposit.

Section 28.6. Refer to Figure 28-1. **Demonstration:** Pass sparks from an induction coil or Tesla coil through a sample of confined air. The electrodes may be of copper inserted through stoppers into a glass tube. A piece of inserted moistened blue litmus turns red. On occasion some color change to nitrogen dioxide may be observed. See Alyea, p. 38, 17-10; p. 99, 7-17s. **Exhibit:** Roots of legume having nodules of nitrogen-fixing bacteria. Refer to *Foundations of Chemistry*, p. 142 and Figure 4-22, "Nitrogen Cycle." **References:** Schrauzer, G. N., "Biological Nitrogen Fixation," *Chemistry*, 50(2), 13 (1977); Safrany, D. R., "Nitrogen Fixation," *Scientific American*, 231(4), 64 (1974); Douglas, J. H., "Improving Nitrogen Fixation," *Science News*, 108(20), 374 (1976); "Nitrogen Fixation the Synthetic Way," *Science News*, 107(9), 132 (1975); Skinner, K. J., "Nitrogen Fixation," *Chemical and Engineering News*, Oct. 4, 1976. Brill, V. J., "Biological Nitrogen Fixation," *Scientific American*, 236(3), 68 (1977); "Nitrogen Fixation: A Piece of the action," *Science News*, 112(10), 149 (1977); "Fixations," *SciQuest*, 52(7), 24 (1979). **Film:** CORF: *Nitric Acid Compounds and the Nitrogen Cycle*. Exhibit a variety of nitrogen fertilizers.

Section 28.7. Display apparatus setup for Figure 28-2. Have students write equation. **Demonstration:** *Destructive distillation of bituminous coal*. The apparatus consists of a test tube connected to a collecting bottle. The delivery tube leads almost to the bottom of the bottle, which also has a short glass jet exit tube. A large piece of moistened red litmus paper is inserted into the bottle and held in position by the stopper. Heat the coal. (Cannel coal works very well.) The coal gas is ignited at the jet exit. The litmus turns blue. Write the equation for the $NH_3(g) + H_2SO_4(aq)$ reaction. *Haber process:* Discuss the conditions under which the process operates in the light of application of Le Chatelier's principle and equilibrium. Simultaneously demonstrate that a catalyst speeds up the reaction in both directions. Show the effect of high temperature on the equilibrium by passing dry NH_3 [prepared by NH_3(aq) dropping onto pellets of NaOH in generator]. Pass NH_3 (dry) over heated steel wool. Collect the products by displacement of water. Test for hydrogen. Refer to marginal note and Figure 28-3. **References:** Medeiros, R. W., "Of Swords and Plowshares," *Chemistry*, 48(7), 12 (1975), discusses Haber, Ostwald, and World War I. Simpson, C. H., *Chemicals from the Atmosphere*, Dept. SIS American Chemical Society (1973); Bayless, P. L., Ammonia Synthesis," *Journal of Chemical Education*, 53(5), 318 (1976). **Film:** CORF: *Nitrogen and Ammonia;* UA: *Ammonia* (19 min.). **Transparency:** W: 78-8000, *Ammonia*.

Section 28.8. Demonstrate the ammonia fountain (Alyea, pp. 12, 27, 149, 174) or show the EBE **Loop** S-81548, *Ammonia Fountain*. Use these and invert a bottle of stoppered

NH_3 into water. Remove the stopper and have students note rapid rise of water into bottle as evidence of the great solubility of NH_3. Test the resultant solution with red litmus paper. Exhibit model of NH_3 molecule (Figure 6-12). Review the sp^3 hybridization, the pyramidal structure, and the electron-dot formula of NH_3 (Figure 6-12). Compare with water: polarity, hydrogen bonding, high boiling and high melting point. Use models and chalkboard electron-dot equations to illustrate the $NH_3 + H_2O$ reaction. Demonstrate the liquefaction of NH_3: Dry NH_3, prepared by dropping concentrated $NH_3(aq)$ onto pellets of NaOH, is passed into a test tube cooled by a Dry Ice–acetone mix (CAUTION: Use the hood). Film: EBE: 2940 *Solution of Alkali Metal in Liquid Ammonia* (24 min.) or 2941, a shorter 6-min. version. Transparency: HM: 2-10536 *The Ammonia Molecule—Hybridized*.

Section 28.9. Demonstrate that a flaming splint is extinguished in NH_3. See Alyea, p. 37, 17-6, for burning NH_3 in O_2. Write the equation for the reaction. The catalytic thermal decomposition of NH_3 has already been described. Bring moistened stoppers from concentrated $NH_3(aq)$ and concentrated HCl together. Also use models, and write the formula and electron-dot equations. Differentiate between ammonia, NH_3, and ammonium, NH_4^+. Perform test for ammonium compound: Heat solid with $Ca(OH)_2$ or solution of NaOH; identify NH_3 by waft test, litmus reaction, and reaction with HCl(g). Reference: Lagowski, J. J., "The Chemistry of Liquid Ammonia," *Journal of Chemical Education*, 55(12), 753 (1978).

Section 28.10. Display a bottle of household ammonia. Have students read the label, detect the odor, and test the vapor with litmus paper. Refer to TV commercials mentioning ammonia. Demonstrate cleaning glass with $NH_3(aq)$ versus cleaning with NaOH solution. Have students test for the odor of rubber latex, then coagulate with $HC_2H_3O_2$. Discuss the uses of ammonia and ammonium compounds as in the text. Refer to Figure 28-4. Write structural and electron-dot formulas for hydrazine, as in Table 6-5. Have students determine oxidation number of nitrogen in hydrazine. Warn students about accidentally mixing the cleaning agents ammonia water and sodium hypochlorite. Have them read label on bottle of household ammonia, which reads: "Do not mix with bleach." Discuss the uses of ammonia and its compounds.

Section 28.11. Demonstrations: Laboratory preparation of HNO_3 from nitrate (Figure 28-5). Have students attempt to explain why a retort is used. Why does the acid react with copper? Why is there no evidence of free hydrogen when the acid reacts with zinc? The last two questions are based on an initial demonstration of these facts. The highlight of the lesson is the demonstration of the oxidation reaction of the acid on excelsior and/or the ignition of a glowing splint in the vapors of a heated sample of the acid produced in the retort preparation. (Hold the splint with tongs to prevent staining of hand by the vapors and make sure that the mouth of the test tube is pointed away from the instructor and the class.) What does the method of collection reveal about HNO_3? (Tap water can be used instead of ice water.) Write two forms of the equation. Ostwald process: Demonstrate the catalytic oxidation of ammonia to oxides of nitrogen. Dry NH_3, prepared by dropping concentrated $NH_3(aq)$ on pellets of NaOH, is passed over heated platinized asbestos with the simultaneous admission of air

through a two-hole stopper at the reaction tube inlet. The outlet tube leads into a large flask in which the brown NO_2 becomes visible. This is then dissolved in water and tested with litmus, and for the nitrate ion. To avoid formation of a white cloud of NH_4NO_3, preheat the catalyst before starting NH_3 production. (An electrically heated coil of platinum wire can be substituted for the platinized asbestos.) See Alyea, p. 28, 17-11, 17-12; p. 169; p. 179; p. 188; p. 224; and *Journal of Chemical Education*, 41, A973 (1964); 47, A534 (1970). Write the equations in this section of the text. Related demonstrations are: (a) Open a flask of NO to air and have class observe change. Add H_2O, stopper, and shake the flask. Reopening the flask produces more NO_2. (b) Prepare and collect sample of NO and NO_2. Test solubility, reaction with H_2O, and other properties. Open small bottle of NO. The NO turns brown. Add a small amount of H_2O to the flask. Moisten your palm and use it to cover the bottle opening. Shake. The glass bottle held vertically adheres to the hand. The yellow stain on the demonstrator's palm indicates the formation of xanthoproteic acid (a test for proteins, which can be demonstrated by heating boiled egg white with HNO_3). Films: W: 140-4136 *Nitric Acid*; CORF: *Preparation and Properties of Nitric Acid*; UA: *Preparation and Properties of Nitric Acid* (21 min.); UA: *Oxides of Nitrogen* (16 min.).

Sections 28.12 and 28.13. Refer to method of collection and discuss details. Heat the sample of HNO_3 collected in the laboratory preparation (CAUTION). Insert a glowing splint into the vapor. Remove splint. Into the mouth of the test tube place a loosely packed wad of wool or excelsior. Reheat the HNO_3. Write the equation. Indicate instability. Relate to use of retort and HNO_3 as an oxidizing agent. Add HNO_3 to zinc and copper. Test for hydrogen and note production of oxides of nitrogen. (NO_2 observable.) Ask why no hydrogen is produced with zinc and why copper reacts. Write equations for reaction of copper with HNO_3 (dilute and concentrated). To show that hydrogen is produced with an active metal, use magnesium and HNO_3 (1:25 or greater dilution). Write the equation. Add concentrated HNO_3 to gold leaf. Then add concentrated HCl. This combination shows the action of aqua regia. Write the equations in Section 28.13. See Ophardt, C. E., "Nitrogen Oxide Experiments," *Journal of Chemical Education*, 53(6), 374 (1976) for use of Mg + HNO_3 for determination of the gram-molecular volume of hydrogen. The article also describes preparation of NO from 2 g of Fe filings, 3 mL of H_2O, and 15 mL of 6 M HNO_3. Describes tests for the NO_3^- and NO_2^- ions. Other Demonstrations: Al foil and Sn foil with concentrated HNO_3; Fe with concentrated HNO_3. Transparency: W: 75-8000, *Nitric Oxide*.

Section 28.14. Discuss the uses of HNO_3 as in text. Exhibit $NaNO_3$, KNO_3, cans of preserved meat (corned beef), and hot dogs. (Have labels read for use of nitrate and nitrite.) Discuss nitrosamine possibility from bacon. Exhibit fertilizers, aniline dyes, plastics. Ignite samples of cellulose acetate and cellulose nitrate film. Film: UA: *Nitrous Acid and Sodium Nitrite* (18 min.). As summary use Filmstrip I: 67105, *Nitrogen and Its Compounds*. Also use two PH filmstrips (with cassettes or records), WCC 464 *Air Pollution*. Chapter References: Ondrus, M. G., "The Determination of NO and Particulates in Cigarette Smoke," *Journal of Chemical Education*, 56(8), 551 (1979); Miller, J. A., "Beyond the Ice

Pack," *Science News*, 114(15), 250 (1978). *Scientific American* Offprints: 1194, *The Nitrogen Cycle;* 1193, *The Carbon Cycle;* 1192, *The Oxygen Cycle*.

Teacher Notes
Chapter 29

Chapter Note

Current concern with ecology and pollution as it relates to sulfur and its compounds may be made the focal point of the chapter. Student reports on pollution and on sulfuric acid should be used at appropriate times. Suitable **References** are: Likens, G. E., Wright, R. F., Galloway, J. N., and Butler, T. J., "Acid Rain," *Scientific American*, 241(4), 43 (1979); "It's Raining H_2SO_4," Research Reporter, *Chemistry*, 50(8), 24 (1977); Stokes, J. C., and Lockhart, W. L., "Where Has All the Sulfuric Acid Gone?" *Chemistry*, 51(8), 10 (1978); Wittcoff, H., and Fernelius, W. C., "The Chemical Industry, What Is It?" *Journal of Chemical Education*, 56(4), 253 (1979); "Acid rain clouds gather," *Science News*, 117(13), 199 (1980).

The chapter requires three periods. One possible arrangement is:

Lesson 1 Sections 29.1–29.6: Sulfur: Occurrence, Production, Allotropes, Properties, Uses
Lesson 2 Sections 29.7–29.12: Sulfur Dioxide: Occurrence, Preparation, Properties, Uses, Acid Rain. May require more than one period for student reports and discussion on pollution.
Lesson 3 Sections 29.13–29.16: Sulfuric Acid: Preparation, Properties, Uses

Section 29.1. Exhibit samples of sulfur (if possible, volcanic), roll sulfur, flowers of sulfur, and sulfur minerals. Discuss occurrence and pose the problem of recovery from deposits in Texas and Louisiana. **Film:** *Sulfur*, U. S. Department of Mines, 4800 Forbes St., Pittsburgh, PA (Frasch mining operations).

Section 29.2. Activities: Precede the discussion of the Frasch process by demonstrating **(a)** the insolubility of sulfur in water and **(b)** the low melting point of sulfur. Exhibit pressure cooker and relate boiling point to pressure in connection with the use of superheated water in the process. Make a chalkboard replica of Figure 29-2. Demonstration model of the Frasch process: Fowles, G., *et al., The Science Masters' Book, Series 4, Part 2: Chemistry*, J. Murray, London 1964, p. 114, uses a modified Liebig condenser and yellow wax. **Film:** EBE: 2952 *Sulfur, Its Physical States and Properties*.

Section 29.3. Activities: Have students test sulfur for odor, for density by dropping roll sulfur into water, for solubility in water. Demonstrate solubility in CS_2 and CCl_4. Relate solubility to preparing rhombic sulfur. Have students note the color and phase changes during the preparation of monoclinic and amorphous sulfur. Outline these on chalkboard table and indicate temperatures involved.

Section 29.4. Refer to Sections 9.11–14 and 17.3 for other examples of allotropy. If you do not let students use CS_2, demonstrate the preparation of rhombic sulfur. Crystals of good size are obtained by covering the watch glass or evaporating dish with a large inverted beaker. Provide a support so that a small opening at the beaker mouth permits slow evaporation

of CS_2. **CAUTION:** Use the hood or window sill. Have students examine the rhombic crystals with a hand lens. **Demonstrate** the various changes in color, phase, viscosity, and allotropic form. Tabulate these on the chalkboard table with the addition of significant temperatures. **Exhibit** and discuss the models, Figures 29-3 and 29-4. Construct a ball-and-stick model of S_8. Open the S_8 model and add more balls for sulfur.

Section 29.5. Demonstrations: (a) Burn a chunk of sulfur in a deflagrating spoon. Insert the spoon into a bottle using a cover plate. Insert a piece of moistened blue litmus paper. Have students detect odor by waft test. Extinguish burning sulfur by submersion in H_2O. **(b)** Insert a 6-inch strip of copper into the vapors of boiling sulfur. **(c)** Ignite (**CAUTION**) a small cone of a mixture of zinc powder and flowers of sulfur on an asbestos sheet. Write equations for **(a)**–**(c)**. Discuss stability of sulfur at room temperature and bond energy between sulfur atoms. Write electron-dot formulas for H_2S, SO_2, and SO_3, and exhibit models and determine oxidation state of sulfur in each compound. Discuss similarities and differences between oxygen and sulfur—allotropism, support combustion, electronegativity, relative reactivity, comparison of formulas of compounds. **Film:** UA: *Sulfur and Hydrogen Sulfide* (21 min.). **Loop:** LB: 13 *Sulfur*. **Filmstrip:** I: 67154 *Chemistry of Group VI-A*.

Section 29.6. Activity: Discuss uses as in text. Exhibit CS_2, H_2SO_4, matches, sulfa drugs, sulfur hair ointment. Discuss vulcanization, referring back to Chapter 17. See Feinstein, H. I., and Hutchinson, C., "Detection of SO_2 in a Burning Match Head," *Journal of Chemical Education*, 51(11), A558 (1974).

Section 29.7. Activity: Discuss sources of SO_2 in air and problems of pollution, particularly the burning of coal containing sulfur and roasting of ores. Write a representative equation for roasting ZnS. **Reference:** Toon and Ellis, *Foundations of Chemistry*, pp. 396–399: "Photochemical Smog."

Section 29.8. Demonstrations: Preparation by methods 1, 3, 4 as in text.

Section 29.9. Activity: The great solubility of SO_2 in water can be demonstrated by moistening the palm of the hand, placing the hand over an open bottle, and shaking. The mouth of the bottle adheres to the palm of the hand with the bottle hanging downward. Alternatively, removing the thumb that seals a test tube of SO_2 below water results in the rapid rise of the water in the test tube. This is then tested with blue litmus paper. **Demonstration of liquefaction:** Pass the dry gas through a U-tube cooled in Dry Ice–acetone. Under the hood, insert a small test tube containing H_2O into a larger test tube containing liquid SO_2. The evaporation of the liquid SO_2 results in freezing H_2O.

Section 29.10. Activity: Thrust a burning splint into a bottle of SO_2. This shows that the gas neither burns nor supports combustion, showing its stability. The litmus test for dissolved SO_2 shows it is an acid anhydride. Write the two equations for its step-by-step ionization and discuss the magnitudes of the ionization constants. A water solution can be shaken with air and subjected to the test for a sulfate. You may also wish to perform litmus or pH paper tests on a sulfite and hydrogen sulfite solution to show hydrolysis and weakness of the acid. **Other Demonstrations:** "Wine to water to milk." Pour dilute $KMnO_4$ solution into an "empty" cylinder (small amount of bisulfite of a very small quantity of SO_2 solution) and then into a second cylinder containing "water" [$BaCl_2$(aq)]. Also see Alyea, p. 42, 197-17, for another color change.

Section 29.11. Exhibit boxes of dried apricots and prunes. Have student read labels. Also, read label on a bottle of maraschino cherries. **Demonstration:** Bleach a flower in solution of SO_2 and restore its color by immersing in H_2O_2. Discuss use as a bleaching agent and in preparation of paper pulp (no longer used in this country). You may mix sulfurous acid with limewater to demonstrate production of calcium hydrogen sulfite. Exhibit bottle of sulfuric acid. **Film:** UA: *Sulfur Dioxide and Sulfurous Acid* (25 min.). **Transparency:** W: 75 W 800, SO_2, H_2S. **Loop:** LB: 14 *Sulfur Compounds*.

Section 29.12. Use student reports based on the listed references. Discuss the details of production of sulfuric and nitric acids, and the dispersal of acid rain. Demonstrate the pH of tap water and rainwater, if available, using pH meter or pH paper. **Film:** *Measures for Air Quality* (4 min.) (about SO_2), Association Films (local distributors), 600 Grand Ave., Ridgefield, N. J. 07657. **References:** "Clean Coal," *Scientific American*, 241(4), 76 (1979); "An Acid Can Be Basic," *Journal of Chemical Education*, 56(8), 529 (1979); "Acid Rain Network Planned," *Science News*, 113(25), 407 (1978); "Acid Rain in the Spotlight," *Science News*, 116(15), 244 (1979); West, S., "Acid from Heaven," *Science News*, 117(5), 76 (1980); West, S., "Acid Solutions," *Science News*, 117(7), 106 (1980); "Acid Rain Clouds Gather," *Science News*, 117(13), 199 (1980); "A Blow to Acid Rain," *Science News*, 117(26), 407 (1980).

Section 29.13. **Activities:** Introduce sulfuric acid by illustrating and/or citing the many uses of H_2SO_4. **Exhibit** storage battery, superphosphate fertilizer, rayon, cellophane, etc. **Demonstrations:** *Charring action (dehydration):* **(1)** Wood splint or cloth dipped into H_2SO_4. **(2)** Add H_2SO_4 to sugar in a beaker and stir. *Removal of oxide coat:* Immerse a rusted article in the acid. Identify H_2SO_2 as a "key chemical." Quote Aldous Huxley: "Chemists cheer for the flag and H_2SO_4." Pose the problem of production of sulfuric acid arising from the fact that H_2SO_4 has been used in the production of other acids (both binary and oxyacids). Have students decide on the formula of the anhydride. Burn sulfur and then attempt to burn SO_2. This identifies the key problem—the conversion of SO_2 to SO_3. **Demonstration:** Contact process: An evaporating dish covered with a funnel that is burning in the dish. The mixture of air and SO_2 is drawn over heated platinized asbestos, and the products are drawn through H_2O in a side-arm test tube. The aspirator is attached to the side arm. The H_2O is tested for hydronium and sulfate ions before and after the run. Attention is drawn to the undissolved cloud of SO_3, which did not react with the H_2O. This indicates the need for solution of SO_3 in H_2SO_4. No white cloud forms when, in a second run, a test tube containing H_2SO_4 is substituted for the H_2O. The catalyst can also be V_2O_5 or an electrically heated platinum. See Alyea, p. 41, for another version of the contact process and for a lead chamber process demonstration. **References:** See Fowles, pp. 216–222. **Student report:** "The Early Days of Sulfuric Acid," *Chemistry*, 45, Oct. (1972). **References:** Martin, J. A., Baudot, P., Manai, J. L., and Lejaille, M. F., "Synthesis of Sulfuric Acid by the Contact Process," *Journal of Chemical Education*, 52(3), 188 (1975), for a more elaborate demon-

stration. In stepwise fashion, develop the flowchart in Figure 29-10, writing the appropriate equations where the chemical changes take place. Discuss the production of sulfuric acid droplets in automobiles catalytic converters. **Film:** UA: *Sulfuric Acid* (16 min.). **Filmstrip:** I: 67101 *Putting Sulfur to Work*.

Section 29.14. Have a student lift a small bottle of H_2SO_4 (**CAUTION**) and an identical bottle with an identical volume of H_2O. Have students observe oily viscosity as you swirl the acid in a bottle. Carefully heat a sample of the acid with a 360°C thermometer inserted. Demonstrate the correct method of dilution. Have a student feel the outside of the beaker in which this is done or observe an inserted thermometer. **Reference:** Wolf, W. A., and Solomon, J. A., "Chem Compacts," *Journal of Chemical Education*, 53(6), 370 (1976). Dilute H_2SO_4 by adding the acid to ice. The heat of fusion of ice permits the preparation of barely warm acid.

Section 29.15. **Activities:** Write the equations for the ionizations of the diprotic acid, indicating the degree of ionization for each stage. Write neutralization equations for formation of $NaHSO_4$ and Na_2SO_4. Add dilute H_2SO_4 to Zn and test for H_2. Refer to Table 22-3. Recall or repeat the Cu + H_2SO_4 reaction. Write the equation and determine change in the oxidation state of the sulfur. Demonstrate the reaction between Zn and hot, slightly diluted acid, testing for the H_2S produced. Write the equation and have students determine change in oxidation state of the sulfur. To sugar (sucrose) in a beaker add H_2SO_4 while stirring and observe the results. Have students note the steam produced and the rise of the mass of carbon produced. Precede this by thrusting a wood splint into H_2SO_4 (concentrated); withdraw the splint and have students note charred bottom part of the splint. Drop H_2SO_4 onto paper and cloth. Write equation for charring of sucrose. Drop a large crystal of $CuSO_4 \cdot 5H_2O$ into H_2SO_4 (concentrated) and have students note production of white anhydrous $CuSO_4$ on exterior of crystal. Have students read the **CAUTION** in the text. Refer to dehydration of formic acid to produce CO. Write the equation for the production of nitroglycerin.

Section 29.16. **Activities:** Refer to previous exhibits, indicating uses of sulfuric acid. Exhibit $Ca_3(PO_4)_2$ and $CaSO_4 \cdot 2H_2O$ (gypsum), fertilizers, superphosphate. Have students state properties of sulfuric acid that permit its use in making other acids. Dip rusted iron into H_2SO_4. **Exhibit** nitrocellulose plastics, photographic film, cellophane. As the chapter summary, show the **Film:** CORF: 1436 *Sulfur and Its Compounds* (13+ min.). **Chapter References:** "By Jove," *Scientific American*, 241(2), 72 (1979); Soderblom, L. A., "The Galilean Moons of Jupiter," *Scientific American*, 242(1), 88 (1980); "Chemical Analogies between the Stars," *Science News*, 117(2), 22 (1980); "An Acid Can Be Basic," *Journal of Chemical Education*, 56(8), 529 (1979).

Teacher Notes
Chapter 30

Chapter Note

The chapter topic may be introduced by a variety of approaches such as the **Film:** W: 140-4112 *Chemical Families* (22 min.); W: 140-4160 *A Research Problem: Inert (?) Gas Compounds*

(19 min.). Discuss fluoridation and chlorination of water, TV commercials on dentifrices, pesticides, and ecology (DDT), chlorinated biphenyls, fluorocarbon propellants, the Kepone episode as related in "Research Reporter," *Chemistry,* 49, 20 [1976] and 49, 24 [1976]). Discuss the noble gas compounds of fluorine. The role of theoretical chemistry as an instrument of prediction is typified by the suggestions of Pauling in 1933. A good source is Selig, H., Malm, J. G., and Classen, H., "The Chemistry of the Noble Gases, *Scientific American*. 210(5), 66–77 (1964). Student reports may be given based on this or other references. For instance, two reports on Teflon appear in *Chemistry,* 38 June and August, 1965. **Exhibits:** Salt, iodized salt, tincture of iodine, Teflon cookware, liquid bleach, and so on. If these activities are not used as an introduction, they may be used at appropriate times during the chapter development.

This chapter requires five periods. One possible arrangement is:

Lesson 1 Sections 30.1–30.3: Halogen Family, Fluorine
Lesson 2 Sections 30.4–30.8: Chlorine
Lesson 3 Sections 30.9–30.12: Hydrogen Chloride
Lesson 4 Sections 30.13–30.16: Bromine
Lesson 5 Sections 30.17–30.21: Iodine, Summary

Section 30.1. Exhibit samples, ball-and-stick and spatial models. Develop a chalkboard and student notebook table like Table 30-1. Add the data relating to ionization energy (Figure 5-7), electron affinity (Figure 5-10), and electronegativity (Figure 6-14). Give the students the symbol and atomic number, then let them determine the electron configuration, orbital notation, electron-dot symbol, etc. Have students explain how the atom X becomes the X^- ion, leading to the principal oxidation number. You may wish to review the acids of chlorine and have students determine other oxidation numbers, indicating that fluorine is unique in that it has only the oxidation number -1 in its compounds. Mention the meaning of halogen. Write the electron-dot formula(s) for X_2.

In each instance have students discuss the reasons for variations among the halogens. On the basis of electronegativities and electronegativity differences, discuss hydrogen bonding and acid strengths of the hydrogen halides. **Films:** CORF: 1643 *The Halogens (2nd Ed.)* (16+ min.); W: 140-4112 *Chemical Families* (22 min.); MH: 61200 or 612025 (C) *The Family of Halogens*.

Section 30.2. Discuss the discovery and preparation of fluorine, the reason for using a carbon anode (action of fluorine on metals of an electrolytic cell). **Reference:** Waggoner, W. H., "The Naming of Fluorine," *Journal of Chemical Education,* 53(1), 27 (1976); "Freon Refrigerants," *Journal of Chemical Education,* 52(6), 413 (1975). Discuss properties as in text. Emphasize the reasons for extreme electronegativity and reactivity as evidenced by explosion with H_2 in dark. Exhibit some fluorides. **Transparencies:** HM: 2-10528, *The Fluorine Molecule;* 2-10531 *The F_2O Molecule.* **References For Student Reports:** Muhler, J. C., "Fluoridated Water," *Journal of Chemical Education,* 57(7), 496 (1980); Miller, J. A., "Protecting Those Pearly Whites," *Science News* 116(23), 394 (1979); "Fluoride may find Wider Medicinal Use," *Chemical and Engineering News,* April 9 (1979).

Section 30.3. Exhibit fluorspar, fluoride insecticide (Merck Sodium Fluoride label includes warning about inhaling, swal-

lowing, and gives antidote), Freon, cryolite, toothpaste Teflon-coated cookware. Discuss uses of these substance Refer to Figure 29-2 and discuss the noble gas compound of fluorine. Discuss water fluoridation. **References:** Groth, E "Science and the Fluoridation Controversy," *Chemistr* 49(May), 5 (1976); Morton, W. E., "Fluoridation Contr versy Continues," *Chemistry,* 49(9), 28 (1976); "The Nob Gas Compounds," *Chemistry,* 37 (Jan.), (1964); "The Nob Gases and the Periodic Table," *Journal of Chemical Educ tion,* 46, 569 (1969). **Filmstrip:** I: 67108 The Noble Gase **Demonstration:** Exhibit plastic bottle (no-drip spout) hydrofluoric acid. Your laboratory may stock older typ containers: wax or lead bottles. Prepare H_2F_2 by mixing Cal and H_2SO_4 (concentrated) in a lead dish with a splint. waxed glass plate has some wax removed by a sharp instr ment and this side of the waxed plate is placed face downwa on the lead dish. The vapors of H_2F_2 etch the glass leavir a pattern after the wax is removed by hot water. See Alye p. 34 (15–34).

Section 30.4. Exhibit chlorides, table salt, iodized sa salt substitutes, rock salt, halite crystal, salt tablets, and model of NaCl. A student may report on the booklet, *Sa Today and Yesterday,* Morton Salt, Division of Morto Norwich, 110 North Wacker Drive, Chicago, IL 6060 **Reference:** Black, M. R., "The Social Influence of Salt, *Scientific American,* July (1963).

Sections 30.5 and 30.6. Demonstration: Demonstra the electrolysis of brine using a U-tube and carbon electrode Collect hydrogen through outlet tube and test by "bark test. Use red and blue litmus at both electrodes. Test for chlorir by odor and bleaching and test for NaOH with litmus. Devel electrode, net formula, and net ionic equations. Consider review equations for preparations as oxidation-reductic phenomena and, if desired, balance by redox technique Prepare and collect several bottles of Cl_2 using MnO_2 ar HCl (or $NaCl + H_2SO_4$). Stress the relationship betwee method of collection and properties as well as use of Na_2S_2O solution as safety trap for excess Cl_2. Use hood. Prepare rel tively "dry" Cl_2 by passing it through H_2SO_4 and calciu hypochlorite or bleaching powder. **Films:** SUTH: *Chlorine– A Representative Halogen;* PPG: *Electrolysis of Brine* (1 min.); PPG: *Commercial Production of Chlorine* (9+ min. **Transparency:** W: 75 W 8000 Cl_2. **Loops:** EBE: S-8156 *Electrolysis of an Aqueous Salt Solution.*

Section 30.7. Demonstrations: Powder Sb into Cl_2 Heated steel wool or Cu into Cl_2. Hydrogen jet into Cl_2 Turpentine soaked paper dropped into Cl_2. Dry red and blu litmus paper into "dry" Cl_2 prepared from bleaching pow der + H_2SO_4, then moistened litmus paper into same bottle Newspaper (printer's ink) into Cl_2. Write formula equatior for the above reactions and analyze as oxidation-reductio reactions. **Loop:** 168W 1003(T) *Alkali Metal Reactions wit Chlorine and Water.*

Section 30.8. Activities: Exhibit household bleache (i.e., liquid and dry bleaches). Read labels. **Demonstrat** $Cl_2 + Na_2CO_3$ for production of NaClO. Discuss **CAUTIO** and the warning "Do not mix household ammonia and hypc chlorite solution." **Activities:** Discuss chlorination as in te and necessity for removal of organic materials before chlorina tion. Exhibit and discuss use of chlorine in swimming pools isplay and use chlorine and pH tester used for swimming ools. Exhibit compounds and discuss their uses (Subsection 3). clude ethyl chloride. **Reference:** ''Chlorine and Hydrochloric cid: They Touch Our Lives Daily,'' *Journal of Chemical ducation,* 55(7), 466 (1978). ''How Halogens Reduce olymer Flammability,'' *Chemical and Engineering News,* ept. 13, 1976, p. 23.

Section 30.9. Prepare and collect HCl using a flask enerator as in Figure 30-3 and collecting HCl by upward dis- lacement of air. Have one bottle containing about 3–4 cm of ater. After collecting 3 bottles of the gas, place the delivery be about one cm above the water in the bottle. Have the udents observe the solution of HCl occurring as evidenced the oily convection currents that are observable when the ater is viewed from the side. Write equations and discuss her preparations including the burning of hydrogen in chlorine d chlorination processes (Sections 18.12 and 18.21). For notochemical reaction of H_2 and Cl_2 (explosion) see Alyea, 243 (20-8) and p. 154. **Reference:** ''More HCl Producers urn to Chlorine Burning,'' *Chemical and Engineering News,* ly 2, 1979, p. 9.

Section 30.10. **Activities:** Blow across top of bottle of Cl. Test for odor by waft test. Invert a bottle or test tube HCl in H_2O, remove cover, note rapid rise of H_2O. Test ith litmus. **Alternate Activity:** Demonstrate HCl fountain hange in color of blue litmus or change phenolphthalein to lorless). Repeat reaction of NH_3 + HCl by bringing moist- ed stoppers from HCl (con) and NH_3(aq). **Transparency:** : 75 W80000, *HCl.*

Section 30.11. **Demonstrations:** Test a sample of the eceding solution made with litmus. (The solution is concen- ated enough to react with magnesium if not with zinc.) edemonstrate protolysis by conductivity and litmus tests of luene + HCl before and after additions of H_2O. Mix luene solutions of HCl and NH_3. Bring moistened stoppers om concentrated hydrochloric acid and NH_3(aq) together. ote accumulation of solid on the outside of bottles of hydro- loric acid that may have been stored near NH_3(aq) in ockroom. Wash out a 500-mL cylinder with NH_3(aq). Posi- n the end of the delivery tube from HCl generator at bottom cylinder and pass in the HCl. A cloud and solid deposit of H_4Cl forms on the walls of the cylinder and, on occasion, a rceptible amount of H_2O may be poured from the inverted linder. Test HCl(g) with a burning splint for combustibility d for supporting combustion. Write equations for protolysis HCl (Brønsted acid) with H_2O and then with NH_3. Write uations for acid-base neutralization. If you do not demon- ate HCl toluene series, use **Loop:** W: 168 W 1041(T) *HCl Water and in Benzene.* **References:** Giguère, P. A., ''The eat Fallacy of the H^+ Ion: and the True Nature of H_3O^+,'' urnal of Chemical Education,* 56(9), 571 (1979).

Section 30.12. **Demonstrations:** Remove coating from ass doorknob or other brass fixture by rubbing with cotton oistened with concentrated hydrochloric acid. Discuss acid ncentration in gastric juice and recall or demonstrate the gestion of boiled egg white in pepsin + HCl. Precipitate rmation of $PbCl_2$ and Hg_2Cl_2. Demonstrate the test for $^-$ ion. Show the nonspecificity of merely adding $AgNO_3$ by monstrating precipitation with solutions of carbonate, osphate, and oxalate. Precipitates are somewhat white but

will dissolve in HNO_3. Develop the chloride ion test sequence by demonstrating solution of AgCl in NH_3(aq) and its reprecipitation with HNO_3. Write the equations.

Section 30.13. **Demonstrations:** Prepare and collect Br_2, using retort as in Figure 30-7. Have students guess why a test tube, glass, and rubber tubing assembly is not used. Hold mouth of retort under water in test tube. Have students note and explain. Have them note formation of dark red globule of Br_2 under water in test tube. The water solution of Br_2 above may be used as bromine water in later demonstra- tions. Add Cl_2 water to solution of a bromide. Perform the shake-out test with perchloroethylene (CS_2, $CHCl_3$, CCl_4). As a control, demonstrate shake-out test with bromine water. Write the equations in the text.

Section 30.14. If necessary redo solubility tests (Section 30.13). **Film:** W: 140 4175 *Bromine—Element from the Sea.*

Section 30.15. **Activity:** Discuss as in text. **Demonstra- tion:** Water solution of bromine bleaches litmus paper and dye in cloth. Have students explain, as for bleaching by chlorine water. **Loop:** W: 168 W 1036(T) *Bromine Reactions with Red Phosphorus, Hydrogen, and Aluminum.*

Section 30.16. Refer to or show again **Film:** *Bromine— Element from the Sea.* Refer to Dow booklet, ''Bromine and Brominated Compounds.'' Discuss uses as in text. Exhibit Bromoseltzer, AgBr in photography. **Demonstrate:** NaBr + $AgNO_3$. Test for bromide ion. Differentiate between test for free, elemental bromine and the colorless bromide ion, which must be replaced by the more active chlorine.

Section 30.17. Discuss discovery, occurrence, and re- covery of iodine. Refer to Toon and Ellis, *Foundations of Chemistry,* p. 594, for explanation of production from iodates. For production of iodine, refer to Figure 30-9. Phosphoric acid may be used instead of sulfuric acid, which on occasion will not produce the sublimed crystals of I_2 on the bottom of the evaporating dish. Demonstrate replacement in iodide solution both by chlorine and bromine, thus establishing relative reactivities.

Sections 30.18 and 30.19. **Demonstration: (1)** Subli- mate a few small iodine crystals in a test tube by heating. Pour out the vapor. Note iodine crystals on the upper part of the test tube. **(2)** Solubility: Procedure 2, Experiment ''Halide Ions.'' **(3)** Starch test for free iodine. **(4)** Liquefaction of Iodine (Alyea, p. 203). **(5)** I_2 + White P **(CAUTION). (6)** Comparative reactivity: antimony + chlorine; antimony heated in deflagrating spoon + Br_2(g); antimony (heated) into hot iodine (g). Replacement of I^- by both chlorine water and bromine water with shake-out test. Refer to Tables 22-3 and 22-4 for oxidation and reduction data of the halogens and halide ions.

Sections 30.20 and 30.21. Exhibit tincture of iodine, current iodine-complexed organic compounds (antiseptic), iodized salt. Discuss use of radioactive iodine in medicine. **Demonstrate:** KI + $AgNO_3$ to produce precipitate of AgI. Have students note color and reaction to light (photography). Refer to organic iodides and use in Grignard and Williamson reactions. Repeat tests for iodide using both Cl_2 and Br_2 solu- tions. Demonstrate starch test for I_2 and its failure with iodide solutions. **Other Halogen Demonstrations:** *Journal of Chemical Education,* 46, A107-108, A355-356, A309-310, A451 (1969). Hydrogen halides: Fowles, Experiment 325, 326 for preparation from PBr_3 and PI_3. **Demonstrations:** Place a sample of the sodium or potassium halide in Erlenmeyer flasks. Add H_2SO_4 to each halide and heat. The vapors from the fluoride etch the flask; from the bromide they are red-brown; from the iodide they are violet; and from the chloride, colorless. (HCl will fume if you blow across the top of the flask.) The results are representative of the methods for producing HF and HCl and of the smaller resistance to oxidation by the HBr and HI. **Demonstration of Interhalide Compound: (ICl_3 or $KICl_4$):** Place a long strip of filter paper in a 500-mL cylinder. Chlorine enters the cylinder through a glass delivery tube reaching the cylinder bottom. At first, the expected happens (the paper turns brown), but the iodine then reacts with excess chlorine to form the yellow compound(s) from the bottom up (of the paper in the cylinder). **Summary: Films:** *Preparation and Properties of the Halogens* (32 min.). CORF: 1643 *The Halogens (2nd ed.)* (16 + min.). **Filmstrip:** I: 67104 *Group VI—The Halogens.* Useful booklets may be available from: The Chlorine Institute, 342 Madison Ave., New York, NY 10017; The Dow Chemical Co., Midland, MI. **References:** Spadaro, J. J., "Qualitative Analysis of the Halogens," *Journal of Chemical Education,* 57(5), 372 (1980), (uses hexane as a solvent instead of CCl_4); Muhler, J. C., "Fluoridated Water," *Journal of Chemical Education,* 57(7), 496 (1980); "Fluoride May Find Wider Medicinal Use," *Chemical and Engineering News,* Apr. 9, 1979, p. 29; "Fluoride: Prevents Caries Longer," *Science News,* 116(21) 358 (1979); "Chlorine and Hydrochloric Acid: They Touch Our Lives Daily," *Journal of Chemical Education,* 55(7), 66 (1978); Linda, F. W., Hollenbach, R. C., "The Backyard Pool," *SciQuest,* 52(5), 6 (1979); "Health Effects and Hydrocarbons," *Chemistry,* 51(8), 20 (1970), (DDT, HCP, PCB, PBB); Leddy, J. J., "The Chlor-Alkali Industry," *Journal of Chemical Education,* 57(9), 640 (1980).

Teacher Notes
Chapter 31

Chapter Note

The chapter content affords many opportunities for student reports and class discussion of such related problems as nuclear energy and nuclear reactors; dangers of radioactive fallout; disposal of radioactive wastes; nuclear weapons; national and international policies; nuclear research; usefulness of radioisotopes. Such discussions alert students to the political, social, economic, and international aspects of radioactivity and nuclear energy.

Many teachers make use of demonstrations of radioactivity in establishing the details of atomic structure in Chapter 3. Students have also learned details of Rutherford's experiment and its implications in Chapter 3. Review nuclear changes as considered in Chapter 2.

This chapter requires five periods. One possible arrangement is:

Lesson 1 Sections 31.1–31.5: Natural Radioactivity: Discoveries, Properties, Half-life, Nature of Radiation(s)

Lesson 2 Sections 31.6–31.8: Natural Radioactivity: Radioactive Decay, Radioactive Series, Nuclear Equations

Lesson 3 Sections 31.9–31.13: Artificial Radioactivity Nuclear Stability, Historical Nuclear Disintegrations, Neutron Emission

Lesson 4 Sections 31.14–31.17: Artificial Radioactivity: Accelerators, Neutron Bullets, Artificial Radioactive Elements (atoms)

Lesson 5 Sections 31.18–31.21: Uranium Fission, Nuclear Chain Reaction, Nuclear Reactor(s), Fusion Reactions

Sections 31.1 and 31.2. Exhibit a radiophoto of an object such as a key as an example of Becquerel's discovery. Exhibit a mineral that fluoresces and a sample of uranium ore. Have radioactivity defined. **References:** Becquerel biography, *Journal of Chemical Education,* 39, 533 (1962); Biggs, K., "Pierre and Marie Curie," *Chemistry,* 49(7), 21 (1976). Consult the *Twenty-Five Year Cumulative Index of the Journal of Chemical Education* for articles on the Curies.

Sections 31.3 and 31.4. Review the physical and chemical properties of radium listed in Table 25-1. **Demonstrations:** Refer to Figure 31-2 and demonstrate the discharge of a Braun electroscope by a radioactive source. Demonstrate the change in count of a Geiger counter exposed to a radioactive source. Test a luminous watch with the Geiger counter. Define half-life. Refer students to Table 31-1 for half-life data. Mention other half-life data: iodine-131, 8 days; phosphorus-34, 14.3 days; strontium-90, 20 years. You may wish to discuss fallout and strontium-90. **Demonstrate:** Wilson cloud chamber (student project or commercial variety). **Half-life Demonstration:** Use "Minigenerator," available from Welch or other science apparatus supply companies. Use Table 31-1 for student location of natural radioactive nuclides with atomic number less than 83(Bi). Mention use of rubidium-strontium dating in determining the age of the earth and of moon rocks, and of carbon-14 in dating artifacts. Discuss the generalizations in Section 31.3. Ask why astatine and francium are not included among the natural radioactive nuclides. State the use of radon: refer to *Chemistry,* "Latest on Chemistry of Radon," 42, Dec. (1969). See the "Minigenerator" Laboratory Manual, Welch 219M for related demonstrations. Discuss factors that may alter the half-life of a nuclide. **Reference:** Hopke, P. K., "Extranuclear Effects on Nuclear Decay Rates," *Journal of Chemical Education,* 51(8), 517 (1974). Use the Practice Problems of Section 31.3. Discuss the details of Section 31.4. **Film:** EBE: 2937 *Geiger Counter* (8 min.). **Filmstrip:** I: 67249 *Radioactivity;* EBE: Series 10690 *Radioisotopes, Natural and Man-made;* **Loop:** EBE: S 81261 *Determining the Half-life of a Radioisotope.* **References:** Section 31.4, Gottlieb, H. H., "Half-life Using Short-lived Radioisotopes," *The Physics Teacher,* Apr. 1968, p. 176; Skinner, S. B., "A Simple Experiment to Illustrate Exponential Decay, Half-life and Time Constant," *The Physics Teacher,* May 1971, p. 269.

Section 31.5. Since students may have difficulty in interpreting the effects of a powerful magnetic field on the complex radiation given off by a small particle of radioactive material (Figure 31-5), use a chalkboard diagram that shows the effect of two oppositely charged plates on the beam of radiation given off. Indicate that a Geiger counter would locate only a single beam if the plates are not superposed. Then show the results when the charged plates are used. The direction and relative amounts of deflection due to the charged plates are used to help the students realize the identity and properties of the radiation particles and rays. Use a beta source (Uranyl nitrate) and a gamma source (Thorium nitrate) and sheets of paper, glass, aluminum, and lead to show penetration and shielding effects. Impress students by showing that gamma radiations (rays) go through the hand but betas are stopped. **Transparency:** EYE: 003-36 *Types of Radiation;* EYE: 003-33 *Ionizing Radiations.*

Sections 31.6 and 31.7. Activities: Illustrate Figures 31-6 and 31-7 with nuclear equations in stepwise fashion. Define transmutation. Stress the energy concomitant and the effects of alpha and beta emissions on the mass number and atomic number of the product nucleus in each transmutation. **Transparency:** HRW: PP transparency T44 *Radioactive Displacement Rules* details changes in the number and kinds of nucleons. For beta emission use: neutron → proton + electron. Overlays for PP T44, 44E, and 44F deal with positron emission (β^+). Write nuclear equations for alpha and beta emissions. Have students do the Practice Problems. **Transparency:** EYE: 003-37 *Radioactive Decay.* **Reference:** Wolsey, W. C., "Variations of Radioactive Decay Rates," *Journal of Chemical Education,* 55(5), 302 (1978).

Section 31.8. Discuss: The uses of radioactivity in determining age of earth, moon dust, moon rocks, and the use of carbon-dating. Also discuss potassium-argon dating and write equation for orbital electron capture changing potassium-40 to argon-40. **Student Report References:** Garrett, A. B., "The Flash of Genius," 13, Van Nostrand, 1962; "Carbon-14 Dating," Willard F. Libby (original article in *Journal of Chemical Education,* 40, 76 (1963)); Kamen, M. D., "The Early History of Carbon-14," *Journal of Chemical Education,* 40 276 (1963); *Scientific American,* "Clocks," 234(3), 60D (1976); Schramm, D. N., "The Age of the Elements," *ibid.,* 230(1), 69 (1974); "A Rock from the Moon's Early Days," *Science News,* 105(13), 205 (1974); "Getting More Out of Carbon-14," *Scientific American,* 239(2), 69 (1978); Moorbath, S., "The Oldest Rocks and the Growth of Continents," *Scientific American,* 236(3), 92 (1977). **Filmstrips:** EYE (Nuclear Radiation series): 2-5A *Use of Detectors,* 2-5B *Uses in Medicine,* 2-5C *Uses in Earth Science,* 2-5D *Outer Space,* 2-5E *Uses in Industry,* 2-5F *Fallout;* EBE: Series 10690 *Radiation and Practical Uses, Measuring with Radiation, The Atomic Detective.* **Film:** EBE: 2784 *Radioisotopes: Tools of Discovery* (11 min.).

Sections 31.9 and 31.10. Define and illustrate nuclear mass defect and nuclear binding energy. Develop the generalizations pertaining to the stability of a nucleus and nuclides: atomic number increase, neutron-proton ratio, the even-odd relationships of the number of protons and neutrons. Illustrate as in Section 31.9. Discuss the four types of nuclear reactions and the related changes in stability. Discuss how the release of alpha particles from a radioactive nucleus decreases the number of protons and neutrons (alpha particle release) and how the release of beta particles both yield a product nucleus that is more stable than the original nucleus. Refer to Figures 31-6, 31-9, and Section 31.7. **Filmstrips** from individual programs: PH: WCC 856 *The Nucleus, Stability and Decay;* Ward's Solo-Learn: 78-0770 *Introduction to Artificial Radioactivity.* **Transparencies:** EYE: 003-37 *Radioactive Decay;*

EYE: 003-34 *Nuclear Binding Energy.* **References:** Bodner, G., "Binding Energy and Atomic Weight Calculations," *Journal of Chemical Education,* 55(9), 598 (1978); Loveland, W., "Nuclear Beta Decay," *Journal of Chemical Education,* 56(4), 250 (1979). See pp. 559 and 571, *Modern Physics,* 1980 ed. for a calculation of binding energy and Section 21.2, *Foundations of Chemistry.*

Section 31.11. Write the equation for Rutherford's first artificial nuclear disintegration. See page 569 and Figure 24-7, *Modern Physics,* 1980 ed. for details of the experiment. Use the text Figure 31-11.

Section 31.12. Write the equation for the Cockroft-Walton experiment. Calculate the loss in μ and convert to Mev by multiplying by 931. See Appendix Table 5, *Modern Physics,* 1980 ed. for converting Mev to ergs and joules.

Section 31.13. Write the partial equation for Chadwick's discovery of the neutron, writing $^{12}_{6}C$ as one product. Have students attempt to determine the atomic number and mass of the other product. Refer to Section 23.9, *Modern Physics,* 1980 ed. for details and see Figure 23-12.

Section 31.14. Discuss details of the accelerators described in this section with the aid of Figures 31-12, 31-13, and 31-14. **Films:** USDE: 495 *Building an Atomic Accelerator* (28 min.); USDE: 431 *Exploring the Atomic Nucleus* (13+ min.), USDE: 500 *The Heart of the Matter* (6 min.). **Filmstrip:** I: 67255 *Particle Accelerators.* **References:** Sections 25.4–25.7, Particle Accelerators, *Modern Physics,* 1980 ed. Use the model Van de Graff generator or a student-constructed model to demonstrate stimulating experiments including some "hair-raising" experiments. **References:** *Scientific American* Offprints: 234, "The Linear Accelerator"; 251, Particle Accelerators"; 322, "The Two-Mile Electron Accelerator"; Rosen, L., "Particle Accelerators: Instruments of Basic Research and Human Welfare, *The Physics Teacher,* Nov. 1970, p. 432; Trower, W. P., "The Accelerator in Particle Physics," *The Science Teacher,* Nov. 1969, p. 25; Wilson, R. R., "The Next Generation of Particle Accelerators," *Scientific American,* 242(1), 42 (1980); Thomson, D. E., "Tom Swift and His Electric Synchrotron," *Science News,* 111(18), 282 (1977); Thomson, D. E., "Atom Smashers—50 Years," *Science News,* 112(25), 410 (1977); Frazier, K., "Superheavy Elements," *Science News,* 113(15), 236 (1978).

Sections 31.15 and 31.16. Refer to the nuclear equation for Chadwick's experiment as neutron production. Discuss fast neutrons, possible nuclear disintegration, production of slow neutrons (deuterium oxide and graphite), capture of any unstable nucleus that may result. Develop the equation series for neutron capture by uranium-238. Use the equations in Table 31-2 to illustrate methods for the production of the transuranium elements. **References:** *Chemistry,* Reprint 90 "Plutonium, the Lively Element, Parts I and II"; "Discovery of Element 105," 43, Nov. (1970); "Predicted Properties of Elements 113 and 114," 43, Nov. (1970); *Scientific American* Offprints: Seaborg, G. T., and Perlman, I., "The Synthetic Elements" (I) 242; (II) 243; (III) 293; Seaborg, G. T., *Manmade Transuranium Elements,* Prentice-Hall, 1963; Seaborg, G. T., "Some Recollections of Early Nuclear Chemistry," *Journal of Chemical Education,* 45, 278 (1968). Waldrop, M., "Nuclear Chemistry," *Chemical and Engineering News,* May 21, 1979, p. 16; Frazier, K., "Superheavy Elements,"

Science News, 113(15), 236 (1978). **Film:** W: 140-4178 *Transuranium Elements* (23 min.).

Section 31.17. Write equations for the preparation of cobalt-60 and phosphorus-32. Discuss the uses of radioactive isotopes. **Films:** USDE: 466 *Isotopes in Environmental Control* (14 min.); USDE: 304 *Radioisotope Scanning in Medicine* (16 min.); USDE: 471 *Short-lived Radioisotopes in Nuclear Medicine*.

Sections 31.18 and 31.19. Write the nuclear equation for fission. Redefine fission (Section 31.9). Have students examine Figure 31-15 and determine the most probable products (mass numbers). Discuss fission-track dating (Figure 31-16). Review the equations in Section 31.16 for the production of plutonium-239. Use Figure 31-17 as the basis of the definition of a chain reaction. **References:** Starke, K., "The Detours Leading to the Discovery of Nuclear Fission," *Journal of Chemical Education*, 56(12), 771 (1979); Deffeyes, K. S., and MacGregor, I. D., "World Uranium Resources," *Scientific American*, 242(1), 66 (1980); Mickey, "Nuclear Energy," *Journal of Chemical Education*, 57(5), 360 (1980); "Energy from Uranium," *Journal of Chemical Education*, 56(2), 119 (1979) (various types of nuclear reactors with good diagrams); West, R. J., "Natural Nuclear Reactors," *Journal of Chemical Education*, 53(6), 336 (1976); Cowan, G. A., "Natural Fission Reactor," *Scientific American*, 235(1), 36 (1976); "The Fossil Reactors of Gabon," *Scientific American*, 232(6), 41 (1975).

Section 31.20. Construct a chalkboard equivalent of Figure 31-18 in outline form. Discuss details of structure and operation (shield, fuel, moderator, control rods, heat exchange coolant). Define nuclear reactor. Discuss critical mass. Outline the present problems. Possible student reports. **Films:** EBE: 3397 *Learning About Nuclear Energy*, 2nd ed. (15 min.); NAVC: 001445-HH *Basic Principles of Power Reactors;* NAVC: 558924-HH *Nuclear Power and the Environment* (14 min.); CVF(G.E.) *How a Boiling Water Reactor Operates* (11 min.); USDE: 180 *Introducing Atoms and Nuclear Energy* (11 min.). **Filmstrips:** EBE: Series 10690 *Introducing Atomic Energy, Harnessing the Atom*. **Individualized Programs:** PH: WCC 857 *Fission and Fusion Reactions;* Ward's Solo-Learn: 78-0760 *Introduction to Nuclear Fission and Fusion*. **Filmstrip or Slides:** R: *The Storage and Disposal of Radioactive Waste*. **Transparency:** W: 167 Q 0120 series *Atomic Fission, Nuclear Reactor*. **References:** Cohen, B. L., "The Disposal of Radioactive Wastes from Fission Reactors, *Scientific American*, 236(6), 21 (1977); Rose, D. J., and Lester, R. K., "Nuclear Power, Nuclear Weapons and International Stability," *Scientific American*, 238(4), 45 (1978); Lewis, K. N., "The Prompt and Delayed Effects of Nuclear War," *Scientific American*, 241(1), 35 (1979); Lewis, H. W., "The Safety of Fission Reactors," *Scientific American*, 242(3), 53 (1980); "Political Problem," *Scientific American*, 242(5), 78 (1980); Epstein, W., "A Ban on the Production of Fissionable Material for Weapons," *Scientific American*, 243(1), 43 (1980); Guillan, M. A., "Protecting Nuclear Material: 'Combative' Research," *Science News*, 112(7), 108 (1977); "More Cancer Links to Low-level Radiation," *Science News*, 113(8), 117 (1978); Duaglas, J. H., "The Nuclear Dilemma," *Science News*, 113(244), 394 (1978); Raloff, J., "Radiation: Can a Little Hurt?" *Science News*,

115(3), 44 (1979); Raloff, J., "A Nuclear Watershed," *Science News*, 116(3), 45 (1979); West, S., "Rad Wastes," *Science News*, 116(3), 47 (1979); Weaver, K. F., and Krostof E., "The Promise and Peril of Nuclear Energy," *National Geographic*, 155(4), 459 (1979). From *The Science Teacher* series by Moore, J. W., and Moore, E. A.: "Fission Power—Panacea or Faustian Bargain, 1. Types of Reactors," 42(8) 21 (1975); 2. Possible Hazards," 42(9), 34 (1975).

Section 31.21. Define fusion (Section 31.9). Write the nuclear equations for $2{}_1^2\text{H}$ to ${}_2^3\text{He} + {}_0^1\text{n}$, $4\,{}_1^1\text{H}$ to ${}_2^4\text{He}$, and ${}_3^6\text{Li}{}_1^2\text{H}$ to $2{}_2^4\text{He}$ as described in *Modern Physics*, 1980 ed. Section 24.8. Identify these as thermonuclear reactions. Discuss details of fusion reactions. **Films:** BFA: 11649 *Fusion The Ultimate Fire* (also USDE 532) (13+ min.); NAVC 008861-HH *The Ultimate Energy* (also USDE 509) (28 min.) NAVC: 007707-HH *Challenge of the Future* (Fusion) (29 min.). **Filmstrips:** See Section 31.20. **Transparency:** W 167 Q 0120 set *Atomic Fusion*. **References:** "Tandem Mirror," *SciQuest*, 52 (5), 24 (1979) (experimental fusion machines); "Fusion Power—Here and Now," *Chemistry* 51(9), 24 (1979); Yonas, G., "Fusion Power with Particle Beams," *Scientific American*, 239(5), 50 (1978); Furth, H. P. "Progress toward a Tokomak Fusion Reactor," *Scientific American*, 241(2), 51 (1979); "Carbon Dioxide Laser: Fusion at Last," *Science News*, 111(11), 166 (1977); "Fusion by Electron Beam Produced at Sandia," *Science News*, 112(1) 4 (1977); "Thermonuclear Burn In Laser Fusion," *Science News*, 112(2), 21 (1977); Fowler, T. K., and Post, R. F. "Progress Toward Fusion Power," *Scientific American*, 215(6), 21 (1966); Freilich, F. G., "Radiation and People," *The Physics Teacher*, 8 49 (1970). **Questions:** 10–20, 31–40. **References:** Walters, E. A., and Wewerka, E. M., "An Overview of the Energy Crisis," *Journal of Chemical Education*, 52(5), 282 (1975); Bethe, H. A., "The Necessity of Fission Power," *Scientific American*, 234(1), 21 (1976); Anderson, E. V., "Nuclear Energy: A Key Role Despite Problems," *Chemical and Engineering News*, 8, March (1977); York, H. P., "The Debate over the Hydrogen Bomb," *Scientific American*, 233(4), 106 (1975); McDougall, J. D., "Fission—Track Dating," *Scientific American*, 235(6), 114 (1976). The series below gives a history of recent fusion developments: Emmett, J. L., Nuckolls, J., and Wood, L., "Fusion Power by Laser Implosion," *Scientific American*, 230(6), 24 (1974); "Laser Fusion: Breakeven Within 3 Years," *Science News*, 107(23), 364 (1975); "Fusion Targets Disclosed," *Science News*, 107(24), 384 (1975); "Hope on the Road to Controlled Fusion," *Science News*, 108(21), 324 (1975); "Laser Fusion: Toward 'Brand X,'" *Science News*, 109(14), 212 (1976); "Electron Beam Fusion," *Science News*, 109(14) 212 (1976); Thomsen, D. E., "Shiva, Argus & Co.," *Science News*, 110(8), 74 (1976); Thomsen, D. E., "Mirror, Mirror in the Lab," *Science News*, 110(8), 121 (1976); "X-ray Photos Confirm Fusion Calculations," *Science News*, 110(12), 182 (1976); "Argus Hits a Billion," *Science News*, 110(20), 311 (1976); "Laser Fusion: Frequency Not So Critical," *Science News*, 110(22), 340 (1976); "High-beta Baseball Plasma," *Science News*, 110(24), 380 (1976); Thomsen, D. E., "Double Your Pleasure, Double Your Fun," *Science News*, 111(4), 61 (1977). Write for *Scientific American* catalog of offprints, which lists about fifty related articles.

Key to Suppliers

PART 3

Audiovisual Aids

These general sources are highly recommended by the High School Editor of the *Journal of Chemical Education* for your chemistry or school library.

   1. *Educator's Guide to Free Science Materials,* Mary H. Saterson (editor), Educators Progress Service, Randolph, WI, 1979 (audiovisual and printed items).
   2. ACS publication, *Topics-Aids—A Guide to Instructional Resources for General Chemistry.*
   3. National Information for Educational Media, University of Southern California, University Park, Los Angeles, CA 90007. (A complete listing of all 16-mm films available—both free and for rent.)

The **Key to Audiovisual Aids** lists the identifying letter(s) for producers or distributors (with their addresses) used throughout the **Teacher Notes,** PART 2, *Teacher's Edition, Modern Chemistry 1982.*

There are many features of the Secondary School Section of the *Journal of Chemical Education* that provide a wide variety of timely source materials. These include (1) Chemical Bingo: largely printed material; (2) AV review: evaluation and details of available products.

Booklets

Teachers may inquire from the following sources as to the availability of free or inexpensive booklets that may be useful as supplemental materials.

Alcoa, 818 Alcoa Building, Pittsburgh, PA 15219. "Alcoa Information Aids," list of literature and motion pictures (Chap. 26).

Aluminum Association, 818 Connecticut Ave., NW, Washington, DC 20006.

American Gas Association, 1515 Wilson Blvd., Arlington, VA 22209.

American Iron and Steel Institute, 150 W. 42 St., New York, NY 10017.

American Paper Institute, 260 Madison Ave., New York, NY 10017.

American Petroleum Institute, 1801 K St., NW, Washington, DC 20006.

The Chlorine Institute, Inc., 342 Madison Ave., New York, NY 10017.

Corning Glass Works, Corning, New York.

Foote Mineral Co., Route 100, Exton, PA 19341.

General Electric Co., Room 901, 570 Lexington Ave., New York, NY 10022.

B. F. Goodrich Co., 277 Park Ave., New York, NY 10017.

The Goodyear Tire and Rubber Co., 50 Rockefeller Plaza, New York, NY 10020.

Hach Chemical Co., P.O. Box 907, Ames, IA 50010.

Manufacturing Chemists' Association, 1825 Connecticut Ave., NW, Washington, DC 20009.

Mobil Oil Co., Room 647, 150 E. 42 St., New York, NY 10017.

Morton-Norwich Products, Inc., 110 North Wacker Drive, Chicago, IL 60606.

Zinc Institute, Inc., 292 Madison Ave., New York, NY 10017.

Demonstration Sources

*Alyea, H. N., Dutton, F. B., *Tested Demonstrations in Chemistry,* 6th ed., Journal of Chemical Education, Chemical Education Publishing Co., 20 & Northhampton Sts., Easton, PA 18042, 1969.

Alyea, N. N., *TOPS in General Chemistry,* Journal of Chemical Education, 1967, 337 Harrison St., Princeton, NJ 08540. Compiler: *TOPS in General Chemistry,* 3rd ed.; *Armchair Chemistry: Using TOPS Equipment,* 2nd ed.; *Microchemistry Projected: The 200 Best TOPS Experiments,* 3rd ed.

Chemistry Handbook, New York State Education Department, Albany, NY 12224, 1962.

Chen, P. S., *Entertaining and Educational Chemical Demonstrations,* Chemical Elements Publishing Co., 529 Mission Drive, Camarillo, CA 93010.

Ford, L. A. *Chemical Magic,* Fawcett World Library, 67 W. 44 St., New York, NY 10036.

Fowles, G., *Lecture Experiments in Chemistry,* Bell & Sons, London, 1957.

Fowles, G., *Science Masters' Book,* Series III, Part II—Chemistry, 1955; Series IV, Part 2—Chemistry, 1964.

Lawrence, W. S., *Chemical Investigations for Changing Times,* Burgess Publishing Co., 7180 Ohms Lane, Minneapolis, MN 55435.

Meiners, H. H. Ed., *Physics Demonstration Experiments,* The Ronald Press Co., 79 Madison Ave., New York, NY 10016

*In the **Teacher Notes,** this reference appears simply as Alyea.

Lab Bench Experiments in Chemistry, SciQuest (formerly *Chemistry*), Reprint Department, 1155 Sixteenth St., NW, Washington, DC 20036.

Physics Handbook, New York State Education Department, Albany, NY 12224, 1970. (The 1956 edition is also available.)

Teacher's Guide for High School Regents Chemistry, Curriculum Report no. 422-1500-SS, Bureau of Curriculum Development, Board of Education, The City of New York, 110 Livingston St., Brooklyn, NY 11201, 1968.

Weaver, E. C., *Experiments in Environmental Pollution; Experiments in the Chemistry of Foods,* Manufacturing Chemists' Association, 1825 Connecticut Ave., NW, Washington, DC 20009.

Vlassis, C. C., *Alchemy Revisited: Chemistry Experiments for Today,* Oxford University Press, 200 Madison Ave., New York, NY 10016.

From Journals: Features

Journal of Chemical Education:
Tested Demonstrations, Gilbert, G. L., Ed.
Chem Ed Compacts, Wold, W. A., Ed.
High School Forum, Herron, J. D., Ed.
50-Minute Experiment, Baruch, G., Ed.
Ideas from Everywhere, Smith, D. D., Ed.
Chem I Supplement, Journal of Chemical Education Staff

The Science Teacher
Idea Bank, Talesnick, L., Ed.

CHEM 13 News
Lab Bench, University of Waterloo, Waterloo, Ontario, N213 G1, Canada.

Equipment Sources

Aloe Scientific Div. of Brunswick Corp., 1150 Flower St., Los Angeles, CA 90015.

Atomic Accessories, Inc., 811 West Merrick Rd., Valley Stream, NY 11580.

Atomic Laboratories, Inc., 3088 Claremont Ave., Berkeley, CA 94705.

Baird-Atomic, 35 University Road, P.O. Box 400, Cambridge, MA 02138.

Cenco (Central Scientific Co.), 2600 S. Kostner Ave., Chicago, IL 60623.

Ealing Corp., 2225 Massachusetts Ave., Cambridge, MA 02140.

Edmund Scientific Co., 103 Gloucester Pike, Barrington, NJ 08007.

Educational Materials and Equipment Co., 41 Lafayette Ave., New Rochelle, NY 10801.

Fisher Scientific Co., Educational Materials Division, 4901 W. LeMoyne Ave., Chicago, IL 60651.

Klinger Scientific Apparatus Corp., 83-45 Parsons Blvd., Jamaica, NY 11432.

Labasco (Standard Scientific Supply Corp.), 808 Broadway, New York, NY 10003.

Lab Safety Supply Co., P.O. Box 1368, Janesville, WI 53545.

La Pine Scientific Co., 6001 S. Knox Ave., Chicago, IL 60629.

Lemont Specialties, Box 271, Lemont, PA 16581.

Merrell Scientific Division, The Educational Modules, Inc., 1685 Buffalo Road, Rochester, NY 14624.

Metrologic Instruments, Inc., 143 Harding Ave., Bellmar, NJ 08030.

Nuclear-Chicago Corp., 301 E. Howard Ave., Des Plaines, IL 60618.

Sargent-Welch Scientific Co., 7300 N. Linder Ave., Skokie, IL 60076.

Scientific Glass Apparatus Co., 737 Broad St. Bloomfield, NJ 07003.

Sesco, Inc., 1312 S. Thirteenth St., Vincennes, IN 47591.

Stansi Scientific Co., 1231-45 N. Honore St., Chicago, IL 60622.

Wilkens-Anderson Co., 4515 W. Division St., Chicago, IL 60651.

Will Corporation, Wilco Drive, Rochester, NY 14603.

Note: Many of the companies listed above supply models in great variety. The following companies specialize in models

Dyna-Slide Co., 1566 Sherman Ave., Evanston, IL 60201 (Stereofold).

Ealing Corp., 2225 Massachusetts Ave., Cambridge, MA 02140. (Ask for Atomic Model Reference Library.) (SRM Molecular, Orbital, and Crystal Model Systems, Scale Model Molecular Models.)

Edmund Scientific Co., Barrington, NJ 08007 (Atomic, Molecular, and Crystal Models).

Klinger Scientific Co., 83-45 Parsons Blvd., Jamaica, NY 11432.

Macro Models, 948 Howard St., San Francisco, CA 94103.

Scientific Educational Products Corp., 30 E. 42 St., New York NY 10017.

Science Related Materials, Inc., P.O. Box 1422, Janesville WI 53545 (Large-scale models for class display studen kits).

Thomas, Arthur H., Co., Ninth St. at Third, P.O. Box 779 Philadelphia, PA.

Class-constructed models: Student-constructed types may be assembled from plastic spheres, eggs, and teardrops, which may be purchased from such companies as:

Ace Plastic Co., 91-30 Van Wyck Expressway, Jamaica, NY 11435.

Lemont Specialties (see above).

Plasteel Corp., 26970 Princeton St., Inkster, MI.

Star Band Co., Inc., Board and Commerce Sts., Portsmouth VA.

Student Kits: Cenco or O. H. Jons Glas Co., Ltd., 219 Broad view Ave., Toronto, Canada (Jonsglas Student Molecula Models).

Sargent-Welch: 5736 Student Molecular Kit. (See list of sup pliers for address.)

Printed Matter Related to Models

Gordon, A. J., "A Survey of Atomic and Molecular Models," *Journal of Chemical Education,* 47, 30 (1970). Lists mode types, commercially available model sets, suppliers, an specific references to articles.

Wells, A. F., *Models in Structural Inorganic Chemistry*, Oxford University Press, New York, NY (1970), paper. Kit available.

Sanderson, R. T., *Principles and Construction of New Chemistry Aids*, Bureau of Audio-Visual Instruction, State University of Iowa, Iowa City, IA.

King, L. C., "Molecular Architecture," *Chemistry*, 37, 12 (1964); "Molecular Architecture," *The Science Teacher*, 33, 6 (1966)

Bassow, H., *Construction and Use of Atomic and Molecular Models*, Pergamon Press, Inc., 395 Sawmill River Rd., Elmsford, NY 10523.

McNab, W. K., McClellan, A. L., *Modeling Chemical Structures*, 10 Morningside Drive, San Anselmo, CA 94960.

Indexes, Guides, Handbooks

American Chemical Society, *Aids and Sources for the Science Teacher: A Guide for the Science Teacher; Topic-Aids* (A guide to instructional resources), O'Connor, R., Ed.

Chemistry (now *SciQuest*) List of Reprints, Reprint Dept; *12 Year Chemistry Index (1964–1975)*, 1155 Sixteenth St., NW, Washington, DC 20036.

Chen, P. S., *A New Handbook of Chemistry*, Chemical Elements Publishing Co., 529 Mission Drive, Camarillo, CA 93010.

Journal of Chemical Education, 25-year Cumulative Index (Vol. 1–25, 1924–49); 10-year Cumulative Index (Vol. 26–35, 1949–58); 10-year Cumulative Index (Vol. 26–45, 1959–68).

Lange's Handbook of Chemistry, Dean, J. A., Ed., Ace Scientific Supply Co., Inc., 1420 E. Linden Ave., Linden, NJ 07036.

Scientific American Cumulative Index: May 1948–June 1978, 415 Madison Ave., New York, NY 10017.

Scientific American Offprints. Annual Catalog listing all available reprints, W. H. Freeman Co., 660 Market St., San Francisco, CA 94104.

The Merck Index, Merck & Co., Inc., Rahway, NJ 07065.

Handbook of Chemistry and Physics, Annual, CRC Press, Inc., Boca Raton, FL 33431.

Note

1. The April issues of *Journal of Chemical Education* contain a section listing the paperback publications of the National Bureau of Standards Reference Data System, U.S. Dept. of Commerce, National Bureau of Standards, Washington, DC 20234.

2. The December issues of such publications as *Chemistry, Journal of Chemical Education* and *Scientific American* include a yearly Index.

3. The September issue of the *Journal of Chemical Education* includes a section, Book Buyers' Guide: Texts, Laboratory Manuals, Programmed Instruction, Paperbacks, and Audiovisual Materials.

Journals

Chem 13 News, University of Waterloo, Waterloo, Ontario, N2L 3G1, Canada

Chemical and Engineering News, American Chemical Society, 1155 Sixteenth St., NW, Washington, DC 20036.

Journal of Chemical Education, Chemical Education Publishing Co., 20th and Northhampton Sts., Easton, PA 18042.

Science News, Science Service, 231 W. Center St., Marion, OH 43302.

Science '80, American Association for the Advancement of Science, 1515 Massachusetts Ave., NW, Washington, DC 20005.

SciQuest (formerly *Chemistry*), American Chemical Society, 1155 Sixteenth St. NW, Washington, DC 20036.

Scientific American, Scientific American, Inc., 415 Madison Ave., New York, NY 10017.

The Physics Teacher, American Institute of Physics, 335 E. 45 St., New York, NY 10017.

The Science Teacher, National Science Teachers Association, 1201 Sixteenth St., NW, Washington, DC 20036.

Key to Publishers

Academic Press, Inc., 111 Fifth Ave., New York, NY 10003

Addison-Wesley Publishing Co., Reading, MA 01867.

Allyn & Bacon, Inc. 470 Atlantic Ave., Boston, MA 02210.

American Chemical Society, 1155 Sixteenth St., NW, Washington, DC 20036.

Appleton-Century Crofts, Inc., 440 Park Ave., S., New York, NY 10016.

W. A. Benjamin, Inc., South St., Reading, MA.

Cambridge University Press, 32 E. 57 St., New York, NY 10022.

Chemical Rubber Co., 18901 Cranwood Pkwy., Cleveland, OH 44128.

Chemical Education Publishing Co., 20th and Northhampton, Easton, PA 18042.

Cornell University Press, 124 Roberts Place, Ithaca, NY 14850.

Thomas Y. Crowell Co., 666 Fifth Ave., New York, NY 10019.

Doubleday & Company Inc. 277 Park Ave., New York, NY 10017.

W. H. Freeman & Co., 660 Market St., San Francisco, CA 94104.

Harcourt Brace Jovanovich, Inc., 757 Third Ave., New York, NY 10017.

Harper & Row, 10 E. 53 St., New York, NY 10022.

D. C. Heath, 125 Sprint St., Lexington, MA 02173.

Holt, Rinehart and Winston, Inc., 383 Madison Ave., New York, NY 10017.

Houghton Mifflin Co., 1 Beacon St., Boston, MA 02108.

Longman, Inc. 19 W. 44 St., New York, NY 10036.

McGraw-Hill Book Co., 1221 Avenue of the Americas, New York, NY 10020.

Macmillan, Inc., 866 Third Ave., New York, NY 10022.

National Science Teachers Association, 1742 Connecticut Ave., NW, Washington, DC 20009.

Oxford University Press, Inc., 200 Madison Ave., New York, NY 10016.

Prentice-Hall, Inc., Englewood Cliffs, NJ 07632.

W. B. Saunders Co., 218 W. Washington Sq., Philadelphia, PA 19105.

U.S. Dept. of Commerce, National Bureau of Standards, Clearing House, Springfield, VA 22151.

D. Van Nostrand Company, 135 W. 50 St., New York, NY 10020.

John Wiley & Sons, Inc., 605 Third Ave., New York, NY 10016.

Key to Suppliers of Audiovisual Aids

AEC — Audio Visual Branch, Division of Public Information, U.S. Atomic Energy Commission, Washington, DC 20545

AFL — Anargyros Film Library, 1813 Fairburn Ave., Los Angeles, CA 90025

AGA — American Gas Association, 1515 Wilson Blvd., Arlington, VA 22209

AIM — Association Instructional Materials, Associated Films, 347 Madison Avenue, New York, NY 10017

API — American Petroleum Institute, 2101 L St., NW, Washington, DC 20037

ACS — ACS Film Video Courses, American Chemical Society, 1155 Sixteenth St., NW, Washington, DC 20036

BFA — BFA Educational Media (A Division of CBS), 2211 Michigan Ave., Santa Monica, CA 90404

BL — Bell Laboratories, 600 Mountain Ave., Murray Hill, NJ 07974

C — John Colburn Associates, 1122 Central Ave., Willemette, IL (transparencies)

CHUR — Churchill Films, 662 North Robertson Blvd., Los Angeles, CA 90069

CN — Centron Films, 1621 W. 9 St., Box 687, Lawrence, KS 66044

CORF — Coronet Films, 65 East South Water St., Chicago, IL 60601

DUART — Du Art Film Laboratories, Inc., U.S. Government Film Service, 245 West 55 St., New York, NY 10019

EBE — Encyclopedia Britannica Educational Corporation, 425 North Michigan Ave., Chicago, IL 60611

EYE — Eye Gate Media Inc., 146-01 Archer Ave., Jamaica, NY 11435

FAC — Film Associates of California, 11559 Santa Monica Blvd., Los Angeles, CA 90025

GE — Creative Venture Films, Box 599, Pringhouse, PA 19477 (distributes General Electric films)

HM — Houghton Mifflin Co., 1 Beacon St., Boston, MA 02107

HR — Harper & Row, 49 East 53 St., New York, NY 10016

HRW — Holt, Rinehart and Winston, 383 Madison Ave., New York, NY 10017 (Transparencies for Project Physics designated as PP.)

ICF — International Communications Films, 1371 Reynolds Ave., Santa Ana, CA 92705

IFB — International Film Bureau Inc., 332 S. Michigan Ave., Chicago, IL 60604

INDU — Indiana University, Audiovisual Center, Bloomington, IN 47405

I — Inquiry Audiovisuals, 1754 W. Farragut Ave., Chicago, IL 60640 (filmstrips, slides, transparencies)

LBF — LB Films, 3435 Grant St., Corvallis, OR 97330

LGC — Longmans, Green & Co., 48 Grosvenor St., London, W.I., England

MG — The Media Guild, 118 South Acacia, Box 881, Solana Beach, CA 92075

MH — McGraw-Hill Films, Dept. 455, 1221 Avenue of the Americas, New York, NY 10020

NAVC — National Audiovisual Center (National Archives Trust Fund Board), Washington, DC 20409

PH — Prentice-Hall Media, 150 White Plains Road, Tarrytown, NY 10591 (Communication Skills Programs: identified as WCC, consist of a filmstrip, a set of matching 35-mm slides, a cassette and a workbook; some have a microfiche.) Chem-Review, Series WCF 1000 (8 microfiche)

PPG — PPG Industries Inc., One Gateway Center, Pittsburgh, PA 15222

R — James J. Ruhle & Associates, P.O. Box 4301, Fullerton, CA 92631

ROB — Peter M. Robeck & Co., 230 Park Ave., New York, NY 10017

SRM — Science Related Materials, P.O. Box 1422, Jamesville, WI 53545

STER — Sterling Movies, Inc., 43 West 61 St., New York, NY 10023

SUTH — Sutherland Educational Films, Inc., 201 N. Occidental Blvd., Los Angeles, CA 90026

UA — University of Akron, Audio Visual Services, 302 E. Buchtel Ave., Akron, OH 44325

USDE — U.S. Department of Energy, Washington, DC 20545

USDC — U.S. Department of Commerce, National Bureau of Standards (order from Association Films, Distribution Centers, 410 Great Road, Littleton, MA 01460)

W — Ward's (Ward's Natural Science Establishment, Inc.) P.O. Box 1712, Rochester, NY 14603 (CHEM films and loops, PSSC films, some transparencies, and Solo-Learn units: each having a filmstrip, cassette, manual, student review sheets, and answers to student review sheets.)

V — Visual Products Division, 3M Center, St. Paul, MN 55101 (Overhead Transparency Masters)

Answers to Questions and Problems

PART

4

CHAPTER 1
Answers to Questions pp. 36–37
Group A

1. Some variation of the definition given in Section 1.1: Chemistry is the science of materials, their composition and structure, and the changes they undergo.
2. (a) Analytical, organic, inorganic, physical, biological, and nuclear chemistry. (b) It would not be possible for a person to acquire knowledge in depth over the breadth of chemistry. By organizing chemical knowledge into several systems of related information, learning is made easier and the gathering of new information is facilitated.
3. Combustible materials contained a substance called phlogiston, which was released as heat or flame during burning.
4. The discoveries of the radioactive elements polonium and radium.
5. What occurs? How does it occur?
6. Observing, generalizing, theorizing, and testing.
7. (a) The resistance to change of motion or position of a body. (b) The measure of the inertia of a body. (c) The measure of the earth's attraction for a body.
8. (a) A solid has definite shape; a liquid does not. (b) A liquid has definite volume; a gas does not.
9. Color, odor, solubility, density, hardness, melting point, and boiling point.
10. Chemical activity; reactions with air gases, with water, and with acids; burning characteristics.
11. Matter and energy are interchangeable, and the total matter and energy in the universe is constant.
12. The most commonly used prefixes are: milli-, centi-, and kilo-.
13. (a) cm^2, (b) L, (c) mm, (d) kg, (e) km/hr.
14. cm^2, L, km/hr.
15. Length—meter; mass—kilogram; time—second; temperature—degree; amount of substance—mole.
16. (a) Heat is the energy transferred between two systems that is associated exclusively with the difference in temperature between them. Temperature is a measure of the ability of a system to transfer heat to, or acquire heat from, another system. It refers to the heat intensity of matter. (b) Heat is measured in cal or j; temperature is measured in C°.
17. Accuracy pertains to the nearness of a measurement to its true or accepted value and is expressed in terms of error. Precision pertains to the reproducibility of measurement data, or to the amount of detail, and is expressed in terms of deviation.
18. Significant figures in a measurement expression comprise all digits that are known with certainty, plus the first digit that is uncertain.
19. The exponent of 10 is −7.
20. (a) The two variables are inversely proportional to one another. (b) The two variables are directly proportional to one another.

Group B
21. Answers will vary but may represent efforts to analyze the definition stated in Section 1.1.
22. Answers will vary.
23. Two bodies of equal mass have the same weight while in the same location.
24. (a) A successful argument will be based on the notion that the attractive force between the object and the earth is related to the distance separating the two masses. (It is an inverse-square-law relationship.) (b) The argument will need to recognize that the object in the deep mine shaft has an appreciable portion of the earth mass "above" it and that the attractive force between the object and this portion of the earth mass opposes the "downward" attractive force between the object and the bulk portion of the earth mass.
25. A liquid has a definite volume, but requires lateral support in order to retain a given shape. The upper surface is not confined or supported by the container and thus is a free surface. A liquid is a fluid that can be contained in an open vessel.
26. Both liquids and gases have the characteristic of flowing.

27. The property is chemical if its demonstration involves a change in the identity of the material. If the identity is not changed, it is physical.
28. (*a*) No. (*b*) No. (*c*) Yes. The ratio of mass to volume is useful in distinguishing one material from another. This ratio yields density information.
29. Both a number and a unit are required because the number of measurement units counted depends on the unit used.
30. (*a*) Speed has the dimensions of length/time. Therefore, acceleration has the dimensions of $\dfrac{length}{time} \div time$, or $\dfrac{l}{t^2}$. (*b*) Meters per second squared, or m/s^2.
31. (*a*) By estimating the point of balance to be 0.4 of the scale division between 70.1 g and 70.2 g. (*b*) Four significant figures.
32. (*a*) 12.95 cm accepted because it contains one doubtful digit and the unit of measure used. (*b*) 12.95—no unit; 12.9 cm—failed to include one estimated digit; 12.955 cm—included two doubtful digits; 129.55 mm—included two doubtful digits; 13 cm—two additional significant figures were possible.
33. (*a*) *127.50* km; (*b*) *1200* m; (*c*) *90027.00* cm^3; (*d*) *0.0053* g; (*e*) *67$\overline{0}$* mg; (*f*) *0.0730* g; (*g*) *43.053* L; (*h*) *30090$\overline{0}$* kg; (*i*) *147* cm; (*j*) *6271.9* cm^2.
34. (*a*) 9; (*b*) 299,792,458 m/s; (*c*) 299,800,000 m/s; (*d*) 30$\overline{0}$,000,000 m/s; (*e*) 300,000,000 m/s; (*f*) km/10^3 m; (*g*) 3.00 × 10^5 km/s; (*h*) 3 × 10^{10} cm/s.
35. Both sides of the equation must have the same dimensions.
36. If the answer unit is found to be dimensionally correct for the physical quantity being sought, it indicates that the correct solution expression has been assembled and the indicated arithmetic computation should yield the correct answer. If the answer unit is not dimensionally correct for the quantity being sought, the solution expression has not been assembled correctly and the arithmetic should not be computed until the expression is corrected.

Solutions to Problems p. 38
Group A

1. (*a*) $1\ \cancel{cm} \times \dfrac{10\ mm}{\cancel{cm}} = 10\ mm$

   (*b*) $1\ \cancel{m} \times \dfrac{1000\ mm}{\cancel{m}} = 1000\ mm$

   (*c*) $1\ \cancel{km} \times \dfrac{1{,}000{,}000\ mm}{\cancel{km}} = 1{,}000{,}000\ mm$

2. (*a*) $1.00\ \cancel{ft} \times \dfrac{30.5\ cm}{\cancel{ft}} = 30.5\ cm$

   (*b*) $2.0\ \cancel{m} \times \dfrac{100\ cm}{\cancel{m}} = 2\overline{0}0\ cm$

   (*c*) $3.35\ \cancel{m} \times \dfrac{39.37\ in}{\cancel{m}} = 132\ in$

3. (*a*) $1.5\ \cancel{L} \times \dfrac{1000\ mL}{\cancel{L}} = 1500\ mL$

   (*b*) $10\ \cancel{L} \times \dfrac{1000\ cm^3}{\cancel{L}} = 10{,}000\ cm^3$

   (*c*) $1\ \cancel{m^3} \times \dfrac{1000\ L}{\cancel{m^3}} = 1000\ L$

4. (*a*) $0.425\ \cancel{kg} \times \dfrac{1{,}000{,}000\ mg}{\cancel{kg}} = 425{,}000\ mg$

   (*b*) $1.15\ \cancel{lb} \times \dfrac{453.6\ \cancel{g}}{\cancel{lb}} \times \dfrac{1000\ mg}{\cancel{g}} = 522{,}000\ mg$

   (*c*) $2.65\ \cancel{kg} \times \dfrac{1000\ g}{\cancel{kg}} = 2650\ g$

5. (a) Student answer. Model: $68.5 \cancel{\text{in}} \times \dfrac{2.54 \text{ cm}}{\cancel{\text{in}}} = 174 \text{ cm}$

   (b) Student answer. Model: $145 \cancel{\text{lb}} \times \dfrac{0.4536 \text{ kg}}{\cancel{\text{lb}}} = 65.8 \text{ kg}$

6. (a) $2.50 \times 10^2 \cancel{\text{mL}} \times \dfrac{\text{L}}{10^3 \cancel{\text{mL}}} = 2.50 \times 10^{-1} \text{ L}$

   (b) $2.50 \times 10^{-1} \cancel{\text{L}} \times \dfrac{10^3 \text{ g water}}{\cancel{\text{L}}} = 2.50 \times 10^2 \text{ g water}$

7. (a) $1.415 \times 10^8 \cancel{\text{mi}} \times \dfrac{\text{km}}{6.214 \times 10^{-1} \cancel{\text{mi}}} = 2.277 \times 10^8 \text{ km}$

   (b) $687 \cancel{\text{da}} \times \dfrac{\text{yr}}{365 \cancel{\text{da}}} = 1.88 \text{ yr}$

8. $0.0000005 \text{ cm} = 5 \times 10^{-7} \text{ cm}$

9. $\text{lt yr} = \dfrac{3.00 \times 10^8 \cancel{\text{m}}}{\cancel{\text{s}}} \times \dfrac{1 \text{ km}}{10^3 \cancel{\text{m}}} \times \dfrac{60 \cancel{\text{s}}}{\cancel{\text{min}}} \times \dfrac{60 \cancel{\text{min}}}{\cancel{\text{hr}}} \times \dfrac{24 \cancel{\text{hr}}}{\cancel{\text{da}}} \times 365 \cancel{\text{da}}$

   $\text{lt yr} = 9.46 \times 10^{12} \text{ km}$

10. (a) $736 \cancel{\text{cal}} \times \dfrac{4.19 \text{ j}}{\cancel{\text{cal}}} = 3080 \text{ j}$

    (b) $3080 \cancel{\text{j}} \times \dfrac{1 \text{ kj}}{1000 \cancel{\text{j}}} = 3.08 \text{ kj}$

11. (a) $100\overline{0} \cancel{\text{g water}} \times \dfrac{1 \text{ mL}}{\cancel{\text{g water}}} = 100\overline{0} \text{ mL}$

    (b) $100\overline{0} \cancel{\text{mL}} \times \dfrac{1 \text{ cm}^3}{\cancel{\text{mL}}} = 100\overline{0} \text{ cm}^3$

    (c) $\sqrt[3]{100\overline{0} \text{ cm}^3} = 10.00 \text{ cm}$

    (d) $10.00 \cancel{\text{cm}} \times \dfrac{1 \text{ m}}{100 \cancel{\text{cm}}} = 0.10000 \text{ m}$

12. (a) $V = \pi r^2 h = 3.14 \times (12.5 \cancel{\text{mm}})^2 \times 125 \cancel{\text{mm}} \times \dfrac{1 \cancel{\text{cm}^3}}{1000 \cancel{\text{mm}^3}} \times \dfrac{1 \text{ mL}}{1 \cancel{\text{cm}^3}} = 61.3 \text{ mL}$

    (b) $61.3 \cancel{\text{mL}} \times \dfrac{1 \text{ g water}}{\cancel{\text{mL}}} = 61.3 \text{ g water}$

13. $m = 1.000 \cancel{\text{lb}} \times \dfrac{453.6 \text{ g}}{\cancel{\text{lb}}} - \left(\dfrac{8.600 \text{ g}}{\cancel{\text{student}}} \times 24 \cancel{\text{students}} \right)$

    $m = 453.6 \text{ g} - 206.4 \text{ g} = 247.2 \text{ g of the salt remains}$

14. $h = h_g + h_u = (V_g \div \pi r^2) + h_u$

    $h = \left[1.00 \cancel{\text{L}} \times \dfrac{1000 \text{ cm}}{\cancel{\text{L}}} \div 3.14 \times (4.12 \text{ cm})^2 \right] + \left(52 \cancel{\text{mm}} \times \dfrac{1 \text{ cm}}{10 \cancel{\text{mm}}} \right)$

    $h = 18.8 \text{ cm} + 5.2 \text{ cm} = 24.0 \text{ cm}$

15. (a) $D = m/V$ and $m = DV = \dfrac{13.5 \text{ g}}{\cancel{\text{mL}}} \times 8.20 \cancel{\text{mL}} = 111 \text{ g}$

    (b) $V = m/D = \dfrac{12\overline{0} \cancel{\text{g}}}{13.5 \cancel{\text{g}}/\text{mL}} = 8.89 \text{ mL}$

16. (a) $152.20 \text{ cm} \times \dfrac{1 \text{ m}}{100 \text{ cm}} = 1.5220 \text{ m}$

(b) $152.20 \text{ cm} \times \dfrac{10 \text{ mm}}{\text{cm}} = 1522.0 \text{ mm}$

(c) $152.20 \text{ cm} \times \dfrac{1 \text{ km}}{100,000 \text{ cm}} = 0.0015220 \text{ km}$

(d) $152.20 \text{ cm} \times \dfrac{1 \text{ in}}{2.54 \text{ cm}} = 59.921 \text{ in}$

17. $\dfrac{3.70 \text{ mL} \times 6.02 \times 10^{23} \text{ mol}}{18.0 \text{ g} \times 1 \text{ mL/g}} = 1.24 \times 10^{23} \text{ mol}$

18. $\dfrac{1.24 \times 10^{23} \text{ mol}}{\dfrac{1 \text{ mol}}{\text{s}} \times \dfrac{8.64 \times 10^4 \text{ s}}{\text{da}} \times \dfrac{365 \text{ da}}{\text{yr}}} = \dfrac{1.24 \times 10^{23}}{3.15 \times 10^7} \text{ yr} = 3.94 \times 10^{15} \text{ yr}$

CHAPTER 2
Answers to Questions pp. 56–57
Group A
1. The three general classes of matter are elements, compounds, and mixtures.
2. Matter is anything that occupies space and has mass. A substance is a homogeneous material consisting of one particular kind of matter.
3. A complex substance is composed of two or more elements combined chemically. An elementary substance consists of a single element.
4. (a) Elements are classed as metals and nonmetals. (b) No, some elements have characteristics intermediate between metals and nonmetals and are called metalloids.
5. A compound is composed of two or more elements combined chemically in a definite proportion by mass. A mixture consists of two or more substances intermingled in any proportion.
6. Oxygen, silicon, aluminum, iron, and calcium.
7. (a) Metals have luster, reflect heat and light, and conduct heat and electricity. They are ductile, malleable, and tenacious. (b) Nonmetals are poor conductors of heat and electricity. They may be brittle solids; several are normally gaseous.
8. (a) 107 elements are known. (b) 92 were known prior to the Atomic Age.
9. The symbol identifies a certain element and stands for one atom of that element.
10. (a), (b), (c) Student answers.
11. In a physical change only physical properties are altered; the identifying properties of the substance remain unchanged. In a chemical change the identifying properties of the substance are altered; a new substance or substances with new properties are formed.
12. By increasing the temperature of the reactants. By using a catalyst.
13. By the second letter of the symbol.
14. (a) The first is always capitalized. (b) The second is always lower case.
15. (a) sulfur; (b) zinc; (c) potassium; (d) nitrogen; (e) nickel; (f) cobalt; (g) barium; (h) iron; (i) chlorine; (j) chromium; (k) magnesium; (l) manganese; (m) arsenic; (n) lead; (o) sodium.
16. (a) Al; (b) W; (c) Hg; (d) C; (e) Br; (f) Si; (g) Sn; (h) H; (i) Au; (j) Ag; (k) F; (l) Sr; (m) Ca; (n) P; (o) Bi.
17. (a) Unnilunium, Unu. (b) Unnilbium, Unb. (c) Unniltrium, Unt.
18. Exothermic process: one in which energy is released. Endothermic process: one in which energy is absorbed.

Group B
19. Difference in solubility. Sand is insoluble in water and sugar is soluble.
20. Place the mixture in water. Separate the sand by filtration and recover the sugar by evaporation of water from the sugar-water solution.
21. A solution does not consist of a single substance. The properties of the different substances may be recognized. They may be separated by physical means. The composition can be varied.
22. The mass relationship of constituents is constant.
23. It assures the chemist of the constancy of mass relationship of the elements of a compound.

24. Student answer.
25. Student answer. Separation of the solution by physical means since it is a mixture.
26. In the first case, the solid combined with a gas from the air; in the second, the solid decomposed giving up a gaseous product to the air; in the third, no reaction occurred.
27. Gold, silver, and copper are sufficiently inactive that they do not readily combine with other substances and were thus found free in nature long before processes for recovery of other more active metals were developed.
28. Student answer, which should recognize that iodine (but not antimony) is soluble in such solvents as carbon tetrachloride and trichloroethane, in which it imparts a characteristic color. By extraction, the iodine is taken up by the solvent. By filtration, the antimony is recovered. By evaporation of the solvent, the iodine is recovered.
29. (a) chemical, (b) chemical, (c) physical, (d) chemical, (e) physical, (f) physical.
30. (a), (b), and (d).
31. Student answers.
32. Evidence of chemical reaction is the production of heat, light, mechanical energy, or electric energy. The production of a gas and the formation of a precipitate are also evidences of chemical reaction.
33. Student answer.
34. Chemical change is indicated by evidence of chemical reaction and evidence of new substances with new properties. Physical change is indicated by change in appearance or other physical properties without loss of identifying properties.
35. Reaction processes are influenced by the tendency to proceed toward a lower energy state and the tendency to proceed toward a more disordered state.
36. The endothermic change (melting) occurs at the higher temperature and is in the direction of higher entropy. The exothermic change (freezing) occurs at the lower temperature and is in the direction of lower energy. It would appear that the influence of the entropy-change factor increases as the temperature of the system rises.

Solutions to Problems p. 57

Group B

1. $D = m/V$ and $V = m/D$

$$V = \frac{4.05 \text{ kg}}{7.87 \text{ g/cm}^3} \times \frac{10^3 \text{ g}}{\text{kg}} = 515 \text{ cm}^3$$

2. $450\overline{\text{g}} \times \dfrac{\text{kg}}{10^3 \text{ g}} \times \dfrac{1 \text{ kcal}}{\text{kg C}^\circ} \times 79.0 \text{ C}^\circ = 35.6 \text{ kcal}$

3. $\dfrac{45.5 \text{ kcal}}{1.25 \text{ L} \times 1 \text{ kg/L} \times 1 \text{ kcal/kg C}^\circ} = 36.4 \text{ C}^\circ$

4. $68 \text{ kcal} \times \dfrac{1.0 \text{ g}}{2.1 \times 10^{10} \text{ kcal}} = 3.2 \times 10^{-9} \text{ g}$

5. $10.0 \text{ g Na} \times \dfrac{10\overline{0} \text{ g NaCl}}{39.3 \text{ g Na}} = 25.4 \text{ g NaCl}$

CHAPTER 3
Answers to Questions pp. 73–74

Group A

1. Even with a microscope one cannot see the particles of sugar in a sugar-water solution. One cannot see particles of gas escaping from a gas valve into the air.
2. The modern atomic theory includes information concerning the structure and properties of atoms, the kinds of compounds they form, and the properties of these compounds. It also includes information about the mass, volume, and energy relationships in reactions between atoms.
3. *1.* All matter is made up of very small structures called atoms. *2.* Atoms of the same element are chemically alike; atoms of different elements are chemically different. *3.* Individual atoms of an element may not all have the same mass. However, the atoms of an element, as it occurs naturally, have, for practical purposes, a definite average mass that is characteristic of the element. *4.* Individual atoms of different elements may have nearly identical masses. However, the atoms of different naturally occurring elements have different average masses. *5.* Atoms are not subdivided in chemical reactions.
4. (a) The nucleus and the electron cloud. (b) Nucleus: protons and neutrons. Electron cloud: electrons. (c) Proton—positively charged particle with a mass of 1.673×10^{-24} g, which is 1836/1837 of the mass of a protium atom. Neutron—

neutral particle with a mass of 1.675×10^{-24} g, which is about the same mass as a proton. Electron—negatively charged particle with a mass of 9.110×10^{-28} g, which is 1/1837 of the mass of a protium atom.

5. The diameter of the nucleus is about 1/10,000 of the diameter of the atom.
6. A region about the nucleus of an atom in which electrons move.
7. Electrons move about the nucleus in such a manner as to effectively occupy the relatively vast empty space around the nucleus.
8. Protium—one proton in nucleus, one electron in first energy level. Deuterium—one proton and one neutron in nucleus, one electron in first energy level. Tritium—one proton and two neutrons in nucleus, one electron in first energy level.
9. (a) The number of protons in the nucleus of that atom. (b) It indicates the number of electrons in the neutral atom.
10. (a) The different varieties of atoms as determined by their nuclear composition. (b) Nuclides having the same atomic number; atoms of the same element that have different masses.
11. The mass number is the sum of the number of protons and neutrons.
12. (a) 8. (b) 17. (c) Oxygen-17.
13. Beryllium and fluorine.
14. An atomic mass unit is 1/12 the mass of a carbon-12 atom.
15. The mass of an atom expressed in atomic mass units.
16. (a) 6.022045×10^{23}. (b) The Avogadro number. (c) Mole.
17. The atomic weight of an element is the ratio of its gram-atomic weight to 1/12 the mass in grams of one mole of carbon-12 atoms.
18. They indicate relative mass relationships between reacting elements.
19. (a) Silver: at. no. 47, at. wt. 107.868. (b) Gold: at. no. 79, at. wt. 196.9665. (c) Copper: at. no. 29, at. wt. 63.546. (d) Sulfur: at. no. 16, at. wt. 32.06. (e) Uranium: at. no. 92, at. wt. 238.029.
20. (a) 2.00 moles × 4.00260 g/mole = 8.01 g. (b) 5.00 moles × 10.81 g/mole = 54.0 g. (c) 0.500 mole × 20.179 g/mole = 10.1 g. (d) 0.250 mole × 24.305 g/mole = 6.08 g. (e) 0.100 mole × 28.0855 g/mole = 2.81 g.

21. (a) $\dfrac{20.823 \text{ g}}{6.941 \text{ g/mole}} = 3.000$ moles. (b) $\dfrac{160.93 \text{ g}}{22.98977 \text{ g/mole}} = 7.0001$ moles.

(c) $\dfrac{3.995 \text{ g}}{39.948 \text{ g/mole}} = 0.1000$ mole. (d) $\dfrac{8.016 \text{ g}}{32.06 \text{ g/mole}} = 0.2500$ mole.

(e) $\dfrac{20.24 \text{ g}}{26.9815 \text{ g/mole}} = 0.7501$ mole.

Group B
22. The law of definite composition; and the way and the proportions in which substances react with one another.
23. Most of a platinum atom is space through which high-speed positively charged particles readily pass. However, platinum atoms contain a very small, positively charged nucleus that repels the high-speed positively charged particles if they approach head-on or very nearly so.
24. (a) The atoms of each successive element have one more proton. (b) The atoms of each successive element have one more electron. (c) There is no definite pattern, but generally the number of neutrons increases.
25. Two electrons in the first energy level and from one to eight electrons in the second energy level.
26.

Name of nuclide	Atomic number	Mass number	Composition of nucleus		Electron configuration		
			Protons	Neutrons	K	L	M
sodium-23	11	23	11	12	2	8	1
magnesium-24	12	24	12	12	2	8	2
aluminum-27	13	27	13	14	2	8	3
silicon-28	14	28	14	14	2	8	4
phosphorus-31	15	31	15	16	2	8	5
sulfur-32	16	32	16	16	2	8	6
chlorine-35	17	35	17	18	2	8	7
argon-40	18	40	18	22	2	8	8

27. Approximately 75% chlorine-35 and 25% chlorine-37.
28. They will be the same.
29. (*a*) They are isotopes. (*b*) They are of different elements but have the same mass number.
30. Divide the atomic mass in grams by the Avogadro number.
31. It is the weighted average mass of an atom of the element in grams.

32. $0.99759 \text{ mole} \times \dfrac{15.99491 \text{ g}}{1 \text{ mole}} = 15.9564 \text{ g}$

$\quad 0.00037 \text{ mole} \times \dfrac{16.99914 \text{ g}}{1 \text{ mole}} = 0.0063 \text{ g}$

$\quad 0.00204 \text{ mole} \times \dfrac{17.99916 \text{ g}}{1 \text{ mole}} = 0.0367 \text{ g}$

$15.9564 \text{ g} + 0.0063 \text{ g} + 0.0367 \text{ g} = 15.9994 \text{ g}$, the gram-atomic weight. The atomic weight is 15.9994.

CHAPTER 4
Answers to Questions pp. 87–88
Group A
1. (*a*) Electromagnetic radiations are forms of energy that travel through space as waves at the rate of 3.00×10^8 m/s. (*b*) Light, X rays, radio waves.
2. (*a*) They travel through space as waves. (*b*) They are transferred to matter in quanta (units) of energy called photons.
3. By the absorption of a photon.
4. (*a*) 3rd energy level to 2nd energy level. (*b*) 6th energy level to 2nd energy level.
5. A nucleus surrounded by electrons in definite energy levels—that is, only at certain distances from the nucleus and with only certain speeds. Electrons do not give off energy while in an energy level. They give off energy when they change to lower energy levels.
6. A highly probable location about a nucleus in which an electron may be found.
7. (*a*) The space surrounding a nucleus bounded by the occupied space orbitals. (*b*) It gives size and shape to an atom and prevents two free atoms, or portions of free atoms, from occupying the same space.
8. The principal quantum number indicates the most probable distance of the electron from the nucleus of the atom. The orbital quantum number indicates the shape of the space orbital. The magnetic quantum number indicates the position in space of the space orbital. The spin quantum number indicates the two possibilities for the property of an electron called electron spin.
9. (*a*) A hollow sphere. (*b*) One. (*c*) Two. (*d*) They must have opposite spin. (*e*) The first.
10. (*a*) Approximately that of two footballs or watermelons each tangent to the other at an end; two ellipsoids each tangent to the other at a point of greatest curvature. (*b*) Three. (*c*) At 90° angles along the three axes in space. (*d*) The second.
11. (*a*) No. The amounts of energy of two electrons in the same atom cannot be the same. (*b*) Yes. (*c*) Their first three quantum numbers must be alike, but they must have opposite spins.
12. In its ground state, the electrons of an atom occupy the lowest energy orbitals available. In an excited state, one or more electrons of an atom occupy orbitals of higher energy.
13. (*a*) Two electrons of opposite spin occupying the same space orbital. (*b*) Eight electrons occupying the *s* and *p* orbitals of an outer energy level.

Group B
14. The attraction between oppositely charged particles requires that atoms collapse. Since this is not so, this explanation is unsatisfactory.
15. $c = f\lambda$. So $f = c/\lambda$. $E = hf$. So $f = E/h$. Then $c/\lambda = E/h$. And $\lambda = ch/E$.
16. Because electrons may only possess definite amounts of energy.
17. (*a*) 1000 Å. (*b*) 18,800 Å.
18. (*a*) Five. (*b*) Ten. (*c*) The third.
19. (*a*) Seven. (*b*) Fourteen. (*c*) The fourth.
20. (*a*) One. (*b*) Four. (*c*) Two. (*d*) One. (*e*) Three.
21. Krypton.

22.

Chemical symbol	Orbital notation					Electron-configuration notation	Electron-dot notation
	1s	2s	2p	3s	3p		
Na	↓↑	↓↑	↓↑ ↓↑ ↓↑	↑	__ __ __	$1s^2 2s^2 2p^6 3s^1$	Na •
Mg	↓↑	↓↑	↓↑ ↓↑ ↓↑	↓↑	__ __ __	$1s^2 2s^2 2p^6 3s^2$	Mg :
Al	↓↑	↓↑	↓↑ ↓↑ ↓↑	↓↑	↑ __ __	$1s^2 2s^2 2p^6 3s^2 3p^1$	Ȧl :
Si	↓↑	↓↑	↓↑ ↓↑ ↓↑	↓↑	↑ ↑ __	$1s^2 2s^2 2p^6 3s^2 3p^2$	• S̈i :
P	↓↑	↓↑	↓↑ ↓↑ ↓↑	↓↑	↑ ↑ ↑	$1s^2 2s^2 2p^6 3s^2 3p^3$	• Ṗ :
S	↓↑	↓↑	↓↑ ↓↑ ↓↑	↓↑	↓↑ ↑ ↑	$1s^2 2s^2 2p^6 3s^2 3p^4$	• S̈ :
Cl	↓↑	↓↑	↓↑ ↓↑ ↓↑	↓↑	↓↑ ↓↑ ↑	$1s^2 2s^2 2p^6 3s^2 3p^5$	: C̈l :
Ar	↓↑	↓↑	↓↑ ↓↑ ↓↑	↓↑	↓↑ ↓↑ ↓↑	$1s^2 2s^2 2p^6 3s^2 3p^6$	: Är :

23. Seven.
24. The completion of s and p sublevels of the outer energy level is interrupted by the occupation of the d sublevel of the next-to-outside energy level.
25. The completion of s and p sublevels of the outer energy level and the d sublevel of the next-to-outside energy level is interrupted by the occupation of the f sublevel in the second-from-outside energy level.
26. (a) Fourth. (b) s, p, d, and f. (c) One s, three p's, five d's, and seven f's. (d) Two in the s orbital, six in the p orbitals, ten in the d orbitals, and fourteen in the f orbitals. (e) 32.
27. (a) s and p. (b) s, p, and d.
28. $1s^2 2s^2 2p^6 3s^2 3p^6 3d^{10} 4s^2 4p^6 4d^{10} 4f^{14} 5s^2 5p^6 5d^{10} 5f^{14} 6s^2 6p^6 6d^7 7s^2$.

CHAPTER 5
Answers to Questions pp. 107–108
Group A
1. (a) In order of increasing atomic weights. (b) In order of increasing atomic numbers.
2. He predicted the discovery of new elements and their properties.
3. The wavelengths of X rays become shorter as the elements used as a target contain more protons in their nuclei.
4. The physical and chemical properties of the elements are periodic functions of their atomic numbers.
5. (a) Chemical symbol, atomic number, atomic weight, distribution of electrons in the energy levels of the atoms of the element. (b) The chemical symbol is in the center with the atomic number below, the atomic weight above, and the electron distribution to the right.
6. (a) A vertical column of elements in the periodic table. (b) One of the vertical columns.
7. (a) A horizontal row of elements in the periodic table. (b) One of the horizontal rows.
8. (a) Lithium, beryllium, boron, carbon, nitrogen, oxygen, fluorine, neon. (b) The number increases from one to eight as you go across the series from lithium to neon. (c) The properties range from an active metallic element to an active non-metallic element, with the last element in the period being a noble gas.
9. They have the same number of electrons in their outer energy levels.
10. They increase in activity from the top to the bottom of a group.
11. They decrease in activity from the top to the bottom of the group.
12. (a) Metalloids. (b) Metalloids show both metallic and nonmetallic properties under different conditions.
13. Ar-40 and K-39.
14. The boundary of an atom's electron cloud is not a distinct surface because the space occupied by an atom is that taken by charged electrons moving rapidly about a nucleus.
15. (a) The radii of the Group I elements are greatest among the elements of their period. (b) The single outer energy level electron is rather loosely bound to the nucleus.
16. It is next to smallest.

17. Sodium, 1.54 Å; chlorine, 0.99 Å. The greater nuclear charge of chlorine draws the electron cloud closer.
18. Magnesium, 1.36 Å; barium, 1.98 Å. Barium atoms have three more electron shells. This produces a larger atom despite the increased nuclear charge.
19. (a) K + energy → K^+ + e^-. (b) Br + e^- → Br^- + energy. (c) A singly positively charged potassium ion and a singly negatively charged bromide ion.
20. (a) The few outer shell electrons of the metal atoms are not strongly held by nuclear attraction. (b) The outer shell electrons of nonmetal atoms are more strongly held by nuclear attraction.
21. Sodium, 119 kcal/mole; chlorine, 299 kcal/mole. The first chlorine electron to be removed is closer to the nucleus and held by a greater nuclear charge.
22. Aluminum, 138 kcal/mole; chromium, 156 kcal/mole. While the first electron to be removed from each atom is at the same distance from the nucleus (the atoms are the same size), the chromium electron is held by the larger nuclear charge.
23. Electron affinity is the energy change that occurs when an electron is acquired by a neutral atom.
24. (a) Na + e^- → Na^- + energy (12.6 kcal/mole); (b) Cl + e^- → Cl^- + energy (83.4 kcal/mole); (c) Ar + e^- → Ar^- − energy (−8.3 kcal/mole); (d) In the Na^- ion, the electron is weakly bound. In the Cl^- ion, the electron is strongly bound. The Ar^- ion is unstable. It will spontaneously release the electron to form the more stable neutral atom.

Group B

25. The noble gases.
26. (a) Electromagnetic radiations that have a high frequency and a short wavelength. (b) By high-speed electrons striking the metal target in an evacuated tube.
27. (a) By studying the properties of the elements he already knew. (b) By unusual variations in the wavelengths of X rays between two supposedly successive elements.
28. (a) Because of its many unique properties. (b) Because it has one electron in its outermost energy level.
29. (a) Elements that usually differ in electron configuration from that of the next lower or higher atomic number only in the number of electrons in the next-to-the-outside energy level. (b) Fourth, fifth, sixth, and seventh periods.
30. (a) Elements that usually differ in electron configuration from that of the next lower or higher atomic number only in the number of electrons in the second-from-outside energy level. (b) Sixth and seventh periods.
31. (a) Atomic size generally increases with atomic number within a family of elements. (b) Each element in a family has one more energy level than the element above it. The addition of an energy level increases atomic size more than increased nuclear charge reduces it.
32. (a) Atomic size generally decreases with atomic number. (b) The attraction of the increased nuclear charge for the electrons pulls them closer to the nucleus.
33. (a) The atom with higher atomic number should have the higher ionization energy. (b) The nuclear attraction for its outer energy level electrons should be greater.
34. (a) The atom is more stable because it has less energy than the ion. (b) The ion is more stable because it has less energy than the atom.
35. Atoms of elements in these groups acquire an additional electron by endothermic reactions. Thus the ions formed are less stable than the neutral atoms. This is evidence of a stable outer electron configuration in the neutral atoms. Specifically it is related to a filled s sublevel in Group II elements and filled s and p sublevels in the Group VIII elements.
36. This is evidence for the stability of half-filled p sublevels. Much more energy is released when an electron is added to a p sublevel containing two electrons than when an electron is added to a p sublevel containing three electrons.
37. The number of orbitals that have energies between the completed p sublevels of successive noble gas configurations. The number of elements in a period is twice the number of such orbitals.
38. 16.
39. It serves as a useful and systematic, though not perfect, classification of elements according to their properties.
40.

Chemical element	Electron-configuration notation
K	$1s^2 2s^2 2p^6 3s^2 3p^6 4s^1$
Ca	$1s^2 2s^2 2p^6 3s^2 3p^6 4s^2$
Ga	$1s^2 2s^2 2p^6 3s^2 3p^6 3d^{10} 4s^2 4p^1$

In general, the ionization energy increases with each electron removed from an atom because each successive electron must be removed from a particle with an increasingly greater net positive charge. Also, the lower the energy level of an electron, the more ionization energy is required for its removal. Potassium: The first electron is a $4s$ electron, in a higher energy level than the second, third, and fourth electrons, which are $3p$ electrons. Calcium: The first two electrons are $4s$ electrons, in a higher energy level than the third and fourth electrons, which are $3p$ electrons. Gallium: The first electron is a $4p$ electron. The second and third are $4s$ electrons, in a lower energy sublevel than the first. The fourth electron is a $3d$ electron, in a still lower energy level.

Group A

1. (a) The electrons in an incomplete outer shell; the valence electrons. (b) Usually by the transfer of valence electrons from the outer shell of one atom to the outer shell of another atom, or by the sharing of valence electrons among the outer shells of combining atoms.
2. (a) Ionic bonding and covalent bonding. (b) Ionic bonding produces ions; covalent bonding produces molecules.
3. (a) A stable one having a noble-gas configuration. (b) Because atoms with such outer shells have no tendency to transfer and little tendency to share electrons.
4. (a) Exothermic. (b) Usually exothermic, but can be endothermic.
5. (a) A chemical formula is a shorthand method of using chemical symbols to represent the composition of a substance. (b) An empirical formula merely indicates the kind and simplest whole-number ratio of the constituent atoms in a substance. A molecular formula indicates the actual composition of a molecule.
6. (a) An empirical formula. (b) A molecular formula.
7. (a) $K\cdot$ (b) K^+
8. (a) $\times\overset{\times\times}{\underset{\times}{S}}\times$ (b) $\overset{\times\times}{\underset{\times\bullet}{:S:}}^{--}$

9. K^+ $\overset{\times\times}{\underset{\times\times}{:S:}}^{--}$ K^+

10. (a) A chemical reaction in which an element attains a more positive oxidation state. (b) A chemical reaction in which an element attains a more negative oxidation state.
11. (a) Because it effects the reduction of the other reactant. (b) Because it effects the oxidation of the other reactant.
12. A barium atom has electrons in two more energy levels than a calcium atom, and the effect of additional energy levels more than offsets the greater nuclear charge of the barium atom.
13. A bromide ion has electrons in one more energy level than a chloride ion. The effect of the addition of an energy level is greater than the effect of greater nuclear charge.

14. (a) F $\quad\underset{1s}{\downarrow\uparrow}\quad\underset{2s}{\downarrow\uparrow}\quad\underbrace{\downarrow\uparrow\quad\downarrow\uparrow\quad\uparrow}_{2p}$

    F $\quad\underset{1s}{\downarrow\uparrow}\quad\underset{2s}{\downarrow\uparrow}\quad\underbrace{\downarrow\uparrow\quad\downarrow\uparrow\quad\downarrow}_{2p}$

(b) $\overset{\bullet\bullet}{\underset{\bullet\bullet}{:F:}}\overset{\times\times}{\underset{\times\times}{F\times}}$

(c) F_2

15. An atom is the smallest particle of an element that can exist either alone or in combination. A molecule is the smallest chemical unit of an element or a compound that is capable of stable, independent existence.
16. A symbol represents one atom of an element, while a formula represents the composition of a substance.
17. (a) N_2 is most stable. (b) Cl_2 is least stable.
18. The property of an atom of attracting the shared electrons forming a bond between it and another atom.
19. (a) Approximately 1.7 or more. (b) Greater than about 0.5 but less than about 1.7. (c) Less than about 0.5.
20. (a) Sodium. (b) Chlorine. (c) Chlorine. (d) Lithium. (e) Hydrogen.
21. (a) Mn +4, O −2. (b) H +1, P +5, O −2. (c) H +1, N +5, O −2. (d) P +5, O −2. (e) Na +1, O −2, H +1.
22. (a) Hydrogen, nitrogen, oxygen, fluorine, chlorine. (b) H_2, N_2, O_2, F_2, Cl_2.
23. (a) Helium, neon, argon, krypton, xenon, radon. (b) He, Ne, Ar, Kr, Xe, Rn.
24. Sugar: 12 atoms of carbon, 22 atoms of hydrogen, 11 atoms of oxygen. Sand: 1 atom of silicon, 2 atoms of oxygen. Salt: 1 atom of sodium, 1 atom of chlorine. Hydrogen peroxide: 2 atoms of hydrogen, 2 atoms of oxygen. Soap: 18 atoms of carbon, 35 atoms of hydrogen, 2 atoms of oxygen, 1 atom of sodium.
25. (a) 1 atom of argon. (b) 4 molecules of nitrogen, each molecule of which consists of two atoms of nitrogen. (c) 1 molecule of a substance, each molecule of which consists of 1 atom of hydrogen and 1 atom of iodine. (d) 6 molecules of a substance, each molecule of which consists of 2 atoms of hydrogen, 1 atom of sulfur, and 4 atoms of oxygen. (e) 3 atoms of copper. (f) 2 chemical units, each consisting of 1 potassium ion and 1 bromide ion. (g) 1 molecule of a substance, each molecule of which consists of 1 atom of carbon and 1 atom of oxygen. (h) 1 atom of cobalt.

Group B

26. (*a*) Ca   ↓↑ ↓↑ ↓↑ ↓↑ ↓↑ ↓↑ ↓↑ ↓↑ ↓↑ ↓↑
              1s 2s ⸜___2p___⸝ 3s ⸜___3p___⸝ 4s

   (*b*) Ca^{++} ↓↑ ↓↑ ↓↑ ↓↑ ↓↑ ↓↑ ↓↑ ↓↑ ↓↑ ___
                   1s 2s ⸜___2p___⸝ 3s ⸜___3p___⸝ 4s

27. (*a*) F   ↓↑ ↓↑ ↓↑ ↓↑ ↑
              1s 2s ⸜__2p__⸝

   (*b*) F$^-$ ↓↑ ↓↑ ↓↑ ↓↑ ↓↑
               1s 2s ⸜___2p___⸝

28. F$^-$ ↓↑ ↓↑ ↓↑ ↓↑ ↑
           1s 2s ⸜__2p__⸝
                        ↑

   Ca^{++} ↓↑ ↓↑ ↓↑ ↓↑ ↓↑ ↓↑ ↓↑ ↓↑ ↓↑ ↓↑
             1s 2s ⸜___2p___⸝ 3s ⸜___3p___⸝ 4s

   F$^-$ ↓↑ ↓↑ ↓↑ ↓↑ ↓↓
          1s 2s ⸜___2p___⸝

29. The greater nuclear charge of the calcium atom draws the 4*s* electrons closer to the nucleus.

30. Each has an outer shell consisting of an octet of M-shell electrons. The nuclear charge of the sulfur is weaker, thus the octet of this ion is further from the nucleus.

31. (*a*) H
                                                                    ↓
                                                                    1s
   Br ↓↑ ↓↑ ↓↑ ↓↑ ↓↑ ↓↑ ↓↑ ↓↑ ↓↑ ↓↑ ↓↑ ↓↑ ↓↑ ↓↑ ↓↑ ↓↑ ↓↑ ↑
      1s 2s ⸜___2p___⸝ 3s ⸜___3p___⸝ ⸜_____3d_____⸝ 4s ⸜___4p___⸝

   (*b*) H ⁝Br⁝

32. H
                                       ↑
                                       1s
   S ↓↑ ↓↑ ↓↑ ↓↑ ↓↑ ↓↑ ↓↑ ↓ ↓
     1s 2s ⸜___2p___⸝ 3s ⸜__3p__⸝

   H
                                       ↑
                                       1s

   H⁝S⁝   H$_2$S
     H

33. (*a*) Pyramidal, similar to NH_3. (*b*) Bent, similar to H_2O.
34. (*a*) 63%, ionic. (*b*) 22%, polar covalent. (*c*) 82%, ionic. (*d*) 4%, essentially nonpolar covalent. (*e*) 0%, nonpolar covalent.
35. (*a*) +7. (*b*) +2. (*c*) Reduction. (*d*) Oxidizing agent.
36. (*a*) +2, +3; (*b*) +3, +6, +6.
37. HClO, +1; $HClO_2$, +3; $HClO_3$, +5; $HClO_4$, +7.
38. (*a*) S +6, O −2. (*b*) S +4, O −2. (*c*) N +3, O −2. (*d*) C +4, O −2. (*e*) Cr +6, O −2.

39. (a) :Ö: (b) :Ö: (c) It must be a resonance hybrid.

40. (a) Ionic crystal. (b) Nonpolar covalent molecule. (c) Polar covalent molecule. (d) Polar covalent molecule. (e) Nonpolar covalent molecule.

Solutions to Problems p. 136
Group A

1. $\frac{1}{2}$ mole H_2 + 52 kcal $\rightarrow$ 1 mole H
   $\frac{1}{2}$ mole Br_2 + 23 kcal $\rightarrow$ 1 mole Br
   1 mole H + 1 mole Br $\rightarrow$ 1 mole HBr + 87 kcal

   $\frac{1}{2}$ mole H_2 + $\frac{1}{2}$ mole Br_2 $\rightarrow$ 1 mole HBr + 12 kcal

   Energy change is exothermic; 12 kcal/mole HBr.
   (Note to teacher: The reason this heat of reaction does not equal the heat of formation of hydrogen bromide is because we have not considered the approximately 3 kcal required to convert $\frac{1}{2}$ mole Br_2(l) to $\frac{1}{2}$ mole Br_2(g). In the elementary bond energy calculations in this chapter all substances are in the gaseous state for the sake of simplicity.)

2. 1 mole H_2 + 104 kcal $\rightarrow$ 2 moles H
   $\frac{1}{2}$ mole O_2 + 59 kcal $\rightarrow$ 1 mole O
   2 moles H + 1 mole O $\rightarrow$ 1 mole H_2O + 222 kcal

   1 mole H_2 + $\frac{1}{2}$ mole O_2 $\rightarrow$ 1 mole H_2O + 59 kcal

   Exothermic energy change; 59 kcal/mole H_2O.

Group B

3. 1 mole Mg + 523 kcal $\rightarrow$ 1 mole Mg^{++} + 2 moles e^-
   2 moles Br + 2 moles e^- $\rightarrow$ 2 moles Br^- + 155 kcal
   1 mole Mg^{++} + 2 moles Br^- $\rightarrow$ 1 mole $Mg^{++}Br^-_2$ + 587 kcal

   1 mole Mg + 2 moles Br $\rightarrow$ 1 mole $Mg^{++}Br^-_2$ + 219 kcal

   Exothermic energy change; 219 kcal/mole $MgBr_2$.

4. 1 mole H_2 + 104 kcal $\rightarrow$ 2 moles H
   1 mole O_2 + 118 kcal $\rightarrow$ 2 moles O
   2 moles H + 2 moles O $\rightarrow$ 2 moles H—O + 222 kcal
   2 moles H—O $\rightarrow$ 1 mole H_2O_2 + 34 kcal

   1 mole H_2 + 1 mole O_2 $\rightarrow$ 1 mole H_2O_2 + 34 kcal

   Exothermic energy change; 34 kcal/mole H_2O_2.

5. 1 mole N_2 + 225 kcal $\rightarrow$ 2 moles N
    2 moles H_2 + 208 kcal $\rightarrow$ 4 moles H

    2 moles N + 4 moles H $\rightarrow$ 2 moles N$\underset{H}{\overset{H}{\diagup}}$ + 4(92 kcal)

    2 moles N$\underset{H}{\overset{H}{\diagup}}$ $\rightarrow$ 1 mole N_2H_4 + 37 kcal

    1 mole N_2 + 2 moles H_2 + 28 kcal $\rightarrow$ 1 mole N_2H_4

   Energy change is endothermic; 28 kcal/mole N_2H_4.
   (Note to teacher: In this problem the heat evolved when N_2H_4(g) condenses to N_2H_4(l) has not been considered. The heat of formation of N_2H_4(l) is +12 kcal/mole.)

CHAPTER 7
Answers to Questions p. 159
Group A

1. The molecular formula NH_3 represents the composition of one molecule of ammonia—one atom of nitrogen and three atoms of hydrogen. Since the atomic weight of nitrogen is 14.0 and that of hydrogen is 1.0, the molecular weight of ammonia is 17.0. The mass of one mole of ammonia is 17.0 g.

2. Because it applies to all types of substances, not just to those that are molecular.

3. (a) Na^+; (b) Cu^+; (c) Fe^{+++}; (d) Ni^{++}; (e) Pb^{++}; (f) Fe^{++}; (g) Cl^-; (h) O^{--}; (i) S^{--}; (j) I^-; (k) Cu^{++}; (l) K^+; (m) Ag^+; (n) Hg_2^{++}.

4. (a) Ammonium, $+1$; (b) sulfate, -2; (c) nitrate, -1; (d) carbonate, -2; (e) acetate, -1; (f) dichromate, -2; (g) chlorate, -1; (h) hydrogen sulfate, -1; (i) hydroxide, -1; (j) nitrite, -1.

5. (a) HCO_3^-; (b) Br^-; (c) CrO_4^{--}; (d) SO_3^{--}; (e) PO_4^{---}; (f) O_2^{--}; (g) Mg^{++}; (h) Zn^{++}; (i) Ba^{++}; (j) F^-.

6. (a) $BaCl_2$; (b) CaO; (c) $MgSO_4$; (d) $AgBr$; (e) $ZnCO_3$.

7. (a) Sodium hydrogen carbonate; (b) potassium peroxide; (c) mercury(II) chloride; (d) iron(III) hydroxide; (e) nickel(II) acetate.

8. (a) NH_4NO_3; (b) Al_2S_3; (c) $Cu(OH)_2$; (d) $Pb_3(PO_4)_2$; (e) $Fe_2(SO_4)_3$.

9. (a) Copper(II) chloride; (b) calcium sulfide; (c) potassium hydrogen sulfate; (d) sodium nitrite; (e) nickel(II) phosphate.

10. (a) CrF_3; (b) $Ni(ClO_3)_2$; (c) $KHCO_3$; (d) $CaCrO_4$; (e) HgI_2.

11. (a) Sodium peroxide; (b) ammonium nitrite; (c) magnesium phosphate; (d) iron(II) sulfate; (e) silver carbonate; (f) sodium oxide; (g) mercury(I) chloride; (h) mercury(II) chloride; (i) hydrogen peroxide.

12. (a) $NaHSO_4$; (b) $PbCrO_4$; (c) $CuCl$; (d) $Hg_2(NO_3)_2$; (e) FeO.

13. (a) potassium sulfate; (b) barium dichromate; (c) chromium(III) hydroxide; (d) lead(II) bromide; (e) mercury(II) iodide.

14. (a) $Al(OH)_3$; (b) Cu_2O; (c) $(NH_4)_2S$; (d) $Pb(C_2H_3O_2)_2$; (e) $FeBr_3$.

15. (a) $Mg(HCO_3)_2$; (b) Ag_2S; (c) K_2SO_3; (d) $Cr_2(SO_4)_3$; (e) Na_3PO_4.

Group B

16. Atoms of essentially constant average mass combine in definite proportions to form the particles of more complex substances. Hence substances have a fixed percentage composition by mass.

17. The atomic theory provides for the possibility that atoms may combine in more than one way and in more than one proportion.

18. (a) Sulfur trioxide; (b) silicon tetrachloride; (c) phosphorus tribromide; (d) diarsenic pentoxide; (e) lead monoxide.

19. (a) SO_2; (b) $BiCl_3$; (c) MnO_2; (d) AsI_5; (e) CI_4.

20. (a) Carbon monoxide; (b) carbon dioxide; (c) carbon tetrabromide; (d) dinitrogen trioxide; (e) dinitrogen pentoxide.

Solutions to Problems pp. 159–160
Group A

1. Formula weight of $N_2H_4 = 2(14.0) + 4(1.0) = 32.0$
2. Formula weight of $H_2SO_4 = 2(1.0) + 32.1 + 4(16.0) = 98.1$
3. Formula weight of $C_6H_{12}O_6 = 6(12.0) + 12(1.0) + 6(16.0) = 180.0$
4. Formula weight of $C_2H_5OH = 2(12.0) + 6(1.0) + 16.0 = 46.0$
5. Formula weight of $Ca_3(PO_4)_2 = 3(40.1) + 2(31.0) + 8(16.0) = 310.3$
6. Formula weight of $MgSO_4 \cdot 7H_2O = 24.3 + 32.1 + 4(16.0) + 14(1.0) + 7(16.0) = 246.4$
7. (a) Formula weight of $HNO_3 = 1.0 + 14.0 + 3(16.0) = 63.0$
   (b) Formula weight of $NaOH = 23.0 + 16.0 + 1.0 = 40.0$
   (c) Formula weight of $HgO = 200.6 + 16.0 = 216.6$
   (d) Formula weight of $CuSO_4 \cdot 5H_2O = 63.5 + 32.1 + 4(16.0) + 10(1.0) + 5(16.0) = 249.6$
   (e) Formula weight of $HC_2H_3O_2 = 4(1.0) + 2(12.0) + 2(16.0) = 60.0$
   (f) Formula weight of $MgBr_2 = 24.3 + 2(79.9) = 184.1$
   (g) Formula weight of $Al_2S_3 = 2(27.0) + 3(32.1) = 150.3$
   (h) Formula weight of $Ca(NO_3)_2 = 40.1 + 2(14.0) + 6(16.0) = 164.1$
   (i) Formula weight of $Fe_2(Cr_2O_7)_3 = 2(55.8) + 6(52.0) + 21(16.0) = 759.6$
   (j) Formula weight of $KMnO_4 = 39.1 + 54.9 + 4(16.0) = 158.0$

8. Formula weight of $HC_2H_3O_2 = 4(1.0) + 2(12.0) + 2(16.0) = 60.0$

   H: $\dfrac{(4.0)\ H}{(60.0)\ HC_2H_3O_2} \times 100\%\ HC_2H_3O_2 = 6.7\%\ H$

   C: $\dfrac{(24.0)\ C}{(60.0)\ HC_2H_3O_2} \times 100\%\ HC_2H_3O_2 = 40.0\%\ C$

O: $\dfrac{(32.0)\ O}{(60.0)\ HC_2H_3O_2} \times 100\%\ HC_2H_3O_2 = 53.3\%\ O$

9. Formula weight of $NaHCO_3 = 23.0 + 1.0 + 12.0 + 3(16.0) = 84.0$

Na: $\dfrac{(23.0)\ Na}{(84.0)\ NaHCO_3} \times 100\%\ NaHCO_3 = 27.4\%\ Na$

H: $\dfrac{(1.0)\ H}{(84.0)\ NaHCO_3} \times 100\%\ NaHCO_3 = 1.2\%\ H$

C: $\dfrac{(12.0)\ C}{(84.0)\ NaHCO_3} \times 100\%\ NaHCO_3 = 14.3\%\ C$

O: $\dfrac{(48.0)\ O}{(84.0)\ NaHCO_3} \times 100\%\ NaHCO_3 = 57.1\%\ O$

10. Formula weight of $C_{17}H_{35}COONa = 18(12.0) + 35(1.0) + 2(16.0) + 23.0 = 306.0$

C: $\dfrac{(216.0)\ C}{(306.0)\ C_{17}H_{35}COONa} \times 100\%\ C_{17}H_{35}COONa = 70.6\%\ C$

H: $\dfrac{(35.0)\ H}{(306.0)\ C_{17}H_{35}COONa} \times 100\%\ C_{17}H_{35}COONa = 11.4\%\ H$

O: $\dfrac{(32.0)\ O}{(306.0)\ C_{17}H_{35}COONa} \times 100\%\ C_{17}H_{35}COONa = 10.5\%\ O$

Na: $\dfrac{(23.0)\ Na}{(306.0)\ C_{17}H_{35}COONa} \times 100\%\ C_{17}H_{35}COONa = 7.5\%\ Na$

11. (*a*) Formula weight of $SO_2 = 32.1 + 2(16.0) = 64.1$

S: $\dfrac{(32.1)\ S}{(64.1)\ SO_2} \times 100\%\ SO_2 = 50.1\%\ S$

O: $\dfrac{(32.0)\ O}{(64.1)\ SO_2} \times 100\%\ SO_2 = 49.9\%\ O$

(*b*) Formula weight of $Ca(OH)_2 = 40.1 + 2(16.0) + 2(1.0) = 74.1$

Ca: $\dfrac{(40.1)\ Ca}{(74.1)\ Ca(OH)_2} \times 100\%\ Ca(OH)_2 = 54.1\%\ Ca$

O: $\dfrac{(32.0)\ O}{(74.1)\ Ca(OH)_2} \times 100\%\ Ca(OH)_2 = 43.2\%\ O$

H: $\dfrac{(2.0)\ H}{(74.1)\ Ca(OH)_2} \times 100\%\ Ca(OH)_2 = 2.7\%\ H$

(*c*) Formula weight of $Ca(H_2PO_4)_2 \cdot H_2O = 40.1 + 4(1.0) + 2(31.0) + 8(16.0) + 18.0 = 252.1$

Ca: $\dfrac{(40.1)\ Ca}{(252.1)\ Ca(H_2PO_4)_2 \cdot H_2O} \times 100\%\ Ca(H_2PO_4)_2 \cdot H_2O = 15.9\%\ Ca$

H: $\dfrac{(4.0)\ H}{(252.1)\ Ca(H_2PO_4)_2 \cdot H_2O} \times 100\%\ Ca(H_2PO_4)_2 \cdot H_2O = 1.6\%\ H$

P: $\dfrac{(62.0)\ P}{(252.1)\ Ca(H_2PO_4)_2 \cdot H_2O} \times 100\%\ Ca(H_2PO_4)_2 \cdot H_2O = 24.6\%\ P$

O: $\dfrac{(128.0)\ O}{(252.1)\ Ca(H_2PO_4)_2 \cdot H_2O} \times 100\%\ Ca(H_2PO_4)_2 \cdot H_2O = 50.8\%\ O$

H$_2$O: $\dfrac{(18.0)\ H_2O}{(252.1)\ Ca(H_2PO_4)_2 \cdot H_2O} \times 100\%\ Ca(H_2PO_4)_2 \cdot H_2O = 7.1\%\ H_2O$

(d) Formula weight of $MgSO_4 \cdot 7H_2O = 24.3 + 32.1 + 4(16.0) + 7(18.0) = 246.4$

Mg: $\dfrac{(24.3)\ Mg}{(246.4)\ MgSO_4 \cdot 7H_2O} \times 100\%\ MgSO_4 \cdot 7H_2O = 9.9\%\ Mg$

S: $\dfrac{(32.1)\ S}{(246.4)\ MgSO_4 \cdot 7H_2O} \times 100\%\ MgSO_4 \cdot 7H_2O = 13.0\%\ S$

O: $\dfrac{(64.0)\ O}{(246.4)\ MgSO_4 \cdot 7H_2O} \times 100\%\ MgSO_4 \cdot 7H_2O = 26.0\%\ O$

H_2O: $\dfrac{(126.0)\ H_2O}{(246.4)\ MgSO_4 \cdot 7H_2O} \times 100\%\ MgSO_4 \cdot 7H_2O = 51.1\%\ H_2O$

12. (a) Formula weight of $Ca(NO_3)_2 = 40.1 + 2(14.0) + 6(16.0) = 164.1$

N: $\dfrac{(28.0)\ N}{(164.1)\ Ca(NO_3)_2} \times 100\%\ Ca(NO_3)_2 = 17.1\%\ N$

(b) Formula weight of $CaCN_2 = 40.1 + 12.0 + 2(14.0) = 80.1$

N: $\dfrac{(28.0)\ N}{(80.1)\ CaCN_2} \times 100\%\ CaCN_2 = 35.0\%\ N$

(c) Formula weight of $(NH_4)_2SO_4 = 2(14.0) + 8(1.0) + 32.1 + 4(16.0) = 132.1$

N: $\dfrac{(28.0)\ N}{(132.1)\ (NH_4)_2SO_4} \times 100\%\ (NH_4)_2SO_4 = 21.2\%\ N$

13. Mass of oxygen $= 7.956\ g - 6.356\ g = 1.600\ g$

Cu: $\dfrac{6.356\ g\ Cu}{7.956\ g\ Cpd} \times 100\%\ Cpd = 78.89\%\ Cu$

O: $\dfrac{1.600\ g\ O}{7.956\ g\ Cpd} \times 100\%\ Cpd = 20.11\%\ O$

14. (a) 1.00 mole $\times 35.5$ g Cl/mole $= 35.5$ g Cl
(b) 5.00 moles $\times 14.0$ g N/mole $= 70.0$ g N
(c) 3.00 moles $\times 159.8$ g Br_2/mole $= 479$ g Br_2
(d) 6.00 moles $\times 36.5$ g HCl/mole $= 219$ g HCl
(e) 10.0 moles $\times 120.4$ g $MgSO_4$/mole $= 1200$ g $MgSO_4$
(f) 2.50 moles $\times 166$ g KI/mole $= 415$ g KI
(g) 0.500 mole $\times 170$ g $AgNO_3$/mole $= 85.0$ g $AgNO_3$
(h) 0.100 mole $\times 58.5$ g NaCl/mole $= 5.85$ g NaCl

15. (a) $\dfrac{25.0\ g\ CaO}{56.1\ g/mole} = 0.446$ mole CaO

(b) $\dfrac{25.0\ g\ Na_2CO_3 \cdot 10H_2O}{286\ g/mole} = 0.0874$ mole $Na_2CO_3 \cdot 10H_2O$

(c) $\dfrac{25.0\ g\ BaCl_2 \cdot 2H_2O}{244.3\ g/mole} = 0.102$ mole $BaCl_2 \cdot 2H_2O$

(d) $\dfrac{25.0\ g\ (NH_4)_2SO_4}{132.1\ g/mole} = 0.189$ mole $(NH_4)_2SO_4$

(e) $\dfrac{25.0\ g\ Fe(NO_3)_3 \cdot 6H_2O}{349.8\ g/mole} = 0.0715$ mole $Fe(NO_3)_3 \cdot 6H_2O$

(f) $\dfrac{25.0\ g\ Al_2(SO_4)_3 \cdot 18H_2O}{666\ g/mole} = 0.0375$ mole $Al_2(SO_4)_3 \cdot 18H_2O$

(g) $\dfrac{25.0\ g\ K_2CrO_4}{194\ g/mole} = 0.129$ mole K_2CrO_4

16. Formula weight of $Fe_3O_4 = 3(55.8) + 4(16.0) = 231.4$

    1.000 metric ton $\times 10^6$ g/metric ton $\times$ 1 mole $Fe_3O_4/231.4$ g $\times$ 3 moles Fe/1 mole $Fe_3O_4 = 1.296 \times 10^4$ moles Fe

17. Formula weight of $HgS = 200.6 + 32.1 = 232.7$

    1.00 kg $\times 10^3$ g/kg $\times$ 1 mole $HgS/232.7$ g $\times$ 1 mole Hg/1 mole HgS $= 4.297$ moles Hg

18. Formula weight of $Cu_2O = 2(63.5) + 16.0 = 143.0$

    Cu: $\dfrac{(127.0)\ Cu}{(143.0)\ Cu_2O} \times 100\%\ Cu_2O = 88.81\%\ Cu$

    Formula weight of $CuCO_3 \cdot Cu(OH)_2 = 2(63.5) + 12.0 + 5(16.0) + 2(1.0) = 221.0$

    Cu: $\dfrac{(127.0)\ Cu}{(221.0)\ CuCO_3 \cdot Cu(OH)_2} \times 100\%\ CuCO_3 \cdot Cu(OH)_2 = 57.47\%\ Cu$

    Formula weight of $CuFe_2S_4 = 63.5 + 2(55.8) + 4(32.1) = 303.5$

    Cu: $\dfrac{(63.5)\ Cu}{(303.5)\ CuFe_2S_4} \times 100\%\ CuFe_2S_4 = 20.9\%\ Cu$

19. Formula weight of $CaCO_3 = 40.1 + 12.0 + 3(16.0) = 100.1$
    Formula weight of $CaO = 40.1 + 16.0 = 56.1$

    $\dfrac{(56.1)\ CaO}{(100.1)\ CaCO_3} \times 100\%\ CaCO_3 = 56.0\%\ CaO$

20. Formula weight of $CuSO_4 \cdot 5H_2O = 63.5 + 32.1 + 4(16.0) + 5(18.0) = 249.6$
    Formula weight of $5H_2O = 5(18.0) = 90.0$

    $\dfrac{(90.0)\ H_2O}{(249.6)\ CuSO_4 \cdot 5H_2O} \times 100\%\ CuSO_4 \cdot 5H_2O = 36.1\%\ H_2O$

Group B

21. % Pt $= 100.0\% - 42.1\% = 57.9\%$

    Pt: $\dfrac{57.9\ g\ Pt}{195.1\ g/mole} = 0.297$ mole Pt

    Cl: $\dfrac{42.1\ g\ Cl}{35.5\ g/mole} = 1.19$ moles Cl

    Pt:Cl $= 0.297/0.297 : 1.19/0.297 = 1:4$
    Empirical formula $= PtCl_4$
    % Pt $= 100.0\% - 26.7\% = 73.3\%$

    Pt: $\dfrac{73.3\ g\ Pt}{195.1\ g/mole} = 0.376$ mole Pt

    Cl: $\dfrac{26.7\ g\ Cl}{35.5\ g/mole} = 0.752$ mole Cl

    Pt:Cl $= 0.376/0.376 : 0.752/0.376 = 1:2$
    Empirical formula $= PtCl_2$

22. % F $= 100\% - 85\% = 15\%$

    Ag: $\dfrac{85\ g\ Ag}{107.9\ g/mole} = 0.79$ mole Ag

    F: $\dfrac{15\ g\ F}{19.0\ g/mole} = 0.79$ mole F

    Ag:F $= 1:1$ Empirical formula $= AgF$

23. Formula weight of $C_{11}H_{12}N_2O_5Cl_2 = 11(12.0) + 12(1.0) + 2(14.0) + 5(16.0) + 2(35.5) = 323.0$

C: $\dfrac{132.0\ C}{323.0\ C_{11}H_{12}N_2O_5Cl_2} \times 100\%\ C_{11}H_{12}N_2O_5Cl_2 = 40.9\%\ C$

H: $\dfrac{12.0\ H}{323.0\ C_{11}H_{12}N_2O_5Cl_2} \times 100\%\ C_{11}H_{12}N_2O_5Cl_2 = 3.7\%\ H$

N: $\dfrac{28.0\ N}{323.0\ C_{11}H_{12}N_2O_5Cl_2} \times 100\%\ C_{11}H_{12}N_2O_5Cl_2 = 8.7\%\ N$

O: $\dfrac{80.0\ O}{323.0\ C_{11}H_{12}N_2O_5Cl_2} \times 100\%\ C_{11}H_{12}N_2O_5Cl_2 = 24.8\%\ O$

Cl: $\dfrac{71.0\ Cl}{323.0\ C_{11}H_{12}N_2O_5Cl_2} \times 100\%\ C_{11}H_{12}N_2O_5Cl_2 = 22.0\%\ Cl$

24. P: $\dfrac{43.67\ g\ P}{31.0\ g/mole} = 1.41\ moles\ P$

O: $\dfrac{56.33\ g\ O}{16.0\ g/mole} = 3.52\ moles\ O$

P:O = 1.41/1.41 : 3.52/1.41 = 1.00 : 2.50 = 2.00 : 5.00
Empirical formula = P_2O_5

25. K: $\dfrac{24.58\ g\ K}{39.1\ g/mole} = 0.629\ mole\ K$

Mn: $\dfrac{34.81\ g\ Mn}{54.9\ g/mole} = 0.634\ mole\ Mn$

O: $\dfrac{40.50\ g\ O}{16.0\ g/mole} = 2.53\ moles\ O$

K:Mn:O = 0.629/0.629 : 0.634/0.629 : 2.53/0.629 = 1.00 : 1.01 : 4.02
Empirical formula = $KMnO_4$

26. Na: $\dfrac{37.70\ g\ Na}{23.0\ g/mole} = 1.64\ moles\ Na$

Si: $\dfrac{22.95\ g\ Si}{28.1\ g/mole} = 0.817\ mole\ Si$

O: $\dfrac{39.34\ g\ O}{16.0\ g/mole} = 2.46\ moles\ O$

Na:Si:O = 1.64/0.817 : 0.817/0.817 : 2.46/0.817 = 2.01 : 1.00 : 3.01
Empirical formula = Na_2SiO_3

27. Na: $\dfrac{28.05\ g\ Na}{23.0\ g/mole} = 1.22\ moles\ Na$

C: $\dfrac{29.26\ g\ C}{12.0\ g/mole} = 2.44\ moles\ C$

H: $\dfrac{3.66\ g\ H}{1.01\ g/mole} = 3.62\ moles\ H$

O: $\dfrac{39.02\ g\ O}{16.0\ g/mole} = 2.44\ moles\ O$

Na:C:H:O = 1.22/1.22 : 2.44/1.22 : 3.62/1.22 : 2.44/1.22 = 1.00 : 2.00 : 2.97 : 2.00
Empirical formula = $NaC_2H_3O_2$

28. N: $\dfrac{21.20 \text{ g N}}{14.0 \text{ g/mole}} = 1.51$ moles N

H: $\dfrac{6.06 \text{ g H}}{1.01 \text{ g/mole}} = 6.00$ moles H

S: $\dfrac{24.30 \text{ g S}}{32.1 \text{ g/mole}} = 0.757$ mole S

O: $\dfrac{48.45 \text{ g O}}{16.0 \text{ g/mole}} = 3.03$ moles O

N:H:S:O = 1.51/0.757:6.00/0.757:0.757/0.757:3.03/0.757 = 1.99:7.93:1.00:4.00
Empirical formula = $N_2H_8SO_4$ or $(NH_4)_2SO_4$

29. K: $\dfrac{44.82 \text{ g K}}{39.1 \text{ g/mole}} = 1.15$ moles K

S: $\dfrac{18.39 \text{ g S}}{32.1 \text{ g/mole}} = 0.573$ mole S

O: $\dfrac{36.79 \text{ g O}}{16.0 \text{ g/mole}} = 2.30$ moles O

K:S:O = 1.15/0.573:0.573/0.573:2.30/0.573 = 2.01:1.00:4.01
Empirical formula = K_2SO_4

30. Ca: $\dfrac{24.7 \text{ g Ca}}{40.1 \text{ g/mole}} = 0.616$ mole Ca

H: $\dfrac{1.2 \text{ g H}}{1.0 \text{ g/mole}} = 1.2$ moles H

C: $\dfrac{14.8 \text{ g C}}{12.0 \text{ g/mole}} = 1.23$ moles C

O: $\dfrac{59.3 \text{ g O}}{16.0 \text{ g/mole}} = 3.71$ moles O

Ca:H:C:O = 0.616/0.616:1.2/0.616:1.23/0.616:3.71/0.616 = 1.00:1.9:2.00:6.02
Empirical formula = $CaH_2C_2O_6$ or $Ca(HCO_3)_2$

31. Fe: $\dfrac{72.4 \text{ g Fe}}{55.8 \text{ g/mole}} = 1.30$ moles Fe

O: $\dfrac{27.6 \text{ g O}}{16.0 \text{ g/mole}} = 1.72$ moles O

Fe:O = 1.30/1.30:1.72/1.30 = 1.00:1.32 = 3.00:3.96
Empirical formula = Fe_3O_4

32. C: $\dfrac{92.3 \text{ g C}}{12.0 \text{ g/mole}} = 7.7$ moles C

H: $\dfrac{7.7 \text{ g H}}{1.0 \text{ g/mole}} = 7.7$ moles H

C:H = 1:1
Empirical formula = CH
$(\text{CH weight})_x = (12.0 + 1.0)_x = 26.0 \quad x = 2$
Molecular formula = $(CH)_2$ or C_2H_2

33. C: $\dfrac{80 \text{ g C}}{12 \text{ g/mole}} = 6.7$ moles C

H: $\dfrac{2\bar{0}\text{ g H}}{1.0\text{ g/mole}} = 2\bar{0}$ moles H

C:H = 6.7/6.7 : 2$\bar{0}$/6.7 = 1.0 : 3.0
Empirical formula = CH_3
(CH_3 weight)$_x$ = (12.0 + 3.0)$_x$ = 30.0   x = 2
Molecular formula = $(CH_3)_2$ or C_2H_6

34. (a) I: $\dfrac{76.0\text{ g I}}{127\text{ g/mole}} = 0.598$ mole I

O: $\dfrac{24.0\text{ g O}}{16.0\text{ g/mole}} = 1.50$ mole O

I:O = 0.598/0.598 : 1.50/0.598 = 1.00 : 2.51 = 2 : 5
Empirical formula = I_2O_5
(I_2O_5 weight)$_x$ = (254 + 80.0)$_x$ = 334   x = 1
Molecular formula = I_2O_5
(b) Oxidation state of I = +5

35. % O = 100.0% − 42.8% = 57.2%

C: $\dfrac{42.8\text{ g C}}{12.0\text{ g/mole}} = 3.57$ moles C

O: $\dfrac{57.2\text{ g O}}{16.0\text{ g/mole}} = 3.58$ moles O

C:O = 1.1
% O = 100.0% − 27.3% = 72.7%

C: $\dfrac{27.3\text{ g C}}{12.0\text{ g/mole}} = 2.28$ moles C

O: $\dfrac{72.7\text{ g O}}{16.0\text{ g/mole}} = 4.54$ moles O

C:O = 2.28/2.28 : 4.54/2.28 = 1.00 : 1.99
In the two oxides, if C is constant, 1:1, then O is 1:1.99, or 1:2.

CHAPTER 8
Answers to Equations pp. 180–181
Group A
1. Zn + S → ZnS. Composition.
2. KCl + $AgNO_3$ → AgCl(s) + KNO_3. Ionic, precipitate.
3. CaO + H_2O → $Ca(OH)_2$. Composition.
4. NaOH + HCl → NaCl + H_2O. Ionic, molecular product (H_2O).
5. $MgBr_2$ + Cl_2 → $MgCl_2$ + Br_2. Replacement of halogens.
6. 2NaCl + H_2SO_4 → Na_2SO_4 + 2HCl(g). Ionic, gaseous product.
7. 2Al + Fe_2O_3 → Al_2O_3 + 2Fe. Replacement of a metal by a more active metal.
8. NH_4NO_2 → N_2(g) + 2H_2O. Decomposition.
9. 2$AgNO_3$ + Ni → $Ni(NO_3)_2$ + 2Ag(s). Replacement of a metal by a more active metal.
10. 3H_2 + N_2 → 2NH_3(g). Composition.
11. sodium + iodine → sodium iodide. 2Na + I_2 → 2NaI.
12. calcium + oxygen → calcium oxide. 2Ca + O_2 → 2CaO.
13. hydrogen + chlorine → hydrogen chloride(g). H_2 + Cl_2 → 2HCl(g). Reactions 11, 12, and 13 are exothermic (Chapter 6). The products are more stable than the reactants.
14. nickel(II) chlorate → nickel(II) chloride + oxygen(g). $Ni(ClO_3)_2$ → $NiCl_2$ + 3O_2(g). Decomposition of a metallic chlorate.
15. barium carbonate → barium oxide + carbon dioxide(g). $BaCO_3$ → BaO + CO_2(g). Decomposition of a metallic carbonate.
16. zinc hydroxide → zinc oxide + steam(g). $Zn(OH)_2$ → ZnO + H_2O(g). Decomposition of a metallic hydroxide.

17. aluminum + sulfuric acid → aluminum sulfate + hydrogen(g). $2Al + 3H_2SO_4 \rightarrow Al_2(SO_4)_3 + 3H_2(g)$. Aluminum is more active than hydrogen.

18. potassium iodide + chlorine → potassium chloride + iodine. $2KI + Cl_2 \rightarrow 2KCl + I_2$. Chlorine is more active than iodine.

19. iron + copper(II) nitrate → iron(II) nitrate + copper(s). $Fe + Cu(NO_3)_2 \rightarrow Fe(NO_3)_2 + Cu(s)$. Iron is more active than copper.

20. silver nitrate + zinc chloride → silver chloride(s) + zinc nitrate. $2AgNO_3 + ZnCl_2 \rightarrow 2AgCl(s) + Zn(NO_3)_2$. Silver chloride precipitates.

21. copper(II) hydroxide + acetic acid → copper(II) acetate + water. $Cu(OH)_2 + 2HC_2H_3O_2 \rightarrow Cu(C_2H_3O_2)_2 + 2H_2O$. Water is a molecular product.

22. iron(II) sulfate + ammonium sulfide → iron(II) sulfide(s) + ammonium sulfate. $FeSO_4 + (NH_4)_2S \rightarrow FeS(s) + (NH_4)_2SO_4$. Iron(II) sulfide precipitates.

Group B

23. barium chloride + sodium sulfate → barium sulfate(s) + sodium chloride. $BaCl_2 + Na_2SO_4 \rightarrow BaSO_4(s) + 2NaCl$. Ionic. Barium sulfate precipitates.

24. calcium + hydrochloric acid → calcium chloride + hydrogen(g). $Ca + 2HCl \rightarrow CaCl_2 + H_2(g)$. Replacement. Calcium is more active than hydrogen.

25. iron(II) sulfide + hydrochloric acid → hydrogen sulfide(g) + iron(II) chloride. $FeS + 2HCl \rightarrow H_2S(g) + FeCl_2$. Ionic. Hydrogen sulfide is a gas.

26. zinc chloride + ammonium sulfide → zinc sulfide(s) + ammonium chloride. $ZnCl_2 + (NH_4)_2S \rightarrow ZnS(s) + 2NH_4Cl$. Ionic. Zinc sulfide precipitates.

27. $NH_3 + 2O_2 \rightarrow HNO_3 + H_2O$.

28. magnesium + nitric acid → magnesium nitrate + hydrogen(g). $Mg + 2HNO_3 \rightarrow Mg(NO_3)_2 + H_2(g)$. Replacement. Magnesium is more active than hydrogen.

29. potassium + water → potassium hydroxide + hydrogen(g). $2K + 2H_2O \rightarrow 2KOH + H_2(g)$. Replacement. Potassium is more active than hydrogen.

30. sodium iodide + bromine → sodium bromide + iodine. $2NaI + Br_2 \rightarrow 2NaBr + I_2$. Replacement. Bromine is more active than iodine.

31. silver + sulfur → silver sulfide. $2Ag + S \rightarrow Ag_2S$. Composition. Exothermic reaction. Silver sulfide is more stable than elemental silver and sulfur.

32. sodium chlorate → sodium chloride + oxygen(g). $2NaClO_3 \rightarrow 2NaCl + 3O_2(g)$. Decomposition. Metallic chlorates yield metallic chlorides and oxygen.

33. $C + H_2O \rightarrow CO(g) + H_2(g)$.

34. zinc + lead(II) acetate → zinc acetate + lead(s). $Zn + Pb(C_2H_3O_2)_2 \rightarrow Zn(C_2H_3O_2)_2 + Pb(s)$. Replacement. Zinc is more active than lead.

35. iron(III) hydroxide → iron(III) oxide + steam. $2Fe(OH)_3 \rightarrow Fe_2O_3 + 3H_2O(g)$. Decomposition. Metallic hydroxides yield metallic oxides and steam.

36. $Fe_2O_3 + 3CO \rightarrow 2Fe + 3CO_2(g)$.

37. lead(II) acetate + hydrogen sulfide → lead(II) sulfide(s) + acetic acid. $Pb(C_2H_3O_2)_2 + H_2S \rightarrow PbS(s) + 2HC_2H_3O_2$. Ionic. Lead(II) sulfide precipitates.

38. aluminum bromide + chlorine → aluminum chloride + bromine. $2AlBr_3 + 3Cl_2 \rightarrow 2AlCl_3 + 3Br_2$. Replacement. Chlorine is more active than bromine.

39. magnesium carbonate → magnesium oxide + carbon dioxide(g). $MgCO_3 \rightarrow MgO + CO_2(g)$. Decomposition. Metallic carbonates yield metallic oxides and carbon dioxide.

40. iron(III) chloride + sodium hydroxide → iron(III) hydroxide(s) + sodium chloride. $FeCl_3 + 3NaOH \rightarrow Fe(OH)_3(s) + 3NaCl$. Ionic. Iron(III) hydroxide precipitates.

41. $3CaO + P_2O_5 \rightarrow Ca_3(PO_4)_2$.

42. chromium + oxygen → chromium(III) oxide. $4Cr + 3O_2 \rightarrow 2Cr_2O_3$. Composition. Exothermic reaction. Chromium(III) oxide is more stable than elemental chromium and oxygen.

43. sodium + water → sodium hydroxide + hydrogen(g). $2Na + 2H_2O \rightarrow 2NaOH + H_2(g)$. Replacement. Sodium is more active than hydrogen.

44. calcium carbonate + hydrochloric acid → calcium chloride + carbon dioxide(g) + water. $CaCO_3 + 2HCl \rightarrow CaCl_2 + CO_2(g) + H_2O$. Ionic and decomposition of carbonic acid. Carbon dioxide is a gas.

45. calcium hydroxide + phosphoric acid → calcium phosphate + water. $3Ca(OH)_2 + 2H_3PO_4 \rightarrow Ca_3(PO_4)_2 + 6H_2O$. Ionic. Water is a molecular product.

46. sodium carbonate + nitric acid → sodium nitrate + carbon dioxide(g) + water. $Na_2CO_3 + 2HNO_3 \rightarrow 2NaNO_3 + CO_2(g) + H_2O$. Ionic and decomposition of carbonic acid. Carbon dioxide is a gas.

47. aluminum hydroxide + sulfuric acid → aluminum sulfate + water. $2Al(OH)_3 + 3H_2SO_4 \rightarrow Al_2(SO_4)_3 + 6H_2O$. Ionic. Water is a molecular product.

48. sodium sulfite + sulfuric acid → sodium sulfate + sulfur dioxide(g) + water. $Na_2SO_3 + H_2SO_4 \rightarrow Na_2SO_4 + SO_2(g) + H_2O$. Ionic and decomposition of sulfurous acid. Sulfur dioxide is a gas.

49. $Cu + 2H_2SO_4 \rightarrow CuSO_4 + 2H_2O + SO_2(g)$.

50. $Ca(OH)_2 + (NH_4)_2SO_4 \rightarrow CaSO_4 + 2NH_3(g) + 2H_2O$.

Solutions to Problems pp. 181–182

Group A

1. $\quad$ 25.0 g $\qquad\qquad$ X
    $$2HgO \rightarrow 2Hg + O_2(g)$$
    2 moles $\qquad\qquad$ 1 mole
    1 mole HgO = 216.6 g $\qquad$ 1 mole O_2 = 32.0 g

    (a) 25.0 g HgO $\times \dfrac{\text{mole}}{216.6 \text{ g}}$ = 0.115 mole HgO

    (b) 0.115 mole HgO $\times \dfrac{1 \text{ mole } O_2}{2 \text{ moles HgO}}$ = 0.0575 mole O_2

    (c) 0.0575 mole $O_2 \times$ 32.0 g/mole = 1.84 g O_2

2. $\quad$ 25.0 g $\qquad\qquad$ X
    $$2KClO_3 \rightarrow 2KCl + 3O_2(g)$$
    2 moles $\qquad\qquad$ 3 moles
    1 mole $KClO_3$ = 122.6 g $\qquad$ 1 mole O_2 = 32.0 g

    (a) 25.0 g $KClO_3 \times \dfrac{\text{mole}}{122.6 \text{ g}}$ = 0.204 mole $KClO_3$

    (b) 0.204 mole $KClO_3 \times \dfrac{3 \text{ moles } O_2}{2 \text{ moles } KClO_3}$ = 0.306 mole O_2

    (c) 0.306 mole $O_2 \times$ 32.0 g/mole = 9.79 g O_2

3. $\quad$ X $\qquad\qquad\qquad\qquad$ 0.10 g
    $$Zn + H_2SO_4 \rightarrow ZnSO_4 + H_2(g)$$
    1 mole $\qquad\qquad\qquad\qquad$ 1 mole
    1 mole Zn = 65.4 g $\qquad$ 1 mole H_2 = 2.0 g

    (a) 0.10 g $H_2 \times \dfrac{\text{mole}}{2.0 \text{ g}}$ = 0.050 mole H_2

    (b) 0.050 mole $H_2 \times \dfrac{1 \text{ mole Zn}}{1 \text{ mole } H_2}$ = 0.050 mole Zn

    (c) 0.050 mole Zn $\times$ 65.4 g/mole = 3.3 g Zn

4. $\quad$ X $\qquad\quad$ 10.0 g
    $$NaCl + AgNO_3 \rightarrow AgCl(s) + NaNO_3$$
    1 mole $\quad$ 1 mole $\quad$ 1 mole
    1 mole $AgNO_3$ = 169.9 g $\qquad$ 1 mole NaCl = 58.5 g

    (a) 10.0 g $AgNO_3 \times \dfrac{\text{mole}}{169.9 \text{ g}}$ = 0.0589 mole $AgNO_3$

    (b) 0.0589 mole $AgNO_3 \times \dfrac{1 \text{ mole NaCl}}{1 \text{ mole } AgNO_3}$ = 0.0589 mole NaCl

    (c) 0.0589 mole NaCl $\times$ 58.5 g/mole = 3.45 g NaCl

5. (a) 0.0589 mole $AgNO_3 \times \dfrac{1 \text{ mole AgCl}}{1 \text{ mole } AgNO_3}$ = 0.0589 mole AgCl

    (b) 1 mole AgCl = 143.4 g
    $\qquad$ 0.0589 mole AgCl $\times$ 143.4 g/mole = 8.45 g AgCl

6. X   80.0 g
    S + $O_2 \rightarrow SO_2(g)$
    1 mole   1 mole
    1 mole SO_2 = 64.1 g   1 mole S = 32.1 g

$$X = 80.0 \text{ g } SO_2 \times \frac{\text{mole}}{64.1 \text{ g}} \times \frac{1 \text{ mole S}}{1 \text{ mole } SO_2} \times 32.1 \text{ g/mole} = 40.1 \text{ g S}$$

7. 25 g   X
    Fe_3O_4 + $4H_2$ → $3Fe$ + $4H_2O(g)$
    1 mole   4 moles
    1 mole Fe_3O_4 = 231.4 g   1 mole H_2 = 2.0 g

$$X = 25 \text{ g } Fe_3O_4 \times \frac{\text{mole}}{231.4 \text{ g}} \times \frac{4 \text{ moles } H_2}{1 \text{ mole } Fe_3O_4} \times 2.0 \text{ g/mole} = 0.86 \text{ g } H_2$$

8. 1.00 kg   X
    $2Cu$ + $O_2 \rightarrow$ $2CuO$
    2 moles   2 moles
    1 mole Cu = 63.5 g   1 mole CuO = 79.5 g

$$X = 1.00 \text{ kg Cu} \times \frac{1000 \text{ g}}{\text{kg}} \times \frac{\text{mole}}{63.5 \text{ g}} \times \frac{2 \text{ moles CuO}}{2 \text{ moles Cu}} \times 79.5 \text{ g/mole}$$

$$= 1250 \text{ g CuO}$$

9. 40.0 g   X
    Cu   + $2AgNO_3 \rightarrow$ $2Ag(s)$ + $Cu(NO_3)_2$
    1 mole   2 moles
    1 mole Cu = 63.5 g   1 mole Ag = 107.9 g

$$X = 40.0 \text{ g Cu} \times \frac{\text{mole}}{63.5 \text{ g}} \times \frac{2 \text{ moles Ag}}{1 \text{ mole Cu}} \times 107.9 \text{ g/mole} = 136 \text{ g Ag}$$

10. 10.0 g   X
    FeS + $2HCl \rightarrow FeCl_2$ + $H_2S(g)$
    1 mole   1 mole
    1 mole FeS = 87.9 g   1 mole H_2S = 34.1 g

$$X = 10.0 \text{ g FeS} \times \frac{\text{mole}}{87.9 \text{ g}} \times \frac{1 \text{ mole } H_2S}{1 \text{ mole FeS}} \times 34.1 \text{ g/mole} = 3.88 \text{ g } H_2S$$

Group B

11. $15\overline{0}$ g   X   Y
    H_2SO_4 + BaO_2 → H_2O_2 + $BaSO_4(s)$
           1 mole 1 mole   1 mole
    1 mole BaO_2 = 169.3 g

(a) $X = 15\overline{0} \text{ g } BaO_2 \times \dfrac{\text{mole}}{169.3 \text{ g}} \times \dfrac{1 \text{ mole } H_2O_2}{1 \text{ mole } BaO_2} = 0.886 \text{ mole } H_2O_2$

(b) $Y = 0.886 \text{ mole } H_2O_2 \times \dfrac{1 \text{ mole } BaSO_4}{1 \text{ mole } H_2O_2} = 0.886 \text{ mole } BaSO_4$

12. $10\overline{0}$ g   X
    Zn + $2HCl$ → $ZnCl_2$ + $H_2(g)$
          2 moles   1 mole
    1 mole HCl = 36.5 g

$$X = 10\overline{0} \text{ g HCl} \times \frac{\text{mole}}{36.5 \text{ g}} \times \frac{1 \text{ mole } H_2}{2 \text{ moles HCl}} = 1.37 \text{ moles } H_2$$

13. 10.0 g   Y   X
    Fe +   S   → FeS
    1 mole 1 mole 1 mole
    1 mole Fe = 55.8 g   1 mole S = 32.1 g   1 mole FeS = 87.9 g

(a) $X = 10.0$ g Fe $\times \dfrac{\text{mole}}{55.8 \text{ g}} \times \dfrac{1 \text{ mole FeS}}{1 \text{ mole Fe}} \times 8.79$ g/mole $= 15.8$ g FeS

(b) $Y = 10.0$ g Fe $\times \dfrac{\text{mole}}{55.8 \text{ g}} \times \dfrac{1 \text{ mole S}}{1 \text{ mole Fe}} \times 32.1$ g/mole $= 5.75$ g S used; 10.0 g $- 5.8$ g $= 4.2$ g S remaining

$$\begin{matrix} 4.2 \text{ g} & & X \\ S & + O_2 \rightarrow & SO_2 \\ 1 \text{ mole} & & 1 \text{ mole} \end{matrix}$$
1 mole S $= 32.1$ g   1 mole $SO_2 = 64.1$ g

$X = 4.2$ g S $\times \dfrac{\text{mole}}{32.1 \text{ g}} \times \dfrac{1 \text{ mole } SO_2}{1 \text{ mole S}} \times 64.1$ g/mole $= 8.4$ g SO_2

14. 1.00 kg
$$CaCO_3 \rightarrow \quad CaO \quad + CO_2(g)$$
1 mole   1 mole

Equal
mole
quantities   X
$$CaO + H_2O \rightarrow Ca(OH)_2$$
   1 mole   1 mole
1 mole $CaCO_3 = 100.1$ g   1 mole $Ca(OH)_2 = 74.1$ g

$X = 1.00$ kg $CaCO_3 \times \dfrac{10^3 \text{ g}}{\text{kg}} \times \dfrac{\text{mole}}{100.1 \text{ g}} \times \dfrac{1 \text{ mole } Ca(OH)_2}{1 \text{ mole } CaCO_3} \times 74.1$ g/mole $= 74\bar{0}$ g $Ca(OH)_2$

15. 93 g   X
$$4P \quad + \quad 5O_2 \quad \rightarrow \quad P_4O_{10}$$
4 moles   5 moles
1 mole P $= 31.0$ g   1 mole $O_2 = 32.0$ g

$X = 93$ g P $\times \dfrac{\text{mole}}{31.0 \text{ g}} \times \dfrac{5 \text{ moles } O_2}{4 \text{ moles P}} \times 32.0$ g/mole $\times \dfrac{100\% \text{ air}}{23\% O_2} = 520$ g air

16.   X
$$C \quad + O_2 \rightarrow CO_2(g)$$
1 mole   1 mole
1 mole C $= 12.0$ g   1 mole $CO_2 = 44.0$ g

$X = 1.000$ metric ton coke $\times \dfrac{9\bar{0}\% \text{ C}}{100\% \text{ coke}} \times \dfrac{\text{mole}}{12.0 \text{ g}} \times \dfrac{1 \text{ mole } CO_2}{1 \text{ mole C}} \times 44.0$ g/mole $= 3.3$ metric tons CO_2

17.   X   0.50 mole   Y
$$2Al + 3H_2SO_4 \rightarrow Al_2(SO_4)_3 + 3H_2(g)$$
     3 moles   1 mole   3 moles
1 mole $H_2SO_4 = 98.1$ g

(a) $X = 0.50$ mole $Al_2(SO_4)_3 \times \dfrac{3 \text{ moles } H_2SO_4}{1 \text{ mole } Al_2(SO_4)_3} \times 98.1$ g/mole $= 150$ g H_2SO_4

(b) $Y = 0.50$ mole $Al_2(SO_4)_3 \times \dfrac{3 \text{ moles } H_2}{1 \text{ mole } Al_2(SO_4)_3} = 1.5$ moles H_2

18. 1.00 kg   X
$$2C_4H_{10} + \quad 13O_2 \quad \rightarrow 8CO_2 + 10H_2O$$
2 moles   13 moles
1 mole $C_4H_{10} = 58.0$ g   1 mole $O_2 = 32.0$ g

$X = 1.00$ kg $C_4H_{10} \times \dfrac{\text{mole}}{58.0 \text{ g}} \times \dfrac{13 \text{ moles } O_2}{2 \text{ moles } C_4H_{10}} \times 32.0$ g/mole $= 3.59$ kg O_2

19. $\quad$ 45 g $\qquad$ X $\qquad$ Y

$$2C_2H_6 + 7O_2 \rightarrow 4CO_2 \times 6H_2O$$

2 moles $\qquad$ 4 moles $\quad$ 6 moles

1 mole C_2H_6 = 30.0 g

(a) X = 45 g $C_2H_6 \times \dfrac{\text{mole}}{30.0 \text{ g}} \times \dfrac{4 \text{ moles } CO_2}{2 \text{ moles } C_2H_6}$ = 3.0 moles CO_2

(b) Y = 45 g $C_2H_6 \times \dfrac{\text{mole}}{30.0 \text{ g}} \times \dfrac{6 \text{ moles } H_2O}{2 \text{ moles } C_2H_6}$ = 4.5 moles H_2O

20. $\quad$ 15̄0 g $\qquad$ Y $\qquad$ X $\qquad$ Z

$$H_2SO_4 + 2NaCl \rightarrow Na_2SO_4 + 2HCl$$

1 mole $\quad$ 2 moles $\qquad$ 1 mole $\qquad$ 2 moles

1 mole H_2SO_4 = 98.1 g $\qquad$ 1 mole NaCl = 58.5 g $\qquad$ 1 mole Na_2SO_4 = 142.1 g

1 mole HCl = 36.5 g

(a) X = 15̄0 g $H_2SO_4 \times \dfrac{\text{mole}}{98.1 \text{ g}} \times \dfrac{1 \text{ mole } Na_2SO_4}{1 \text{ mole } H_2SO_4} \times$ 142.1 g/mole = 217 g Na_2SO_4

(b) Y = 15̄0 g $H_2SO_4 \times \dfrac{\text{mole}}{98.1 \text{ g}} \times \dfrac{2 \text{ moles NaCl}}{1 \text{ mole } H_2SO_4} \times$ 58.5 g/mole = 179 g NaCl

(c) Z = 15̄0 g $H_2SO_4 \times \dfrac{\text{mole}}{98.1 \text{ g}} \times \dfrac{2 \text{ moles HCl}}{1 \text{ mole } H_2SO_4} \times$ 36.5 g/mole = 112 g HCl

CHAPTER 9
Answers to Questions pp. 201–202
Group A

1. (a) Free oxygen consists of diatomic covalent molecules, O_2. Combined oxygen has united with other elements to form compounds. (b) The atmosphere is the most abundant source of free oxygen. Water is the most abundant source of combined oxygen.
2. (a) Scheele heated manganese dioxide with concentrated sulfuric acid. (b) Priestley used a lens to focus the sun's rays on mercury(II) oxide. The heat from the sun's rays decomposed the mercury(II) oxide into oxygen gas and liquid mercury.
3. (a) A catalyst is a substance or combination of substances that increases the rate of a chemical reaction without being permanently changed. (b) To increase the rate of decomposition of hydrogen peroxide at room temperature. (c) To lower the decomposition temperature of potassium chlorate.
4. Oxygen is not very soluble in water.
5. (a) Nitrogen boils away first. (b) Nitrogen has a lower boiling point than oxygen.
6. Oxygen gas is colorless, odorless, tasteless, slightly more dense than air, and slightly soluble in water.
7. An oxide is a compound consisting of oxygen and usually one other element; in oxides the oxidation number of oxygen is −2.
8. If a glowing splint is lowered into a colorless, odorless, tasteless gas and bursts into flame, the gas is oxygen.
9. Oxygen is used in the basic-oxygen method of steel production. It is used for removing surface impurities and for welding and cutting.
10. It can destroy bacteria and oxidize harmful substances to harmless products.
11. (a) Ozone occurs to the extent of 5 to 10 parts per million in the stratosphere, between 15 km and 50 km above the earth. (b) This ozone layer absorbs most of the harmful ultraviolet rays from the sun.
12. (a) Allotropy is the existence of an element in two or more forms in the same physical phase. (b) Oxygen exists as two kinds of molecules: oxygen molecules, O_2, and ozone molecules, O_3.
13. Its oxidizing property.
14. Free hydrogen is very scarce on the earth. Combined hydrogen occurs in water, plant and animal tissues, and most fuels.
15. Hydrogen is much more abundant than oxygen.
16. (a) An acid and a metal more active than hydrogen. (b) Hydrogen and a compound in solution formed from the metal and the negative ion of the acid.
17. Hydrogen gas is colorless, odorless, tasteless, very much less dense than air, and very slightly soluble in water.
18. Adsorption is an acquisition of one substance by the surface of another. Absorption is the soaking up of one substance through the entire mass of another.
19. (a) No. (b) If a bottle of hydrogen is held mouth downward while a blazing splint is thrust slowly upward into the bottle, the hydrogen ignites and burns at the mouth of the bottle. But the splint does not burn inside the bottle in an atmosphere of hydrogen.

20. If a colorless, odorless, tasteless gas burns in air or oxygen with a nearly colorless flame and water is the only product, the gas is hydrogen.
21. For preparing ammonia and methanol.
22. (a) An atmosphere free of oxygen. (b) It prevents oxidation of metals at high temperatures required for working them.

Group B

3. Lavoisier extended and interpreted the experiments of others. He used logical procedures and measured masses and volumes. He worked out the correct explanations for what he observed.
4. $2H_2\overset{-1}{O_2} \rightarrow 2H_2\overset{-2}{O} + \overset{0}{O_2}$ Oxygen is both oxidized and reduced.

   $2Na_2\overset{-1}{O_2} + 2H_2\overset{-2}{O} \rightarrow 4NaOH + \overset{0}{O_2}$ Oxygen is both oxidized and reduced.

   $2K\overset{-2}{ClO_3} \rightarrow 2KCl + 3\overset{0}{O_2}$ Oxygen is oxidized.

   $2H_2\overset{-2}{O} \rightarrow 2H_2 + \overset{0}{O_2}$ Oxygen is oxidized.

5. Because liquid oxygen is slightly attracted by a magnet.
6. (a) $2K + O_2 \rightarrow K^+_2O^-_2$
   (b) $2Ca + O_2 \rightarrow 2Ca^{++}O^{--}$
   (c) $N_2 + O_2 \rightarrow 2NO$
7. No. In this compound the oxidation number of oxygen is $+2$. In oxides, the oxidation number of oxygen is -2.
8. Their bodies can receive an adequate amount of oxygen without as much lung and heart effort.
9. Ozone molecules have a higher energy content and are more active than oxygen molecules.
10. The bonding in ozone molecules is a resonance hybrid of two electron-dot structures. Each oxygen-oxygen bond is the same, and is intermediate in properties between single and double covalent bonds.
11. Because Cavendish not only prepared the gas, but he studied its properties.
12. The amount of metal surface exposed to the acid, the temperature, the strength of the acid, and the purity of the iron filings.
13. (a) It should react more vigorously. (b) The activity of Group I metals increases with atomic number.
14. $CH_4 + H_2O \rightarrow CO(g) + 3H_2(g)$
15. (a) Hydrogen; (b) carbon; (c) carbon; (d) hydrogen.
16. The change in its electric conductivity.
17. (a) Hydrogen chloride; (b) ammonia; (c) polar covalent bonds; (d) polar molecules.
18. (a) Potassium hydride; (b) strontium hydride; (c) ionic bonds; (d) positive and negative ions.
19. (a) Tin; (b) hydrogen; (c) hydrogen; (d) tin.
20. (a) Because of their greatly different masses. (b) Their reaction rates are different.

CHAPTER 10
Answers to Questions p. 220
Group A

1. Matter is composed of very tiny particles. The particles of matter are in continual motion. The total kinetic energy of colliding particles remains constant.
2. Because the collisions of the gas particles with each other and with the walls of the container do not change the total kinetic energy of the system.
3. (a) The higher the temperature of a gas, the more kinetic energy its particles have: the lower the temperature of a gas, the less kinetic energy its particles have. (b) No. The kinetic energy possessed by individual gas particles, all of which are at the same temperature, varies widely. However, most of the particles will have kinetic energies near the average kinetic energy of all the particles.
4. (a) The lowest temperature at which a substance can exist as a gas at atmospheric pressure. (b) The gas may condense to a liquid. (c) The kinetic energy of the gas particles is not sufficient to overcome the forces of attraction between them.
5. Dispersion interaction and dipole–dipole attraction. Dispersion interaction is a close-range attractive force between molecules that depends on the number of electrons in a molecule and the tightness with which they are held. The greater the number of electrons and the less tightly they are bound, the stronger is the attractive force of dispersion interaction. Dipole–dipole attraction is the attraction between the oppositely charged portions of neighboring polar molecules.
6. It does not indicate the conditions of temperature and pressure under which the measurement is made.
7. (a) Exactly 0 °C. (b) Exactly 760 mm of mercury.
8. (a) Boyle's law: The volume of a definite quantity of dry gas is inversely proportional to the pressure, provided the temperature remains constant. Charles' law: The volume of a definite quantity of dry gas varies directly with the Kelvin temperature, provided the pressure remains constant. (b) $V' = Vp/p'$. $V' = VT'/T$.
9. (a) -273 °C. (b) Kelvin temperature = Celsius temperature $+273$ °.
10. Its pressure may be greater than, less than, or the same as that of the air in the room.

Group B

11. (a) The particles of a gas move apart. (b) The particles of a gas bombard the walls of the container. (c) The particles of a gas are far apart. (d) The particles of a gas can move in and occupy truly empty space, or the spaces between other gas particles.

12. If each linear dimension is increased tenfold, the volume is increased 10^3, or 1000 times.

13. The condensation temperatures of polar covalent molecular substances are generally higher than those of nonpolar covalent molecular substances; hence, the strength of the attractive forces between particles of polar covalent molecular substances is greater than that between particles of nonpolar covalent molecular substances.

14. The condensation temperatures of ionic, covalent network, and metallic substances are generally higher than those of molecular substances; hence, the strength of the attractive forces between particles of ionic, covalent network, and metallic substances is greater than that between particles of molecular substances.

15. Pressure is directly proportional to the Kelvin temperature.

16. Volume is directly proportional to the Kelvin temperature.

17. Volume is inversely proportional to the pressure.

18. (a) The partial pressure exerted by water vapor. (b) It makes the pressure of the gas appear greater than it actually is. (c) By subtracting the water vapor pressure at the given temperature from the measured total pressure of the gas within the tube.

19. (a) No correction. (b) Subtract difference in levels from barometric pressure. (c) Subtract water vapor pressure. (d) Subtract water vapor pressure and difference in levels divided by 13.5.

20. At temperatures near room temperature and at pressures of less than a few atmospheres.

Solutions to Problems pp. 220–221
Group A

1. $V' = Vp/p'$. $V' = 25\bar{0}$ mL $\times$ $72\bar{0}$ mm/75$\bar{0}$ mm. $V' = 24\bar{0}$ mL.

2. $V' = Vp/p'$. $V' = 38\bar{0}$ mL $\times$ 800 mm/76$\bar{0}$ mm. $V' = 40\bar{0}$ mL.

3. $V' = Vp/p'$. $V' = 100$ mL $\times$ 735 mm/70$\bar{0}$ mm. $V' = 105$ mL.

4. $V' = Vp/p'$. $p' = pV/V'$. $p' = 70.0$ cm $\times$ 240.0 mL/60.0 mL. $p' = 28\bar{0}$ cm.

5. (a) 293 °K. (b) 358 °K. (c) 258 °K. (d) 83 °K.

6. 27 °C = 300 °K. 42 °C = 315 °K. $V' = VT'/T$. $V' = 90.0$ mL $\times$ 315 °K/300 °K. $V' = 94.5$ mL.

7. 43 °C = 316 °K. $V' = VT'/T$. $T' = TV'/V$. $T' = 316$ °K $\times$ 135 mL/18$\bar{0}$ mL. $T' = 237$ °K. 237 °K = −36 °C. The temperature must be lowered 79 C°.

8. −23 °C = 25$\bar{0}$ °K. 23 °C = 296 °K. $V' = VT'/T$. $V' = 500$ mL $\times$ 296 °K/25$\bar{0}$ °K. $V' = 592$ mL.

9. 27 °C = 300 °K. $\bar{0}$ °C = 273 °K. $V' = VT'/T$. $V' = 50.0$ L $\times$ 273 °K/300 °K. $V' = 45.5$ L.

10. 30 °C = $30\bar{3}$ °K. $\bar{0}$ °C = 273 °K. $V' = V \times p/p' \times T'/T$. $V' = 2280$ mL $\times$ 808 mm/760 mm $\times$ 273 °K/303 °K. $V' = 2.18 \times 10^3$ mL.

11. −23 °C = 25$\bar{0}$ °K. $\bar{0}$ °C = 273 °K. $V' = V \times p/p' \times T'/T$. $V' = 100\bar{0}$ mL $\times$ 70$\bar{0}$ mm/760 mm $\times$ 273 °K/25$\bar{0}$ °K. $V' = 1.01 \times 10^3$ mL.

12. −33 °C = 24$\bar{0}$ °K. $\bar{0}$ °C = 273 °K. $V' = V \times p/p' \times T'/T$. $V' = 1520$ mL $\times$ 72$\bar{0}$ mm/760 mm $\times$ 273 °K/24$\bar{0}$ °K. $V' = 1.64 \times 10^3$ mL.

13. 27 °C = $30\bar{0}$ °K. −3 °C = 27$\bar{0}$ °K. $V' = V \times p/p' \times T'/T$. $V' = 50\bar{0}$ mL $\times$ 80.0 cm/75.0 cm $\times$ 270 °K/300 °K. $V' = 48\bar{0}$ mL.

14. 17 °C = 29$\bar{0}$ °K. 307 °C = 58$\bar{0}$ °K. $V' = V \times p/p' \times T'/T$. $V' = 10\bar{0}$ mL $\times$ 38$\bar{0}$ mm/50$\bar{0}$ mm $\times$ 58$\bar{0}$ °K/29$\bar{0}$ °K. $V' = 152$ mL.

Group B

15. 740.0 mm − 4$\bar{0}$ mm = 70$\bar{0}$ mm. 25 °C = 298 °K. $\bar{0}$ °C = 273 °K. $V' = V \times p/p' \times T'/T$. $V' = 35.0$ mL $\times$ 700 mm/760 mm $\times$ 273 °K/298 °K. $V' = 29.5$ mL.

16. 715 mm − 25 mm = 690 mm. 20 °C = 293 °K. $\bar{0}$ °C = 273 °K. $V' = V \times p/p' \times T'/T$. $V' = 60.0$ mL $\times$ 69$\bar{0}$ mm/760 mm $\times$ 273 °K/293 °K. $V' = 50.8$ mL.

17. 720.0 mm − 14.5 mm = 705.5 mm. 17 °C = 29$\bar{0}$ °K. $\bar{0}$ °C = 273 °K. $V' = V \times p/p' \times T'/T$. $V' = 25.0$ mL $\times$ 705.5 mm/760.0 mm $\times$ 273 °K/290 °K. $V' = 21.8$ mL.

18. 732.0 mm − 21.1 mm = 710.9 mm. 23 °C = 296 °K. $\bar{0}$ °C = 273 °K. $V' = V \times p/p' \times T'/T$. $V' = 45.0$ mL $\times$ 710.9 mm/760.0 mm $\times$ 273 °K/296 °K. $V' = 38.8$ mL.

19. 727.0 mm − (65 mm ÷ 13.5) = 722.2 mm. 722.2 mm − 23.8 mm = 698.4 mm. 25 °C = 298 °K. $\bar{0}$ °C = 273 °K. $V' = V \times p/p' \times T'/T$. $V' = 50.0$ mL $\times$ 698.4 mm/760.0 mm $\times$ 273 °K/298 °K. $V' = 42.1$ mL.

20. 745.0 mm − (95 mm ÷ 13.5) = 738.0 mm. 738.0 mm − 15.5 mm = 722.5 mm. 18 °C = 291 °K. $\bar{0}$ °C = 273 °K. $V' = V \times p/p' \times T'/T$. $V' = 12.0$ mL $\times$ 722.5 mm/760.0 mm $\times$ 273 °K/291 °K. $V' = 10.7$ mL.

21. 1.98 g/L $\times$ (760 mm − 4$\bar{0}$ mm)/760 mm = 2.08 g/L.

22. $\bar{0}$ °C = 273 °K. 39 °C = 312 °K. 1.43 g/L $\times$ 273 °K/312 °K = 1.25 g/L.

23. $\bar{0}$ °C = 273 °K. 27 °C = 300 °K. 1.25 g/L $\times$ 273 °K/300 °K $\times$ 90.0 cm/76.0 cm = 1.35 g/L.

24. 25 °C = 298 °K. $V' = V \times p/p' \times T'/T$. $T' = T \times V'/V \times p'/p$. $T' = 298$ °K $\times$ 350 mL/40$\bar{0}$ mL $\times$ 74$\bar{0}$ mm/800 mm. $T' = 241$ °K. 241 °K = −32 °C.

CHAPTER 11

Solutions to Problems pp. 241–242

Group A

1. g-mol wt of HCl = (1.0 + 35.5) g = 36.5 g. D = g-mol wt/molar volume = 36.5 g/22.4 L = 1.63 g/L at STP.

2. g-mol wt of H_2S = 2(1.0) g + 32.1 g = 34.1 g. D = g-mol wt/molar volume = 34.1 g/22.4 L = 1.52 g/L at STP.

3. g-mol wt of CH_4 = 12.0 g + 4(1.0) g = 16.0 g. D = g-mol wt/molar volume = 16.0 g/22.4 L = 0.714 g/L at STP. The mass of 1.00 L is 0.714 g.

4. g-mol wt = D × molar volume = 2.75 g/1.00 L × 22.4 L = 61.6 g. mol wt = 61.6.

5. (a) g-mol wt = D × molar volume = 1.25 g/1.00 L × 22.4 L = 28.0 g. mol wt = 28.0. (b) If the atomic weight of nitrogen is 14.0 and its molecular weight is 28.0, there must be 28.0/14.0 or 2.00 atoms/molecule.

6. g-mol wt of H_2 = 2(1.01)g = 2.02 g. D = m/V = g-mol wt/molar volume. m = g-mol wt/molar volume × V = 2.02 g/22.4 L × 0.300 L = 0.0271 g, the mass of 300 mL of H_2 at STP.

7. m/V = g-mol wt/molar volume. g-mol wt = m/V × molar volume = 0.6428 g/0.225 L × 22.4 L = 64.0 g. mol wt = 64.0.

8. g-mol wt of CO_2 = 12.0 g + 2(16.0)g = 44.0 g. m/V = g-mol wt/molar volume. m = g-mol wt/molar volume × V = 44.0 g/22.4 L × 0.750 L = 1.47 g.

9. m/V = g-mol wt/molar volume. g-mol wt = m/V × molar volume = 0.179 g/0.250 L × 22.4 L = 16.0 g. mol wt = 16.0.

10. (a) mol wt of HBr = 1.0 + 79.9 = 80.9
    mol wt of PH_3 = 31.0 + 3(1.0) = 34.0
    mol wt of N_2O = 2(14.0) + 16.0 = 44.0

    (b) D of HBr = g-mol wt/molar volume = 80.9 g/22.4 L = 3.61 g/L
    D of PH_3 = g-mol wt/molar volume = 34.0 g/22.4 L = 1.52 g/L
    D of N_2O = g-mol wt/molar volume = 44.0 g/22.4 L = 1.96 g/L

11. m/V = g-mol wt/molar volume. m = g-mol wt/molar volume × V.
    N_2: m = 28.0 g/22.4 L × 4.00 L = 5.00 g
    NH_3: m = 17.0 g/22.4 L × 4.00 L = 3.04 g
    C_2H_2: m = 26.0 g/22.4 L × 4.00 L = 4.64 g

12. $\qquad$ Y $\qquad$ X $\qquad$ $\overline{20}$ L
    $N_2(g)$ + $3H_2(g)$ → $2NH_3(g)$
    1 mole $\quad$ 3 moles $\quad$ 2 moles

    $X = \overline{20}$ L NH_3 × $\dfrac{3 \text{ moles } H_2}{2 \text{ moles } NH_3}$ = $\overline{30}$ L H_2

    $Y = \overline{20}$ L NH_3 × $\dfrac{1 \text{ mole } N_2}{2 \text{ moles } NH_3}$ = $\overline{10}$ L N_2

13. 15 L $\qquad$ Y $\qquad$ X
    $2CO(g)$ + $O_2(g)$ → $2CO_2(g)$
    2 moles $\quad$ 1 mole $\quad$ 2 moles

    (a) $X = 15$ L CO × $\dfrac{2 \text{ moles } CO_2}{2 \text{ moles } CO}$ = 15 L CO_2

    (b) $Y = 15$ L CO × $\dfrac{1 \text{ mole } O_2}{2 \text{ moles } CO}$ = 7.5 L O_2

14. 25.0 L $\qquad$ X $\qquad$ Y
    $2C_2H_2(g)$ + $5O_2(g)$ → $4CO_2(g)$ + $2H_2O(l)$
    2 moles $\quad$ 5 moles $\quad$ 4 moles

    (a) $X = 25.0$ L C_2H_2 × $\dfrac{5 \text{ moles } O_2}{2 \text{ moles } C_2H_2}$ = 62.5 L O_2

    (b) $Y = 25.0$ L C_2H_2 × $\dfrac{4 \text{ moles } CO_2}{2 \text{ moles } C_2H_2}$ = 50.0 L CO_2

15. 12 L $\qquad\qquad\qquad$ X(L) $\quad$ Y(moles)
    $2C_2H_6(g)$ + $7O_2(g)$ → $4CO_2(g)$ + $6H_2O(l)$
    2 moles $\quad$ 7 moles $\quad$ 4 moles $\quad$ 6 moles

(a) $X = 12 \text{ L } C_2H_6 \times \dfrac{4 \text{ moles } CO_2}{2 \text{ moles } C_2H_6} = 24 \text{ L } CO_2$

(b) $Y = \dfrac{12 \text{ L } C_2H_6}{22.4 \text{ L/mole}} \times \dfrac{6 \text{ moles } H_2O}{2 \text{ moles } C_2H_6} = 1.6 \text{ moles } H_2$

16. $12 \text{ L } C_2H_6 \times \dfrac{7 \text{ moles } O_2}{2 \text{ moles } C_2H_6} \times \dfrac{100\% \text{ air}}{21\% \text{ } O_2} = 2\bar{0}0 \text{ L air}$

17. $\begin{array}{lll} 40\bar{0} \text{ mL} & X & Y \\ 2H_2(g) & + \ O_2(g) & \to 2H_2O(g) \\ 2 \text{ moles} & 1 \text{ mole} & 2 \text{ moles} \end{array}$

(a) $X = 40\bar{0} \text{ mL } H_2 \times \dfrac{1 \text{ mole } O_2}{2 \text{ moles } H_2} = 20\bar{0} \text{ mL } O_2 \text{ required}$

$40\bar{0} \text{ mL} - 20\bar{0} \text{ mL} = 20\bar{0} \text{ mL } O_2 \text{ uncombined}$

(b) $Y = 40\bar{0} \text{ mL } H_2 \times \dfrac{2 \text{ moles } H_2O}{2 \text{ moles } H_2} = 40\bar{0} \text{ mL } H_2O \text{ vapor}$

18. $\begin{array}{ll} X(g) & 4.0 \text{ L} \\ 2Na(s) \ + \ 2H_2O(l) \to 2NaOH(aq) \ + & H_2(g) \\ 2 \text{ moles} & 1 \text{ mole} \\ 1 \text{ mole Na} = 23.0 \text{ g} \qquad 1 \text{ mole } H_2 = 22.4 \text{ L} \end{array}$

$X = 4.0 \text{ L } H_2 \times \dfrac{\text{mole}}{22.4 \text{ L}} \times \dfrac{2 \text{ moles Na}}{1 \text{ mole } H_2} \times 23.0 \text{ g/mole} = 8.2 \text{ g Na}$

19. $\begin{array}{lll} 25.0 \text{ g} & X(L) & Y(\text{moles}) \\ CuO(s) \ + \ H_2(g) & \to Cu(s) \ + & H_2O(l) \\ 1 \text{ mole} \quad 1 \text{ mole} & 1 \text{ mole} \\ 1 \text{ mole CuO} = 79.5 \text{ g} \qquad 1 \text{ mole } H_2 = 22.4 \text{ L} \end{array}$

(a) $X = 25.0 \text{ g CuO} \times \dfrac{\text{mole}}{79.5 \text{ g}} \times \dfrac{1 \text{ mole } H_2}{1 \text{ mole CuO}} \times 22.4 \text{ L/mole} = 7.04 \text{ L } H_2$

(b) $Y = 25.0 \text{ g CuO} \times \dfrac{\text{mole}}{79.5 \text{ g}} \times \dfrac{1 \text{ mole } H_2O}{1 \text{ mole CuO}} = 0.314 \text{ mole } H_2O$

20. $\begin{array}{lll} 13\bar{0} \text{ g} & 15\bar{0} \text{ g} & X \\ Zn(s) \ + & 2HCl(aq) \to ZnCl_2(aq) \to & H_2(g) \\ 1 \text{ mole} & 2 \text{ moles} & 1 \text{ mole} \\ 1 \text{ mole Zn} = 65.4 \text{ g} \quad 1 \text{ mole HCl} = 36.5 \text{ g} \quad 1 \text{ mole } H_2 = 22.4 \text{ L} \end{array}$

By inspection HCl is seen to be in excess.

$X = 13\bar{0} \text{ g Zn} \times \dfrac{\text{mole}}{65.4 \text{ g}} \times \dfrac{1 \text{ mole } H_2}{1 \text{ mole Zn}} \times 22.4 \text{ L/mole} = 44.5 \text{ L } H_2$

21. $\begin{array}{lll} 90.0 \text{ g} & X & Y \\ 2H_2O(l) \to & O_2(g) \ + & 2H_2(g) \\ 2 \text{ moles} & 1 \text{ mole} & 2 \text{ moles} \\ 1 \text{ mole } H_2O = 18.0 \text{ g} \quad 1 \text{ mole } O_2 = 22.4 \text{ L} \quad 1 \text{ mole } H_2 = 22.4 \text{ L} \end{array}$

(a) $X = 90.0 \text{ g } H_2O \times \dfrac{\text{mole}}{18.0 \text{ g}} \times \dfrac{1 \text{ mole } O_2}{2 \text{ moles } H_2O} \times 22.4 \text{ L/mole} = 56.0 \text{ L } O_2$

(b) $Y = 90.0 \text{ g } H_2O \times \dfrac{\text{mole}}{18.0 \text{ g}} \times \dfrac{2 \text{ moles } H_2}{2 \text{ moles } H_2O} \times 22.4 \text{ L/mole} = 112 \text{ L } H_2$

22. $\begin{array}{lll} 39.5 \text{ g} & Y(L) & X(g) \\ CuO(s) \ + & H_2(g) \ \to & Cu(s) \ + H_2O(l) \\ 1 \text{ mole} & 1 \text{ mole} & 1 \text{ mole} \\ 1 \text{ mole CuO} = 79.5 \text{ g} \quad 1 \text{ mole Cu} = 63.5 \text{ g} \quad 1 \text{ mole } H_2 = 22.4 \text{ L} \end{array}$

(a) X = 39.75 g CuO $\times \dfrac{\text{mole}}{79.5 \text{ g}} \times \dfrac{1 \text{ mole Cu}}{1 \text{ mole CuO}} \times$ 63.5 g/mole = 31.8 g Cu

(b) Y = 39.75 g CuO $\times \dfrac{\text{mole}}{79.5 \text{ g}} \times \dfrac{1 \text{ mole H}_2}{1 \text{ mole CuO}} \times$ 22.4 L/mole = 11.2 L H_2

23.   25 g   X
      $Ca(s)$ + $2HCl(aq)$ → $CaCl_2(aq)$ + $H_2(g)$
      1 mole   1 mole
      1 mole Ca = 40.1 g   1 mole H_2 = 22.4 L

X = 25 g Ca $\times \dfrac{\text{mole}}{40.1 \text{ g}} \times \dfrac{1 \text{ mole H}_2}{1 \text{ mole Ca}} \times$ 22.4 L/mole = 14 L H_2

Group B

24. (a) $\dfrac{30.51 \text{ g N}}{14.0 \text{ g/mole}}$ = 2.18 moles N

$\dfrac{69.49 \text{ g O}}{16.0 \text{ g/mole}}$ = 4.34 moles O

N:O = 2.18/2.18 : 4.34/2.18 = 1.00 : 1.99
Empirical formula = NO_2
(b) g-mol wt = $D \times$ molar volume = 4.085 g/L $\times$ 22.4 L = 91.5 g. mol wt = 91.5.
(c) $(NO_2 \text{ weight})_x = (14.0 + 32.0)_x$ = 91.5.x = 2.0
Molecular formula = $(NO_2)_2$ or N_2O_4

25. g-mol wt = $m/V \times$ molar volume = 1.30 g/[1.00 L $\times$ $72\bar{0}$ mm/$76\bar{0}$ mm $\times$ 273 °K/$30\bar{0}$ °K] $\times$ 22.4 L = 33.8 g. mol wt = 33.8.

26. (a) $\dfrac{46.7 \text{ g N}}{14.0 \text{ g/mole}}$ = 3.33 moles N

$\dfrac{53.3 \text{ g O}}{16.0 \text{ g/mole}}$ = 3.33 moles O

N:O = 3.33/3.33 : 3.33/3.33 = 1 : 1
Empirical formula = NO
(b) g-mol wt = $D \times$ molar volume = 1.34 g/L $\times$ 22.4 L = 30.0 g.
mol wt = 30.0. molecular formula = NO.
(c) Given: 1.00 L of nitrogen + 1.00 L of oxygen → 2.00 L of NO. From Avogadro's principle: 1 molecule of nitrogen + 1 molecule of oxygen → 2 molecules of NO. Each of two molecules of NO contains one atom of N and one atom of O. Thus each nitrogen molecule must consist of two atoms, and each oxygen molecule must consist of two atoms.

27. m/V = g-mol wt/molar volume. $V = m/$[g-mol wt/molar volume] = 2.0 g/[76.2 g/22.4 L] = 0.59 L at STP.
$V_{50 °C, 756 \text{ mm}}$ = 0.59 L $\times$ $76\bar{0}$ mm/756 mm $\times$ 323 °K/273 °K = 0.70 L.

28. 6.02×10^{23} molecules $\times \dfrac{1.00 \text{ L}}{22.4 \text{ L}} \times \dfrac{1.00 \times 10^{-4} \text{ mm}}{7\bar{6}0 \text{ mm}}$ = 3.54×10^{15} molecules.

29. g-mol wt = $m/V \times$ molar volume = 0.865 g/[0.174 L $\times$ 273 °K/373 °K $\times$ 745 mm/$76\bar{0}$ mm] $\times$ 22.4 L = 155 g. mol wt = 155.

30. (a) $5\bar{0}$ g   X
          $S(s)$ + $O_2(g)$ → $SO_2(g)$
          1 mole   1 mole
          1 mole S = 32.1 g   1 mole SO_2 = 22.4 L

X = $5\bar{0}$ g S $\times \dfrac{\text{mole}}{32.1 \text{ g}} \times \dfrac{1 \text{ mole SO}_2}{1 \text{ mole S}} \times$ 22.4 L/mole = 35 L SO_2 at STP.

(b) $V_{25 °C, 745 \text{ mm}}$ = 35 L $\times$ $76\bar{0}$ mm/745 mm $\times$ 298 °K/273 °K = 39 L.

31. $V_{STP} = 40\bar{0}$ mL $\times$ $74\bar{0}$ mm/$76\bar{0}$ mm $\times$ 273 °K/293 °K = 363 mL.

    X   0.363 L

$Mg(s) + 2HCl(aq) \rightarrow MgCl_2(aq) + H_2(g)$

1 mole   1 mole

1 mole H_2 = 22.4 L   1 mole Mg = 24.3 g

X = 0.363 L H_2 $\times$ $\dfrac{mole}{22.4\ L}$ $\times$ $\dfrac{1\ mole\ Mg}{1\ mole\ H_2}$ $\times$ 24.3 g/mole = 0.394 g Mg

32. 6.0 g   X

$Mg(s) + H_2SO_4(aq) \rightarrow MgSO_4(aq) + H_2(g)$

1 mole   1 mole

1 mole Mg = 24.3 g   1 mole H_2 = 22.4 L

X = 6.0 g Mg $\times$ $\dfrac{mole}{24.3\ g}$ $\times$ $\dfrac{1\ mole\ H_2}{1\ mole\ Mg}$ $\times$ 22.4 L/mole = 5.5 L H_2 at STP.

$V_{25\,°C,\ 755.0\ mm}$ = 5.5 L $\times$ $76\bar{0}$ mm/(755.0 mm $-$ 23.8 mm) $\times$ 298 °K/273 °K = 6.2 L.

33. $V_{STP} = 12.0$ L $\times$ (745.0 mm $-$ 21.2 mm)/$76\bar{0}$ mm $\times$ 273 °K/296 °K = 10.5 L at STP. 10.5 L $\times$ 32.0 g/22.4 L = 15.0 g.

34. 5.0 g   X

$2Al(s) + 3H_2SO_4(aq) \rightarrow Al_2(SO_4)_3(aq) + 3H_2(g)$

2 moles   3 moles

1 mole Al = 27.0 g   1 mole H_2 = 22.4 L

X = 5.0 g Al $\times$ $\dfrac{mole}{27.0\ g}$ $\times$ $\dfrac{3\ moles\ H_2}{2\ moles\ Al}$ $\times$ 22.4 L/mole = 6.2 L H_2 at STP.

$V_{2\bar{0}\,°C,\ 765\ mm}$ = 6.2 L $\times$ $76\bar{0}$ mm/(765 mm $-$ 18 mm) $\times$ 293 °K/273 °K = 6.8 L.

35. 1.00 mole

$CS_2(l) + 3O_2(g) \rightarrow CO_2(g) + 2SO_2(g)$

1 mole   3 moles

By inspection 3.00 moles of O_2 is required. This is 3.00 moles $\times$ 22.4 L/mole = 67.2 L at STP.

Volume of air = 67.2 L $\times$ $\dfrac{10\bar{0}\%\ air}{21.0\%\ O_2}$ = $32\bar{0}$ L air at STP. $V_{29\,°C,\ 744\ mm}$ = $32\bar{0}$ L $\times$ $76\bar{0}$ mm/744 mm $\times$

302 °K/273 °K = 362 L air.

36. By inspection there will be 3.00 moles of CO_2—SO_2 mixture, or 67.2 L of mixture at STP. $V_{29\,°C,\ 744\ mm} =$ 67.2 L $\times$ 760 mm/744 mm $\times$ 302 °K/273 °K = 75.9 L.

37.   X   Y   1.00 L

$MnO_2(s) + 4HCl(aq) \rightarrow MnCl_2(aq) + 2H_2O(l) + Cl_2(g)$

 1 mole   4 moles   1 mole

1 mole MnO_2 = 86.9 g   1 mole HCl = 36.5 g   1 mole Cl_2 = 22.4 L

(a) X = 1.00 L Cl_2 $\times$ $\dfrac{mole}{22.4\ L}$ $\times$ $\dfrac{1\ mole\ MnO_2}{1\ mole\ Cl_2}$ $\times$ 86.9 g/mole = 3.88 g MnO_2

(b) Y = 1.00 L CL_2 $\times$ $\dfrac{mole}{22.4\ L}$ $\times$ $\dfrac{4\ moles\ HCl}{1\ mole\ Cl_2}$ $\times$ 36.5 g/mole = 6.52 g HCl

38. 6.52 g HCl $\times$ $\dfrac{10\bar{0}\%\ HCl\ soln}{37.4\%\ HCl}$ $\times$ $\dfrac{1\ mL}{1.189\ g}$ = 14.7 mL HCl soln

39. $V_{STP} = 10\bar{0}$ L $\times$ 747 mm/760 mm $\times$ 273 °K/293 °K = 91.5 L

      X   91.5 L

$C(s) + O_2(g) \rightarrow CO_2(g)$

1 mole   1 mole

1 mole C = 12.0 g   1 mole CO_2 = 22.4 L

$$X = 91.5 \text{ L CO}_2 \times \frac{\text{mole}}{22.4 \text{ L}} \times \frac{1 \text{ mole C}}{1 \text{ mole CO}_2} \times 12.0 \text{ g/mole} = 49.0 \text{ g C}$$

$$49.0 \text{ g C} \times \frac{100\% \text{ charcoal}}{90.0\% \text{ C}} = 54.4 \text{ g charcoal.}$$

0. $5.00 \text{ L} \times 60\bar{0} \text{ mm}/76\bar{0} \text{ mm} \times 273 \text{ °K}/293 \text{ °K} \times 1 \text{ mole}/22.4 \text{ L} \times 71.0 \text{ g Cl}_2/\text{mole} = 11.7 \text{ g Cl}_2$

1. $pV = nRT$
   $T = pV/nR$
   $T = [745 \text{ mm}/76\bar{0} \text{ mm}] \times 2.50 \text{ L}/0.100 \text{ mole} \times [0.0821 \text{ L atm/mole °K}]$
   $T = 298 \text{ °K or } 25 \text{ °C}$

2. $pV = nRT$ and $n = pV/RT$ where $n = $ no. of moles of gas. Thus $n = m/M$ (mass of gas in grams $\div$ g-mol wt). Substituting $m/M = pV/RT$ and $m/V = pM/RT$. By definition: $D = m/V$. Substituting: $D = pM/RT$. At STP, p, R, and T are constants. Therefore D is directly proportional to M.

3. $pV = nRT$ where $n = m/M$ (mass of gas in grams $\div$ g-mol wt). $pV = mRT/M$. $M = mRT/pV$. $p = 74\bar{0}/76\bar{0}$ atm = 0.974 atm.

$$M = \frac{1.98 \text{ g} \times 0.0821 \text{ L atm/mole °K} \times 285 \text{ °K}}{0.974 \text{ atm} \times 1.07 \text{ L}}$$

$M = 44.4 \text{ g/mole}$ mol wt = 44.4

CHAPTER 12
Answers to Questions pp. 266–268
Group A

1. (a) The forces of attraction between the particles of a liquid are strong enough to permit it to have one free surface; thus it has a definite volume. (b) The kinetic energy of the particles of a liquid is sufficient to enable single particles or groups of particles to move with respect to one another. (c) The particles of a liquid are almost as close together as it is possible for them to be. (d) The particles of one liquid may intermingle with the particles of another liquid. (e) The kinetic energy of some particles of a liquid is great enough for the particles to escape from the liquid surface into the space above.

2. Finely divided particles of a solid suspended in a liquid and viewed through a microscope are observed to move about in a random manner. The use of lighter or smaller particles and higher temperatures increases the motion.

3. Two opposing processes in the same system proceeding simultaneously at equal rates.

4. No. The vapor can continually escape, so that the process of condensation can never occur as fast as the process of evaporation. Hence, no equilibrium is possible.

5. The rate of evaporation is reduced and the rate of condensation is increased. This causes the quantity of liquid to increase and the quantity of vapor to decrease. Ultimately the rate of condensation will become equal to the rate of evaporation, and equilibrium will be restored at a lower equilibrium vapor pressure.

6. The greater the pressure on the water surface, the higher the boiling temperature of the water.

7. (a) The highest temperature at which it is possible to liquefy a gas with any amount of pressure. (b) The pressure required to liquefy a gas at its critical temperature. (c) The volume occupied by one mole of gas under the conditions of critical temperature and critical pressure.

8. Its temperature must be lowered to or below its critical temperature, and its pressure must be raised to or above the vapor pressure of the liquefied gas at this temperature.

9. (a) Vapor. (b) Gas.

10. (a) The particles of a solid are held close together in fixed positions by strong forces. (b) Same as (a). (c) Same as (a). (d) The particles of a solid are in weak vibratory motion back and forth about fixed equilibrium positions. (e) The particles of a solid are held in fixed equilibrium positions which, if in a regular pattern, produce crystals.

11. (a) Both have three equal axes. Cubic has all right angles. Trigonal has three equal oblique angles. (b) Both have all right angles. Tetragonal has two axes of equal length. Orthorhombic has three unequal axes. (c) All three have three unequal axes. Orthorhombic has all right angles. Monoclinic has one oblique intersection. Triclinic has three unequal oblique intersections.

12. (a) Hard, brittle, rather high melting point, good insulator. (b) Low melting point, fairly soft, volatile, good insulator. (c) Very hard, brittle, rather high melting point, nonconductor. (d) High electric conductivity, hardness and melting point extremely variable.

13. Abundantly on the earth. Water exists on some of the other planets.

14. Transparent, odorless, almost colorless, tasteless, freezes at 0 °C, boils at 100 °C.

15. The volume of the steam is about 1700 times the volume of the water at 100 °C and 1 atm pressure.

16. (a) $H_2O(s) + 1.44 \text{ kcal} \rightarrow H_2O(l)$ (b) $H_2O(l) + 9.70 \text{ kcal} \rightarrow H_2O(g)$

17. A water molecule is composed of two atoms of hydrogen joined to an atom of oxygen by covalent bonds, with an angle of about 105° between the bonds. Because of the higher electronegativity of the oxygen, the molecule has regions of partial electric charge that make it polar.

18. (a) A weak chemical bond between a hydrogen atom in one polar molecule and a very electronegative atom in a second polar molecule. (b) They cause the boiling point to be higher than it otherwise would be.

19. (a) A compound that does not decompose easily. Water. (b) A compound that decomposes easily. Mercury(II) oxide.

20. (a) Sodium, potassium, calcium, lithium, magnesium, etc. (b) Sodium, potassium, lithium, and calcium will react with cold water; magnesium will react with boiling water.

21. (a) An oxide that forms either a basic solution or an acid solution when combined with water. (b) A basic anhydride is an ionic oxide of a metal that forms a basic solution with water, while an acid anhydride is a covalent oxide of a nonmetal that forms an acid solution with water. (c) A nonmetallic oxide. (d) A metallic oxide.

22. This represents the loose attachment of water molecules to the ions of a hydrate.

23. The chemical changes that occur when water is added to an effervescent alkalizing tablet.

24. No. Sodium carbonate decahydrate crystals are efflorescent and lose water of crystallization to air in which the water vapor pressure is lower than the vapor pressure of the crystals.

25. (a) Anhydrous calcium chloride is deliquescent and so removes water vapor from the air, finally forming a concentrated solution. (b) The calcium chloride may be placed in bags or perforated metal cones and supported above shallow pans. The solution drips into the pans.

26. By electrolysis.

27. As a moderator in nuclear reactors and as a "tracer" in research work in physiology.

28. (a) The H_2O_2 molecule is a double-bent molecule, H—O , with single covalent bonds between the atoms. (b) Each
$$O—H$$
hydrogen atom has an oxidation number of $+1$; each oxygen atom has an oxidation number of -1.

29. (a) $BaO_2(aq) + H_2SO_4(aq) \rightarrow H_2O_2(aq) + BaSO_4(s)$ (b) Exchange reaction. (c) $BaSO_4$ is insoluble and precipitates.

30. As a bleaching agent, in waste purification, in metal extraction processes, etc.

Group B

31. (a) Low-molecular-weight nonpolar molecules. (b) High-molecular-weight nonpolar molecules and low-molecular-weight polar molecules. (c) Ions, covalent networks, and metallic ions permeated by electron "gas."

32. (a) About 92 °C. (b) About 72 °C. (c) About 28 °C.

33. (a) Equilibrium shifts to right to absorb energy. (b) Equilibrium shifts to right to occupy larger volume. (c) No effect, since system is in closed container.

34. (a) Work is done on the gas during compression, and this increases its energy. (b) Gas molecules do work during expansion, and this decreases their energy.

35. (a) No, this temperature is higher than its critical temperature. (b) Yes, this temperature is lower than its critical temperature.

36. (a) It increases their potential energy as they do work against attractive forces in becoming particles of vapor. (b) It increases their potential energy as they do work against attractive forces in becoming particles of liquid.

37. (a) An amorphous metal alloy. (b) In transformer cores, in heads of magnetic tape recorders and players, and for magnetic bubble memories in computers.

38. By observing the crystal structure. Sodium chloride forms cubic crystals. Alum forms octahedral crystals.

39. Camphor forms molecular crystals, the lattice of which is bound by weak dispersion interaction forces. The crystal lattice is easily distorted and molecules can easily acquire enough energy to overcome completely the weak dispersion interaction forces and escape as free molecules.

40. Water makes up 70% to 90% of living things. Chemical reactions of life processes occur in water, with water frequently also being a reactant or product.

41. Ice has a rigid open lattice structure in which the molecules are farther apart than in the liquid.

42. (a) Equilibrium shifts to right to absorb energy. (b) Equilibrium shifts to left to supply energy. (c) Equilibrium will shift slightly to right, since water occupies slightly less volume than an equal mass of ice.

43. When water is warmed, the breaking down of some of the hydrogen bonds enables water molecules to crowd closer together, while the increased energy of the molecules causes them to spread apart. Up to 4 °C, the first effect predominates causing an increase in density. Above 4 °C, the second effect predominates and the density becomes less.

44. They are strong bonds.

45. Tobacco is hygroscopic; thus in damp weather the leaves are not so brittle.

46. Molecules composed of the isotopes of both hydrogen and oxygen as well as ions formed from each of these isotopes.

47. Oxygen molecules are nonpolar. The attractive forces between them are weak. Hydrogen peroxide molecules are polar and associate by hydrogen bonding. The forces between them are much stronger.

48. (a, b) $\overset{+1}{2}\overset{-1}{H_2}O_2 \rightarrow \overset{+1}{2}\overset{-2}{H_2}O + \overset{0}{O_2}$. (c) $\overset{-1}{O}$ to $\overset{0}{O}$. (d) $\overset{-1}{O}$ to $\overset{-2}{O}$.

Solutions to Problems p. 268

Group A

1. Oxygen. 5.0 mL.
2. Hydrogen. 40.0 mL.
3. (*a*) 75.0 mL.

$$\begin{array}{cc} 37.5 \text{ mL} & X\text{(mole)} \\ (b) \ 2H_2(g) + \ O_2(g) \ \rightarrow \ 2H_2O \\ 1 \text{ mole} & 2 \text{ moles} \end{array}$$

1 mole O_2 = 22.4 L

$$X = 37.5 \text{ mL } O_2 \times \frac{\text{mole}}{22.4 \text{ L}} \times \frac{1 \text{ L}}{1000 \text{ mL}} \times \frac{2 \text{ moles } H_2O}{1 \text{ mole } O_2} = 3.35 \times 10^{-3} \text{ mole } H_2O$$

4. (*a*) Oxygen, 25.0 mL.

$$\begin{array}{cc} (b) \ 50.0 \text{ mL} & X\text{(mmole)} \\ 2H_2(g) + O_2(g) \rightarrow & 2H_2O \\ 2 \text{ moles} & 2 \text{ moles} \end{array}$$

1 mmole H_2 = 22.4 mL

$$X = 50.0 \text{ mL } H_2 \times \frac{\text{mmole}}{22.4 \text{ mL}} \times \frac{2 \text{ moles } H_2O}{2 \text{ moles } H_2} = 2.23 \text{ mmoles } H_2O$$

5.
$$\begin{array}{ccc} X(g) & Y(g) & 15.0 \text{ moles} \\ 2H_2 & + \ O_2 \ \rightarrow & 2H_2O \\ 2 \text{ moles} & 1 \text{ mole} & 2 \text{ moles} \end{array}$$

1 mole H_2 = 2.02 g   1 mole O_2 = 32.0 g

$$X = 15.0 \text{ moles } H_2O \times \frac{2 \text{ moles } H_2}{2 \text{ moles } H_2O} \times 2.02 \text{ g } H_2/\text{mole} = 30.3 \text{ g } H_2$$

$$Y = 15.0 \text{ moles } H_2O \times \frac{1 \text{ mole } O_2}{2 \text{ moles } H_2O} \times 32.0 \text{ g } O_2/\text{mole} = 24\overline{0} \text{ g } O_2$$

6. (*a*)
$$\begin{array}{cc} X & Y \\ BaO_2 + H_2SO_4 \rightarrow & H_2O_2 + BaSO_4 \\ 1 \text{ mole} & 1 \text{ mole} \quad 1 \text{ mole} \end{array}$$

1 mole BaO_2 = 169.3 g   1 mole H_2O_2 = 34.0 g

$$X = 51.0 \text{ g } H_2O_2 \times \frac{\text{mole}}{34.0 \text{ g}} \times \frac{1 \text{ mole } BaO_2}{1 \text{ mole } H_2O_2} \times \frac{169.3 \text{ g}}{\text{mole}} = 254 \text{ g } BaO_2$$

(*b*) 1 mole $BaSO_4$ = 233.4 g

$$Y = 51.0 \text{ g } H_2O_2 \times \frac{\text{mole}}{34.0 \text{ g}} \times \frac{1 \text{ mole } BaSO_4}{1 \text{ mole } H_2O_2} \times \frac{233.4 \text{ g}}{\text{mole}} = 35\overline{0} \text{ g } BaSO_4$$

7. (*a*) $\dfrac{15 \text{ Å}^3}{\text{molecule}} \times \dfrac{6.02 \times 10^{23} \text{ molecules}}{\text{mole}} \times \left(\dfrac{10^{-8} \text{ cm}}{1 \text{ Å}}\right)^3 \times \dfrac{\text{mL}}{\text{cm}^3} = 9.0 \text{ mL/mole}$

(*b*) $\dfrac{18.0 \text{ g}}{\text{mole}} \times \dfrac{1 \text{ mL } H_2O}{1 \text{ g } H_2O} = 18.0 \text{ mL/mole}$

(*c*) About one-half the volume of water is empty space.

Group B

8. Formula wt $Na_2CO_3 \cdot 10H_2O$ = 2(23.0) + 12.0 + 3(16.0) + 10(18.0) = 286.0
   Formula wt Na_2CO_3 = 2(23.0) + 12.0 + 3(16.0) = 106.0

$$10\overline{0} \text{ g } Na_2CO_3 \cdot 10H_2O \times \frac{106.0 \ Na_2CO_3}{286.0 \ Na_2CO_3 \cdot 10H_2O} = 37.1 \text{ g } Na_2CO_3$$

9. Formula wt $CoCl_2 \cdot 6H_2O = 58.9 + 2(35.5) + 6(18.0) = 237.9$

Co: $\dfrac{58.9\ Co}{237.9\ CoCl_2 \cdot 6H_2O} \times 100\%\ CoCl_2 \cdot 6H_2O = 24.8\%\ Co$

Cl: $\dfrac{71.0\ Cl}{237.9\ CoCl_2 \cdot 6H_2O} \times 100\%\ CoCl_2 \cdot 6H_2O = 29.8\%\ Cl$

H_2O: $\dfrac{108.0\ H_2O}{237.9\ CoCl_2 \cdot 6H_2O} \times 100\%\ CoCl_2 \cdot 6H_2O = 45.4\%\ H_2O$

10. $ZnSO_4$: $\dfrac{56.14\ g\ ZnSO_4}{161.5\ g/mole} = 0.348\ mole\ ZnSO_4.$

H_2O: $\dfrac{43.86\ g\ H_2O}{18.0\ g/mole} = 2.44\ moles\ H_2O$

$ZnSO_4$: $H_2O = 0.348/0.348 : 2.44/0.348 = 1 : 7.01$
Empirical formula $= ZnSO_4 \cdot 7H_2O$

11. H_2O: $\dfrac{45.0\ g\ H_2O}{124.8\ g\ CuSO_4 \cdot 5H_2O} \times 100\%\ CuSO_4 \cdot 5H_2O = 36.1\%\ H_2O$

12. Cu: $\dfrac{31.8\ g\ Cu}{63.5\ g/mole} = 0.501\ mole\ Cu$

S: $\dfrac{16.0\ g\ S}{32.1\ g/mole} = 0.498\ mole\ S$

O: $\dfrac{32.0\ g\ O}{16.0\ g/mole} = 2.00\ moles\ O$

H_2O: $\dfrac{45.0\ g\ H_2O}{18.0\ g/mole} = 2.50\ moles\ H_2O$

Cu: S:O:$H_2O = 0.501/0.498 : 0.498/0.498 : 2.00/0.498 : 2.50/0.498 = 1:1:4:5$
Empirical formula $= CuSO_4 \cdot 5H_2O$

13. (a) 1 mole $CCl_4 = 154.0\ g$

$\dfrac{154.0\ g}{mole} \times \dfrac{1}{1.600\ g/mL} \times \dfrac{1\ mole}{6.023 \times 10^{23}\ molecules} = 1.598 \times 10^{-22}\ mL/molecule$

(b) $V = 4/3\pi r^3 = \pi d^3/6.\ d = \sqrt[3]{6V/\pi}.$
$d = \sqrt[3]{6 \times 1.598 \times 10^{-22}\ mL/3.1416} = 6.73 \times 10^{-8}\ cm = 6.73\ Å$

14. Radius of atom of Hg $= 1.49\ Å$
(a) $V = 4/3\pi r^3$

$V = \dfrac{4 \times 3.14 \times (1.49\ Å)^3}{3} = 13.9\ Å^3$

(b) Effective volume of Hg atom in cubic array is that of a cube $2 \times 1.49\ Å$ on a side $= (2.98\ Å)^3 = 26.5\ Å^3$

$\dfrac{6.02 \times 10^{23}\ atoms}{1.00\ mole} \times \dfrac{26.5\ Å^3}{atom} \times \dfrac{1\ mL}{10^{24}\ Å^3} = 16.0\ mL/mole.$

CHAPTER 13
Answers to Questions pp. 293–294
Group A
1. (a) A homogeneous mixture of two or more substances, the composition of which may vary within characteristic limits. (b) The dissolving medium of a solution. (c) The substance dissolved in a solution.
2. They are indefinite and give only general information as to concentration. These terms have no quantitative significance.
3. (a) Gas in gas, in liquid, in solid; liquid in gas, in liquid, in solid; solid in gas, in liquid, in solid. (b) Solid in liquid is the most common.

4. The carbon dioxide is less soluble in water at atmospheric pressure than at the higher pressure within the soda fountain. Therefore most of the carbon dioxide comes out of solution and escapes as a gas when the carbonated water is drawn from the fountain.

5. Solution equilibrium limits the quantity of solute in solution.

6. The term dissolve refers to the solution process in which a solute goes into solution diffusing throughout the solvent. The term melt refers to the change from solid to liquid phase.

7. (a) The solubility of a gas in a liquid increases with pressure. (b) The effect of pressure on the solubility of a solid in a liquid is negligible.

8. (a) The solubility of a gas in a liquid decreases with rise in temperature. (b) The solubility of a solid in a liquid generally increases with rise in temperature; however, there are exceptions.

9. (a) The term miscible refers to the mutual solubility of two liquids. Immiscibility refers to liquids that do not mix. (b) Miscible: alcohol and water, alcohol and ether. Immiscible: oil and water, water and carbon tetrachloride.

10. Polar molecules are covalent structures having a negative region and a positive region.

11. By stirring, by powdering the solid, and by heating the solvent.

12. Under existing conditions the rate at which a solute goes into solution and the rate at which the solute separates from solution may become equal. When these opposing processes are equal, solution equilibrium exists and the concentration is the greatest possible.

13. (a) 25 g/100 g H_2O. (b) 124 g/100 g H_2O.

14. Prepare a hot saturated solution, filter, and allow to cool slowly without any disturbance.

15. Liquids with similar structures tend to be miscible. Ether molecules are nonpolar and water molecules are polar. The molecules of ethanol have both polar and nonpolar regions, giving them miscibility with both water and ether.

Group B

16. The solubility of air in water decreases as the temperature of the water increases. Thus cold water may have air in solution that remains suspended in the ice when the water freezes and causes the ice to be cloudy. Any dissolved air was driven out of the hot water as it was heated.

17. Alcohol is a volatile substance; thus the boiling point of the solution will be lower than that of water.

18. (a) The partial pressure of oxygen in the atmosphere determines the amount of oxygen dissolved since they are in equilibrium. (b) Oxygen would come out of solution because of the shift in equilibrium.

19. Powder the copper(II) sulfate crystals, add to hot water, and stir the mixture.

20. The carbon tetrachloride molecule is a regular tetrahedral structure in which the four polar bonds are symmetrically arranged.

21. The alcohol molecule has a region that is distinctly nonpolar and a region that is polar. The molecule of carbon tetrachloride is nonpolar and that of water is polar. Applying the rough rule that like dissolves like, the solubility of carbon tetrachloride may be due to the nonpolar region of the alcohol molecule. The solubility of water may be due to the polar region of the alcohol molecule.

22. The solubility of carbon dioxide decreases as the temperature rises. The gas collects in the neck of the bottle and may build up enough pressure to blow off the cap.

23. Calcium hydroxide is more soluble in cold water.

24. The number of grams of the salt that can be dissolved in 100 g of water at a given temperature is plotted as the ordinate against that temperature in °C as the abscissa. A succession of such points is plotted, and the points are then joined by a smooth curve.

25. (a) The mixture of two different kinds of molecules has greater randomness than the separate pure liquids and is, therefore, more probable. The entropy is increased by formation of the solution. (b) The entropy change favors the solution since entropy is increased in this dissolving process. (c) The dissolving action is exothermic. The negative sign means that the solution has less energy than the separate components. Thus heat is given up during dissolving. (d) The energy change is toward minimum energy and favors the solution. (e) Both the entropy change toward maximum entropy and the energy change toward minimum energy favor the dissolving process. The two driving forces work together to promote miscibility.

Solutions to Problems p. 294

Group A

1. g-mol wt of C_2H_5OH = 46.0 g

$$\frac{0.175 \text{ mole } C_2H_5OH}{\text{kg } H_2O} \times \frac{46.0 \text{ g}}{\text{mole}} \times 40\overline{0} \text{ g } H_2O \times \frac{\text{kg}}{10^3 \text{ g}} = 3.22 \text{ g } C_2H_5OH$$

2. g-mol wt of $C_{12}H_{22}O_{11}$ = 342 g

$$\frac{0.100 \text{ mole } C_{12}H_{22}O_{11}}{\text{kg } H_2O} \times \frac{342 \text{ g}}{\text{mole}} \times 250\overline{0} \text{ g } H_2O \times \frac{\text{kg}}{10^3 \text{ g}} = 85.5 \text{ g } C_{12}H_{22}O_{11}$$

3. g-mol wt of $C_6H_{12}O_6 = 18\bar{0}$ g

$$\frac{6.75 \text{ g } C_6H_{12}O_6}{325 \text{ g } H_2O} \times \frac{\text{mole}}{18\bar{0} \text{ g}} \times \frac{10^3 \text{ g}}{\text{kg}} = \frac{0.115 \text{ mole } C_6H_{12}O_6}{\text{kg } H_2O} = 0.115 \text{ } m$$

4. g-mol wt of $C_3H_5(OH)_3 = 92.0$ g

$$\frac{46.0 \text{ g } C_3H_5(OH)_3}{75\bar{0} \text{ g } H_2O} \times \frac{\text{mole}}{92.0 \text{ g}} \times \frac{10^3 \text{ g}}{\text{kg}} = \frac{0.667 \text{ mole } C_3H_5(OH)_3}{\text{kg } H_2O} = 0.667 \text{ } m$$

5. g-mol wt of $CH_3OH = 32.0$ g

$$\frac{96.0 \text{ g } CH_3OH}{350\bar{0} \text{ g } H_2O} \times \frac{\text{mole}}{32.0 \text{ g}} \times \frac{10^3 \text{ g}}{\text{kg}} = \frac{0.857 \text{ mole } CH_3OH}{\text{kg } H_2O} = 0.857 \text{ } m$$

6. g-mol wt of $C_6H_{12}O_6 = 18\bar{0}$ g

$$\frac{\text{kg } H_2O \times 90.0 \text{ g } C_6H_{12}O_6}{0.250 \text{ mole } C_6H_{12}O_6} \times \frac{\text{mole}}{18\bar{0} \text{ g}} \times \frac{10^3 \text{ g}}{\text{kg}} = 200\bar{0} \text{ g } H_2O$$

7. g-mol wt of $C_{10}H_8 = 128$ g

$$\frac{\text{kg } C_6H_6 \times 32.0 \text{ g } C_{10}H_8}{0.400 \text{ mole } C_{10}H_8} \times \frac{\text{mole}}{128 \text{ g}} \times \frac{10^3 \text{ g}}{\text{kg}} = 625 \text{ g } C_6H_6$$

8. g-mol wt $C_2H_4(OH)_2 = 62.0$ g

$$\frac{31.0 \text{ g } C_2H_4(OH)_2}{10\bar{0} \text{ g } H_2O} \times \frac{\text{mole}}{62.0 \text{ g}} \times \frac{10^3 \text{ g}}{\text{kg}} = \frac{5.00 \text{ mole } C_2H_4(OH)_2}{\text{kg } H_2O} = 5.00 \text{ } m$$

9. g-mol wt of $I_2 = 254$ g

$$\frac{0.762 \text{ g } I_2}{45\bar{0} \text{ g } CCl_4} \times \frac{\text{mole}}{254 \text{ g}} \times \frac{10^3 \text{ g}}{\text{kg}} = \frac{0.00667 \text{ mole } I_2}{\text{kg } CCl_4} = 0.00667 \text{ } m$$

10. g-mol wt $C_{12}H_{22}O_{11} = 342$ g

$$\Delta T_f = K_f m = \frac{1.86 \text{ C}°}{\text{mole } C_{12}H_{22}O_{11}/\text{kg } H_2O} \times \frac{15.0 \text{ g } C_{12}H_{22}O_{11}}{150.0 \text{ g } H_2O} \times \frac{\text{mole}}{342 \text{ g}} \times \frac{10^3 \text{ g}}{\text{kg}}$$

$\Delta T_f = 0.544 \text{ C}°$
f. p. $= -0.544 \text{ °C}$

11. $\Delta T_b = K_b m = \dfrac{0.51 \text{ C}°}{\text{mole } C_{12}H_{22}O_{11}/\text{kg } H_2O} \times \dfrac{15.0 \text{ g } C_{12}H_{22}O_{11}}{150.0 \text{ g } H_2O} \times \dfrac{\text{mole}}{342 \text{ g}} \times \dfrac{10^3 \text{ g}}{\text{kg}}$

$\Delta T_b = 0.15 \text{ C}°$
b. p. $= 100.15 \text{ °C}$

12. $\Delta T_f = K_f m = \dfrac{1.86 \text{ C}°}{\text{mole solute}/\text{kg } H_2O} \times \dfrac{11.25 \text{ g solute}}{250 \text{ g } H_2O} \times \dfrac{\text{mole}}{180 \text{ g}} \times \dfrac{10^3 \text{ g}}{\text{kg}}$

$\Delta T_f = 0.46 \text{ C}°$
f. p. $= -0.46 \text{ °C}$

13. ΔT_f for benzene $= 5.5 \text{ °C} - 4.3 \text{ °C} = 1.2 \text{ C}°$
$\Delta T_f = K_f m$

$$m = \frac{\Delta T_f}{K_f} = \frac{1.2 \text{ C}°}{5.1 \text{ C}°/\text{molal}} = 0.24 \text{ molal}$$

14. ΔT_b for water $= 100.11 \text{ °C} - 100.00 \text{ °C} = 0.11 \text{ C}°$
$\Delta T_b = K_b m$

$$m = \frac{\Delta T_b}{K_b} = \frac{0.11 \text{ C}°}{0.51 \text{ C}°/\text{molal}} = 0.22 \text{ molal}$$

Group B

15. (a) $C:H:O = \dfrac{32.0}{12.0} : \dfrac{4.0}{1.0} : \dfrac{64.0}{16.0} = 2.67:4.0:4.00$

$= \dfrac{2.67}{2.67} : \dfrac{4.0}{2.67} : \dfrac{4.00}{2.67} = 1.0:1.5:1.5 = 2:3:3$

empirical formula $= C_2H_3O_3$

(b) g-mol wt $= \dfrac{1.86\ C° \times 15.0\ \text{g solute}}{\text{mole solute/kg } H_2O \times 0.186\ C° \times 1.00\ \text{kg } H_2O}$

g-mol wt $= 15\bar{0}$ g/mole
mol wt $= 150$

(c) $(C_2H_3O_3)_x = 15\bar{0}$ $x = 15\bar{0} \div 75 = 2.0$ molecular formula $= (C_2H_3O_3)_2$ or $C_4H_6O_6$ (tartaric acid)

16. (a) $C:H:O = \dfrac{40.00}{12.0} : \dfrac{6.67}{1.0} : \dfrac{53.33}{16.0} = 3.33:6.7:3.33 = 1:2:1$

empirical formula $= CH_2O$

(b) g-mol wt $= \dfrac{0.51\ C° \times 9.0\ \text{g solute}}{\text{mole solute/kg } H_2O \times 0.051\ C° \times 50\bar{0}\ \text{g } H_2O \times \text{kg}/10^3\ \text{g}}$

g-mol wt $= 180$ g/mole
mol wt $= 180$

(c) $(CH_2O)_x = 180$ $x = 180 \div 3\bar{0} = 6.0$
molecular formula $= (CH_2O)_6$ or $C_6H_{12}O_6$

17. (a) $C:H:Br = \dfrac{30.3}{12.0} : \dfrac{1.7}{1.0} : \dfrac{68}{8\bar{0}} = 2.52:1.7:0.85$

$= \dfrac{2.52}{0.85} : \dfrac{1.7}{0.85} : \dfrac{0.85}{0.85} = 3:2:1$

empirical formula $= C_3H_2Br$

(b) g-mol wt $= \dfrac{5.12\ C° \times 10.0\ \text{g solute}}{\text{mole solute/kg } C_6H_6 \times 2.1\ C° \times 10\bar{0}\ \text{g } C_6H_6 \times \text{kg}/10^3\ \text{g}}$

g-mol wt $= 240$ g/mole
mol wt $= 240$

(c) $(C_3H_2Br)_x = 240$
$x = 240 \div 118 = 2.0$
molecular formula $= (C_3H_2Br)_2$ or $C_6H_4Br_2$

18. $\Delta T_b = K_b m$ and $\Delta T_f = K_f m$

$m = \dfrac{\Delta T_b}{K_b} = \dfrac{\Delta T_f}{K_f}$ and $\Delta T_f = \dfrac{\Delta T_b \times K_f}{\Delta K_b}$

$\Delta T_f = \dfrac{0.42\ C° \times 1.86\ C°/\text{molal}}{0.51\ C°/\text{molal}} = 1.5\ C°$

f.p. $= -1.5\ °C$

CHAPTER 14

Answers to Questions pp. 311–312
Group A

1. An electrolyte is a substance whose water solution conducts electricity. Solutions of nonelectrolytes do not conduct electricity.
2. Electrolytes lower the freezing point and raise the boiling point of their solvents more than nonelectrolytes.
3. The theory of ionization.

4. (a) That electrolytes in solution exist in the form of ions. (b) That an ion is an atom or a group of atoms that carries an electric charge. (c) That the water solution of an electrolyte contains an equal number of positive and negative charges.

5. An ion is an atom or a group of atoms that carries an electric charge.

6. $2H_2O \rightarrow H_3O^+ + OH^-$.

7. The greater positive nuclear charge of the oxygen atom attracts the electrons shared with the two hydrogen atoms (covalent bonds) more strongly. This causes the oxygen end of the molecule to be more negative, and the hydrogen end to be more positive.

8. It is a lattice-like structure of positive and negative ions arranged in a pattern determined by their oxidation states and their size.

9. An atom is electrically neutral, and except for the noble gases, has an unstable outer shell of electrons. An ion is electrically unbalanced, having an excess of either positive or negative charges, and a stable outer shell of electrons.

10. As an atom gains or loses electrons it forms an ion having the stable electron configuration of a noble gas.

11. (a) The water dipoles surround the ions of an ionic compound and weaken the bonds between them. The hydrated ions diffuse throughout the solvent as the ionic compound dissolves. (b) The process is reversed by evaporating the solvent.

12. All the dissolved particles exist as ions in the solution.

13. Potassium chloride is an ionic crystalline substance. When it is fused, its ions are free to move about and conduct an electric current.

14. (a) 0.0372 C°. (b) 0.0186 C°. (c) 0.0930 C°.

Group B

15. (a) Water molecules are polar. The more negative oxygen end of several water molecules is attracted to the more positive hydrogen end of a hydrogen chloride molecule. The more positive hydrogen end of several other water molecules is attracted to the more negative chlorine end of a hydrogen chloride molecule. The collection of such dipoles around the hydrogen chloride molecule weakens the attractive force between the hydrogen and chloride, and the bond between them is broken. The chlorine keeps the electron from the hydrogen because of its stronger positive nucleus. Both the hydrogen and chlorine atoms are thus converted to hydrated ions. (b) $HCl + H_2O \rightarrow H_3O^+ + Cl^-$.

16. Dissociation is the separation of ions already existing in the solid by the action of the solvent. Ionization is the formation of ions from covalent molecules by the action of the solvent.

17. A solution equilibrium condition exists in which the rate at which Na^+ ions and NO_3^- ions are being hydrated equals the rate at which these hydrated ions are rejoining the crystal lattice of the undissolved sodium nitrate.

$$Na^+NO_3^- \rightleftarrows Na^+ + NO_3^-$$

18. (a) They are covalent molecules that have a symmetrical bond distribution and thus have a net structure that is nonpolar. (b) They do not ionize because of the nonpolar nature of the molecule as a whole. They are not likely to be very soluble in polar solvents and such solvent molecules can exert little influence on them.

19. The freezing-point depression and boiling-point elevation are dependent on the number of particles in solution, not on their identity. Electrolytes provide more particles per mole, because of dissociation or ionization, than do nonelectrolytes. Thus electrolytes cause a greater freezing-point depression and boiling-point elevation than do nonelectrolytes.

20. (a) $Ca^{++}Cl^-_2 \rightarrow Ca^{++} + 2Cl^-$. (b) The dissociation results in 3 ions, thus the freezing-point depression will be 3×1.86 C° or -5.58 °C (ideally).

21. By measuring the freezing-point depression or boiling-point elevation, or by measuring the electric conductivity.

22. It is assumed that the hydrated ions in concentrated solutions interfere with each other's activity, causing the apparent ionization to be less than the actual ionization.

23. A concentrated solution of a weak electrolyte is one in which there is a large amount of solute which does not readily ionize. A dilute solution of a strong electrolyte contains a small amount of solute which readily ionizes.

24. (a) The temperature of the solution is lowered. (b) The lattice energy is greater than the hydration energy. (c) The increase in entropy is the driving force for dissolving.

25. (a) The solubility of KNO_3 increases with temperature. (b) By Le Chatelier's principle raising the temperature of the KNO_3 solution increases the action that takes up heat, the endothermic dissolving process.

26. (a) The substance is an electrolyte and the solution will be a conductor of electricity. The greater freezing-point depression is due to the presence of ions in solution, giving a greater number of particles per mole than nonelectrolytes. The depression per mole of solute is approximately twice the molal-freezing point constant. (b) The ionic charges have a 1:1 ratio.

27. $Ba^{++} + 2Br^- + 2NH_4^+ + SO_4^{--} \rightarrow BaSO_4(s) + 2NH_4^+ + 2Br^-$ $\qquad Ba^{++} + SO_4^{--} \rightarrow BaSO_4(s)$

28. $2Ag^+ + 2NO_3^- + Mg^{++} + 2Cl^- \rightarrow 2AgCl(s) + Mg^{++} + 2NO_3^-$ $\qquad 2Ag^+ + 2Cl^- \rightarrow 2AgCl(s)$

29. $Mn^{++} + SO_4^{--} + 2NH_4^+ + S^{--} \rightarrow MnS(s) + 2NH_4^+ + SO_4^{--}$ $\qquad Mn^{++} + S^{--} \rightarrow MnS(s)$

30. $Zn^{++} + 2I^- + Ca^{++} + 2OH^- \rightarrow Zn(OH)_2(s) + Ca^{++} + 2I^-$ $\qquad Zn^{++} + 2OH^- \rightarrow Zn(OH)_2(s)$

31. $HI(g) + H_2O(l) \rightarrow H_3O^+(aq) + I^-(aq)$

32. $NH_3(g) + H_2O(l) \rightarrow NH_4^+(aq) + OH^-(aq)$

Solutions to Problems p. 312

Group B

1. (a) $\dfrac{10.0 \text{ mL}}{185 \text{ drops}} \times \dfrac{1 \text{ g}}{\text{mL}} \times \dfrac{\text{mole}}{18.0 \text{ g}} \times \dfrac{6.02 \times 10^{23} \text{ molecules}}{\text{mole}} = 1.81 \times 10^{21} \dfrac{\text{molecules}}{\text{drop}}$

 (b) $\dfrac{1.81 \times 10^{21} \text{ molecules}}{\text{drop}} \times \dfrac{2H_3O^+ \text{ ion}}{10^9 \text{ molecules}} = \dfrac{4 \times 10^{12} \text{ H}_3O^+ \text{ ions}}{\text{drop}}$

 (c) 4×10^{12} OH$^-$ ions/drop

2. $\dfrac{0.0155 \text{ mole CuSO}_4 \cdot 5H_2O}{\text{kg H}_2O} \times \dfrac{249.7 \text{ g}}{\text{mole}} \times 125 \text{ g H}_2O \times \dfrac{\text{kg}}{10^3 \text{ g}} = 0.484 \text{ g CuSO}_4 \cdot 5H_2O$

3. $\Delta T_f = K_f m = \dfrac{1.86 \text{ C}°}{\text{mole C}_2H_5OH/\text{kg H}_2O} \times \dfrac{12.0 \text{ g C}_2H_5OH \times \text{mole}/36.0 \text{ g}}{0.600 \text{ kg H}_2O} = 1.03 \text{ C}°$

 f. p. $= -1.03$ °C

4. $C:H:Cl = \dfrac{10.1 \text{ g}}{12.0 \text{ g/mole}} : \dfrac{0.846 \text{ g}}{1.01 \text{ g/mole}} : \dfrac{89.1 \text{ g}}{35.5 \text{ g/mole}}$

 $= 0.842 \text{ mole} : 0.838 \text{ mole} : 2.51 \text{ mole}$

 $= 1:1:3$

 Empirical formula $= CHCl_3$ Empirical formula weight $= 119.5$

 $\Delta T_f = K_f m$ where $m = \dfrac{\text{g solute/g-mol wt}}{\text{kg solvent}}$

 g-mol wt $= \dfrac{K_f \text{ g solute}}{\Delta T_f \text{ kg solvent}} = \dfrac{5.12 \text{ C}° \times 2.50 \text{ g solute}}{\dfrac{\text{mole solute}}{\text{kg solvent}} \times 1.07 \text{ C}° \times 0.100 \text{ kg solvent}}$

 g-mol wt $= 12\overline{0}$ g/mole
 mol wt $= 120$ Therefore, molecular formula $= CHCl_3$

5. $V_{STP} = 15.0 \text{ mL HCl} \times \dfrac{748 \text{ mm}}{760 \text{ mm}} \times \dfrac{273 \text{ °K}}{294 \text{ °K}} = 13.7 \text{ mL HCl at STP}$

 $D_{HCl} = 1.64$ g/L
 $m = DV = 1.64 \text{ g/L} \times 1.37 \text{ mL HCl} \times \text{L}/10^3 \text{ mL} = 0.0225 \text{ g HCl}$
 (1 mole HCl $\rightarrow$ 2 moles solute ions)

 $\Delta T_f = 2K_f m = \dfrac{2 \times 1.86 \text{ C}°}{\text{mole HCl/kg H}_2O} \times \dfrac{0.0225 \text{ g HCl} \times \text{mole}/36.5 \text{ g}}{1.00 \text{ kg H}_2O} = 0.00230 \text{ C}°$

CHAPTER 15
Answers to Questions pp. 339–340
Group A

1. Sulfuric acid—making phosphoric acid, other chemicals. Phosphoric acid—making fertilizer, detergents. Nitric acid—making fertilizer, explosives. Hydrochloric acid—cleaning iron and steel.
2. The hydronium ion.
3. (1) Contain ionizable hydrogen, (2) donate protons to bases, (3) have a sour taste, (4) affect color of indicators, (5) neutralize hydroxides, (6) react with metals, (7) react with metallic oxides, and (8) react with carbonates.
4. An acid gives up protons to particles capable of accepting them, hence it is a proton donor.
5. (a) An acid anhydride is a nonmetallic oxide that reacts with water to form an acid. (b) A basic anhydride is a metallic oxide that reacts with water to form the basic OH$^-$ ion. (c) Examples of acid anhydrides: SO_2, CO_2, P_2O_5. Examples of basic anhydrides: CaO, MgO.
6. (a) Binary acids are named by using the prefix *hydro-*, the root of the name of the element other than hydrogen in the acid, and the ending *-ic*. (b) Oxyacids are named by a system that depends on the amount of oxygen in the acid. The prefix *per-*, the root of the name of the third element in the acid, and the ending *-ic* are used with the acid containing the greatest amount of oxygen. Only the root and ending *-ic* are used with the acid containing the next greatest amount of oxygen. The root and

the ending *-ous* are used for the next acid. The acid containing the smallest amount of oxygen is named by using the prefix *hypo-*, the root of the name of the third element, and the ending *-ous*.

7. Bases are substances that react with acids by acquiring protons; bases are proton acceptors.

8. $H_3O^+ + OH^- \rightarrow 2H_2O$

9. (1) Supply OH^- ions in solution, (2) have a bitter taste, (3) have a slippery feel, (4) affect color of indicators, (5) neutralize acids, (6) react with nonmetallic oxides, and (7) some are amphoteric.

10. Amphoteric.

11. A salt is an ionic compound composed of the positive ions of an aqueous base and the negative ions of an aqueous acid.

12. Salts are named by combining the names of the positive and negative ions of which they are composed.

13. Ionic reaction: Sodium sulfate and calcium chloride are soluble salts and are readily available. There is little energy change in the reaction. Calcium sulfate is only very slightly soluble and will precipitate while sodium chloride will remain in solution. Calcium sulfate can be recovered by filtering, washing, and drying.

$$2Na^+ + SO_4^{--} + Ca^{++} + 2Cl^- \rightarrow 2Na^+ + 2Cl^- + CaSO_4(s)$$

14. No. $BaSO_4$ is insoluble.

Group B

15. HCl consists of polar molecules that are ionized in water solution due to the hydrating action of the water dipoles. The water solution contains hydrated protons giving it acidic properties.

16. (*a*) $4Zn^{++}(aq) + 10H^+(aq) + 5SO_4^{--}(aq) \rightarrow 4Zn^{++}(aq) + 4SO_4^{--}(aq) + H_2S(g) + 4H_2O(l)$
    (*b*) $4Zn(s) + 10H^+(aq) + SO_4^{--}(aq) \rightarrow 4Zn^{++}(aq) + H_2S(g) + 4H_2O(l)$

17. (*a*) $3Cu(s) + 8H^+(aq) + 8NO_3^-(aq) \rightarrow 3Cu^{++}(aq) + 6NO_3^-(aq) + 2NO(g) + 4H_2O(l)$
    (*b*) $3Cu(s) + 8H^+(aq) + 2NO_3^-(aq) \rightarrow 3Cu^{++}(aq) + 2NO(g) + 4H_2O(l)$

18. (*a*) $Cu(s) + 4H^+(aq) + 4NO_3^-(aq) \rightarrow Cu^{++}(aq) + 2NO_3^-(aq) + 2NO_2(g) + 2H_2O(l)$
    (*b*) $Cu(s) + 4H^+(aq) + 2NO_3^-(aq) \rightarrow Cu^{++}(aq) + 2NO_2(g) + 2H_2O(l)$

19. (*a*) When the HCl dissolves in ammonia it gives up a proton to ammonia, forming the ammonium ion and a chloride ion. The HCl acts as a proton donor and in this sense is an acid. (*b*) $HCl + NH_3 \rightarrow NH_4^+ + Cl^-$.

20. (*a*) A water molecule may yield a proton to an ammonia molecule dissolved in it to form the ammonium ion and the hydroxide ion. Since the water molecule donates a proton, it can be called an acid.

(*b*) $H:\overset{..}{N}:H + H:\overset{..}{\underset{..}{O}}: \rightarrow H:\overset{\overset{H}{|}}{\underset{H}{N}}:H^+ + :\overset{..}{\underset{..}{O}}:^-$

21. (*a*) Greasy sink traps are cleaned with sodium hydroxide. The hydroxide reacts with the grease to form soap, which may be washed down the drain. (*b*) Ammonia water may be used to remove grease spots from clothing. It is weakly basic and leaves no residue in the fabric on evaporation.

22. Calcium hydroxide solution or ammonia water may be used to neutralize acid stains on clothing. Both are relatively harmless to fabrics.

23. NaCl—soluble. $CaCO_3$—partly soluble. $BaSO_4$—insoluble. $(NH_4)_2S$—soluble. $Al(C_2H_3O_2)_3$—soluble. Ag_2SO_4—slightly soluble. $Pb(NO_3)_2$—soluble. Hg_2Cl_2—insoluble. $Mg_3(PO_4)_2$—slightly soluble. CuS—insoluble.

24. (*a*) hydrogen selenide (hydroselenic acid), (*b*) iodic acid, (*c*) gallium hydroxide, (*d*) cesium hydroxide, (*e*) radium bromide, (*f*) potassium manganate, (*g*) magnesium sulfate, (*h*) iron(II) perchlorate, (*i*) potassium permanganate, (*j*) copper(II) iodate, (*k*) calcium iodide, (*l*) barium sulfite, (*m*) ammonium fluoride, (*n*) aluminum phosphate, (*o*) sodium chlorate.

25. (*a*) The H_3O^+ ion. (*b*) The OH^- ion.

26. (*a*) The NH_4^+ ion. (*b*) The NH_2^- ion.

27. $HF(g) + H_2O(l) \rightleftarrows H_3O^+(aq) + F^-(aq)$
    acid   base   acid   base

28. $H_2SO_4 + H_2O \rightarrow H_3O^+ + HSO_4^-$
    acid   base   acid   base
    $HSO_4^- + H_2O \rightarrow H_3O^+ + SO_4^{--}$
    acid   base   acid   base

29. $Zn(H_2O)_4^{++}(aq) + 2OH^-(aq) \rightarrow Zn(OH)_2(H_2O)_2(s) + 2H_2O$

30. $Zn(OH)_2(H_2O)_2(s) + 2OH^-(aq) \rightarrow Zn(OH)_4^{--}(aq) + 2H_2O$

31. $Zn(OH)_2(H_2O)_2(s) + 2H_3O^+ \rightarrow Zn(H_2O)_4^{++} + 2H_2O$

Solutions to Problems p. 340

Group A

1.   X   50.0 g   Y
$$H_2SO_4 + NaNO_3 \rightarrow HNO_3 + NaHSO_4$$
   1 mole   1 mole   1 mole

$$\frac{98.1 \text{ g}}{\text{mole}} \qquad \frac{63.0 \text{ g}}{\text{mole}} \quad \frac{12\bar{0} \text{ g}}{\text{mole}}$$

(a) $X = 50.0 \text{ g } HNO_3 \times \dfrac{\text{mole}}{63.0 \text{ g}} \times \dfrac{1 \text{ mole } H_2SO_4}{\text{mole } HNO_3} \times \dfrac{98.0 \text{ g}}{\text{mole}} = 77.8 \text{ g } H_2SO_4$

(b) $Y = 50.0 \text{ g } HNO_3 \times \dfrac{\text{mole}}{63.0 \text{ g}} \times \dfrac{1 \text{ mole } NaHSO_4}{\text{mole } HNO_3} \times \dfrac{12\bar{0} \text{ g}}{\text{mole}} = 95.2 \text{ g } NaHSO_4$

2.   25.0 g   X
$$CaCO_3 + 2HCl \rightarrow CaCl_2 + H_2O + CO_2$$
   1 mole   1 mole

$$\frac{10\bar{0} \text{ g}}{\text{mole}} \qquad\qquad\qquad \frac{22.4 \text{ L}}{\text{mole}}$$

$X = 25.0 \text{ g } CaCO_3 \times \dfrac{\text{mole}}{10\bar{0} \text{ g}} \times \dfrac{1 \text{ mole } CO_2}{\text{mole } CaCO_3} \times \dfrac{22.4 \text{ L}}{\text{mole}} = 5.60 \text{ L } CO_2 \text{ at STP}$

$V' = 5.60 \text{ L} \times \dfrac{293 \text{ °K}}{273 \text{ °K}} \times \dfrac{760 \text{ mm}}{745 \text{ mm}} = 6.13 \text{ L at } 2\bar{0} \text{ °C and 745 mm pressure}$

3.   75.0 g   90.0 g   X
$$CaO + SiO_2 \rightarrow CaSiO_3$$
   1 mole   1 mole   1 mole

$$\frac{56.1 \text{ g}}{\text{mole}} \quad \frac{60.1 \text{ g}}{\text{mole}} \quad \frac{116 \text{ g}}{\text{mole}}$$

(SiO_2 is in excess)

$X = 75.0 \text{ g } CaO \times \dfrac{\text{mole}}{56.1 \text{ g}} \times \dfrac{1 \text{ mole } CaSiO_3}{\text{mole } CaO} \times \dfrac{116 \text{ g}}{\text{mole}} = 155 \text{ g } CaSiO_3$

4. (a) $V_{STP} = 75.0 \text{ L} \times 755 \text{ mm}/760 \text{ mm} \times 273 \text{ °K}/298 \text{ °K}$
      $V_{STP} = 68.2 \text{ L}$

       X   68.2 L   Y
$$CaO + CO_2 \rightarrow CaCO_3$$
   1 mole   1 mole   1 mole

$$\frac{56.1 \text{ g}}{\text{mole}} \quad \frac{22.4 \text{ L}}{\text{mole}} \quad \frac{10\bar{0} \text{ g}}{\text{mole}}$$

$X = 68.2 \text{ L} \times \dfrac{\text{mole}}{22.4 \text{ L}} \times \dfrac{1 \text{ mole } CaO}{\text{mole } CO_2} \times \dfrac{56.1 \text{ g}}{\text{mole}} = 171 \text{ g } CaO$

(b) $Y = 68.2 \text{ L} \times \dfrac{\text{mole}}{22.4 \text{ L}} \times \dfrac{1 \text{ mole } CaCO_3}{\text{mole } CO_2} \times \dfrac{10\bar{0} \text{ g}}{\text{mole}} = 304 \text{ g } CaCO_3$

CHAPTER 16

Answers to Questions p. 367

Group A

1. Molality: moles of solute per kilogram of solvent. Molarity: moles of solute per liter of solution.
2. (a) One equivalent of an acid is the number of grams required to supply 1 mole of H_3O^+ ions. (b) One equivalent of a base is the number of grams required to accept one mole of protons, or to supply one mole of OH^- ions.
3. (a) 82.0 g (b) 32.7 g (c) 61.0 g (d) 74.6 g (e) 6.9 g (f) 19.0 g (g) 80.8 g (h) 17.0 g (i) 60.0 g (j) 57.0 g.

4. (a) 2 (b) 1 (c) 2 (d) 3 (e) 2 (f) 1 (g) 1 (h) 2 (i) 2 (j) 3.
5. $H_2SO_4 + H_2O \rightarrow H_3O^+ + HSO_4^-$
   $HSO_4^- + H_2O \rightarrow H_3O^+ + SO_4^{--}$
6. CO_3^{--} ion.
7. Ammonium ion concentration in moles per liter.
8. (a) pH is the symbol for the hydronium ion index. It is the common logarithm of the reciprocal of the hydronium ion concentration of a solution. $pH = \log \dfrac{1}{[H_3O^+]}$, where $[H_3O^+]$ is expressed in gram-ion per liter. (b) The usual range of the pH scale is from 0 to 14.
9. (a) pH = 3. (b) $[OH^-] = 1 \times 10^{-11}$ mole/liter.
10. (a) The transition interval lies between pH of 3.0 and 4.4. The pH at the end point in this titration is above 7. (b) Phenol red or phenolphthalein.

Group B

11. The strength of an acid depends on the extent to which ionization occurs in water solution. HCl is highly ionized, yielding a low concentration of hydronium ions.
12. (a) Place several pieces of red and blue litmus paper in the bottom of a beaker and cover with a piece of moist filter paper. In another beaker mix several teaspoons of soil with enough water to make a thin paste. Pour this mixture onto the filter paper in the first beaker. Allow to stand for 20 minutes and observe the litmus paper through the bottom of the beaker. If it has changed to red, the soil is acid; if to blue, the soil is basic. (b) Slaked lime or ground limestone may be added to the soil if acidic.
13. Student answer. Toothpastes are likely to be basic.
14. (a) The K^+ ion and the Cl^- ion take no part in the neutralization reaction. They are present as ions in the water solution when the reaction is complete. (b) KCl may be recovered as a crystalline salt by evaporation of the water after the neutralization reaction is complete.
15. Litmus. A neutralization reaction between a strong acid and a strong hydroxide has an end point at a pH of about 7. The color change for litmus occurs at a pH of 6–8, thus the color change would show that equivalent quantities of the two solutes were present. Bromthymol blue or phenol red may be selected for the same reason.
16. (a) 1 mole of NaOH. (b) 2 moles of NaOH. (c) 3 moles of NaOH.
    (d) $NaOH + HCl \rightarrow NaCl + H_2O$
    $2NaOH + H_2SO_4 \rightarrow Na_2SO_4 + 2H_2O$
    $3NaOH + H_3PO_4 \rightarrow Na_3PO_4 + 3H_2O$
17. (a) Formula: $Ca(OH)_2$. Formula weight = 74. One equiv = 74 g ÷ 2 = 37 g. 0.01-N solution requires 0.01 · 37 g/liter = 0.37 g of calcium hydroxide per liter of solution. (b) 0.74 g per liter of solution.
18. (a) Ten million, or 10^7 liters of water. (b) 1 equiv of hydronium ions. (c) 19 g of H_3O^+ ion. (d) 1 mole of OH^- ion. (e) 1 equiv of hydroxide ions. (f) 17 g of OH^- ion.
19. (a) 0.0040-M $CuCl_2$ is 0.0080 N. (b) 0.15-M KOH is 0.15 N. (c) 2-M H_2SO_4 is 4 N.
20. (a) 0.006-M HI. (b) 0.0006-M $Al_2(SO_4)_3$. (c) 0.015-M $Ba(OH)_2$.

Solutions to Problems p. 368
Group A

1.   X   54.75 g
    $NaOH + HCl \rightarrow NaCl + H_2O$
    1 mole   1 mole
    1 mole NaOH = 40.0 g   1 mole HCl = 36.5 g

    (a) $X = 54.75$ g HCl $\times \dfrac{mole}{36.5\ g} \times \dfrac{1\ mole\ NaOH}{1\ mole\ HCl} \times \dfrac{40.0\ g}{mole} = 60.0$ g NaOH

    (b) 54.75 g HCl $\times \dfrac{mole}{36.5\ g} = 1.50$ moles HCl = 1.50 moles NaOH

2. Formula: KNO_3. Formula weight = 101
   0.250 mole = 0.250 × 101 g = 25.2 g KNO_3/kg H_2O
   or 12.6 g KNO_3/500 g H_2O

3. 1 mole of $C_{12}H_{22}O_{11}$ = 342 g

   $0.800 \times \dfrac{342\ g/L}{1000\ mL/L} \times 50.0$ mL = 13.7 g sugar.

4. $M = \dfrac{49.0 \text{ g}}{98.1 \text{ g/mole} \times 3.00 \text{ L}} = 0.166 \ \dfrac{\text{mole}}{\text{L}} = 0.166 \text{ molar}$

5. $M = \dfrac{446 \text{ g}}{223 \text{ g/mole} \times 5.00 \text{ L}} = 0.400 \ \dfrac{\text{mole}}{\text{L}} = 0.400 \text{ molar}$

6. $X = 0.500 \ \dfrac{\text{mole}}{\text{L}} \times 0.250 \text{ L} \times \dfrac{58.5 \text{ g}}{\text{mole}} = 7.31 \text{ g}$

7. $X = 0.300 \ \dfrac{\text{mole}}{\text{L}} \times 0.800 \text{ L} \times \dfrac{666 \text{ g}}{\text{mole}} = 16\overline{0} \text{ g}$

8. (a) 39.1 g; (b) 20.0 g; (c) 58.5 g; (d) 79.8 g; (e) 143 g; (f) 90.1 g

9. $N = \dfrac{4.0 \text{ g}}{71 \text{ g/equiv} \times 1.0 \text{ L}} = 0.056 \text{ equiv/L} = 0.056 \text{ normal}$

10. $N = \dfrac{71\overline{0} \text{ g}}{71.0 \text{ g/equiv} \times 15.0 \text{ L}} = 0.667 \text{ equiv/L} = 0.667 \text{ normal}$

11. $X = 0.100 \ \dfrac{\text{equiv}}{\text{L}} \times 0.500 \text{ L} \times \dfrac{125 \text{ g}}{\text{equiv}} = 6.25 \text{ g}$

12. $X = 0.500 \ \dfrac{\text{equiv}}{\text{L}} \times 0.200 \text{ L} \times \dfrac{90.1 \text{ g}}{\text{equiv}} = 9.01 \text{ g}$

13. (a) Assuming complete ionization of a dilute solution of a strong acid, $[H_3O^+] = 0.01 \text{ mole/L} = 10^{-2} \text{ mole/L}$

$$pH = \log \dfrac{1}{[H_3O^+]} = \log \dfrac{1}{10^{-2}} = \log 10^2$$

pH = 2

(b) NaOH is an ionic compound, all water solutions are completely ionized. $[OH^-] = 0.01 \text{ mole/L} = 10^{-2} \text{ mole/L}$

(c) $[H_3O^+][OH^-] = 10^{-14}$ (constant)

$\quad [H_3O^+] = 10^{-14} \div 10^{-2} = 10^{-12}$

$$pH = \log \dfrac{1}{[H_3O^+]} = \log \dfrac{1}{10^{-12}} = \log 10^{12}$$

pH = 12

14. $30.0 \text{ mL} \times \dfrac{0.500 \ N}{0.150 \ N} = 10\overline{0} \text{ mL of } 0.150\text{-}N \text{ hydroxide solution required.}$

15. $0.50 \ N \times \dfrac{34 \text{ mL}}{1\overline{0} \text{ mL}} = 1.7\text{-}N \text{ ammonia-water solution.}$

Group B

16. 1 liter of a 1-M solution of any molecular solute contains 6.02×10^{23} molecules of solute (the Avogadro Number). 1 mL of 0.1-M solution contains $0.0001 \times 6.02 \times 10^{23}$ molecules $= 10^{-4} \times 6.02 \times 10^{23} = 6.02 \times 10^{19}$ molecules of solute per milliliter.

17. Pressure of the dry gas = 745.0 mm − 17.5 mm = 727.5 mm.

$$\text{Vol. of } H_2 \text{ at STP} = 2.55 \text{ L} \times \dfrac{727.5 \text{ mm}}{760 \text{ mm}} \times \dfrac{273 \ ^\circ\text{K}}{293 \ ^\circ\text{K}} = 2.27 \text{ L}$$

$$\begin{array}{cccc} & X & & 2.27\text{L} \\ Zn + & 2HCl & \rightarrow ZnCl_2 + & H_2 \\ & 2 \text{ moles} & & 1 \text{ mole} \end{array}$$

1 mole HCl = 36.5 g　　1 mole H_2 = 22.4 L

$$X = 2.27 \text{ L } H_2 \times \dfrac{\text{mole}}{22.4 \text{ L}} \times \dfrac{2 \text{ moles HCl}}{1 \text{ mole } H_2} \times \dfrac{36.5 \text{ g}}{\text{mole}} = 7.40 \text{ g HCl}$$

7.40 g HCl are contained in $40\overline{0}$ mL solution

$$\frac{7.40 \text{ g HCl}}{40\overline{0} \text{ mL soln}} \times \frac{1000 \text{ mL}}{L} = 18.5 \text{ g HCl/L solution}$$

$$\frac{18.5 \text{ g HCl/L soln}}{36.5 \text{ g/mole}} = 0.507 \text{ mole HCl/L soln} = 0.507\text{-}M \text{ solution}$$

18. (a) $\dfrac{1.00 \text{ mole HCl}}{L} \times \dfrac{36.5 \text{ g}}{\text{mole}} \times 1.00 \text{ L} = 36.5 \text{ g HCl required}$

$\dfrac{1.19 \text{ g}}{\text{mL}} \times \dfrac{37.2 \text{ g HCl}}{10\overline{0} \text{ g conc soln}} = 0.443 \text{ g HCl/mL conc soln}$

$36.5 \text{ g HCl} \times \dfrac{\text{mL conc soln}}{0.443 \text{ g HCl}} = 82.4 \text{ mL conc soln}$

(b) $\dfrac{3.00 \text{ mole HCl}}{L} \times \dfrac{36.5 \text{ g}}{\text{mole}} \times 2.00 \text{ L} \times \dfrac{\text{mL conc soln}}{0.443 \text{ g HCl}} = 494 \text{ mL conc soln}$

(c) $\dfrac{0.100 \text{ equiv HCl}}{L} \times \dfrac{36.5 \text{ g}}{\text{g-eq}} \times 5.00 \text{ L} \times \dfrac{\text{mL conc soln}}{0.443 \text{ g HCl}} = 41.2 \text{ mL conc soln}$

(d) $\dfrac{0.200 \text{ equiv HCl}}{L} \times \dfrac{36.5 \text{ g}}{\text{mole}} \times 0.250 \text{ L} \times \dfrac{\text{mL conc soln}}{0.443 \text{ g HCl}} = 4.12 \text{ mL conc soln}$

19. (a) $\dfrac{0.500 \text{ mole H}_2\text{SO}_4}{L} \times \dfrac{98.1 \text{ g}}{\text{mole}} \times 2.50 \text{ L} = 123 \text{ g H}_2\text{SO}_4 \text{ required}$

$\dfrac{1.84 \text{ g}}{\text{mL}} \times \dfrac{95.0 \text{ g H}_2\text{SO}_4}{10\overline{0} \text{ g conc soln}} = 1.75 \text{ g H}_2\text{SO}_4/\text{mL conc soln}$

$123 \text{ g H}_2\text{SO}_4 \times \dfrac{\text{mL conc soln}}{1.75 \text{ g H}_2\text{SO}_4} = 70.3 \text{ mL conc soln}$

(b) $\dfrac{0.250 \text{ mole H}_2\text{SO}_4}{L} \times \dfrac{98.1 \text{ g}}{\text{mole}} \times 0.100 \text{ L} \times \dfrac{\text{mL conc soln}}{1.75 \text{ g H}_2\text{SO}_4} = 1.40 \text{ mL conc soln}$

(c) $\dfrac{1.00 \text{ equiv H}_2\text{SO}_4}{L} \times \dfrac{49.0 \text{ g}}{\text{g-eq}} \times 1.00 \text{ L} \times \dfrac{\text{mL conc soln}}{1.75 \text{ g H}_2\text{SO}_4} = 28.0 \text{ mL conc soln}$

(d) $\dfrac{0.200 \text{ equiv H}_2\text{SO}_4}{L} \times \dfrac{49.0 \text{ g}}{\text{g-eq}} \times 3.00 \text{ L} \times \dfrac{\text{mL conc soln}}{1.75 \text{ g H}_2\text{SO}_4} = 16.8 \text{ mL conc soln}$

20. $\text{H}_2\text{SO}_4 + 2\text{NaOH} \rightarrow \text{Na}_2\text{SO}_4 + 2\text{H}_2\text{O}$

$0.0150 \text{ L} \times \dfrac{0.275 \text{ mole H}_2\text{SO}_4}{L} = 0.00412 \text{ mole H}_2\text{SO}_4 \text{ used}$

2 moles NaOH used per mole H_2SO_4
0.00824 mole NaOH in 20.0 mL NaOH soln
0.00824 mole NaOH/0.0200 L = 0.412 mole NaOH/L = 0.412-M NaOH

21. Reaction requires 1 mole NaOH per mole $\text{HC}_2\text{H}_3\text{O}_2$
1 mole $\text{HC}_2\text{H}_3\text{O}_2 = 60.0 \text{ g}$

$25.0 \text{ mL NaOH} \times \dfrac{L}{1000 \text{ mL}} \times \dfrac{0.100 \text{ mole}}{L} = 0.00250 \text{ mole NaOH used.}$

$\text{HC}_2\text{H}_3\text{O}_2$ neutralized = 0.00250 mole
contained in 30.0 mL dilute solution, or 3.00 mL vinegar.

$\dfrac{0.00250 \text{ mole HC}_2\text{H}_3\text{O}_2}{3.00 \text{ mL vinegar}} \times \dfrac{1000 \text{ mL}}{L} = 0.833 \text{ mole HC}_2\text{H}_3\text{O}_2/\text{L vinegar}$

$\dfrac{0.833 \text{ mole HC}_2\text{H}_3\text{O}_2}{\text{L vinegar}} \times \dfrac{60.0 \text{ g}}{\text{mole}} = 50.0 \text{ g HC}_2\text{H}_3\text{O}_2/\text{L vinegar}$

Assuming mass of L of vinegar to be $100\overline{0}$ g:

$$\frac{50.0 \text{ g HC}_2\text{H}_3\text{O}_2}{100\overline{0} \text{ g}} \times 100\% = 5.00\% \text{ HC}_2\text{H}_3\text{O}_2$$

22. (a) $\text{pH} = -\log [\text{H}_3\text{O}^+]$
$[\text{H}_3\text{O}^+] = \text{antilog} (-\text{pH}) = \text{antilog} (-2.9)$
$[\text{H}_3\text{O}^+] = \text{antilog} (0.1 - 3) = \text{antilog} (0.1) \times \text{antilog} (-3)$
$[\text{H}_3\text{O}^+] = 1.26 \times 10^{-3}$
(b) $[\text{H}_3\text{O}^+][\text{OH}^-] = 1.00 \times 10^{-14}$

$$[\text{OH}^-] = \frac{1.00 \times 10^{-14}}{1.26 \times 10^{-3}} = 0.795 \times 10^{-11} = 7.95 \times 10^{-12}$$

23. $[\text{H}_3\text{O}^+] = \dfrac{1 \times 10^{-14}}{[\text{OH}^-]} = \dfrac{1 \times 10^{-14}}{2 \times 10^{-2}} = 0.5 \times 10^{-12}$

$\text{pH} = -\log [\text{H}_3\text{O}^+] = -\log (0.5 \times 10^{-12})$
$\text{pH} = -(\log 0.5 + \log 10^{-12}) = -\log \frac{1}{2} - \log 10^{-12}$
$\text{pH} = \log 2 + \log 10^{12} = 0.30 + 12 = 12.3$

24. Dilute solutions of strong acids are completely ionized, thus $[\text{H}_3\text{O}^+] = 0.054$.

$$\text{pH} = \log \frac{1}{[\text{H}_3\text{O}^+]} = -\log [\text{H}_3\text{O}^+] = -\log 0.054$$

$\text{pH} = -(8.73 - 10) = -(-1.27) = 1.27$

25. 25.0 mL of 0.150-M NaOH $= 0.0250 \text{ L} \times 0.150 \text{ mole/L}$
$\qquad\qquad\qquad\qquad\qquad = 0.00375$ mole of NaOH.
50.0 mL of 0.100-M HCl $= 0.0500 \text{ L} \times 0.100 \text{ mole/L}$
$\qquad\qquad\qquad\qquad\qquad = 0.00500$ mole of HCl.
HCl in excess $= 0.00500$ mole $- 0.00375$ mole $= 0.00125$ mole.

$$\text{Concentration of HCl in resulting solution} = \frac{0.00125 \text{ mole}}{0.0250 \text{ L} + 0.050 \text{ L}} = \frac{0.00125 \text{ mole}}{0.0750 \text{ L}} = 0.0167\text{-}M \text{ HCl}$$

$\text{pH} = -\log (0.0167) = -(8.22 - 10) = -(-1.78) = 1.78$

CHAPTER 17
Answers to Questions pp. 388–390
Group A

1. (a) Because of the large number of compounds of carbon. (b) Organic chemistry.
2. They are directed in space toward the four vertices of a regular tetrahedron, if we assume the center of the atom is at the center of the tetrahedron.
3. They join readily with other elements. They also link together in chains, rings, plates, and networks.
4. (a) Allotropy is the existence of an element in two or more forms in the same physical phase. (b) Diamond and graphite. (c) Because X-ray scattering shows that amorphous carbon contains regions in which the carbon atoms are arranged in an orderly way.
5. Because diamond is the hardest material.
6. Heat is conducted through diamond by transfer of energy of vibration from atom to atom. This process is efficient because carbon atoms have a small mass and are strongly bonded to one another. The diamond structure has no mobile electrons; thus diamond is a nonconductor of electricity.
7. The carbon atom layers in graphite slide over one another easily, accounting for the softness. The atoms within the layers are strongly bonded and are difficult to pull apart in the direction of the layer. Hence, carbon fibers are strong.
8.

It is possible to write three valence bond structures for graphite. Evidence indicates, however, that all the bonds in graphite are the same. None of these structures has an independent existence. The actual structure is a resonance hybrid of the written structures. The carbon-carbon bonds are intermediate in character between single and double bonds.

9. The flat scale-like plates slide over one another easily. It is not soluble or subject to corrosion. It is not affected by heat.

10. (a) Coal is a solid, rocklike material, containing at least 50% carbon, that burns readily. (b) By long-time decomposition of buried vegetation at high temperature and pressure in the absence of air.

11. (a) Peat, lignite, subbituminous coal, bituminous coal, and anthracite. (b) The length of decomposition time and increasingly higher temperatures and pressures.

12. (a) The process of decomposing materials by heating them in a closed container without access to air or oxygen. (b) It is destructive only in the sense that it breaks up or decomposes substances. It is not actually destructive, however, since many new, useful substances are formed by this process.

13. Because the elemental carbon produced by the destructive distillation of coal or wood is not volatile at the temperature at which the destructive distillation is carried out.

14. Adsorption is the concentration of a gas, liquid, or solid on the surface of a liquid or solid with which it is in contact.

15. It usually contains considerable amounts of calcium phosphate.

16. The tremendous internal surface area created during the preparation of activated carbon.

17. The two steps are destructive distillation of a carbon-containing material, and treatment of the residue with steam or carbon dioxide at about 100 °C.

18. It is used as a filler and reinforcing agent in natural and synthetic rubber.

19. It is used for electrodes in the cells in which aluminum is produced by electrolysis.

20. Because it is a part of the oxygen-carbon dioxide cycle upon which many forms of life depend.

21. (a) It is increasing. (b) The burning of carbon-containing fuels and the destruction of forests.

22. The increase in the amount of carbon dioxide in the atmosphere enables more of the sun's heat to be held by the earth. This increased heat absorption could raise the earth's temperature enough to change local growing conditions, cause the polar ice caps to melt, and raise the ocean levels. .

23. (a) By burning carbonaceous material, by reaction of steam and natural gas, by fermentation of molasses, and by heating a carbonate. (b) By the action of an acid on a carbonate. (c) C (combined) $+ O_2 \rightarrow CO_2$. $CH_4 + 2H_2O \rightarrow 4H_2 + CO_2$. $C_6H_{12}O_6 \rightarrow 2C_2H_5OH + 2CO_2$. $CaCO_3 \rightarrow CaO + CO_2$. $CaCO_3 + 2HCl \rightarrow CaCl_2 + H_2O + CO_2$.

24. It is a catalyst.

25. (a) Carbon dioxide is appreciably soluble in water. (b) It will be contaminated with air.

26. Stable gas that neither burns nor supports combustion (except of burning magnesium), anhydride of carbonic acid, forms precipitate of calcium carbonate with limewater, can cause death by suffocation.

27. (a) By the reaction of carbon dioxide with water. (b) It is a weak acid because the reaction of carbon dioxide with water is slight even though H_2CO_3 ionizes extensively.

28. The reaction of limewater and carbon dioxide to produce a white precipitate.

29. Photosynthesis and the various natural and artificial methods of producing atmospheric carbon dioxide.

30. (a) Sodium hydrogen carbonate. (b) By reaction with an acid or acid-forming substance in water solution.

31. (a) $2NaHCO_3 + H_2SO_4 \rightarrow Na_2SO_4 + 2H_2O + 2CO_2$. (b) Ionic: $2Na^+ + 2HCO_3^- + 2H_3O^+ + SO_4^{--} \rightarrow 2Na^+ + SO_4^{--} + 4H_2O + 2CO_2$. Net ionic: $2HCO_3^- + 2H_3O^+ \rightarrow 4H_2O + 2CO_2$.

32. By blanketing the fire with a dense gas to shut off oxygen. By cooling the burning material below its kindling temperature.

33. Most carbon monoxide in the atmosphere comes from automobile engine exhaust. Other sources are other incompletely burned fuels, decaying plants, and live algae.

34. The sulfuric acid acts as a dehydrating agent.

35. Hydrogen, carbon monoxide, oxygen, carbon dioxide.

36. As a reducing agent, as a fuel, and for synthesizing organic compounds.

Group B

37. Because of their very strong tendency to share electrons and form covalent bonds.

38. The $2s$ orbital and the three $2p$ orbitals are combined to form four tetrahedrally-oriented equivalent orbitals.

39. (a) An element has two or more kinds of molecules, each with different numbers of atoms, which exist in the same phase; or an element has two or more different arrangements of atoms or molecules in a crystal. (b) The second reason.

40. When diamonds are burned in pure oxygen, an amount of carbon dioxide is formed which equals the theoretical amount that would be formed if a diamond were pure carbon.

41. In diamond the carbon atoms are covalently bonded to each other in a strong compact fashion. The rigidity of the structure gives diamond its hardness. Since all the electrons are firmly bound in the giant molecular structure, diamond is a nonconductor of electricity. In graphite the carbon atoms are arranged in layers of thin hexagonal plates. The layered structure accounts for the softness. The mobile electrons in the layers account for the electric conductivity. The atoms are closer, on the average, in diamond than in graphite, giving diamond the higher density. The bond strengths in both diamond and graphite are high, giving them both ability to withstand high temperatures without melting.

42. (a) Coating the molds used in metal casting, increasing the carbon content of steel, and making clay-graphite crucibles. (b) Its high melting point.
43. (a) Electrodes for electric-arc steelmaking furnaces. (b) Its electric conductivity.
44. (a) It decreases. (b) It increases. (c) It decreases. (d) It increases.
45. The coke.
46. Charcoal will burn. Copper(II) oxide is reduced to copper by hydrogen when it is hot. Manganese dioxide responds to neither of these processes.
47. Activated carbon might be used to recover dry-cleaning solvent vapors from exhaust gases. It might be used to purify the dry-cleaning solvent.
48. (a) A spray of liquid fuel or gaseous fuel vapor, an additional fuel, and air. (b) The fuels supply oxidizable material and the carbon which becomes carbon black. The air is a source of oxygen.
49. The carbon in printer's ink is not soluble.
50. $Ca^{++}CO_3^{--} + 2H_3O^+ \rightarrow Ca^{++} + 3H_2O + CO_2$.
51. $CO_3^{--} + 2H_3O^+ \rightarrow 3H_2O + CO_2$.
52. Its vapor pressure.
53. It is hot enough to decompose carbon dioxide and produce oxygen in which it continues to burn.
54. $CO_2 + H_2O \rightleftarrows H_2CO_3$
$H_2CO_3 + 2H_2O \rightleftarrows 2H_3O^+ + CO_3^{--}$
$2Na^+OH^- \rightarrow 2Na^+ + 2OH^-$
$2H_3O^+ + 2OH^- \rightarrow 4H_2O$
55. $Ca^{++}(OH^-)_2 \rightarrow Ca^{++} + 2OH^-$
$CO_2 + H_2O \rightleftarrows H_2CO_3$
$H_2CO_3 + 2H_2O \rightleftarrows 2H_3O^+ + CO_3^{--}$
$Ca^{++} + 2OH^- + 2H_3O^+ + CO_3^{--} \rightarrow Ca^{++}CO_3^{--}(s) + 4H_2O$
56. The ring is calcium carbonate formed by the reaction between the limewater and the carbon dioxide in the air. Dilute hydrochloric acid will remove it.
57. (a) Low critical temperature. (b) Chemical stability.
58. Baking soda is sodium hydrogen carbonate. Baking powder is a dry mixture of sodium hydrogen carbonate, a powdered acid or acid-forming substance, and cornstarch.
59. High temperature to supply energy and low pressure because of the volume increase during the reaction.
60. While the carbon-oxygen bonds in carbon dioxide are slightly polar, the symmetrical arrangement of the molecule prevents it from being polar as a whole. The carbon monoxide molecule is unsymmetrical. The 50% contribution of the $^-\!:C\!:\!:\!:O\!:^+$ structure causes the carbon atom to be more electronegative.
61. Since carbon dioxide molecules are nonpolar and carbon monoxide molecules are only weakly polar, the attractive forces between these molecules are weak, and at rather low temperatures the kinetic energies of the molecules are sufficient to overcome them. Water molecules, on the other hand, are so strongly polar that they form chains by hydrogen bonding. A higher temperature is necessary before the kinetic energy of the molecules can overcome these bonding forces.
62. Carbon dioxide asphyxiates because of lack of oxygen to breathe. Carbon monoxide combines with the hemoglobin of the blood in preference to oxygen, and prevents the hemoglobin from transporting oxygen.

Solutions to Problems p. 390
Group A
1. Formula weight of HCOOH = 2(1.0) + 12.0 + 2(16.0) = 46.0

H: $\dfrac{2.0\ H}{46.0\ HCOOH} \times 100\%\ HCOOH = 4.3\%\ H$

C: $\dfrac{12.0\ C}{46.0\ HCOOH} \times 100\%\ HCOOH = 26.1\%\ C$

O: $\dfrac{32.0\ O}{46.0\ HCOOH} \times 100\%\ HCOOH = 69.6\%\ O$

2. (a)
$$\begin{array}{ccccccc} X\,(moles) & & 2.00\ moles & & Y\,(moles) & & Z\,(moles) \\ Fe_2O_3 & + & 3CO & \rightarrow & 2Fe & + & 3CO_2 \\ 1\ mole & & 3\ moles & & 2\ moles & & 3\ moles \end{array}$$

$X = 2.00\ moles\ CO \times \dfrac{1\ mole\ Fe_2O_3}{3\ moles\ CO} = 0.667\ mole\ Fe_2O_3$

(b) $Y = 2.00\ moles\ CO \times \dfrac{2\ moles\ Fe}{3\ moles\ CO} = 1.33\ moles\ Fe$

(c) Z = 2.00 moles CO $\times$ $\dfrac{3 \text{ moles } CO_2}{3 \text{ moles } CO}$ = 2.00 moles CO_2

3.   12.2 g   X   Y   Z

     ZnO + CO → Zn + $CO_2(g)$

     1 mole   1 mole   1 mole   1 mole

     1 mole ZnO = 81.4 g   1 mole CO = 28.0 g

     X = 12.2 g ZnO $\times$ $\dfrac{\text{mole}}{81.4 \text{ g}}$ $\times$ $\dfrac{1 \text{ mole } CO}{1 \text{ mole } ZnO}$ $\times$ 28.0 g/mole = 4.20 g CO

4. (a) 1 mole Zn = 65.4 g

     Y = 12.2 g ZnO $\times$ $\dfrac{\text{mole}}{81.4 \text{ g}}$ $\times$ $\dfrac{1 \text{ mole } Zn}{1 \text{ mole } ZnO}$ $\times$ 65.4 g/mole = 9.81 g Zn

   (b) 1 mole CO_2 = 22.4 L

     Z = 12.2 g ZnO $\times$ $\dfrac{\text{mole}}{81.4 \text{ g}}$ $\times$ $\dfrac{1 \text{ mole } CO_2}{1 \text{ mole } ZnO}$ $\times$ 22.4 L/mole = 3.36 L

5.   1.00 kg   X   Y

     $2NaHCO_3$ + H_2SO_4 → Na_2SO_4 + $2H_2O$ + $2CO_2(g)$

     2 moles   1 mole   2 moles

     1 mole $NaHCO_3$ = 84.0 g   1 mole H_2SO_4 = 98.1 g

     X = 1.00 kg $\times$ $\dfrac{10^3 \text{ g}}{\text{kg}}$ $\times$ $\dfrac{1 \text{ mole } NaHCO_3}{84.0 \text{ g}}$ $\times$ $\dfrac{1 \text{ mole } H_2SO_4}{2 \text{ moles } NaHCO_3}$ $\times$ 98.1 g/mole = 584 g H_2SO_4

6. 1 mole CO_2 = 22.4 L

     Y = 1.00 kg $\times$ $\dfrac{10^3 \text{ g}}{\text{kg}}$ $\times$ $\dfrac{1 \text{ mole } NaHCO_3}{84.0 \text{ g}}$ $\times$ $\dfrac{2 \text{ moles } CO_2}{2 \text{ moles } NaHCO_3}$ $\times$ 22.4 L/mole = 267 L CO_2

Group B

7. $23\overline{0}$ g   X

     $HCOOH$ → H_2O + CO

     1 mole   1 mole

     1 mole $HCOOH$ = 46.0 g   1 mole CO = 28.0 g

     X = $23\overline{0}$ g $HCOOH$ $\times$ $\dfrac{\text{mole}}{46.0 \text{ g}}$ $\times$ $\dfrac{1 \text{ mole } CO}{1 \text{ mole } HCOOH}$ $\times$ 28.0 g/mole = $14\overline{0}$ g CO

8. $14\overline{0}$ g CO $\times$ $\dfrac{22.4 \text{ L}}{28.0 \text{ g}}$ $\times$ $\dfrac{30\overline{0} \text{ °K}}{273 \text{ °K}}$ $\times$ $\dfrac{760 \text{ mm}}{75\overline{0} \text{ mm}}$ = 125 L CO

9. $2CO(g)$ + O_2 → $2CO_2(g)$

   2 moles   2 moles

     125 L CO $\times$ $\dfrac{2 \text{ moles } CO_2}{2 \text{ moles } CO}$ = 125 L CO_2

10. V_{STP} = 2.50 L $\times$ $\dfrac{273 \text{ °K}}{29\overline{0} \text{ °K}}$ $\times$ $\dfrac{74\overline{0} \text{ mm}}{760 \text{ mm}}$ = 2.29 L at STP

     X   2.29 L

     $CaCO_3$ + $2HCl$ → $CaCl_2$ + H_2O + $CO_2(g)$

     1 mole   2 moles   1 mole

     1 mole $CaCO_3$ = 100.1 g   1 mole CO_2 = 22.4 L

     X = 2.29 L CO_2 $\times$ $\dfrac{\text{mole}}{22.4 \text{ L}}$ $\times$ $\dfrac{1 \text{ mole } CaCO_3}{1 \text{ mole } CO_2}$ $\times$ 100.1 g/mole = 10.2 g $CaCO_3$

11. 1 mole HCl = 36.5 g

$$2.29 \text{ L CO}_2 \times \frac{\text{mole}}{22.4 \text{ L}} \times \frac{2 \text{ moles HCl}}{1 \text{ mole CO}_2} \times 36.5 \text{ g/mole} \times \frac{100\%}{38.0\%} \times \frac{1 \text{ mL}}{1.20 \text{ g}} = 16.4 \text{ mL conc. HCl}$$

12. C: $\dfrac{52.9 \text{ g C}}{12.0 \text{ g/mole}} = 4.41$ moles C

O: $\dfrac{47.1 \text{ g O}}{16.0 \text{ g/mole}} = 2.94$ moles O

C:O = 4.41/2.94 : 2.94/2.94 = 1.50 : 1.00 = 3.00 : 2.00
Empirical formula C_3O_2
$C_3O_2 + O_2 \rightarrow CO_2$ (not balanced)
$C_3O_2 + 2O_2 \rightarrow 3CO_2$ (balanced according to conservation of atoms)
Since the balanced equation shows 2 moles of O_2 for each mole of C_3O_2 and the volume relations are also known to be 2 volumes of O_2 for each volume of C_3O_2, C_3O_2 is proved to be the molecular formula by Avogadro's principle.

CHAPTER 18
Answers to Questions pp. 415–416
Group A

1. Carbon atoms link together by means of covalent bonds and the same atoms may be arranged in several different isomeric structures.
2. A pair of shared electrons.
3. The kinds of atoms, how many of each, and their arrangement in the molecule.
4. Most organic compounds do not dissolve in water. Organic compounds are decomposed by heat more easily than most inorganic compounds. Organic reactions generally proceed at much slower rates. Organic reactions are greatly affected by reaction conditions. Organic compounds exist as molecules that consist of atoms joined by covalent bonds.
5. (a) Natural gas is a mixture of hydrocarbon gases and vapors. Up to about 97% of natural gas is methane. The remainder consists of hydrocarbons whose molecules contain from two to seven carbon atoms. (b) Petroleum is a complex mixture of hydrocarbons that varies greatly in composition from place to place. The hydrocarbon molecules in petroleum contain from one to more than 50 carbon atoms, and are of several different types.
6. (a) Fractional distillation is a method of separating the components of a mixture on the basis of differences in their boiling points. (b) It is fairly easy to separate the lower members of the alkane series. However, it is usually only possible to separate the higher-boiling substances into mixtures of compounds with similar boiling points.
7. (a) Solvent and dry cleaner. (b) Furnace fuel, Diesel engine fuel, cracking processes for gasoline production.
8. (a) C_nH_{2n+2}. (b) C_nH_{2n}. (c) C_nH_{2n-2}.
9. (a) C_6H_{14}. (b) C_6H_{12}. (c) C_6H_{10}.
10. By using the Greek or Latin prefixes which show the number of carbon atoms in the molecule and the suffix -ane.
11. A generalized formula for an alkane.
12. By heating a mixture of soda lime and sodium acetate.
13. (a) $CH_4 + 2O_2 \rightarrow CO_2 + 2H_2O$. (b) $C_2H_4 + 3O_2 \rightarrow 2CO_2 + 2H_2O$. (c) $2C_2H_2 + 5O_2 \rightarrow 4CO_2 + 2H_2O$. (d) $2C_4H_6 + 11O_2 \rightarrow 8CO_2 + 6H_2O$.
14. $CH_4 + Br_2 \rightarrow CH_3Br + HBr$; $CH_3Br + Br_2 \rightarrow CH_2Br_2 + HBr$; $CH_2Br_2 + Br_2 \rightarrow CHBr_3 + HBr$; $CHBr_3 + Br_2 \rightarrow CBr_4 + HBr$.
15. (a) Cracking is a process by which complex organic molecules are broken up into simpler molecules. (b) Thermal cracking is done by heat alone. Catalytic cracking involves the use of both heat and a catalyst.
16.

17. (a) A single unit of a polymer. (b) A compound formed by two simpler molecules or radicals. (c) A compound formed by two or more simpler molecules or radicals with repeating structural units. (d) A union of two or more similar structures in which the atoms remain in similar relative position.
18. It is used in the synthesis of complex organic compounds and in the oxyacetylene torch.
19. They refer to the bonding in hydrocarbon molecules. Saturated molecules have only single bonds between carbon atoms, while unsaturated molecules have at least one double or triple bond.
20. Because any moisture in the air would react with the calcium carbide, and liberate ethyne.

21. They have structures that consist of two and three benzene molecules joined together, respectively.
22. (*a*) Knocking occurs in an automobile engine when the mixture of gasoline vapor and air within the cylinders does no burn at a uniform rate. (*b*) By using a large proportion of molecules of branched-chain and ring hydrocarbons that bur more uniformly. Lead tetraethyl is sometimes added also.
23. The gasoline performs in a test engine like a mixture of 96% iso-octane and 4% *n*-heptane.
24. By heating the oil shale, which drives out the oil.
25. By adding formic acid.
26. The monomers are joined in a zigzag chain.
27. By mixing the rubber with sulfur and various other powders.
28. The organic catalysts speed vulcanization. Other organic chemicals slow the aging process caused by oxygen in the ai
29. The heating of rubber with other materials to a definite temperature for a definite time to improve its properties.
30. It is little affected by oils and greases.

Group B

31. Ionic bonds are usually stronger than covalent bonds and more energy (higher temperature) is needed to break them.
32. In Figure 12-6 a pure liquid is shown. In Figure 18-7 a mixture of liquids is shown. In both cases, whether the vapor bubbl reaches the surface or collapses depends on the relationship between the vapor pressure of the bubble and the pressure o the liquid surface. The vapor pressure depends on the temperature.

33.
```
    H   H   H   H   H   H              H   H   H   H   H
    |   |   |   |   |   |              |   |   |   |   |
H—C—C—C—C—C—C—H                    H—C—C—C—C—C—H
    |   |   |   |   |   |              |   |   |   |   |
    H   H   H   H   H   H              H   |   H   H   H
                                         H—C—H
                                           |
                                           H

    H   H   H   H   H
    |   |   |   |   |
H—C—C—C—C—C—H
    |   |   |   |   |
    H   H   |   H   H
          H—C—H
            |
            H

          H                              H
          |                              |
        H—C—H                          H—C—H
    H   |       H   H          H   H   |       H
    |   |       |   |          |   |   |       |
H—C——C——C—C—H          H—C——C——C——C—H
    |   |       |   |          |   |   |       |
    H   |       H   H          H   H   |       H
      H—C—H                          H—C—H
        |                              |
        H                              H
```

34. $2C_{10}H_{22} + 31O_2 \rightarrow 20CO_2 + 22H_2O$.

35.
```
    H  Cl  H
    |   |  |
H—C—C—C—H
    |   |  |
    H  Cl  H
```

36.
```
    H   H   H   H   Cl             Cl  Cl  Cl  H   H
    |   |   |   |   |              |   |   |   |   |
H—C—C—C—C—C—Cl           H—C—C—C—C—C—H
    |   |   |   |   |              |   |   |   |   |
    H   H   H   H   Cl             H   H   H   H   H

    Cl  H  Cl   H  Cl
    |   |   |   |   |
H—C—C—C—C—C—H        etc.
    |   |   |   |   |
    H   H   H   H   H
```

37. Almost all carbon compounds contain hydrogen. In addition, hydrogen is contained in acids, hydroxides, ammonium compounds, etc.

38.

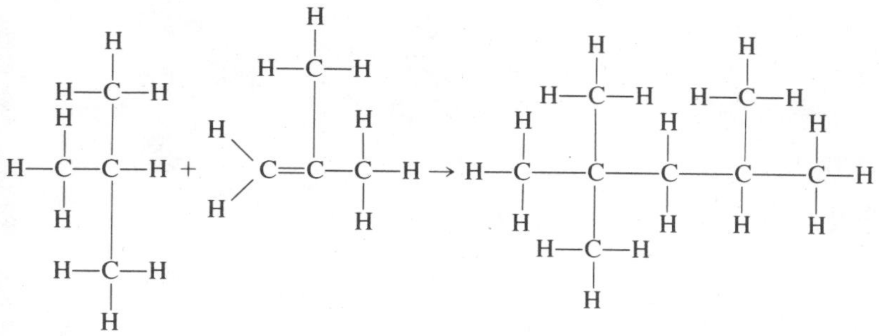

39. $2H-C\equiv C-H \xrightarrow[\text{NH}_4\text{Cl}]{\text{Cu}_2\text{Cl}_2}$

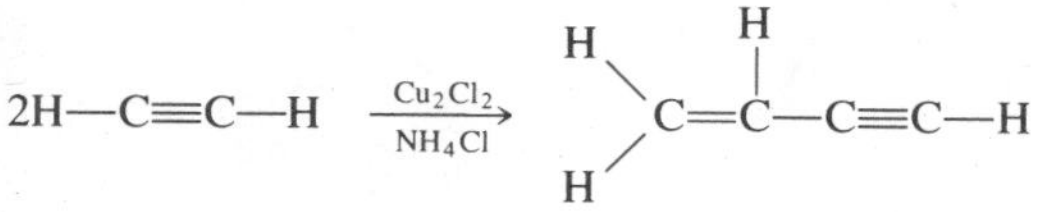

40. (a) Yes. (b) Yes. The structural formula would be

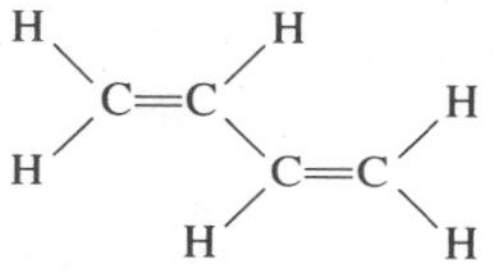

(c) The six hydrogen atoms and the four carbon atoms would all lie in the same plane.

41. (a)

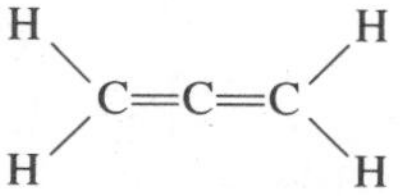

(b)

(c) Student drawing.
(d) They do not lie in the same plane.

42. C_6H_{2n-6}.

43. (a) Resonance is an attempt to make up for the deficiencies of the valence-bond structures of certain molecules written in accord with the valence-bond rules. (b) Benzene is represented by the resonance formula

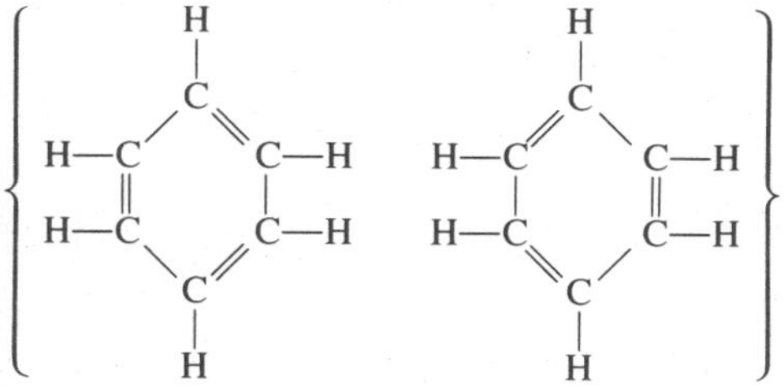

in which the two structures contribute equally. The bonds in benzene are resonance hybrid bonds. All the carbon-carbon bonds in the molecule are equivalent. (c) No.

44. $C_6H_6 + Br_2 \rightarrow C_6H_5Br + HBr$; $C_6H_5Br + Br_2 \rightarrow C_6H_4Br_2 + HBr$; $C_6H_4Br_2 + Br_2 \rightarrow C_6H_3Br_3 + HBr$; $C_6H_3Br_3 + Br_2 \rightarrow C_6H_2Br_4 + HBr$; $C_6H_2Br_4 + Br_2 \rightarrow C_6HBr_5 + HBr$; $C_6HBr_5 + Br_2 \rightarrow C_6Br_6 + HBr$.

45. 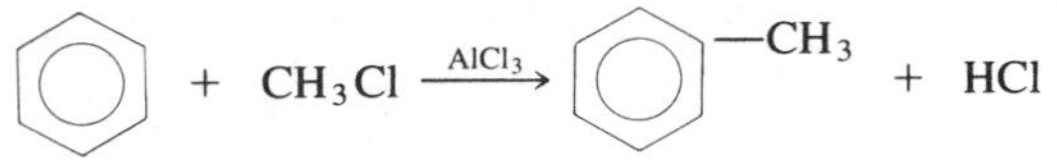 $\bigcirc$ + CH_3Cl $\xrightarrow{AlCl_3}$ $\bigcirc$—CH_3 + HCl

46. (a)

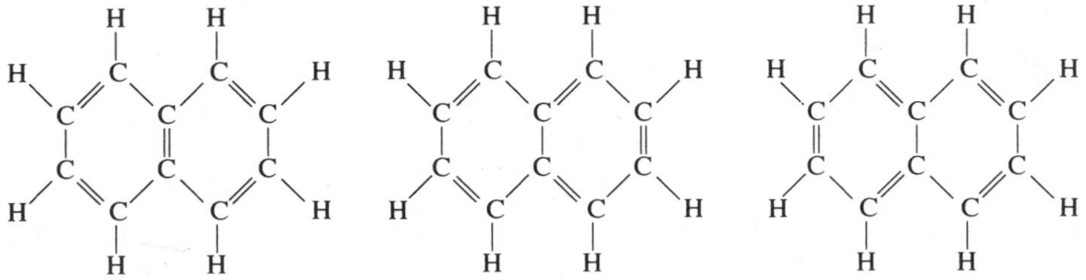

(b)

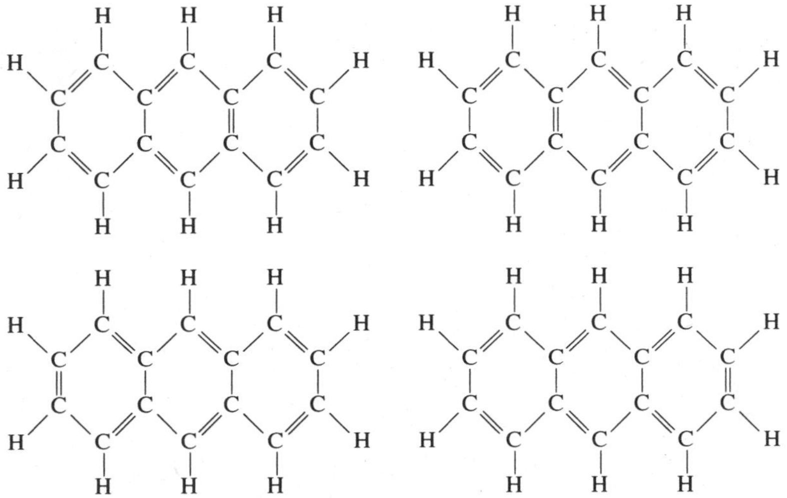

47. (a) Carbon monoxide and hydrogen are reactants. A variety of saturated and unsaturated straight-chain hydrocarbons is the product. (b) Finely powdered coal suspended in oil and hydrogen are reactants. Liquid hydrocarbons are products.

48. (a) Butadiene and styrene. (b) Tire treads. (c) It resists wear better than the other synthetic rubbers.

Solutions to Problems p. 416

Group A

1. $D = m/V$. $m = DV$. $m = 0.692$ g/mL $\times$ 15.0 gal $\times$ 4 qt/gal $\times$ 945 mL/qt $\times$ 1 kg/1000 g. $m = 39.3$ kg.

2. Molecular weight of $C_4H_{10} = 4(12.0) + 10(1.0) = 58.0$

C: $\dfrac{48.0\ C}{58.0\ C_4H_{10}} \times 100\%\ C_4H_{10} = 82.8\%$ C

H: $\dfrac{10.0\ H}{58.0\ C_4H_{10}} \times 100\%\ C_4H_{10} = 17.2\%$ H

3. $\quad$ 25.0 L $\qquad\qquad$ X

$\quad C_3H_8\ +\ 5O_2 \rightarrow\ 3CO_2\ +\ 4H_2O$

$\quad$ 1 mole $\qquad\qquad$ 3 moles

X = 25.0 L $C_3H_8 \times \dfrac{3\ moles\ CO_2}{1\ mole\ C_3H_8} = 75.0$ L CO_2

4. $\quad$ X $\qquad\qquad\quad$ 2.0 L

$\quad CaC_2\ +\ 2H_2O \rightarrow\ C_2H_2\ +\ Ca(OH)_2$

$\quad$ 1 mole $\qquad\qquad$ 1 mole

1 mole $CaC_2 = 64.1$ g $\qquad$ 1 mole $C_2H_2 = 22.4$ L

X = 2.0 L $C_2H_2 \times \dfrac{1\ mole}{22.4\ L} \times \dfrac{1\ mole\ CaC_2}{1\ mole\ C_2H_2} \times \dfrac{64.1\ g}{mole} = 5.7$ g CaC_2

Group B

5. C: $\dfrac{60.0 \text{ g C}}{12.0 \text{ g/mole}} = 5.00$ moles C

O: $\dfrac{26.7 \text{ g O}}{16.0 \text{ g/mole}} = 1.67$ moles O

H: $\dfrac{13.3 \text{ g H}}{1.0 \text{ g/mole}} = 13.3$ moles H

C:O:H $= 5.00/1.67 : 1.67/1.67 : 13.3/1.67 = 2.99 : 1.00 : 7.96$
Empirical formula C_3OH_8
$(C_3OH_8)_x = 60$
$\quad x = 60 \div 60.0 = 1.0$
Molecular formula $= (C_3OH_8)_1$ or C_3OH_8

6. 1 mole CH_4 + 98 kcal $\rightarrow$ 1 mole CH_3^- + 1 mole H
    1 mole Br_2 + 46 kcal $\rightarrow$ 2 moles Br
    1 mole CH_3^- + 1 mole Br $\rightarrow$ 1 mole CH_3Br + 66 kcal
    1 mole H + 1 mole Br $\rightarrow$ 1 mole HBr + 87 kcal
    _____
    1 mole CH_4 + 1 mole $Br_2 \rightarrow$ 1 mole CH_3Br + 1 mole HBr + 9 kcal

Exothermic energy change; 9 kcal/mole CH_3Br formed

7. $V'_{STP} = V \times p/p' \times T'/T$. $V'_{STP} = 135 \text{ mL} \times \dfrac{738 \text{ mm} - 20 \text{ mm}}{760 \text{ mm}} \times \dfrac{273 \text{ °K}}{295 \text{ °K}}$

$V'_{STP} = 118$ mL.

8. (a) C: $\dfrac{93.75 \text{ g C}}{12.0 \text{ g/mole}} = 7.81$ moles C

H: $\dfrac{6.25 \text{ g H}}{1.0 \text{ g/mole}} = 6.25$ moles H

C:H $= 7.81/6.25 : 6.25/6.25 = 1.25 : 1.00 = 5 : 4$
Empirical formula C_5H_4

(b) g-mol wt $= \dfrac{5.1 \text{ C°} \times 6.40 \text{ g solute}}{\text{mole solute/kg } C_6H_6 \times 2.55 \text{ C°} \times 100 \text{ g } C_6H_6 \times \text{kg}/10^3 \text{ g}}$

g-mol wt $= 128$ g/mole
  mol wt $= 128$

(c) $(C_5H_4)_x = 128$
$\quad\quad x = 128 \div 64 = 2.0$
$\quad\quad$ Molecular formula $= (C_5H_4)_2$ or $C_{10}H_8$

CHAPTER 19
Answers to Questions pp. 429–430
Group A
1. (a) RX; (b) ROH; (c) ROR'; (d) RCHO; (e) RCOR'; (f) RCOOH; (g) RCOOR'.
2. (a) As a solvent for oil and grease and as a starting material for preparing other halogenated hydrocarbons. (b) Good ventilation is needed.

3.

$$\begin{array}{cccccc} H & H & H & H & H & H \\ | & | & | & | & | & | \\ -C-&C-&C-&C-&C-&C- \\ | & | & | & | & | & | \\ H & Cl & H & Cl & H & Cl \end{array}$$

4. Alcohols do not yield hydroxide ions in water.
5. It destroys the cells of the optic nerve, causing blindness and eventually death.
6. An increase in octane number, better mileage, and reduced exhaust pollution.
7. It is hygroscopic.
8. Sodium reacts with water to yield hydrogen and sodium hydroxide. Sodium reacts with methanol to yield hydrogen and sodium methoxide.
9. Six.
10. For making adhesives for plywood and particle board and resins for plastics.
11. (a) The reduction of alkaline copper(II) sulfate solution to a brick-red precipitate of copper(I) oxide. (b) The formyl group.
12. As a solvent in the manufacture of acetate rayon, as a cleaning agent, and in preparing synthetic organic chemicals.
13. (a) Vinegar made from apple cider. (b) By permitting apple cider to ferment to hard cider and oxidizing the ethanol in the hard cider to acetic acid. Oxygen of air acts as the oxidizing agent. The reaction is catalyzed by enzymes from certain bacteria.
14. (a) $H_2C_2O_4 + H_2O \rightleftarrows H_3O^+ + HC_2O_4^-$
$HC_2O_4^- + H_2O \rightleftarrows H_3O^+ + C_2O_4^{--}$
(b) Eight moles.
15. The oxygen and one hydrogen come from the acid. The other hydrogen comes from the alcohol.
16. Dehydration of alcohols to ethers or alkenes. Esterification.
17. (a) They are esters of glycerol and long-carbon-chain acids. (b) A fat is a solid at room temperature while an oil is a liquid. (c) Oils usually contain hydrocarbon chains that are more unsaturated and have lower melting points.
18. Saponification is the alkaline hydrolysis of a fat.

Group B

19.

(a) $\text{Cl}-\overset{\displaystyle H}{\underset{\displaystyle H}{C}}-\text{Cl}$;

(b) $H-\overset{\displaystyle H}{\underset{\displaystyle O}{C}}-\overset{\displaystyle H}{\underset{\displaystyle O}{C}}-\overset{\displaystyle H}{\underset{\displaystyle O}{C}}-H$ (with H on each O);

(c) $H-\overset{\displaystyle H}{\underset{\displaystyle H}{C}}-\overset{\displaystyle H}{\underset{\displaystyle H}{C}}-O-\overset{\displaystyle H}{\underset{\displaystyle H}{C}}-\overset{\displaystyle H}{\underset{\displaystyle H}{C}}-H$;

(d) $H-C\overset{\displaystyle O}{\underset{\displaystyle H}{\Big\langle}}$;

(e) $H-\overset{\displaystyle H}{\underset{\displaystyle H}{C}}-\overset{\displaystyle H}{\underset{\displaystyle H}{C}}-\overset{\displaystyle }{\underset{\displaystyle O}{C}}=\overset{\displaystyle H}{\underset{\displaystyle H}{C}}-\overset{\displaystyle H}{\underset{\displaystyle H}{C}}-H$;

(f) $H-\overset{\displaystyle H}{\underset{\displaystyle H}{C}}-C\overset{\displaystyle O}{\underset{\displaystyle O-H}{\Big\langle}}$;

(g) $H-C\overset{\displaystyle O}{\underset{\displaystyle O-\overset{\displaystyle H}{\underset{\displaystyle H}{C}}-H}{\Big\langle}}$

20. (a) $C_2H_6 + Cl_2 \rightarrow C_2H_5Cl + HCl$
(b) $C_2H_4 + HCl \rightarrow C_2H_5Cl$
(c) $C_2H_5OH + HCl \rightarrow C_2H_5Cl + H_2O$
21. Alkyl halides react with water solutions of strong hydroxides to yield alcohols and the halide ion. Alkyl halides react with benzene to form alkyl benzenes and hydrogen chloride. Preparation of dichlorodifluoromethane from carbon tetrachloride and hydrofluoric acid.
22. $CH_4 + 4Cl_2 \rightarrow CCl_4 + 4HCl$

$CCl_4 + 2HF \xrightarrow{\text{catalyst}} CCl_2F_2 + 2HCl$
23. Freons in the stratosphere are believed to react with and deplete the ozone which protects the earth's surface from excess ultraviolet radiation from the sun.

24.

(a)

(b)

(c) $C_{12}H_{22}O_{11} + H\text{—}O\text{—}H \rightarrow 4O{=}C{=}O + 4H\text{—}$

(d)

25. In order of increasing molecular weight, methanol, ethanol, ethylene glycol, increasing masses are required per unit mass of water to produce the same freezing-point depression. However, in this same order, the boiling points increase. So while a smaller mass of methanol is required for a given freezing-point lowering, it evaporates most readily. A larger mass of ethylene glycol is required, but it does not evaporate appreciably.

26. $C_3H_7OH + HI \rightarrow C_3H_7I + H_2O$

27. (a) By dehydration of propyl alcohol.

   (b) $2C_3H_7OH \xrightarrow{H_2SO_4} C_3H_7OC_3H_7 + H_2O.$

28. Methylethylketone.

29. (a) $CH_3OH + CO \xrightarrow{catalyst} CH_3COOH;$

   (b) $C_2H_5OH + CuO \rightarrow CH_3CHO + H_2O + Cu; \quad CH_3CHO + O \text{ (from oxidizing agent)} \rightarrow CH_3COOH.$

30. (a) The carbon–oxygen bonds in formic acid are a single and a double bond, because they have different lengths. (b) The carbon–oxygen bonds in sodium formate are alike because they have the same length. (c) The carbon–oxygen bonds in sodium formate are resonance hybrid bonds intermediate between single and double covalent bonds.

31. $C_4H_9OH + CH_3COOH \xrightarrow{H_2SO_4} CH_3COOC_4H_9 + H_2O$

32. $(C_{17}H_{35}COO)_3C_3H_5 + 3NaOH \rightarrow 3C_{17}H_{35}COONa + C_3H_5(OH)_3$

Solutions to Problems p. 430

Group A

1. Molecular weight of $CCl_2F_2 = 12.0 + 2(35.5) + 2(19.0) = 121.0$

2. $V_aN_a = V_bN_b. \quad N_b = V_aN_a/V_b. \quad N_b = (35.0 \text{ mL} \times 0.150\text{-}N)/40.0 \text{ mL}. \quad N_b = 0.131\text{-}N$

3. G-mol wt $C_3H_5(OH)_3 = 92.0$

$$\frac{0.400 \text{ mole } C_3H_5(OH)_3}{kg \ H_2O} \times \frac{92.0 \text{ g}}{mole} \times 0.300 \text{ kg } H_2O = 11.0 \text{ g}$$

4. G-equiv wt $(COOH)_2 = \dfrac{\text{g-mol wt } (COOH)_2}{2} = \dfrac{90.0 \text{ g}}{2} = 45.0 \text{ g}$

$$\frac{0.200 \text{ g-eq } (COOH)_2}{L} \times \frac{45.0 \text{ g}}{g\text{-eq}} \times 1.50 \text{ L} = 13.5 \text{ g}$$

5. Formula weight of $C_{12}H_{25}OSO_2ONa$ = $12(12.0) + 25(1.0) + 4(16.0) + 32.1 + 23.0 = 288.1$

C: $\dfrac{144.0 \text{ C}}{288.1 \text{ cpd}} \times 100\% \text{ cpd} = 49.98\% \text{ C}$

H: $\dfrac{25.0 \text{ H}}{288.1 \text{ cpd}} \times 100\% \text{ cpd} = 8.68\% \text{ H}$

O: $\dfrac{64.0 \text{ O}}{288.1 \text{ cpd}} \times 100\% \text{ cpd} = 22.2\% \text{ O}$

S: $\dfrac{32.1 \text{ S}}{288.1 \text{ cpd}} \times 100\% \text{ cpd} = 11.1\% \text{ S}$

Na: $\dfrac{23.0 \text{ Na}}{288.1 \text{ cpd}} \times 100\% \text{ cpd} = 7.98\% \text{ Na}$

6. (a) $C = \dfrac{54.4 \text{ g C}}{12.0 \text{ g/mole}} = 4.54 \text{ moles}$

$H = \dfrac{9.1 \text{ g H}}{1.0 \text{ g/mole}} = 9.1 \text{ moles}$

$O = \dfrac{36.4 \text{ g O}}{16.0 \text{ g/mole}} = 2.28 \text{ moles}$

$C:H:O = 4.54/2.28 : 9.1/2.28 : 2.28/2.28 = 1.99 : 4.0 : 1.00$
Empirical formula = C_2H_4O
(b) $(C_2H_4O)_x = 88$
$x = 88 \div 44 = 2$
Molecular formula = $(C_2H_4O)_2 = C_4H_8O_2$. The compound could be ethyl acetate, $CH_3COOC_2H_5$.

7. $pH = -\log [H_3O^+] = -\log (9.4 \times 10^{-4}) = -(\log 9.4 + \log 10^{-4}) = -(0.97 - 4) = 3.03$

8. G-mol wt $C_2H_5OH = 46.0$ g

$$\dfrac{0.750 \text{ mole } C_2H_5OH}{L \text{ } H_2O} \times \dfrac{46.0 \text{ g}}{\text{mole}} \times \overline{500} \text{ mL} \times \dfrac{1 \text{ L}}{1000 \text{ mL}} \times \dfrac{1 \text{ mL}}{0.789 \text{ g}} = 21.9 \text{ mL}$$

CHAPTER 20
Answers to Questions pp. 459–460
Group A
1. A definite amount of energy is released or absorbed when a substance reacts to form new substances even though both reactant and product are at the same temperature.
2. (a) Lower. (b) Higher.
3. The molar heat of formation of a compound is the heat evolved or absorbed when 1 mole of the compound is formed from its elements.
4. Two factors in the driving force of reactions are the tendency toward lowest state of energy, and the tendency toward higher state of disorder.
5. In an exothermic system the heat content of the products is lower than that of the reactants, so the heat of reaction is lost to the system and the heat content changes in a negative sense.
6. Changes of phase in the direction of the solid phase are accompanied by decreases in entropy.
7. Rise in temperature favors an increase in entropy.
8. Activation energy is the energy required to transform reactants into the activated complex.
9. The activation energy required for the endothermic change is greater than that required for the exothermic change by the amount of the energy of reaction of the system.
10. The collision may not be energetic enough to supply the necessary activation energy, and the colliding molecules may not be oriented in a way that favors their interaction.
11. The term *activated complex* refers to the transitional structure resulting from an effective collision between reactant particles that persists while old bonds are breaking and new bonds are forming.

Group B
12. The energy change in a reaction system is related to the change that occurs in the number and strengths of bonds during the reaction.

3. $43.8 \text{ kcal} - 3.0 \text{ kcal} = 40.8 \text{ kcal} = \Delta H_a(HI)$

4. A high negative heat of formation suggests that the compound is very stable. The heat content of the compound is much lower than that of its separate elements, so a large energy input is required for its decomposition.

5. If the temperature of the gases remained constant throughout the mixing, this would indicate that the heat content did not change.

6. The self-mixing of the two gases is accompanied by an increase in entropy, a driving force in natural processes.

7. If an exothermic reaction is accompanied by a decrease in entropy such that the unfavorable change in entropy, expressed as $T\Delta S$, exceeds the favorable change in energy content, the reaction will not be spontaneous. This is to say, the free energy change is positive and the reaction is not spontaneous.

8. An endothermic reaction in which the entropy change is favorable and the increase in entropy, expressed as $T\Delta S$, exceeds the unfavorable energy change will proceed spontaneously since it is accompanied by a decrease in free energy.

9. (a) This is the pathway by which the potential energy of the reactants is raised to the minimum level needed for effective collisions. (b) The maximum energy region of the minimum energy pathway for reaction is reached when the activated complex is formed.

10. Since the formation of a single activated complex by the simultaneous collision of 5 molecules is highly improbable, the reaction mechanism must involve some sequence of simple steps.

11. (a) The rate is increased. (b) The rate is doubled. (c) The rate is cut in half. (d) The rate is increased. (e) The rate is increased.

12. $NO_2 + O \rightarrow NO + O_2$

13. (a) Rapid, gas chain reaction. (b) Rapid, ionic, no bonds to break, limited only by addition rate. (c) Slow, limited surface area of contact.

14. Measure pressure of the reaction system. Since 2 moles of gas reactant form 1 mole of gas product, the pressure will decrease as the reaction proceeds.

15. $\quad O_3 \rightarrow O_2 + O$
    $O + O_3 \rightarrow 2O_2$

Solutions to Problems p. 460

Group A

1. $2C_2H_6 + 7O_2 \rightarrow 4CO_2 + 6H_2O + 745.64 \text{ kcal}$
   $2\Delta H_f(C_2H_6) = 4\Delta H_f(CO_2) + 6\Delta H_f(H_2O) - 2\Delta H_c(C_2H_6)$

   $$\Delta H_f(C_2H_6) = 2\left(-94.05 \frac{\text{kcal}}{\text{mole}}\right) + 3\left(-68.32 \frac{\text{kcal}}{\text{mole}}\right) - \left(-372.82 \frac{\text{kcal}}{\text{mole}}\right)$$

   $\Delta H_f(C_2H_6) = -20.24 \text{ kcal/mole}$

2. $2C_2H_2(g) + 5O_2(g) \rightarrow 4CO_2(g) + 2H_2O(l) + 621.24 \text{ kcal}$
   $C_2H_2(g) + \frac{5}{2}O_2(g) \rightarrow 2CO_2(g) + H_2O(l) + 310.62 \text{ kcal}$
   $\Delta H_{f(C_2H_2)} = 2\Delta H_{f(CO_2)} + \Delta H_{f(H_2O)} - \Delta H_{c(C_2H_2)}$
   $\Delta H_{c(C_2H_2)} = -188.10 \text{ kcal} + (-68.32) \text{ kcal} - (-310.62 \text{ kcal}) = +54.20 \text{ kcal/mole}$

3. $2C_6H_6(l) + 15O_2(g) \rightarrow 12CO_2(g) + 6H_2O(l) + 1561.96 \text{ kcal}$
   $C_6H_6(l) + \frac{15}{2}O_2(g) \rightarrow 6CO_2(g) + 3H_2O(l) + 780.98 \text{ kcal}$
   $\Delta H_{f(C_6H_6)} = 6\Delta H_{f(CO_2)} + 3\Delta H_{f(H_2O)} - \Delta H_{c(C_6H_6)}$
   $\Delta H_{f(C_6H_6)} = -564.30 \text{ kcal} + (-204.96) \text{ kcal} - (-780.98) \text{ kcal} = +11.72 \text{ kcal/mole}$

4. $2H_2(g) + O_2(g) \rightarrow 2H_2O(l) + 2\Delta H_c$
   $H_2(g) + \frac{1}{2}O_2(g) \rightarrow H_2O(l) + \Delta H_c$
   $\Delta H_{c(H_2)} = \Delta H_{f(H_2O)} - \Delta H_{f(H_2)}$
   $\Delta H_{c(H_2)} = -68.32 \text{ kcal} - 0.00 \text{ kcal} = -68.32 \text{ kcal/mole}$

5. $S(s) + O_2(g) \rightarrow SO_2(g)$
   $\Delta H_f(S) = \Delta H_f(SO_2) = \Delta H_c(S)$
   $\Delta H_c(S) = \Delta H_f(SO_2) - \Delta H_f(S)$
   $\Delta H_c(S) = (-70.96 \text{ kcal/mole}) - (-0.00 \text{ kcal/mole}) = -70.96 \text{ kcal/mole}$

6. $C_2H_5OH(l) + 3O_2(g) \rightarrow 2CO_2(g) + 3H_2O(l)$
   $\Delta H_f(C_2H_5OH) = 2\Delta H_f(CO_2) + 3\Delta H_f(H_2O) - \Delta H_c(C_2H_5OH)$
   $\Delta H_c(C_2H_5OH) = 2\Delta H_f(CO_2) + 3\Delta H_f(H_2O) - \Delta H_f(C_2H_5OH)$

   $$\Delta H_c(C_2H_5OH) = 2\left(-94.05 \frac{\text{kcal}}{\text{mole}}\right) + 3\left(-68.32 \frac{\text{kcal}}{\text{mole}}\right) - \left(-66.36 \frac{\text{kcal}}{\text{mole}}\right) = -326.7 \frac{\text{kcal}}{\text{mole}}$$

7. (a) $0.0375 \, M - 0.0268 \, M = 0.0107 \, M$
   $0.0107 \text{ mole/L} \div 18.0 \text{ min} = 5.94 \times 10^{-4} \text{ mole/L/min}$
   (b) $5.94 \times 10^{-4} \text{ mole/L/min} \div 60 \text{ s/min} = 9.90 \times 10^{-6} \text{ mole/L/s}$

Group B

8. $S(s) \quad + O_2(g) \qquad \rightarrow SO_2(g) \qquad \Delta H = -70.96 \text{ kcal} \qquad (1)$
$SO_2(g) + 1/2O_2(g) \quad \rightarrow SO_3(g) \qquad \Delta H = -23.49 \text{ kcal} \qquad (2)$
$SO_3(g) + H_2O(l) \quad \rightarrow H_2SO_4(l) \qquad \Delta H = -31.14 \text{ kcal} \qquad (3)$
$H_2(g) \quad + 1/2O_2(g) \quad \rightarrow H_2O(l) \qquad \Delta H = -68.32 \text{ kcal} \qquad (4)$

$S(s) + 2O_2(g) + H_2(g) \rightarrow H_2SO_4(l) \qquad \Delta H = -193.91 \text{ kcal}$

9. (a) (1) $\dfrac{-57.8 \text{ kcal}}{18.0 \text{ g reactants}} \times \dfrac{10^3 \text{ g}}{\text{kg}} = \dfrac{-3210 \text{ kcal}}{\text{kg reactants}}$

   (2) $\dfrac{-64.2 \text{ kcal}}{20.0 \text{ g reactants}} \times \dfrac{10^3 \text{ g}}{\text{kg}} = \dfrac{-3210 \text{ kcal}}{\text{kg reactants}}$

   (b) Reaction (1) preferred since mol wt H_2O is lower

10. (a) $R = k[A][B]^2$

   (b) $k = \dfrac{R}{[A][B]^2} = \dfrac{2.0 \times 10^{-4} \text{ mole/L/min}}{0.20 \text{ mole/L} \times (0.20 \text{ mole/L})^2}$

   $k = 2.5 \times 10^{-2} \text{ L}^2/\text{mole}^2/\text{min}$
   (c) $R = k[A][B]^2$

   $R = \dfrac{2.5 \times 10^{-2} \text{ L}^2}{\text{mole}^2 \text{ min}} \times \dfrac{0.30 \text{ mole}}{L} \times \left(\dfrac{0.30 \text{ mole}}{L}\right)^2$

   $R = 6.8 \times 10^{-4} \text{ mole/L/min (or } M/\text{min)}$

CHAPTER 21
Answers to Questions pp. 490–491
Group A

1. (1) Water in contact with its saturated vapor in a closed vessel. (2) Sugar crystals in contact with a saturated solution. (3) Sodium chloride crystals in contact with a saturated solution. (Other examples of physical equilibrium may be given.)
2. $HC_2H_3O_2 + H_2O \rightleftarrows H_3O^+ + C_2H_3O_2^-$
   $H_2CO_3 + H_2O \rightleftarrows H_3O^+ + HCO_3^-$.
   $H_3PO_4 + H_2O \rightleftarrows H_3O^+ + H_2PO_4^-$.
   (Other examples may be given using soluble polar compounds recognized as weak electrolytes.)
3. Equilibrium is a dynamic state; the opposite reactions do not stop but continue at the same rate so that the net change is zero.
4. The speed of a reaction is proportional to the product of the concentrations of the reacting substances, each raised to the appropriate power.
5. (a) The speed of the reaction increases decidedly. (b) Air is one-fifth oxygen; thus pure oxygen at the same pressure as the air will provide 5 times the number of collisions between the reactants.
6. (a) If a system at equilibrium is subjected to a stress, the equilibrium will be displaced in such direction as to relieve the stress. (b) Le Chatelier's principle applies to all dynamic equilibria, physical, chemical, and ionic.
7. (a) (1) Concentration. (2) Pressure. (3) Temperature. (b) A change in the temperature of the system causes a change in the value of the equilibrium constant for that system.
8. (1) If an insoluble product is formed.
   $Ag^+ + Cl^- \rightarrow AgCl$
   (2) If a gaseous product is formed.
   $H_3O^+ + HCO_3^- \rightarrow 2H_2O + CO_2$
   (3) If a product is very slightly ionized.
   $H_3O^+ + OH^- \rightarrow 2H_2O$
   (All spectator ions have been omitted from these equations.)
9. Salts that are sparingly soluble in water, generally described as insoluble.
10. The product of the molar concentrations of the ions of a sparingly soluble substance in saturated solution, each raised to the appropriate power.

Group B

11. Place the steam and iron in a closed container and heat. Neither the steam nor the hydrogen can escape. When the tube is opened, all 4 substances will be present.
12. The term dynamic means active as opposed to static. Dynamic equilibria involve opposing processes that are occurring at the same time at the same speed.

13. $\dfrac{[CH_3OH]}{[CO][H_2]^2} = K$

14. The reaction to the right is exothermic. A rise in temperature would act as a stress on the system and the equilibrium would shift in the direction of the endothermic reaction to relieve the stress. This would reduce the concentration of methanol. By lowering the temperature of the system the yield of methanol would be increased.

15. An increase in pressure would act as a stress and the equilibrium would shift in the direction that produces fewer gas molecules to relieve the stress. Increasing the pressure on the system would increase the yield of methanol.

16. $K = \dfrac{[C]}{[A][B]} = \dfrac{1.0}{2.0 \times 3.0} = \dfrac{1.0}{6.0} = 0.17$

17. (a) $BaCO_3 + 2H_3O^+ \rightarrow Ba^{++} + 3H_2O + CO_2(g)$
    (b) $Pb^{++} + 2Cl^- \rightarrow PbCl_2(s)$ (low solubility in cold water)
    (c) NO REACTION
    (d) NO REACTION
    (e) $Ba^{++} + SO_4^{--} \rightarrow BaSO_4(s)$
    (f) NO REACTION
    (g) $AgC_2H_3O_2 + H_3O^+ + Cl^- \rightarrow HC_2H_3O_2 + AgCl(s) + H_2O$
    (h) $3Cu^{++} + 2PO_4^{---} \rightarrow Cu_3(PO_4)_2(s)$
    (i) $Ba^{++} + SO_4^{--} \rightarrow BaSO_4(s)$
    (j) $CuO + 2H_3O^+ \rightarrow Cu^{++} + 3H_2O$

18. Acetic acid is a weak electrolyte and is slightly ionized in water solution. Equilibrium is quickly established between acetic acid molecules and hydronium and acetate ions in the solution. $HC_2H_3O_2 + H_2O \rightleftarrows H_3O^+ + C_2H_3O_2^-$. Sodium acetate is an ionic salt and is therefore completely ionized in water solution. When added to the acetic acid solution the concentration of the acetate ion is increased, driving the equilibrium to the left. This removes hydronium ions from solution and increases the concentration of un-ionized acetic acid molecules. Thus the solution is less acidic and has a higher pH value.

19. (1) $K = \dfrac{[NH_3]^2}{[N_2][H_2]^3}$ (2) $K = \dfrac{[NH_3]^2}{[N_2][H_2]^3}$ (3) $K = \dfrac{[NH_3]^2}{[N_2][H_2]^3}$

   (4) $K = \dfrac{[H_2S]^2}{[H_2]^2[S_2]}$ (5) $K = \dfrac{[H_2O][CO]}{[H_2][CO_2]}$ (6) $K = \dfrac{[H_2]^2[O_2]}{[H_2O]^2}$

   (7) $K = \dfrac{[CO_2]^2}{[CO]^2[O_2]}$ (8) $K = \dfrac{[HI]^2}{[H_2][I_2]}$ (9) $K = \dfrac{[HI]^2}{[H_2][I_2]}$

  (10) $K = \dfrac{[HI]^2}{[H_2][I_2]}$ (11) $K = \dfrac{[CO]^2}{[CO_2]}$ (12) $K = \dfrac{[Cu^{++}]}{[Ag^+]^2}$

  (13) $K = \dfrac{[I]^2}{[I_2]}$ (14) $K = \dfrac{[O_2]^3}{[O_3]^2}$ (15) $K = \dfrac{[N]^2}{[N_2]}$

20. In the first two experiments $[H_2] = [I_2]$ because the data were acquired by starting with hydrogen iodide. The equilibrium equation shows that HI decomposition gives equal quantities of H_2 and I_2.

21. The $H_2 + I_2 \rightleftarrows HI$ equilibrium is not affected by changes in pressure since both sides of the equilibrium equation show the same number of gas molecules.

22. (a) $NH_3 + H_2O \rightleftarrows NH_4^+ + OH^-$

$$K_b = \dfrac{[NH_4^+][OH^-]}{[NH_3]}$$

(b) The value of K_b is very small, showing that there are comparatively few NH_4^+ and OH^- ions in the equilibrium.

23. $B^- + H_2O \rightleftarrows HB + OH^-$ (1)

$$K_h = \dfrac{[HB][OH^-]}{[B^-]}$$ (2)

From $2H_2O \rightleftarrows H_3O^+ + OH^-$ (3)
$K_w = [H_3O^+][OH^-]$ (4)
From $HB + H_2O \rightleftarrows H_3O^+ + B^-$ (5)

$$K_a = \dfrac{[H_3O^+][B^-]}{[HB]}$$ (6)

Solving Eq. (6) for $[HB]$: $[HB] = \dfrac{[H_3O^+][B^-]}{K_a}$ (7)

Subs. Eq. (7) in Eq. (2): $K_h = \dfrac{[H_3O^+][B^-][OH^-]}{K_a[B^-]} = \dfrac{[H_3O^+][OH^-]}{K_a}$ (8)

Subs. Eq. (4) in Eq. (8): $K_h = \dfrac{K_w}{K_a}$

24. The concentration of molecular acetic acid is high and the concentrations of H_3O^+ and $C_2H_3O_2^-$ ions are low. Equilibrium is established early, before the forward reaction has progressed very far. This shows that acetic acid is a weak electrolyte.

25.

pH	$[H_3O^+]$ (moles/liter)	$[OH^-]$ (moles/liter)	$\dfrac{[H_3O^+]}{[OH^-]}$	Property
0	$10^0 = 1.0$	$10^{-14} = 0.00000000000001$	10^{-14}	↑
1	$10^{-1} = 0.1$	$10^{-13} = 0.0000000000001$	10^{-14}	Stronger
3	$10^{-3} = 0.001$	$10^{-11} = 0.00000000001$	10^{-14}	acid
5	$10^{-5} = 0.00001$	$10^{-9} = 0.000000001$	10^{-14}	
7	$10^{-7} = 0.0000001$	$10^{-7} = 0.0000001$	10^{-14}	Neutral
9	$10^{-9} = 0.000000001$	$10^{-5} = 0.00001$	10^{-14}	
11	$10^{-11} = 0.00000000001$	$10^{-3} = 0.001$	10^{-14}	Stronger
13	$10^{-13} = 0.0000000000001$	$10^{-1} = 0.1$	10^{-14}	base
14	$10^{-14} = 0.00000000000001$	$10^0 = 1.0$	10^{-14}	↓

Solutions to Problems p. 492

Group A

1. $[H_3O^+] = 0.00040$ mole/L $= 4.0 \times 10^{-4}$ mole/L
   $\log 0.00040 = -4.60 = 6.60 - 10 = -3.40$
   or, $\log (4.0 \times 10^{-4}) = \log 4.0 + \log 10^{-4} = 0.60 - 4 = -3.40$

   $pH = \log \dfrac{1}{[H_3O^+]} = -\log [H_3O^+] = -(-3.40) = 3.40$

2. $[H_3O^+] = 0.002$ mole/L $= 2 \times 10^{-3}$ mole/L
   $\log 0.002 = -3.30 = 7.30 - 10 = -2.70$
   or, $\log (2 \times 10^{-3}) = \log 2 + \log 10^{-3} = 0.30 - 3 = -2.70$

   $pH = \log \dfrac{1}{[H_3O^+]} = -\log [H_3O^+] = -(-2.70) = 2.70$

3. $[OH^-] = 0.02$ mole/L $= 2 \times 10^{-2}$ mole/L
   $\log 0.02 = -2.30 = 8.30 - 10 = -1.70$
   or, $\log (2 \times 10^{-2}) = \log 2 + \log 10^{-2} = 0.30 - 2 = -1.70$
   $pH = 14 - 1.70 = 12.30$
   (Alternate answer to No. 3)
   $[H_3O^+][OH^-] = 1 \times 10^{-14}$ mole/L

   $[H_3O^+] = \dfrac{1 \times 10^{-14} \text{ mole/L}}{[OH^-]} = \dfrac{1 \times 10^{-14} \text{ mole/L}}{2 \times 10^{-2} \text{ mole/L}}$

   $[H_3O^+] = 5 \times 10^{-13}$ mole/L
   $\log (5 \times 10^{-13}) = \log 5 + \log 10^{-13} = 0.70 - 13 = -12.30$

   $pH = \dfrac{1}{[H_3O^+]} = -\log [H_3O^+] = -(-12.30) = 12.30$

4. (a) Gram-formula weight of NaOH $= \overline{40}$ g
   0.50-M solution $= 0.50$ mole solute/L solution

   Mass NaOH $= \dfrac{\overline{40} \text{ g NaOH}}{\text{mole}} \times \dfrac{0.50 \text{ mole}}{L} \times 0.25 \text{ L} = 5.0 \text{ g NaOH}$

5.0 g NaOH dissolved in water in volumetric flask and diluted with water to 250 mL volume.

(b) Normality = 0.50 N

5. Gram-formula weight of $CuSO_4 \cdot 5H_2O$ = 249.7 g

2.00-M solution = 2.00 moles solute/L solution

$$\text{Mass } CuSO_4 \cdot 5H_2O = \frac{249.7 \text{ g}}{\text{mole}} \times \frac{2.00 \text{ moles}}{L} \times 0.750 \text{ L} = 375 \text{ g}$$

Group B

6. $[H_3O^+] = [C_2H_3O_2^-] = 10^{-3.3799}$

antilog (-3.3799) = antilog $(0.6201 - 4) = 4.17 \times 10^{-4}$

$[H_3O^+] = [C_2H_3O_2^-] = 4.17 \times 10^{-4}$

$[HC_2H_3O_2] = 0.01000 - 0.000417 = 0.00958$

$$K_a = \frac{[H_3O^+][C_2H_3O_2^-]}{[HC_2H_3O_2]} = \frac{(4.17 \times 10^{-4})^2}{9.58 \times 10^{-3}} \qquad K_a = \frac{17.4 \times 10^{-8}}{9.58 \times 10^{-3}} = 1.82 \times 10^{-5}$$

7. (*Determination of* $[OH^-]$)

$NH_3 + H_2O \rightleftarrows NH_4^+ + OH^-$

$$K_b = \frac{[NH_4^+][OH^-]}{[NH_3]}$$

At equilibrium,

$[NH_4^+] = [OH^-]$

$[NH_3] \simeq 0.50 \, M$ *(See problem Note)*

$K_b = 1.8 \times 10^{-5}$

$$K_b = \frac{[NH_4^+][OH^-]}{[NH_3]} = \frac{[OH^-]^2}{0.50} = 1.8 \times 10^{-5}$$

$[OH^-]^2 = 0.90 \times 10^{-5}$

$[OH^-] = \sqrt{9.0 \times 10^{-6}} = 3.0 \times 10^{-3}$

(Determination of pH)

$K_w = [H_3O^+][OH^-] = 1.0 \times 10^{-14}$

$$[H_3O^+] = \frac{K_w}{[OH^-]} = \frac{1.0 \times 10^{-14}}{3.0 \times 10^{-3}}$$

$[H_3O^+] = 3.3 \times 10^{-12}$

pH $= -\log [H_3O^+] = -\log (3.3 \times 10^{-12}) = -(0.52 - 12) = 11.5$

8. *At equilibrium*

$AgBr \rightleftarrows Ag^+ + Br^-$

$$1.3 \times 10^{-4} \text{ g AgBr/L} = \frac{1.3 \times 10^{-4} \text{ g AgBr/L}}{188 \text{ g/mole}} = 6.9 \times 10^{-7} \, M \text{ AgBr}$$

$6.9 \times 10^{-7} \, M \text{ AgBr} \rightarrow 6.9 \times 10^{-7} \, M \text{ Ag}^+ + 6.9 \times 10^{-7} \, M \text{ Br}^-$

$K_{sp} = [Ag^+][Br^-] = (6.9 \times 10^{-7})(6.9 \times 10^{-7}) = 4.8 \times 10^{-13}$

9. $$\frac{0.86 \text{ g PbBr}_2}{100 \text{ g}} \times \frac{1000 \text{ g}}{L} \times \frac{\text{mole}}{367 \text{ g}} = \frac{2.3 \times 10^{-2} \text{ mole PbBr}_2}{L}$$

$PbBr_2(s) \rightleftarrows Pb^{++}(aq) + 2Br^-(aq)$

$[Pb^{++}] = (2.3 \times 10^{-2})$ $\qquad [Br^-] = 2(2.3 \times 10^{-2})$

$K_{sp} = [Pb^{++}][Br^-]^2 = (2.3 \times 10^{-2})(4.6 \times 10^{-2})^2$

$K_{sp} = (2.3 \times 10^{-2})(2.1 \times 10^{-3}) = 4.8 \times 10^{-5}$

10. $Ag_2CO_3(s) \rightleftarrows 2Ag^+(aq) + CO_3^{--}(aq)$

$[Ag^+] = 2(1.26 \times 10^{-4})$ $\qquad [CO_3^{--}] = (1.26 \times 10^{-4})$

$K_{sp} = [Ag^+]^2[CO_3^{--}] = (2.52 \times 10^{-4})^2(1.26 \times 10^{-4})$

$K_{sp} = (6.35 \times 10^{-8})(1.26 \times 10^{-4}) = 8.00 \times 10^{-12}$

11. *At equilibrium*

$AgC_2H_3O_2 \rightleftarrows Ag^+ + C_2H_3O_2^-$
1 mole $AgC_2H_3O_2 \to$ 1 mole $Ag^+ +$ 1 mole $C_2H_3O_2^-$
$K_{sp} = [Ag^+][C_2H_3O_2^-] = 2.5 \times 10^{-3}$
$[Ag^+] = [C_2H_3O_2^-] = [AgC_2H_3O_2]$ dissolved
$[AgC_2H_3O_2]^2 = 2.5 \times 10^{-3} = 25 \times 10^{-4}$
$[AgC_2H_3O_2] = 5.0 \times 10^{-2}\ M$

$$\frac{5.0 \times 10^{-2}\ \text{mole}\ AgC_2H_3O_2}{L} \times \frac{167\ g}{\text{mole}} \times 10.0\ L = 84\ g\ AgC_2H_3O_2$$

12. (*a*) $PbSO_4$ might precipitate.
(*b*) $PbSO_4 \rightleftarrows Pb^{++} + SO_4^{--}$
$\quad K_{sp} = [Pb^{++}][SO_4^{--}] = 1.8 \times 10^{-8}$
If the $Pb(NO_3)_2$ dissolves completely,
$\quad [Pb^{++}] = 0.0015$ mole/L
$\quad [SO_4^{--}] = 0.0015$ mole/L
Ion product $[Pb^{++}][SO_4^{--}] = (1.5 \times 10^{-3})(1.5 \times 10^{-3}) = 2.2 \times 10^{-6}$
Since $2.2 \times 10^{-6} > 1.8 \times 10^{-8}$, $PbSO_4$ precipitates.

CHAPTER 22
Answers to Questions pp. 521–522
Group A

1. Oxidation involves a change by an element to a more positive oxidation number. Reduction involves a change by an element to a more negative oxidation number.
2. In a chemical action in which an element acquires a more positive oxidation number, another element must acquire a comparable, more negative oxidation number.
3. The oxidation state becomes more negative.
4. Oxidation-reduction reactions: (*a*), (*b*), (*c*), (*f*), (*g*), (*h*), and (*j*).

5. *Equation*

	(*a*)	(*b*)	(*c*)	(*d*)
(*a*)	sodium	chlorine	chlorine	sodium
(*b*)	carbon	oxygen	oxygen	carbon
(*c*)	oxygen	hydrogen	hydrogen (indirectly)	oxygen (indirectly)
(*f*)	oxygen	chlorine	chlorine	oxygen
(*g*)	hydrogen	chlorine	chlorine	hydrogen
(*h*)	hydrogen	oxygen	oxygen	hydrogen
(*j*)	zinc	copper(II) ion	copper(II) ion	zinc

6. (*a*) $Ca = +2$, $Cl = +5$, $O = -2$. (*b*) $Na = +1$, $H = +1$, $P = +5$, $O = -2$. (*c*) $K = +1$, $S = +4$, $O = -2$. (*d*) $H = +1$, $P = +3$, $O = -2$. (*e*) $Fe = +3$, $O = -2$, $H = +1$.

7. (*a*) $\overset{+2\ +6\ -2}{PbSO_4}$; (*b*) $\overset{+1\ -1}{H_2O_2}$; (*c*) $\overset{+1\ +6\ -2}{K_2Cr_2O_7}$; (*d*) $\overset{+1\ +4\ -2}{H_2SO_3}$; (*e*) $\overset{+1\ +7\ -2}{HClO_4}$.
8. Anode—lead(IV) oxide; cathode—lead; electrolyte—moderately dilute sulfuric acid solution.
9. (*a*) Electrode potential is the potential difference between an electrode and its solution in a half-reaction. (*b*) Half-reaction is the reaction taking place at the electrode in a half-cell. (*c*) Half-cell is the portion of a voltaic cell consisting of an electrode in contact with a solution of its ions.
10. By assigning an arbitrary potential of 0.00 volt to the standard hydrogen electrode, the potential difference across a cell using hydrogen as the reference electrode can be attributed to the other half-reaction.
11. Step 1: Write skeleton equation.
    Step 2: Assign oxidation numbers.
    Step 3: Write electronic equations for the oxidation and the reduction.
    Step 4: Interbalance the electronic equations.
    Step 5: Transfer coefficients to skeleton equation.
    Step 6: Adjust coefficients of the remainder of the equation.

12. (*a*)　$\overset{0}{Zn} + \overset{+1}{HCl} \to \overset{+2}{ZnCl_2} + \overset{0}{H_2}$
    $Zn \to Zn^{++} + 2e^-$
    $2H^+ + 2e^- \to H_2$

(*b*)　$\overset{0}{Fe} + \overset{+2}{CuSO_4} \to \overset{+2}{FeSO_4} + \overset{0}{Cu}$
    $Fe \to Fe^{++} + 2e^-$
    $Cu^{++} + 2e^- \to Cu$

(c) $\overset{+6}{K_2Cr_2}O_7 + \overset{0}{S} + H_2O \rightarrow \overset{+4}{S}O_2 + KOH + \overset{+3}{Cr_2}O_3$

$\overset{+6}{4Cr} + 12e^- \rightarrow \overset{+3}{4Cr}$

$\overset{0}{3S} \rightarrow \overset{+4}{3S} + 12e^-$

(d) $\overset{0}{Br_2} + H_2O \rightarrow \overset{-1}{H}Br + \overset{+1}{H}BrO$

$Br \rightarrow \overset{+1}{Br} + e^-$

$Br + e^- \rightarrow Br^-$

Group B

13. $\overset{+6}{2Cr} + 6e^- \rightarrow \overset{+3}{2Cr}$

$\overset{0}{3Zn} \rightarrow 3Zn^{++} + 6e^-$

$3Zn + 2Na_2CrO_4 + 4NaOH \rightarrow 3Na_2ZnO_2 + 2NaCrO_2 + 2H_2O$

14. $\overset{+6}{K_2Cr_2}O_7 + \overset{-1}{H}Cl \rightarrow KCl + \overset{+3}{Cr}Cl_3 + H_2O + \overset{0}{Cl_2}$

$Cl^- \rightarrow Cl + e^-$ (multiply by 6) $6Cl^- \rightarrow 3Cl_2 + 6e^-$

$\overset{+6}{Cr} + 3e^- \rightarrow \overset{+3}{Cr}$ (multiply by 2) $\overset{+6}{2Cr} + 6e^- \rightarrow \overset{+3}{2Cr}$

$K_2Cr_2O_7 + 14HCl \rightarrow 2KCl + 2CrCl_3 + 7H_2O + 3Cl_2$

15. $K_2CO_3 + \overset{0}{Br_2} \rightarrow \overset{-1}{K}Br + \overset{+5}{K}BrO_3 + CO_2$

$\overset{0}{Br} \rightarrow \overset{+5}{Br} + 5e^-$

$\overset{0}{5Br} + 5e^- \rightarrow \overset{-1}{5Br}$

$3K_2CO_3 + 3Br_2 \rightarrow 5KBr + KBrO_3 + 3CO_2$

16. $\overset{+7}{K}MnO_4 + Na_2\overset{+4}{S}O_3 + H_2SO_4 \rightarrow K_2\overset{+6}{S}O_4 + \overset{+2}{Mn}\overset{+6}{S}O_4 + Na_2\overset{+6}{S}O_4 + H_2O$

$\overset{+7}{2Mn} + 10e^- \rightarrow \overset{+2}{2Mn}$

$\overset{+4}{5S} \rightarrow \overset{+6}{5S} + 10e^-$

$2KMnO_4 + 5Na_2SO_3 + 3H_2SO_4 \rightarrow K_2SO_4 + 2MnSO_4 + 5Na_2SO_4 + 3H_2O$

17. (a) $\overset{+5}{2N} + 2e^- \rightarrow \overset{+4}{2N}$

$\overset{0}{Cu} \rightarrow \overset{+2}{Cu^{++}} + 2e^-$

$Cu + 4HNO_3 \rightarrow Cu(NO_3)_2 + 2NO_2 + 2H_2O$

(b) $4H^+(aq) + \overset{+5}{2N}O_3^- + 2e^- \rightarrow \overset{+4}{2N}O_2 + 2H_2O$

$\overset{0}{Cu} \rightarrow \overset{+2}{Cu^{++}} + 2e^-$

$Cu + 4H^+(aq) + 2NO_3^- \rightarrow Cu^{++} + 2NO_2 + 2H_2O$

$Cu + 4HNO_3 \rightarrow Cu(NO_3)_2 + 2NO_2 + 2H_2O$

18. (a) $\overset{+5}{2N} + 6e^- \rightarrow \overset{+2}{2N}$

$\overset{0}{3Cu} \rightarrow \overset{+2}{3Cu^{++}} + 6e^-$

$3Cu + 8HNO_3 \rightarrow 3Cu(NO_3)_2 + 2NO + 4H_2O$

(b) $8H^+(aq) + \overset{+5}{2N}O_3^- + 6e^- \rightarrow \overset{+2}{2N}O + 4H_2O$

$\overset{0}{3Cu} \rightarrow \overset{+2}{3Cu^{++}} + 6e^-$

$3Cu + 8H^+(aq) + 2NO_3^- \rightarrow 3Cu^{++} + 2NO + 4H_2O$

or $\quad 3Cu + 8HNO_3 \rightarrow 3Cu(NO_3)_2 + 2NO + 4H_2O$

19. (a) $\overset{+6}{S} + 8e^- \rightarrow \overset{-2}{S^{--}}$

$\overset{0}{4Zn} \rightarrow \overset{+2}{4Zn^{++}} + 8e^-$

$4Zn + 5H_2SO_4 \rightarrow 4ZnSO_4 + H_2S + 4H_2O$

(b) $10H^+(aq) + \overset{+6}{S}O_4^{--} + 8e^- \rightarrow H_2\overset{-2}{S} + 4H_2O$

$\overset{0}{4Zn} \rightarrow \overset{+2}{4Zn^{++}} + 8e^-$

$4Zn + 10H^+(aq) + SO_4^{--} \rightarrow 4Zn^{++} + H_2S + 4H_2O$

or $\quad 4Zn + 5H_2SO_4 \rightarrow 4ZnSO_4 + H_2S + 4H_2O$

20. (a)
$$\overset{+5}{2N} + 6e^- \rightarrow \overset{+2}{2N}$$
$$\overset{-2}{3S} \rightarrow \overset{0}{3S} + 6e^-$$
$$2HNO_3 + H_2S \rightarrow 2NO + 3S + 4H_2O$$

(b)
$$8H^+(aq) + \overset{+5}{2NO_3^-} + 6e^- \rightarrow \overset{+2}{2NO} + 4H_2O$$
$$\overset{-2}{3S^{--}} \rightarrow \overset{0}{3S} + 6e^-$$
$$\overline{8H^+(aq) + 2NO_3^- + 3S^{--} \rightarrow 2NO + 3S + 4H_2O}$$
or $\quad 2HNO_3 + 3H_2S \rightarrow 2NO + 3S + 4H_2O$

21. $\quad 8H^+(aq) + \overset{+5}{2NO_3^-} + 6e^- \rightarrow \overset{+2}{2NO} + 4H_2O$
$$\overset{0}{3Zn} \rightarrow \overset{+2}{3Zn^{++}} + 6e^-$$
$$\overline{3Zn + 8H^+(aq) + 2NO_3^- \rightarrow 3Zn^{++} + 2NO + 4H_2O}$$
or $\quad\quad 3Zn + 8HNO_3 \rightarrow 3Zn(NO_3)_2 + 2NO + 4H_2O$

22. $\quad 16H^+(aq) + \overset{+7}{2MnO_4^-} + 10e^- \rightarrow \overset{+2}{2Mn^{++}} + 8H_2O$
$$\overset{+2}{10Fe^{++}} \rightarrow \overset{+3}{10Fe^{+++}} + 10e^-$$
$$\overline{16H^+(aq) + 2MnO_4^- + 10Fe^{++} \rightarrow 2Mn^{++} + 10Fe^{+++} + 8H_2O}$$
or
$$2KMnO_4 + 10FeSO_4 + 8H_2SO_4 \rightarrow K_2SO_4 + 2MnSO_4 + 5Fe_2(SO_4)_3 + 8H_2O$$

23. The metals at the top of the table are strong reducing agents. They readily give up electrons to oxidized substances appearing below them. This property diminishes to the extent that metals near the bottom give up electrons only in the presence of strong oxidizing agents.

24. $\overset{0}{Cu} \rightarrow \overset{+2}{Cu^{++}} + 2e^- \quad\quad E = -0.34$ v

$\overset{+1}{Ag^+} + e^- \rightarrow \overset{0}{Ag} \quad\quad E = +0.80$ v

25. (a) -0.34 v $+ 0.80$ v $= 0.46$ v
Cu electrode is negative with respect to the Ag electrode.
(b) $Cu + 2Ag^+ \rightarrow Cu^{++} + 2Ag$

CHAPTER 23
Answers to Questions pp. 531–532
Group A

1. The first element, sodium, one electron in the outer shell, is a highly reactive metal. The next two elements, magnesium and aluminum, two and three outer-shell electrons, respectively, are metals of decreasing activity. The fourth element silicon, four outer-shell electrons, is a metalloid. The fifth, sixth, and seventh elements, phosphorus, sulfur, and chlorine five, six, and seven outer-shell electrons, respectively, are nonmetals of increasing activity. The eighth element, argon eight outer-shell electrons, is an inert noble gas.

2. (a) Good conduction of heat and electricity, metallic luster, ductility, malleability. (b) Poor conduction of heat, no conduction of electricity, no luster, brittleness.

3. (a) Attraction between positive ions and negative electron gas; (b) strong covalent bonds; (c) covalent bond; (d) dispersion interaction forces; (e) dispersion interaction forces.

4. Aluminum has a metallic structure while silicon has a covalent network structure. The bonding forces are much stronger between the atoms of solid silicon than between the ions of solid aluminum within their electron gas.

5. The interatomic forces of elements that are malleable are stronger than those of elements that are brittle.

6. Because the sodium ion has no third-energy-level electron.

7. Because it has one excess electron and the chlorine nucleus does not hold the outer shell octet as close as it holds the seven outer-shell electrons in the neutral atom.

8. Na_2O reacts with water to form a strongly basic sodium hydroxide solution. SiO_2 does not react with water. Cl_2O reacts with water to form a weak hypochlorous acid solution.

9. NaH reacts with water to produce hydrogen and sodium hydroxide solution. SiH_4 reacts with water to form silicon dioxide and hydrogen. HCl reacts with water to form hydronium ions and chloride ions.

10. The silicon-silicon bonds and silicon-hydrogen bonds of the silanes are weaker than the carbon-carbon bonds and carbon-hydrogen bonds of the alkanes.

Group B

11. The silvery luster of metals can be attributed to the free electrons in the crystal surfaces. When light strikes these surfaces, the valence electrons absorb energy and are set into vibratory motions that re-radiate the energy in all directions as light.

12. Because the heavier aluminum atoms are smaller and pack more closely together.

13. The binding force between atoms of liquid argon is very much smaller than the binding force between atoms of liquid aluminum, as shown by the very much higher boiling temperature of aluminum as compared to argon.

14. There are no free valence electrons in diamond, while there are some free valence electrons in silicon.

15. By using three single covalent bonds, it is possible for four phosphorus atoms to bond to each other in a pyramidal-type structure. Sulfur atoms bond together in eight-membered puckered rings, with each atom using only two covalent bonds. Chlorine atoms can only bond together in pairs, since each atom has only one covalent bond.

16. The first electron removed from an aluminum atom structure is a $3p$ electron, while the first electron removed from a magnesium atom structure is a $3s$ electron. Since the $3p$ electron is in a higher energy sublevel, it requires less energy to remove it than it does to remove a $3s$ electron. There appears to be structural stability to half-filled sublevels. The first electron to be removed from a sulfur atom structure is the fourth $3p$ electron. The first electron to be removed from a phosphorus atom structure is the third $3p$ electron. Since a half-filled $3p$ sublevel has greater stability, it requires less energy to remove the fourth electron from it than it does to remove the third.

17. (a) Na· Mg: Al: ·Si: ·P: ·S: :Cl: :Ar: (b) Sodium attains its oxidation state of $+1$ by losing its single outer-shell electron. Magnesium and aluminum attain their oxidation states of $+2$ and $+3$, respectively, in the same manner. Silicon attains its oxidation state of $+4$ by sharing its four outer-shell electrons. Phosphorus attains its $+3$ oxidation state by sharing its $3p$ electrons. It attains its $+5$ state by sharing all its third energy level electrons. Sulfur attains its -2 oxidation state by acquiring two additional electrons to complete the octet. It attains its $+4$ state by sharing its $3p$ electrons and attains its $+6$ state by sharing all its third energy level electrons. Chlorine attains its -1 state by acquiring one electron to complete the octet. It attains its $+5$ state by sharing its $3p$ electrons and its $+7$ state by sharing all its third energy level electrons. Argon does not gain, lose, or share electrons. Its oxidation state is 0.

18. (a)

Formula	Electronegativity Difference	Percentage Ionic Character	Type of Bonding
Na_2O	$3.5 - 0.9 = 2.6$	82%	Ionic
MgO	$3.5 - 1.2 = 2.3$	73%	Ionic
Al_2O_3	$3.5 - 1.5 = 2.0$	68%	Ionic
SiO_2	$3.5 - 1.8 = 1.7$	51%	Polar covalent
P_4O_{10}	$3.5 - 2.1 = 1.4$	39%	Polar covalent
SO_2	$3.5 - 2.5 = 1.0$	22%	Polar covalent
Cl_2O	$3.5 - 3.0 = 0.5$	7%	Slightly polar covalent
(b) NaH	$2.1 - 0.9 = 1.2$	30%	{ Polar covalent predicted / Actually ionic
$(MgH_2)_x$	$2.1 - 1.2 = 0.9$	19%	Polar covalent
$(AlH_3)_x$	$2.1 - 1.5 = 0.6$	9%	Polar covalent
SiH_4	$2.1 - 1.8 = 0.3$	3%	Slightly polar covalent
PH_3	$2.1 - 2.1 = 0$	0%	Covalent
H_2S	$2.5 - 2.1 = 0.4$	4%	Slightly polar covalent
HCl	$3.0 - 2.1 = 0.9$	19%	Polar covalent

19. Elemental silicon has each silicon atom tetrahedrally bonded to four other silicon atoms. Silicon dioxide has a similar structure except that an oxygen atom is inserted into each silicon-silicon bond. Hence the separation of silicon atoms from each other is greater in silicon dioxide than in elemental silicon.

20. (a) Same shape: PH_3 is slightly larger; bonding in PH_3 covalent, but not polar as in NH_3. (b) H_2S has same shape but smaller bond angle; H_2S is slightly larger, bonding in both is polar covalent, but polarity is less in H_2S.

21. $AlH_3 + 3H_2O \rightarrow Al(OH)_3 + 3H_2$

Answers to Problems p. 532

Group A

1. $D = m/V$. $m = D \times V$. $m = 2.70 \text{ g/cm}^3 \times 5.0 \text{ cm} \times 2.0 \text{ cm} \times 1.5 \text{ cm}$. $m = 4\overline{0}$ g.

2. $0.472 \text{ g Mg} \times \dfrac{\text{mole}}{24.3 \text{ g}} \times \dfrac{6.02 \times 10^{23} \text{ atoms}}{\text{mole}} = 1.17 \times 10^{22} \text{ atoms.}$

3. Formula weight of $P_4O_{10} = 4(31.0) + 10(16.0) = 284.0$

P: $\dfrac{(124.0)\ P}{(284.0)\ P_4O_{10}} \times 100\%\ P_4O_{10} = 43.66\%\ P$

4. $\overset{160\ mL}{SiH_4} + 2H_2O \rightarrow SiO_2 + \overset{X}{4H_2}$
    1 volume   4 volumes

$X = 16\bar{0}\ mL\ SiH_4 \times \dfrac{4\ vols\ H_2}{1\ vol\ SiH_4} = 64\bar{0}\ mL\ H_2$

5. $\overset{X}{Ca_3P_2} + 6H_2O \rightarrow 3Ca(OH)_2 + \overset{5.0\ g}{2PH_3}$
    1 mole   2 moles

1 mole $Ca_3P_2 = 182.3\ g$ 1 mole $PH_3 = 34.0\ g$

$X = 5.0\ g\ PH_3 \times \dfrac{mole}{34.0\ g} \times \dfrac{1\ mole\ Ca_3P_2}{2\ moles\ PH_3} \times \dfrac{182.3\ g}{mole} = 13\ g\ Ca_3P_2$

6. $\overset{12\ g}{SiO_2} + 4HF \rightarrow 2H_2O + \overset{X}{SiF_4}$
    1 mole   1 mole

1 mole $SiO_2 = 60.1\ g$ 1 mole $SiF_4 = 22.4\ L$

$X = 12\ g\ SiO_2 \times \dfrac{mole}{60.1\ g} \times \dfrac{1\ mole\ SiF_4}{1\ mole\ SiO_2} \times \dfrac{22.4\ L}{mole} = 4.5\ L\ SiF_4$

Group B

7. (a) g-mol wt $= \dfrac{5.1\ C° \times 0.14\ g\ solute}{mole\ solute/kgC_6H_6 \times 0.58\ C° \times 10.0\ g\ C_6H_6 \times kg/10^3\ g}$

     g-mol wt $= 120\ g$
     mol wt $= 120$

   (b) $(P)_x = 120$
       $x = 120 \div 31 = 4$
       molecular formula $= P_4$

8. $[OH^-] = 3.1 \times 10^{-5}$, so
    $[H^+] = 3.2 \times 10^{-10}$
    pH $= -\log [H^+] = -\log [3.2 \times 10^{-10}] = -\log 3.2 + 10 = -0.51 + 10 = 9.49$

CHAPTER 24
Answers to Questions pp. 545–546
Group A

1. The atoms in this family have electron configurations like the preceding noble gases with the addition of one electron in the next higher shell. The ions have the electron configurations of the preceding noble gases.
2. Sodium is prepared by electrolysis of its fused chloride. Potassium is prepared by the reaction of metallic sodium and potassium chloride.
3. In making tetraethyl lead for antiknock gasolines, in making dyes, in sodium vapor lamps, as a reducing agent, etc.
4. Caustic substances are capable of changing some types of animal and vegetable matter into soluble materials by chemical action. Corrosive substances eat away by chemical action, such as the action of an acid on a metal.
5. (a) Common salt, limestone, and coal. (b) Coal tar, sodium carbonate, sodium hydrogen carbonate, and calcium chloride.
6. (a) Sodium hydroxide. (b) Sodium carbonate. (c) Sodium hydrogen carbonate.
7. Molasses contains acids that liberate carbon dioxide from baking soda.
8. Large deposits of potassium chloride, crystallized with magnesium and calcium compounds, are found in Texas and New Mexico. Some potassium compounds are extracted from Searles Lake in California.
9. (a) Under kerosene. (b) Because they react with oxygen and water vapor in the air.
10. $2K(s) + 2H_2O \rightarrow 2K^+(aq) + 2OH^-(aq) + H_2(g)$
11. A clean platinum wire is dipped into a solution of either a sodium or potassium compound and then placed in an almost colorless oxidizing flame. The sodium atoms cause a yellow flame; the potassium, a violet flame.

12. $CO_2(g) + NH_3(g) + H_2O \rightarrow NH_4^+(aq) + HCO_3^-(aq)$
$Na^+(aq) + HCO_3^-(aq) \rightarrow NaHCO_3(s)$
$2NaHCO_3(s) \rightarrow Na_2CO_3(s) + H_2O(g) + CO_2(g)$
13. $CaCO_3(s) \rightarrow CaO(s) + CO_2(g)$
$CaO + H_2O \rightarrow Ca(OH)_2$
$NH_4^+(aq) + OH^-(aq) \rightarrow NH_3(g) + H_2O$
14. (a) The lattice structure consists of monopositive ions of the metal. This lattice is permeated by an electron gas consisting of "free" valence electrons. (b) The alkali metal unit cell is a body-centered cubic structure in which each metallic ion is surrounded by eight nearest neighbors at the corners of the cube.

Group B

15. Because the atoms in the solid metals are rather widely spaced and are held together by only weak attractive forces.
16. Sodium chloride is essential for proper functioning of the body, but it is lost through perspiration and must be replaced.
17. It is the cheapest, most readily available source of sodium.
18. (a) Sodium compounds are cheaper per gram, and one gram of a sodium compound goes further. (b) In black gunpowder and in fertilizers.
19. Calcium chloride.
20. The salt contains magnesium chloride, which is very deliquescent.
21. The increase in volume between sodium and potassium atoms is proportionally greater than the increase in mass between the two.
22. $CO_2 + 2OH^- \rightarrow CO_3^{--} + H_2O$
23. Because the sodium hydrogen carbonate is practically insoluble under the conditions of the reaction.
24. A water solution of sodium carbonate has basic properties because of hydrolysis of the CO_3^{--} ion.
25. Lithium hydroxide. You obtain more hydroxide ions per pound.
26. Common-ion effect: the presence of $NaC_2H_3O_2$ greatly increases the $[C_2H_3O_2^-]$ and shifts the $HC_2H_3O_2 + H_2O \rightleftharpoons H_3O^+ + C_2H_3O_2^-$ equilibrium to the left. The $[H_3O^+]$ decreases and the pH rises.

Solutions to Problems p. 546
Group A

1. (a) $\underset{2\text{ moles}}{10.0\text{ g}}$ $\overset{X}{}$
    $\underset{2\text{ moles}}{2NaOH} + \underset{1\text{ mole}}{H_2SO_4} \rightarrow Na_2SO_4 + 2H_2O$
    1 mole NaOH = 40.0 g   1 mole H_2SO_4 = 98.1 g

    $X = \dfrac{10.0\text{ g NaOH}}{40.0\text{ g/mole}} \times \dfrac{1\text{ mole }H_2SO_4}{2\text{ moles NaOH}} \times \dfrac{98.1\text{ g}}{\text{mole}} = 12.3\text{ g }H_2SO_4$

    (b) $\underset{2\text{ moles}}{10.0\text{ g}}$ $\overset{X}{}$
    $\underset{2\text{ moles}}{2KOH} + \underset{1\text{ mole}}{H_2SO_4} \rightarrow K_2SO_4 + 2H_2O$
    1 mole KOH = 56.1 g   1 mole H_2SO_4 = 98.1 g

    $X = \dfrac{10.0\text{ g KOH}}{56.1\text{ g/mole}} \times \dfrac{1\text{ mole }H_2SO_4}{2\text{ moles KOH}} \times \dfrac{98.1\text{ g}}{\text{mole}} = 8.74\text{ g }H_2SO_4$

2. $\underset{1\text{ mole}}{\underset{1.00\text{ kg}}{NaNO_3}} + \underset{1\text{ mole}}{\underset{1.00\text{ kg}}{KCl}} \rightarrow \underset{1\text{ mole}}{\overset{X}{KNO_3}} + NaCl$
    1 mole $NaNO_3$ = 85.0 g   1 mole KCl = 74.6 g   1 mole KNO_3 = 101.1 g
    KCl is in excess. Therefore the mass of KNO_3 produced will depend on the mass of $NaNO_3$ used.

    $X = \dfrac{1.00\text{ kg }NaNO_3}{85.0\text{ g/mole}} \times \dfrac{1\text{ mole }KNO_3}{\text{mole }NaNO_3} \times \dfrac{101.1\text{ g}}{\text{mole}} = 1.19\text{ kg }KNO_3$

3. $286/106 \times 12.5¢/\text{kg} = 33.7¢/\text{kg}$.

4. (a) $X = 50.0\text{ g }Na_2CO_3 \times \dfrac{\text{mole}}{106\text{ g}} \times \dfrac{1\text{ mole }CO_2}{\text{mole }Na_2CO_3} \times \dfrac{22.4\text{ L}}{\text{mole}} = 10.6\text{ L }CO_2$

    (b) $X = 50.0\text{ g }NaHCO_3 \times \dfrac{\text{mole}}{84.0\text{ g}} \times \dfrac{1\text{ mole }CO_2}{\text{mole }NaHCO_3} \times \dfrac{22.4\text{ L}}{\text{mole}} = 13.3\text{ L }CO_2$

(c) $X = 50.0 \text{ g } K_2CO_3 \times \dfrac{\text{mole}}{138 \text{ g}} \times \dfrac{1 \text{ mole } CO_2}{\text{mole } K_2CO_3} \times \dfrac{22.4 \text{ L}}{\text{mole}} = 8.12 \text{ L } CO_2$

(d) $X = 50.0 \text{ g } KHCO_3 \times \dfrac{\text{mole}}{10\bar{0} \text{ g}} \times \dfrac{1 \text{ mole } CO_2}{\text{mole } KHCO_3} \times \dfrac{22.4 \text{ L}}{\text{mole}} = 11.2 \text{ L } CO_2$

Group B

5. $X = \dfrac{1.00 \times 10^3 \text{ kg } Na_2CO_3 \times 117 \text{ g } NaCl}{106 \text{ g } Na_2CO_3} = 1.10 \times 10^3 \text{ kg } NaCl$

6. $X = \dfrac{1.00 \times 10^3 \text{ kg } Na_2CO_3 \times 22.4 \text{ L } CO_2}{106 \text{ g } Na_2CO_3} \times \dfrac{m^3}{10^3 \text{ L}} \times \dfrac{10^3 \text{ g}}{\text{kg}} = 211 \text{ m}^3 \text{ } CO_2$

7. $V' = 211 \text{ m}^3 \text{ } CO_2 \times \dfrac{760 \text{ mm}}{745 \text{ mm}} \times \dfrac{423 \text{ }^\circ K}{273 \text{ }^\circ K} = 334 \text{ m}^3 \text{ } CO_2$

8.
$$
\begin{array}{ccccc}
2.50 \times 10^3 \text{ kg} & & X & & Y \\
CaCO_3(s) & \rightarrow & CaO(s) & + & CO_2(g) \\
1 \text{ mole} & & 1 \text{ mole} & & 1 \text{ mole} \\
10\bar{0} \text{ g/mole} & & 56.1 \text{ g/mole} & & 22.4 \text{ L/mole}
\end{array}
$$
$2.72 \times 10^3 \text{ kg} \times 0.920 = 2.50 \times 10^3 \text{ kg } CaCO_3$

$X = 2.50 \times 10^3 \text{ kg } CaCO_3 \times \dfrac{\text{mole}}{10\bar{0} \text{ g}} \times \dfrac{1 \text{ mole } CaO}{\text{mole } CaCO_3} \times \dfrac{56.1 \text{ g}}{\text{mole}}$

$\quad = 1.40 \times 10^3 \text{ kg } CaO$

9. $Y = 2.50 \times 10^3 \text{ kg } CaCO_3 \times \dfrac{\text{mole}}{10\bar{0} \text{ g}} \times \dfrac{1 \text{ mole } CaO}{\text{mole } CaCO_3} \times \dfrac{22.4 \text{ L}}{\text{mole}} \times \dfrac{10^3 \text{ g}}{\text{kg}} = 5.60 \times 10^5 \text{ L } CO_2 \text{ (at STP)}$

$V' = \dfrac{5.60 \times 10^5 \text{ L } CO_2 \times 760 \text{ mm} \times 298 \text{ }^\circ K}{855 \text{ mm} \times 273 \text{ }^\circ K} = 5.43 \times 10^5 \text{ L } CO_2$

10. $\dfrac{1.1 \text{ g } NaOH}{50\bar{0} \text{ mL soln}} \times \dfrac{\text{mole}}{40.0 \text{ g}} \times \dfrac{10^3 \text{ mL}}{L} = 0.055 \dfrac{\text{mole } NaOH}{\text{L soln}}$

$[H_3O^+] = \dfrac{1.0 \times 10^{-14} \text{ mole}^2/L^2}{5.5 \times 10^{-2} \text{ mole/L}} = 1.8 \times 10^{-13} \text{ mole/L}$

$pH = -\log [H_3O^+] = -\log (1.8 \times 10^{-13})$
$pH = -(\log 1.8 + \log 10^{-13}) = -(0.26 - 13) = 12.74$

CHAPTER 25
Answers to Questions pp. 559–560
Group A
1. (a) $CaCO_3 \rightarrow CaO + CO_2$. (b) Carbon dioxide is removed from the kiln as it is formed.
2. (a) A double carbonate of magnesium and calcium. (b) As a building stone and for lining steel furnaces.
3. It forms a protective coating on the surface that prevents further action on the metal below the surface.
4. Calcium is prepared by electrolyzing fused calcium chloride. Sodium is prepared by electrolyzing fused sodium chloride.
5. To deoxidize copper, to harden lead for cables and storage battery grids, and as an alloy with lead for bearings.
6. Limestone, calcite, marble, and shells.
7. (a) Water containing ions such as calcium and magnesium that form precipitates with soap. (b) Water that does not contain these ions. (c) Temporary hardness is due to HCO_3^- ions that are removed by boiling. Permanent hardness is due to more stable negative ions such as SO_4^{--} ions.
8. By allowing a concentrated solution of common salt to stand in contact with the zeolite—the law of mass action.
9. (a) Calcium carbonate. (b) Calcium oxide. (c) Calcium hydroxide. (d) Calcium oxide. (e) Calcium hydroxide.
10. Carbon dioxide.
11. Put a drop of hydrochloric acid on the coral. Carbon dioxide will be liberated in the reaction that results.
12. $CaCO_3 + H_2O + CO_2 \rightleftarrows Ca(HCO_3)_2$.
13. Powdered limestone and clay are mixed in the proper proportions and heated strongly in a cement kiln.

Group B

14. $Mg^{++}(aq) + 2OH^-(aq) \rightarrow Mg(OH)_2(s)$
$Mg(OH)_2 + 2HCl \rightarrow MgCl_2 + 2H_2O$
$Mg^{++} + 2Cl^- \rightarrow Mg + Cl_2(g)$
15. Beryllium compounds are covalent, extensively hydrolyzed in water, and very toxic.
16. Because the attraction between the metal ions and the electron "gas" of the metallic crystals is stronger in the members of the Calcium Family than in the corresponding members of the Sodium Family.
17. (a) $CaO + H_2O \rightarrow Ca(OH)_2$ (b) $Ca(OH)_2$ is very slightly soluble in water. The reaction is strongly exothermic.
18. Calcium is a less active metal and the calcium hydroxide produced by the reaction coats the surface of the calcium.
19. (a) Ca^{++} and Mg^{++}. (b) HCO_3^-. (c) SO_4^{--}.
20. Ion exchange reaction, with the formation of a precipitate.
21. (a) $CaSO_4 + Na_2CO_3 \rightarrow CaCO_3(s) + Na_2SO_4$.
(b) $Mg(HCO_3)_2 + Na_2CO_3 \rightarrow MgCO_3(s) + 2NaHCO_3$.
22. (a) By gently heating gypsum. (b) By uniting with water and forming crystals.
23. (a) Carbon dioxide. (b) For making solutions of salts whose positive ions form insoluble carbonates. For making solutions whose pH must be precisely regulated.
24. Each mole of $Ca(OH)_2$ added supplies 2 moles of OH^- ions and 1 mole of Ca^{++} ions, but neutralizes 2 moles of HCO_3^- ions to form 2 moles of CO_3^{--} ions. Thus 2 moles of Ca^{++} ions are precipitated, 1 mole from the hard water and 1 mole from the limewater.

Solutions to Problems p. 560
Group A

1. 1000 kg $- (0.125 \times 1000$ kg$) = 875$ kg $CaCO_3$

$$875 \text{ kg} \qquad X$$
$$CaCO_3 \rightarrow \quad CaO \ + CO_2$$
$$1 \text{ mole} \qquad 1 \text{ mole}$$
$$1 \text{ mole } CaCO_3 = 100 \text{ g} \qquad 1 \text{ mole } CaO = 56.1 \text{ g}$$

$$X = \frac{875 \text{ kg } CaCO_3}{100 \text{ g/mole}} \times \frac{1 \text{ mole } CaO}{1 \text{ mole } CaCO_3} \times \frac{56.1 \text{ g}}{\text{mole}} = 491 \text{ kg } CaO$$

2.
$$86.0 \text{ kg} \qquad\qquad\qquad X$$
$$2CaSO_4 \cdot 2H_2O \rightarrow (CaSO_4)_2 \cdot H_2O + \ 3H_2O$$
$$2 \text{ moles} \qquad\qquad\qquad 3 \text{ moles}$$
$$1 \text{ mole } CaSO_4 \cdot 2H_2O = 172 \text{ g} \qquad 1 \text{ mole } H_2O = 18.0 \text{ g}$$

$$X = \frac{86.0 \text{ kg } CaSO_4 \cdot 2H_2O}{172 \text{ g/mole}} \times \frac{3 \text{ moles } H_2O}{2 \text{ moles } CaSO_4 \cdot 2H_2O} \times \frac{18.0 \text{ g}}{\text{mole}} = 13.5 \text{ kg } H_2O$$

3. $Be_3Al_2Si_6O_{18}$: formula weight, 537. Weight of beryllium, $27.0/537 = 0.0502$ or 5.02%

4. 1000 kg $\times \frac{24}{40} = 600$ kg magnesium.

5. 4.0×10^6 kg $MgCl_2 \times \frac{24 \text{ g Mg}}{95 \text{ g } MgCl_2} = 1.0 \times 10^6$ kg Mg

6.
$$8.10 \text{ g} \qquad\qquad\qquad X$$
$$Mg \ + 2HCl \rightarrow MgCl_2 + \ H_2$$
$$1 \text{ mole} \qquad\qquad\qquad 1 \text{ mole}$$
$$1 \text{ mole } Mg = 24.3 \text{ g} \qquad 1 \text{ mole } H_2 = 22.4 \text{ L}$$

$$X = \frac{8.10 \text{ g Mg}}{24.3 \text{ g/mole}} \times \frac{1 \text{ mole } H_2}{1 \text{ mole } Mg} \times \frac{22.4 \text{ L}}{\text{mole}} = 7.47 \text{ L } H_2$$

Group B

7. Dolomite is $24.3/184$ Mg $= 13.2\%$. $13.2\% \times 0.950 = 12.5\%$ magnesium in sample.
8. 1000 kg $\times 0.810 = 810$ kg

$$810 \text{ kg} \qquad\qquad X$$
$$CaCO_3 \quad \rightarrow CaO + \quad CO_2(g)$$
$$1 \text{ mole} \qquad\qquad 1 \text{ mole}$$
$$100 \text{ g/mole} \qquad\qquad 44.0 \text{ g/mole}$$

$$X = 81\overline{0} \text{ kg CaCO}_3 \times \frac{\text{mole}}{10\overline{0} \text{ g}} \times \frac{1 \text{ mole CO}_2}{1 \text{ mole CaCO}_3} \times \frac{44.0 \text{ g}}{\text{mole}}$$

$$X = 356 \text{ kg CO}_2$$

9. $356 \text{ kg CO}_2 \times \dfrac{10^3 \text{ g}}{\text{kg}} \times \dfrac{\text{L}}{1.98 \text{ g}} = 1.80 \times 10^5 \text{ L CO}_2$

10. $1.80 \times 10^5 \text{ L CO}_2 \times \dfrac{760 \text{ mm}}{72\overline{0} \text{ mm}} \times \dfrac{293 \,^{\circ}\text{K}}{273 \,^{\circ}\text{K}} = 2.04 \times 10^5 \text{ L CO}_2$

11. $pV = nRT$
$T = 273^{\circ} + 28^{\circ} = 301 \,^{\circ}\text{K}$

$$p = \frac{95\overline{0} \text{ mm}}{760 \text{ mm/atm}} = 1.25 \text{ atm}$$

$V = 50\overline{0} \text{ m}^3 \times 10^3 \text{ L/m}^3 = 5.00 \times 10^5 \text{ L}$
$R = 8.21 \times 10^{-2} \text{ L atm/mole} \,^{\circ}\text{K}$

$$n = \frac{pV}{RT} = \frac{1.25 \text{ atm} \times 5.00 \times 10^5 \text{ L}}{8.21 \times 10^{-2} \text{ L atm/mole} \,^{\circ}\text{K} \times 301 \,^{\circ}\text{K}}$$

$n = 2.53 \times 10^4 \text{ mole}$

CHAPTER 26
Answers to Questions p. 584
Group A
1. The metallic character of transition elements is attributed to the small number of electrons in the outermost shell of their atoms.
2. Yellow, the complement of blue light.
3. (a) It is reduced. (b) It is purified.
4. All are found as the native metal. They are soft, dense, and inactive metals. They all have an oxidation state of +1 in some compounds.
5. In moist air the coating is a basic copper carbonate. Sulfur dioxide in the air may also form basic copper sulfate. Probably both are formed in most cases. Both are green compounds.
6. (a) 0; (b) +4; (c) +2; (d) +7; (e) +6.

Group B
7. The metals used in early times were largely the ones that occur in the native state. Those difficult to extract from their ores have been obtained within the last century because of increased knowledge of chemistry which made their extraction possible.
8. A polyatomic ion is a charged structure made up of two or more atoms covalently bonded. A complex ion is a charged structure composed of a central metal ion combined with a specific number of polar molecules or ions.
9. Iron(II) ions gradually oxidize to the +3 state and the blue color characteristic of Fe ions present in two different oxidation states in the $KFeFe(CN)_6 \cdot H_2O$ product develops.
10. $K_4Fe(CN)_6$ forms the blue precipitate $KFeFe(CN)_6 \cdot H_2O$ with iron(III) ions. $K_3Fe(CN)_6$ forms the same blue precipitate with iron(II) ions.
11. Enough gold and silver are recovered to pay for the process.

Solutions to Problems p. 584
Group A
1. $165 \text{ g Fe} \times \dfrac{126.8 \text{ g FeCl}_2}{55.8 \text{ g Fe}} = 375 \text{ g FeCl}_2$

2. $375 \text{ g FeCl}_2 \times \dfrac{162.3 \text{ g FeCl}_3}{126.8 \text{ g FeCl}_2} = 48\overline{0} \text{ g FeCl}_3$

3. $4Fe = 223.$ $9O = 144.$ $6H = 6.$ Formula weight $= 373$
$223 \div 373 \times 100\% = 59.8\%$

4. $X = \dfrac{10\overline{0} \text{ g Ag} \times 17\overline{0} \text{ g AgNO}_3}{108 \text{ g Ag}} = 157 \text{ g AgNO}_3$

5. $\dfrac{112 \text{ g Fe}}{160 \text{ g Fe}_2\text{O}_3} \times 87.0\% \text{ Fe}_2\text{O}_3 = 60.9\% \text{ Fe}$

6. $1.0 \times 10^6 \text{ metric tn} \times 4.0 \times 10^{-2} = 4.0 \times 10^4 \text{ metric tn}$

Group B

7. $8.0 \times 10^4 \text{ metric tn SiO}_2 \times \dfrac{100 \text{ g CaCO}_3}{60 \text{ g SiO}_2} = 1.3 \times 10^5 \text{ metric tn CaCO}_3$

8. (a) $8.7 \times 10^3 \text{ metric tn Fe}_2\text{O}_3 \times \dfrac{84 \text{ g CO}}{160 \text{ g Fe}_2\text{O}_3} = 4.6 \times 10^5 \text{ metric tn CO}$

   (b) $4.6 \times 10^5 \text{ metric tn CO} \times \dfrac{24 \text{ g C}}{56 \text{ g CO}} = 2.0 \times 10^5 \text{ metric tn C}$

9. $\text{FeSO}_4 + \text{H}_2\text{SO}_4 + \text{HNO}_3 \rightarrow \text{Fe}_2(\text{SO}_4)_3 + \text{NO} + \text{H}_2\text{O}$

   $3\overset{+2}{\text{Fe}} \rightarrow 3\overset{+3}{\text{Fe}} + 3e^-$

   $\overset{+5}{\text{N}} + 3e^- \rightarrow \overset{+2}{\text{N}}$

   $6\text{FeSO}_4 + 3\text{H}_2\text{SO}_4 + 2\text{HNO}_3 \rightarrow 3\text{Fe}_2(\text{SO}_4)_3 + 2\text{NO} + 4\text{H}_2\text{O}$

10. $3\overset{0}{\text{Ag}} \rightarrow 3\overset{+1}{\text{Ag}} + 3e^-$

    $\overset{+5}{\text{N}} + 3e^- \rightarrow \overset{+2}{\text{N}}$

    $3\text{Ag} + 4\text{HNO}_3 \rightarrow 3\text{AgNO}_3 + \text{NO} + 2\text{H}_2\text{O}$

11. $\overset{0}{\text{Cu}} \rightarrow \overset{+2}{\text{Cu}} + 2e^-$

    $\overset{+6}{\text{S}} + 2e^- \rightarrow \overset{+4}{\text{S}}$

    $\text{Cu} + 2\text{H}_2\text{SO}_4 \rightarrow \text{CuSO}_4 + \text{SO}_2 + 2\text{H}_2\text{O}$

CHAPTER 27
Answers to Questions pp. 595–596
Group A

1. Many clays, rocks, and other mineral materials.
2. Silver-white in color; density 2.70 g per cm^3; ductile; malleable; not as tenacious as copper, brass, or steel; good conductor of electricity; can be welded, spun, or cast; difficult to solder.
3. (a) Both are oxides of aluminum. (b) Al_2O_3. (c) As abrasives.
4. Aluminum oxide is an infusible substance. It can be dissociated by being dissolved in fused cryolite.
5. To produce a carbon-free metal. Also because aluminum is a more powerful reducing agent.
6. $\text{KAl(SO}_4)_2 \cdot 12\text{H}_2\text{O}$; $\text{NaAl(SO}_4)_2 \cdot 12\text{H}_2\text{O}$; $\text{KFe(SO}_4)_2 \cdot 12\text{H}_2\text{O}$; $\text{KCr(SO}_4)_2 \cdot 12\text{H}_2\text{O}$.
7. The salt brines of Searles Lake, California.
8. It dissolves metallic oxides leaving a clean metallic surface.
9. Second among the elements of the earth's crust.
10. Arsenic dust and vapor and most compounds of arsenic are very toxic.

Group B

11. (a) $2\text{Al(s)} + 6\text{H}_3\text{O}^+ + 6\text{H}_2\text{O} \rightarrow 2\text{Al(H}_2\text{O)}_6^{+++} + 3\text{H}_2\text{(g)}$
    (b) $2\text{Al(s)} + 2\text{OH}^- + 6\text{H}_2\text{O} \rightarrow 2\text{Al(OH)}_4^- + 3\text{H}_2\text{(g)}$
    (c) The protective oxide coating isolates the aluminum from the water.
12. Cathode: $\text{Al}^{+++} + 3e^- \rightarrow \text{Al}$. Anode: $2\text{O}^{--} \rightarrow \text{O}_2 + 4e^-$.
13. Aluminum cannot be produced economically from clay.
14. Availability of cheap electricity usually generated by waterpower.
15. (a) Small atomic radius; (b) ionization energy intermediate between metals and nonmetals; (c) electronegativity of about 2; (d) form covalent bonds; (e) low electric conductivity at ordinary temperature; electric conductivity increases with an increase in temperature.

16. Boric acid and an alcohol form the corresponding ester. When the alcohol vapor is ignited, the flame shows a green color due to the presence of the ester. The green flame indicates the presence of the boric acid.
17. Cobalt.
18. Yes. The similarity in crystal structure gives them similar hardness.
19. (*a*) As molecules. (*b*) It may be safely used as an antiseptic and eye wash.
20. (*a*) A compound containing a chain of alternate silicon and oxygen atoms, with organic groups attached to the silicon atoms. (*b*) As lubricants, as a varnish for the windings of electric motors, as a water repellent, and in automobile and furniture polishes.
21. Because of the hydrocarbon groups attached to the silicon atoms.

Solutions to Problems p. 596
Group A

1.

$$\begin{array}{ccc} X & Y & 10.0 \text{ kg} \\ 2Al & + Fe_2O_3 \rightarrow Al_2O_3 + & 2Fe \\ 2 \text{ moles} & 1 \text{ mole} & 2 \text{ moles} \end{array}$$

1 mole Al = 27.0 g   1 mole Fe_2O_3 = 16$\overline{0}$ g   1 mole Fe = 55.8 g

$$X = \frac{10.0 \text{ kg Fe}}{55.8 \text{ g/mole}} \times \frac{2 \text{ moles Al}}{2 \text{ moles Fe}} \times \frac{27.0 \text{ g}}{\text{mole}} = 4.84 \text{ kg Al}$$

$$Y = \frac{10.0 \text{ kg Fe}}{55.8 \text{ g/mole}} \times \frac{1 \text{ mole } Fe_2O_3}{2 \text{ moles Fe}} \times \frac{16\overline{0} \text{ g}}{\text{mole}} = 14.3 \text{ kg } Fe_2O_3$$

2. $27.0 \div 458 \times 100\% = 5.90\%$ Al

3.

$$\begin{array}{cccc} 50.0 \text{ g} & 10\overline{0} \text{ g} & & X \\ 2Al & + 2NaOH & + 6H_2O \rightarrow 2NaAl(OH)_4 & + 3H_2 \\ 2 \text{ moles} & 2 \text{ moles} & & 3 \text{ moles} \\ 27.0 \text{ g/mole} & 40.0 \text{ g/mole} & & 22.4 \text{ L/mole} \end{array}$$

By inspection: NaOH is in excess.

$$X = \frac{50.0 \text{ g Al}}{27.0 \text{ g/mole}} \times \frac{3 \text{ moles } H_2}{2 \text{ moles Al}} \times \frac{22.4 \text{ L}}{\text{mole}} = 62.2 \text{ L } H_2$$

4. $Ca_2B_6O_{11} \cdot 5H_2O = 411.0$ 6B = 64.8
$64.8 \div 411.0 \times 100\% = 15.8\%$ boron

5.

$$\begin{array}{cc} 10.0 \text{ g} & X \\ 2Sb & + 3Cl_2 \rightarrow 2SbCl_3 \\ 2 \text{ moles} & 2 \text{ moles} \end{array}$$

1 mole Sb = 122 g   1 mole $SbCl_3$ = 228 g

$$X = \frac{10.0 \text{ g Sb}}{122 \text{ g/mole}} \times \frac{1 \text{ mole } SbCl_3}{1 \text{ mole Sb}} \times \frac{228 \text{ g}}{\text{mole}} = 18.7 \text{ g } SbCl_3$$

Group B

6. As: H = $\dfrac{96.2 \text{ g}}{74.9 \text{ g/mole}} : \dfrac{3.85 \text{ g}}{1.01 \text{ g/mole}} = \dfrac{1.28 \text{ mole}}{1.28 \text{ mole}} : \dfrac{3.81 \text{ mole}}{1.28 \text{ mole}}$

As:H = 1.00 : 2.98 or 1.00 : 3.00
Empirical formula = AsH_3 formula weight = 77.9
g-mol wt = $D \times$ molar vol = 3.48 g/L $\times$ 22.4 L = 78.0 g
molecular formula = AsH_3

7.

$$\begin{array}{cc} 5.00 \text{ g} & X \\ Na_2B_4O_7 + 5H_2O + H_2SO_4 \rightarrow 4H_3BO_3 & + Na_2SO_4 \\ 1 \text{ mole} & 4 \text{ moles} \end{array}$$

1 mole $Na_2B_4O_7$ = 201 g   1 mole H_3BO_3 = 61.8 g

$$X = 5.00 \text{ g } Na_2B_4O_7 \times \frac{1 \text{ mole}}{201 \text{ g}} \times \frac{4 \text{ moles } H_3BO_3}{1 \text{ mole } Na_2B_4O_7} \times \frac{61.8 \text{ g}}{\text{mole}} = 6.15 \text{ g } H_3BO_3$$

8. Te-120: 0.0009 mole $\times$ 119.904 g/mole = 0.1 g
   Te-122: 0.0246 mole $\times$ 121.903 g/mole = 3.00 g
   Te-123: 0.0087 mole $\times$ 122.904 g/mole = 1.1 g
   Te-124: 0.0461 mole $\times$ 123.903 g/mole = 5.71 g
   Te-125: 0.0699 mole $\times$ 124.904 g/mole = 8.73 g
   Te-126: 0.1871 mole $\times$ 125.903 g/mole = 23.56 g
   Te-128: 0.3179 mole $\times$ 127.905 g/mole = 40.66 g
   Te-130: 0.3448 mole $\times$ 129.906 g/mole = 44.79 g

   127.6 g = g-at wt

   I-127: 1.0000 mole $\times$ 126.904 g/mole = 126.90 g = g-at wt

   at wt Te = 127.6
   at wt I = 126.9

CHAPTER 28
Answers to Questions pp. 605–606
Group A

1. (a) In the air. (b) In plant and animal proteins and in sodium nitrate and potassium nitrate.
2. (a) Liquid oxygen. (b) The separation of liquid nitrogen from liquid oxygen by fractional distillation.
3. When catalyzed by the sun's ultraviolet radiation, the oxides of nitrogen react with unburned hydrocarbons to form photochemical smog.
4. The process of converting elemental nitrogen into nitrogen compounds.
5. (a) Growing crops that restore nitrogen compounds to the soil, and electric storms. (b) Manufacturing ammonia.
6. (a) To shift the equilibrium to the right. (b) To increase the speed of the reaction.
7. (a) A pyramid with the hydrogen atoms forming an equilateral triangular base and the nitrogen atom forming the apex. (b) sp^3-s hybrid bonds with an unshared electron pair at the top of the nitrogen atom.
8. Because it emulsifies the film of grease, yet leaves no streaky residue as it dries.
9. Nitric acid vapors would destroy rubber quickly.
10. The nitric acid produced must be driven off by heating.
11. $4NH_3 + 5O_2 \xrightarrow{Pt} 4NO + 6H_2O$. $2NO + O_2 \rightarrow 2NO_2$. $3NO_2 + H_2O \rightarrow 2HNO_3 + NO$.
12. Sunlight promotes its decomposition, and nitrogen dioxide is formed in sufficient amounts to color the acid yellow.

Group B

13. (a) The gas molecules acquire more energy as work is done on them in crowding them together. (b) The molecules lose energy as they do work in spreading apart.
14. The strong triple covalent bond between the atoms of the molecule.
15. As a blanketing atmosphere during the processing of food—inactivity. Used with argon in filling electric lamps—inactivity, pressure reduces filament evaporation. To make ammonia—reacts with hydrogen at moderate temperatures, high pressures, and in the presence of a catalyst. Etc.
16. It must be alkaline.
17. Corn removes nitrogen compounds from the soil; lima beans replace them.
18. (a) $Ca(OH)_2(s) + 2NH_4NO_3(s) \rightarrow 2NH_3(g) + 2H_2O(g) + Ca(NO_3)_2(s)$. (b) $OH^- + NH_4^+ \rightarrow NH_3(g) + H_2O(g)$. (c) They are all the same.
19. Ammonia molecules are polar, and the forces of attraction between them are stronger.
20. Ammonia molecules are polar, methane molecules are not. Water is a polar solvent. The solubility follows the general rule that like dissolves like.
21. Ammonia will dissolve many salts, dissociate many salts, and form complex ions with metallic ions.
22. The zinc will reduce the nitrogen of the nitric acid more readily than it will reduce the hydrogen.
23. The colorless nitrogen monoxide when released to the air is oxidized to reddish-brown nitrogen dioxide.
24. (a) −3. (b) −2. (c) 0. (d) +2. (e) +3. (f) +4. (g) +5.

Solutions to Problems p. 606
Group A

1.

$$\overset{15.0\ g}{Ca(OH)_2} + 2NH_4Cl \rightarrow CaCl_2 + \overset{X}{2NH_3} + 2H_2O$$

   2 moles   2 moles

   1 mole NH_4Cl = 53.5 g   1 mole NH_3 = 17.0 g

   $$X = 15.0\ g\ NH_4Cl \times \frac{mole}{53.5\ g} \times \frac{2\ moles\ NH_3}{2\ moles\ NH_4Cl} \times 17.0\ g/mole = 4.77\ g\ NH_3$$

2.   X   Y $20\bar{0}$ L

$$N_2(g) + 3H_2(g) \rightarrow 2NH_3(g)$$

1 mole   3 moles   2 moles

By inspection: X = $10\bar{0}$ L nitrogen; Y = $30\bar{0}$ L hydrogen

3.   X   15 g

$$NaNO_3 + H_2SO_4 \rightarrow NaHSO_4 + HNO_3$$

1 mole   1 mole

1 mole $NaNO_3$ = 85.0 g   1 mole HNO_3 = 63.0 g

$$X = 15 \text{ g } HNO_3 \times \frac{\text{mole}}{63.0 \text{ g}} \times \frac{1 \text{ mole } NaNO_3}{1 \text{ mole } HNO_3} \times 85.0 \text{ g/mole} = 2\bar{0} \text{ g } NaNO_3$$

Group B

4. $1\bar{0}$ g $1\bar{0}$ g   X

$$NH_4Cl + NaNO_2 \rightarrow N_2(g) + 2H_2O + NaCl$$

1 mole   1 mole   1 mole

1 mole NH_4Cl = 53.5 g   1 mole $NaNO_2$ = 69.0 g   1 mole N_2 = 22.4 L

The NH_4Cl is in excess.

$$X = 1\bar{0} \text{ g } NaNO_2 \times \frac{\text{mole}}{69.0 \text{ g}} \times \frac{1 \text{ mole } N_2}{1 \text{ mole } NaNO_2} \times 22.4 \text{ L/mole} = 3.2 \text{ L } N_2$$

5. 50.0 g (80.0%)   X

    KNO_3 + $H_2SO_4 \rightarrow KHSO_4 + HNO_3$

    1 mole   1 mole

1 mole KNO_3 = 101.1 g   1 mole HNO_3 = 63.0 g

$$X = 50.0 \text{ g } KNO_3 \times 0.800 \times \frac{\text{mole}}{101.1 \text{ g}} \times \frac{1 \text{ mole } HNO_3}{1 \text{ mole } KNO_3} \times 63.0 \text{ g/mole} = 24.9 \text{ g } HNO_3$$

6. (a)   254 g   X   Y

    3Cu   + $8HNO_3 \rightarrow 3Cu(NO_3)_2 + 2NO(g) + 4H_2O$

   3 moles   3 moles   2 moles

  1 mole Cu = 63.5 g   1 mole $Cu(NO_3)_2$ = 187.5 g

$$X = 254 \text{ g Cu} \times \frac{\text{mole}}{63.5 \text{ g}} \times \frac{3 \text{ moles } Cu(NO_3)_2}{3 \text{ moles Cu}} \times 187.5 \text{ g/mole} = 75\bar{0} \text{ g } Cu(NO_3)_2$$

(b) 1 mole NO = 22.4 L

$$Y = 254 \text{ g Cu} \times \frac{\text{mole}}{63.5 \text{ g}} \times \frac{2 \text{ moles NO}}{3 \text{ moles Cu}} \times 22.4 \text{ L/mole} = 59.7 \text{ L NO}$$

CHAPTER 29
Answers to Questions pp. 615–616
Group A

1. Between 150 and 600 meters underground in Texas and Louisiana near the Gulf of Mexico.
2. (a) To melt the sulfur. (b) To force the melted sulfur and water mixture to the surface. (c) There is usually a layer o quicksand between the surface of the ground and the sulfur bed.
3. (a) Odorless. (b) A suffocating, choking odor.
4. This was the result of a change in the sulfur from amorphous sulfur back to rhombic sulfur.
5. For making sulfur dioxide, carbon disulfide, sulfuric acid, and other sulfur compounds. For making matches, fireworks gunpowder, sulfur dyes, agricultural sprays, and in vulcanization of rubber.
6. From volcanic gases or mineral waters, as a product of the combustion of coal, and from roasting sulfide ores.
7. (a) $S(s) + O_2(g) \rightarrow SO_2(g)$
   (b) $Cu(s) + 2H_2SO_4(aq) \rightarrow CuSO_4(aq) + 2H_2O(l) + SO_2(g)$
8. (a) Upward displacement of air. (b) Its solubility in water and greater density than air.
9. Making sulfuric acid.
10. (a) $H_2SO_3 + NaOH \rightarrow NaHSO_3 + H_2O$. (b) $H_2SO_3 + 2NaOH \rightarrow Na_2SO_3 + 2H_2O$.
11. (a) The pH of normal rainwater is 5.6. (b) Because of the slight acidity caused by dissolved carbon dioxide.
12. Because the mixture of sulfur dioxide and oxygen comes in contact with the catalyst.

3. By slowly adding sulfuric acid to water with constant stirring.
4. To remove the oxide coating from iron or steel before the metal is plated.
5. Sulfuric acid acts as a dehydrating agent to absorb the water formed in the reaction between the nitric acid and the glycerol, thus causing the reaction to proceed more readily.

Group B

6. (a) S_8. (b) It would complicate an equation by making it necessary to multiply all the coefficients by 8.
7. At the melting point, sulfur is a pale-yellow liquid that flows easily. As it is heated further it becomes more viscous; above about 160 °C, it hardly pours. The color at this time has changed from light yellow to reddish-brown to almost black. Near the boiling point the fluidity increases again.
8. Endothermic. Monoclinic sulfur is stable only at a higher temperature than rhombic.

9.

20. Easy to liquefy. It requires only three atmospheres pressure at room temperature to liquefy it.
21. It combines readily with water to form sulfurous acid.
22. Sulfur dioxide is formed by the combustion of sulfur impurities in fuels. Sulfur dioxide dissolves in water drops in the air to form sulfurous acid. This sulfurous acid is oxidized to sulfuric acid by oxygen in the air.
23. (a) $Hg + 2H_2SO_4 \rightarrow HgSO_4 + SO_2(g) + 2H_2O$. (b) $2Cu_2S + 3O_2 \rightarrow 2Cu_2O + 2SO_2(g)$.
24. It has a high temperature and is also a powerful oxidizing and dehydrating agent.

Solutions to Problems p. 616

Group A

1. $$\begin{array}{cc} 1.0 \text{ kg} & X \\ S + O_2 \rightarrow & SO_2 \\ 1 \text{ mole} & 1 \text{ mole} \end{array}$$
    1 mole S = 32.1 g   1 mole SO_2 = 64.1 g

    $$X = 1.0 \text{ kg S} \times \frac{\text{mole}}{32.1 \text{ g}} \times \frac{1 \text{ mole } SO_2}{1 \text{ mole S}} \times 64.1 \text{ g/mole} = 2.0 \text{ kg } SO_2$$

2. 100.0% cpd − 86.6% Pb = 13.4% S.

    Pb: $\dfrac{86.6 \text{ g Pb}}{207.2 \text{ g/mole}} = 0.418 \text{ mole Pb}$

    S: $\dfrac{13.4 \text{ g S}}{32.1 \text{ g/mole}} = 0.417 \text{ mole S}$

    Pb:S = 0.418:0.417 = 1:1
    Empirical formula: PbS

3. Formula weight of H_2SO_4 = 2(1.0) + 32.1 + 4(16.0) = 98.1

    H: $\dfrac{(2.0) \text{ H}}{(98.1) \text{ H}_2SO_4} \times 100\% \text{ H}_2SO_4 = 2.0\% \text{ H}$

    S: $\dfrac{(32.1) \text{ S}}{(98.1) \text{ H}_2SO_4} \times 100\% \text{ H}_2SO_4 = 32.7\% \text{ S}$

    O: $\dfrac{(64.0) \text{ O}}{(98.1) \text{ H}_2SO_4} \times 100\% \text{ H}_2SO_4 = 65.2\% \text{ O}$

4. $$\begin{array}{cc} X & 1.00 \text{ L} \\ Na_2SO_3 + H_2SO_4 \rightarrow H_2O + & SO_2(g) + Na_2SO_4 \\ 1 \text{ mole} & 1 \text{ mole} \end{array}$$
    1 mole Na_2SO_3 = 126.1 g   1 mole SO_2 = 22.4 L

    $$X = 1.00 \text{ L } SO_2 \times \frac{\text{mole}}{22.4 \text{ L}} \times \frac{1 \text{ mole } Na_2SO_3}{1 \text{ mole } SO_2} \times 126.1 \text{ g/mole} = 5.63 \text{ g } Na_2SO_3$$

5. For each mole of ZnS roasted, one mole of H_2SO_4 may be theoretically produced.
   1 mole ZnS = 97.5 g   1 mole H_2SO_4 = 98.1 g

$$500 \text{ tons ZnS} \times \frac{10^3 \text{ kg}}{\text{ton}} \times \frac{98.1 \text{ g } H_2SO_4}{97.5 \text{ g ZnS}} = 5.03 \times 10^5 \text{ kg } H_2SO_4$$

Group B

6. From one mole of sulfur, one mole of sulfuric acid may be theoretically produced.
   1 mole S = 32.1 g   1 mole H_2SO_4 = 98.1 g

$$5.00 \text{ kg S} \times 0.995 \times \frac{98.1 \text{ g } H_2SO_4}{32.1 \text{ g S}} = 15.2 \text{ kg } H_2SO_4$$

7. 1200 kg   X
   $4FeS_2 + 11O_2 \rightarrow 2Fe_2O_3 + 8SO_2(g)$
   4 moles   8 moles
   1 mole FeS_2 = 120.0 g   1 mole SO_2 = 22.4 L

$$X = 1200 \text{ kg } FeS_2 \times \frac{10^3 \text{ g}}{\text{kg}} \times \frac{1 \text{ mole}}{120.0 \text{ g}} \times \frac{8 \text{ moles } SO_2}{4 \text{ moles } FeS_2} \times 22.4 \text{ L/mole} \times \frac{298 \text{ °K}}{273 \text{ °K}} \times \frac{760 \text{ mm}}{740 \text{ mm}} = 5.02 \times 10^5 \text{ L S}$$

8. (a) 140 kg   Y   X
   Fe + $H_2SO_4 \rightarrow FeSO_4 + H_2$
   1 mole   1 mole   1 mole
   1 mole Fe = 55.8 g   1 mole $FeSO_4$ = 151.9 g

$$X = 140 \text{ kg Fe} \times \frac{\text{mole}}{55.8 \text{ g}} \times \frac{1 \text{ mole } FeSO_4}{1 \text{ mole Fe}} \times 151.9 \text{ g/mole} = 381 \text{ kg } FeSO_4$$

   (b) 1 mole H_2SO_4 = 98.1

$$Y = 140 \text{ kg Fe} \times \frac{\text{mole}}{55.8 \text{ g}} \times \frac{1 \text{ mole } H_2SO_4}{1 \text{ mole Fe}} \times 98.1 \text{ g/mole} \times \frac{100\% \text{ acid}}{95\% \ H_2SO_4} = 259 \text{ kg acid}$$

9. 100 g 100 g   X
   Cu + $2H_2SO_4 \rightarrow CuSO_4 + 2H_2O + SO_2(g)$
   1 mole   2 moles   1 mole
   1 mole Cu = 63.5 g   1 mole H_2SO_4 = 98.1 g   1 mole SO_2 = 22.4 L
   The copper is in excess.

$$X = 100 \text{ g } H_2SO_4 \times \frac{\text{mole}}{98.1 \text{ g}} \times \frac{1 \text{ mole } SO_2}{2 \text{ moles } H_2SO_4} \times 22.4 \text{ L/mole} = 11.4 \text{ L } SO_2$$

10. $[Ba^{++}][SO_4^{--}] = 1.5 \times 10^{-9}$
    $10^{-2}[SO_4^{--}] = 1.5 \times 10^{-9}$
    $[SO_4^{--}] = 1.5 \times 10^{-7}$

CHAPTER 30
Answers to Questions pp. 626–627
Group A
1. Halogen atoms tend to bond more strongly to other atoms than to another halogen atom.
2. Astatine, iodine, bromine, chlorine, fluorine.
3. Salt producer.
4. A special carbon steel container.
5. As a catalyst in the manufacture of high-octane gasoline, in the manufacture of synthetic cryolite, and for etching glass
6. (a) Sodium chloride. (b) Sodium.

7. (a) $\overset{+4}{Mn}\overset{-2}{O_2} + 4\overset{+1}{H}\overset{-1}{Cl} \rightarrow \overset{+2}{Mn}\overset{-1}{Cl_2} + 2\overset{+1}{H_2}\overset{-2}{O} + \overset{0}{Cl_2}$

   (b) $2\overset{+1}{Na}\overset{-1}{Cl} + 2\overset{+1}{H_2}\overset{+6}{S}\overset{-2}{O_4} + \overset{+4}{Mn}\overset{-2}{O_2} \rightarrow \overset{+1}{Na_2}\overset{+6}{S}\overset{-2}{O_4} + \overset{+2}{Mn}\overset{+6}{S}\overset{-2}{O_4} + 2\overset{+1}{H_2}\overset{-2}{O} + \overset{0}{Cl_2}$

   (c) See (a) and (b) above. Chlorine is oxidized; manganese is reduced.
   (d) They are essentially the same.

8. When inhaled in small quantities, it produces about the same symptoms as a bad head cold. In larger quantities, it causes death.

9. (a) More dense than air and very soluble in water. (b) Upward displacement of air.

10. (a) $2Br^-(aq) + Cl_2(g) \rightarrow 2Cl^-(aq) + Br_2(l)$. (b) Displacement reaction.

11. Dark-red volatile liquid, three times as dense as water, and moderately soluble in water. Readily soluble in carbon tetrachloride, carbon disulfide, and in water solutions of bromides.

12. $:\overset{\cdot\cdot}{\underset{\cdot\cdot}{I}}: + e^- \rightarrow :\overset{\cdot\cdot}{\underset{\cdot\cdot}{I}}:^-$

13. (a) $Zn + Cl_2 \rightarrow ZnCl_2$
    (b) $Ca + F_2 \rightarrow CaF_2$
    (c) $Ni + Br_2 \rightarrow NiBr_2$
    (d) $2Ag + I_2 \rightarrow 2AgI$

Group B

14. (a) $2Br^- + F_2 \rightarrow Br_2 + 2F^-$
    (b) $2I^- + Br_2 \rightarrow I_2 + 2Br^-$
    (c) No reaction.
    (d) No reaction.
    (e) $2Cl^- + F_2 \rightarrow Cl_2 + 2F^-$

15. There are no elements more electronegative than fluorine.

16. $2\overset{+1\ -2}{H_2O} + 2\overset{+2\ -1}{XeF_2} \rightarrow 2\overset{0}{Xe} + \overset{0}{O_2} + 4\overset{+1\ -1}{HF}$

17. It is easily converted to a liquid by pressure at room temperature. It is odorless, nonflammable, and nontoxic.

18. Because otherwise they would react with one another.

19. (a) Hydrogen. (b) When a paraffin candle burns in chlorine, the chlorine unites with the hydrogen of the paraffin and leaves the carbon uncombined.

20. (a) The greenish-yellow color of chlorine is imparted to the chlorine water. (b) The chlorine unites with water to form hypochlorous acid and hydrochloric acid, which are colorless.

21. (a) Bluish black; (b) dark-brown; (c) violet; (d) violet.

22. (a) HF, HCl, HBr, HI. (b) The polarity of the bonds should decrease as one goes from HF to HI. (c) $HF(g) + H_2O(l) \rightarrow H_3O^+(aq) + F^-(aq)$. $HCl(g) + H_2O(l) \rightarrow H_3O^+(aq) + Cl^-(aq)$. $HBr(g) + H_2O(l) \rightarrow H_3O^+(aq) + Br^-(aq)$. $HI(g) + H_2O(l) \rightarrow H_3O^+(aq) + I^-(aq)$.

23. (a) HF: Concentration of hydrogen-bonded hydronium ion–fluoride ion pairs is much higher than the concentrations of either separate hydronium ions and fluoride ions or hydrogen fluoride molecules. HCl, HBr, and HI: Concentrations of hydronium and halide ions are much higher than the concentration of hydrogen halide molecules. (b) Hydrogen-bonded hydronium ion–fluoride ion pairs are more stable than either separate hydronium ions and fluoride ions or hydrogen fluoride molecules. Hydrogen chloride, hydrogen bromide, and hydrogen iodide molecules are less stable than hydronium ions and the corresponding halide ions.

24. Aluminum is not as highly electropositive a metal as sodium and calcium.

Solutions to Problems p. 627
Group A

1.
$$\underset{\text{2 moles}}{2NaCl} + 2H_2O \xrightarrow{\text{elect}} \overset{X}{2NaOH} + H_2 + \underset{\text{1 mole}}{\overset{71\bar{0}\text{ kg}}{Cl_2}}$$

1 mole Cl_2 = 71.0 g   1 mole NaOH = 40.0 g

$X = 71\bar{0}\text{ kg }Cl_2 \times \dfrac{\text{mole}}{71.0\text{ g}} \times \dfrac{\text{2 moles NaOH}}{\text{1 mole }Cl_2} \times 40.0\text{ g/mole} = 80\bar{0}\text{ kg NaOH}$

2.
$$\underset{\text{2 moles}}{2NaBr} + MnO_2 + 2H_2SO_4 \rightarrow \underset{\text{1 mole}}{\overset{10.0\text{ g}}{Br_2}} + Na_2SO_4 + MnSO_4 + 2H_2O$$

1 mole NaBr = 102.9 g   1 mole Br_2 = 159.8 g

$X = 10.0\text{ g }Br_2 \times \dfrac{\text{mole}}{159.8\text{ g}} \times \dfrac{\text{2 moles NaBr}}{\text{1 mole }Br_2} \times 102.9\text{ g/mole} = 12.9\text{ g NaBr}$

3. (a)

$$\begin{array}{cccc} & Y & X & 25\bar{0}\text{ g} \\ & Cl_2 & + Ca(OH)_2 \rightarrow & Ca(ClO)Cl & + H_2O \\ & 1\text{ mole} & 1\text{ mole} & 1\text{ mole} \end{array}$$

1 mole $Ca(OH)_2$ = 74.1 g   1 mole $Ca(ClO)Cl$ = 127.1 g

$$X = 25\bar{0}\text{ g } Ca(ClO)Cl \times \frac{\text{mole}}{127.1\text{ g}} \times \frac{1\text{ mole } Ca(OH)_2}{1\text{ mole } Ca(ClO)Cl} \times 74.1\text{ g/mole} = 146\text{ g } Ca(OH)_2$$

(b) 1 mole Cl_2 = 71.0 g

$$Y = 25\bar{0}\text{ g } Ca(ClO)Cl \times \frac{\text{mole}}{127.1\text{ g}} \times \frac{1\text{ mole } Cl_2}{1\text{ mole } Ca(ClO)Cl} \times 71.0\text{ g/mole} = 14\bar{0}\text{ g } Cl_2$$

4.

$$\begin{array}{ccc} & 11.2\text{ L} & X \\ Zn + & Cl_2(g) \rightarrow & ZnCl_2 \\ & 1\text{ mole} & 1\text{ mole} \end{array}$$

1 mole Cl_2 = 22.4 L   1 mole $ZnCl_2$ = 136.4 g

$$X = 11.2\text{ L } Cl_2 \times \frac{\text{mole}}{22.4\text{ L}} \times \frac{1\text{ mole } ZnCl_2}{1\text{ mole } Cl_2} \times 136.4\text{ g/mole} = 68.2\text{ g } ZnCl_2$$

Group B

5. Formula weight of $C_2H_4Br_2$ = 2(12.0) + 4(1.0) + 2(79.9) = 187.8

Br: $\dfrac{159.8\ (Br)}{187.8\ (C_2H_4Br_2)} \times 100\%\ C_2H_4Br_2 = 85.1\%\ Br$

6.

$$\begin{array}{cccc} 468\text{ g} & & & X \\ 2\ NaCl & \xrightarrow{\text{elect}} & 2\ Na\ + & Cl_2 \\ 2\text{ moles} & & & 1\text{ mole} \end{array}$$

1 mole $NaCl$ = 58.5 g   1 mole Cl_2 = 22.4 L

$$X = 468\text{ g } NaCl \times \frac{\text{mole}}{58.5\text{ g}} \times \frac{1\text{ mole } Cl_2}{2\text{ moles } NaCl} \times 22.4\text{ L/mole} = 89.6\text{ L } Cl_2$$

7. $5 \times 25\bar{0}\text{ mL} \times \dfrac{1\text{ L}}{10^3\text{ mL}} \times \dfrac{273\ ^\circ K}{30\bar{0}\ ^\circ K} \times \dfrac{75\bar{0}\text{ mm}}{76\bar{0}\text{ mm}} = 1.12\text{ L } Cl_2$ at STP

$$\begin{array}{cccccc} X & Y & & & 1.12\text{ L} \\ 4HCl & + MnO_2 \rightarrow & MnCl_2 & + 2H_2O & + Cl_2(g) \\ 4\text{ moles} & 1\text{ mole} & & & 1\text{ mole} \end{array}$$

1 mole HCl = 36.5 g   1 mole Cl_2 = 22.4 L

$$X = 1.12\text{ L } Cl_2 \times \frac{\text{mole}}{22.4\text{ L}} \times \frac{4\text{ moles } HCl}{1\text{ mole } Cl_2} \times 36.5\text{ g/mole} \times \frac{100\%\text{ acid}}{38\%\text{ HCl}} \times \frac{1\text{ mL}}{1.20\text{ g}} = 16.0\text{ mL conc HCl}$$

1 mole MnO_2 = 86.9 g

$$Y = 1.12\text{ L } Cl_2 \times \frac{\text{mole}}{22.4\text{ L}} \times \frac{1\text{ mole } MnO_2}{1\text{ mole } Cl_2} \times 86.9\text{ g/mole} = 4.34\text{ g } MnO_2$$

8.

$$\begin{array}{cccc} 50\bar{0}\text{ g} & 60\bar{0}\text{ g }(95\%) & X \\ 2NaCl\ + & H_2SO_4 \rightarrow & 2HCl\ + & Na_2SO_4 \\ 2\text{ moles} & 1\text{ mole} & 2\text{ moles} \end{array}$$

1 mole $NaCl$ = 58.5 g   1 mole H_2SO_4 = 98.1 g   1 mole HCl = 36.5 g

500 g $NaCl$ = 8.55 moles; 570 g H_2SO_4 = 5.81 moles; H_2SO_4 is in excess.

$$X = 50\bar{0}\text{ g } NaCl \times \frac{\text{mole}}{58.5\text{ g}} \times \frac{2\text{ moles } HCl}{2\text{ moles } NaCl} \times 36.5\text{ g/mole} = 312\text{ g } HCl$$

CHAPTER 31

Answers to Questions pp. 648–649

Group A

1. (a) Henri Becquerel. (b) By accident, Becquerel found that uranium ore gives off invisible rays that affect a photographic plate in the same way light does.
2. Pitchblende was four times as radioactive as the amount of uranium it contained warranted.
3. Radium is more than 1,000,000 times as radioactive as uranium.
4. In producing luminous paint.
5. The length of time required for the decay of one-half of any number of atoms of a radioactive nuclide.
6. The nucleus.
7. The nuclide is changed to one having an atomic number two less and a mass number four less.
8. The nuclide is changed to one having an atomic number one greater and a mass number remaining the same.
9. By measuring the amount of parent nuclide and daughter nuclides in the sample.
10. Radioactive decay, nuclear disintegration, fission, and fusion.
11. The emission of an alpha particle decreases the mass of the nucleus; it also decreases the number of protons and neutrons by an even number. Beta particle emission brings the neutron-proton ratio nearer the value for stable nuclei of the same mass number.
12. By Chadwick during the bombardment of beryllium by alpha particles.
13. Because they do not carry any charge. They are not attracted or repelled by a nucleus and can easily penetrate it.
14. It may go through the atom, or it may be caught by the nucleus. It may cause the nucleus to disintegrate.
15. In medical diagnosis and treatment and as tracers in research.
16. (a) $^{238}_{92}$U, $^{235}_{92}$U, and $^{234}_{92}$U. (b) 99.3%, 0.7%, and insignificant traces, respectively.
17. (a) Fission is the breakup of a very heavy nucleus of an atom into medium-weight parts. (b) It is produced in $^{235}_{92}$U by the capture of a slow neutron, which produces a highly unstable nucleus. The nucleus immediately undergoes fission.
18. The amount of radioactive material required to provide sufficient neutrons to sustain a chain reaction.
19. Because of the heat generated during the chain reaction. If this heat were allowed to accumulate it would soon destroy the reactor.
20. A fusion reaction in which four hydrogen nuclei combine to form a helium nucleus.

Group B

1. Because it is more important for its radioactivity than for its chemical or physical properties.
2. The radiation easily penetrates the black paper and affects the film.
3. The more radioactive a substance is, the faster it will discharge an electroscope.
4. (a) Chemical form, low temperature, high pressure, a varying electric field, interaction of the decaying nucleus and its valence electrons. (b) Slight.
5. Beyond bismuth in the periodic table.
6.

Particle	Identity	Mass number	Charge	Speed	Penetrating ability
α particle	helium nucleus	4	+2	1/10 the speed of light	low penetrating ability
β particle	electron	0	−1	near the speed of light	100 times the penetrating ability of α particles

7. High-energy electromagnetic waves.

8. $^{226}_{88}$Ra $\rightarrow$ $^{222}_{86}$Rn + $^{4}_{2}$He.

9. $^{214}_{82}$Pb $\rightarrow$ $^{214}_{83}$Bi + $^{0}_{-1}$e.

10. $^{214}_{84}$Po $\rightarrow$ $^{210}_{82}$Pb + $^{4}_{2}$He.
$^{210}_{82}$Pb $\rightarrow$ $^{210}_{83}$Bi + $^{0}_{-1}$e.

11. (a) The lightest and heaviest elements. (b) The intermediate-weight elements. (c) The greater the binding energy per nuclear particle is, the more stable the nucleus is.

32. Mass, ratio of neutrons to protons, and the even-odd nature of the number of neutrons and the number of protons.
33. Each type of nuclear reaction results in more stable nuclei because the products are nuclei with greater binding energie per nuclear particle.
34. (a) Rutherford. (b) $^{14}_{7}N + ^{4}_{2}He \rightarrow ^{17}_{8}O + ^{1}_{1}H$.
35. By bombarding lithium with high-speed protons and comparing the actual energy release with Einstein's prediction.
36. (a) It is a spiral path. (b) The combined action of the magnetic field and the alternating voltage on the dees.
37. $^{238}_{92}U$ is bombarded with neutrons to produce the unstable isotope of uranium, $^{239}_{92}U$. This emits a beta particle to for neptunium, $^{239}_{93}Np$. This in turn emits a beta particle to form plutonium, $^{239}_{94}Pu$.
38. (a) By bombarding normally nonradioactive substances with neutrons or deuterons. (b) $^{59}_{27}Co + ^{1}_{0}n \rightarrow ^{60}_{27}Co$. (c) Used treatment of cancer.
39. (a) A chain reaction is one in which the material or energy that starts the reaction is also one of the products. (b) The fissi of $^{235}_{92}U$ is started by a neutron. During the fission process, several neutrons are emitted. Some of these initiate fission other $^{235}_{92}U$ nuclei, which in turn produce other neutrons.
40. It is constructed of blocks of natural uranium alternated with blocks of graphite that serve as a moderator. Control ro and cooling apparatus are also incorporated.

Solutions to Problems p. 649
Group A
1. For three-fourths to decay requires 2 half-lives. 2×18.2 da $= 36.4$ da.
2. 20.25 hr $\div$ 6.75 hr/half-life $= 3.00$ half-lives. After 3 half-lives, one-eighth remains.
3. 4860 yr $\div$ 1620 yr/half-life $= 3.00$ half-lives. After 3 half-lives, one-eighth remains. 0.250 g/8 $= 0.0312$ g.
4. $[3(1.007276\ u) + 4(1.008664\ u)] - 7.01436\ u = 0.04212\ u$.
5. $[10(1.007276\ u) + 10(1.008664\ u)] - 19.98695\ u = 0.17245\ u$.

Group B
6. 7.646 $\div$ 3.823 da/half-life $= 2.000$ half-lives. After 2 half-lives, one-fourth remains. 0.0500 g $\times$ 4 $= 0.200$ g.
7. 10^{5} yr $\div$ 24,390 yr/half-life $=$ approximately 4 half-lives. After 4 half-lives, one-sixteenth remains. 100 g/16 $= 6.25$ Approximately 6 g remains.
8. 4.51×10^{9} yr/1.62×10^{3} yr $= 2.78 \times 10^{6}$. The proportion is one radium-226 atom to 2.78×10^{6} uranium-238 atom
9. 0.04212 u/7 nuclear particles $= 0.006017\ u$/nuclear particle. $0.006017\ u \times 931$ Mev/$u = 5.60$ Mev.
10. $[92(1.007276\ u) + 146(1.008664\ u)] - 238.0003\ u = 1.9340\ u$. $1.9340\ u$/238 nuclear particles $= 0.0081261\ u$/nucle particle. $0.0081261\ u \times 931$ Mev/$u = 7.57$ Mev.

Modern Chemistry

H. Clark Metcalfe
John E. Williams
Joseph F. Castka

The Holt Modern Chemistry Program
Metcalfe, Williams, and Castka

Modern Chemistry (Student Text)
Modern Chemistry (Teacher's Edition)
Laboratory Experiments in Modern Chemistry
Exercises and Experiments in Modern Chemistry
Tests in Modern Chemistry (Duplicating Masters)

HOLT, RINEHART AND WINSTON, PUBLISHERS
New York • London • Toronto • Sydney

H. Clark Metcalfe

P.O. Box V2, Wickenburg, Arizona, 85358; formerly teacher of chemistry at Winchester-Thurston School, Pittsburgh, Pennsylvania, and Head of the Science Department, Wilkinsburg Senior High School, Wilkinsburg, Pennsylvania.

John E. Williams

Formerly teacher of chemistry and physics at Newport Harbor High School, Newport Beach, California, and Head of the Science Department, Broad Ripple High School, Indianapolis, Indiana.

Joseph F. Castka

Formerly Assistant Principal for the Supervision of Physical Science, Martin Van Buren High School, New York City, and Adjunct Associate Professor of General Science and Chemistry, C. W. Post College, Long Island University, New York.

Editorial Development William N. Moore, Roland J. Cormier, Pamela Hirschfeld, Elizabeth Mastalski

Editorial Processing Margaret M. Byrne, Regina Chilcoat

Art, Production, and Photo Resources Vivian Fenster, Fred C. Pusterla, Robin M. Swenson, Russell Dian, Annette Sessa-Galbo, Beverly Silver, Anita Dickhuth, Louise Hannibal

Product Manager Laura Zuckerman

Advisory Board Rhenida Bennett, John W. Griffiths, David J. Miller, Douglas A. Nash, William Paul, George Salinger, Jean Slankard, John Taggart

Consultant John Matejowsky

Researcher James R. George, Erica S. Felman

The cover photograph of MODERN CHEMISTRY 1982 is a computer drawing of a portion of the crystal lattice of ice. The computer program used to produce the diagram was written by William G. Davies, John W. Moore, and Robert Williams.

Photo credits appear on pages 693–694.

Preface

Nearly 65 years ago, Charles E. Dull, then a teacher at West Side High School, Newark, New Jersey, wrote the first edition of ESSENTIALS OF MODERN CHEMISTRY. Now, well into a second generation of authors with extensive secondary school teaching experience, the 1982 edition of MODERN CHEMISTRY still continues the tradition of an accurate, up-to-date, easily understood textbook that fulfills the various curriculum requirements of an introductory course in chemistry. Teachers will find ample material in MODERN CHEMISTRY for an outstanding college-preparatory program. For those students who do not plan to go further in science, there is sufficient elementary theory and descriptive information for a complete general course of study. The Teacher's Edition of MODERN CHEMISTRY gives suggestions for implementing both types of chemistry courses and suggestions for an advanced course as well. It has been the authors' purpose to include more text material than can be covered in one year. This wealth of material permits a wide choice of topics and allows for selective emphasis. Teachers should choose those topics that best meet their needs.

In MODERN CHEMISTRY the subject matter of chemistry is organized in a logical, workable sequence. Descriptive and theoretical topics are alternated to provide classroom variety and a well-correlated laboratory program. Special attention has been given to the introduction of technical vocabulary words. Each of these words is printed in **bold-face italics** and carefully defined when first introduced. Refresher definitions of these words occur at appropriate intervals in the text. Sample Problems and Solutions are used to illustrate important quantitative relationships and concepts. New to this edition are Practice Problems, with answers, that appear frequently throughout the text and immediately reinforce the understanding of important concepts; a vocabulary review list at the end of each chapter; and chapter objectives.

Significant content changes in this edition of MODERN CHEMISTRY include the following: an introductory section telling the beginning chemistry student about the importance and value of chemistry in everyday life; a complete rewrite of Chapter 1 to emphasize measurements and computations, with emphasis on dimensional analysis; the use of L as the abbreviation for liter; the explanation and use of systematic nomenclature of elements with atomic numbers above 100; an updating of definitions of atomic mass and atomic weight; the introduction of arrows for orbital notation; the explanation of oxidation and reduction in terms of oxidation number changes; the inclusion of an alternate method for balancing redox equations; a more detailed exposition of the mole concept; the inclusion of descriptive chemistry of hydrogen peroxide; a more extensive explanation of molar and normal solutions; the review of logarithms prior to the calculation of hydronium and hydroxide ion concentrations; an explanation of coal formation and types of coal; an extensive revision of Unit 7, Chemical Reactions; the restoration to the text of Chapter 23, Elements of Period Three; a careful revision of the descriptive chemistry of metallic and nonmetallic elements; and many minor changes to update and improve the clarity and readability of the text.

The material for each chapter includes an introductory paragraph, which relates chemistry to other fields of human endeavor in science, art, literature, and history. At the beginning of each chapter there is a list of Objectives. At the end of each chapter there is a Summary, a Vocabulary list, and suitable Questions and Problems. The Questions, which are based on the text itself, are graded according to difficulty into Groups A and B. The Problems are similarly graded. The average student should master all the Group A Questions and Problems; the better student will be able to do both Group A and Group B exercises. In the back of the book are an Appendix containing Data Tables, a Glossary, and an Index.

Because of their clarity and great learning value, line drawings are used extensively. The text is also illustrated with many fine photographs. Marginal notes are strategically placed throughout the text to reinforce concepts, provide supplementary information, and assist the student in developing productive study techniques. There are Photo Essays on Careers, Pioneers in Chemistry, and Crystals. In these, pictorial and graphic materials are combined with brief text to highlight special topics in chemistry.

The text was written by H. Clark Metcalfe and John E. Williams. Joseph F. Castka was mainly responsible for the preparation of all supplementary materials that accompany the text: the Teacher's Edition, EXERCISES AND EXPERIMENTS IN CHEMISTRY, LABORATORY EXPERIMENTS IN CHEMISTRY, and TESTS IN CHEMISTRY. The introductory paragraphs that preface each chapter were written by Thomas Szalkiewicz.

The following persons have assisted in preparing this revision by their helpful criticism: Sister Irene Haché, R.C.E., Newton Country Day School of the Sacred Heart, Newton, Massachusetts; Henry Hubinger, Professor, Department of Chemistry, University of Miami, Coral Gables, Florida; Franklin D. Kizer, Executive Secretary, Council of State Science Supervisors; Richard A. Marble, Casady School, Oklahoma City, Oklahoma; Stanley Starr, Chairman of the Science Department, Briarcliff High School, Briarcliff Manor, New York; and Paul L. Willems, Chairman of the Science Department, Manitowoc Lutheran High School, Manitowoc, Wisconsin. Our thanks, too, to Elinor Entelis, Valley Stream North High School, Franklin Square, New York, and her students and to Dr. Joel Aroughetti and the students of High School of Art and Design, New York City, New York, for providing the facilities for the special color photographs of laboratory activities.

H. Clark Metcalfe, John E. Williams, Joseph F. Castka

Contents

How to Use This Book

Introductory Paragraphs relate chemistry to a variety of other topics and preview the chapter.

The twelve **Units** are divided into thirty-one **Chapters. Subtopic** and numbered **Section** headings point out the main ideas of the section.

Major **Objectives** help the student focus on the important concepts of the chapter.

New terms, definitions, and principles are printed in *italics* and ***boldface italics*** for emphasis and rapid review.

Important equations are printed in **boldface** and sometimes in color.

Numerous **Marginal Notes** reinforce concepts, offer additional information, and assist student development of effective study techniques.

Photographs and **Diagrams** enhance and illustrate ideas presented in the chapter.

Hydrocarbon Substitution Products

Many great scientific achievements have been realized by men and women endowed with the gift of imagination. The deciphering of the ring structure of benzene is such an example. For many years scientists had toiled to unravel the geometry of this important hydrocarbon, when in 1865 the German chemist August Kekulé saw it in a dream. In his reverie: "Again the atoms were before my eyes. Little groups kept modestly in the background. My mind's eye, trained by the observation of similar forms, could now distinguish more complex structures of various kinds. Long chains here and there more firmly joined, all winding and turning with a snake-like motion. Suddenly one of the serpents caught its own tail and the ring thus formed whirled exasperatingly before my eyes. . . ." From his experience, Kekulé advised other scientists: "If we learn to dream, we shall perhaps discover truth."

☐ 19.1 Preparation of alkyl halides

An alkyl halide is an alkane in which a halogen atom—fluorine, chlorine, bromine, or iodine—is substituted for a hydrogen atom. Since **R** is often used to represent an alkyl group and **X** any halogen, an alkyl halide can be represented as **RX.**

1. Direct halogenation. In Section 18.12, you learned that the halogens react with alkanes to form substitution products. For example, under suitable conditions halogen atoms can be substituted for each of the four hydrogen atoms in methane. This reaction occurs in four stages.

$$\mathbf{CH_4 + X_2 \rightarrow CH_3X + HX}$$
$$\mathbf{CH_3X + X_2 \rightarrow CH_2X_2 + HX}$$
$$\mathbf{CH_2X_2 + X_2 \rightarrow CHX_3 + HX}$$
$$\mathbf{CHX_3 + X_2 \rightarrow CX_4 + HX}$$

2. From alkenes and alkynes. As discussed in Sections 18.15 and 18.18, alkenes and alkynes react with halogens or hydrogen halides to form alkyl halides.

3. From alcohols. Alcohols are alkanes in which the hydroxyl group, **—OH,** has been substituted for hydrogen. Hence, an alcohol has the type formula **ROH.** The reaction of an alcohol with a hydrogen halide, HCl, HBr, or HI, yields the corresponding alkyl halide.

$$\mathbf{ROH + HX \rightarrow RX + H_2O}$$

HALOGEN SUBSTITUTION PRODUCTS

In this chapter you will gain an understanding of:

- the preparation and reactions of alkyl halides
- the structure, preparations, and reactions of alcohols
- the general structural formulas of ethers, aldehydes, ketones, carboxylic acids, and esters
- the preparations and reactions of these organic compounds
- the reactions of esterification and saponification

Many halogenated hydrocarbons are toxic, affecting the liver or the heart muscle. Some are believed to cause cancer.

Figure 12-18. A computer-generated drawing of a portion of an ice crystal.

vi

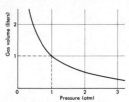

Figure 10-11. The variation of volume with pressure at constant temperature of 1 liter of an ideal gas measured at 1 atmosphere pressure. $pV = constant$.

Table 10-1
CONDENSATION TEMPERATURES OF REPRESENTATIVE SUBSTANCES

Type of substance	Substance	Condensation temperature (1 atm, °C)
nonpolar covalent molecular	H_2	−253
	O_2	−183
	CH_4	−164
	CCl_4	77
	C_6H_6	80

Graphs and **Tables** present data in a clear, concise manner.

SAMPLE PROBLEM

A 50.0-mL volume of gas is measured at $2\overline{0}$ °C. If the pressure remains unchanged, what will be the volume of the gas at $\overline{0}$ °C?

SOLUTION

Change the Celsius temperatures to Kelvin temperatures:

$$2\overline{0} \text{ °C} + 273° = 293 \text{ °K}; \overline{0} \text{ °C} + 273° = 273 \text{ °K}$$
$$V' = VT'/T$$
$$V'_{\overline{0}°C} = 50.0 \text{ mL} \times 273 \text{ °K}/293 \text{ °K}$$
$$V'_{\overline{0}°C} = 46.6 \text{ mL}$$

Sample Problems and **Solutions** illustrate important quantitative relationships.

PRACTICE PROBLEMS

1. A 50.0-mL volume of gas is measured at $2\overline{0}$ °C. If the pressure remains unchanged, what will be the volume of the gas at $4\overline{0}$ °C? *ans.* $V'_{4\overline{0}°C} = 53.4$ mL
2. A gas volume, 149 mL, is measured at 25 °C. What is the gas volume at $\overline{0}$ °C if the pressure does not change? *ans.* $V'_{\overline{0}°C} = 136$ mL

Practice Problems, with answers, provide reinforcement of the understanding of basic concepts.

SUMMARY

The kinetic theory helps explain the properties of gases, liquids, and solids in terms of the forces between the particles of matter and the energy these particles possess. The three basic assumptions of the kinetic theory are: (1) matter is composed of very tiny particles; (2) the particles of becomes smaller. Gas volumes are related to the temperature and pressure of the gas.

Standard temperature is zero degrees Celsius. Standard pressure is the pressure exerted by a column of mercury exactly 760 millimeters high. The temperature of a gas is measured by means

End-of-chapter **Summary** is a brief review of the major concepts.

VOCABULARY

absolute zero	diffusion	Kelvin scale
Boyle's law	dipole-dipole attraction	kinetic theory
Charles' law	dispersion interaction	STP

Key words covered in the chapter are reviewed in the **Vocabulary.**

QUESTIONS

Group A
1. What structural similarity determines the metallic character of transition elements?
2. Copper(II) sulfate crystals are blue. To what

Group B
7. Why were some metals used in very early times, while many other metals were obtained only within the last century?

PROBLEMS

Group A
1. How much iron(II) chloride can be produced by adding 165 g of iron to an excess of hydrochloric acid?

Group B
7. How much limestone will be needed to combine with the silica in 1.0×10^6 metric tons of the ore of Problem 5?

Questions and **Problems,** graded according to difficulty, are designed to check student progress in understanding chapter material.

Table 8

WATER-VAPOR PRESSURE					
Temperature (°C)	Pressure (mm Hg)	Temperature (°C)	Pressure (mm Hg)	Temperature (°C)	Pressure (mm Hg)
0.0	4.6	17.0	14.5	27.0	26.7
5.0	6.5	17.5	15.0	28.0	28.3
10.0	9.2	18.0	15.5	29.0	30.0
12.5	10.9	18.5	16.0	30.0	31.8
15.0	12.8	19.0	16.5	35.0	42.2
15.5	13.2	22.0	19.8	40.0	55.3
16.0	13.6	22.5	20.4	50.0	92.5
16.5	14.1	23.0	21.1	60.0	149.4
17.0	14.5	23.5	21.7	70.0	233.7
17.5	15.0	24.0	22.4	80.0	355.1
18.0	15.5	24.5	23.1	90.0	525.8
18.5	16.0	25.0	23.8	95.0	633.9
19.0	16.5	26.0	25.2	100.0	760.0

Table 9

DENSITY OF GASES AT STP			
Gas	Density (g/L)	Gas	Density (g/L)
air, dry	1.2929	hydrogen	0.0899
ammonia	0.771	hydrogen chloride	1.639
carbon dioxide	1.977	hydrogen sulfide	1.539
carbon monoxide	1.250	methane	0.716
chlorine	3.214	nitrogen	1.251
dinitrogen monoxide	1.977	nitrogen monoxide	1.340
ethyne (acetylene)	1.171	oxygen	1.429
helium	0.1785	sulfur dioxide	2.927

Important **Tables** are contained in the **Appendix.** A **Glossary** provides definitions of important words. The **Index** gives page references for key terms.

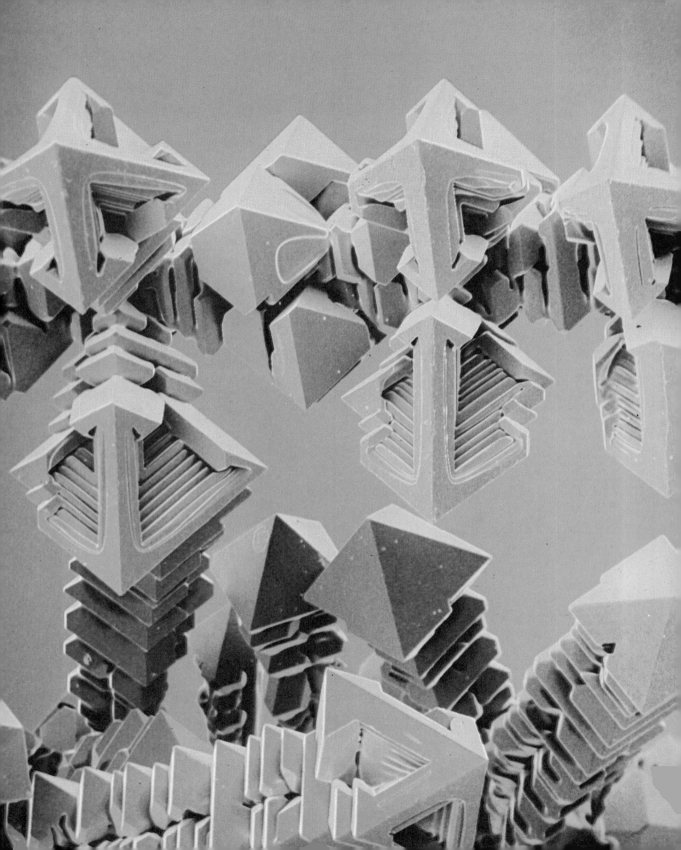

Measurements in Chemistry

The pyramids, one of the seven wonders of the world, rise high above the sandy plains that border the Nile. Built to entomb the mummies of ancient Egyptian rulers, these palaces of the dead attest to the accomplishments of a great civilization — one that transformed a desert oasis into a mecca of culture and science. The Egyptians, like all great civilizations, possessed a powerful invention: a system of measurement. Crude when compared with modern systems, the Egyptian method nonetheless enabled them to shape nearly 2,000,000 stone blocks into pyramids 147 meters high and over 52,000 square meters in area. Today, highly refined systems of measurement play an essential role in a wide range of scientific activities. In chemistry, as in all exact sciences, measurement is the foundation for developing, explaining, and applying ideas.

You are about to begin your study of chemistry. Perhaps you are wondering what this science is about and how it is important to you. Chemistry is the study of materials, their composition and structure, and the changes they undergo. Chemistry is a body of systematized knowledge gained from observation, study, and experimentation—as opposed to guesswork and opinions. By studying chemistry you will be able to understand the nature of the materials around you and the changes they undergo.

The study of chemistry has many practical benefits. The food, clothing, building ·materials, and medicines that are necessary to life are products of the application of chemical knowledge. Many of the materials used in such fields as architecture, engineering, and nuclear science are the results of the work of chemists. Without these and other innovations, our way of life would be radically different.

You are beginning your study of chemistry at a time when there is great concern about complex problems relating to the quality of life. Some of these problems involve sources of energy. Natural gas and petroleum, which would be better used as sources of chemical raw materials, continue to be burned as primary sources of energy. Increased development of energy sources such as coal and nuclear reactors is immediately essential. More research and experimentation will be required before oil shale and fermentation of waste materials from living things can become significant energy sources. Other problems relate to the contamination of the environment. Chemical research has been responsible for the production of many synthetic materials. Yet

INTRODUCTION

In this chapter you will gain an understanding of:

- **the nature of chemistry**
- **the scientific process**
- **matter and energy**
- **scientific measurement and mathematical operations**

Figure 1-1. The realms of chemistry range from the futuristic configurations of crystals of palladium (left), seen with the aid of an electron microscope, to the familiar shapes of laboratory apparatus (above).

1

such production is accompanied by environmental pollution. Mining of coal and metal ores scars the landscape. Burning of coal and smelting of metal ores foul the atmosphere. Some medicines, products of chemical laboratories, have serious and sometimes fatal side effects. The introduction of chemicals into poorly understood natural processes has the possibility of upsetting established balances in nature. Through the study of chemistry and the efforts of chemists, solutions to these and other problems may be revealed.

Chemistry can help you gain a deeper and more satisfying understanding of your environment than you now have. Knowledge of basic concepts in chemistry enables you to recognize and appreciate order in nature. The Greek thinker Aristotle called human beings "creatures who delight to know." If you are curious and wish to know more about natural processes, minerals of the earth, water and solutions, and gases of the atmosphere, the activities of chemistry beckon to you.

Chemical knowledge of a practical nature dates far back in history. Prehistoric people produced watertight pottery by shaping, baking, and glazing certain clays. About 5000 years ago, fire was found to be useful in preparing copper, bronze, and iron. Nearly 2500 years ago, the Egyptians found methods for manufacturing glass and extracting medicines from plant sources. Each of these early discoveries was a chemical operation that greatly influenced the course of civilization. Progress in understanding the underlying causes of these and other chemical transformations, however, was slow in coming. Although as early as 300 B.C. the Greeks attempted to analyze materials and describe their various properties, it was not until 2000 years later that adequate chemical explanations began to appear. Since then, tremendous progress has been made in both understanding and applying the marvels of chemistry. Frontiers, however, still remain. As chemical research continues to unravel the complexity of materials, chemists will continue to make valuable contributions to human progress. Research is an ongoing process in all the sciences, including chemistry. Chemical research promises a brighter future for all. To be a chemist is to be an architect of the future.

Although scientists are interested in learning facts, a mere collection of facts about the physical world does not constitute a science. One of the major activities of scientists is using such facts to build models or provide explanations that can relate the facts to each other and be used to predict future observations. Another activity of scientists is testing the models and explanations. Testing serves to confirm the validity of scientific concepts.

If, over a long time, experimental evidence supports an explanation, it is accepted as valid. If even one observation does not follow the behavior predicted, however, the explanation is no longer valid and must be revised or discarded. Explanations and models are never certain, and scientists must learn to accept and work with a degree of uncertainty.

Scientists are naturally curious people who attempt to find interrelationships among their many observations. Scientists are patient people, for nature only slowly reveals its secrets. Scientists are careful people. They must constantly test their conclusions, knowing full well that scientific explanations are at best imperfect and often temporary. Finally, scientists are optimistic people who have great faith in the orderliness of nature. What scientists should hope to accomplish is appropriately expressed in the words of the famous English philosopher Alfred North Whitehead: "The progress of Science consists in observing interconnections and in showing with a patient ingenuity that the events of the ever-shifting world are but an example of a few general relations, called laws. To see what is general in what is particular, and what is permanent in what is transitory, is the aim of scientific thought."*

❏ 1.1 Chemistry: a physical science

A convenient way to organize the various sciences is to group them into two general categories: (1) *biological sciences,* which are concerned with living things, and (2) *physical sciences,* which deal with the relationships in nature.

Chemistry is a physical science. It is a body of systematized knowledge gained from observation, study, and experimentation—as opposed to guesswork and opinion. *Chemistry is the science of materials, their composition and structure, and the changes they undergo.*

The scope of chemistry is very broad. In order to make the study of chemistry easier, chemical knowledge is arranged in separate systems or branches. Six main branches of chemistry are listed below.

1. Analytical chemistry is concerned with the separation, identification, and composition of materials.

2. Organic chemistry is the chemistry of carbon compounds.

3. Inorganic chemistry is the chemistry of materials other than those classed as organic.

4. Physical chemistry involves the study of the physical characteristics of materials and the mechanisms of their reactions.

5. Biochemistry includes the study of materials and processes that occur in living things.

6. Nuclear chemistry involves the study of subatomic particles and nuclear reactions.

Each of these branches of chemistry is further divided into more specialized areas.

*A. N. Whitehead, *An Introduction to Mathematics*

THE ORGANIZATION OF CHEMISTRY

Figure 1-2. Chemists check the progress of an experiment for evaluating the properties of a new product.

Chemistry is a tool for investigating the materials that constitute the environment. By knowing the composition and structure of materials, the changes these materials undergo in natural processes and in planned experiments are understood. Chemistry is both an experimental and an intellectual science.

Figure 1-3. An industrial research chemist prepares a new chemical for future production.

◻ 1.2 Careers in chemistry

Because chemistry covers a broad scope of both intellectual and experimental activities, various opportunities exist for those who wish to pursue careers as chemists, chemical engineers, or chemical technicians. In chemistry, as in other fields of endeavor, education, ability, and interest determine a person's career opportunities.

Chemists pursue gratifying careers in a wide range of scientific activities. They conduct basic research in the quest for new knowledge and understanding. They are involved in the technology of applied chemistry—the application of chemistry to those processes that supply material needs. They perform chemical analyses, supervise production, develop manufacturing processes, or manage chemically oriented organizations. They do technical writing, work in sales and marketing, or become consultants. They teach chemistry in universities, colleges, or high schools. Chemists sometimes earn law degrees and become patent attorneys with special technical qualifications.

Chemical engineers are chemists with engineering training. They are usually concerned with large-scale industrial processes. They are involved in the design, construction, and operation of equipment required in chemical processes. Frequently they specialize in the marketing aspects of industry.

Chemical technicians usually work under the supervision of a professional chemist. The chemist may design and plan procedures for the technician to carry out in the laboratory. Chemical technicians are trained to use instruments and to perform various laboratory operations.

◻ 1.3 The modern era of chemistry

Centuries ago skilled workers undoubtedly used some practical chemical knowledge in working with bronze, in recovering iron from its ore, and in making pigments and pottery. The practice of alchemy in the Middle Ages was the forerunner of chemistry. Seeking a means to change metals into gold, the alchemists conducted their work in an atmosphere of mystery and magic. However, by the seventeenth century, the transition from alchemy to chemistry had begun; the use of reliable quantitative measurements challenged the beliefs of the alchemists.

A plausible theory of combustion, called the *phlogiston* (flo-*jis*-tun) *theory* was introduced in 1669. According to this theory, all combustible materials contain a mystical substance

Figure 1-4. A chemical engineer may specialize in processing problems, marketing, or production. This engineer is studying results from a trial run in a miniature plant.

called *phlogiston*. During the combustion process the phlogiston is released in the form of heat and flame. The phlogiston theory required that a body lose weight during combustion because the phlogiston escaped.

Although the phlogiston theory was easily understood and applied, some early scientists doubted its correctness. They argued that if it is true a material gives off phlogiston during combustion, the ash that remains must always weigh less than the original material. These doubters challenged the phlogiston theory experimentally. They showed that the "ashes" of burned metals weighed more than the metals themselves. Despite such strong challenges, this idea about the nature of fire dominated all chemical thought for more than a century. It was the last important generalization of the alchemy era.

The initial concept of modern chemistry, that elements are the stuff of which things are made, was being developed in Europe at about the time of the American Revolution. Oxygen was first prepared in 1771 and was quickly recognized as the part of the air actively involved in ordinary combustion processes. These events set the stage for a basic understanding of chemical reactions and a determined search for chemical elements.

Through the efforts of many investigators about 90 elements were eventually recognized. By 1920 most of these elements had been isolated and their properties studied. As in other areas of science, chemical research—creatively conceived and skillfully performed—is primarily responsible for the refinement and growth of chemical knowledge to its present state.

◻ 1.4 The scientific method

Some important scientific discoveries have come about quite by accident. Others have been the result of brilliant new ideas. Most scientific knowledge, however, is the result of carefully planned work carried on by trained scientists. Their technique, known as the *scientific method, is a logical approach to the solution of problems that lend themselves to investigation.* The scientific method requires honesty, the ability to withhold a decision until all the evidence is gathered, and a desire for knowledge.

Scientists believe that there is order in nature, that natural events occur in an orderly way, and that the rules governing these events can be discovered and described. Chemists, like other scientists, strive to explain a large number of related observations in terms of broad principles or *generalizations*. Basic scientific research is devoted to the discovery of these principles. *The generalizations that describe behavior in nature are called laws or principles.* Unlike laws that restrict behavior, scientific laws describe what occurs in nature. Laws of science may be expressed by concise statements or by mathematical equations.

Figure 1-5. A technician draws a sample for chemical analysis in a minicomputer-based analysis system designed to recognize the approximately 200 drugs banned by the Olympic Committee. The automated and computerized system processed approximately 3000 samples in a 12-hour period during the Montreal Olympiad.

Figure 1-6. Marie Sklodowska Curie (1867–1934) was born in Warsaw, Poland, where her father was a professor of physics. She studied chemistry and physics in Warsaw and at the Sorbonne in Paris. In 1898 she discovered the element polonium. That same year Madame Curie and her husband, Pierre Curie, discovered the element radium. Madame Curie shared the Nobel prize in physics with her husband and A.H. Becquerel in 1903. She was the first woman to receive the Nobel prize in chemistry (1911) and the first person to share in two Nobel prizes.

Figure 1-7. Chemistry is built on a foundation of experimentation.

Scientists are interested in "what" and "how" natural phenomena occur.

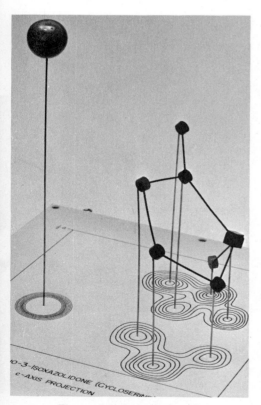

10-3-ISOXAZOLIDONE (CYCLOSERINE)
c-AXIS PROJECTION

Figure 1-8. A physical model is often used by chemists to help them understand the behavior of matter.

One of the distinguishing qualities of scientists is their curiosity. It prompts them to ask two important questions: *"what occurs?"* and *"how does it occur?"* When an event or situation in nature, called a *phenomenon,* is observed, the answers to these questions are sought by conducting systematic, disciplined, and persistent investigations.

There are four distinct phases in applying the scientific method: *observing, generalizing, theorizing,* and *testing.*

1. Observing. The scientist accumulates as much reliable data as possible about an observed phenomenon. The initial interest is the discovery of *what* actually occurs. These data may come from direct observations, from a search for information previously reported in scientific literature, and from well-planned and skillfully performed experiments.

Chemists know that observing is most productive when the conditions that affect the observations are brought under their control. Thus, observing is generally done in the *laboratory,* where conditions can be controlled by the observer. *A sequence of observations carried out under controlled conditions is called an experiment.* Experimentation provides the foundation upon which modern science is built.

2. Generalizing. The scientist organizes the accumulated data and looks for relationships among them. Relationships that are discovered may enable the scientist to formulate a broad generalization describing what does occur. When well established by abundant supporting data, this generalization may be recognized as a new law or principle that describes the behavior.

3. Theorizing. When the scientist knows *what* occurs, it becomes possible to move on to the more stimulating task of determining *how* it occurs. The scientist attempts to develop a plausible explanation and construct a simple physical or mental model that relates the observed behavior to familiar and well-understood phenomena. *A plausible explanation of an observed natural phenomenon in terms of a simple model with familiar properties is called a theory.*

4. Testing. Once a satisfactory theory is developed, it is tested and retested to establish its validity. In fact, scientists continually test observational and experimental data and predictions by subjecting them to new experiments. A theory is retained only as long as it is useful. It may be discarded or modified as a result of new experimentation. A theory that stands up under scientific testing is valuable because it serves as a basis for predicting behavior not previously investigated. This testing and predicting is the heart of the scientific method and the stimulus for the growth of scientific knowledge.

The term "theory" is often used by chemists to refer to the laws and experimental evidence that make up a body of related knowledge. Some examples of broad chemical theories concerning the behavior of matter that you will study in later chapters are the *atomic theory,* the *kinetic theory* of gases, and the *theory of ionization.*

☐ 1.5 The concept of matter

All materials consist of matter. Through the senses of sight, touch, taste, and smell, various kinds of matter can be recognized. This book, your desk, the air you breathe, the water you drink are all examples of matter. Some kinds of matter are easily observed. A stone or a piece of wood can be seen and held in the hand. Water, even in a quiet pool, is easily recognized. Other kinds of matter, such as the air, are recognized less readily. You ride on compressed air in automobile tires. You know of the tremendous damage caused by the rapidly moving air in a hurricane or tornado.

Matter is described as anything that occupies space and has mass. Matter may be acted upon by *forces* that change its motion or position. Matter possesses *inertia,* a resistance to change in position or motion. The concept of inertia as a property of matter is important in the study of physics and chemistry. Imagine a basketball being used as a substitute for a bowling ball. Its effect on the pins would not be the same as that observed in Figure 1-9. Although approximately the same size, the bowling ball contains more matter (and of a different kind) than the basketball. The inertia of the bowling ball is correspondingly greater than that of the basketball. Thus its tendency to remain in motion is also greater.

While these comments are descriptive of matter, they do not give a completely satisfactory definition of matter. Scientists, even with great knowledge of the properties and behavior of matter, are not able to define it precisely.

☐ 1.6 Mass and weight

The quantity of matter that a body possesses is known as its mass. If an object is at rest and you move it, you notice that it

MATTER AND ENERGY

Figure 1-9. A hollow bowling ball would not produce the results shown in this photograph.

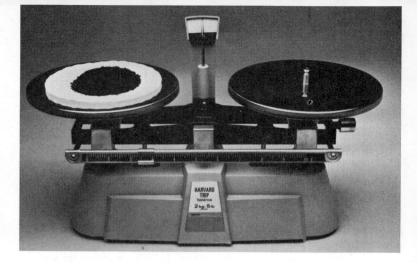

Figure 1-10. The mass of the materials on the left pan is determined to be 12.7 g because it is counterbalanced by the combination of the known 10-g mass on the right pan and the 2.7-g mass indicated by the slider position on the graduated beam.

The weight of an object can vary from place to place.

Figure 1-11. The densities of materials vary. The cork floats because it is less dense than water. The metal key sinks because it is more dense than water. Both mass and volume measurements are required to express density.

resists your effort. If the object is moving and you stop it, you notice that it resists this effort also. The object's *mass* is the measure of its resistance to change in position or motion. This property has been identified as *inertia*. Thus, **mass is the measure of the inertia of a body** and is responsible for it.

Mass is also responsible for the weight of a body. **Weight is the measure of the earth's attraction for a body.** An object weighs less at a high altitude and at the bottom of a deep mine shaft than it does at sea level. Although the weight of the object varies, its mass remains unchanged. *The mass of a body is constant.*

Mass is usually measured by comparison with known masses, as shown in Figure 1-10. If the masses of two objects are the same, they have equal weights while in the same location. Thus the mass of an object, when determined by "weighing" it on a platform balance, is sometimes referred to as its "weight." The measurement of mass by "weighing" is common in chemistry and is not confusing if the meanings of the terms *mass* and *weight* are understood. Chemists are primarily concerned with measurements of mass, and the term *mass* shall be used here with its proper meaning.

◻ 1.7 Density

Matter occupies space and therefore has *volume*. From everyday experiences, you recognize that materials have different masses. Lead can be described as "heavy" and cork as "light." Such statements have little meaning unless *equal volumes* of lead and cork are being compared. *The mass of a unit volume of a material is called its* **density**. Density is expressed by the equation

$$D = \frac{m}{V}$$

Where m is the mass of a material and V is its volume, D is its density. A comparison of the masses of equal volumes of different materials indicates that the densities of different kinds of matter vary. Thus density reveals the *concentration* of matter. See Figure 1-11.

☐ 1.8 Phases of matter

A block of ice is a *solid*. When it melts it forms a *liquid*. When liquid water evaporates it forms a *gas*. Iron is another familiar solid which melts and becomes a liquid if its temperature is high enough. And, at a temperature near that of the surface of the sun, liquid iron boils to form a gas, iron vapor. Materials exist either in the *solid, liquid,* or *gas* phase and may undergo changes of phase under suitable conditions.

A block of wood placed on a table retains its shape and its volume. To change either its shape or its volume, considerable external force would have to be applied. A solid does not require lateral (side) support in order to retain its shape. A solid resists compression. **Solids** *have both definite shape and definite volume.*

Suppose water is poured onto a table. It flows out over the surface because a liquid is not rigid. To retain water, lateral support must be provided. If you attempt to pour a quart of milk into a pint bottle, you observe that the volume of milk doesn't change. The pint bottle holds only half of the milk. **Liquids** *have definite volume, but not definite shape.* A liquid assumes the shape of its container.

When an automobile tire is inflated with air, the air assumes the shape of the tire, which is its container. The tire is actually full of air. If a blowout occurs, however, the air escapes and thus expands in volume. A pint of a gas expands and fills all the space when placed in a truly empty quart bottle. **Gases** *have neither definite volume nor definite shape.* A confined gas has both the volume and shape of its container. Models of solid, liquid, and gas phases of matter are shown in Figure 1-12.

From your experiences with toy balloons, bicycle tires, and volley balls, you know that the volume of a gas is affected by heat

Gas, liquid, and solid are also called the "states" of matter.

A "phase" is a uniform part of a system separated from other uniform parts by boundary faces.

Ice in water represents a two-phase system, a solid phase and a liquid phase.

Figure 1-12. Models of solid, liquid, and gas phases of matter.

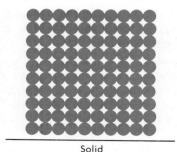

Solid

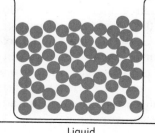

Liquid

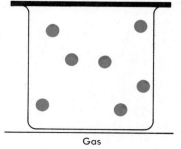

Gas

and pressure. Because of this behavior, a measurement of volume of a gas has meaning only if the temperature and pressure of the gas are specified.

Both liquids and gases are known as *fluids*. Liquid and gaseous materials flow and require vessels to contain them. Although solids are considered rigid, none is perfectly rigid. Given two different solids of the same size and shape, one is likely to be more flexible (less rigid) than the other. Similarly, there are no perfectly fluid materials. Molasses, water, and carbon dioxide all flow as fluids, but certainly at different rates.

Because a liquid has a definite volume, it may have a *free surface*. A free surface is one that is not confined or supported by its container. Thus water can be contained in an open vessel. In ordinary situations, gases must be confined on all sides of their containers. A gas is a fluid that does not have a free surface.

Fluids that cannot exist as liquids having a free surface at ordinary conditions of temperature and pressure are correctly called *gases*. *Vapor is the term used for the gaseous phase of materials that normally exist as liquids or solids.* Thus the correct descriptions are *oxygen gas* and *water vapor*.

The structure of a solid is usually well-ordered. Particles of the material are arranged in a regular pattern. They are closely packed and rigidly bound in fixed positions. This gives the solid its definite size and shape.

The particles of a liquid are also closely packed. This explains why the volume of a solid changes very little when the solid melts. The particles of a liquid, however, are not bound in fixed positions. A liquid has fluidity; its structure is less orderly than that of a solid and it is without shape.

The particles of a gas are widely dispersed (separated) in a random, disorganized fashion. Under ordinary conditions of temperature and pressure, the attraction between such particles is so small that it can be disregarded. A gas is a fluid of very low density.

☐ 1.9 Properties of matter

Matter can be identified by studying its properties. Many liquids, like water, are colorless. Some colorless liquids have distinctive odors; water is odorless. Water freezes at 0 °C, boils at 100 °C, and has a density of 1 gram per cubic centimeter at 4 °C. Because no other liquid exhibits exactly these properties, they can be used to help identify liquid water. *Properties of matter that are useful in identifying it are called* **specific (or characteristic) properties.** The most useful specific properties are those that can be measured quantitatively and expressed by a number of measurement units.

When determining the identity of matter, it is helpful to distinguish between *physical* properties and *chemical* properties.

Physical properties *are those that can be determined directly without altering the identity or composition of a material.* They include *color, odor, solubility, density, hardness, melting* and *boiling points,* and *crystalline* or *amorphous* (noncrystalline) *form.* These properties do not apply equally to all phases of matter. For example, hardness and crystalline form are not properties of fluids. Similarly, odor is of little value in describing many solids.

Chemical properties *are those that describe the behavior of a material in processes that alter its identity.* Chemical properties include *chemical activity* or behavior, which results in a change of identity. Some materials are chemically *active,* reacting vigorously with certain other materials. Some are *inactive.* They do react with other materials, but not very readily. Still others, said to be *inert,* do not react with other materials under the ordinary conditions for chemical reactivity. Information about whether a material burns and how it reacts with the gases of the air, with water, and with acids is valuable to the chemist.

☐ 1.10 The concept of energy

Scientists experience the same difficulty in defining energy as they do in defining matter. They know a great deal about energy and how it can be used and controlled, but they cannot define it precisely. **Energy** *is described as the capacity for doing work.* It is an action quantity associated with changes in matter. Energy is related to matter, but is not a form of matter. Matter possesses energy.

Work, in a physical sense, involves the application of a force through a distance. Work = force × distance.

The most familiar forms of energy are *mechanical energy* and *heat energy.* Mechanical energy can be of two types: *potential energy* or energy of position, and *kinetic energy* or energy of motion. Water held behind a dam has potential energy because of its elevated position. The potential energy of a given mass of water increases with the height of its position. When water is released from the dam, its potential energy is converted to kinetic energy as it falls to a lower level. The kinetic energy of the mass of falling water increases with the *square* of its speed.

When you double the speed of your automobile, its destructive capability (its kinetic energy) increases fourfold.

Energy is released as heat when fuels are burned. The heat energy of burning fuels and the kinetic energy of falling water are major sources of industrial and domestic energy supply.

Other forms of energy are *electric* energy, *chemical* energy, *radiant* energy, and *nuclear* energy. Chemical energy is a basic concern of chemistry. Radio waves, infrared and ultraviolet radiations, visible light, X rays, and gamma rays are examples of radiant energy. Solar energy is a familiar example of radiant energy. The role of solar energy and nuclear energy as basic energy sources is of increasing importance today.

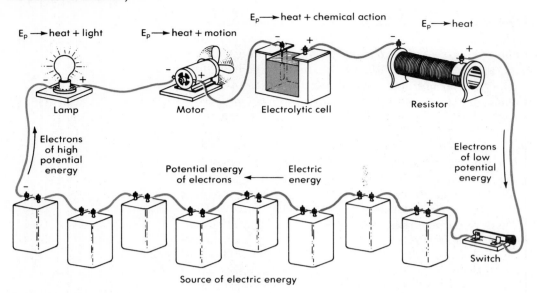

$E_p \longrightarrow$ heat + light $E_p \longrightarrow$ heat + motion $E_p \longrightarrow$ heat + chemical action $E_p \longrightarrow$ heat

Lamp   Motor   Electrolytic cell   Resistor

Electrons of high potential energy

Electrons of low potential energy

Potential energy of electrons ← Electric energy

Switch

Source of electric energy

Figure 1-13. Examples of energy transformations.

Chemical energy can be thought of as a kind of potential (stored) energy.

One form of energy can be transformed into other forms of energy. The transformation of potential energy to kinetic energy for falling water has already been mentioned. As coal or oil is burned, some of the chemical energy of the fuel and of the oxygen from the air is released as heat energy. The heat energy may be transferred to water, and the water converted to steam. The steam then drives a turbine that produces mechanical (rotational) energy. The turbine drives a generator producing electric energy. This electric energy can be transformed into heat and light (radiant energy) in an incandescent lamp. The electric energy can also be transformed into mechanical energy in an electric motor that drives a clock or a locomotive. It is the *transformation* of energy that is usually observed, and the *energy change* during the transformation that is measured. Some familiar energy transformations are illustrated in Figure 1-13.

◻ 1.11 Conservation of matter and energy

In 1905, Albert Einstein (1879–1955) suggested that matter and energy are related. His famous equation

$$E = mc^2$$

represents this relationship. In the equation, E is the amount of energy, m is the amount of matter, and c is a constant equal to the speed of light. Many experiments have established the validity of this equation.

Matter can be converted to energy and energy to matter. The conversion factor, c^2, has a very large numerical value, because the value of c is of the order of 3×10^8 meters per second. Con-

Figure 1-14. An electric power generating plant in which nuclear reactions are the source of energy.

sequently, a very small amount of matter is converted to a very large amount of energy. This conversion suggests that matter and energy are not two independent physical quantities that can be defined individually. Instead, *matter and energy may represent two different forms of a single, more fundamental, physical quantity.* From their studies of matter and energy, scientists have formulated a law of nature known as **the law of conservation of matter and energy:** *matter and energy are interchangeable, and the total matter and energy in the universe is constant.*

Chemical reactions are always accompanied by energy changes. Energy is either released or acquired. Only in nuclear reactions, involving tremendous quantities of energy, does the amount of matter transformed into energy become significant. Changes in mass are not measurable in ordinary chemical reactions. This fact leads to the following generalization: *In ordinary chemical reactions, the total mass of the reacting materials is equal to the total mass of the products.*

◻ 1.12 The metric system

Progress in science is dependent on a precise system of measurements based on a set of *universal standards.* The English system used in daily activities presents some problems in scientific use. In a sense, it is a system that just grew. The units have practical size for common use, and the unit subdivisions are based on the convenient practice of halving and quartering. For example, the pound is subdivided into half-pounds, quarter-pounds, etc. However, the chief disadvantage of the English system is that no single, simple numerical relationship exists between dif-

MEASUREMENTS IN CHEMISTRY

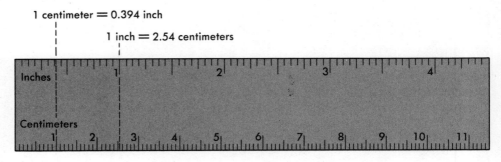

Figure 1-15. The common English/metric rule illustrates one relationship between English and metric measurements.

ferent units of measure. In linear measure, for example, 12 inches = 1 foot, 3 feet = 1 yard, and 5½ yards = 1 rod.

The *metric system,* developed in France near the end of the eighteenth century, is used in scientific work throughout the world. It is in general use in practically all countries except the United States, Great Britain, and other English-speaking countries. Great Britain is in the midst of a long-range program of conversion to metric measurements. Australia, New Zealand, and Canada are also moving from English to metric measure.

Many American industries that participate in foreign markets have already adopted the metric system. This move was necessary to keep them competitive in markets that are almost entirely metric. By the Metric Conversion Act of 1975, the United States was formally committed to encourage, but not to require, the change to metric measurements.

The metric system is a *decimal* system that has a single, simple numerical relationship between units. Computations with measurements are easily performed. The disadvantage of the metric system in everyday usage is that metric units do not have the practical sizes of English units.

A standard set of prefixes is used to expand the basic metric system and provide a simple, uniform structure for expressing measurements of very large and very small magnitudes. Latin prefixes identify descending values. Examples are *deci-*, 0.1, *centi-*, 0.01, and *milli-*, 0.001. Greek prefixes identify ascending values. Examples are *deka-*, 10, *hecto-*, 100, and *kilo-*, 1000. Common prefixes, their symbols, and factors are listed in Table 1-1. A more extensive list is provided in Appendix Table 1.

Metric measurements are used exclusively in chemistry. You will be concerned mainly with measurements of *length, mass,* and *capacity* (volume of liquids and gases). These measurements are expressed in terms of the *meter* (m), the *gram* (g), and the *liter* (L), respectively. The metric prefixes most commonly used are *milli-, centi-,* and *kilo-*. Examples are milliliter (mL), centimeter (cm), and kilogram (kg). The relationships shown in Table 1-2 will be used throughout your study of chemistry. You will find it helpful to memorize them.

Table 1-1
COMMON METRIC PREFIXES

Factor	Prefix	Symbol
10^6	mega-	M
10^3	kilo-	k
10^2	hecto-	h
10^1	deka-	da
10^{-1}	deci-	d
10^{-2}	centi-	c
10^{-3}	milli-	m
10^{-6}	micro-	μ (Greek mu)

Table 1-2
COMMON METRIC EQUIVALENTS

Length
10 millimeters (mm)	= 1 centimeter (cm)
100 centimeters (cm)	= 1 meter (m)
1000 meters (m)	= 1 kilometer (km)

Capacity
1000 milliliters (mL)	= 1 liter (L)
1000 liters (L)	= 1 kiloliter (kL)

Mass
1000 milligrams (mg)	= 1 gram (g)
1000 grams (g)	= 1 kilogram (kg)

Figure 1-16. The standard meter, the unit of length in the metric system.

When the metric system was originally established, it was based on natural standards. The meter was the fundamental unit of measure from which all other units were derived. Today, *the standard meter is the distance between two parallel lines engraved on a special metal bar preserved at the International Bureau of Weights and Measures in Sèvres, France, near Paris.*

This standard meter bar is a physical instrument that could be damaged, lost, or destroyed. Accordingly, the International Conference of Weights and Measures has defined an *indestructible* standard meter that can be reproduced in any properly equipped laboratory. This reproducible standard meter is based on the wavelength of a certain spectral line of the gas krypton at a specific temperature.

One gram (1 g) was intended to be the mass of one cubic centimeter (1 cm^3) of water measured at its temperature for maximum density. Because the gram is an inconveniently small unit of mass, the *standard* unit of mass today is the *kilogram*. *The **gram** is now defined as one-thousandth of the standard kilogram preserved at the International Bureau of Weights and Measures.*

1 g = 0.0353 oz
1 kg = 2.20 lb

$$1 \text{ g} = 0.001 \text{ kg}$$

Figure 1-17. Some comparisons between the English and metric systems.

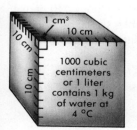

1 cm³
10 cm
10 cm
10 cm
1000 cubic centimeters or 1 liter contains 1 kg of water at 4 °C

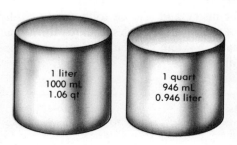

1 liter
1000 mL
1.06 qt

1 quart
946 mL
0.946 liter

1 pound
454 grams

1 kilogram
1000 grams
2.2 pounds

Table 1-3
METRIC-ENGLISH EQUIVALENTS

Metric to English

$$1 \text{ cm} = 0.3937 \text{ in} = 0.03281 \text{ ft}$$
$$1 \text{ m} = 39.37 \text{ in} = 3.281 \text{ ft} = 1.094 \text{ yd}$$
$$1 \text{ km} = 3281 \text{ ft} = 0.6214 \text{ mi}$$
$$1 \text{ cm}^3 = 0.0610 \text{ in}^3 = 0.0000353 \text{ ft}^3$$
$$1 \text{ L} = 1.06 \text{ qt} = 0.265 \text{ gal} = 0.0353 \text{ ft}^3$$
$$1 \text{ g} = 0.0353 \text{ oz} = 0.00220 \text{ lb}$$
$$1 \text{ kg} = 2.20 \text{ lb} = 0.00110 \text{ tn}$$
$$1 \text{ metric tn } (10^3 \text{ kg}) = 2200 \text{ lb} = 1.10 \text{ tn}$$

English to Metric

$$1 \text{ in} = 2.54 \text{ cm} = 0.0254 \text{ m}$$
$$1 \text{ ft} = 30.5 \text{ cm} = 0.305 \text{ m}$$
$$1 \text{ yd} = 91.4 \text{ cm} = 0.914 \text{ m}$$
$$1 \text{ mi} = 1609 \text{ m} = 1.609 \text{ km}$$
$$1 \text{ qt} = 946 \text{ mL} = 0.946 \text{ L}$$
$$1 \text{ oz} = 28350 \text{ mg} = 28.35 \text{ g}$$
$$1 \text{ lb} = 453.6 \text{ g} = 0.4536 \text{ kg}$$
$$1 \text{ tn} = 907 \text{ kg} = 0.907 \text{ metric tn}$$

The liter (**L**) *is a special name for a cubic decimeter.* One cubic decimeter (1 dm^3) is equal to one-thousand cubic centimeters (1000 cm^3). Therefore, a one-liter flask holds 1000 cubic centimeters of a fluid when filled. One milliliter (1 mL) is then equivalent to one cubic centimeter.

$$1 \text{ L} = 1 \text{ dm}^3 = 1000 \text{ cm}^3$$

$$1 \text{ mL} = 0.001 \text{ dm}^3 = 1 \text{ cm}^3$$

Representative metric units and their English equivalents are listed in Table 1-3.

Fluids are usually measured in flasks and other containers graduated in capacity units. Consequently, the volumes of liquids and gases are most conveniently expressed in milliliter (mL), liter (L), and kiloliter (kL) units. This practice is common in chemistry and will be followed generally in this book. Because water is a universal standard, the remarkable simplicity of the metric system can be recognized in the relationships shown in Table 1-4.

Table 1-4
VOLUME-MASS RELATIONS FOR WATER

1 L of water has a volume of 1000 cm^3 and a mass of 1 kg
1 mL of water has a volume of 1 cm^3 and a mass of 1 g

◻ 1.13 Measurement dimensions

A *physical quantity* is the description of a measurement process. *Length* is a physical quantity. The measurement process is indicated by the definition of **length** *as a measured distance or dimension*. The measurement procedure determines the magnitude, or size, of the physical quantity. The magnitude *is described by a number and a unit*. Both are required because the number of measurement units counted depends on the unit used. *The number without the unit is worthless.*

Basic physical quantities are measured in *arbitrary units* established by international agreement. These quantities are the *fundamental quantities* of the measurement system, and their measurement units are *fundamental units*. *Length* (l), *mass* (m), and *time* (t), are examples of fundamental physical quantities. Their standardized measurement units are the *meter* (m), the *kilogram* (kg), and the *second* (s), respectively. (Recall that the gram unit of mass is now defined in terms of the standard kilogram.) These quantities, together with *temperature* (T), measured in degrees, and *amount of substance,* measured in moles, are the important fundamental quantities in chemistry.

All other physical quantities are *defined* in terms of fundamental quantities. They are known as *derived quantities*. In this way, the magnitudes of many different physical quantities can be determined by the measurements of a few fundamental quantities.

Volume is a derived quantity. The volume (V) of a cube is defined as the product of the lengths (l) of its three dimensions.

$$V = l \times l \times l = l^3$$

The volume may be expressed in km^3, m^3, dm^3, or cm^3, depending upon the unit of length used. All are derived volume units and represent the length unit cubed, l^3. Volume, as a derived quantity, has the dimensions of *length*^{3}, or l^3.

Density is also a derived physical quantity. Density (D) is defined in Section 1.7 as the mass (m) per unit volume (V) of an object or a material.

$$D = \frac{m}{V}$$

The density of a material can be determined by measuring its mass and its volume. The densities of solids are expressed in grams per cubic centimeter or kilograms per cubic meter. The densities of liquids are expressed in grams per cubic centimeter or grams per liter (cubic decimeter). The densities of gases are expressed in grams per liter. These derived units—g/cm^3, kg/m^3, g/mL, and g/L—represent a mass unit divided by a length unit cubed. Density has the dimensions of *mass*/*length*^{3}, or m/l^3.

Symbols for physical quantities are printed in italic typeface.

Symbols for measurement units are printed in roman typeface.

The degree is discussed in Section 1.15; the mole is discussed in Section 3.14.

Recall that a dm^3 is called a liter.

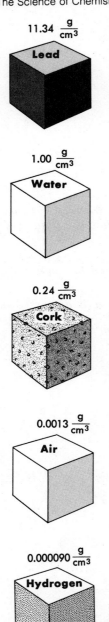

11.34 $\frac{g}{cm^3}$
Lead

1.00 $\frac{g}{cm^3}$
Water

0.24 $\frac{g}{cm^3}$
Cork

0.0013 $\frac{g}{cm^3}$
Air

0.000090 $\frac{g}{cm^3}$
Hydrogen

Figure 1-18. Density is a specific property of a material.

The mass of 10.0 cm³ of iron is 78.7 g and the mass of the same volume of mercury is 135 g. The mass of 6.50 L of oxygen is 9.29 g. Their respective densities are

$$D_{iron} = \frac{78.7 \text{ g}}{10.0 \text{ cm}^3} = 7.87 \text{ g/cm}^3$$

$$D_{mercury} = \frac{135 \text{ g}}{10.0 \text{ cm}^3} = 13.5 \text{ g/cm}^3$$

$$D_{oxygen} = \frac{9.29 \text{ g}}{6.50 \text{ L}} = 1.43 \text{ g/L}$$

Density can be expressed only in derived units that represent the dimensions of mass/length³.

◻ 1.14 Temperature and heat

Temperature and heat are different, but related, physical quantities. It is important to understand the subtle distinction between them. Just as you can push an object to estimate its mass or lift it to estimate its weight, you can touch an object to determine its *hotness* or *coldness*. You then describe the sensation by using a term such as hot, warm, cool, or cold. Your sense perceptions of hotness and coldness are used to assign a property called *temperature* to the object.

Temperature sense, while generally useful, may be unreliable under some conditions. If you place one hand in cold water and then in cool water, the cool water feels warm. If your hand had been in hot water first, however, the cool water would feel cold.

This experiment suggests that the temperature sensation depends on the transfer of heat energy to the hand or away from it. If a system, a body of matter, has a higher temperature than its surroundings, energy flows away from the system. If the temperature of the system is lower than its surroundings, energy flows to the system. The energy that is *in transit* is called heat. *Heat is the energy transferred between two systems that is associated exclusively with the difference in temperature between the systems. The temperature of a system is a measure of its ability to transfer heat to or acquire heat from other systems.*

When two systems with different temperatures are in contact, heat energy flows from one to the other. *Temperature* is the property that determines the direction of the heat transfer. The warmer system cools as it gives up heat, and the cooler system warms as it acquires heat. This is true as long as neither system experiences a change of phase. When the temperatures of the two systems are equal, the tendencies for heat to flow between them are equal, and no further net transfer of heat occurs. The two systems are now said to be in *thermal* (heat) *equilibrium*. It follows that *systems in thermal equilibrium have the same temperature.*

Heat and temperature are different physical quantities that can be sensed qualitatively. They can be determined quantitatively, however, only in terms of measurable quantities that are independent of sense perceptions. Heat is measured as a *quantity of energy,* whereas temperature is measured as the *heat intensity* of matter. A burning match and a campfire might both be at the same *temperature,* but the quantities of *heat* given up are quite different. A small warm object will transfer heat to a large cool object whose total heat content is greater than that of the small warm object.

◻ 1.15 Measuring temperature

Some properties of matter vary with temperature and, therefore, can be used to measure temperature. For example, most materials expand when warmed and contract when cooled. The most familiar instrument for measuring temperature, the mercury thermometer, is based on the nearly linear expansion and contraction of liquid mercury with changing temperature.

In Section 1.13, temperature was described as a fundamental physical quantity. Its measurement unit, the *degree,* is an arbitrary unit determined by international agreement.

Mercury thermometers for scientific use are calibrated in the *Celsius* temperature scale. This scale was devised by the Swedish astronomer Anders Celsius (1701–1744). Celsius established his thermometer scale by defining two *fixed points:* the normal freezing point of water, the *ice point,* as 0 °C, and the normal boiling point of water, the *steam point,* as 100 °C. He divided the interval between the ice point and the steam point into 100 equal parts. Each part represents a temperature change of 1 C°. By extending the same scale divisions beyond the two fixed points, he could measure temperatures below 0 °C and above 100 °C. See Figure 1-19.

In modern thermometry, an absolute (thermodynamic) temperature scale is constructed by defining a single standard fixed point. This temperature scale, called the *Kelvin scale,* is described in Section 10.10.

◻ 1.16 Measuring heat

As heat is transferred *to* a material, the temperature of the material *increases;* as heat is transferred *from* the material, its temperature *decreases.* This is true only if neither heat-transfer process is accompanied by a change in phase. Heat quantities are measured during the heat-transfer processes associated with *thermal* properties of matter. Some important thermal properties

At equilibrium, opposing tendencies are equal.

Heat flows from a region of high heat intensity to a region of low heat intensity.

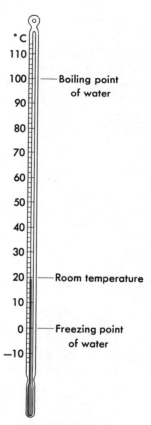

Figure 1-19. The Celsius thermometer scale is used in science. Compare the labeled temperatures with those on the common Fahrenheit thermometer scale.

Thermal: pertaining to heat or temperature.

of matter are *heat of solution* (Chapter 13), *heat of combustion, heat of formation,* and *heat of reaction* (Chapter 20). The measurement of thermal properties is called *calorimetry.*

The unit of heat energy commonly used in calorimetry is the *calorie. The **calorie** (**cal**) is traditionally defined as the quantity of heat required to raise the temperature of 1 gram of water through 1 Celsius degree.*

The calorie is a very small unit of heat and is sometimes inconvenient to use. A larger unit, the *kilocalorie,* is often used in calorimetry measurements. *The **kilocalorie** (**kcal**) is the quantity of heat required to raise the temperature of 1 kilogram of water through 1 Celsius degree.*

$$1 \text{ kcal} = 10^3 \text{ cal}$$

Dietetics: The application of principles of nutrition.

The kilocalorie is the "large Calorie" used for calorie counting in dietetics.

The calorie as traditionally defined lacks good measurement precision because the heat required to raise the temperature of one gram of water through one Celsius degree varies slightly with the water temperature. The calorie is now defined as an auxiliary heat unit in terms of a dimensional unit of energy, E.

The kinetic energy, E_K, of a moving body is determined by the mass of the body and its velocity (speed) according to the equation

$$E_K = \tfrac{1}{2} mv^2$$

Speed is determined by measuring the distance (length) traveled and the time required. Kinetic energy then has the dimensions of mass $\times$ (length $\div$ time)^2, or ml^2/t^2. Other forms of energy can be shown to have the same dimensions as kinetic energy.

If mass is measured in kilograms, length in meters, and time in seconds, the dimensional unit for energy is kg m^2/s^2. Generally, complex dimensional units are assigned special names. This dimensional unit, kg m^2/s^2, is called a *joule* (j).

It is easier to say or write "10 joules" than "10 kilogram meter square per second square."

$$1 \text{ j} = 1 \, \frac{\text{kg m}^2}{\text{s}^2}$$

For example, if

$$E = 15.2 \text{ kg m}^2/\text{s}^2,$$

then

$$E = 15.2 \text{ j}$$

is an equivalent expression.

The calorie can now be defined as an auxiliary unit of heat energy in terms of the joule. *One **calorie** is equivalent to 4.19 joules of heat energy.*

Look up the value of the mechanical equivalent of heat in Appendix Table 3.

$$1 \text{ cal} = 4.19 \text{ j}$$

$$1 \text{ kcal} = 4.19 \text{ kj}$$

Table 1-5
AVERAGE ENERGY VALUES OF SOME COMMON FOODS

Food	Measure	Energy (kcal)	(kj)
apple	1 large	100	419
bacon	2 slices	95	398
banana	1 medium	130	545
bread	1 slice	60	250
cottage cheese	25 cm^3	93	390
cupcake	1 average	200	838
custard	100 mL	125	524
hamburger	113 g (¼ lb) patty	420	1760
hot dog	1 average	138	578
honey	10 mL	67	280
ice cream	100 g	185	775
orange juice	200 mL	83	350
peach	1 medium	50	210
peanut butter	32 g (1 tbsp)	190	796
potato	1 medium	100	419
skim milk	200 mL	74	310
sugar (sucrose)	4 g (1 tsp)	16	67
whole milk	200 mL	133	557

In Table 1-5 the energy values of some common foods are given in both kilocalories (nutritional Calories) and kilojoules. A comparison of the kcal and kj columns may be helpful in visualizing the relative magnitudes of these two heat units.

Heat energy measurements are converted from calories to joules and from joules to calories as follows:

$$23.8 \text{ cal} \times \frac{4.19 \text{ j}}{\text{cal}} = 99.7 \text{ j} \qquad 25.1 \text{ kcal} \times \frac{4.19 \text{ kj}}{\text{kcal}} = 105 \text{ kj}$$

$$99.7 \text{ j} \times \frac{\text{cal}}{4.19 \text{ j}} = 23.8 \text{ cal} \qquad 105 \text{ kj} \times \frac{\text{kcal}}{4.19 \text{ kj}} = 25.1 \text{ kcal}$$

◻ 1.17 Uncertainty in measurement

The experimental process is an essential part of chemistry, and reliable measurement information is an essential part of the experimental process. Unfortunately, *the measurement of any physical quantity is subject to some uncertainty.* If a measurement is to have much worth, it must include some indication of its *reliability.* Consequently, the complete expression of a measured quantity must include the *number value,* the *measurement unit* used, and some indication of *how reliable the number is.*

Contributions to the uncertainty in measurements of physical quantities accrue from *limitations in accuracy* and *limitations in precision* inherent in all measurement processes. In common usage, *accuracy* and *precision* are practically synonymous

Corollary: No measurement of a physical quantity is absolutely certain.

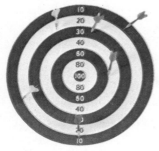

Figure 1-20. An illustration of the distinction between accuracy and precision. Top to bottom: poor accuracy, good precision; poor accuracy, poor precision; good accuracy, good precision.

Table 1-6
AVERAGE DEVIATION OF A SET OF MEASUREMENTS

Sample	Mass of oxygen	Deviation
1	3.92 g	0.02 g
2	3.97 g	0.03 g
3	3.93 g	0.01 g
Average	3.94 g	0.02 g

terms. In regard to measurements, however, they have distinctly different meanings. If you wish to become competent in making measurements and interpreting measurement data, you must understand this distinction.

1. Accuracy denotes the nearness of a measurement to its accepted value. It refers to the correctness of measurement data. Accuracy is expressed in terms of *absolute* or *relative error.*

An *absolute error*, E_a, is the difference between an *observed* (measured) value, O, and the *accepted* value, A, of a physical quantity.

$$E_a = O - A$$

In laboratory experiments, absolute errors are referred to as *experimental errors.*

If the absolute error, E_a, is compared to the accepted value, A, the resulting ratio is called the *relative error*, E_r. It is ordinarily expressed as a percentage.

$$E_r = \frac{E_a}{A} \times 100\%$$

In laboratory experiments, relative errors are referred to as *percentage errors.*

Observe that the accepted value of a measured quantity is used to determine both the absolute error and the relative error. Thus, the accuracy of a measurement can be determined *only* if the accepted value of the measurement is known.

2. Precision is the agreement between the numerical values of a set of measurements that have been made in the same way. Precision refers to the reproducibility of measurement data or to the amount of measurement detail. It relates to the $\pm$ uncertainty in a set of measurements. *Precision conveys nothing about accuracy.* Good measurement precision can be obtained from an instrument even though it may introduce appreciable error in the measurement. The distinction between measurement error and measurement precision is illustrated in Figure 1-20.

The precision of measurement data is expressed in terms of *absolute* or *relative deviation.* One simple form of deviation, the *absolute deviation,* of a set of identical measurements shall be considered.

An *absolute deviation*, D_a, is the difference between an observed value, O, and the arithmetic mean, M, for a set of several identical measurements.

$$D_a = O - M$$

A set of three *identical* samples of potassium chlorate are decomposed to determine the mass of oxygen in each sample. The results are recorded in Table 1-6. Assuming that there is an equal chance for the individual mass measurements to be either high or low, the average (mean) mass for the set is taken as the "best" value.

The absolute deviations of the individual values from the average value are calculated using the expression for D_a given above. The average of these deviations, $D_{a(av)}$, provides a measure of the precision of the experiment. The uncertainty in measurement is ± 0.02 g. The mass of oxygen derived from the experimental data can be expressed as 3.94 ± 0.02 g.

An understanding of the distinction between measurement accuracy and measurement precision is necessary for using measurement instruments properly and processing measurement data.

You will use instruments for measuring length, mass, time, temperature, etc. These instruments can provide measurement detail within their design limits. Instruments of good quality that provide large measurement detail (good precision) are also designed for small error tolerance (good accuracy). Such instruments are periodically recalibrated against dependable standards to maintain their proficiency.

Figure 1-21. Typical new-generation laboratory balance that is readable to 1 mg. Just place an item on the pan and read its mass to 1 mg in an instant.

◻ 1.18 Significant figures

In Section 1.17 you learned that all measurements are subject to some uncertainty. The mass of oxygen recovered from each of three identical samples of potassium chlorate was shown to be 3.94 g. The uncertainty in this measurement set was expressed as a deviation of ± 0.02 g, and the mass of oxygen per sample was expressed as 3.94 ± 0.02 g.

This deviation of ± 0.02 g indicates that there is uncertainty in the *second decimal place* of the recorded measurement. The digit occupying this place could be as low as 2 and as high as 6. That is, the actual mass of oxygen lies between 3.92 g and 3.96 g. Furthermore, *all digits to the left of this uncertain digit are certain.* Of course, any digit carried to the right of this uncertain digit makes no contribution to the measurement information. Its presence would, instead, create a false impression of the measurement reliability.

For all ordinary uses made of measurement data in chemistry, it is sufficient to recognize that *the last digit of the measurement expression is uncertain.* In the example given, the magnitude of this uncertainty, ± 0.02 g, can be omitted and the measurement can be recorded simply as 3.94 g *with the knowledge that the last digit, 4, is uncertain.* This measurement, 3.94 g, consists entirely of digits that have *physical significance;* they are called *significant figures.* **Significant figures** *in a measurement expression comprise all digits that are known with certainty, plus the first digit that is uncertain.* The position of the decimal point is irrelevant.

Measurement detail relates to precision.

Tolerance: the maximum allowable error in the scale graduations of a measuring instrument.

The concept of uncertainty in measurements gives meaning to the method of significant figures.

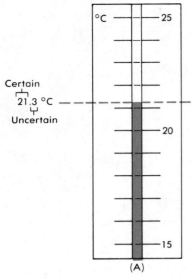

(A)

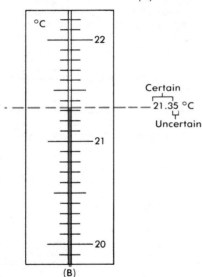

(B)

Figure 1-22. Sections of two thermometer temperature scales. Scale (A) has 1-degree graduations and scale (B) has 0.1-degree graduations. The temperature readout from scale (A) has three significant figures and from scale (B) has four significant figures. Observe that the estimated digit in each readout does make a significant contribution to the temperature information.

All uncertain digits in this series of calculations are shown in bold typeface.

The method of significant figures provides a simple and convenient way of expressing measured quantities. The ± uncertainty in the last significant digit is not required and, therefore, does not have to be calculated. It is necessary only to keep track of the uncertain digit in calculations involving measurement data and to recognize that this uncertain digit is the last digit retained in the result of the calculations.

In your use of measuring instruments, the last digit (the uncertain digit) of a measurement can ordinarily be estimated one place beyond the smallest graduation of the readout scale. For example, the temperature readout from thermometer **A** of Figure 1-22 consists of 3 significant figures; that from thermometer **B** consists of 4 significant figures. Observe that the uncertain digit in each readout *represents an estimate beyond which no further significant contribution to the measurement precision is possible.* The significant measurement detail is limited to the one estimated place.

Suppose you wish to determine the volume of a metal block. Your measuring instrument is a centimeter rule having 1-mm scale divisions, as shown in Figure 1-15. You find the sides to be 3.5**4** cm, 4.8**5** cm, and 5.4**2** cm, estimating the value of the last digit in each case. Observe that the last digit in each measurement represents a reasonable estimate to the nearest 0.1 mm. You can have no idea of the digit that should occupy the next decimal place. Each measurement consists of two *certain figures* and one *uncertain figure*, thus *three significant figures.*

The area of one surface is

$$3.5\textbf{4} \text{ cm} \times 4.8\textbf{5} \text{ cm} = 17.\textbf{1690} \text{ cm}^2$$

The product of any number multiplied by a doubtful figure is also doubtful. Therefore, only one such doubtful figure can be carried. The result is rounded off to 17.**2** cm².

The volume of the block is then calculated.

$$17.\textbf{2} \text{ cm}^2 \times 5.4\textbf{2} \text{ cm} = 93.\textbf{224} \text{ cm}^3$$

Again, the result is properly rounded off to 93.**2** cm³, the volume of the metal block. Had all of the doubtful figures been retained throughout the computations, the volume would have been expressed as 93.**055980** cm³. Obviously, precision to a millionth of a cubic centimeter cannot be obtained from a centimeter scale having 0.1-cm graduations. *Assuming more decimal places does not improve the measurement accuracy or precision.*

In the example given above, the number of significant figures in both the measurements and computation results are easily recognized because all figures are nonzero digits. It is not as easy to determine *when* zeros in a measurement expression are significant. For example, the mean distance to the moon to *six* significant figures is 384,558 km. The distance is more commonly

Table 1-7
ZEROS IN MEASUREMENT EXPRESSIONS

Rule	Measurement expression	Significant figures
1. All nonzero digits **are** significant.	127.34 g	5
2. All zeros between two nonzero digits **are** significant.	120.007 m	6
3. Zeros to the right of a nonzero digit, but to the left of an understood decimal point, **are not** significant **unless** specifically indicated as significant by a bar placed above the rightmost such zero that is significant.	109,000 km 109,0̄00 km 109,00̄0 km 109,000̄ km	3 4 5 6
4. All zeros to the right of a decimal point but to the left of a nonzero digit **are not** significant.*	0.00406 kg	3
5. All zeros to the right of a decimal point and to the right of a nonzero digit **are** significant.	0.04060 cm 30.0000 s	4 6

*The single zero conventionally placed to the left of the decimal point in such an expression is never significant.

expressed as 385,000 km, precise to *three* significant figures. The three zeros that follow the digit 5 merely serve to locate the (understood) decimal point. Similarly, a measured length of 0.00531 cm is precise to *three* significant figures. Here again the zeros are used to locate the decimal point. However, the measurements 104.06 m and 100.60 m each contains *five* significant figures. The question naturally arises: When are zeros significant?

A person using a measuring instrument knows, of course, whether a zero in the readout represents a significant contribution to the measurement information or a method of properly locating the decimal point. This information can be communicated to others by following accepted rules for identifying zeros as significant figures in measurement data. The rules concerning zeros in a measurement expression are stated and illustrated in Table 1-7. These rules are followed throughout this book.

Uncertainty is inherent in any measurement procedure. The accuracy of a measurement can be determined if the accepted value is known. The precision can always be expressed by the proper use of significant figures. Judgments based on precision alone must be considered with caution.

PRACTICE PROBLEMS

In each of the following measurements, (*a*) determine the number of significant figures, and (*b*) identify the applicable rules (Table 1-7).

1. 1.030 cm	*ans.* 4; 5	6. 0.00320 m	*ans.* 3; 4, 5
2. 2,074,000.0 s	*ans.* 8; 2, 5	7. 601,500 km	*ans.* 4; 2, 3
3. 0.00080 kg	*ans.* 2; 4, 5	8. 1,570,5̄00 cm/s	*ans.* 6; 2, 3
4. 0.00001 g	*ans.* 1; 4	9. 47,000 kg	*ans.* 4; 3
5. 367.52 g	*ans.* 5; 1	10. 0.1020 L	*ans.* 4; 2, 5

◻ 1.19 Scientific notation

Scientific work often involves the use of numbers that are extremely large or exceedingly small. The speed of light is approximately 30,000,000,000 cm/s. The mass of the earth is approximately 6,000,000,000,000,000,000,000,000,000 g. An electron's mass is 0.000,000,000,000,000,000,000,000,000,910,953 g. The wavelength of yellow light is about 0.000059 cm. These numbers are inconvenient to write, difficult to read, and cumbersome to use in calculations.

To express such numbers in a simpler way, they can be written as powers of 10. This *exponential notation,* commonly referred to as *scientific notation,* has the form

$$M \times 10^n$$

The set of integers consists of positive integers, negative integers, and zero.

where M is a number between 1 and 10 (having one digit to the left of the decimal point) and n is an integer. For example, the speed of sound in water is about 1500 m/s. Written in scientific notation, it has the form

$$1500 = 1.5 \times 1000 = 1.5 \times 10^3$$

and

$$1500 \text{ m/s} = 1.5 \times 10^3 \text{ m/s}$$

The unusual quantities given above in positional (ordinary) notation are written in scientific notation in Table 1-8. To change a number from positional notation to scientific notation:

1. Determine M by moving the decimal point in the original number to the left or the right so that only one nonzero digit is to the left of it.

2. Determine n by counting the number of places the decimal point has been moved. If moved to the left, n is positive; if moved to the right, n is negative.

The laws of exponents apply in computations involving numbers expressed in scientific notation.

Laws of exponents are reviewed in Section 1.20.

When a measurement is written in the form $M \times 10^n$, all digits, zero and nonzero, expressed in M are *significant.* For example, the distance 402,500 m is precise to five significant figures. Expressed in scientific notation, it becomes 4.0250×10^5 m. If rounded off to three significant figures, it becomes 4.02×10^5 m.

Table 1-8
NUMBERS IN SCIENTIFIC-NOTATION FORM

$$30{,}000{,}000{,}000 \text{ cm/s} = 3 \times 10^{10} \text{ cm/s}$$
$$6{,}000{,}000{,}000{,}000{,}000{,}000{,}000{,}000{,}000 \text{ g} = 6 \times 10^{27} \text{ g}$$
$$0.000{,}000{,}000{,}000{,}000{,}000{,}000{,}000{,}000{,}910{,}953 \text{ g} = 9.10953 \times 10^{-28} \text{ g}$$
$$0.000059 \text{ cm} = 5.9 \times 10^{-5} \text{ cm}$$
$$1000 \text{ mL} = 1.000 \times 10^3 \text{ mL}$$
$$1000 \text{ mL} = 1 \times 10^3 \text{ mL}$$
$$1000 \text{ mL} = 1.00 \times 10^3 \text{ mL}$$
$$10050 \text{ mL} = 1.005 \times 10^4 \text{ mL}$$

The distance from the earth to the sun is 149,740,000 km, or 1.4974×10^8 km. Rounded off to three significant figures, the distance is 15$\bar{0}$,000,000 km, or 1.50×10^8 km. Because *only significant figures* comprise M, the implied precision of the measurement can be determined at a glance.

See Table 1-9 for rounding-off rules.

1. Express each measurement to *3 significant figures* in scientific notation.
   - (*a*) 9,454,500,000,000 km   *ans.* 9.45×10^{12} km
   - (*b*) 22.4136 L/mole   *ans.* 2.24×10^1 L/mole
   - (*c*) 0.0032416 m   *ans.* 3.24×10^{-3} m
   - (*d*) 0.0000000140 cm   *ans.* 1.40×10^{-8} cm
   - (*e*) 2,21$\bar{0}$,000,000 beats   *ans.* 2.21×10^9 beats
2. Express each measurement in positional notation.
   - (*a*) 6.022045×10^{23}/mole
      ans. 602,204,500,000,000,000,000,000 mole
   - (*b*) 1.05602×10^7 kg   *ans.* 10,560,200 kg
   - (*c*) 2.7316×10^2 °K   *ans.* 273.16 °K
   - (*d*) 2.2×10^4 m/hr   *ans.* 22,000 m/hr
   - (*e*) 1.4×10^{-8} cm   *ans.* 0.000000014 cm

◻ 1.20 Operations with significant figures

The results of calculations involving measurements of physical quantities can be no more precise than the measurements themselves. Certain rules must be observed when performing calculations so that the results do not imply greater precision than the measurements. The following rules are valid for most purposes and should be used unless otherwise indicated.

1. Addition and subtraction. Recall that the rightmost significant figure in a measurement is uncertain. Therefore, *the rightmost significant figure in a sum or difference occurs in the leftmost place at which the doubtful figure occurs in any of the measurements involved.* The following addition exercise demonstrates this rule.

"Rules of thumb" are generally useful, but they do not cover all cases.

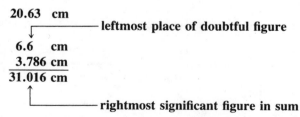

The sum 31.016 cm is then rounded off to allow only the first doubtful figure, and is recorded as 31.0 cm. This is the best expression for the sum in this addition problem. *Before adding or subtracting measurements expressed in scientific notation, all terms must be adjusted to the same power of ten.*

2. Multiplication and division. Three points discussed in Section 1.18 must be remembered in multiplication and division operations involving measured quantities: (*a*) The rightmost significant figure in a measurement is uncertain. (*b*) The product of any digit multiplied by an uncertain digit is also uncertain. (*c*) Only one uncertain digit is retained in the result. Therefore, *the product or quotient is precise to the number of significant figures contained in the least precise factor.* The result in either operation is rounded to the same number of significant figures contained in the factor having the least number of significant figures.

In each of the following examples, typical computation results obtained by slide rule and by calculator are given. These results are then adjusted to the proper number of significant figures representing the numerical product or quotient. The conventions for rounding off computation results are illustrated in Table 1-9.

Multiplication: 9.25 m $\times$ 0.52 m $\times$ 11.35 m
By slide rule, the product is 54.6 m^3
By calculator, the product is 54.5935 m^3
Observe that the factor 0.52 m has only two significant figures. The product can have no greater precision than this least precise factor. Therefore, the result is properly rounded off to two significant figures.

$$\textbf{9.25 m} \times \textbf{0.52 m} \times \textbf{11.35 m} = \textbf{55 m}^3$$

Division: 69.48 m $\div$ 3.62 s
By slide rule, the quotient is 19.2 m/s
By calculator, the quotient is 19.19337 m/s
The result is properly expressed to three significant figures.

$$\textbf{69.48 m} \div \textbf{3.62 s} = \textbf{19.2 m/s}$$

Table 1-9
ROUNDING OFF THE RESULT OF A COMPUTATION

Rule 1. Choose the required number of significant figures that is closest to the number to be rounded off.
Rule 2. When two choices are equally close, choose the one ending in an even digit.

Computation result	4 sig fig	Rounded-off result 3 sig fig	2 sig fig
1.6666 g	1.667 g	1.67 g	1.7 g
27.155 s	27.16 s	27.2 s	27 s
2.3145 kg	2.314 kg	2.31 kg	2.3 kg
150.33 °C	150.3 °C	150 °C	150 °C
8.5455 g/cm^3	8.546 g/cm^3	8.55 g/cm^3	8.5 g/cm^3
30.050 cm	30.05 cm	30.0 cm	30 cm

In multiplication or division operations with measurements expressed in scientific notation, the expressions for M are handled according to the rule above. Keep in mind that all digits are significant. The laws of exponents govern the multiplication and division of 10^n terms. In multiplication, the exponents are added.

$$10^3 \times 10^4 = 10^{3+4} = 10^7$$
$$10^6 \times 10^{-2} = 10^{6+(-2)} = 10^4$$
$$10^4 \times 10^{-6} = 10^{4+(-6)} = 10^{-2}$$

In division, the exponent of the divisor is subtracted from the exponent of the dividend. (Simply change the sign of the exponent of the divisor and add exponents.)

$$10^3 \div 10^2 = 10^{3-2} = 10^1$$
$$10^4 \div 10^{-3} = 10^{4+3} = 10^7$$
$$10^{-5} \div 10^2 = 10^{-5-2} = 10^{-7}$$

Number expressions that are not measurements should not be interpreted as having limited significance. When such exact or defined values are included in a computation with measurements, they have no influence on the number of significant figures in the result. For example, the freezing point of water is *defined* as 0 °C. It is exactly zero degrees. A thermometer readout, on the other hand, is a measurement and is subject to some uncertainty.

A defined number value is not a measurement.

◻ 1.21 Operations with units

You will recall from Section 1.13 that a system of measurement is based on a few selected physical quantities—such as *length, mass, time,* and *temperature*—that are measured in arbitrary units. All other quantities are derived from the fundamental quantities and are measured in derived units. Speed (or velocity) is a derived quantity. The average speed of a moving object is defined as the ratio of the distance (length) traveled to the elapsed time of travel.

$$\text{speed} = \frac{\text{length}}{\text{time}} = \frac{l}{t}$$

Suppose an object travels 576 m in 20.0 s. Its average speed is

$$\text{speed} = \frac{l}{t} = \frac{576 \text{ m}}{20.0 \text{ s}} = 28.8 \text{ m/s}$$

Based on the definition of speed, its *dimensions* are length/time, or l/t. Observe that the dimensions of speed are also specified in terms of the derived unit m/s. Speed *can be expressed* in any derived unit *that represents its dimensions of length/time.* Speed *cannot be expressed* in any derived unit *that does not represent*

Speed has the dimensions of length/time.

its dimensions of length/time. This concept is fundamental in computations involving the dimensions of physical quantities.

A measurement is expressed as a significant number of some kind of dimensional unit: 12.5 g, 6.72 cm, 10.0 s, 42.1 °C, 0.09 g/L, 28.8 m/s. For a mathematical equation to represent the correct solution to a problem, the equation must be *dimensionally correct.* That is, *both sides of the equation must have the same dimensions.* For example, density is defined as the ratio of mass/volume and is shown in Section 1.13 to have the dimensions of mass/length^3. The dimensional unit can be g/cm^3. If,

$$D = \frac{m}{V} \qquad \text{then,} \quad \frac{\mathbf{g}}{\mathbf{cm}^3} = \frac{\mathbf{g}}{\mathbf{cm}^3}$$

$$m = D \times V \qquad \text{then,} \quad \mathbf{g} = \frac{\mathbf{g}}{\mathbf{cm}^3} \times \mathbf{cm}^3 \quad \text{and} \quad \mathbf{g} = \mathbf{g}$$

$$V = \frac{m}{D} \qquad \text{then,} \quad \mathbf{cm}^3 = \frac{\mathbf{g}}{\mathbf{g/cm}^3} \quad \text{or,} \quad \mathbf{cm}^3 = \mathbf{g} \times \frac{\mathbf{cm}^3}{\mathbf{g}} \quad \text{and} \quad \mathbf{cm}^3 = \mathbf{cm}^3$$

Terms common to both numerator and denominator are "canceled" by dividing both by the common term.

Observe that dimensional units *common to both numerators and denominators* are "canceled" and removed from the expressions in the same familiar way as numerical factors.

Only *identical* units cancel, as the above operations illustrate. If mass is given in gram units in the numerator of an expression and in kilogram units in the denominator, the units do not cancel directly. For the mass units to cancel, either the measurement in grams must be converted to kilograms, or the measurement in kilograms must be converted to grams. A valid *conversion factor* that can be introduced into the expression for the purpose of making the desired unit conversion is needed.

Exact conversion factors derived from defined relationships are not involved in significant-figure operations.

Metric units are related as powers of 10 by the system of prefixes. One kilogram is *exactly* one thousand grams; one centimeter is *exactly* one one-hundredth meter; one second is *exactly* one thousand milliseconds. Such a unit relationship can be expressed as a fraction and inserted into an equation as a conversion factor. The form of this conversion factor must allow for the cancellation of the unit to be converted and the retention of the unit required.

Suppose a length *l* is measured to three significant figures as 1.30 m. How is *l* expressed in centimeters? By definition, 1 m is exactly 100 cm. A conversion factor with the cm unit in the numerator (unit required) and the m unit in the denominator (unit to be canceled) can be assembled.

$$\text{(correct)} \qquad l = 1.30 \ \mathbf{m} \times \frac{100 \ \mathbf{cm}}{\mathbf{m}} = 13\overline{0} \ \mathbf{cm}$$

The result, $13\overline{0}$ cm, remains precise to three significant figures. Had the conversion factor been assembled in the inverted form, the meter units would not cancel, the answer unit would not be in centimeters, and the *numerical result would not be correct.*

The conversion factor 100 cm/m does not have limited significance.

(incorrect) $\quad l = \mathbf{1.30\ m} \times \dfrac{\mathbf{m}}{\mathbf{100\ cm}} = \dfrac{\mathbf{0.0130\ m^2}}{\mathbf{cm}}$

Compare these two examples. Both forms of the conversion factor are valid expressions. The second form, m/100 cm, however, is the conversion factor for converting centimeters to meters. Observe that

$$\cancel{\mathbf{m}} \times \frac{\mathbf{cm}}{\cancel{\mathbf{m}}} = \mathbf{cm} \quad \text{and} \quad \cancel{\mathbf{cm}} \times \frac{\mathbf{m}}{\cancel{\mathbf{cm}}} = \mathbf{m}$$

The conversion factor used in the first (correct) example not only yields the intended unit in the answer *but also sets up the arithmetic computation that gives the correct numerical answer.*

These simple examples of the use of conversion factors reveal an important strategy for solving problems involving measurements and their dimensional units. *In any numerical equation, the units associated with the various quantities are treated algebraically and are canceled, combined, etc., just like factors in the equation.*

Measurement units are treated as factors in equations.

When the numerical expression for the solution to a problem has been assembled, the units in the expression should be "solved" for the answer unit *before* the arithmetic is done. If the answer unit is dimensionally correct for the physical quantity required, such as g/cm^3 for density or m/s for speed, this indicates that the arithmetic computation should yield the correct numerical answer. On the other hand, unit operations that yield an incorrect answer unit signal that the expression is incorrect and cannot give a correct answer to the problem.

This *first* unit-operations step is a simple and rapid analysis of the dimensional character of the solution setup for the problem. It is the key step in the problem-solving technique called *dimensional analysis*. This technique is often called the *factor-label* method. It is the method used in this book. Later, the factor-label method will be extended to include chemical formulas in the unit-operations step of problem solving. The following Sample Problems illustrate this factor-label method.

The factor-label method uses unit operations to set up the arithmetic in problem solutions.

◖ SAMPLE PROBLEM

A chemistry student was asked to determine the density of an irregularly shaped sample of lead, but was not supplied with any measurement data.

SOLUTION

The student measured the mass of the lead on a "centigram" balance as 49.33 g. Recalling from General Science that a solid displaces its own volume in a liquid, the student immersed the lead in water contained in a cylinder graduated in 0.1-mL divisions. The sample displaced 4.35 mL of water, the 0.05 mL being estimated.

Because the volume of a solid is normally expressed in cubic measure, the measured volume was converted to cubic centimeters.

Since 1 mL = 1 cm^3,

$$4.35 \; \cancel{mL} \times \frac{1 \; cm^3}{\cancel{mL}} = 4.35 \; cm^3$$

By definition:

$$D = \frac{m}{V} = \frac{49.33 \; g}{4.35 \; cm^3} = 11.34 \; g/cm^3$$

The multiplication/division rule for significant figures indicates an answer to 3 significant figures in this computation. Therefore, the result is rounded off to 11.3 g/cm^3.

A more efficient solution setup for this problem is

$$D = \frac{m}{V} = \frac{49.33 \; g}{4.35 \; \cancel{mL} \times 1 \; cm^3/\cancel{mL}} = 11.3 \; g/cm^3$$

SAMPLE PROBLEM

Determine the concentration of table salt (sodium chloride), in grams of salt per gram of solution, when $40\overline{0}$ mg of the salt is dissolved in $10\overline{0}$ mL of water at $6\overline{0}$ °C.

SOLUTION 1   (Two solution methods are demonstrated.)

The problem requires that the solution concentration be expressed in grams of salt per gram of solution. Therefore, the solution concentration is derived from the ratio: mass salt/mass solution. The mass of the solution is the sum of the mass of salt dissolved and the mass of water used. The volume of water at $6\overline{0}$ °C is known, but its mass is required. Density relates the mass and volume of a material. The density of water at $6\overline{0}$ °C is listed in Appendix Table 10. Locate this table and verify that the density of water at $6\overline{0}$ °C is 0.983 g/mL.

By definition:

$$D = \frac{m}{V}$$

Solving for m:

$$m = D \times V$$

Substituting: $m = 0.983 \dfrac{\text{g}}{\text{mL}} \times 10\overline{0}\ \text{mL} = 98.3\ \text{g water}$

Observe that the unit operations yield the correct answer unit for the mass of water.

The mass of salt is given in milligrams. As milligrams and grams cannot be added, milligrams of salt must be converted to grams.

By definition: $1\ \text{mg} = 0.001\ \text{g}$

$$40\overline{0}\ \text{mg salt} \times \frac{0.001\ \text{g}}{\text{mg}} = 0.400\ \text{g salt}$$

Observe that the factor 0.001 g/mg is exact.

$$\text{mass of solution} = 0.400\ \text{g salt} + 98.3\ \text{g water}$$

$$\text{mass of solution} = 98.7\ \text{g solution}$$

$$\text{solution concentration} = \frac{\text{mass salt}}{\text{mass solution}} = \frac{0.400\ \text{g salt}}{98.7\ \text{g solution}}$$

$$\text{solution concentration} = 0.00405\ \text{g salt/g solution}$$

◖ SOLUTION 2

In this example, the complete solution setup is developed in literal terms (without number values) as an algebraic equation. Measurement values are then substituted, and the indicated unit operations are performed to verify the correct answer unit—grams salt per gram solution. It is an efficient method and a productive approach to the problem-solving process.

$$\text{solution concentration} = \frac{\text{mass salt}}{\text{mass solution}} = \frac{m_\text{s}}{m_\text{soln}}$$

But, $m_\text{soln} = \text{mass salt} + \text{mass water} = m_\text{s} + m_\text{w}$

And, $m_\text{w} = \text{density of water} \times \text{volume of water} = D_\text{w} \times V_\text{w}$

Therefore, $\text{soln conc} = \dfrac{m_\text{s}}{[m_\text{s} + (D_\text{w} \times V_\text{w})]_\text{soln}}$

$$\text{soln conc} = \frac{40\overline{0}\ \text{mg salt} \times 0.001\ \text{g/mg}}{(40\overline{0}\ \text{mg} \times 0.100\ \text{g/mg} + 0.983\ \text{g/mL} \times 10\overline{0}\ \text{mL})_\text{soln}}$$

$$\text{soln conc} = \frac{0.400\ \text{g salt}}{(0.400\ \text{g} + 98.3\ \text{g})\,\text{soln}} = \frac{0.400\ \text{g salt}}{98.7\ \text{g soln}}$$

$$\text{soln conc} = 0.00405\ \text{g salt/g soln}$$

PRACTICE PROBLEMS

Table 1-10
VARIATIONS OF MASS WITH VOLUME OF WATER AT 4 °C

Volume (ml)	Mass (g)
$1\overline{0}$	$1\overline{0}$
$2\overline{0}$	$2\overline{0}$
55	55
75	75
95	95
110	110

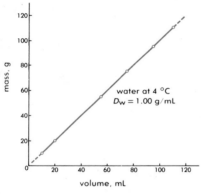

water at 4 °C
$D_w = 1.00$ g/mL

Mass of water at 4 °C as a function of its volume

Figure 1-23. A graph of a direct proportion is a straight line.

Table 1-11
VARIATIONS OF TIME WITH SPEED OVER A CONSTANT DISTANCE

Speed (m/s)	Time (s)
2.0	$30\overline{0}$
5.0	120
$1\overline{0}$	$6\overline{0}$
$1\overline{5}$	$4\overline{0}$
$2\overline{0}$	30
$2\overline{5}$	24
$3\overline{0}$	$2\overline{0}$

1. Using a platform balance, the mass of an irregular block of iron is found to be 280.2 g. The iron was immersed in water and found to displace 35.6 mL of the water. Determine the density of the iron.   *ans*. 7.87 g/cm³

2. Determine the concentration of a solution in grams of salt per gram of solution when the solution is prepared by dissolving 10.2 g of a certain salt in $50\overline{0}$ mL of water at $5\overline{0}$ °C. *ans*. 0.0202 g salt/g soln

☐ 1.22 Proportions

1. Direct proportions. Two variables are said to be *directly proportional* to one another if their *quotient* has a constant value. If the quantity y is proportional to the quantity x, then y varies directly as x and their quotient (or ratio) has the constant value k.

$$y \propto x \quad \text{and} \quad \frac{y}{x} = k$$

where $\propto$ is a proportionality sign, and k is the proportionality constant.

Then,

$$y = kx$$

The density of a material has been defined as the ratio of its mass to its volume.

$$D = \frac{m}{V} \quad \text{then,} \quad m = DV$$

The expression $m = DV$ has the form $y = kx$ when D is constant.

At 4 °C the density of water, D_w, has the constant value of 1.00 g/mL, and the mass of water, m_w, varies as its volume, V_w.

$$m_w = D_w V_w$$

At 4 °C,

$$m_w = \frac{1.00 \text{ g}}{\text{mL}} \times V_w$$

From this expression it is apparent that the mass of water varies directly with its volume at a constant water temperature. The mass and volume of water at a constant temperature are examples of variables that are directly proportional to one another. Representative variations of mass with volume are tabulated in Table 1-10.

The relation between the variables in Table 1-10 can be summarized by means of a graph in which mass m_w is plotted as a function of volume V_w. The assigned values of V_w, called the *independent variable,* are plotted horizontally on the x axis. The determined values of m_w, called the *dependent variable,* are plotted vertically on the y axis. This is shown in Figure 1-23. Observe that the graph of a direct proportion is *linear* (straight-lined).

2. Inverse proportion. Two variables are said to be *inversely proportional* to one another if their *product* has a constant value.

If the quantity y is inversely proportional to the quantity x, then y varies *inversely* as x and their product has the constant value k, the proportionality constant.

$$xy = k \quad \text{and} \quad y = \frac{k}{x}$$

From your experience, you know that the *time* required to travel a *certain distance* is a function of the *average speed* maintained over the distance. For a constant distance, d, the time, t, varies *inversely* as the speed, v.

$$vt = d \quad \text{and} \quad t = \frac{d}{v}$$

Observe that the expression $t = d/v$ has the form $y = k/x$ when d is a constant distance.

The data listed in Table 1-11 illustrate the variations in time required to traverse the same distance at different speeds. The relation between the variables can be summarized by a graph of these data in which time t is plotted as a function of speed v. The graph is shown in Figure 1-24. Observe that the graph of an inverse proportion is a *hyperbola*.

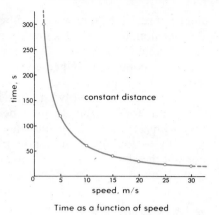

Figure 1-24. A graph of an inverse proportion is a hyperbola.

SUMMARY

Chemistry is the science dealing with materials, their composition, and the changes they undergo. The scientific method is a logical approach to the solutions of problems that lend themselves to investigation. Four steps are usually involved in the application of the scientific method: observing, generalizing, theorizing, and testing.

Matter is anything that occupies space and has mass. Matter has inertia. The mass of an object is a measure of its inertia. Weight is the measure of the earth's gravitational attraction for an object. A material's mass is determined indirectly by comparing its weight with that of a known mass in the same location on earth.

The three phases of matter are solid, liquid, and gas. These phases are largely a function of temperature. The properties of matter are classified as either physical or chemical.

Energy is the capacity for doing work. The law of conservation of matter and energy states that matter and energy are interchangeable and the total matter and energy in the universe is constant.

The metric system is a decimal system with a simple numerical relationship between units. A single set of prefixes extends the basic system of measurement. A few fundamental quantities are measured in terms of arbitrary units. All other physical quantities are derived from these fundamental quantities. A derived quantity has measurement dimensions that are determined by its definition.

Heat is defined in terms of the energy transfer associated with a difference in temperature between two systems. Temperature is an indication of heat intensity within a system. It is a fundamental quantity measured in an arbitrary unit, the °C. Heat is a form of energy commonly measured in calories. Heat energy is also measured in joules. The calorie is defined in terms of the joule.

There is some uncertainty inherent in the measurement of any physical quantity. For measurement information to be useful, the nature of the uncertainty must be indicated. Accuracy and precision are used to express the nature and degree of measurement uncertainty. A measurement expression includes a number magnitude, a dimensional unit, and some indication of the measurement reliability. The measurement reliability is commonly indicated by the method of significant figures.

Computations involving measurement information follow the factor-label method of operations. Measurement units are treated algebraically as factors in the mathematical expressions of the solutions to problems. By the proper application of factor-label and computation rules for significant figures, the reliability of problem solving is enhanced.

Measured quantities that vary with one another are directly proportional if their quotient is constant. They have a linear relation, and a graph in which one variable is plotted as a function of the other is a straight line. Measured quantities that vary with one another are inversely proportional if their product is constant. A graph in which one variable is plotted as a function of the other is a hyperbola.

◖ VOCABULARY

accuracy	energy	law	precision
calorie	gram	liter	scientific method
centi-	heat	mass	scientific notation
chemical property	inertia	matter	significant figures
chemistry	inverse proportion	meter	temperature
density	joule	milli-	theory
dimensional analysis	kilo-	physical property	weight
direct proportion	kinetic energy	potential energy	

◖ QUESTIONS

Group A

1. Define chemistry.
2. (a) Identify six main branches of chemistry. (b) Why is chemical knowledge organized into separate branches?
3. What was the phlogiston theory?
4. What important contributions to chemistry are attributed to Marie Curie?
5. Scientists who investigate natural phenomena are seeking the answers to what two important questions?
6. Describe the scientific method.
7. Define: (a) inertia, (b) mass, in terms of inertia, (c) weight.
8. What distinguishes (a) a solid from a liquid? (b) a liquid from a gas?
9. Compile a list of properties of materials that are classified as physical properties.
10. Compile a list of properties of materials that are classified as chemical properties.
11. State the law of conservation of matter and energy.
12. Which metric prefixes are most commonly used in chemistry?
13. In what metric units would you express: (a) the area of the cover of this book? (b) your family's daily milk consumption? (c) the length of the eye of a darning needle? (d) your own mass? (e) the speed of a moving automobile?
14. Which of the units required in Question 13 are derived units?
15. Name five fundamental quantities that are important in chemistry and give the standard unit for each.
16. (a) What is the distinction between heat and temperature? (b) In what units is each measured?
17. Distinguish between accuracy and precision in measurements.
18. Define significant figures as they relate to measurement information.
19. To change a measurement recorded in positional notation to scientific notation, the

decimal point is moved seven places to the right. What is the exponent of 10?

20. What relationship exists between two variables (a) whose product has a constant value? (b) whose quotient has a constant value?

Group B

21. Having defined chemistry in response to Question 1, in your own words state briefly the meaning the term "chemistry" conveys to you.

22. Of what importance is the study of chemistry in the attainment of your educational goals?

23. What fact enables a chemistry student to determine the mass of a body by comparison with a known mass, as illustrated in Figure 1-10?

24. Accepting the fact that an object weighs less at a high altitude above the earth than it does at the surface, (a) can you develop an argument that supports this fact? (b) Will your argument, or a modified version of it, support the fact that the object also weighs less at the bottom of a deep mine shaft than it does at the surface?

25. Explain the meaning of the term "free surface" as used in the following statement: "A liquid has a single free surface."

26. Why are both liquids and gases classified as fluids?

27. What determines whether a certain property of a material is classed as physical or chemical?

28. Volume is a property of a material. (a) Is it a specific property? (b) Is mass a specific property? (c) Is the ratio of mass to volume a specific property? Explain.

29. Explain why the expression of the magnitude of any measurement requires both a number and a unit.

30. Acceleration is defined as the change in velocity (speed) per unit of time. (a) What are the dimensions of acceleration? (b) What is the derived unit of measure for acceleration if distance is measured in meters and time is measured in seconds?

31. A platform balance has scale graduations to 0.1 g and is known to be sensitive to 0.01 g.

Using this balance, a student records the mass as 70.14 g. (a) How was the digit in the hundredth-gram place determined? (b) The recorded measurement contains how many significant figures?

32. Your laboratory partner was given the task of measuring the length of a block with as much measurement detail as possible, using a meter stick graduated in millimeters. The set of measurements were: 12.95, 12.9 cm, 12.95 cm, 12.955 cm, 129.55 mm, 13 cm. (a) State which one of these reported measurements you would accept, giving the reason. (b) Give your reason for rejecting each of the other reported measurements.

33. Copy each of these measurements and underscore all significant figures in each. (*Do not mark in this book.*) (a) 127.50 km; (b) 1200 m; (c) 90027.00 cm^3; (d) 0.0053 g; (e) 67$\overline{0}$ mg; (f) 0.0730 g; (g) 43.053 L; (h) 300900 kg; (i) 147 cm; (j) 6271.9 cm^2.

34. The speed of light in vacuum, an important physical constant, is listed in Appendix Table 3. (a) How many significant figures are included in the constant expression? (b) Convert the expression to positional notation retaining all significant figures given in Table 3. (c) Round off your expression for (b) to four significant figures. (d) Round off your expression in (c) to three significant figures. (e) Round off your expression in (d) to one significant figure. (f) What conversion factor would you use to convert your constant to one expressed in km/s? (g) Express the constant in scientific notation to three significant figures with the dimensional unit of km/s. (h) Express the constant in scientific notation to one significant figure with the dimensional unit of cm/s.

35. Explain the meaning of the following statement: "For an equation to represent the correct solution to a problem, the equation must be dimensionally correct."

36. When solving a chemistry problem by the factor-label method, the units in the solution expression are first solved for the answer unit. What advantage accrues from this factor-label technique?

◖ PROBLEMS

Group A

1. Using the appropriate conversion factors, demonstrate the conversion of the following measurements to millimeters: (*a*) 1 cm, (*b*) 1 m, (*c*) 1 km.

2. By the method of Problem 1, demonstrate the conversion of (*a*) 1.00 ft to centimeters, (*b*) 2.0 m to centimeters, (*c*) 2.0 m to inches. (Note: use Table 1-3 as required.)

3. Convert (*a*) 1.5 L to milliliters, (*b*) 10 L to cubic centimeters, (*c*) 1 m^3 to liters.

4. Calculate the number of milligrams in (*a*) 0.425 kg, (*b*) 1.15 lb. (*c*) How many grams are there in 2.65 kg?

5. (*a*) What is your height in centimeters? (*b*) What is your mass in kilograms?

6. A Florence flask has a capacity of 2.5 × 10^2 mL. (*a*) What is its capacity in liters? (*b*) How many grams of water will the flask hold?

7. Mars revolves around the sun at an average distance of 141,500,000 mi in a period of 687 days. (*a*) Express the distance in scientific notation as kilometers. (*b*) Express the period in years. (Assume a 365-day year.)

8. The thickness of an oil film on water is 0.0000005 cm. Express this thickness in scientific notation.

9. The distance light travels through space in one year is called a light year. Using the speed of light in vacuum listed in Appendix Table 3 rounded off to 3 significant figures and assuming a 365-day year, determine the distance of a light year in kilometers.

10. In a calorimetry experiment, the quantity of heat released during the combustion of a sample was measured as 736.2 cal. (*a*) How many joules of heat energy were released? (*b*) Express this quantity of heat in kilojoules.

Group B

11. A cubic box holds $10\overline{0}0$ g of water. (*a*) What is the capacity of the box in milliliters? (*b*) What is the length of one side in centimeters? (*c*) What is this length in meters?

12. A laboratory test tube is 125 mm long and 25.0 mm in diameter. (*a*) Neglecting the fact that the bottom of the test tube is rounded, calculate its capacity in milliliters. (*b*) How many grams of water will it hold?

13. Each member of a class of 24 students needs 8.600 g of sodium chloride for an experiment. The instructor sets out a new 1.000-lb jar of the salt. What mass, in grams, of the salt remains at the end of the laboratory period?

14. A 1.00-L graduated cylinder has an inside diameter of 8.24 cm. There is a 52-mm ungraduated portion at the top. What is the total height of the cylinder in centimeters?

15. The density of mercury, to three significant figures, is 13.5 g/mL. (*a*) What is the mass of 8.20 mL of mercury? (*b*) What volume would $12\overline{0}$ g of mercury occupy?

16. Express the distance 152.20 cm in each of the following units, showing the conversion computation in each case: (*a*) meters, (*b*) millimeters, (*c*) kilometers, (*d*) inches.

17. Chemists have determined that 18.0 g of water consists of 6.02 × 10^{23} molecules. Assuming that a teaspoon holds 3.70 mL of water, determine the number of water molecules the teaspoon can hold.

18. Suppose you are able to remove individual molecules of water from the teaspoon of Problem 17 at the rate of 1 molecule per second. How many years would be required to empty the spoon?

Matter and Its Changes

On a clear, moonless night, the stars appear little different from those seen by ancient Egyptian astronomers thousands of years ago. In fixed patterns, they still adorn the black emptiness of endless space. It is as if nothing changes, as if these starry sentries will keep their vigil to the end of time. . . . Yet even distant stars lose their luster. Like dying embers unable to feed brilliant flames, they too will fall victim to ceaseless change in a restless universe. Matter to energy . . . energy to matter — this is the never-ending cycle of nature. Transformations occur all around us. Flowers bloom . . . wood burns . . . iron rusts. Nothing stays the same. And scientists, by measuring and plotting, counting and timing, hope to illuminate this landscape — to explain our universe.

⬚ 2.1 Classes of matter

Chemistry has been described as the study of the structure and composition of matter, of changes in its composition, and of the mechanisms by which these changes occur. The methods of chemistry involve metric measurements and require some basic computations with measurement data. To pursue this study, it is essential that some basic concepts of matter be recognized.

Matter is anything that occupies space and has mass. It includes all materials found in nature. Some materials are made up of parts that are not alike. The dissimilarities may be subtle, or they may be readily apparent. *Matter that has parts with different properties is **heterogeneous*** (het-er-oh-*jee*-nee-us). Granite, a common rock, is heterogeneous because it is composed of several different minerals, each having characteristic properties. Distinctly different parts are easily observed.

Other materials appear uniform throughout; all parts are alike. The properties of any one part are identical to the properties of all other parts. *Matter that has identical properties throughout is **homogeneous*** (hoh-muh-*jee*-nee-us). Sugar and ordinary table salt are examples of homogeneous materials.

The many different kinds of matter throughout the world are the materials with which chemists work. It would be difficult and time-consuming to study these materials without first organizing them into similar groups. One method of classifying matter is according to its three different phases: solid, liquid, and gas. Matter is also divided into three general classes on the basis of its properties: *elements, compounds,* and *mixtures*. These and

COMPOSITION OF MATTER

In this chapter you will gain an understanding of:

- **elements, compounds, and mixtures**
- **physical and chemical changes**
- **endothermic and exothermic processes**
- **the relationship between processes in nature, energy, and entropy**

Matter is either heterogeneous or homogeneous in its makeup.

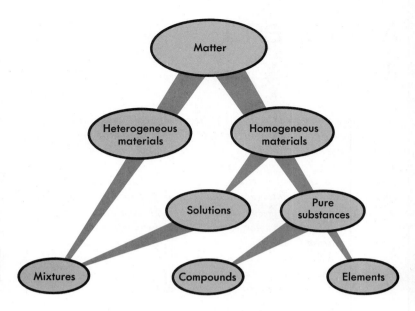

Figure 2-1. All matter is divided into three general classes: elements, compounds, and mixtures. Solutions are homogeneous mixtures.

other ways of classifying matter make the study of chemistry simpler. Figure 2-1 will be helpful in the study of Sections 2.2 and 2.3.

◻ 2.2 Mixtures

Suppose you examine a piece of granite closely with a hand lens. Three different crystalline materials can be seen. They are quartz, feldspar, and mica. The properties of each differ greatly. Granite is a heterogeneous material, having parts with different properties. It is a *mixture*. One part of a piece of quartz has the same properties as every other part. This fact is also true of feldspar and of mica. Each of these components of granite is a homogeneous material. Heterogeneous materials are mixtures of homogeneous materials.

Heterogeneous materials are mixtures.

A heterogeneous mixture does not have a set of unique properties. Instead, its properties are a combination of the properties of its homogeneous parts. All mixtures are not heterogeneous, however. When sugar is dissolved in water, the resulting solution has similar properties throughout. Thus the solution is homogeneous. The amount of sugar or water may be increased, but the solution remains a homogeneous mixture of the two materials. The solution has the sweet taste of the sugar it contains. The water may be removed by evaporation and the sugar recovered in its original form. Solutions are homogeneous mixtures. Air is a solution of gases. It is a mixture composed principally of nitrogen and oxygen. Other gases that are present in air are argon, carbon dioxide, and water vapor. Each gas displays its own unique properties. Alloys, primarily combinations of metals, are usually

Some homogeneous materials are mixtures.

Solutions are mixtures that are homogeneous.

solid solutions. *A **mixture** is a material consisting of two or more kinds of matter, each retaining its own characteristic properties.*

Mixtures are not substances in a chemical sense. Elements and compounds are substances.

2.3 Substances include compounds and elements

Materials with identical properties throughout are homogeneous. In chemistry, such homogeneous materials are called *pure substances,* or simply *substances. A **substance** is a homogeneous material consisting of one particular kind of matter.* Both the sugar and the water of a sugar-water solution are substances in this sense. Unlike granite, which has properties attributable to quartz, feldspar, and mica, sugar has properties attributable to the sugar itself, properties that stem from its particular composition. *A substance has a definite chemical composition.*

Suppose a small quantity of sugar is heated in a test tube over a low flame. The substance melts and changes color. Finally a black residue remains in the bottom of the test tube. Drops of a clear, colorless liquid appear around the cool, open end. The black substance has the properties of carbon and the liquid has the properties of water. The properties of the sugar no longer exist. In fact, the sugar no longer exists. Instead, two different substances, carbon and water, are observed.

Each time the experiment is repeated, the sugar decomposes in the same way to yield the same proportions of carbon and water. Sugar is recognized as a complex substance showing a constant composition. It is an example of a *compound. A **compound** is a substance that can be decomposed into two or more simpler substances by ordinary chemical means.*

Water can be decomposed into two simpler substances, hydrogen and oxygen. Thus water is also a compound. Chemists have not succeeded in decomposing carbon, hydrogen, or oxygen into simpler substances. The conclusion is that they are elemental substances or *elements. **Elements** are substances that cannot be further decomposed by ordinary chemical means.*

2.4 The known elements

One of the fascinating facts of science is that all known matter is composed of approximately 100 elements. A few elemental substances, such as gold, silver, copper, and sulfur, have been known since ancient times. During the Middle Ages and the Renaissance, more elements were discovered. Through the years, improved research techniques have enabled scientists to add to the list of elements.

The list of elements has grown to 107. The 92 elements ranging from hydrogen to uranium are traditionally known as *natural* elements. That is, most of them are found in nature in either free or combined form. They make up the pre–Atomic Age list of

The decomposition of sugar by heat is an example of a chemical process.

A

Figure 2-2. The components of a mixture can be separated by using differences in their physical properties. In (A) the mixture of two solids is separated by shaking it in a liquid because the components settle out at different rates. In (B) the mixture is separated by filtration after shaking it in a liquid in which one component (but not the other) is soluble.

B

Figure 2-3. Plutonium, transuranium element number 94, being prepared for fabrication into atomic reactor fuel.

known elements. Those beyond uranium are called the *transuranium* elements. They are "artificial" elements prepared from other elements during *synthesis* procedures.

In the decade before World War II, a great experimental study of atomic structure was undertaken. Enrico Fermi, an Italian theoretical physicist, stated that it should be possible to prepare the ninety-third and ninety-fourth elements from uranium. Element 93 was first produced in the laboratories of the University of California, Berkeley, in 1940. It was named *neptunium* for the planet Neptune. This planet is beyond the planet Uranus just as element 93 is beyond uranium (element 92) on the list of elements. Later, element 94 was produced in the same laboratories. It was given the name *plutonium* for the planet Pluto, which is beyond Neptune.

These triumphs were followed by the production of *americium* (am-er-*ih*-see-um), named for America; *curium* (*ku*-ree-um), named in honor of Marie and Pierre Curie; *berkelium* (*berk*-lee-um), named for Berkeley (the site of the University of California); and *californium,* named for the university and the state. More recently, *einsteinium,* named for Albert Einstein, *fermium,* named for Enrico Fermi, and *mendelevium* (men-del-*ev*-ee-um), named for Dmitri Mendeleev, have brought the total to 101.

In 1957, a team of American, British, and Swedish scientists working at the Nobel Institute in Sweden announced the discovery of element 102. They suggested the name *nobelium*. Careful experiments by other scientists, however, failed to confirm their discovery.

The following year, a research group at Lawrence Radiation Laboratory of the University of California produced element 102 and identified it by chemical means. They retained the name *nobelium* to honor Alfred Nobel, who made a significant contribution to the advancement of science through his establishment of the Nobel Prizes.

In 1961, element 103 was produced by scientists at the Lawrence Radiation Laboratory. The name *lawrencium* has been assigned to element 103 in honor of Ernest O. Lawrence, the inventor of the cyclotron and founder of the laboratory in which the element was first produced.

Russian scientists reported the production of element 104 in 1964, element 105 in 1970, element 106 in 1974, and element 107 in 1976. Counterclaims have been made by American scientists who believe they produced element 104 in 1968, element 105 in 1970, and element 106 in 1974. The "discoverer" of a new element traditionally proposes its name, but the element is not officially named until after its discovery has been clearly established by the scientific community. Currently, none of the claims of production of elements 104, 105, 106, and 107 have been decided, so

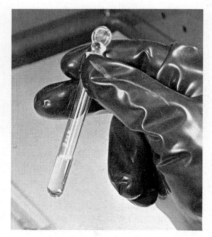

Figure 2-4. A vial containing californium, transuranium element number 98.

there are no officially recognized names for these elements.

To fill a need for names for these elements, as well as others that may be predicted but have not yet been produced, a systematic nomenclature for elements numbered over 100 has been devised. It is intended that the systematic names be used for such elements until official names are established. The systematic name is composed of numerical roots as listed in Table 2-1. The roots are assembled in the order of the digits in the element number and followed by the suffix "ium." Using this scheme, the systematic name for element 104 is un-nil-quad-ium, or unnilquadium (oon-nill-kwawd-ee-um). The name for element 105 is unnilpentium; for 106, unnilhexium; and for 107, unnilseptium. The predicted element 118 would be named ununoctium. The name for element 201 is binilunium (by-nill-oon-ee-um).

Table 2-1
SYSTEMATIC NOMENCLATURE FOR ELEMENTS

---

1. The systematic name is derived from the element number using the following numerical roots:

0 = nil		
1 = un	4 = quad	7 = sept
2 = bi	5 = pent	8 = oct
3 = tri	6 = hex	9 = enn

2. The roots are assembled in the order of the digits in the element number and terminated by "ium" to spell out the element name—with the following exceptions:
   (*a*) The final "n" of "enn" is omitted when it occurs before "nil."
   (*b*) The final "i" of "bi" and of "tri" is omitted when it occurs before "ium."

3. The symbol of the element is composed of the initial letters of the numerical roots that make up the name.

4. In the element name each root is pronounced separately. The root "un" is pronounced to rhyme with "moon."

Element number	Element name	Element symbol
101	Mendelevium	Md
102	Nobelium	No
103	Lawrencium	Lr
104	Unnilquadium	Unq
105	Unnilpentium	Unp
116	Ununhexium	Uuh
127	Unbiseptium	Ubs
238	Bitrioctium	Bto
349	Triquadennium	Tqe
490	Quadennilium	Qen

Pure and Applied Chemistry, February 1979, pp. 383–384. *International Union of Pure and Applied Chemistry*. Used by permission.

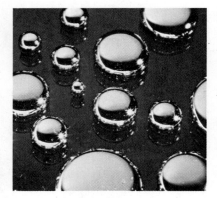

A

B

Figure 2-5. Mercury (A) is the only metallic element that is a liquid at room temperature. Sulfur (B) is a nonmetallic element. Its stable form at room temperature has a rhombic crystalline structure.

Graphite, one form of carbon, is a fairly good conductor of electricity.

☐ 2.5 General classes of elements

Each element has its own set of properties. General similarities among the properties of large groups of elements provide one way of classifying them. In this sense, chemists recognize two general classes of elements, *metals* and *nonmetals*.

Metals. Many familiar metals are recognized because of their appearance. They have a *metallic* luster; that is, they shine like silver. Copper and gold have this metallic luster and they also have distinctive colors. Metals are good reflectors of heat and light. They are good conductors of heat and electricity. Metals are *ductile;* they can be drawn out into fine wire. They are *malleable;* they can be hammered (or rolled) into thin sheets. They are *tenacious;* they can resist being stretched and pulled apart. Metals have these metallic properties of ductility, malleability, and tenacity (tensile strength) to varying degrees.

Familiar metals include gold, silver, copper, aluminum, mercury, magnesium, tin, and zinc. At ordinary temperatures mercury is a liquid metal, as shown in Figure 2-5. Less familiar metals include platinum, sodium, potassium, calcium, cobalt, titanium, gallium, tungsten, and uranium. Gallium is a liquid metal at body temperature, as illustrated in Figure 2-6.

Nonmetals. Nonmetallic elements are usually poor conductors of heat and electricity. As solids, they are brittle and are neither ductile nor malleable. Sulfur is a typical solid nonmetal. Crystalline sulfur is shown in Figure 2-5. Other common nonmetals that are solids at room temperature are iodine, carbon, and phosphorus. Bromine is a liquid nonmetal. Nonmetals such as oxygen, nitrogen, chlorine, and hydrogen are gases.

A few elements are not accommodated entirely by either of these two general classes of elements. For example, the elements helium, neon, argon, krypton, xenon, and radon are gases at ordinary temperatures. As such they are nonmetallic. But unlike nonmetallic elements, they are essentially without chemical reactivity. Some form no known compounds; others form only certain compounds under unusual conditions. Ordinarily these elements are not included in the general classes of metals and nonmetals, but are classified as *noble* gases.

A few other elements have some properties midway between those of metals and nonmetals. Silicon, for example, is usually described as a nonmetal. However, it is a much better conductor of electricity than sulfur, but much poorer than silver or copper. It is called a *semiconductor*. Silicon and other elements such as arsenic, boron, and germanium are generally called *metalloids*. They are solids under normal conditions and have semiconducting properties to varying degrees. They are basically nonmetals, but silicon and germanium are important for their semiconducting (metal-like) properties.

☐ 2.6 Chemical symbols

Ancient alchemists apparently recognized a need for symbols to represent the various substances known to them. For example, the outline of a crescent moon was commonly used as a symbol for silver. An inverted triangle, a short wavy line, or a combination of the two was the symbol for water. The symbols used today to represent chemical elements evolved from this ancient shorthand.

In 1808, John Dalton (1766–1844) introduced a framework for the symbols of the known chemical elements. He used a circle as the symbol for oxygen, a circle with a dot at its center for hydrogen, and a circle with a particular inscribed design or letter for each of the remaining elements, as shown in Figure 2-7. Observe that he represented compounds by appropriate combinations of symbols of elements.

Jöns Jakob Berzelius (1779–1848), a Swedish chemist, was the first to use letters as symbols for elements, instead of Dalton's small circles with identifying marks. Berzelius used the first letter of the name of an element as its symbol. For example, he used the letter **O** as the symbol for oxygen and the letter **H** as the symbol for hydrogen.

As the number of known elements increased, and with only 26 letters in the alphabet, the names of several elements would have begun with the same letter. In such cases, Berzelius added a second letter whose sound is conspicuous when the name of the element is pronounced. For example, the symbol for carbon is **C**; for calcium, **Ca**; for chlorine, **Cl**; for chromium, **Cr**; and for cobalt, **Co**. The first letter of a symbol is *always* capitalized, but the second letter of a symbol is *never* capitalized. For example, **Co** is the *symbol* for cobalt; **CO** is the *formula* for the *compound* carbon monoxide, which is composed of the elements carbon, **C**, and oxygen, **O**. Compare Dalton's and Berzelius' representations of water in Figure 2-7 with the familiar H_2O used today.

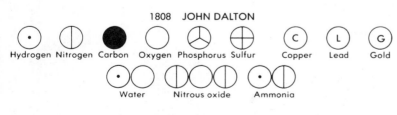

1808   JOHN DALTON

| Hydrogen | Nitrogen | Carbon | Oxygen | Phosphorus | Sulfur | Copper | Lead | Gold |

Water   Nitrous oxide   Ammonia

1814   J. J. BERZELIUS

Cu + O	Copper oxide	$2SO^3 + PoO^2$	Potassium sulfate (K, from kalium, was used later)
S + 3O	Sulfur trioxide	──╫──	A bar through the letter denoted a double atom
CuO + SO³	Copper sulfate	$H^2O = \dot{\ddot{H}}$	A dot denoted an oxygen atom

A

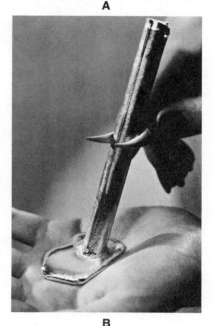

B

Figure 2-6. (A) The metallic element gallium occurs as gray-black rhombic crystals. (B) Gallium melts in your hand. Its melting point is about 30 °C and normal body temperature is 37 °C. Its boiling point is nearly 2000 °C.

Figure 2-7. John Dalton simplified the system of astrological symbols used by the early alchemists. He developed symbol notations for elements and used them to describe the composition of compounds. Berzelius adopted Dalton's system but replaced his graphic symbols with the first letter or letters of the Latin names of the elements.

The first letter of a symbol is always capitalized.

The second letter of a symbol is never capitalized.

Table 2-2
COMMON ELEMENTS AND THEIR SYMBOLS

Name	Symbol
aluminum	Al
antimony	Sb
arsenic	As
barium	Ba
bismuth	Bi
bromine	Br
calcium	Ca
carbon	C
chlorine	Cl
chromium	Cr
cobalt	Co
copper	Cu
fluorine	F
gold	Au
hydrogen	H
iodine	I
iron	Fe
lead	Pb
magnesium	Mg
manganese	Mn
mercury	Hg
nickel	Ni
nitrogen	N
oxygen	O
phosphorus	P
platinum	Pt
potassium	K
silicon	Si
silver	Ag
sodium	Na
strontium	Sr
sulfur	S
tin	Sn
titanium	Ti
tungsten	W
zinc	Zn

In several cases the symbol for an element is derived from the Latin name of the element. For example, the symbol for iron is **Fe**, from the Latin *ferrum*. **Pb**, the symbol for lead, comes from the Latin *plumbum*. The symbols for silver, **Ag**, and sodium, **Na**, come from the Latin *argentum* and *natrium*. Some familiar elements and their symbols are listed in Table 2-2.

A chemical symbol is more than an abbreviation; it has quantitative significance. The symbol **K** not only represents the element potassium, but also *one atom* of potassium. Similarly, **Fe** represents 1 atom of iron. Atoms, the basic units of elements, combine with other elements to form chemical compounds. The symbol for an element will acquire additional significance as the study of chemistry progresses.

◻ 2.7 The earth's elemental composition

Approximately 90 elements are known to occur in measurable amounts in either a free or combined state in the earth's crust. The atmosphere consists almost entirely of two elements, nitrogen and oxygen. Water, which covers a great portion of the earth's surface, is a compound of hydrogen and oxygen. Natural water also contains many dissolved substances.

Only about 30 elements are fairly common. Table 2-3 shows the relative mass distribution of the 10 most abundant elements in the atmosphere, lakes, rivers, oceans, and the solid earth's crust.

Although the solid crust of the earth is the foundation of human existence, it constitutes only about 0.4% of the total mass of the

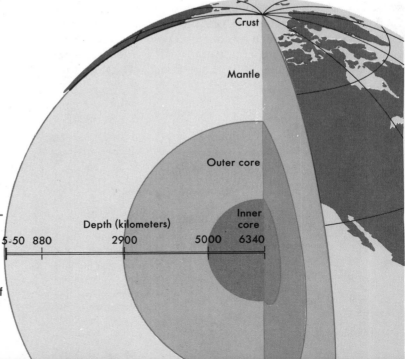

Crust

Mantle

Outer core

Inner core

Depth (kilometers)

5-50   880   2900   5000   6340

Figure 2-8. Regions of the interior of the earth.

earth and less than 1% of its volume. The mantle accounts for about 67.2% and the core 32.4% of the earth's total mass.

The two most abundant elements in the solid crust are oxygen and silicon. Together they account for almost 75% of the mass of the continental crust. Eight elements make up over 98% of the mass of the continental crust. They are listed in Table 2-4. These eight common elements, along with the less common ones, are combined in many ways to produce the more than 2000 different minerals found in the solid earth's crust.

Scientists at the Smithsonian Institution have estimated that five elements account for more than 94% of the mass of the solid earth (including the continental crust, mantle, and core). These elements are listed in Table 2-5.

The mantle is believed to consist almost entirely of compounds of four elements—magnesium, iron, silicon, and oxygen. Earth scientists believe that the earth's core contains about 85% elemental iron, about 7% nickel, and 8% of a mixture of silicon, cobalt, and sulfur.

◻ 2.8 Compounds differ from mixtures

When matter is made up of two or more elements, the elements are either mixed mechanically or combined chemically. The material is either a *mixture* or a *compound,* depending on what has happened to the elements. If the material is a mixture, the properties of each element present will persist. On the other hand, if the elements are chemically combined, a complex substance with its own characteristic properties is observed.

Suppose powdered sulfur and powdered iron are mixed thoroughly on a sheet of paper. There is no evidence of a chemical reaction; neither light nor heat is produced. The two substances may be mixed in any proportion. It is possible to use a large portion of iron and a small portion of sulfur or a large portion of sulfur and a small portion of iron.

As the paper containing this mixture is moved back and forth over a strong magnet, the iron particles separate from the sulfur. When a small portion of the mixture is added to a solution of hydrochloric acid, the iron reacts with the acid and disappears from view, leaving the sulfur unaffected. When another portion of the mixture is added to liquid carbon disulfide, the sulfur dissolves, leaving the iron unchanged.

In each of these tests, the properties of iron and sulfur persist. This is typical of a mixture; the *components* do not lose their identity. They may be mixed in any proportion without showing any evidence of chemical activity.

It is possible to cause the iron and sulfur to react chemically and form a compound. Suppose these two elements are mixed in the ratio of 7 g iron to 4 g sulfur, and the mixture is heated strongly

Table 2-3
COMPOSITION OF SURFACE ENVIRONMENT

Element	Mass distribution
oxygen	49.5%
silicon	25.8%
aluminum	7.5%
iron	4.7%
calcium	3.4%
sodium	2.6%
potassium	2.4%
magnesium	1.9%
hydrogen	0.9%
titanium	0.6%
all other elements	0.7%

Table 2-4
COMPOSITION OF THE CONTINENTAL CRUST

Element	Mass distribution
oxygen	46.6%
silicon	27.7%
aluminum	8.1%
iron	5.0%
calcium	3.6%
sodium	2.8%
potassium	2.6%
magnesium	2.1%

Table 2-5
COMPOSITION OF THE SOLID EARTH

Element	Mass distribution
iron	34.6%
oxygen	29.5%
silicon	15.2%
magnesium	12.7%
nickel	2.4%

The process of combining two or more substances to form a single, more complex substance is called synthesis.

Figure 2-9. A mixture of powdered iron and sulfur can be separated by a magnet because iron, but not sulfur, is attracted to the magnet.

Analysis is the process of determining the identity and quantity of each constituent element in a compound.

in a test tube over a Bunsen burner flame. With a rise in temperature the mixture begins to glow. Even after its removal from the flame, the mixture continues to react and the whole mass soon becomes red hot. *Both heat and light are produced during the chemical reaction in which sulfur and iron combine to form a compound.*

After the reaction has ceased and the product has been removed, careful examination shows that it no longer resembles either the iron or the sulfur. Each element has lost its characteristic properties. The iron cannot be removed by a magnet. The sulfur cannot be dissolved out of the product with carbon disulfide. In the original mixture, hydrochloric acid reacted chemically with the iron and odorless hydrogen gas was produced. Hydrochloric acid also reacts chemically with this new product and a gas is again produced. However, in this reaction, the gas is distinctly different from that formed in the previous reaction. This gas has an odor. It is *hydrogen sulfide,* a poisonous gas that is notorious for its rotten-egg odor. This different product gives evidence that a new substance with a new set of properties is formed during the reaction between the iron and sulfur. It is a *compound* composed of iron and sulfur.

By chemical analysis, this new compound is found to consist of iron, Fe, and sulfur, S, in a definite mass relationship. It is an *iron sulfide* compound consisting of 63.5% Fe and 36.5% S. This composition represents a mass ratio Fe : S of 7 : 4. Had the starting mixture for the reaction been in the ratio of 8 g Fe : 4 g S, 1 g of iron would remain as an unused surplus after the reaction was complete. *A compound is always composed of the same elements in a definite mass relationship.* Significant differences between mixtures and compounds are summarized in Table 2-6.

◻ 2.9 Law of definite composition

Louis Proust (1755–1826), a French chemist, was one of the first to observe that elements combine with one another in a

Table 2-6
DIFFERENCES BETWEEN MIXTURES AND COMPOUNDS

Mixture	Compound
1. In a mixture, the components can be present in any proportion.	1. In a compound, the constituents have a definite proportion by mass.
2. In the preparation of a mixture, there is no evidence of any chemical action taking place.	2. In the preparation of a compound, evidence of chemical action is usually apparent (light, heat, etc.).
3. In a mixture, the components do not lose their identity. They can be separated by physical means.	3. In a compound, the constituents lose their identity. They can be separated only by chemical means.

definite mass ratio. About 50 years later, Jean Servais Stas, a Belgian chemist, performed a series of precise experiments that confirmed this observation. Proust's observation is now known as the *law of definite composition: Each compound has a definite composition by mass.*

Using the law of definite composition, a manufacturer of chemical compounds can determine precisely the quantity of each constituent required to prepare a specific compound.

◻ 2.10 Common examples of mixtures and compounds

In Section 2.2, air was described as a mixture. Its composition varies somewhat in different localities. Other familiar examples of mixtures are baking powders, concrete, and various kinds of soil. There is practically no limit to the number of possible mixtures. They may be made up of two or more elements, of two or more compounds, or of both elements and compounds. For example, brass is a mixture of two elements, copper and zinc. Common gunpowder is a mixture of two elements, carbon and sulfur, with a compound, potassium nitrate. A solution of common salt is a mixture of two compounds, sodium chloride and water.

A large dictionary may define almost a half-million words. All of these words are formed from one or more of the 26 letters of our alphabet. Try to imagine the number of compounds possible from different combinations of 100 or more elements. Of course, some elements do not react readily with others to form compounds. Helium, **He,** exists only in the free state. It forms no known compounds. Enough elements do combine, however, to make possible the several million compounds known to chemists. Water, table salt, sugar, alcohol, baking soda, ether, glycerol, cellulose, nitric acid, and sulfuric acid are examples of common compounds.

The simplest compounds consist of two different elements chemically combined. Iron sulfide is such a compound. It is composed of iron and sulfur. Carbon dioxide is composed of carbon and oxygen. Hydrogen and oxygen combine to form water. Table salt consists of sodium combined with chlorine. Sodium is an active metallic element that must be protected from contact with air and water. Chlorine is a poisonous gas. However, when combined chemically, the two elements form common table salt or *sodium chloride.*

Many compounds are composed of three different elements. Carbon, hydrogen, and oxygen are the constituent elements in sugar. These same three elements occur combined in different proportions in many other compounds having decidedly different properties. Examples are acetic acid, alcohol, ether, and formaldehyde.

CHANGES IN MATTER

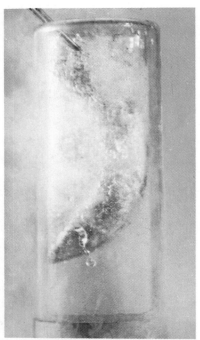

Figure 2-10. After a banana is dipped in liquid nitrogen at -195.8 °C, it can be used as a hammer to drive the nail into the block of wood.

☐ 2.11 Physical changes

Solids melt, liquids boil, gases condense, liquids freeze, and many solids, liquids, and gases dissolve in water. A length of platinum wire glows when heated in a Bunsen flame. As the platinum wire cools, its characteristic metallic luster is observed to have remained unchanged. In each of these actions, matter undergoes a change that involves some quantity of energy. The form of matter may be different or a change of phase may have occurred. However, the *identity* of matter has not changed. A reversal of the action that caused a change may restore the material to its original form and the original identifying properties may again be recognized. For example, water is rapidly converted to water vapor when heated to its boiling point. As the vapor loses heat, it condenses to water and the properties of liquid water are again recognized.

These examples together with Figure 2-10 illustrate *physical changes*. Only physical properties are altered during physical changes. No new substances with new properties are formed. *Physical changes are those in which certain physical properties of substances change and their identifying properties remain unchanged.*

Modern concepts of the solution process suggest that some types of physical changes may involve intermediate processes that are not physical in nature. These considerations will be treated in Chapter 13.

☐ 2.12 Chemical changes

Wood burns, iron rusts, silver tarnishes, milk sours, plants decay, and acids react with metals. These reactions are examples of processes in which the identifying properties of the original substances disappear as new substances with different properties are formed. Changes occur that alter the composition of matter. *Chemical changes are those in which different substances with new properties are formed.*

Chemical reactions may involve the formation of compounds from elemental substances. Complex substances may be broken down into simpler compounds or into the constituent elements. Compounds may react with other compounds or elements to form new and different substances.

Chemistry is concerned specifically with the chemical changes substances undergo, and with the methods of controlling the chemical reactions in which the changes occur. To recognize these processes and control them, chemists need to know how the reactions occur. They observe changes in the properties of substances in bulk, and try to interpret these changes in terms of the behavior of the particles of the substances involved.

◻ 2.13 Chemical reactions involve energy

Chemical changes are always accompanied by energy changes. Substances possess energy because of their composition and structure. It is a kind of potential energy that chemists refer to as *chemical energy*.

The products of chemical reactions differ in composition and structure from the original reactants. Thus they have larger or smaller quantities of chemical energy than those of the original reactants. If the product has a *smaller* quantity of energy, energy is *liberated* during the reaction—usually as heat and sometimes light or electric energy. If the product has a *larger* quantity of energy, energy is *absorbed* during the reaction.

Calcium carbide, a compound formed of the elements calcium and carbon, is produced in the intense heat of an electric furnace. The compound carbon disulfide is formed when hot sulfur vapor is passed over white-hot carbon in an electric furnace. Heat energy is absorbed continuously while these chemical reactions proceed. *Any process that absorbs energy as it progresses is said to be* **endothermic**.

Some chemical reactions are important because of their products. Others are important because of the energy that is released. When fuels are burned, large amounts of heat energy are released rapidly. Many similar reactions occur in nature but take place so slowly that the release of heat is not noticed. *Any process that liberates energy as it proceeds is said to be* **exothermic**. The majority of chemical reactions that occur spontaneously in nature are exothermic. One notable exception is the photosynthesis process in green plants. This process is endothermic. Solar energy is stored in the product of photosynthesis (a sugar) as chemical energy.

As fuels are burned, light energy usually accompanies the release of heat. A photoflash lamp is designed to release a maximum amount of energy as light. The final proof of a chemical reaction rests with the analysis of the products. However, *the evolution of heat and light* usually indicates a chemical reaction, as illustrated in Figure 2-11.

The explosion of dynamite is a violent exothermic chemical reaction that is ordinarily used to produce mechanical energy. Similarly, the combustion of a mixture of gasoline vapor and air in the cylinder of an automobile engine produces mechanical energy.

The zinc cup in a flashlight cell acts as the negative electrode in a chemical reaction when the cell is in use. During the reaction, chemical energy is converted to electric energy. The resulting *electric current* gives evidence of the chemical reaction by heating the lamp filament to incandescence.

The production of a gas usually indicates that a chemical reaction is taking place. However, a boiling liquid, a dissolved

Energy is absorbed in endothermic reactions.

Energy is released in exothermic reactions.

A

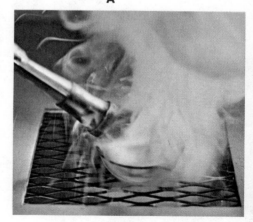

B

Figure 2-11. The elements sulfur and zinc mixed in the evaporating dish at room temperature (A) do not react chemically until the temperature of the mixture is raised as in (B). Once started, the reaction is exothermic.

gas escaping from a solution, or gas escaping from the surface of a solid should not be mistaken as evidence of chemical reaction.

The formation of a precipitate, an insoluble solid formed when one solution is added to another, provides evidence that a chemical reaction occurred as the two solutions were mixed.

Chemists make use of various agents to initiate chemical reactions or to control reactions already started. Some form of energy is often used.

1. Heat energy. A match is kindled by rubbing it over a rough surface to heat it by friction. If paper is held in the flame of the burning match, the paper ignites and begins to burn. Heat from the burning match is required to start this combustion; once started, however, it proceeds as an exothermic reaction. It is not necessary to continue supplying heat from the burning match in order to keep the paper burning.

Many chemical reactions that occur in the preparation of foods are endothermic. Heat is supplied to sustain these reactions. As a rule, increasing the temperature increases the rate of chemical reaction. *Each increase in temperature of 10 C° approximately doubles the rate of many chemical reactions.*

2. Light energy. Photosynthesis, the endothermic reaction by which green plants manufacture food, requires light energy. In photography, a camera shutter is opened for a fraction of a second and light falls on the light-sensitive film. This light energy triggers a chemical reaction in the film, and a "latent" (invisible) image is formed. From this image a picture can be developed at some future time.

3. Electric energy. If a direct current of electricity is passed through water (to which a little acid has been added to improve its conductivity), the water is decomposed to hydrogen and oxygen. Similar procedures are used for recharging storage batteries, electroplating one metal on the surface of another, recovering aluminum and other metals from their ores, and purifying some metals. Electric energy is also used to produce heat for thermal processes. The use of an electric furnace in the production of calcium carbide and carbon disulfide was mentioned earlier in this section.

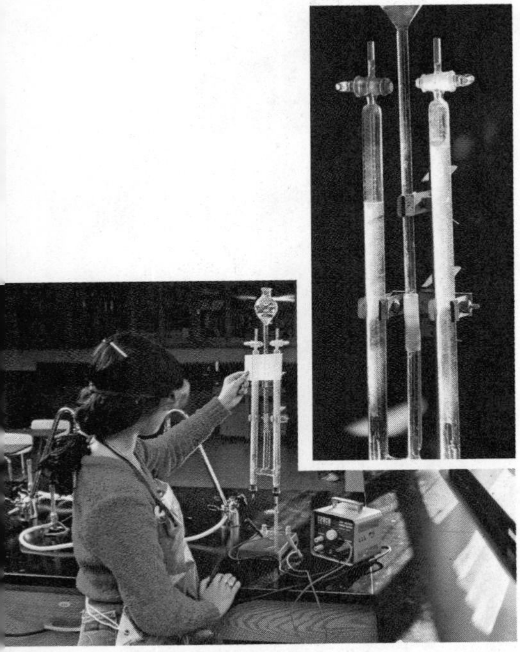

4. Solution in water. Baking powder is a mixture of two or more compounds. No chemical reaction occurs as long as the mixture is kept *dry.* However, when water is added to baking powder, a chemical reaction begins immediately and a gas is released. Many chemicals that do not react in the *dry* state begin to react as soon as they are dissolved in water.

5. Catalysis (kuh-*tal*-uh-sis). Some chemical reactions are promoted by *catalysts* (*kat*-uh-lists). These are specific agents that promote reactions that would otherwise be difficult or impractical to carry out. A catalyst does not start a chemical reaction that would not occur of and by itself. For example, oxygen

A Celsius temperature readout of 10 degrees is expressed as 10 °C. A Celsius temperature interval or temperature difference of 10 degrees is expressed as 10 C°.

Figure 2-12. Electric energy can be used to decompose water. Oxygen gas is collected at the positive electrode and hydrogen gas is collected at the negative electrode.

can be prepared in the laboratory by heating a mixture of potassium chlorate and manganese dioxide. Without the manganese dioxide, the preparation would have to be carried out at a higher temperature. Also, the gas would be produced more slowly. The manganese dioxide aids the reaction by its presence. It can be recovered in its original form at the conclusion of the experiment. *A **catalyst** is a substance or combination of substances that increases the rate of a chemical reaction without itself being permanently changed.*

Many chemical processes, such as the production of vegetable shortening, the manufacture of synthetic rubber, and the preparation of high-octane gasoline, depend on specific catalytic agents for their successful operation.

◻ 2.14 Reaction tendencies

It is not surprising to see a ball roll down an incline unaided; it is just what would be expected. Potential energy is given up in this process, and the ball attains a more stable state at a lower energy level. It would be surprising, however, if the ball rolled up the incline by and of itself. From such experiences with nature, a basic rule for natural processes becomes apparent: *There is a tendency for processes to occur that lead to a lower energy state.* This tendency in nature is toward greater *stability* (resistance to change) in a system.

The great majority of chemical reactions in nature are exothermic. As the reactions proceed, energy is liberated and the products have less energy than the original reactants. With the above rule in mind, one would expect exothermic reactions to occur spontaneously; that is, they have the potential to proceed without the assistance of an external agent.

It should follow that endothermic reactions, in which energy is absorbed, would not occur spontaneously but would proceed only with the assistance of an external agent. Certainly energy must be expended on the ball to roll it up the incline. At the top of the incline its potential energy is high and its stability is low.

There are several processes that occur spontaneously with the absorption of energy. When steam is passed over hot carbon, carbon monoxide gas and hydrogen gas are produced and heat is absorbed. The products are in a higher energy state than the reactants. This spontaneous reaction is endothermic and the rule appears to have failed. Apparently the tendency of a reaction to proceed spontaneously is not determined exclusively by the energy-change rule.

An ice cube melts spontaneously at room temperature as heat is transferred from the warm body of air to the cool ice and to the ice water formed. The well-ordered structure of the ice crystal (the solid phase) is lost, and the less orderly liquid phase of higher

Spontaneous chemical reactions are self-acting because of inherent properties of the system.

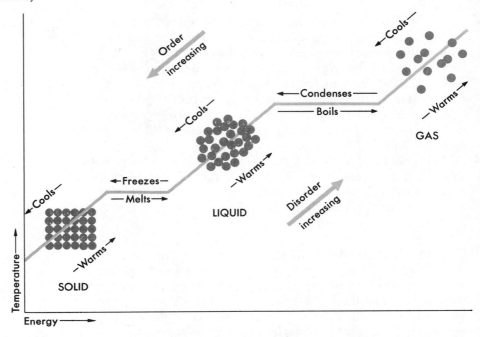

Figure 2-13. Change of phase. Observe that each change of phase occurs at a constant temperature.

energy content is formed. This phase-change mechanism is illustrated in Figure 2-13.

What is observed here is a tendency for the ice to move into the less orderly liquid phase. This observation suggests a second basic rule for natural processes: *There is a tendency for processes to occur that lead to a less orderly or a more disordered state.* This tendency in nature is toward greater *disorder* in a system. A disordered system is one that lacks a regular arrangement of its parts. *That property which describes the disorder of a system is called* **entropy**. The more disordered or more random the system, the *higher* is its entropy. Liquid water has higher entropy than ice.

Entropy is a measure of the disorder of a system.

Thus, processes in nature are driven in two ways: toward *lowest* energy and toward *highest* entropy. Where these two oppose each other, the dominant factor determines the direction of the spontaneous change. In the steam-plus-hot-carbon reaction, the temperature is high enough that the entropy factor overcomes the unfavorable energy-change factor. The spontaneous endothermic reaction occurs.

If the ice cube is subjected to a temperature below 0 °C, it does not melt. Liquid water placed in this environment freezes. The temperature is low enough that the energy-change factor overcomes the entropy-change factor. Heat is given up by the water (lower energy), and the well-ordered ice crystal is formed (lower entropy). These examples suggest that an entropy change is favored by high temperatures and an energy change is favored by low temperatures. Entropy as a factor in reaction systems will be considered in more detail in Section 20.7.

☐ 2.15 Nuclear changes

New substances are produced during a chemical reaction by rearranging the atoms of the original substances. In a *nuclear change,* new substances with new properties are also produced. There is a difference, however. *In a **nuclear change,** the new substances are formed by changes in the identity of the atoms themselves.*

In nature, some nuclear changes take place spontaneously. Radium atoms disintegrate in successive stages, finally becoming lead. Scientists are able to bring about many important nuclear changes. The elements beyond uranium named in Section 2.4 are products of nuclear changes. Nuclear reactions, both natural and artificial, will be discussed in Chapter 31.

SUMMARY

Matter is classified as a mixture or a pure substance. Pure substances are homogeneous and are either compounds or elements. Compounds can be decomposed into two or more simpler substances by ordinary chemical means. Elements cannot be further decomposed by ordinary chemical means. Mixtures are composed of two or more kinds of matter, each retaining its own characteristic properties.

Of the 107 known elements, the 92 ranging from hydrogen to uranium represent the pre–Atomic Age list of elements. Approximately 90 of these elements occur free or combined in the earth's crust. Only about 30 elements are fairly common. Based on their properties, elements are recognized as metals or nonmetals. Some elements having certain properties characteristic of metals and others of nonmetals are called metalloids, or semiconductors.

Symbols are used to represent elements. The symbol of an element stands for one atom of that element. The atom is the smallest particle of an element that can enter into combination with other elements. Compounds are composed of two or more elements. Every compound has a definite composition by mass.

Physical changes are those in which certain identifying properties of a substance remain unchanged. Examples are freezing, boiling, and dissolving. Chemical changes are those in which different substances with new properties are formed. Reactions that absorb energy as they proceed are endothermic. Reactions that liberate energy are exothermic. The rates of some chemical reactions can be accelerated by catalysts.

There is a basic tendency for processes to occur in nature that lead to a lower energy state. A second basic tendency is for processes to occur that lead to a more disordered or more random state. Entropy is the property that describes the disorder of a system. The more disordered the system, the higher is its entropy.

VOCABULARY

catalyst	endothermic	malleable	physical change
chemical change	entropy	metal	precipitate
chemical symbol	exothermic	metalloid	substance
compound	formula	mixture	symbol
ductile	heterogeneous	nonmetal	
element	homogeneous	nuclear change	

QUESTIONS

Group A

1. What are the three general classes of matter?
2. Distinguish between matter and a substance.
3. Distinguish between a complex substance and an elemental substance.
4. (a) What are the two general classes of elements? (b) Do all elements fit definitely into one of these classes?
5. Distinguish between a compound and a mixture.
6. What are the five most abundant elements by mass in the earth's surface environment?
7. (a) What are the properties of metals? (b) of nonmetals?
8. (a) How many elements are known? (b) How many were known prior to the beginning of the Atomic Age?
9. What is the meaning of a chemical symbol?
10. (a) List five familiar substances that are elements. (b) List five that are compounds. (c) List five familiar mixtures.
11. What is the difference between a physical change and a chemical reaction?
12. How can a chemist usually increase the speed of a chemical reaction?
13. If two or more elements have symbols beginning with the same letter, how are they distinguished?
14. If a symbol has two letters, (a) what is always true of the first letter? (b) what is always true of the second letter?
15. Write the names (spelled correctly) of the elements represented by the following symbols: (a) S; (b) Zn; (c) K; (d) N; (e) Ni; (f) Co; (g) Ba; (h) Fe; (i) Cl; (j) Cr; (k) Mg; (l) Mn; (m) As; (n) Pb; (o) Na.
16. Write the symbols for the following elements: (a) aluminum; (b) tungsten; (c) mercury; (d) carbon; (e) bromine; (f) silicon; (g) tin; (h) hydrogen; (i) gold; (j) silver; (k) fluorine; (l) strontium; (m) calcium; (n) phosphorus; (o) bismuth.
17. Write the systematic name and symbol for (a) element 101, (b) element 102, and (c) element 103.

18. Distinguish between exothermic and endothermic processes.

Group B

19. What difference in the properties of white sand and sugar would enable you to separate a mixture of the two substances?
20. How would you carry out the separation and recovery of both components of the sand-sugar mixture of Question 19?
21. Why is a solution recognized as a mixture?
22. What is the meaning of the phrase "definite composition by mass"?
23. Why is the law of definite composition important to chemists?
24. Consult the list of known elements in Appendix Table 4 and compile a list of those about which you already have some knowledge. Give the name, symbol, and pertinent information in column form.
25. Given two liquids, one a solution and the other a compound, how would you distinguish the solution from the compound?
26. Suppose you heat three different solids in open vessels and then allow them to cool. The first gains mass, the second loses mass, and the mass of the third remains unchanged. How can you reconcile these facts with the generalization that in a chemical reaction the total mass of the reacting materials is equal to the total mass of the products?
27. How can you explain the fact that gold, silver, and copper were known long before such metals as iron and aluminum?
28. Suppose you were given a sample of iodine crystals, a sample of antimony, and a sample of a mixture of iodine and antimony that had been ground together to form a fine powder of uniform consistency. Look up the physical and chemical properties of both iodine and antimony. Then list those properties of each element that you believe would be useful in separating and recovering them from the mixture. On the basis of these properties,

devise a procedure that would enable you to separate the two elements from the mixture and recover the separate elements.

29. Which of these changes are physical and which are chemical? (*a*) burning coal; (*b*) tarnishing silver; (*c*) magnetizing steel; (*d*) exploding gunpowder; (*e*) boiling water; (*f*) melting shortening.

30. Which of the chemical changes listed in Question 29 are also exothermic?

31. Show by example how each form of energy produces chemical changes: (*a*) heat energy; (*b*) light energy; (*c*) electric energy.

32. What evidences usually indicate chemical reaction?

33. Can you suggest a reason why iron and sulfur unite in definite proportions when iron sulfide is formed?

34. How can you determine whether a certain change is physical or chemical?

35. What two basic tendencies in nature appear to influence reaction processes?

36. An ice cube melts at room temperature and water freezes at temperatures of 0 °C and below. From these facts, what can you infer concerning the relationship between the temperature of a system and the influence of the entropy factor on the change that the system undergoes?

◀ | PROBLEMS

Group B

   (Show problem solutions by factor-label operations. Refer to Section 1.21.)

1. Determine the volume of an iron sphere that has a mass of 4.05 kg. (See Appendix Table 16 for properties of elements.)

2. How many kilocalories of heat are required to raise the temperature of $45\overline{0}$ g of water from 21.0 °C to 100.0 °C? (Refer to Section 1.16.)

3. If 1.25 L of water absorbs 45.5 kcal of heat, how much does the temperature of the water rise?

4. The Einstein equation $E = mc^2$ shows that 1.0 g of matter is the equivalent of 2.1×10^{10} kcal of energy (Section 1.11). When 2.0 g of hydrogen reacts with 16 g of oxygen to form 18 g of water, 68 kcal of heat energy is given up. To what loss of mass in the reaction system described is this quantity of energy equivalent?

5. Ordinary table salt is the compound sodium chloride, NaCl. According to the law of definite composition, the compound always consists of 39.3% sodium and 60.7% chlorine. What quantity of sodium chloride can be produced given 10.0 g of sodium and 20.0 g of chlorine? (A percentage composition may be interpreted as *grams of element per $10\overline{0}$ g of compound*.)

pioneers in chemistry

pioneer. *n.* One that originates or helps open up a new line of thought or activity; one who goes before, preparing the way for others to follow. —*v.* To discover or explore in advance of others.

Glen Theodore Seaborg
isolated U-233; transuranic elements; actinide series

Ernest Rutherford
atomic nucleus; alpha, beta, gamma radiation; proton

Amedeo Avogadro
1 mole = 6.02×10^{23} units

Henry Gwyn-Jeffreys Moseley
properties of an element are determined by its atomic number

Robert Boyle
$V \propto 1/p$; vacuum pump

John Dalton
atomic theory; law of partial pressure

The history of chemistry is replete with men and women who exemplify the true pioneer. Through new theories, experiments, discoveries, and inventions, they have brought chemistry to where it is today and charted its path for the future.

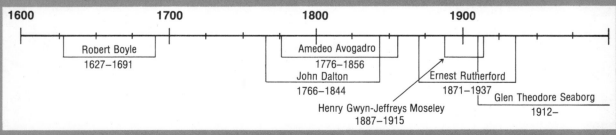

1600	1700	1800	1900

Robert Boyle
1627–1691

Amedeo Avogadro
1776–1856
John Dalton
1766–1844

Ernest Rutherford
1871–1937

Henry Gwyn-Jeffreys Moseley
1887–1915

Glen Theodore Seaborg
1912–

Atomic Structure

Homer, Sappho, Socrates, Plato, these are some of the illustrious citizens of early Greece who have profoundly influenced Western civilization. Their achievements, and those of other Greek thinkers, affect every aspect of our culture, including chemistry. The word entropy, in fact, is derived from the Greek word for change. *Many other chemical terms have Greek roots, and for good reason; the ancient Greeks were important pioneers in studying matter and speculating on its composition and changes. As early as the sixth century B.C., Greek philosophers theorized that all matter could be broken down into four basic substances: fire, air, earth, and water. In the fifth century, Democritus pondered further the nature of these primitive elements and postulated the existence of ultimate, indestructible particles — atoms.*

☐ 3.1 Particles of matter

For a very long time people have believed that matter is made up of simple, indivisible particles. As early as 400 B.C. some Greek thinkers had the idea that matter could not be destroyed. They believed that matter could be divided into smaller and smaller particles until a basic particle of matter that could not be divided further was reached. Such basic particles were thought to be the smallest particles of matter that existed. Democritus called them *atoms*. The word "atom" is from the Greek word meaning "indivisible."

When you crush a lump of sugar, you can see that it is made up of many small particles of sugar. You may grind these particles into very fine powder, but each tiny piece is still sugar. Now suppose you dissolve the sugar in water. The tiny particles disappear completely. Even if you look at the sugar-water solution through a microscope, you cannot see any sugar particles. However, if you taste the solution, you know that the sugar is still there.

If you open a laboratory gas valve, you can smell the escaping gas. Yet you cannot see gas particles in the air of the room, even if you use the most powerful microscope. These observations and many others like them have led scientists to believe that the basic particles of matter must be very, very small.

☐ 3.2 The atomic theory

Invention of the chemical balance gave chemists a tool for studying the composition of substances quantitatively. Chemists

In this chapter you will gain an understanding of:

- **the atomic theory**
- **the structure of the atom**
- **atomic number, mass number, and atomic mass**
- **isotopes**
- **the relationship between a mole and the Avogadro number**
- **gram-atomic weight and atomic weight**

Democritus (deh-mock-writ-us) (460–370 B.C.) was a Greek thinker. He believed that the hard atoms of the four primitive elements (earth, air, water, and fire) moved in a vacuum. The shape and size of these atoms explained some of their properties. For example, the atoms of fire were tiny spheres. Because of their smooth surfaces, they did not link with the atoms of the other elements. The atoms of earth, air, and water had shapes that enabled them to connect with each other and form visible matter.

Figure 3-1. The point of a tungsten needle as viewed through a field-ion microscope. This instrument magnifies objects up to 3,000,000 diameters and shows the regular arrangement of tungsten atoms in the metal.

John Dalton was an English schoolmaster. He was interested in the composition and properties of the gases in the atmosphere. He kept a daily record of the weather from 1787 until 1844.

A theory is a plausible explanation of an observed natural phenomenon in terms of a simple model with familiar properties. See Section 1.4(3).

showed, in the half-century prior to the year 1800, that substances they investigated are chemical combinations of a fairly small number of elements. They learned much about how elements combine to form compounds and how compounds can be broken down into their constituent elements. From this knowledge they formulated several quantitative laws of chemical combination, such as Proust's law of definite composition (see Section 2.9).

John Dalton's atomic theory, first conceived in 1803 and published in 1808–1810, postulated the existence of a different kind of atom for each element. His theory was ultimately accepted because it satisfactorily explained these laws. It forms the basis of modern atomic theory.

In science, a theory is never secure. Each new observation tests it. If the theory does not explain the new observation satisfactorily, the theory is either rejected or revised. With increased knowledge, Dalton's original theory has been revised. For example, Dalton thought that atoms of the same element were identical in all respects, particularly mass. But evidence now shows that all atoms of the same element do not have exactly the same mass. Generally, the atomic theory has stood the test of time. It has satisfactorily explained observations and laws in many different fields. It now includes information about

1. the structure and properties of atoms;
2. the kinds of compounds that atoms form;
3. the properties of compounds that atoms form;
4. the mass, volume, and energy relations of reactions between atoms.

*An **atom** is the smallest unit of an element that can exist either alone or in combination with atoms of the same or different elements.* It is the smallest individual structure of an element that retains the properties of the element. The chemical and physical properties of matter lead scientists to make the following statements about atoms and their properties:

1. All matter is made up of very small structures called *atoms.*
2. Atoms of the *same element* are *chemically alike;* atoms of *different elements* are *chemically different.*
3. Individual atoms of an element may not all have the same mass. However, *the atoms of an element,* as it occurs naturally, *have,* for practical purposes, *a definite average mass that is characteristic of the element.*
4. Individual atoms of different elements may have nearly identical masses. However, *the atoms of different naturally occurring elements have different average masses.*
5. Atoms are not subdivided in *chemical reactions.*

Right now statements 3 and 4 may be a bit puzzling. In Section 3.15, their meaning shall be made clearer.

☐ 3.3 The structure of the atom

For nearly 100 years, scientists have been gathering evidence about the structure of atoms. Some of this evidence has come from the study of radioactive elements such as radium and uranium. Particle accelerators, the mass spectrograph, the X-ray tube, the spectroscope, and a variety of other electronic devices have provided additional information. From all this information scientists have developed a theory of atomic structure. This atomic structure model will be described in the following sections of this chapter and in Chapter 4. As you read, remember that this explanation is based on the best, present understanding of experiments on atomic structure. Future experiments may necessitate changes in the model.

At the present time, scientists know that atoms are not simple indivisible particles. Instead, they are composed of several different kinds of still smaller particles arranged in a complex way.

An atom consists of two main parts. *The positively charged central part is called the **nucleus**.* It is very small and very dense. Its diameter is about 10^{-12} cm. Its density is about 20 metric tn/cm^3.

A more useful unit for atomic sizes is the angstrom.

$$1 \text{ angstrom (Å)} = 10^{-8} \text{ cm}$$

To get some idea of the extreme smallness of the angstrom, consider the fact that 1 cm is the same fractional part of 10^3 km (about 600 miles) as 1 Å is of 1 cm.

The diameter of a nucleus is about 10^{-12} cm, or about 10^{-4} Å. This is about one ten-thousandth of the diameter of the atom itself, since atoms range from 1 Å to 5 Å in diameter.

The idea that an atom has a nucleus is the result of experiments conducted about 1910 by the English physicist Ernest Rutherford (1871–1937). Rutherford used an evacuated tube (a tube from which the gas has been pumped). In it, a beam of high-speed, positively charged particles was aimed at a thin sheet of gold. Most of the particles passed straight through the gold. A few were slightly deflected (turned away from a straight course) as they passed through the gold. A very few were greatly deflected back from the gold. These very few great deflections were explained by assuming that the positively charged particles bounced back if they approached a positively charged atomic nucleus head-on. The few slight deflections were explained by assuming that the particles were turned from their paths in near misses of nuclei. But most of the particles passed straight through the gold foil. Therefore, the experimenters reasoned, most of an atom must consist of space through which such particles could move readily. In fact, since a vast majority of the particles went undeflected, the nucleus must occupy a very, very small portion of the volume of an atom.

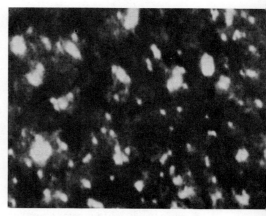

Figure 3-2. Single uranium atoms magnified more than five million times by a scanning transmission electron microscope. The small bright spots are single uranium atoms. The larger white spots are clusters of uranium atoms. The background is a thin carbon filament, about six atoms thick, that supports the uranium atoms.

Figure 3-3. A schematic diagram of Rutherford's experiment. High-speed positively charged particles are given off in many directions by the emitter. The hole in the lead plate allows a beam of particles moving toward the gold foil to pass through. The solid portion of the lead plate absorbs the other particles. Most of the high-speed positively charged particles in the beam passed through the gold foil. A few were slightly deflected, while a very few were very greatly deflected. The screens emit a flash of light when struck by a charged particle.

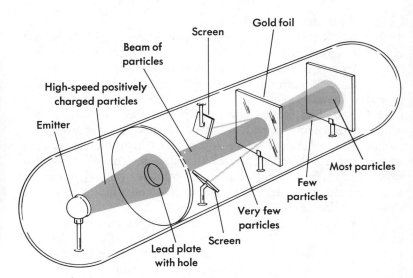

The other part of an atom lies outside the central nucleus. It is made up of negatively charged particles and is called the *electron cloud*. The electron cloud gives an atom its volume and keeps out other atoms.

Each atom is electrically neutral. This electric neutrality indicates that the total positive charge of the nucleus must equal the total negative charge of the electron cloud.

◻ 3.4 The electron cloud

An electron cloud is made up of negatively charged particles called *electrons*. Electrons move about the nucleus with different energies. Several electrons having similar energies comprise a *shell* and are said to be in the same *energy level*.

About 1913, the Danish scientist Niels Bohr (1885–1962) compared the movements of electrons about the nucleus of an atom with the revolution of the planets around the sun. The motion of the electrons is now believed to be much less definite than the orbits of the planets. Electrons move about the nucleus of an atom much as bees move about in the area near their hive. Sometimes the electrons are near the nucleus; sometimes they are farther away. While electrons do have some properties of particles, it is not possible for scientists to determine the paths along which they move. The electrons just seem to occupy the relatively vast empty space around the nucleus. The positions of the electrons are best visualized as an electron cloud about the nucleus.

Electrons were discovered in 1897 by the English scientist J. J. Thomson (1856–1940).

***Electrons** are negatively charged particles with a mass of 9.110 × 10⁻²⁸ g.* The mass of an electron is $\frac{1}{1837}$ of the mass of the most common type of hydrogen atom. The most common type of hydrogen atom has the simplest structure and the least mass of any atom.

The electron is believed to be a pointlike particle. No smaller quantity of electric charge than that on one electron has been found. Regardless of the atom of which an electron is a part, *all electrons are identical.*

◻ 3.5 The nucleus of the atom

Except for the simplest type of hydrogen atom, a nucleus is made up of two kinds of particles, *protons* and *neutrons*. **Protons** *are positively charged particles with a mass of 1.673 × 10⁻²⁴ g.* This mass is $\frac{1836}{1837}$ of the mass of the simplest type of hydrogen atom. This atom consists of a single-proton nucleus with a single electron moving about it. Most of the mass of the simplest type of hydrogen atom is due to the mass of the proton. The diameter of a proton is about 10^{-5} Å. The electric charge on the proton has the same magnitude as that on an electron, but is positive in sign. In any atom, the number of electrons and protons is equal. Since protons and electrons have equal but opposite electric charges, an atom is electrically neutral.

Neutrons *are neutral particles with a mass of 1.675 × 10⁻²⁴ g,* which is about the same mass as a proton. They have no electric charge.

Particles that have the same electric charge generally repel one another. Nevertheless, as many as 100 protons can exist close together in a nucleus. This close existence of protons in the nucleus can occur when up to about 150 neutrons are also present. When a proton and a neutron are very close to each other, there is a strong attraction between them. Proton-proton attractive forces and neutron-neutron attractive forces also exist when these pairs of particles are very close together. These short-range proton-neutron, proton-proton, and neutron-neutron forces hold the nuclear particles together. They are referred to as *nuclear forces.*

The nuclei of atoms of different elements are different. The amounts of positive charge are always different. The nuclei of atoms of different elements also have different masses, although the difference in mass is sometimes very slight.

Protons were discovered in the early years of this century. Today there is evidence that protons have an internal structure. One theory supposes that protons are mostly empty space containing three, hard, fundamental pointlike units called quarks.

Neutrons were discovered by the English scientist James C. Chadwick (1891–1974) in 1932. The experiment during which this discovery was made is described in Section 31.13. Neutrons are also believed to have an internal structure consisting of quarks.

In nuclear changes, particles in addition to protons and neutrons come from the nucleus. We shall describe some of these in Chapter 31. We do not need to know about these particles now to understand atomic structure and chemical changes.

Table 3-1
PARTICLES IN AN ATOM

Name	Mass	Atomic mass (See Section 3.13)	Mass number (See Section 3.7)	Charge
electron	9.110×10^{-28} g	0.0005486 u	0	−1
proton	1.673×10^{-24} g	1.007276 u	1	+1
neutron	1.675×10^{-24} g	1.008664 u	1	0

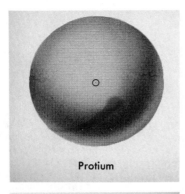

Protium

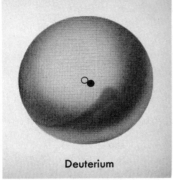

Deuterium

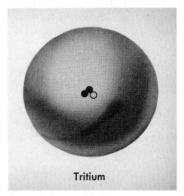

Tritium

Figure 3-4. Tentative models of the three isotopes of hydrogen: protium, deuterium, and tritium. Each has one proton in the nucleus and one electron moving about the nucleus in the 1st energy level. The only structural difference between them is the number of neutrons in the nucleus of each atom. In these diagrams, the nuclei are enlarged in proportion to the size of the atom to show their composition.

☐ 3.6 Hydrogen atoms

The most common type of hydrogen is sometimes called *protium* (*proht*-ee-um). Its atoms have the simplest possible composition. The nucleus of a protium atom consists of *one proton*. This proton has one electron moving about it. This electron could most probably be found at a distance from the nucleus corresponding to the innermost shell, or lowest energy level, that an electron can occupy. This shell or energy level is called the **K shell** or **1st energy level.** An illustration may help you to better understand the sizes and distances between the particles of the protium atom. Picture the nucleus (a proton) as being 1 cm in diameter (about the diameter of the end of your little finger). Comparatively, the much smaller electron is on the average about 48 m from the nucleus. (The 48-m distance is about one-half the length of a football field.) The electron can be thought of as moving about the nucleus and effectively occupying the space surrounding it.

In addition to protium, which makes up 99.985% of naturally occurring hydrogen, there are two other known forms of hydrogen atoms. One of these is *deuterium* (dyou-*tir*-ee-um), which occurs to the extent of 0.015% in nature. Each deuterium atom has a nucleus containing *one proton* and *one neutron,* with one electron moving about it.

The third form of hydrogen is *tritium* (*trit*-ee-um). Tritium is a radioactive form. It exists in nature in very small amounts but can be prepared artificially by a nuclear reaction. Each tritium atom has a nucleus composed of *one proton* and *two neutrons,* with one electron moving about it.

☐ 3.7 Atomic number and mass number

*The **atomic number** of an atom is the number of protons in the nucleus of that atom.* An element consists of atoms, all of which have the same number of protons in their nuclei. Hence, all atoms of the same element have the same atomic number. (All unexcited neutral atoms of an element have the same arrangement of electrons about their nuclei, too.) The atoms of the element hydrogen, whether they be protium, deuterium, or tritium atoms, have one proton in each nucleus. Their atomic number, therefore, is 1. Any atom having the atomic number 1 contains one proton in its nucleus and is a hydrogen atom.

However, because protium, deuterium, and tritium nuclei contain different numbers of neutrons, these atoms have different masses. *Atoms of the same element that have different masses are called **isotopes.***

All elements have two or more isotopes. Isotopes of an element may occur naturally, or they may be prepared artificially. While isotopes have different masses, they do not differ significantly in chemical properties. See Appendix Table 2 for a list of natural and radioactive isotopes of some of the elements.

Each different variety of atom as determined by the number of protons and number of neutrons in its nucleus is called a **nuclide**. Nuclides having *the same number of protons* (the same atomic number) are *isotopes*. The three hydrogen isotopes are the nuclides protium, deuterium, and tritium.

In addition to their names, hydrogen nuclides may also be distinguished by their *mass numbers*. *The* **mass number** *of an atom is the sum of the number of protons and neutrons in its nucleus.* The mass number of protium is 1 (1 proton + 0 neutron). That of deuterium is 2 (1 proton + 1 neutron). That of tritium is 3 (1 proton + 2 neutrons). Sometimes these isotopes are named hydrogen-1, hydrogen-2, and hydrogen-3, respectively.

◻ 3.8 Elements in atomic number order

At the time of this writing, 107 different elements are known or reported to exist. Their atomic numbers range from 1 to 107. The elements may be arranged in the order of increasing atomic number. This arrangement simplifies the understanding of atomic structure. If the elements are arranged in this way, the nuclei of the atoms of one element differ from those of the preceding element by one additional proton per nucleus. (The number of neutrons per nucleus may or may not change from atom to atom.)

An element is a substance all the atoms of which have the same number of protons; that is, they have the same atomic number. This statement is a more precise definition of an element than that given in Section 2.3.

◻ 3.9 Helium atoms

The second element in order of complexity is helium. Since each helium nucleus contains two protons, the atomic number of helium is 2. Natural helium exists as a mixture of two isotopes. Helium-3 occurs to the extent of $1.34 \times 10^{-4}\%$. Helium-4 accounts for practically 100% of natural helium. These helium nuclides contain 1 neutron and 2 neutrons per nucleus, respectively. (Note that the number of neutrons in the nucleus of an atom may be determined by subtracting the atomic number from the mass number.) Moving about each helium nucleus are two electrons, both in the *1st energy level*. The chemical properties and spectrum of helium indicate that the 1st energy level may contain a *maximum* of two electrons. Thus, helium atoms have a *filled* 1st energy level.

The atoms of hydrogen have one 1st-energy-level electron. The atoms of helium have two (the maximum number). Hydrogen and helium, then, form the first *series* of elements.

◻ 3.10 Lithium atoms

Lithium exists in nature as two isotopes. Each atom of one isotope contains 3 protons, 3 neutrons, and 3 electrons. Each atom of the other isotope contains 3 protons, 4 neutrons, and 3 electrons. By the composition of these atoms, the atomic number of lithium is known to be 3 (3 protons). The mass number of the first

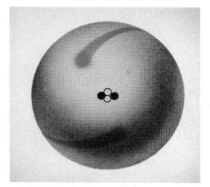

Figure 3-5. Tentative model of a helium-4 atom. Its nucleus consists of two protons and two neutrons. Its two electrons move about this nucleus and completely fill the 1st energy level of the atom.

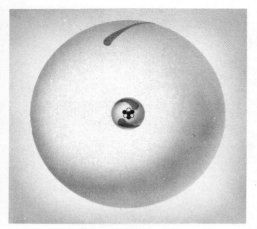

Figure 3-6. Tentative model of a lithium-7 atom. This atom has a nucleus consisting of three protons and four neutrons. Two electrons are in the 1st energy level and one is in the 2nd energy level. Lithium is the first element in the second series.

Atomic masses are measured using a mass spectrograph. This device was developed by F. W. Aston, an English scientist, in 1919.

isotope is 6 (3 protons + 3 neutrons). The mass number of the second isotope is 7 (3 protons + 4 neutrons). These isotopes are lithium-6 and lithium-7.

The chemical properties of lithium help chemists determine its electron arrangement. Two of the three electrons in a lithium atom move in the 1st energy level. The third moves about the nucleus at a greater distance and with higher energy than the other two. It moves in the next larger shell, or next higher energy level. This is called the *L shell* or *2nd energy level*. The 1st energy level contains no more than two electrons. When it has this maximum of two electrons, additional electrons occupy higher energy levels at greater distances from the nucleus.

◻ 3.11 Other atoms of the second series

The element with atomic number 4 is beryllium. Naturally occurring beryllium consists of only one nuclide, beryllium-9. Beryllium nuclei consist of four protons and five neutrons. The four electrons are arranged with two in the 1st energy level and two in the 2nd energy level. Next in order of atomic structure are the elements boron, carbon, nitrogen, oxygen, fluorine, and neon. The atoms of each successive element have one additional proton per nucleus and may have one or two additional neutrons per nucleus. Each successive element has one additional electron in the 2nd energy level of each of its atoms. The atoms of the element neon have eight electrons in the 2nd energy level. The chemical properties and spectrum of neon indicate that the 2nd energy level may contain a maximum of eight electrons. So neon completes the second series of elements.

Table 3-2 contains information about the composition of the nuclei and electron configurations (arrangements) of atoms in the first and second series.

◻ 3.12 The atoms of the third series

The elements in the third series are sodium, magnesium, aluminum, silicon, phosphorus, sulfur, chlorine, and argon. The atoms of these elements have a filled 1st energy level of two electrons and a filled 2nd energy level of eight electrons. Successive electrons occupy the *M shell* or *3rd energy level*. This level contains eight electrons in the atoms of argon.

◻ 3.13 Atomic mass

The actual mass of a single atom is very small. An atom of oxygen-16 has a mass of 2.65×10^{-23} g. A hydrogen-1 atom has a mass of 1.67×10^{-24} g. These numbers are not very easy to use in chemical arithmetic problems. Therefore, a system for expressing the masses of atoms in numbers on a relative scale has been worked out. These relative numbers are easier to use.

Table 3-2
NATURALLY OCCURRING NUCLIDES
(First and Second Series of Elements)

Name of nuclide	Abundance	Atomic number	Mass number	Composition of nucleus		Electron configuration	
				Protons	Neutrons	1st energy level (K shell)	2nd energy level (L shell)
hydrogen-1 (protium)	99.985%	1	1	1	0	1	
hydrogen-2 (deuterium)	0.015%	1	2	1	1	1	
helium-3	0.00013%	2	3	2	1	2	
helium-4	99.99987%	2	4	2	2	2	
lithium-6	7.42%	3	6	3	3	2	1
lithium-7	92.58%	3	7	3	4	2	1
beryllium-9	100%	4	9	4	5	2	2
boron-10	19.78%	5	10	5	5	2	3
boron-11	80.22%	5	11	5	6	2	3
carbon-12	98.892%	6	12	6	6	2	4
carbon-13	1.108%	6	13	6	7	2	4
nitrogen-14	99.635%	7	14	7	7	2	5
nitrogen-15	0.365%	7	15	7	8	2	5
oxygen-16	99.759%	8	16	8	8	2	6
oxygen-17	0.037%	8	17	8	9	2	6
oxygen-18	0.204%	8	18	8	10	2	6
fluorine-19	100%	9	19	9	10	2	7
neon-20	90.92%	10	20	10	10	2	8
neon-21	0.257%	10	21	10	11	2	8
neon-22	8.82%	10	22	10	12	2	8

A relative scale consists of numbers without units or with specially defined units. These relative-scale numbers must be directly proportional to the magnitude of some property of matter that can be measured. An example will make this definition clearer. Suppose you wish to set up a relative scale of weights of the members of your class. First, the weight of one member of the class is selected and given a simple numerical value. In theory, it does not make any difference whose weight is selected or what numerical value it is assigned. In practice, choices should be made on the basis of convenience and usefulness.

Suppose the weight of a 125-lb (pound) pupil is selected and assigned a value of 5.00 units. Now the *relative* weights of the other members of the class can be calculated by comparing their *actual* weights with that of the 125-lb pupil. A 150-lb pupil has a

Zeros to the right of a nonzero digit, but to the left of an understood decimal point, are not significant unless specifically indicated to be significant. The rightmost such zero that is significant is indicated by a bar placed above it.

weight that is $\dfrac{15\overline{0}\ \text{lb}}{125\ \text{lb}}$ or 1.20 times that of the 125-lb pupil. Since the 125-lb pupil has an assigned weight of 5.00 units on the relative weight scale, the 15$\overline{0}$-lb pupil will have a relative weight of 1.20 × 5.00 units = 6.00 units. This relative weight could have been calculated in one step by using the expression $\dfrac{15\overline{0}\ \text{lb}}{125\ \text{lb}} \times 5.00$ units = 6.00 units. Similarly, the weight of a 20$\overline{0}$-lb pupil will have a value of $\dfrac{20\overline{0}\ \text{lb}}{125\ \text{lb}} \times 5.00$ units = 8.00 units on the relative scale. The weight of a 10$\overline{0}$-lb pupil will have a value of $\dfrac{10\overline{0}\ \text{lb}}{125\ \text{lb}} \times$ 5.00 units = 4.00 units on the relative scale. These relative weights, 5.00 units, 6.00 units, 8.00 units, and 4.00 units, are directly proportional to the actual weights of 125 lb, 15$\overline{0}$ lb, 20$\overline{0}$ lb, and 10$\overline{0}$ lb, respectively. If it is the *relationship* between these weights that is important, then it does not matter whether the actual weights or the relative weights are used. In the example given, the actual weights and the relative weights are probably equally convenient to use. But the very small numbers that express the actual masses of atoms in grams are not convenient to use.

In order to set up a relative scale of masses of atoms, one atom is chosen and assigned a relative mass value. The masses of all other atoms are then expressed in relation to this defined relative mass. Such a system of relative masses was set up by the world organizations of chemists and physicists. In this system, the carbon-12 atom was chosen and assigned a relative mass of exactly 12 units. The units of this relative mass scale are called *atomic mass units* and are abbreviated *u*. One atomic mass unit, 1 *u*, is exactly $\frac{1}{12}$ the mass of a carbon-12 atom, or 1.6605655 × 10^{-24} g. The *atomic mass* of a carbon-12 atom is exactly 12 *u*. *The mass of an atom expressed in atomic mass units is called the* **atomic mass** *of the atom*.

The hydrogen-1 atom has a mass about $\frac{1}{12}$ that of the carbon-12 atom. So it has a relative mass (atomic mass) of about $\frac{1}{12}$ of 12 or about 1 *u*. The accurate value for the atomic mass of hydrogen-1 atoms is 1.007825 *u*.

The mass of a hydrogen-2 atom is about $\frac{1}{6}$ that of a carbon-12 atom. Its atomic mass has been measured to be 2.014102 *u*. An oxygen-16 atom has about $\frac{4}{3}$ the mass of a carbon-12 atom. Careful measurements show its atomic mass to be 15.994915 *u*. The mass of a magnesium-24 atom is found to be slightly less than double that of a carbon-12 atom. Its accurate atomic mass is 23.985042 *u*. In the same way, the atomic mass of any nuclide is determined by comparison with the mass of a carbon-12 atom. Atomic masses are very accurately known, as the values given above indicate. You have learned that the *mass number* is the total number of protons and neutrons in the nucleus of an atom. You can now see that it is also *the whole number closest to the atomic mass.*

The masses of the subatomic particles may also be expressed on the atomic-mass scale. The atomic mass of the electron is 0.0005486 u. That of the proton is 1.007276 u, and that of the neutron is 1.008664 u.

◻ 3.14 The Avogadro number and the mole

You have learned (Section 3.13) that the atomic mass of a carbon-12 atom is exactly 12 u. But atomic mass units are so very small that they are impractical for laboratory mass determinations. A chemist would find it much easier to weigh out exactly 12 g of carbon-12 (to the precision limit of the balance). How many atoms are there in exactly 12 g of carbon-12?

$$12.00000 \text{ g C} \times \frac{u}{1.6605655 \times 10^{-24} \text{ g}} \times \frac{1 \text{ atom}}{12 \text{ } u} = 6.022045 \times 10^{23} \text{ atoms C}$$

The number of atoms in the atomic mass of a nuclide in grams is an important unit of measure in chemistry. It is the number of atoms in exactly 12 grams of carbon-12, 6.022045×10^{23} atoms. It is also the number of atoms in 1.007825 g of hydrogen-1.

$$1.007825 \text{ g H} \times \frac{u}{1.6605655 \times 10^{-24} \text{ g}} \times \frac{1 \text{ atom}}{1.007825 \text{ } u} = 6.022045 \times 10^{23} \text{ atoms H}$$

It is also the number of atoms in 15.994915 g of oxygen-16. You should recognize that the number of atoms in these three cases is identical. This is true because the mass taken in grams is directly proportional to the atomic mass of each nuclide. In the calculation, these numbers cancel out.

This quantity, 6.022045×10^{23}, is so important in science that it has been given a special name. It is called the *Avogadro number,* honoring the Italian chemist and physicist Amedeo Avogadro (1776–1856). This constant is quite useful and should be remembered to at least three significant figures: 6.02×10^{23}.

*The amount of substance containing the Avogadro number of any kind of chemical unit is called a **mole** of that substance.* Thus, exactly 12 g of carbon-12 is a mole of carbon-12 atoms; 1.007825 g of hydrogen-1 is a mole of hydrogen-1 atoms; 15.994915 g of oxygen-16 is a mole of oxygen-16 atoms. Note that *mole* is the name of the quantity containing a convenient number (6.02×10^{23}) of chemical units. Here the chemical unit is the atom. "Mole" is used by chemists as a counting unit the way a grocer uses "dozen" or "case," or a stationer uses "gross" or "ream." A dozen eggs is the quantity 12 eggs; a case of soft drink bottles is the quantity 24 bottles; a gross of pencils is the quantity 144 pencils; a ream of paper is the quantity 500 sheets of paper. A mole of atoms is the quantity 6.02×10^{23} atoms. The mole is a

To help you understand the enormous number of units in one mole, imagine this situation. Suppose everyone living today on the earth (4 billion people) were to help count the atoms in one mole of an element (copper, for instance). If each person counted continuously at the rate of one atom per second, it would require about 5 million years for all the atoms to be counted.

1 mole of lead atoms
6.02×10^{23} atoms
207.2 g Pb

Table 3-3
MOLAR QUANTITIES OF NUCLIDES

Nuclide	Atomic mass	Molar quantity	Number of atoms	Mass
C-12	12 u exactly	1 mole	6.02×10^{23}	12 g exactly
H-1	1.007825 u	1 mole	6.02×10^{23}	1.007825 g
O-16	15.994915 u	1 mole	6.02×10^{23}	15.994915 g

1 mole of copper atoms
6.02×10^{23} atoms
63.5 g Cu

1 mole of carbon atoms
6.02×10^{23} atoms
12.0 g C

Figure 3-7. The mass in grams of one mole of atoms of an element, 6.02×10^{23} atoms, is the gram-atomic weight of the element. The numerical portion of this quantity is the atomic weight of the element.

The use of the word "weight" in the expression "atomic weight" is, of course, not correct since the quantity so named is a "mass." However, "atomic weight" has been used historically and still is used today for this concept.

very important unit of measure in chemistry. It will be used throughout this text. See Table 3-3.

◻ 3.15 Atomic weight

Naturally occurring elements usually exist as a mixture of several isotopes. The percentage of each isotope in the naturally occurring element is nearly always the same, no matter where the element is found. Naturally occurring hydrogen consists of 99.985% hydrogen-1 atoms, atomic mass 1.007825 u; and 0.015% hydrogen-2 atoms, atomic mass 2.014102 u. In one mole of atoms of this mixture of isotopes, there will be 0.99985 mole of hydrogen-1 atoms and 0.00015 mole of hydrogen-2 atoms. The mass of 0.99985 mole of hydrogen-1 atoms is

$$0.99985 \text{ mole} \times \frac{1.007825 \text{ g}}{1 \text{ mole}} = 1.00767 \text{ g}$$

and the mass of 0.00015 mole of hydrogen-2 atoms is

$$0.00015 \text{ mole} \times \frac{2.014102 \text{ g}}{1 \text{ mole}} = 0.00030 \text{ g}$$

The mass of one mole of atoms of this mixture is therefore

$$1.00767 \text{ g} + 0.00030 \text{ g} = 1.00797 \text{ g}$$

*The mass in grams of one mole of naturally occurring atoms of an element is called the **gram-atomic weight** of the element.* From the calculation, 1.00797 g is the *gram-atomic weight* of hydrogen.

*The ratio of the gram-atomic weight of an element to one-twelfth the mass in grams of one mole of carbon-12 atoms is the **atomic weight** of the element.* Recall from Section 3.14 that, by definition, one mole of carbon-12 atoms has a mass of exactly 12 g. One-twelfth of exactly 12 g is exactly 1 g. The gram-atomic weight of hydrogen was calculated to be 1.00797 g. So, the *atomic weight* of hydrogen is the ratio $\frac{1.00797 \text{ g}}{1 \text{ g}}$ or 1.00797. The atomic weight of an element is the numerical portion of the gram-atomic weight.

Similarly, naturally occurring carbon consists of 98.89% carbon-12, atomic mass exactly 12 *u* (by definition), and 1.11% carbon-13, atomic mass 13.00335 *u*. One mole of atoms of this mixture has a mass of 12.011 g. Thus, 12.011 g is the gram-atomic weight of carbon and 12.011 is its atomic weight.

Atomic weights are important to the chemist because they indicate relative mass relationships between reacting elements. They enable the chemist to predict the quantities of materials that will be involved in chemical reactions.

Atomic weights appear in the periodic table that is on the inside back cover of this book and in Appendix Table 4. They include the most recent accurate figures. Atomic weights are occasionally revised when new data become available. You need not memorize them. Approximate atomic weights are given on the inside of the front cover and in Appendix Table 5. These values are accurate enough for use in solving problems in high school chemistry. However, for more advanced chemical work the accurate atomic weights in the periodic table or Appendix Table 4 must always be used.

SAMPLE PROBLEM

What is the mass in grams of 3.50 moles of copper atoms?

SOLUTION

The atomic weight of copper from the table inside the back cover or from Appendix Table 4 is 63.546. Therefore, the gram-atomic weight of copper, or the mass of one mole of copper atoms, is 63.546 g. The mass of 3.50 moles of copper atoms is

$$3.50 \text{ moles} \times \frac{63.546 \text{ g Cu}}{\text{mole}} = 222 \text{ g Cu}$$

Since the number of moles of copper atoms is expressed in the problem to only three significant figures, the approximate atomic weight of copper found in the table inside the front cover or in Appendix Table 5, 63.5, could have been used in the solution. The same answer is obtained.

$$3.50 \text{ moles} \times \frac{63.5 \text{ g Cu}}{\text{mole}} = 222 \text{ g Cu}$$

| PRACTICE PROBLEMS

1. What is the mass in grams of 5.75 moles of copper atoms?
   ans. 365 g Cu
2. What is the mass in grams of 5.75 moles of silver atoms?
   ans. 620 g Ag

◖ **SAMPLE PROBLEM**

How many moles of atoms are there in 6.195 g of phosphorus?

◖ **SOLUTION**

Since the mass of phosphorus is given to four significant figures, the atomic weight of phosphorus given to at least four significant figures in the table inside the back cover must be used. Rounded to four significant figures, 30.97376 is 30.97. Thus, there is one mole of phosphorus atoms in 30.97 g of phosphorus. Then 6.195 g of phosphorus contains

$$6.195 \text{ g P} \times \frac{1 \text{ mole}}{30.97 \text{ g P}} = 0.2000 \text{ mole}$$

Note that significant-figure rules permit an answer calculated to four significant figures.

PRACTICE PROBLEMS

1. How many moles of atoms are there in 18.58 g of phosphorus? *ans*. 0.5999 mole
2. How many moles of atoms are there in 18.58 g of nitrogen? *ans*. 1.326 moles

◖ **SUMMARY**

The idea that matter consists of simple, indivisible, indestructible particles called atoms was proposed by Greek thinkers as early as 400 B.C. John Dalton, between 1803 and 1808, was the first to realize that an understanding of the nature and properties of atoms could explain the law of definite composition and the way and proportions in which substances react with one another.

An atom is the smallest unit of an element that can exist either alone or in combination with atoms of the same or different elements. The atomic theory states that

1. All matter is made up of very small structures called atoms.

2. Atoms of the same element are chemically alike; atoms of different elements are chemically different.

3. Individual atoms of an element may not all have the same mass. The atoms of an element, as it occurs naturally, have a definite average mass that is characteristic of the element.

4. Individual atoms of different elements may have nearly identical masses. The atoms of different naturally occurring elements have different average masses.

5. Atoms are not subdivided in chemical reactions.

An atom consists of a positively charged central part called the nucleus and negatively charged particles called electrons, which move about the nucleus in shells or energy levels. Atoms are electrically neutral. Positively charged protons and neutral neutrons are held together in the nucleus by very short-range forces.

The hydrogen atom has a nucleus made up of one proton. One electron moves about this nucleus in the K shell or 1st energy level. Three isotopes of hydrogen (protium, deuterium, and tritium) are possible with nuclei containing, respectively, no neutron, one neutron, and two neutrons. Isotopes are atoms of the same element that have different masses. The atomic number of an atom is the number of protons in the nucleus of that atom. The atomic number of hydrogen is 1.

Each different variety of atom as determined by the number of protons and number of neutrons in its nucleus is called a nuclide. The mass number of an atom is the sum of the number of protons and neutrons in its nucleus.

The K shell or 1st energy level may contain a maximum of two electrons. The L shell or 2nd energy level may contain a maximum of eight electrons. Argon, the final element in the third series, has eight electrons in the M shell or 3rd energy level.

The mass of an atom expressed in atomic mass units is called the atomic mass of the atom. One atomic mass unit is exactly one-twelfth the mass of a carbon-12 atom. The whole number closest to the atomic mass is the mass number of the atom.

The amount of substance containing an Avogadro number of any kind of chemical unit is called a mole of that substance. The Avogadro number is 6.02×10^{23}.

The mass in grams of one mole of naturally occurring atoms of an element is called the gram-atomic weight of the element. The numerical portion of this quantity is the atomic weight of the element.

◖ VOCABULARY

angstrom	atomic theory	gram-atomic weight	nucleus
atom	atomic weight	isotope	nuclide
atomic mass	Avogadro number	mass number	proton
atomic mass unit	electron	mole	shell
atomic number	energy level	neutron	

◖ QUESTIONS

Group A

1. What evidence is there that the particles of matter are very small?
2. What topics in chemistry are included today in the atomic theory?
3. What statements may be made about atoms of the elements and their properties?
4. (a) What are the main parts of an atom? (b) What particles are found in each part? (c) Describe each type of particle.
5. How does the size of the nucleus of an atom compare with the size of an atom?
6. What is a shell or energy level?
7. Describe the movement of electrons about the nucleus of an atom.
8. Describe the structure of each of the three isotopes of hydrogen.
9. (a) What is the atomic number of an atom? (b) How is it related to the number of electrons in a neutral atom?
10. (a) What are nuclides? (b) What are isotopes?
11. If you know the number and kinds of particles in an atom, how can you calculate its mass number?
12. An atomic nucleus that contains 8 protons and 9 neutrons is surrounded by 8 electrons: 2 in the 1st energy level and 6 in the 2nd energy level. (a) What is the atomic number of this nuclide? (b) What is its mass number? (c) What is the name of this nuclide?
13. Which elements among the first ten exist naturally as a single nuclide?
14. What is an atomic mass unit?
15. What is the atomic mass of an atom?
16. (a) How many atoms are there in exactly 12 g of carbon-12? (b) What name is given to this number? (c) What name is given to the amount of substance containing this number of chemical units?
17. What is the atomic weight of an element?

18. Why are atomic weights important to the chemist?

19. From the Table of Atomic Weights, find the atomic numbers and atomic weights of: (*a*) silver; (*b*) gold; (*c*) copper; (*d*) sulfur; (*e*) uranium.

20. What is the mass in grams of: (*a*) 2.00 moles of helium atoms; (*b*) 5.00 moles of boron atoms; (*c*) 0.500 mole of neon atoms; (*d*) 0.250 mole of magnesium atoms; (*e*) 0.100 mole of silicon atoms? Use the Table of Atomic Weights and follow the rules for significant-figure calculations.

21. How many moles of atoms are there in: (*a*) 20.823 g of lithium; (*b*) 160.93 g of sodium; (*c*) 3.995 g of argon; (*d*) 8.016 g of sulfur; (*e*) 20.24 g of aluminum?

Group B

22. What two observations about matter did Dalton believe could be explained by the nature and properties of atoms?

23. In one of the Rutherford experiments, it was found that 1 high-speed positively charged particle in 8000 was deflected by 90° or more when directed at a thin sheet of platinum. What does this observation indicate about the structure of platinum atoms?

24. If you arrange the elements in order of increasing atomic number, how do the atoms of successive elements differ in (*a*) number of protons? (*b*) number of electrons? (*c*) number of neutrons?

25. Describe the electron configurations in atoms of elements of the second series.

26. Copy and complete the table below *on a separate sheet of paper.*

27. Chlorine exists in nature as chlorine-35, atomic mass 34.96885 *u*, and chlorine-37, atomic mass 36.96590 *u*. Its atomic weight is 35.453. What must be the approximate abundance in nature of these two isotopes?

28. The elements sodium, aluminum, and phosphorus have only one naturally occurring nuclide. How will the atomic mass of this nuclide and the atomic weight of the element compare?

29. (*a*) What is the relationship between an atom containing 10 protons, 10 neutrons, and 10 electrons, and one containing 10 protons, 11 neutrons, and 10 electrons? (*b*) What is the relationship between an atom containing 10 protons, 11 neutrons, and 10 electrons, and one containing 11 protons, 10 neutrons, and 11 electrons?

30. How can the mass in grams of a single atom of a nuclide be calculated if the atomic mass of the nuclide is known?

31. What is the significance of the quotient obtained by dividing the gram-atomic weight of an element by the Avogadro number?

32. Calculate the atomic weight of oxygen. The naturally occurring element consists of 99.759% O-16, atomic mass 15.99491 *u*; 0.037% O-17, atomic mass 16.99914 *u*; and 0.204% O-18, atomic mass 17.99916 *u*.

Name of nuclide	Atomic number	Mass number	Composition of nucleus		Electron configuration		
			Protons	Neutrons	K	L	M
sodium-23	11						
magnesium-24	12						
aluminum-27	13						
silicon-28	14						
phosphorus-31	15						
sulfur-32	16						
chlorine-35	17						
argon-40	18						

Arrangement of Electrons in Atoms

"It is a truth very certain that when it is not in our power to determine, we ought to follow what is probable."

René Descartes, Discourse on Method

Are there limits to what we can know about the physical world? Can science describe exactly all forms of matter and energy? At one time, scientists felt confident that the mysteries of the universe would one day be explained; the refinement of scientific instruments would aid in this pursuit. In the early part of this century, however, their optimism gave way to the realization that the data needed to construct some laws could never be absolutely accurate. Scientific knowledge, therefore, is limited by a degree of uncertainty. However, the mathematical subject of probability enables scientists to give a fairly accurate description of reality and to better understand the universe, even within the confines of uncertainty.

◻ 4.1 The nucleus and moving electrons

In Chapter 3, you learned about the particles that make up atoms. The atom was described as a nucleus, containing protons and usually neutrons, surrounded by electrons. Although the electrons in an atom move about the nucleus, it is not possible to determine their paths. The regions the electrons occupy are called shells or energy levels. Now you will learn more about how the electrons are arranged and held within the atom.

Recall that the nucleus has a positive charge because of its protons. A neutral atom contains an equal number of positively charged protons and negatively charged electrons. Thus you might expect electrons to be held in an atom by the attraction between oppositely charged particles. This arrangement would be similar to the orbiting of a satellite around the earth. Instead of gravitational attraction, which holds a satellite in orbit, the attraction of oppositely charged particles would hold an electron in an atom.

However, scientists have observed that electrically charged particles moving in curved paths give off energy. If an electron moving about a nucleus continually gives off energy, it should slow down. It should gradually move nearer to the nucleus and eventually fall into it. This behavior would be like the slowing down of a satellite by friction with the earth's upper atmosphere. As this slowing down occurs, the satellite falls toward the earth and eventually burns up in the earth's atmosphere. But atoms do not collapse. Electrons do not fall into the nucleus. Thus, the attraction of oppositely charged particles may partly explain how

In this chapter you will gain an understanding of:

- **electromagnetic radiation and spectra**
- **quantum numbers**
- **electron configuration of atoms**
- **electron-dot notation, electron-configuration notation, and orbital notation**

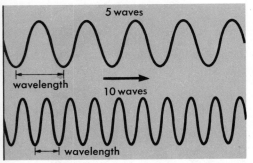

Figure 4-1. Both waves are traveling toward the right at the same speed. Assume they travel the distance shown in 1 s. Then the frequency of the top wave is 5 waves/s and the frequency of the bottom wave is 10 waves/s. The top wave has a wavelength twice that of the bottom wave. The wavelength is inversely proportional to the frequency. The top wave has a lower frequency and a longer wavelength. The bottom wave has a higher frequency and a shorter wavelength.

Inverse proportion is explained in Section 1.22(2).

Direct proportion is explained in Section 1.22(1).

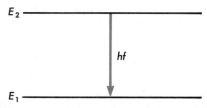

Figure 4-2. When an excited atom with energy E_2 returns to energy E_1, it gives off a photon having energy $E_2 - E_1 = E = hf$.

electrons are held by the nucleus of an atom. But it does not satisfactorily explain the motion of electrons about the nucleus.

◻ 4.2 Electromagnetic radiation

Visible light is one kind of electromagnetic radiation. Other kinds of electromagnetic radiation are X rays, ultraviolet and infrared light, and radio waves. Electromagnetic radiations are forms of energy that travel through space as waves. They move at the rate of 3.00×10^8 m/s, the speed of light in a vacuum. For any wave motion, the speed equals the product of the *frequency* (the number of waves passing a given point in one second) and the *wavelength*. For electromagnetic radiation

$$c = f\lambda$$

where c is the speed of light, f is the frequency, and λ (the Greek letter lambda) is the wavelength. Since c is the same for all electromagnetic radiation, the product $f\lambda$ is a constant, and λ is inversely proportional to f. See Figure 4-1.

In addition to its wave characteristics, electromagnetic radiation has some properties of particles. Electromagnetic radiation is transferred to matter in units or *quanta* of energy called *photons*. The energy of a photon is proportional to the frequency of the radiation. Thus, the energy of a photon and the frequency of the radiation are related by

$$E = hf$$

Here, E is the energy of the photon, h is a proportionality constant called *Planck's constant,* and f is the frequency of the radiation. Planck's constant is the same for all types of electromagnetic radiation. Since f multiplied by Planck's constant equals E, f and E are directly proportional.

Energy is transferred to matter in photon units. Therefore, the absorption of a photon by an atom increases its energy by a definite quantity, hf. An atom that has absorbed energy in this way is called an *excited* atom. When excited atoms radiate energy, the radiation is given off in photon units. See Figure 4-2.

◻ 4.3 Spectra of atoms

Atoms may be excited by heating them in a flame or in an electric arc. As these excited atoms return to their normal energy states, they give off light of a characteristic color. An example is the yellow-orange light given off by sodium atoms in a glass rod heated in a burner flame. Atoms of gases can be excited by passing high-voltage electricity through the gas contained inside a glass tube. The red light of neon advertising signs is a familiar example. If hydrogen gas is used in such a tube, it glows with a characteristic lavender color. See Figure 4-3.

When observed through a spectroscope, the lavender-colored light of hydrogen gas reveals lines of particular colors, as shown in Figure 4-4. Such a spectrum is called a bright-line spectrum. It indicates that the light given off by excited atoms has only certain wavelengths. Light of a particular wavelength has a definite *frequency* ($c = f\lambda$) and a characteristic color. A definite frequency also means a definite energy ($E = hf$). Hence the bright-line hydrogen spectrum shows that excited hydrogen atoms emit (give off) photons having only certain energies. Now, recall from Section 4.2 that λ is inversely proportional to f, but that f is directly proportional to E. So, λ is inversely proportional to E. A long wavelength is thus associated with less energy and a short wavelength is associated with more energy.

Emitted photons have only certain energies. These energies represent differences between the energies of atoms before and after radiation. Therefore, these energies of atoms are *fixed and definite quantities*. And because each species of atom has its own characteristic spectrum, each atom must have its own characteristic energy possibilities. This evidence indicates that the energy changes that occur from time to time within an atom involve definite amounts of energy rather than a continuous flow of energy.

The energy changes of an excited atom returning to its normal energy state are actually changes in the energy of its electrons. Therefore, a diagram that shows the electron energy levels of the atom can be devised. Figure 4-5 includes lines in the ultraviolet and infrared regions of the hydrogen spectrum. Figure 4-6 gives the corresponding electron energy-level transitions in the hydrogen atom. For example, when electrons in excited hydrogen atoms move from the second energy level to the first energy level, the energy released produces ultraviolet line *a* in the Lyman series, wavelength 1215 Å. Similarly, electrons in excited hydrogen atoms that move from the fourth energy level to the second energy level release energy that produces the greenish-blue line *b* in the Balmer series, wavelength 4861 Å.

The idea of electron energy levels in the hydrogen atom was developed by Niels Bohr in 1913. The definite energy levels of the atom indicate two properties of the electron moving about the hydrogen nucleus. First, it can move at only certain distances from the nucleus. Second, it can move with only certain

Figure 4-3. Hydrogen atoms are excited when high-voltage electricity is passed through a glass tube containing hydrogen gas. The lavender glow is characteristic of hydrogen.

The continuous spectrum at the top of page 543 shows the relationship between wavelength and color of light.

Figure 4-4. The visible bright-line spectrum of hydrogen seen through a spectroscope.

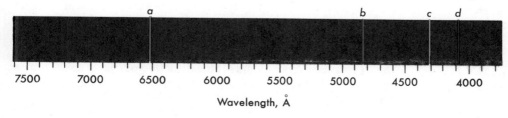

Wavelength, Å

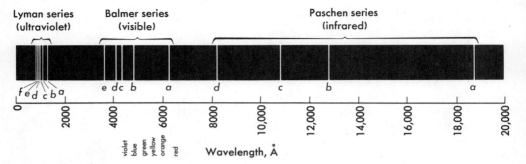

Figure 4-5. Representative lines in the hydrogen spectrum. The small letter below each line indicates which of the energy-level transitions in Figure 4-6 produces it.

speeds. Bohr's theory states that electrons do not give off energy when they remain in given energy levels. They only give off energy when they change to lower energy levels. This helps explain why electrons in atoms do not lose energy, fall into the nucleus, and cause the atom to collapse.

This model works well in explaining the spectra of the one-electron hydrogen atom. But it does not satisfactorily explain the spectra of more complex atoms.

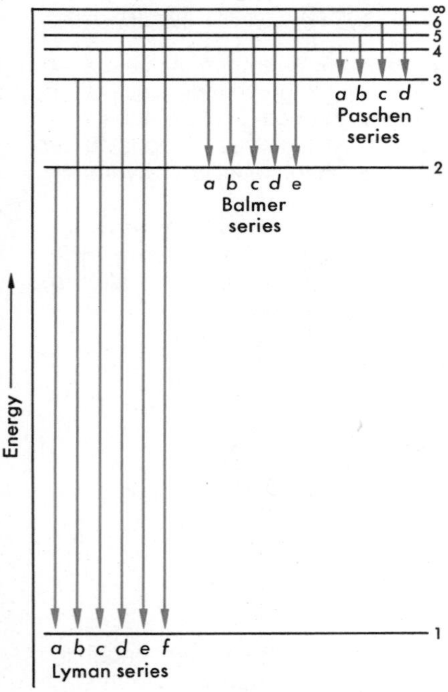

4.4 Wave-mechanics concept of an atom

During the past half century, the work of theoretical physicists, including Heisenberg, de Broglie, and Schrödinger, helped develop a theory of atomic structure based on wave mechanics. The basic ideas of wave mechanics are beyond the scope of a high school chemistry course. It will be useful, however, to consider some of its conclusions.

The motion of an electron about an atom is not in a definite path like that of the earth about the sun. In fact, it is impossible to determine an electron's path without changing that path! So an electron's location can be given only in terms of probabilities. This location is described by a *space orbital*. A space orbital may be thought of as a highly probable location in which an electron may be found. The motion of the single hydrogen electron creates a spherical *electron cloud* surrounding the nucleus. The electron cloud gives size and shape to an atom. It also prevents two free atoms (or portions of free atoms) from occupying the same space.

Figure 4-6. An electron energy-level diagram for hydrogen showing some of the transitions that are possible in this atom. Transitions that leave an electron in a particular final energy level belong to a particular spectral series. Some of these series are named for the people who discovered them.

4.5 Quantum numbers

The mathematics of wave mechanics shows that the energy state of an electron in an atom may be described by a set of four numbers. These are called *quantum numbers*. Quantum numbers describe the space orbital the electron occupies in terms of: (1) distance from the nucleus; (2) shape; (3) position with respect to the three axes in space; and (4) the direction of spin of the electron in the orbital. As you read on, refer to the corresponding columns in Table 4-1.

Table 4-1
QUANTUM NUMBER RELATIONSHIPS IN ATOMIC STRUCTURE

Principal quantum number (energy level) (n)	Orbitals (n orbital shapes) (n sublevels)	Number of orbitals per sublevel	Number of orbitals per energy level (n^2)	Number of electrons per sublevel	Number of electrons per energy level $(2n^2)$
1	s	1	1	2	2
2	s	1	4	2	8
	p	3		6	
3	s	1	9	2	18
	p	3		6	
	d	5		10	
4	s	1	16	2	32
	p	3		6	
	d	5		10	
	f	7		14	

The *principal quantum number,* symbolized by n, indicates the most probable distance of the electron from the nucleus of the atom. It is a positive whole number, having values 1, 2, 3, etc. The principal quantum number is the main energy-level designation, or identifying number, of an orbital. The 1st energy level is closest to the nucleus with others at increasing distances. Electrons in the 1st energy level have the lowest energies. Electrons in higher energy levels have increasingly greater energies. Sometimes, the energy levels are designated by letters instead of numbers. These designations are K shell, L shell, M shell, N shell, O shell, etc.

The *orbital quantum number* indicates the shape of the orbital the electron occupies. The letter designations for the first four orbital quantum numbers are *s, p, d,* and *f.* These are listed in order of ascending energies. For a particular energy level, the *s* orbital has the lowest energy. The *p* orbitals have higher energy than the *s* orbital, the *d* orbitals have higher energy than the *p* orbitals, and so on. Sometimes the *s* orbital is called the *s* sublevel, *p* orbitals the *p* sublevel, *d* orbitals the *d* sublevel, etc.

The number of possible orbital shapes in an energy level is equal to the value of the principal quantum number. In the 1st energy level, an orbital of only one shape is possible. So the first energy level has only an *s* orbital, or *s* sublevel. In the 2nd energy level, orbitals of two shapes are possible. The 2nd energy level has *s* and *p* orbitals. The 3rd energy level has three possible orbital shapes: *s, p,* and *d* orbitals. The 4th energy level has four possible orbital shapes; it has *s, p, d,* and *f* orbitals. In the *n*th energy level, orbitals of *n* shapes are possible.

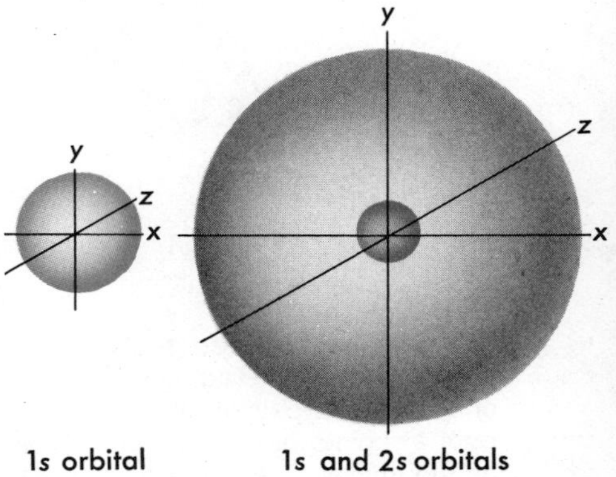

1s orbital   1s and 2s orbitals

Figure 4-7. Position in the space about the nucleus of s orbitals. The s orbitals are spherical in shape.

The *magnetic quantum number* indicates the position of the orbital about the three axes in space. There is only one position in the space around the nucleus for an *s* orbital. There are three positions for a *p* orbital, five positions for a *d* orbital, and seven positions for an *f* orbital. See Figures 4-7 and 4-8.

In the 1st energy level, there is only one *s* orbital. In the 2nd energy level, there are one *s* orbital and three *p* orbitals, for a total of four orbitals. In the 3rd energy level, there are one *s* orbital, three *p* orbitals, and five *d* orbitals, for a total of nine orbitals. Do you see that the total number of orbitals per energy level is the square of the principal quantum number? In the *n*th energy level, there will be n^2 orbitals.

The *spin quantum number* indicates a property of the electron described by just two conditions. These conditions may be thought of as being like the right-handed or left-handed conditions of a glove. That is, they are like mirror images in being ''opposites'' of each other. This property is called *electron spin*. Scientists often refer to the two possibilities for spin as clockwise and counterclockwise. Thus, each of the *positions of orbitals in the space around the nucleus described by the first three quantum numbers can be occupied by only two electrons having opposite spins*. No two electrons in an atom can have exactly the same set of four quantum numbers. This agrees with the observation that no two electrons in an atom have exactly the same energy.

If there are n^2 orbitals in the *n*th energy level, and each may be occupied by a maximum of two electrons, then the maximum number of electrons per energy level is $2n^2$.

◻ 4.6 Electron configuration of atoms of first three series

The quantum numbers that describe the arrangement of electrons about an atom are related to the energies of the electrons. The energies associated with the various electron orbitals as they become occupied by electrons are shown in Figure 4-9. The most stable state of an atom is called its *ground state*. In this condition, the electrons have the lowest possible energies. If the number of electrons in an atom is known, the arrangement of electrons of its ground state can be described. This is because electrons occupy the various orbitals in a reasonably definite order starting with those of lowest energy. The arrangement of electrons is called the *electron configuration*.

Hydrogen atoms have only one electron. In the ground state this electron moves in the 1*s* sublevel, the *s* sublevel of the 1st energy level. The two electrons of helium atoms both occupy the 1*s* sublevel. This may be shown in *orbital notation* as

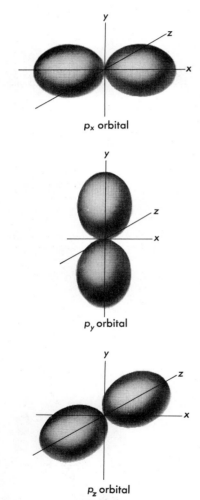

p_x orbital

p_y orbital

p_z orbital

Figure 4-8. The three spatial positions of *p* orbitals. The *p* orbitals are shaped like a pair of ellipsoids tangent at points of greatest curvature at the nucleus. They are oriented along the three axes in space. The superposition of the three *p* orbitals produces a spherical electron cloud.

$$\text{H} \quad \underset{1s}{\uparrow} \qquad \text{He} \quad \underset{1s}{\downarrow\uparrow}$$

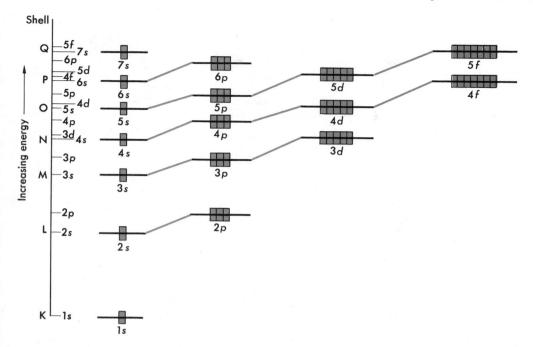

Figure 4-9. This chart shows the approximate relative energies of the atomic sublevels as they are occupied by electrons. Note how the sublevels of an energy level vary in energy and that the sublevels of higher energy levels overlap.

In orbital notation, one electron occupying a space orbital is represented as ↑. Two electrons occupying a space orbital is represented as ↓↑. An unoccupied space orbital is represented as ___. The two helium electrons occupying the same space orbital must have opposite spins. Two electrons of opposite spin in the same space orbital are called an *electron pair*.

In *electron-configuration notation* hydrogen has the designation $1s^1$. This designation shows that hydrogen has one electron (represented by the superscript) in the s sublevel of the 1st energy level. Helium's electron structure is represented as $1s^2$. This means that helium has two electrons (represented by the superscript) in the s sublevel of the 1st energy level.

In *electron-dot notation,* hydrogen and helium are designated as

$$\text{H} \cdot \qquad \text{He} \colon$$

In this notation, the symbol represents the element, and the dots indicate the number of outer-shell electrons. Two dots written together, as in the helium notation, represent an *electron pair*.

The elements in the second series have electrons occupying the 1st and 2nd energy levels. Their ground-state electron arrangements may be represented by orbital notation, electron-configuration notation, and electron-dot notation, as shown in Table 4-2. Note that the orbital notations and electron-configuration notations show *all* of the electrons in the atom. The electron-

Table 4-2
ELECTRON NOTATIONS OF ATOMS
IN THE SECOND SERIES

	Orbital notation			Electron-configuration notation	Electron-dot notation
	1s	2s	2p		
Li	↓↑	↑	_ _ _	$1s^2 2s^1$	Li·
Be	↓↑	↓↑	_ _ _	$1s^2 2s^2$	Be:
B	↓↑	↓↑	↑ _ _	$1s^2 2s^2 2p^1$	·Ḃ:
C	↓↑	↓↑	↑ ↑ _	$1s^2 2s^2 2p^2$	·Ċ:
N	↓↑	↓↑	↑ ↑ ↑	$1s^2 2s^2 2p^3$	·N̈:
O	↓↑	↓↑	↓↑ ↑ ↑	$1s^2 2s^2 2p^4$	·Ö:
F	↓↑	↓↑	↓↑ ↓↑ ↑	$1s^2 2s^2 2p^5$	:F̈:
Ne	↓↑	↓↑	↓↑ ↓↑ ↓↑	$1s^2 2s^2 2p^6$	:N̈e:

dot notations, however, show only the electrons in the *outer* (highest numbered) energy level or shell. See Figure 4-10.

Observe that electrons do not pair up in *p* orbitals until each of the three *p* orbitals is occupied by a single electron. These single electrons have parallel spins. An atom such as that of neon has the *s* and *p* sublevels of its outer (highest numbered) energy level filled with eight electrons. Thus, it is said to have an outer shell consisting of an *octet*.

The electron configurations of the elements of the third series are similar to those of the second series with successive electrons occupying the 3*s* and 3*p* space orbitals.

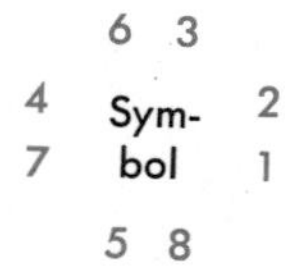

◻ 4.7 Atoms of the fourth series

The first two elements in the fourth series are potassium and calcium. Their atoms have the same electron configuration in the first three energy levels as the argon atom, $1s^2 2s^2 2p^6 3s^2 3p^6$. Electron-dot symbols for these elements are

$$\textbf{K·} \qquad \textbf{Ca:}$$

These symbols show the presence of one and two electrons, respectively, in the 4*s* sublevel. The electron configuration of K is $1s^2 2s^2 2p^6 3s^2 3p^6 4s^1$ and of Ca, $1s^2 2s^2 2p^6 3s^2 3p^6 4s^2$. In the atoms of the next ten elements of this fourth series, the 3*d* sublevel is occupied in successive steps by the addition of electrons. The distribution of electrons in the ground state of these atoms is given in Table 4-3.

See Question 22 at the end of this chapter.

```
    6  3
 4  Sym-  2
 7  bol   1
    5  8
```

Figure 4-10. The order of placing electron dots, which represent outer-shell electrons. If there is only one dot in a position, it is centered. Dots 1 and 2 represent *s* electrons. Dots 3 through 8 represent *p* electrons. The *p* electrons do not form pairs until the three *p* orbitals have one electron each. An atom with electrons in all eight positions has an outer shell consisting of an octet.

Table 4-3
STRUCTURE OF ATOMS IN THE FOURTH SERIES

Name	Symbol	Atomic number	Number of electrons in sublevels							
			1s	2s	2p	3s	3p	3d	4s	4p
potassium	K	19	2	2	6	2	6		1	
calcium	Ca	20	2	2	6	2	6		2	
scandium	Sc	21	2	2	6	2	6	1	2	
titanium	Ti	22	2	2	6	2	6	2	2	
vanadium	V	23	2	2	6	2	6	3	2	
chromium	Cr	24	2	2	6	2	6	5	1	
manganese	Mn	25	2	2	6	2	6	5	2	
iron	Fe	26	2	2	6	2	6	6	2	
cobalt	Co	27	2	2	6	2	6	7	2	
nickel	Ni	28	2	2	6	2	6	8	2	
copper	Cu	29	2	2	6	2	6	10	1	
zinc	Zn	30	2	2	6	2	6	10	2	
gallium	Ga	31	2	2	6	2	6	10	2	1
germanium	Ge	32	2	2	6	2	6	10	2	2
arsenic	As	33	2	2	6	2	6	10	2	3
selenium	Se	34	2	2	6	2	6	10	2	4
bromine	Br	35	2	2	6	2	6	10	2	5
krypton	Kr	36	2	2	6	2	6	10	2	6

Half-filled or completely filled sublevels have extra stability. The structures of both the chromium and copper atoms appear to be irregular. Chromium would be expected to have four $3d$ electrons and two $4s$ electrons. Instead, in the ground state, chromium atoms have five $3d$ electrons and one $4s$ electron. This $3d^5 4s^1$ structure must have higher stability and lower energy than the expected $3d^4 4s^2$ structure. (The $3d^4 4s^2$ configuration can occur in excited chromium atoms.) Apparently a half-filled $3d$ sublevel provides greater stability than a $3d$ sublevel with only four electrons. This greater stability occurs even though the electron-pair in the $4s$ sublevel is broken up. Copper would be expected to have nine $3d$ electrons and two $4s$ electrons. Instead, in the ground state, it has ten $3d$ electrons and one $4s$ electron. Here the filled $3d$ sublevel provides greater stability. (The $3d^9 4s^2$ configuration can occur in excited copper atoms.)

With the element zinc, the 3rd energy level is completely filled and there are two electrons in the 4th energy level. The remaining six elements in the fourth series are gallium, germanium, arsenic, selenium, bromine, and krypton. They all have completely filled 1st, 2nd, and 3rd energy levels. The electrons in the $4s$ and $4p$ sublevels are shown in these electron-dot symbols:

$$\overset{\textstyle\cdot}{\text{Ga}}\text{:} \qquad \cdot\overset{\textstyle\cdot}{\text{Ge}}\text{:} \qquad \cdot\overset{\textstyle\cdot}{\underset{\textstyle\cdot}{\text{As}}}\text{:} \qquad \cdot\overset{\textstyle\cdot\cdot}{\underset{\textstyle\cdot}{\text{Se}}}\text{:} \qquad \text{:}\overset{\textstyle\cdot\cdot}{\underset{\textstyle\cdot}{\text{Br}}}\text{:} \qquad \text{:}\overset{\textstyle\cdot\cdot}{\underset{\textstyle\cdot\cdot}{\text{Kr}}}\text{:}$$

Krypton is the last member of the fourth series. It is a gas that has an octet (two s and six p electrons) in its 4th energy level. Its electron-configuration notation is $1s^2 2s^2 2p^6 3s^2 3p^6 3d^{10} 4s^2 4p^6$. Observe that in this notation all the sublevels of an energy level are grouped together in *s, p, d,* and *f* order.

◻ 4.8 Atoms of the fifth series

The fifth series of elements, like the fourth, consists of 18 elements. The first two of these are rubidium and strontium. The inner shells of these elements resemble the krypton atom. The additional one and two electrons, respectively, occupy the 5*s* sublevel.

Rb·   **Sr:**

In the atoms of the next ten elements, the five 4*d* sublevel orbitals become occupied by the successive addition of electrons.

The atoms of the element cadmium have completely filled 1st, 2nd, and 3rd energy levels. The 4*s, 4p,* and 4*d* sublevels are also filled. There are two electrons in the 5*s* sublevel. The atoms of the remaining six elements of the fifth series are indium, tin, antimony, tellurium, iodine, and xenon. The first four energy levels of these elements are similar to those of cadmium. Successive electrons occupy the 5*p* sublevel, which has the next higher energy.

İn: **·Sn:**   **·Sb:**   **·Te:**   **:İ:**   **:Xe:**

Thus in the fifth series the addition of electrons to sublevels of two different energy levels proceeds as it did in the fourth series.

Table 4-4
STRUCTURE OF ATOMS IN THE FIFTH SERIES

Name	Symbol	Atomic number	Number of electrons in sublevels										
			1s	2s	2p	3s	3p	3d	4s	4p	4d	5s	5p
rubidium	Rb	37	2	2	6	2	6	10	2	6		1	
strontium	Sr	38	2	2	6	2	6	10	2	6		2	
yttrium	Y	39	2	2	6	2	6	10	2	6	1	2	
zirconium	Zr	40	2	2	6	2	6	10	2	6	2	2	
niobium	Nb	41	2	2	6	2	6	10	2	6	4	1	
molybdenum	Mo	42	2	2	6	2	6	10	2	6	5	1	
technetium	Tc	43	2	2	6	2	6	10	2	6	5	2	
ruthenium	Ru	44	2	2	6	2	6	10	2	6	7	1	
rhodium	Rh	45	2	2	6	2	6	10	2	6	8	1	
palladium	Pd	46	2	2	6	2	6	10	2	6	10		
silver	Ag	47	2	2	6	2	6	10	2	6	10	1	
cadmium	Cd	48	2	2	6	2	6	10	2	6	10	2	
indium	In	49	2	2	6	2	6	10	2	6	10	2	1
tin	Sn	50	2	2	6	2	6	10	2	6	10	2	2
antimony	Sb	51	2	2	6	2	6	10	2	6	10	2	3
tellurium	Te	52	2	2	6	2	6	10	2	6	10	2	4
iodine	I	53	2	2	6	2	6	10	2	6	10	2	5
xenon	Xe	54	2	2	6	2	6	10	2	6	10	2	6

Xenon, the last member of the series, has an octet in its 5th energy level and 4*s*, 4*p*, and 4*d* sublevels filled.

◻ 4.9 Atoms of the sixth series

The sixth series of atoms is much longer than the others. It consists of 32 elements. The atoms of the first two, cesium and barium, have inner energy levels that resemble the xenon atom. Successive electrons occupy the 6*s* sublevel.

Cs·   Ba:

At lanthanum, the lowest-energy *d* sublevel (here 5*d*) begins to fill, as 4*d* began to fill at yttrium and 3*d* began to fill at scandium. But with the very next element, cerium, something different happens. In the atoms of cerium and the next 12 elements of the

Table 4-5
STRUCTURE OF ATOMS IN THE SIXTH SERIES

Name	Symbol	Atomic number		Number of electrons in sublevels						
				4d	4f	5s	5p	5d	6s	6p
cesium	Cs	55		10		2	6		1	
barium	Ba	56		10		2	6		2	
lanthanum	La	57		10		2	6	1	2	
cerium	Ce	58		10	1	2	6	1	2	
praseodymium	Pr	59		10	3	2	6		2	
neodymium	Nd	60		10	4	2	6		2	
promethium	Pm	61		10	5	2	6		2	
samarium	Sm	62		10	6	2	6		2	
europium	Eu	63		10	7	2	6		2	
gadolinium	Gd	64		10	7	2	6	1	2	
terbium	Tb	65		10	9	2	6		2	
dysprosium	Dy	66		10	10	2	6		2	
holmium	Ho	67		10	11	2	6		2	
erbium	Er	68	krypton	10	12	2	6		2	
thulium	Tm	69	structure	10	13	2	6		2	
ytterbium	Yb	70	plus	10	14	2	6		2	
lutetium	Lu	71		10	14	2	6	1	2	
hafnium	Hf	72		10	14	2	6	2	2	
tantalum	Ta	73		10	14	2	6	3	2	
tungsten	W	74		10	14	2	6	4	2	
rhenium	Re	75		10	14	2	6	5	2	
osmium	Os	76		10	14	2	6	6	2	
iridium	Ir	77		10	14	2	6	7	2	
platinum	Pt	78		10	14	2	6	9	1	
gold	Au	79		10	14	2	6	10	1	
mercury	Hg	80		10	14	2	6	10	2	
thallium	Tl	81		10	14	2	6	10	2	1
lead	Pb	82		10	14	2	6	10	2	2
bismuth	Bi	83		10	14	2	6	10	2	3
polonium	Po	84		10	14	2	6	10	2	4
astatine	At	85		10	14	2	6	10	2	5
radon	Rn	86		10	14	2	6	10	2	6

sixth series, the 7 orbitals of the $4f$ sublevel are occupied by successive electrons. In atoms of the element ytterbium, the 4th energy level has all of its sublevels filled with 32 electrons.

The atoms of the next ten elements of the sixth series have successive electrons occupying the five orbitals of the $5d$ sublevel. These orbitals have the next higher energies.

The atoms of the remaining six elements of this series are thallium, lead, bismuth, polonium, astatine, and radon. They have the first four energy levels completely filled and filled $5s$, $5p$, and $5d$ sublevels. The $6s$ and $6p$ electrons are shown in these electron-dot symbols:

$$\overset{\bullet}{Tl}\!: \qquad \bullet\overset{\bullet}{Pb}\!: \qquad \bullet\overset{\bullet}{\underset{\bullet}{Bi}}\!: \qquad \bullet\overset{\bullet\bullet}{\underset{\bullet}{Po}}\!: \qquad :\overset{\bullet\bullet}{\underset{\bullet}{At}}\!: \qquad :\overset{\bullet\bullet}{\underset{\bullet\bullet}{Rn}}\!:$$

Radon, the last member of the sixth series, has an octet in its 6th energy level and $5s$, $5p$, and $5d$ sublevels filled.

◻ 4.10 Atoms of the seventh series

The seventh series of elements is an incomplete series of which only 21 elements are known. Table 4-6 shows what is believed to be the arrangement of electrons in the 5th, 6th, and 7th energy levels. Appendix Table 7, Electronic Arrangement of the Elements, gives the complete electron configurations for all of the elements.

Table 4-6
STRUCTURE OF ATOMS IN THE SEVENTH SERIES

Name	Symbol	Atomic number		Number of electrons in sublevels						
				4f	5d	5f	6s	6p	6d	7s
francium	Fr	87		14	10		2	6		1
radium	Ra	88		14	10		2	6		2
actinium	Ac	89		14	10		2	6	1	2
thorium	Th	90		14	10		2	6	2	2
protactinium	Pa	91		14	10	2	2	6	1	2
uranium	U	92		14	10	3	2	6	1	2
neptunium	Np	93		14	10	4	2	6	1	2
plutonium	Pu	94	xenon	14	10	6	2	6		2
americium	Am	95	structure	14	10	7	2	6		2
curium	Cm	96	plus	14	10	7	2	6	1	2
berkelium	Bk	97		14	10	8	2	6	1	2
californium	Cf	98		14	10	10	2	6		2
einsteinium	Es	99		14	10	11	2	6		2
fermium	Fm	100		14	10	12	2	6		2
mendelevium	Md	101		14	10	13	2	6		2
nobelium	No	102		14	10	14	2	6		2
lawrencium	Lr	103		14	10	14	2	6	1	2
unnilquadium	Unq	104		14	10	14	2	6	2	2?
unnilpentium	Unp	105		14	10	14	2	6	3	2?
unnilhexium	Unh	106		14	10	14	2	6	4	2?
unnilseptium	Uns	107		14	10	14	2	6	5	2?

SUMMARY

Electromagnetic radiations are forms of energy that travel through space as waves. The frequency of a wave and its wavelength are inversely proportional. Electromagnetic radiation also has some properties of particles. Electromagnetic radiation is transferred to matter in photon units. The energy of a photon is directly proportional to the frequency of the radiation. An atom that has absorbed energy is called an excited atom. When excited atoms radiate energy, the radiation is given off in photon units.

The bright-line spectra of atoms show that energy changes involving only fixed and definite quantities of energy may occur within atoms. This is evidence for electron energy levels in atoms.

A space orbital is a highly probable location in which an electron may be found. The energy state of an electron in an atom may be described by four quantum numbers. The principal quantum number indicates the most probable distance of the electron from the nucleus of the atom. The orbital quantum number indicates the shape of the orbital the electron occupies. The magnetic quantum number indicates the position of the orbital about the three axes in space. The spin quantum number indicates the direction of spin of the electron. No two electrons in an atom can have exactly the same set of quantum numbers.

The most stable state of an atom is its ground state. If the number of electrons in an atom is known, its electron configuration can be described because electrons occupy the various orbitals in a reasonably definite order. Electron configurations can be described by orbital notation, electron-configuration notation, and electron-dot notation. Two electrons of opposite spin in the same space orbital are an electron pair. An atom with only the s and p orbitals of its outer energy level filled with eight electrons is said to have an outer shell consisting of an octet. Seven series of atoms have been identified. The final element in each series has an octet in its outer shell.

VOCABULARY

electromagnetic radiation	magnetic quantum number	quanta
electron cloud	octet	space orbital
electron pair	orbital quantum number	spectrum
frequency	photon	spin quantum number
ground state	principal quantum number	wavelength

QUESTIONS

Group A

1. (a) What are electromagnetic radiations? (b) Give examples of forms of electromagnetic radiation.
2. (a) In what form do electromagnetic radiations travel through space? (b) In what form are they transferred to matter?
3. How is an excited atom produced?
4. (a) The red line in the visible spectrum of hydrogen has a wavelength of 6563 Å. From Figures 4-5 and 4-6 identify the electron-energy-level transition that produces this line. (b) Which electron-energy-level transition produces the violet line having a wavelength of 4102 Å?
5. What are the principal characteristics of the Bohr model of the hydrogen atom?
6. What is a space orbital?
7. (a) What is an electron cloud? (b) What properties does it give an atom?

8. What are the four kinds of quantum numbers and what does each indicate?
9. (*a*) What is the shape of an *s* orbital? (*b*) How many *s* orbitals can there be in an energy level? (*c*) How many electrons can occupy such an orbital? (*d*) What characteristic must these electrons have? (*e*) Which is the lowest energy level having an *s* orbital?
10. (*a*) What is the shape of a *p* orbital? (*b*) How many *p* orbitals can there be in an energy level? (*c*) How are they arranged with respect to one another? (*d*) Which is the lowest energy level having *p* orbitals?
11. (*a*) May two electrons in the same atom have exactly the same set of quantum numbers? Explain. (*b*) May two electrons occupy the same space orbital in an atom? (*c*) Under what conditions?
12. Distinguish between an atom in its ground state and an excited atom.
13. (*a*) What is an electron pair? (*b*) What is an octet?

Group B
14. What aspect of the attraction between oppositely charged particles makes it unsatisfactory for explaining how electrons move in an atom?
15. Derive the relationship between λ and E for electromagnetic radiation.
16. Why must energy transitions within an atom occur in definite amounts rather than as a continuous flow?
17. (*a*) From Figures 4-5 and 4-6, determine the approximate wavelength of the radiation produced by an electron transition in a hydrogen atom from the 4th energy level to the 1st energy level; (*b*) from the 4th energy level to the 3rd energy level.
18. (*a*) How many *d* orbitals can there be in an energy level? (*b*) How many *d* electrons can there be in an energy level? (*c*) Which is the lowest energy level having *d* orbitals?
19. (*a*) How many *f* orbitals can there be in an energy level? (*b*) How many *f* electrons can there be in an energy level? (*c*) Which is the lowest energy level having *f* orbitals?

20. How many electron pairs are there in the outer shell of each of the following atoms: (*a*) carbon; (*b*) krypton; (*c*) oxygen; (*d*) arsenic; (*e*) iodine?
21. Which of the atoms in Question 20 has an octet as an outer shell?
22. On a separate sheet of paper copy and complete the following table for the atoms in the third series. *Do not write in this book.*

Chemical symbol	Orbital notation	Electron-configuration notation	Electron-dot notation
Na			
Mg			
Al			
Si			
P			
S			
Cl			
Ar			

23. How many energy levels are partially or fully occupied in the mendelevium atom?
24. Why do the fourth and fifth series of elements contain 18 elements, rather than 8 as do the second and third series?
25. Why does the sixth series of elements contain 32 elements, rather than 18 as do the fourth and fifth series?
26. (*a*) Which energy level corresponds to the N shell? (*b*) What types of space orbitals can be found in this energy level? (*c*) How many of each type? (*d*) How many electrons can occupy each of these types of space orbitals? (*e*) How many electrons are needed to completely fill the N shell?
27. Which sublevels of the 3rd energy level are filled (*a*) in the element argon; (*b*) in the element krypton?
28. What is a probable electron configuration for the as yet undiscovered element 109, unnilennium?

The Periodic Law

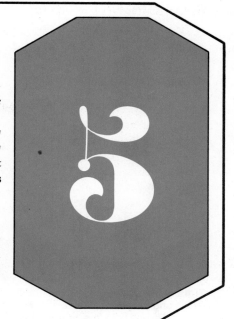

The lean buds of spring precede the full bloom of summer, to be followed by the sumptuous fruit of autumn. Winter comes, and the branches are barren. In the springtime, the cycle begins anew. Nature works in cycles. Repetition is the hallmark of art as well as nature. A characteristic feature of music is its insistent rhythms and the recurrent alternations of its sounds. Beethoven's Moonlight Sonata, Gershwin's Rhapsody in Blue, the Beatles' Here Comes the Sun—all have their own form of repetition. Dance also uses repetition: the pattern of the dancer's steps and body movement. Art mimics nature, and the beauty of art, like that of nature, derives from its rhythms. Science, like art, seeks to discover the repeating pattern in all things—in the smallest crystal or the brightest star. The sensibility of the scientist is very much like that of the artist.

◻ 5.1 Atomic weights and the properties of elements

The law of definite composition states that every compound has a definite composition by weight. By chemical analysis, it is possible to determine the weight of any element that combines with a fixed weight of a particular element. Such a weight is called a *combining weight*. Between 1807 and 1818, Berzelius determined the combining weights with oxygen of 43 elements: almost all of the elements known at his time.

Chemists also recognized that some elements had similar properties. Lithium, sodium, and potassium were found to be similar metals, as were calcium, strontium, and barium. Chlorine, bromine, and iodine were found to be similar nonmetals. So were sulfur, selenium, and tellurium. In 1829 Johann Wolfgang Döbereiner (1780–1849), a German chemist, pointed out that in such groups of three elements, the combining weight of the middle element was the average of the combining weights of the other two elements.

By 1860, it became possible to establish whether the combining weight of an element was indeed its atomic weight, or was a multiple or submultiple of the atomic weight. Stas' atomic weight determinations, begun in 1860, far surpassed the earlier work of Berzelius. Stas used techniques of both analysis and synthesis. His materials were very pure, his balance was a precision instrument, and he exercised the utmost care in his experimentation. The availability of Stas' atomic weights stimulated the search for a meaningful relationship between the properties of elements and their atomic weights.

In this chapter you will gain an understanding of:

- **the development of the periodic table**
- **the periodic law**
- **the modern periodic table and periodic properties**
- **ionization energy and electron affinity**

Some of the ways this decision is made will be described in Chapters 7 and 11.

Analysis and synthesis are defined in Section 2.8.

In 1865, John A. R. Newlands (1838–1898), an English chemist, arranged the elements in order of increasing atomic weight for the first time. He found that similar elements were 7 or a multiple of 7 elements apart. Lithium, the 2nd element, was similar in properties to sodium, the 9th element, and potassium, the 16th element. Fluorine, the 8th element, was similar to chlorine, the 15th element, and to bromine, the 29th element. Iodine was the 42nd element in atomic weight order, not the 43rd as Newlands' arrangement predicted. However, he felt that a more accurate atomic weight determination would clear up this discrepancy.

☐ 5.2 Mendeleev's periodic table

In 1869, the Russian chemist Dmitri Mendeleev (men-deh-*lay*-eff) (1834–1907) published a table of elements based on both their properties and the order of their atomic weights. See Figure 5-1. The elements are arranged in vertical columns in atomic-weight order so that elements having similar chemical properties are in the same horizontal row. Mendeleev realized that all the elements were probably not yet discovered. He carefully studied the properties of the known elements and then left gaps in his table. Note the question marks in the table corresponding to atomic weights 45, 68, and 70. He predicted that new elements would be discovered to fill these gaps. He also predicted the properties of these new elements. When scandium, gallium, and

Figure 5-1. Even though Mendeleev's original periodic table appears quite different from the one we use today, there are similarities. How many elements can you find that we now classify as belonging in the same groups? Which elements did Mendeleev predict would be discovered?

			Ti = 50	Zr = 90	? = 180
			V = 51	Nb = 94	Ta = 182
			Cr = 52	Mo = 96	W = 186
			Mn = 55	Rh = 104,4	Pt = 197,4
			Fe = 56	Ru = 104,4	Ir = 198
		Ni = Co = 59		Pd = 106,6	Os = 199
H = 1			Cu = 63,4	Ag = 108	Hg = 200
	Be = 9,4	Mg = 24	Zn = 65,2	Cd = 112	
	B = 11	Al = 27,4	? = 68	Ur = 116	Au = 197 ?
	C = 12	Si = 28	? = 70	Sn = 118	
	N = 14	P = 31	As = 75	Sb = 122	Bi = 210 ?
	O = 16	S = 32	Se = 79,4	Te = 128 ?	
	F = 19	Cl = 35,5	Br = 80	J = 127	
Li = 7	Na = 23	K = 39	Rb = 85,4	Cs = 133	Tl = 204
		Ca = 40	Sr = 87,6	Ba = 137	Pb = 207
		? = 45	Ce = 92		
		?Er = 56	La = 94		
		?Yt = 60	Di = 95		
		?In = 75,6	Th = 118 ?		

Table 5-1
COMPARISON OF MENDELEEV'S PREDICTIONS
WITH ACTUAL PROPERTIES OF GERMANIUM

Property	Mendeleev's prediction	Actual value
atomic weight	72	72.59
density, g/cm^3	5.5	5.32
atomic volume, cm^3	13	13.6
combining power	4	4
specific heat, cal/g C°	0.073	0.077
density of dioxide, g/cm^3	4.7	4.228
molecular volume of dioxide, cm^3	22	24.74
boiling point of tetrachloride, °C	<100	84
density of tetrachloride, g/cm^3	1.9	1.8443
molecular volume of tetrachloride, cm^3	113	116.26

germanium were discovered, their properties agreed very well with Mendeleev's predictions.

From Mendeleev's table of the elements, it was apparent that a relationship did exist between the properties of elements and their atomic weights. When elements are arranged in order of increasing atomic weights, their chemical properties follow a pattern. Similar chemical properties reoccur at definite intervals. Mendeleev concluded that "the properties of the elements are in periodic dependence on their atomic weights." Thus, Mendeleev's table, and others like it, are called periodic tables.

Lothar Meyer (1830–1895), a German chemist, independently arrived at this same conclusion at about the same time Mendeleev did.

◻ 5.3 Two discoveries alter the periodic table

During the 1890s Sir William Ramsay (1852–1916), a British chemist, discovered the noble gases neon, argon, krypton, and xenon. Another noble gas, helium, had been discovered on the sun in 1868. It was not really accepted as an element until it was found on the earth in 1895. Radon, the noble gas of highest atomic weight, was discovered in 1900. These six elements added an entirely new row to Mendeleev's periodic table. This row of elements goes between the F, Cl, Br, I row and the Li, Na, K, Rb, Cs row.

During 1913–1914 the English scientist Henry Gwyn-Jeffreys Moseley (1887–1915) performed X-ray experiments that showed the manner in which the number of protons per nucleus varied progressively from element to element. Moseley used his experimental evidence to determine the atomic number order of the elements.

X rays are electromagnetic radiations. Light is another form of electromagnetic radiation. But, unlike light, *X rays are not visible and are of higher frequency and shorter wavelength than light.* X rays are produced when high-speed electrons strike a metal target in an evacuated tube. Moseley found that the wave-

The atomic number of an atom is defined in Section 3.7 as the number of protons in its nucleus.

lengths of the X rays produced depend on the kind of metal used as the target. He used various metals ranging in atomic weight from aluminum to gold as the targets. He found that the wavelengths of X rays became shorter as elements with more protons in their nuclei were used. The higher the atomic number of an element, the shorter the wavelength of the X rays produced when that element is used as the target in an X-ray tube.

In three cases Moseley found an unusual variation in the wavelengths of X rays between two successive elements. The variation was twice as great as his calculations indicated. He concluded that in these cases an element was missing from the periodic table. The three elements, technetium, promethium, and rhenium, have since been discovered. They fill the gaps that Moseley indicated.

When the elements in a periodic table are placed in order of increasing atomic numbers instead of increasing atomic weights, some of the problems of arrangement disappear. Arranged according to increasing atomic weights, potassium, 39.1, precedes argon, 39.9. Yet, when arranged according to properties, potassium follows argon. This agrees with the atomic numbers: argon, 18, potassium, 19. A similar case is that of tellurium and iodine.

◯ 5.4 The periodic law

As stated in Section 5.2, Mendeleev concluded that the properties of elements are related in a periodic way to their atomic weights. Today, evidence shows that atomic numbers are better standards for establishing the order of the elements. Mendeleev's conclusion is now restated as the *periodic law: The physical and chemical properties of the elements are periodic functions of their atomic numbers*. In other words, (1) the properties of elements go through a pattern of change; (2) elements of similar properties occur at certain intervals, provided the elements are arranged in a periodic table in order of increasing atomic number.

◯ 5.5 Arrangement of the modern periodic table

The modern periodic table is shown on pages 96–97. As you study this section frequent reference to these pages will help you understand the periodic table and its importance in chemistry.

Each element is assigned a separate block in the table. See Figure 5-2. In the center of the block is the chemical symbol for the element. Below the symbol is the atomic number of the element. Above the symbol is the atomic weight. To the right of each symbol are numbers. These numbers indicate the distribution of electrons in the shells of the atoms of this element. A horizontal row of blocks on the table is called a *period* or *series*. A vertical column is called a *group* or *family*.

Hydrogen, atomic number 1, is placed at the top of the table by itself because of its many unique properties. It is in the first

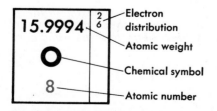

Figure 5-2. This figure shows the position of information found in each block of the periodic table.

column at the left of the table because its atoms have one electron in the outermost shell. Helium, atomic number 2, is at the top of the extreme right-hand column. Helium is classified as an inert gas because it does not react with other elements. It is the simplest member of the group of elements known as the *noble gases.* Note that helium atoms have two electrons in the K shell, or 1st energy level, which makes the K shell complete. Hydrogen and helium compose the first period of elements.

Figure 5-3 illustrates the relationship between the periodic table and the sublevels occupied by electrons in the structures of atoms of the elements. Refer to it also as you continue to study this section.

The second period consists of eight elements: (1) *lithium,* a soft, silvery, active metal, whose atoms have one electron in the L shell, or 2nd energy level; (2) *beryllium,* a silvery metal, less active than lithium, whose atoms have two electrons in the L shell; (3) *boron,* a black solid with some nonmetallic properties, whose atoms have three electrons in the L shell; (4) *carbon,* a

One unique property of hydrogen atoms is their single electron. If an electron is removed from a hydrogen atom, only the nucleus, one ten-thousandth the diameter of the atom, remains. If an electron is removed from any other atom, enough other electrons remain to occupy the space around the nucleus and roughly maintain the diameter of the atom.

Figure 5-3. The periodic table consists essentially of blocks of elements whose structures add support to the modern atomic theory.

SUBLEVEL BLOCKS OF THE PERIODIC TABLE

Period	Sublevels being filled	s sublevel block														p sublevel block					
		I	II												III	IV	V	VI	VII	VIII	
1	1s	H 1	He 2																		
2	2s 2p	Li 3	Be 4												B 5	C 6	N 7	O 8	F 9	Ne 10	
3	3s 3p	Na 11	Mg 12												Al 13	Si 14	P 15	S 16	Cl 17	Ar 18	
4	4s 3d 4p	K 19	Ca 20	Sc 21	Ti 22	V 23	Cr 24	Mn 25	Fe 26	Co 27	Ni 28	Cu 29	Zn 30		Ga 31	Ge 32	As 33	Se 34	Br 35	Kr 36	
5	5s 4d 5p	Rb 37	Sr 38	Y 39	Zr 40	Nb 41	Mo 42	Tc 43	Ru 44	Rh 45	Pd 46	Ag 47	Cd 48		In 49	Sn 50	Sb 51	Te 52	I 53	Xe 54	
6	6s 4f 5d 6p	Cs 55	Ba 56	Lu 71	Hf 72	Ta 73	W 74	Re 75	Os 76	Ir 77	Pt 78	Au 79	Hg 80		Tl 81	Pb 82	Bi 83	Po 84	At 85	Rn 86	
7	7s 5f 6d 7p	Fr 87	Ra 88	Lr 103	Unq 104	Unp 105	Unh 106	Uns 107													

TRANSITION ELEMENTS
d sublevel block

RARE EARTH ELEMENTS
f sublevel block

Period	Sublevels	series														
6	4f	Lanthanide series	La 57	Ce 58	Pr 59	Nd 60	Pm 61	Sm 62	Eu 63	Gd 64	Tb 65	Dy 66	Ho 67	Er 68	Tm 69	Yb 70
7	5f	Actinide series	Ac 89	Th 90	Pa 91	U 92	Np 93	Pu 94	Am 95	Cm 96	Bk 97	Cf 98	Es 99	Fm 100	Md 101	No 102

Sodium
Na

Magnesium
Mg

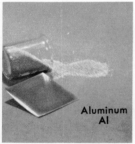

Aluminum
Al

Silicon
Si

Figure 5-4 (A). The first four elements of period three of the periodic table.

solid element with very distinctive chemical properties intermediate between those of metals and nonmetals: four electrons in the L shell; (5) *nitrogen,* a colorless gas with nonmetallic properties and five electrons in the L shell; (6) *oxygen,* a colorless gas having strong nonmetallic properties and six electrons in the L shell; (7) *fluorine,* a pale-yellow gas with very strong nonmetallic properties and seven electrons in the L shell; (8) *neon,* a colorless, inert (unreactive) gas having eight electrons in the L shell. Refer to Appendix Table 7, Electron Arrangement of the Elements.

The elements of Period 2 range from an active metallic element (Li) through two metalloids (Be and B, whose properties are between those of the typical metal and nonmetal) to an active nonmetallic element (F). The last element in the period (Ne) is inert. This variation in properties from metallic through metalloidal to nonmetallic is accompanied by an increase in the number of L-shell electrons from 1 to 7. The inert element neon has 8 electrons, an octet, in the L shell.

The third period also consists of eight elements: (1) *sodium,* a soft, silvery, active metal similar to lithium, one electron in the outermost M shell, or 3rd energy level; (2) *magnesium,* a silvery metal similar in properties to beryllium, two electrons in the M shell; (3) *aluminum,* a silvery metal with some nonmetallic properties, three electrons in the M shell; (4) *silicon,* a dark-colored, nonmetallic element with some properties resembling carbon, four electrons in the M shell; (5) *phosphorus,* a nonmetallic, solid element that forms compounds similar to those of nitrogen, five electrons in the M shell; (6) *sulfur,* a yellow, nonmetallic solid element, six electrons in the M shell; (7) *chlorine,* a yellow-green gas with strong nonmetallic properties resembling those of fluorine, seven electrons in the M shell; (8) *argon,* a colorless, inert gas, eight electrons in the M shell. Figure 5-4 illustrates the variations in the properties of these third-period elements. Again the elements range from active metallic through metalloidal to active nonmetallic properties as the number of electrons in the outer shell varies from 1 to 7. The element with an octet as its outer shell is a noble gas.

Elements with similar properties have a similar arrangement of outer-shell electrons. They fall into the same group in the periodic table.

Group I of the periodic table is the *sodium family,* a group of six similar, very active, metallic elements. Their atoms all have only one electron in the outermost shell. *Francium* is the most complex member of the sodium family. The position of francium in the periodic table indicates that it is probably the most active metal.

Group II also consists of six active metals whose chemical properties are very much alike. The atoms of each have two electrons in the outer shell. This is the *calcium family*. The most chemically active member of this family is *radium*.

The properties of elements in Group III vary from nonmetallic to metallic as the atoms become larger and heavier. The atoms of this group have three electrons in the outer shell.

The elements of Group IV vary in similar fashion. Their atoms have four electrons in the outer shell. Atoms of elements in both Group III and Group IV have very stable inner shells.

Group V is the *nitrogen family*. *Nitrogen* and *phosphorus*, the elements at the top of this family, are nonmetallic. The element *bismuth*, at the bottom of the table, is metallic. *Arsenic* and *antimony* exhibit both metallic and nonmetallic properties. The atoms of each of these elements have five electrons in the outer shell and very stable inner shells.

Group VI is the *oxygen family*. The properties of elements in this family vary from active nonmetallic to metallic as the atoms become larger and heavier. The atoms of each of these elements have six electrons in the outer shell and very stable inner shells.

The elements in Group VII, the *halogen family*, are very active nonmetals. Their atoms each have seven electrons in the outer shell and very stable inner shells. The most active member of the halogen family is its simplest element, *fluorine*.

Group VIII is the *noble-gas family*. With the exception of *helium* atoms, which have a pair of electrons in the outer shell, atoms of these elements have an octet as the outer shell. This is the greatest number of electrons found in an outer shell. No compounds of helium, neon, and argon are known. A few compounds of krypton, xenon, and radon have been prepared. The low-atomic-weight noble gases are not considered in a discussion of activity because they form no compounds. Thus, the activity of the elements ranges from the most active metal at the lower left corner of the periodic table to the most active nonmetal at the upper right corner.

The fourth period consists of 18 elements. It is the first long period. In addition to the eight elements in Groups I to VIII, there are also ten **transition elements**. These are metallic elements whose atoms have one or two electrons in the outer shell. Successive electrons usually occupy the group of 5 space orbitals of the $3d$ sublevel.

The fifth period also consists of 18 elements. It includes ten transition elements, in which successive electrons occupy the group of 5 space orbitals of the $4d$ sublevel. The transition elements are all metals.

The sixth period consists of 32 elements. In addition to the elements in Groups I to VIII and the ten transition elements, there is a group of 14 **rare earth elements**. These elements have almost identical chemical properties. They compose the *lanthanide series*. The two outer shells of these atoms are almost

Phosphorus
P

Sulfur
S

Chlorine
Cl

Argon
Ar

Figure 5-4 (B). The last four elements of period three of the periodic table.

PERIODIC TABLE

METALS

TRANSITION ELEMENTS

	I	II								
1	1.0079 **H** 1									

	I	II								
2	6.941 **Li** 3	9.01218 **Be** 4								
3	22.98977 **Na** 11	24.305 **Mg** 12								
4	39.0983 **K** 19	40.08 **Ca** 20	44.9559 **Sc** 21	47.90 **Ti** 22	50.9415 **V** 23	51.996 **Cr** 24	54.9380 **Mn** 25	55.847 **Fe** 26	58.9332 **Co** 27
5	85.4678 **Rb** 37	87.62 **Sr** 38	88.9059 **Y** 39	91.22 **Zr** 40	92.9064 **Nb** 41	95.94 **Mo** 42	[98] **Tc** 43	101.07 **Ru** 44	102.9055 **Rh** 45
6	132.9054 **Cs** 55	137.33 **Ba** 56	Lantha-nide Series / 174.967 **Lu** 71	178.49 **Hf** 72	180.9479 **Ta** 73	183.85 **W** 74	186.207 **Re** 75	190.2 **Os** 76	192.22 **Ir** 77
7	[223] **Fr** 87	226.0254 **Ra** 88	Actinide Series / [260] **Lr** 103	[261] **Unq** 104	[263] **Unp** 105	[263] **Unh** 106	[261] **Uns** 107		

Lantha-nide Series	138.9055 **La** 57	140.12 **Ce** 58	140.9077 **Pr** 59	144.24 **Nd** 60	[145] **Pm** 61	150.4 **Sm** 62	151.96 **Eu** 63

Actinide Series	227.0278 **Ac** 89	232.0381 **Th** 90	231.0359 **Pa** 91	238.029 **U** 92	237.0482 **Np** 93	[244] **Pu** 94	[243] **Am** 95

OF THE ELEMENTS

NONMETALS

			III	IV	V	VI	VII	Noble gases VIII
								4.00260 **He** 2 (2)
			10.81 **B** 5 (2, 3)	12.011 **C** 6 (2, 4)	14.0067 **N** 7 (2, 5)	15.9994 **O** 8 (2, 6)	18.998403 **F** 9 (2, 7)	20.179 **Ne** 10 (2, 8)
			26.98154 **Al** 13 (2, 8, 3)	28.0855 **Si** 14 (2, 8, 4)	30.97376 **P** 15 (2, 8, 5)	32.06 **S** 16 (2, 8, 6)	35.453 **Cl** 17 (2, 8, 7)	39.948 **Ar** 18 (2, 8, 8)
58.70 **Ni** 28 (2, 8, 16, 2)	63.546 **Cu** 29 (2, 8, 18, 1)	65.38 **Zn** 30 (2, 8, 18, 2)	69.72 **Ga** 31 (2, 8, 18, 3)	72.59 **Ge** 32 (2, 8, 18, 4)	74.9216 **As** 33 (2, 8, 18, 5)	78.96 **Se** 34 (2, 8, 18, 6)	79.904 **Br** 35 (2, 8, 18, 7)	83.80 **Kr** 36 (2, 8, 18, 8)
106.4 **Pd** 46 (2, 8, 18, 18, 0)	107.868 **Ag** 47 (2, 8, 18, 18, 1)	112.41 **Cd** 48 (2, 8, 18, 18, 2)	114.82 **In** 49 (2, 8, 18, 18, 3)	118.69 **Sn** 50 (2, 8, 18, 18, 4)	121.75 **Sb** 51 (2, 8, 18, 18, 5)	127.60 **Te** 52 (2, 8, 18, 18, 6)	126.9045 **I** 53 (2, 8, 18, 18, 7)	131.30 **Xe** 54 (2, 8, 18, 18, 8)
195.09 **Pt** 78 (2, 8, 18, 32, 17, 1)	196.9665 **Au** 79 (2, 8, 18, 32, 18, 1)	200.59 **Hg** 80 (2, 8, 18, 32, 18, 2)	204.37 **Tl** 81 (2, 8, 18, 32, 18, 3)	207.2 **Pb** 82 (2, 8, 18, 32, 18, 4)	208.9804 **Bi** 83 (2, 8, 18, 32, 18, 5)	[209] **Po** 84 (2, 8, 18, 32, 18, 6)	[210] **At** 85 (2, 8, 18, 32, 18, 7)	[222] **Rn** 86 (2, 8, 18, 32, 18, 8)

RARE EARTH ELEMENTS

157.25 **Gd** 64 (2, 8, 18, 25, 9, 2)	158.9254 **Tb** 65 (2, 8, 18, 27, 8, 2)	162.50 **Dy** 66 (2, 8, 18, 28, 8, 2)	164.9304 **Ho** 67 (2, 8, 18, 29, 8, 2)	167.26 **Er** 68 (2, 8, 18, 30, 8, 2)	168.9342 **Tm** 69 (2, 8, 18, 31, 8, 2)	173.04 **Yb** 70 (2, 8, 18, 32, 8, 2)

[247] **Cm** 96 (2, 8, 18, 32, 25, 9, 2)	[247] **Bk** 97 (2, 8, 18, 32, 26, 9, 2)	[251] **Cf** 98 (2, 8, 18, 32, 28, 8, 2)	[254] **Es** 99 (2, 8, 18, 32, 29, 8, 2)	[257] **Fm** 100 (2, 8, 18, 32, 30, 8, 2)	[258] **Md** 101 (2, 8, 18, 32, 31, 8, 2)	[259] **No** 102 (2, 8, 18, 32, 32, 8, 2)

A value given in brackets denotes the mass number of the isotope of longest known half-life.

the same. The outermost shell contains two electrons. The next-inner shell contains either eight or nine electrons. As the number of electrons in the 4th energy level increases from 18 to 32, successive electrons occupy the group of 7 space orbitals of the $4f$ sublevel.

The seventh period of elements is at present an incomplete period. It is assumed to be similar to the sixth period. The rare earth elements in the period compose the *actinide series*. To date, 21 members of the seventh period are known or reported.

In the periodic table, the elements are roughly divided into metals, nonmetals, and noble gases. The line separating the metals from the nonmetals is a zigzag line. It runs diagonally down and to the right near the right side of the table. The elements that border this zigzag line are the *metalloids*. These elements show both metallic and nonmetallic properties under different conditions.

Figure 5-5. Periodic table showing radii of the atoms of the elements in angstrom units.

PERIODIC TABLE OF ATOMIC RADII

I	II											III	IV	V	VI	VII	VIII
0.32 H 1																	0.31 He 2
1.23 Li 3	0.89 Be 4											0.82 B 5	0.77 C 6	0.74 N 7	0.70 O 8	0.68 F 9	0.67 Ne 10
1.54 Na 11	1.36 Mg 12											1.18 Al 13	1.11 Si 14	1.06 P 15	1.02 S 16	0.99 Cl 17	0.98 Ar 18
2.03 K 19	1.74 Ca 20	1.44 Sc 21	1.32 Ti 22	1.22 V 23	1.18 Cr 24	1.17 Mn 25	1.17 Fe 26	1.16 Co 27	1.15 Ni 28	1.17 Cu 29	1.25 Zn 30	1.26 Ga 31	1.22 Ge 32	1.20 As 33	1.17 Se 34	1.14 Br 35	1.12 Kr 36
2.16 Rb 37	1.91 Sr 38	1.62 Y 39	1.45 Zr 40	1.34 Nb 41	1.30 Mo 42	1.27 Tc 43	1.25 Ru 44	1.25 Rh 45	1.28 Pd 46	1.34 Ag 47	1.48 Cd 48	1.44 In 49	1.40 Sn 50	1.40 Sb 51	1.36 Te 52	1.33 I 53	1.31 Xe 54
2.35 Cs 55	1.98 Ba 56	1.56 Lu 71	1.44 Hf 72	1.34 Ta 73	1.30 W 74	1.28 Re 75	1.26 Os 76	1.27 Ir 77	1.30 Pt 78	1.34 Au 79	1.49 Hg 80	1.48 Tl 81	1.47 Pb 82	1.46 Bi 83	1.46 Po 84	1.45 At 85	Rn 86
Fr 87	2.20 Ra 88	Lr 103	Unq 104	Unp 105	Unh 106	Uns 107											

1.69 La 57	1.65 Ce 58	1.64 Pr 59	1.64 Nd 60	1.63 Pm 61	1.62 Sm 62	1.85 Eu 63	1.62 Gd 64	1.61 Tb 65	1.60 Dy 66	1.58 Ho 67	1.58 Er 68	1.58 Tm 69	1.70 Yb 70
2.0 Ac 89	1.65 Th 90	Pa 91	1.42 U 92	Np 93	Pu 94	Am 95	Cm 96	Bk 97	Cf 98	Es 99	Fm 100	Md 101	No 102

Atomic radii mostly from R.T. Sanderson, INORGANIC CHEMISTRY, Reinhold Publishing Corporation, New York, 1967, and subsequent private communication.

🞏 5.6 Size of atoms: a periodic property

In Chapter 3 it was established that an atom consists of a central nucleus with electrons moving about it. The nucleus has a diameter about one ten-thousandth that of the atom. Most of the volume of an atom is occupied by moving electrons, whose complex motion makes the atoms appear as spheres, even though they are mostly empty space. The spherical electron cloud gives an atom its volume and excludes other atoms.

The volume of an atom is not a completely definite quantity because the boundary of an atom's electron cloud is not a distinct surface. Rather, the boundary is somewhat fuzzy and indefinite. An atom may be rather easily distorted when it combines with other atoms. But very great force must be used if it is to be compressed.

The reported "size" of an atom varies somewhat with the dimension measured and the method used to measure it. Scientists have measured the distance between adjacent nuclei in the crystalline forms of elements and in the molecules of gaseous elements. One-half of this distance, with slight correction, is used as the radius of one atom. The radius of an atom, and thus its volume, *do not increase regularly* with atomic number. Such an increase might be expected from the regular addition of an electron in successive elements. But atomic size varies in a periodic fashion as shown in Figure 5-5. This figure is a miniature periodic table with element symbols and atomic numbers in black. Atomic radii are shown in color. The radii of atoms of the elements are given in angstroms. Figure 5-6 shows the atomic radius plotted as a function of the atomic number. Two conclusions about the relationship between atomic radius and the periodic table are:

1. The atomic radius generally increases with atomic number in a particular group or family of elements. Each element in a group has one more shell or energy level than the element above it. The increased nuclear charge decreases the radii of the

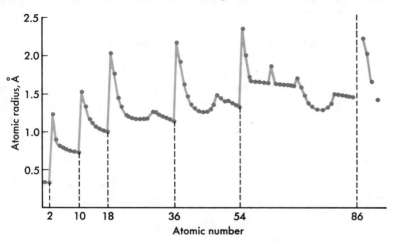

Figure 5-6. Graph showing atomic radius plotted as a function of atomic number.

electron shells by drawing them closer. But the addition of a shell more than counteracts this effect.

2. From Group I to Group VIII in a period, there is a general decrease in the atomic radii of the elements. Each element has a greater positive nuclear charge than the one before it. This greater charge results in a greater total force of attraction between the electrons and the nucleus. This greater force of attraction may explain why the electrons of the elements across a period are successively closer to the nucleus.

Because the number of protons in the nucleus of the elements increases from left to right in any one period, so does the number of electrons in the outermost orbitals about the nucleus. As the number of electrons increases, the force of repulsion between them also increases. Irregularities in the atomic radius pattern may be caused by patterns in this force of repulsion.

5.7 Ionization energy

A negatively charged electron is held in an atom by the attraction of the positively charged protons in the nucleus. By supplying energy, it is possible to remove an electron from an

Figure 5-7. Periodic table showing first ionization energies of the elements in kilocalories per mole.

PERIODIC TABLE OF FIRST IONIZATION ENERGIES

I	II											III	IV	V	VI	VII	VIII
314 H 1																	567 He 2
124 Li 3	215 Be 4											191 B 5	260 C 6	335 N 7	314 O 8	402 F 9	497 Ne 10
119 Na 11	176 Mg 12											138 Al 13	188 Si 14	242 P 15	239 S 16	299 Cl 17	363 Ar 18
100 K 19	141 Ca 20	151 Sc 21	157 Ti 22	155 V 23	156 Cr 24	171 Mn 25	181 Fe 26	181 Co 27	176 Ni 28	178 Cu 29	217 Zn 30	138 Ga 31	182 Ge 32	226 As 33	225 Se 34	272 Br 35	323 Kr 36
96 Rb 37	131 Sr 38	147 Y 39	158 Zr 40	159 Nb 41	164 Mo 42	168 Tc 43	170 Ru 44	172 Rh 45	192 Pd 46	175 Ag 47	207 Cd 48	133 In 49	169 Sn 50	199 Sb 51	208 Te 52	241 I 53	280 Xe 54
90 Cs 55	120 Ba 56	125 Lu 71	161 Hf 72	182 Ta 73	184 W 74	182 Re 75	201 Os 76	210 Ir 77	208 Pt 78	213 Au 79	241 Hg 80	141 Tl 81	171 Pb 82	168 Bi 83	196 Po 84	At 85	248 Rn 86
Fr 87	122 Ra 88	Lr 103	Unq 104	Unp 105	Unh 106	Uns 107											

129 La 57	126 Ce 58	125 Pr 59	127 Nd 60	128 Pm 61	130 Sm 62	131 Eu 63	142 Gd 64	135 Tb 65	137 Dy 66	139 Ho 67	141 Er 68	143 Tm 69	144 Yb 70
159 Ac 89	Th 90	Pa 91	U 92	Np 93	134 Pu 94	138 Am 95	Cm 96	Bk 97	Cf 98	Es 99	Fm 100	Md 101	No 102

atom. Suppose that **A** is used as a symbol for an atom of any element and that → means "yields." Then this electron removal may be shown in equation form as

$$A + energy \rightarrow A^+ + e^-$$

The particle A^+ that remains after the removal of an electron, e^-, is an *ion* with a single positive charge. *An ion is an atom* (or sometimes a group of atoms) *that has a net positive or negative charge.* This net charge results from unequal numbers of positively charged protons and negatively charged electrons. *The energy required to remove an electron from an atom is its ionization energy.* The chart, Figure 5-7, shows the ionization energy required to remove one electron from an atom of each element. One unit in which ionization energy is expressed is kcal/mole. The first ionization energy of oxygen, for example, is 314 kcal/mole. This means that 314 kcal of energy must be supplied to remove the first, or least tightly held, outermost electron from each atom in one mole of oxygen atoms. (Recall that one mole of oxygen atoms is 6.02×10^{23} atoms.) Figure 5-8 is a graph showing first ionization energy plotted as a function of atomic number. From Figures 5-7 and 5-8, the following conclusions can be drawn:

1. Low ionization energy is characteristic of a *metal. High ionization energy* is characteristic of a *nonmetal.* The chemical inertness of the noble gases is strong evidence for the unusual stability, or resistance to change, of the outer-shell octet. As might be expected, the noble gases have unusually high ionization energies.

2. Within a group of nontransition elements, the ionization energy generally decreases with increasing atomic number. This is because increasing atomic number is accompanied by increas-

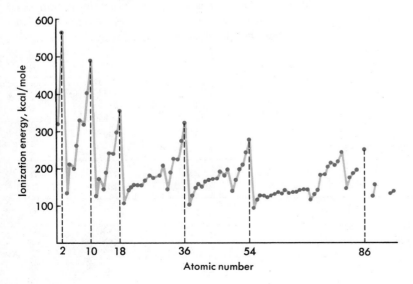

Figure 5-8. Graph showing first ionization energy as a function of atomic number.

ing atomic radius within such groups. The outer-shell electrons of the elements of higher atomic number within a group are farther from the nucleus. Thus, these electrons are attracted less by the nucleus. The ionization energy for removal of one outer-shell electron, therefore, is less as the atomic number of the atom is greater. This reasoning does not hold true for the transition elements.

3. Ionization energy does not vary uniformly from element to element within a series. Instead, it is a *periodic* property. In each series or period, the ionization energy increases from Group I to Group VIII. But the increase is not regular. There is a decrease in ionization energies between Groups II and III in Periods 2 and 3. This decrease occurs as the *s* sublevel is filled and the *p* sublevel is started. In these periods, there is also a decrease between Groups V and VI as the *p* sublevel becomes half-filled. In Periods 4, 5, and 6, there is a sharp decrease in the ionization energy between the last transition element and Group III. This decrease occurs as the *d* sublevel is filled and the *p* sublevel is started. These irregularities are apparently related to the extra stability of completed and half-completed sublevels.

◻ 5.8 Ionization energy to remove successive electrons

It is possible to remove more than one electron from many-electron atoms.

$$\textbf{Na + ionization energy 1st electron} \rightarrow \textbf{Na}^+ + \textbf{e}^-$$

$$\textbf{Na}^+ + \textbf{ionization energy 2nd electron} \rightarrow \textbf{Na}^{++} + \textbf{e}^-$$

$$\textbf{Na}^{++} + \textbf{ionization energy 3rd electron} \rightarrow \textbf{Na}^{+++} + \textbf{e}^-$$

Table 5-2 shows the electron configurations of sodium, magnesium, and aluminum atoms. It also gives the ionization energies required to remove successive electrons from atoms of these elements. Notice the increase in energy for each successive electron removed.

Table 5-2
ELECTRON CONFIGURATIONS AND IONIZATION ENERGIES OF SODIUM, MAGNESIUM, AND ALUMINUM

Elements	*Electron configuration*	*Ionization energy* (kcal/mole)			
		1st electron	*2nd electron*	*3rd electron*	*4th electron*
Na	$1s^2 2s^2 2p^6 3s^1$	119	1090	1652	2281
Mg	$1s^2 2s^2 2p^6 3s^2$	176	347	1848	2519
Al	$1s^2 2s^2 2p^6 3s^2 3p^1$	138	434	656	2767

It is not surprising that the ionization energy increases with each electron removed from an atom. After all, each successive electron must be removed from a particle with an increasingly greater net positive charge. A closer examination of the variations in ionization energies is now needed.

For sodium atoms, there is a great increase between the first and second ionization energies. The first electron, a $3s$ electron, is rather easily removed. But to remove the second electron almost ten times as much energy is needed. This increase occurs because the second electron is a $2p$ electron in a much lower energy level. The lower the energy level, the greater the energy needed to remove an electron from the attraction of the nucleus. Figure 5-9 shows the energy-level transitions involved for the elements sodium, magnesium, and aluminum.

The removal of electrons from magnesium atoms requires little ionization energy for the first two electrons, since both are $3s$ electrons. More energy is required to remove the first $3s$ electron from magnesium atoms than the first $3s$ electron from sodium atoms. This increase occurs because magnesium atoms have a greater nuclear charge and the $3s$ electrons are closer to the nucleus. But to remove the third electron from magnesium atoms requires between five and six times as much energy as is needed to remove the second. This increase occurs because the third electron is a $2p$ electron. Since $2p$ electrons of magnesium are at a much lower energy level than $3s$ electrons, there is a great increase in ionization energy.

It is easy to remove the first three electrons from aluminum atoms. In fact, it is easier to remove the first electron from aluminum atoms than it is to remove the first electron from magnesium atoms. A look at the electron configuration indicates that the first aluminum electron is a $3p$ electron. It is in a slightly higher energy sublevel than the first magnesium electron, which is a $3s$ electron. There is a great increase in ionization energy between the third and fourth aluminum electrons. This increase is explained by the fact that the fourth electron is a $2p$ electron. This electron is in a much lower energy level than the first three electrons, which were all 3rd energy-level electrons.

The order in which electrons are removed from atoms by ionization is not the same as the order in which electrons occupy orbitals in the structures described in Sections 4.6–4.10. This difference is caused by the shifting of the relative positions of energy sublevels as they are occupied by electrons. Electrons are removed from atoms by ionization in the reverse of the order given by the electron-configuration notation. The electron-configuration notation of iron is $1s^2 2s^2 2p^6 3s^2 3p^6 3d^6 4s^2$. The first electron removed from iron atoms is a $4s$ electron. So is the second. The third electron is a $3d$ electron, as are the fourth, fifth, sixth, and so on.

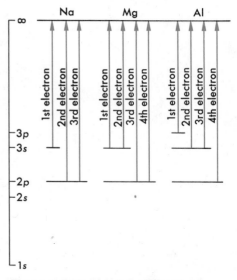

Figure 5-9. Energy-level transitions for the removal of successive electrons from sodium, magnesium, and aluminum atoms.

See Question 40 at the end of this chapter.

□ 5.9 Electron affinity

Neutral atoms can acquire additional electrons. The measure of this tendency is *electron affinity*. **Electron affinity is the energy change that occurs when an electron is acquired by a neutral atom.** When an electron is added to a neutral atom, an ion with a single negative charge is formed. An amount of energy, the electron affinity, is either released or absorbed.

For most atoms the electron affinity is energy that is released. In equation form, the acquiring of an electron and the release of energy may be expressed as

$$A + e^- \rightarrow A^- + \text{energy} \qquad \textbf{(Equation 1)}$$

It may be helpful to review Sections 2.13 and 2.14.

Since energy is released, the change is exothermic. The negative ion will be more stable than the neutral atom. Because the energy is released, it is given a positive sign, as shown in Equation 1. Like ionization energy, electron affinity may be measured in kcal/mole. The electron affinity indicates how tightly an additional electron is bound to an atom. If the electron affinity is positive and low, the electron is weakly bound. If the electron affinity is positive and high, the electron is strongly bound.

Figure 5-10. Periodic table showing the electron affinities of the elements in kilocalories per mole. The values in parentheses are estimated.

PERIODIC TABLE OF ELECTRON AFFINITIES

																		VIII
																		(−5.1) **He** 2
I	**II**												**III**	**IV**	**V**	**VI**	**VII**	
14.3 **Li** 3	(18) **Be** 4												6.5 **B** 5	29.3 **C** 6	0.0 **N** 7	33.8 **O** 8	78.4 **F** 9	(−6.9) **Ne** 10
12.6 **Na** 11	−3.5 **Mg** 12												11 **Al** 13	31.9 **Si** 14	17.2 **P** 15	47.9 **S** 16	83.4 **Cl** 17	(−8.3) **Ar** 18
11.6 **K** 19	(−16) **Ca** 20	(11) **Sc** 21	(14) **Ti** 22	(14) **V** 23	15 **Cr** 24	(−14) **Mn** 25	3.2 **Fe** 26	(21) **Co** 27	26.5 **Ni** 28	28.3 **Cu** 29	−11 **Zn** 30	(8.5) **Ga** 31	27.7 **Ge** 32	18 **As** 33	46.6 **Se** 34	77.6 **Br** 35	(−9.2) **Kr** 36
11.2 **Rb** 37	(−5) **Sr** 38	(16) **Y** 39	(−23) **Zr** 40	23 **Nb** 41	23 **Mo** 42	(−14) **Tc** 43	(16) **Ru** 44	(25) **Rh** 45	(25) **Pd** 46	30.0 **Ag** 47	−7.6 **Cd** 48	8.1 **In** 49	28.8 **Sn** 50	24.2 **Sb** 51	45.4 **Te** 52	70.6 **I** 53	(−9.7) **Xe** 54
10.9 **Cs** 55	(−12) **Ba** 56	**Lu** 71	(5) **Hf** 72	14 **Ta** 73	14 **W** 74	3.5 **Re** 75	(28) **Os** 76	(25) **Ir** 77	49.1 **Pt** 78	53.2 **Au** 79	−14 **Hg** 80	(44) **Tl** 81	24.2 **Pb** 82	24.2 **Bi** 83	(23) **Po** 84	(65) **At** 85	(−9.7) **Rn** 86
(10.5) **Fr** 87	**Ra** 88	**Lr** 103	**Unq** 104	**Unp** 105	**Unh** 106	**Uns** 107											

(28) **La** 57	(0) **Ce** 58	(0) **Pr** 59	(−16) **Nd** 60	**Pm** 61	(−7) **Sm** 62	**Eu** 63	**Gd** 64	**Tb** 65	**Dy** 66	**Ho** 67	**Er** 68	**Tm** 69	**Yb** 70
Ac 89	(0) **Th** 90	**Pa** 91	(25) **U** 92	**Np** 93	**Pu** 94	**Am** 95	**Cm** 96	**Bk** 97	**Cf** 98	**Es** 99	**Fm** 100	**Md** 101	**No** 102

17.4 **H** 1

Values in parentheses are estimated.

Data compiled by E.C.M. Chen and W.E. Wentworth, *J. Chem. Ed.*, August 1975 and subsequent private communications.

For some atoms the electron affinity is energy that is absorbed. In equation form, this change may be expressed as

$$A + e^- + energy \rightarrow A^-$$

Since energy is absorbed, the change is endothermic. A more useful form of this equation is similar to Equation 1, with the energy term to the right of the "yields" sign:

$$A + e^- \rightarrow A^- - energy \qquad \textbf{(Equation 2)}$$

In the case of an endothermic reaction, the energy change is given a negative sign, as shown in Equation 2. If the electron affinity is negative, energy must be used in forming the negative ion. The negative ion, consequently, will be less stable than the neutral atom.

Figure 5-10 gives the known experimental values for electron affinities in kilocalories per mole of atoms. Estimated values are given for some of the other atoms. These data are graphed in Figure 5-11. From these figures, several observations can be made.

The Group II elements, the elements of the zinc subfamily (Zn, Cd, Hg), and the noble gases have zero or negative electron affinities. This is evidence that the atoms of these elements have filled outermost s or p sublevels and stable inner energy levels. An electron can be added to such atoms only by supplying energy. The addition of an electron to these atoms produces a singly charged negative ion that is less stable than the atom.

If only the experimental values are considered, a general decrease in electron affinity in the numbered families from the third through the sixth periods is apparent. The added electron takes a position in the atom farther from the nucleus. Not as much energy is released; the electron is not as strongly held.

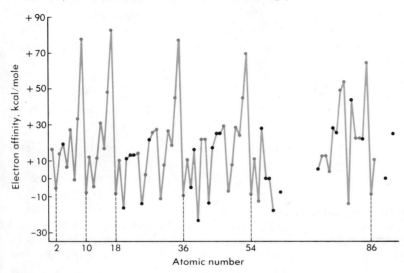

Figure 5-11. Graph showing electron affinity as a function of atomic number. Experimental data are shown by dots in color; estimated data are shown by black dots.

For the Group I elements there is a decrease in electron affinity between the second and third periods. But for Groups III, IV, V, VI, and VII, there is an increase between the second and third periods. The Period Two elements are small in size and frequently show irregularities in properties when compared with other elements in their group.

There is an increase in electron affinity between Groups III and IV. The addition of an electron to a Group III atom results in an ion with 2 electrons in the outer *p* sublevel. The addition of an electron to a Group IV atom results in an ion with 3 electrons in the outer *p* sublevel. These 3 electrons constitute a half-filled *p* sublevel. The greater amount of energy released when an electron is added to a Group IV atom than to a Group III atom is evidence of the greater stability of a half-filled *p* sublevel than one with only 2 electrons.

There is a decrease in electron affinity between Groups IV and V. The Group V atoms have half-filled *p* sublevels, and there is little attraction for another electron.

Ionization energy and electron affinity are important concepts in understanding how compounds are formed from atoms of metallic and nonmetallic elements.

There is a general increase in electron affinity among the atoms of Groups V, VI, and VII. The addition of electrons in turn to Group V, VI, and VII atoms produces ions with increasingly stable outer shells. The addition of an electron to a Group VII atom produces an ion with an outer-shell octet. The quite high electron affinities of the halogens is additional evidence for the stability of outer-shell octets.

◻ 5.10 Value of the periodic table

In former years, the periodic table served as a check on atomic weight determinations. It also was used in the prediction of new elements. These uses are now outdated. Today the periodic table serves as a useful and systematic classification of elements according to their properties. The occurrence of properties such as atomic size, ionization energy, and electron affinity at regular intervals has already been described. This information is valuable in determining the types of compounds that certain elements form. Though not perfect, the periodic table makes the study of chemistry easier.

◖ SUMMARY

About 1869, Mendeleev classified the elements according to physical and chemical properties by arranging them in order of increasing atomic weight. He concluded that the properties of elements are in periodic dependence on their atomic weights.

Moseley found that X rays could be used to determine the atomic number of an element. An increase in the number of protons in the nucleus of atoms of the metal used as the target in an X-ray tube shortens the wavelength of the X rays produced. When elements are arranged in order of their atomic numbers, some discrepancies in Mendeleev's arrangement disappear. As a result of this discovery, the periodic law is now stated as: The physical and chemical properties of the elements are periodic functions of their atomic numbers.

In the modern periodic table, the families of elements with similar properties, also known as groups, are in vertical columns. Each element in a family has a similar number of electrons in its outer shell. At the left of the table, the most active elements are at the bottom. At the right of the table, they are at the top. A row of elements is called a period. In a given period, the properties of the elements gradually pass from strong metallic to strong nonmetallic nature. The last member of a period is a noble gas. Atomic size, ionization energy, and electron affinity vary from element to element in a periodic fashion.

◖ VOCABULARY

actinide series	group	noble gas	series
atomic radius	ion	period	transition elements
electron affinity	ionization energy	periodic law	X rays
family	lanthanide series	rare earth elements	

◖ QUESTIONS

Group A

1. (*a*) On what basis did Mendeleev arrange the elements in his periodic table? (*b*) On what basis are they arranged today?
2. What use did Mendeleev make of his study of the known elements?
3. How are X rays used to determine the atomic number of an element?
4. What is the periodic law?
5. (*a*) What information is given in each block of the periodic table? (*b*) How are these data arranged in each block?
6. (*a*)What is a group or family of elements? (*b*) What position does a family occupy in the periodic table?
7. (*a*) What is a series or period of elements? (*b*) What position does a period occupy in the periodic table?
8. (*a*) Name the elements in the second period. (*b*) How does the number of electrons in the outer shell vary in these elements? (*c*) How do their properties compare?
9. What is similar about the electron configurations of elements with similar properties?
10. How do the elements at the left of the periodic table vary in activity?
11. How do the elements in Group VII vary in activity?
12. (*a*) What name is given to the elements that border the line dividing the metals from the nonmetals? (*b*) What characteristic does this name imply?
13. The mass numbers of the naturally occurring isotopes of argon are 36, 38, and 40. Those of potassium are 39, 40, and 41. From the atomic weights of these elements given in the periodic table, estimate which isotope of each element is most abundant.
14. Why is the radius of an atom not a definitely fixed quantity?
15. (*a*) How do the atomic radii of the Group I elements compare with the radii of other elements of their period? (*b*) For what structural characteristic of these atoms is this evidence?
16. In a period, how does the atomic radius of the Group VII element compare with the atomic radii of the other *numbered group* elements?
17. Compare the atomic radii of sodium and chlorine. What difference in structure is related to the difference in radii?
18. Compare the atomic radii of magnesium and barium. What differences in structure are related to the difference in radii?
19. (*a*) Write an equation to represent the removal of the single outer-shell electron from a potassium atom. (*b*) Write an equation to represent the addition of an electron to a

neutral bromine atom. (*c*) What particles are produced by these reactions?

20. (*a*) What does the low ionization energy of metals indicate about their atomic structure? (*b*) What does the high ionization energy of nonmetals indicate about their atomic structure?

21. Compare the first ionization energies of sodium and chlorine. What differences in structure are related to the difference in ionization energy?

22. Compare the first ionization energies of aluminum and chromium. What difference in structure is related to the difference in ionization energy?

23. What is electron affinity?

24. Write an equation to represent (*a*) the addition of an electron to a sodium atom; (*b*) the addition of an electron to a chlorine atom; (*c*) the addition of an electron to an argon atom. (*d*) Compare the strength with which the electron is bound in the three ions.

Group B

25. What family of elements was missing from Mendeleev's periodic table?

26. (*a*) What are X rays? (*b*) How are they produced?

27. (*a*) How did Mendeleev know where to leave gaps for undiscovered elements in his periodic table? (*b*) How did Moseley know where to leave gaps for undiscovered elements?

28. (*a*) Why is hydrogen placed separately in the periodic table? (*b*) Why is it placed above Group I?

29. (*a*) What are transition elements? (*b*) In which periods of elements do they appear?

30. (*a*) What are rare earth elements? (*b*) In which periods of elements do they appear?

31. (*a*) How does atomic size vary with atomic number within a family of elements? (*b*) How does the explanation of atomic structure account for this variation?

32. (*a*) How does atomic size generally vary with atomic number within a period of elements? (*b*) How does the explanation of atomic structure account for this variation?

33. (*a*) How would you expect the ionization energies of two atoms of about equal size but different atomic number to compare? (*b*) Why?

34. (*a*) If energy must be supplied to remove an outer-shell electron from an atom, which is more stable, the atom or the resulting ion? (*b*) If energy is released during the addition of an electron to a neutral atom, which is more stable, the atom or the resulting ion?

35. Most Group II and all Group VIII elements have negative electron affinities. To what structural features of these atoms is this related?

36. There is a decrease in electron affinity between Groups IV and V. For what structural characteristic of atoms is this evidence?

37. What determines the number of elements in each period of the periodic table?

38. How many 5th energy-level orbitals would theoretically be filled in element 118?

39. What is the present value of the periodic table?

40. On a separate sheet of paper, copy and complete the following table. *Do not write in this book.*

On the basis of the electron configuration, explain the variation in ionization energies for successive electrons.

Chemical element	Electron-configuration notation	Ionization energy (kcal/mole)			
		1st electron	**2nd electron**	**3rd electron**	**4th electron**
K		100	729	1054	1405
Ca		141	274	1174	1547
Ga		138	473	708	1470

Chemical Bonds

The Chinese philosopher Confucius taught that all existence can be analyzed into two opposite principles, the masculine yang and the feminine yin. According to the I-Ching, the book containing the beliefs of this ancient philosophy, when the active and heavenly yang combines in a definite ratio with the passive and earthly yin, a new principle is formed. Each new principle corresponds to a particular law of nature. This idea of the combination of opposites to analyze many phenomena is used in many other Eastern and Western disciplines, including science. In biology, for example, most species of plants and animals are represented by two forms, the male and female. In optics, white light results when two colors called complementary colors combine. Chemists, alongside physicists, biologists, and philosophers, use the concept of interacting opposites in their work.

◻ 6.1 Elements form compounds

In Chapter 2 you learned about the process of chemical change. Forming compounds from elements is one kind of chemical change. In succeeding chapters the theory of the structure of the atoms of the elements was described. In this chapter, atomic theory will be used to explain *how* atoms combine to form the other particles of substances. You will learn what these particles are, how atoms are held together in these particles, and how these particles vary in size and shape.

Here is a series of chemical formulas for some well-known compounds:

HCl	NaCl
H_2O	$CaCl_2$
NH_3	$AlCl_3$
CH_4	CCl_4

Notice that each formula in the left column contains hydrogen. The first formula shows that one atom of hydrogen combines with one atom of chlorine. The second formula shows that two atoms of hydrogen combine with one atom of oxygen. The third and fourth formulas show that three atoms of hydrogen combine with one atom of nitrogen, but four atoms of hydrogen combine with one atom of carbon. In the four formulas, different numbers of hydrogen atoms combine with one atom of other elements.

Now look at the second column. Each formula contains chlorine. One chlorine atom combines with one sodium atom. Two chlorine atoms combine with one calcium atom. Three chlorine

In this chapter you will gain an understanding of:

- **two basic types of chemical bonding**
- **chemical formulas**
- **writing electron-dot formulas for binary compounds**
- **energy changes in bonding**
- **oxidation and reduction**
- **oxidation-number rules**
- **hybridization**
- **electronegativity and its relation to bonding**
- **resonance**

These formulas were originally established by chemical analysis. Methods of working out chemical formulas from the results of analyses are described in Chapters 7 and 11. Ways in which these compounds are formed are described in Chapter 8 and later chapters throughout this book. It is not necessary at this point to know how these compounds are formed or how these formulas are determined.

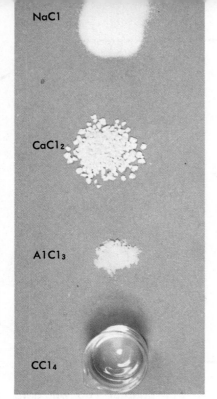

NaCl

CaCl₂

AlCl₃

CCl₄

Figure 6-1. In these compounds, different numbers of chlorine atoms combine with single atoms of other elements.

Recall from Section 2.14 that the products of exothermic reactions have less energy than the reactants. The products of endothermic reactions have more energy than the reactants.

IONIC BONDING

Some experimental evidence for electron transfer is described in Section 22.6.

Orbital notation is explained in Section 4.6.

atoms combine with one aluminum atom, but four chlorine atoms combine with one carbon atom. Different numbers of chlorine atoms combine with one atom of other elements. Why is there a difference in the number of hydrogen and chlorine atoms that will combine with a single atom of another element? Is there any relation between the structure of an atom and the number of other atoms with which it will combine?

◻ 6.2 Valence electrons and chemical bonds

The electrons in the outermost shell of an atom play a very important part in the formation of compounds. The electrons in an *incomplete* outer shell are called **valence electrons.** The remainder of the atom, excluding the valence electrons, is called the **kernel** of the atom. In the formation of chemical compounds from elements, *valence electrons are usually either transferred from the outer shell of one atom to the outer shell of another atom, or shared among the outer shells of the combining atoms.* This transfer or sharing of electrons produces **chemical bonds.** (The formation of some chemical bonds by atoms of transition and rare-earth elements involves not only outer shell electrons but also those of an incomplete next inner shell.)

*Electron transfer results in **ionic bonding** while electron sharing produces **covalent bonding.** When an atom of one element combines chemically with an atom of another element, both atoms usually attain a stable outer shell having a noble-gas configuration. *This kind of electron structure has chemical stability.*

Energy changes are always involved in the process of electron transfer or electron sharing. In *most* cases, when compounds are formed from the elements, energy is given off. The process of electron transfer is *always* exothermic and that of electron sharing is *usually* exothermic. In a *few* cases of compound formation by electron sharing, energy is absorbed. The process of electron sharing may sometimes be endothermic.

◻ 6.3 Ionic bonding

In the formation of a compound by ionic bonding, electrons are actually transferred from the outer shell of one atom to the outer shell of a second atom. By this process both atoms usually attain completed outer shells with noble-gas configurations. For example, sodium reacts with chlorine to form sodium chloride. The single $3s$ electron of a sodium atom is transferred to the singly occupied $3p$ orbital of a chlorine atom.

The sodium, now deficient in one electron, has the stable electron configuration of neon. The chlorine, now with one excess electron, has the stable electron configuration of argon. Only 1 atom of each element is required for the electron transfer that produces these stable electron configurations. Thus, the *formula* of the compound is ˚NaCl. *A chemical formula is a shorthand method of representing the composition of a substance by using chemical symbols.*

The particles produced by this transfer of an electron are no longer electrically neutral atoms of sodium and chlorine. They are: (1) a *sodium ion* with a single excess positive charge, and (2) a *chloride ion* with a single excess negative charge.

$$\text{Na}^+ \quad \underset{1s}{\downarrow\uparrow} \quad \underset{2s}{\downarrow\uparrow} \quad \underset{2p}{\underbrace{\downarrow\uparrow \ \downarrow\uparrow \ \downarrow\uparrow}} \quad \underset{3s}{\underline{\quad}} \quad \underset{3p}{\underbrace{\underline{\quad}\ \underline{\quad}\ \underline{\quad}}}$$

$$\text{Cl}^- \quad \underset{1s}{\downarrow\uparrow} \quad \underset{2s}{\downarrow\uparrow} \quad \underset{2p}{\underbrace{\downarrow\uparrow \ \downarrow\uparrow \ \downarrow\uparrow}} \quad \underset{3s}{\downarrow\uparrow} \quad \underset{3p}{\underbrace{\downarrow\uparrow \ \downarrow\uparrow \ \downarrow\uparrow}}$$

These ions are arranged systematically in crystals of sodium chloride in the ratio of 1 sodium ion to 1 chloride ion. See Figure 6-3.

The formula NaCl, which represents the composition of the compound sodium chloride, is an **empirical formula.** An empirical formula indicates (1) the kinds of atoms in the compound formed, and (2) the simplest whole-number ratio of the atoms in the compound. The formula $Na_{17}Cl_{17}$ shows the kinds and ratio of atoms that make up the compound sodium chloride. But the empirical formula NaCl represents this information in the simplest way.

Table 6-1 shows the number of protons and electrons in the atoms and ions of sodium and chlorine and the charges that result. It also shows their symbols, and their radii in angstroms.

Using only the 3rd energy level electrons, the electron-dot symbol for an atom of sodium is

Na ˚

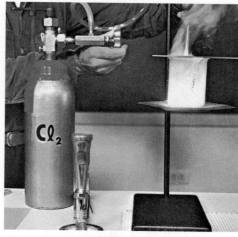

Figure 6-2. Sodium metal, heated in the beaker, combines directly with chlorine gas to form the compound sodium chloride.

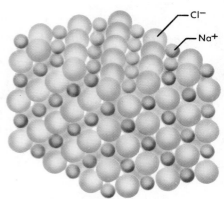

Figure 6-3. This diagram shows the arrangement of the sodium and chloride ions in a portion of a sodium chloride crystal.

Table 6-1
DATA ON ATOMS AND IONS OF SODIUM AND CHLORINE

	Sodium atom	*Sodium ion*	*Chlorine atom*	*Chloride ion*
number of protons	11	11	17	17
number of electrons	11	10	17	18
net charge	0	+1	0	−1
symbol	Na	Na^+	Cl	Cl^-
radius, Å	1.54	0.97	0.99	1.81

Figure 6-4. The regular shape of a naturally formed crystal of sodium chloride results from the regular arrangement of sodium ions and chloride ions in the crystal.

The stable occupation of an orbital by electrons having opposite spins is described in Section 4.5.

Ionization energy is explained in Section 5.7.

Electron affinity is explained in Section 5.9.

That for an atom of chlorine is

$$\cdot \overset{\displaystyle ..}{\underset{\displaystyle ..}{Cl}} :$$

When these atoms react, sodium atoms become sodium ions. The electron-dot symbol for a sodium ion is

$$\mathbf{Na^+}$$

The chlorine atoms become chloride ions, which have the electron-dot symbol

$$\overset{\displaystyle ..}{\underset{\displaystyle ..}{\circ Cl}} : ^-$$

These ions form the compound sodium chloride. The electron-dot formula for sodium chloride may be written as

$$\mathbf{Na^+} \, \overset{\displaystyle ..}{\underset{\displaystyle ..}{\circ Cl}} : ^-$$

or as a simpler ionic formula, $\mathbf{Na^+ Cl^-}$.

Note the symbols for electrons ∘ and ∙, which are used here and in other electron-dot formulas in this chapter. These symbols are used only to show the origin of the electrons in the completed shells. They *do not mean* that electrons from different atoms are different from each other. All electrons, regardless of the atom from which they originate, are identical. However, when two electrons occupy the same space orbital, the electrons must have opposite spins if the orbital is to be occupied in a stable way.

☐ 6.4 Energy change in ionic bonding

Sodium ions and chloride ions in a common salt crystal can be formed from widely separated sodium and chlorine atoms. In order *to study the energy change involved,* this chemical change can be assumed to consist of three separate reactions. The first reaction, the removal of one electron from each sodium atom, is endothermic. The amount of energy required is the *ionization energy* of sodium. For one mole of sodium atoms,

$$\mathbf{1 \ mole \ Na + 119 \ kcal \rightarrow 1 \ mole \ Na^+ + 1 \ mole \ e^-}$$

Only one electron can be readily removed from each sodium atom because a great increase in ionization energy occurs between the first and second electrons. (See Section 5.8.)

The second reaction is the addition of one electron to each neutral chlorine atom. This reaction is exothermic. The energy given off is the *electron affinity* of chlorine. For one mole of chlorine atoms,

$$\mathbf{1 \ mole \ Cl + 1 \ mole \ e^- \rightarrow 1 \ mole \ Cl^- + 83 \ kcal}$$

In the third reaction the oppositely charged sodium ions and chloride ions take up their positions in the sodium chloride crystal. This reaction is also exothermic.

$$1 \text{ mole Na}^+ + 1 \text{ mole Cl}^- \rightarrow 1 \text{ mole Na}^+\text{Cl}^- + 189 \text{ kcal}$$

The first reaction requires energy (119 kcal). This is less than the sum of the energies given off in the second and third reactions (83 kcal and 189 kcal). The overall effect is that energy is given off [(83 kcal + 189 kcal) − (119 kcal) = 153 kcal]. The summation of these three separate reactions is

$$1 \text{ mole Na} + 119 \text{ kcal} \rightarrow \cancel{1 \text{ mole Na}^+} + \cancel{1 \text{ mole e}^-}$$
$$1 \text{ mole Cl} + \cancel{1 \text{ mole e}^-} \rightarrow \cancel{1 \text{ mole Cl}^-} + 83 \text{ kcal}$$
$$\cancel{1 \text{ mole Na}^+} + \cancel{1 \text{ mole Cl}^-} \rightarrow 1 \text{ mole Na}^+\text{Cl}^- + 189 \text{ kcal}$$

$$1 \text{ mole Na} + 1 \text{ mole Cl} \rightarrow 1 \text{ mole Na}^+\text{Cl}^- + 153 \text{ kcal}$$

The net process of electron transfer is exothermic. The formation of all ionic compounds from their elements is exothermic.

☐ 6.5 Oxidation and reduction

Another aspect of the reactions by which sodium ions and chloride ions are produced should now be examined. The formation of a sodium ion from a sodium atom may be considered to involve the loss of an electron. The equation for this change might be written

$$\text{Na} - \text{e}^- \rightarrow \text{Na}^+$$

However, chemists prefer to show only the substances entering a reaction at the left of the "yields" sign. The substances formed by the reaction are written at the right of the "yields" sign. Consequently, the equation showing the formation of a sodium ion from a sodium atom should be written

$$\text{Na} \rightarrow \text{Na}^+ + \text{e}^- \qquad \textbf{(Equation 1)}$$

The *oxidation state* of an element is represented by a signed number called an **oxidation number.** Oxidation numbers are assigned according to a set of seven rules. These rules will be introduced as needed in this chapter.

Rule 1: *The oxidation number of an atom of a free element is zero.*

Rule 2: *The oxidation number of a monatomic (one-atomed) ion is equal to its charge.*

It is apparent from these rules that: (1) the oxidation number of elemental sodium is zero: $\overset{0}{\text{Na}}$. (2) The oxidation number of the sodium ion is plus one: $\overset{+1}{\text{Na}}{}^+$. Note that an oxidation number is written above a symbol, while an ion charge is written as a right superscript. Equation 1 above can now be rewritten to include these oxidation numbers.

$$\overset{0}{\text{Na}} \rightarrow \overset{+1}{\text{Na}}{}^+ + \text{e}^-$$

An ion is an atom or group of atoms that has a net positive or negative charge.

From this equation it is apparent that the oxidation state of sodium has changed from 0 to +1; the oxidation state has become *more positive. A chemical reaction in which an element attains a more positive oxidation state is called* **oxidation.** The particle whose oxidation state becomes *more positive* is said to be *oxidized.* In the reaction above, the sodium atom is oxidized to a sodium ion since its oxidation state has become more positive. The reaction is an oxidation.

The formation of a chloride ion from a chlorine atom involves the gain of an electron.

$$Cl + e^- \rightarrow Cl^- \qquad \text{(Equation 2)}$$

The oxidation number of elemental chlorine is zero: $\overset{0}{Cl}$ (Rule 1). The oxidation number of the chloride ion is minus one: $\overset{-1}{Cl^-}$ (Rule 2). Equation 2 may now be rewritten

$$\overset{0}{Cl} + e^- \rightarrow \overset{-1}{Cl^-}$$

This equation shows that the oxidation state of chlorine has changed from 0 to −1; the oxidation state has become *more negative. A chemical reaction in which an element attains a more negative oxidation state is called* **reduction.** The particle whose oxidation state becomes *more negative* is said to be *reduced.* In the reaction shown, the chlorine atom is reduced to the chloride ion since its oxidation state has become more negative. The reaction is a reduction.

In the reaction

$$\overset{0}{Na} + \overset{0}{Cl} \rightarrow \overset{+1}{Na^+}\overset{-1}{Cl^-}$$

elemental sodium is oxidized and elemental chlorine is reduced. *The substance that is reduced* is called the **oxidizing agent.** (In the reaction represented by the equation, chlorine is the oxidizing agent.) At the same time, *the substance that is oxidized* is called the **reducing agent.** (Sodium is the reducing agent in this reaction.) NaCl is the correct empirical formula for the compound sodium chloride. Note that the algebraic sum of the oxidation numbers written above this formula is zero.

Rule 3: *The algebraic sum of the oxidation numbers of all the atoms in the formula of a compound is zero.*

◻ 6.6 Formation of magnesium bromide from its elements

In the formation of magnesium bromide, the two $3s$ electrons of the magnesium are transferred. *Both* $3s$ electrons must be transferred if magnesium is to acquire the stable electron configuraton of the noble gas neon. Recall that the ionization energies

Figure 6-5. Magnesium and bromine react vigorously to form magnesium bromide.

of the two $3s$ electrons in magnesium are low. The 4th energy level of the bromine atom already contains seven electrons. (Eight, of course, is the number needed for a noble-gas configuration.) Thus, a single bromine atom has a place for only one of the two electrons that the magnesium atom transfers. So two bromine atoms are needed to react with one magnesium atom. Each bromine atom gains one electron. The diagram representing this electron transfer is

There is a great increase in ionization energy between the second and third electrons in a magnesium atom. Hence, only two electrons can be removed chemically.

Initially	Chemical Change	Finally

$$:\overset{\cdot\cdot}{\underset{\cdot}{Br}}: \quad \underset{1s}{\downarrow\uparrow} \quad \underset{2s}{\downarrow\uparrow} \quad \underbrace{\downarrow\uparrow\ \downarrow\uparrow\ \downarrow\uparrow}_{2p} \quad \underset{3s}{\downarrow\uparrow} \quad \underbrace{\downarrow\uparrow\ \downarrow\uparrow\ \downarrow\uparrow}_{3p} \quad \underbrace{\downarrow\uparrow\ \downarrow\uparrow\ \downarrow\uparrow\ \downarrow\uparrow\ \downarrow\uparrow}_{3d} \quad \underset{4s}{\downarrow\uparrow} \quad \underbrace{\downarrow\uparrow\ \downarrow\uparrow\ \uparrow}_{4p} \quad :\overset{\cdot\cdot}{\underset{\circ\circ}{Br}}:^{-}$$

$$Mg \overset{\circ}{\circ} \quad \underset{1s}{\downarrow\uparrow} \quad \underset{2s}{\downarrow\uparrow} \quad \underbrace{\downarrow\uparrow\ \downarrow\uparrow\ \downarrow\uparrow}_{2p} \quad \underset{3s}{\downarrow\uparrow} \quad \underbrace{-\ -\ -}_{3p} \quad \underbrace{-\ -\ -\ -\ -}_{3d} \quad \underset{4s}{-} \quad \underbrace{-\ -\ -}_{4p} \quad Mg^{++}$$

$$:\overset{\cdot\cdot}{\underset{\cdot}{Br}}: \quad \underset{1s}{\downarrow\uparrow} \quad \underset{2s}{\downarrow\uparrow} \quad \underbrace{\downarrow\uparrow\ \downarrow\uparrow\ \downarrow\uparrow}_{2p} \quad \underset{3s}{\downarrow\uparrow} \quad \underbrace{\downarrow\uparrow\ \downarrow\uparrow\ \downarrow\uparrow}_{3p} \quad \underbrace{\downarrow\uparrow\ \downarrow\uparrow\ \downarrow\uparrow\ \downarrow\uparrow\ \downarrow\uparrow}_{3d} \quad \underset{4s}{\downarrow\uparrow} \quad \underbrace{\downarrow\uparrow\ \downarrow\uparrow\ \downarrow}_{4p} \quad :\overset{\cdot\cdot}{\underset{\circ\circ}{Br}}:^{-}$$

The empirical formula for the compound magnesium bromide is $MgBr_2$. The magnesium ions in this compound each have two excess positive charges. The bromide ions each have a single excess negative charge. These particles are arranged in orderly fashion in crystals of magnesium bromide. The ratio of the particles is 2 bromide ions to 1 magnesium ion. See Table 6-2 and also Figure 6-6. The subscript $_2$ following Br in the formula indicates that there are two bromide ions to each magnesium ion in the compound. When no subscript is used, as with Mg, one atom or monatomic ion is understood.

The electron-dot symbols for atoms of magnesium and bromine are

$$Mg \overset{\circ}{\circ} \qquad \cdot \overset{\cdot\cdot}{\underset{\cdot\cdot}{Br}}:$$

and for the magnesium ion and bromide ion are

$$Mg^{++} \qquad :\overset{\cdot\cdot}{\underset{\cdot\cdot}{Br}}:^{-}$$

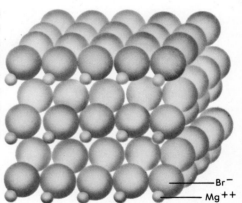

Br⁻
Mg⁺⁺

Figure 6-6. This diagram shows the arrangement of the magnesium and bromide ions in a portion of a magnesium bromide crystal.

Table 6-2
DATA ON ATOMS AND IONS OF MAGNESIUM AND BROMINE

	Magnesium atom	Magnesium ion	Bromine atom	Bromide ion
number of protons	12	12	35	35
number of electrons	12	10	35	36
net charge	0	+2	0	−1
symbol	Mg	Mg⁺⁺	Br	Br⁻
radius, Å	1.36	0.66	1.14	1.96

The electron-dot formula for magnesium bromide is

$$: \overset{..}{\underset{..}{Br}} :^- \ Mg^{++} \ : \overset{..}{\underset{..}{Br}} :^-$$

and the ionic formula is $Mg^{++}Br^-_2$. Note that in the formula $Mg^{++}Br^-_2$, the subscript $_2$ applies to *both* the symbol Br and its charge $^-$. It shows that there are two Br^- ions with each Mg^{++} ion in the formula.

Energy is required to remove two electrons from one magnesium atom. But this energy is less than the electron affinity of two bromine atoms plus the energy released when one magnesium ion and two bromide ions take up their positions in a magnesium bromide crystal. Thus, the formation of the compound magnesium bromide from widely separated magnesium and bromine atoms is another example of the exothermic nature of electron transfer.

See Problem 3 at the end of the chapter.

In forming the compound magnesium bromide, elemental magnesium atoms are *oxidized* from $\overset{0}{Mg}$ to $\overset{+2}{Mg}^{++}$. The oxidation state of magnesium becomes more positive as it changes from 0 to +2.

$$\overset{0}{Mg} \rightarrow \overset{+2}{Mg}^{++} + 2e^-$$

At the same time, for each magnesium atom oxidized, two elemental bromine atoms are *reduced* from $\overset{0}{Br}$ to $\overset{-1}{Br}^-$. The oxidation state of bromine becomes more negative as it changes from 0 to −1.

$$\overset{0}{2Br} + 2e^- \rightarrow \overset{-1}{2Br}^-$$

Bromine is the oxidizing agent; magnesium is the reducing agent.

In the formula $\overset{+2}{Mg}^{++} \overset{-1}{Br}^-_2$ the algebraic sum of +2 and 2(−1) equals zero. Note how the algebraic sum of the oxidation numbers of the atoms in a formula is determined. Each oxidation number must be multiplied by the number of atoms or monatomic ions having that oxidation number. The formulas of ionic compounds merely indicate the relative numbers of positive and negative ions that combine. Therefore, *all formulas for ionic compounds are empirical.*

PRACTICE PROBLEMS

For the formation of the compound $Li^+_2O^{--}$ by ionic bonding:
1. Draw the electron-transfer diagram using orbital notation.
2. Write the electron-dot formula for the compound.
3. Write an equation showing the oxidation.
4. Write an equation showing the reduction.
5. Identify the oxidizing agent and reducing agent.

◻ 6.7 Elements with several oxidation numbers

Many elements exhibit more than one oxidation state. Some differences in the oxidation number of an element depend on the kind of bond that it forms with other elements. However, another factor is important. Transition elements, with from four to seven electron energy levels, can readily transfer the electrons in the outermost level. Many of them can also transfer one or two electrons from the next-to-outermost level with very little additional energy. The electrons in excess of an octet in the next-to-outermost energy level are those available for transfer. Iron is such a transition element. In forming compounds, it can transfer two $4s$ electrons. In more energetic reactions, a $3d$ electron can also be transferred. Thus its oxidation number can be $+2$ or $+3$. This variable number of transferable electrons accounts for the variable oxidation state of many of the transition metals. The table of Common Elements, inside the front cover and Appendix Table 5, lists common oxidation numbers.

◻ 6.8 Relative sizes of atoms and ions

Once again, look at Tables 6-1 and 6-2 accompanying Sections 6.3 and 6.6. These tables give the radii of the atoms and ions of sodium, magnesium, chlorine, and bromine. Notice the great difference in radius between an atom and the ion formed from it.

It is characteristic of metals to form positive ions. *Positive ions are called* **cations**. It is to be expected that metallic ions would be smaller than the corresponding metallic atoms since the outer-shell electrons are no longer present. As a result, the remaining electrons are drawn closer to the nucleus by its unbalanced positive charge.

Nonmetallic elements form negative ions. *Negative ions are called* **anions**. Nonmetallic ions are larger than the corresponding nonmetallic atoms. Electrons have been added, making the outer shell an octet. Since the total positive charge of the nucleus remains the same, the average force of attraction for each electron decreases because there are more electrons.

Table 6-3 shows the sizes of representative atoms and ions. From these data and the generalizations above, it follows that:

1. Within a group or family of elements, the ion size increases with atomic number because of shell addition.

2. Within a period of elements, the Group I, II, and III cations show a sharp decrease in size. On the other hand, the Group VII anion is only slightly smaller than the Group VI anion. Group I and II cations have the same electron configurations, but the Group II cation's greater nuclear charge draws the electrons much closer. Group VI and VII anions have identical electron configurations too. The Group VII anion's greater nuclear charge draws the electrons somewhat closer.

Figure 6-7. Compounds of transition metals have different colors depending on their oxidation states. See Questions 35 and 36 at the end of this chapter.

Table 6-3
RADII OF REPRESENTATIVE ATOMS AND IONS IN ANGSTROMS

	Group I		Group II		Group III		Group VI		Group VII	
Period 2	Li	1.23	Be	0.89	B	0.82	O	0.70	F	0.68
	Li^+	0.68	Be^{++}	0.35	B^{+++}	0.23	O^{--}	1.40	F^-	1.33
Period 3	Na	1.54	Mg	1.36	Al	1.18	S	1.02	Cl	0.99
	Na^+	0.97	Mg^{++}	0.66	Al^{+++}	0.51	S^{--}	1.84	Cl^-	1.81
Period 4	K	2.03	Ca	1.74	Ga	1.26	Se	1.17	Br	1.14
	K^+	1.33	Ca^{++}	0.99	Ga^{+++}	0.62	Se^{--}	1.98	Br^-	1.96
Period 5	Rb	2.16	Sr	1.91	In	1.44	Te	1.36	I	1.33
	Rb^+	1.47	Sr^{++}	1.12	In^{+++}	0.81	Te^{--}	2.21	I^-	2.20
Period 6	Cs	2.35	Ba	1.98	Tl	1.48				
	Cs^+	1.67	Ba^{++}	1.34	Tl^{+++}	0.95				

Figures 6-3 and 6-6 show the arrangement of ions in crystals of the compounds sodium chloride and magnesium bromide. Such arrangements depend on the relative numbers and sizes of each kind of ion present. Crystals are described in more detail in Chapter 12.

COVALENT BONDING

◻ 6.9 Covalent bonding: hydrogen molecules

In covalent bonding electrons are not transferred from one atom to another. Instead, they are *shared* by the bonded atoms. In forming a single covalent bond, two atoms mutually share one of their electrons. These two shared electrons (with opposite spins) effectively fill an orbital in each atom. They make up a *covalent electron pair* that forms the bond.

The atoms of the common elemental gases, hydrogen, oxygen, nitrogen, fluorine, and chlorine, form stable diatomic (two-atomed) *molecules* by covalent bonding. *A **molecule** is the smallest chemical unit of a substance that is capable of stable independent existence.* For these elemental gases, the smallest chemical units capable of stable independent existence are diatomic units. Single atoms of the five gases listed above are chemically unstable under most conditions. Hence, these diatomic units make up molecules of these gases.

In diatomic hydrogen molecules each hydrogen atom shares its single $1s$ valence electron with the other hydrogen atom. These two electrons move about both nuclei so that each atom, in effect, has its $1s$ orbital filled. In essence, each hydrogen atom has the stable electron configuration of a helium atom.

H $\frac{\uparrow}{1s}$

H $\frac{\downarrow}{1s}$

The *electron-dot formula* for a molecule of hydrogen is

H:H

Frequently chemists indicate a shared pair of electrons by a dash (—) instead of the symbol (:). Thus the formula for a molecule of hydrogen may be written

H—H

This type of formula is called a *structural formula.*

The *molecular formula* for hydrogen is H_2. The numerical subscript indicates the number of atoms per molecule. *A formula that indicates the actual composition of a molecule is called a* **molecular formula.**

Hydrogen molecules are linear (straight-line), as shown in Figure 6-8. All diatomic molecules are linear because two points determine a straight line.

Hydrogen molecules have greater stability than separate hydrogen atoms. This statement is supported by the fact that energy is given off in the reaction

2 moles H atoms → 1 mole H_2 molecules + 104 kcal energy

One mole of H_2 molecules has lower energy and is more stable than two moles of uncombined H atoms. The reverse action is that of separating hydrogen molecules into the atoms of which they are made. Energy is required for this reaction.

1 mole H_2 + 104 kcal → 2 moles H

The energy required, 104 kcal/mole, is called the *bond energy* of the **H—H** bond. *Bond energy is the energy required to break chemical bonds and form neutral atoms.* It is usually expressed in kcal per mole of bonds broken.

Diatomic molecules of elements are considered to be free elements. Thus, each atom in the molecule may be assigned a zero oxidation number (Rule 1).

◻ 6.10 Chlorine molecules

Diatomic chlorine molecules can be formed in the same manner as hydrogen molecules. Each atom shares one electron with the other and, in effect, fills an incomplete $3p$ orbital in each. This gives both atoms the stable electron arrangement of the noble gas argon. Both atoms essentially have an octet in the 3rd energy level.

Hydrogen molecule

Oxygen molecule

Nitrogen molecule

Chlorine molecule

Figure 6-8. The molecules of the common gases, such as those of hydrogen, nitrogen, oxygen, and chlorine represented here, consist of two atoms joined by covalent bonding. These are all linear molecules.

Cl ↓↑ ↓↑ ↓↑ ↓↑ ↓↑ ↓↑ ↓↑ ↓↑ ↑
      1s   2s   2p   3s   3p

Cl ↓↑ ↓↑ ↓↑ ↓↑ ↓↑ ↓↑ ↓↑ ↓↑ ↓
      1s   2s   2p   3s   3p

The electron-dot formula for a molecule of chlorine is

$$\overset{\circ\circ}{\underset{\circ\circ}{\circ\,Cl}}\overset{\bullet\bullet}{\underset{\bullet\bullet}{Cl}}\bullet$$

Its structural formula is

$$Cl—Cl$$

and its molecular formula is Cl_2. Chlorine molecules are linear (straight-line) like those of hydrogen. See Figure 6-8.

Energy is required to separate chlorine molecules into chlorine atoms.

$$1 \text{ mole } Cl_2 + 58 \text{ kcal} \rightarrow 2 \text{ moles } Cl$$

The bond energy of the Cl—Cl bond is 58 kcal/mole, and the chlorine molecules are more stable than separate chlorine atoms.

Diatomic molecules of the other halogens have similar formulas and shapes. Their bond energies are given in Table 6-4.

❑ 6.11 Oxygen molecules

Oxygen also exists as diatomic molecules. But the bonding in an oxygen molecule is rather complex. It is not shown very satisfactorily by orbital and electron-dot formulas. A possible orbital notation for an oxygen molecule is shown in the margin at left. The corresponding electron-dot formula for an oxygen molecule is

$$\overset{\circ\circ}{\underset{\circ}{\circ\,O}}\overset{\bullet\bullet}{\underset{\bullet\bullet}{O}}$$

Its structural formula is

$$O{=}O$$

and its molecular formula is O_2.

Note that *two pairs* of electrons are shared in the oxygen molecule. This sharing of two electron pairs makes a *double covalent bond*. A double covalent bond is represented in a structural formula by a double dash. The oxygen molecule is linear. The bond energy of the O=O bond is 118 kcal/mole. Oxygen molecules are more stable than separate oxygen atoms.

❑ 6.12 Nitrogen molecules

The structure of the nitrogen molecule indicates the sharing of *three pairs* of electrons. Nitrogen molecules contain a *triple covalent bond*, as shown in the margin at left. The electron-dot formula for the nitrogen molecule is

$$\overset{\circ}{\circ}N\overset{\bullet}{\underset{\bullet}{\bullet}}N\bullet$$

Its structural formula is

$$N{\equiv}N$$

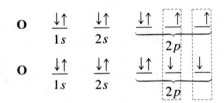

and its molecular formula is N_2. Note that in a structural formula a triple covalent bond is represented by a triple dash. Nitrogen molecules are linear molecules. The bond energy of the $N{\equiv}N$ bond is 225 kcal/mole. With such a high bond energy, nitrogen molecules are much more stable than individual nitrogen atoms.

☐ 6.13 Covalent bonding of unlike atoms: hydrogen chloride molecules

Atoms of different elements may combine by covalent bonding. A hydrogen atom and a chlorine atom combine by covalent bonding to form a hydrogen chloride molecule. In this molecule, the $1s$ hydrogen electron and a $3p$ chlorine electron complete a space orbital, as shown below.

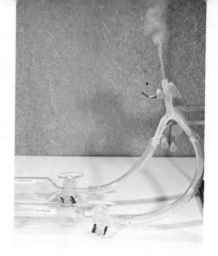

Figure 6-9. Hydrogen burns in chlorine to form hydrogen chloride, a colorless gas. Hydrogen chloride and moisture in the air form the fog visible in the photo.

The electron-dot formula for hydrogen chloride is

$$H \!:\! \overset{\cdot\cdot}{\underset{\cdot\cdot}{Cl}} \!:$$

Its structural formula is

$$H{-}Cl$$

and its molecular formula is **HCl**. The HCl molecule is linear, as shown in Figure 6-10.

Energy is required to separate HCl molecules into H and Cl atoms.

$$\textbf{1 mole HCl} + \textbf{103 kcal} \rightarrow \textbf{1 mole H} + \textbf{1 mole Cl}$$

Hydrogen chloride molecules are more stable than separate hydrogen and chlorine atoms. The bond energy of the $H{-}Cl$ bond is 103 kcal/mole.

Rule 4: *In compounds, the oxidation number of hydrogen is +1.*

By Rule 4 the oxidation number of hydrogen in hydrogen chloride is +1. By Rule 3 (Section 6.5) the oxidation number of chlorine must be −1.

Bond energies can be used to calculate the approximate energy of a chemical reaction. See Table 6-4. This method of calculation assumes that the energy change in a reaction is the net result of the breaking and making of chemical bonds.

The reaction for the formation of one mole of hydrogen chloride molecules can be used as an example. One-half mole of

Hydrogen chloride molecule

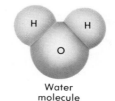

Water molecule

Hydrogen peroxide molecule

Figure 6-10. Hydrogen chloride, water, and hydrogen peroxide are compounds whose simplest particles are molecules composed of covalently bonded atoms. Hydrogen chloride molecules are linear; water molecules are bent molecules; hydrogen peroxide molecules are double-bent molecules.

hydrogen molecules and one-half mole of chlorine molecules combine as follows:

$$\tfrac{1}{2} \text{ mole } H_2 + \tfrac{1}{2} \text{ mole } Cl_2 \rightarrow 1 \text{ mole } HCl$$

For calculation purposes this reaction may be considered to occur in three steps. The first step is the breaking of bonds in one-half mole of hydrogen molecules.

$$\tfrac{1}{2} \text{ mole } H_2 + 52 \text{ kcal} \rightarrow 1 \text{ mole } H$$

(The equation is written for one-half mole of H_2 molecules. The energy needed is one-half the bond energy per mole, 104 kcal.)

The second step is the breaking of bonds in one-half mole of chlorine molecules.

$$\tfrac{1}{2} \text{ mole } Cl_2 + 29 \text{ kcal} \rightarrow 1 \text{ mole } Cl$$

(Again the energy involved is one-half the bond energy per mole, 58 kcal.)

The third reaction is the reverse of the **H—Cl** bond energy reaction written earlier in this section.

$$1 \text{ mole } H + 1 \text{ mole } Cl \rightarrow 1 \text{ mole } HCl + 103 \text{ kcal}$$

Combining these three equations and adding them algebraically,

$$\tfrac{1}{2} \text{ mole } H_2 + 52 \text{ kcal} \rightarrow \cancel{1 \text{ mole } H}$$
$$\tfrac{1}{2} \text{ mole } Cl_2 + 29 \text{ kcal} \rightarrow \cancel{1 \text{ mole } Cl}$$
$$\underline{\cancel{1 \text{ mole } H} + \cancel{1 \text{ mole } Cl} \rightarrow 1 \text{ mole } HCl + 103 \text{ kcal}}$$
$$\tfrac{1}{2} \text{ mole } H_2 + \tfrac{1}{2} \text{ mole } Cl_2 \rightarrow 1 \text{ mole } HCl + 22 \text{ kcal}$$

Thus, the reaction is exothermic. The amount of energy released is 22 kcal.

Table 6-4
BOND ENERGIES

Bond	Energy (kcal/mole)
H—H	104
N—N	37
N≡N	225
O—O	34
O=O	118
Cl—Cl	58
Br—Br	46
I—I	36
C—H	98
N—H	92
O—H	111
Cl—H	103
Br—H	87
I—H	71
C—Cl	78
C—Br	66

☐ 6.14 Water molecules

The common compound water consists of molecules formed by covalent bonding of two hydrogen atoms with one oxygen atom. The orbital representation of this bonding is shown in the margin at left. The electron-dot formula for water is

$$H : \overset{\cdot\cdot}{\underset{\cdot\cdot}{O}} :$$
$$H$$

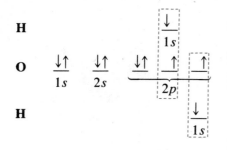

Its structural formula is

$$\overset{\displaystyle O}{\underset{\displaystyle H \qquad H}{\diagup \quad \diagdown}}$$

and its molecular formula is H_2O.

A molecule containing three atoms can have one of only two shapes. Either (1) the atoms lie on the same straight line and form a linear molecule, or (2) the atoms do not lie on one straight line and form a bent molecule. Figure 6-10 shows that the hydrogen atoms and oxygen atom in a water molecule do not lie on the same straight line. Water molecules are bent molecules. Very careful measurements reveal that the distances between the oxygen atom and each of the two hydrogen atoms are the same. This evidence suggests that the two hydrogen atoms act the same way in the molecule.

Energy is required to break up water molecules into the atoms of which they are made.

$$\text{1 mole } H_2O + 222 \text{ kcal} \rightarrow 2 \text{ moles } H + 1 \text{ mole } O$$

Water molecules have lower energy and are more stable than separate hydrogen and oxygen atoms. Two **H—O** bonds are broken per molecule of water decomposed. Therefore, the **H—O** bond energy is 111 kcal/mole, or one-half that shown in the equation.

❑ 6.15 Hydrogen peroxide molecules

It is possible for more than one kind of molecule to be formed from the same kinds of atoms. A second compound that may be formed from hydrogen and oxygen is hydrogen peroxide, a well-known bleaching and oxidizing agent. The orbital notation of hydrogen peroxide is shown in the margin at right. Its electron-dot formula is

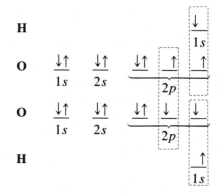

$$\text{H} \overset{\times}{\underset{\times}{\text{O}}} :$$
$$\overset{\times\ \circ}{\underset{\times\times}{\text{O}}} \text{H}$$

Its structural formula is

$$\begin{array}{c} \text{H—O} \\ | \\ \text{O—H} \end{array}$$

Its molecular formula is H_2O_2. Experimental evidence indicates that the hydrogen peroxide molecule is a double-bent shaped molecule. (See Figure 6-10.)

Rule 5: *In compounds, the oxidation number of oxygen is -2.*

One exception to this rule is that in peroxides the oxidation number of oxygen is -1. In water the oxidation number of hydrogen is $+1$ and of oxygen is -2. On the other hand, in hydrogen peroxide the oxidation number of hydrogen is $+1$ and of oxygen is -1. (Use Rule 3 to check this result.)

❑ 6.16 Other molecules containing hydrogen

Table 6-5 gives some examples of covalent bonding between hydrogen and nitrogen and between hydrogen and carbon. The

For review purposes use the statements of Rule 4 and Rule 5 in Section 6.25, since further exceptions are discussed later in this chapter.

oxidation number of hydrogen in each molecule is $+1$. But note that the oxidation numbers of nitrogen and carbon vary from molecule to molecule.

Ammonia molecules, NH_3, have three hydrogen atoms so spaced about a nitrogen atom that the molecule has the shape of a pyramid. Think of the hydrogen atoms as forming the base of the pyramid and the nitrogen atom the peak. In methane, CH_4, the hydrogen atoms are symmetrically spaced in three dimensions about the carbon atom. Methane molecules have a regular tetrahedral shape. A regular tetrahedron is a solid figure that has four sides, each side an equilateral triangle.

Consider the examples of covalent bonding illustrated thus far. Except for hydrazine (Table 6-5), all of the bonded atoms are more stable because they have filled orbitals. They have lower energy than the unbonded atoms. Thus, the reactions in which these molecules are formed from atoms are exothermic. Only the combination of nitrogen and hydrogen atoms to form hydrazine, N_2H_4, is endothermic.

The neutral particle that results from the covalent bonding of atoms is a molecule. Its composition is represented by a molecular formula.

PRACTICE PROBLEM

Calculate the energy change for the reaction

$\frac{1}{2}$ mole N_2 + $\frac{3}{2}$ mole $H_2 \rightarrow$ 1 mole NH_3 *ans.* 8 kcal exothermic

---

Table 6-5
DATA ON SOME REPRESENTATIVE MOLECULES

	Ammonia	*Hydrazine*	*Methane*	*Ethane*
molecular formula	NH_3	N_2H_4	CH_4	C_2H_6
structural formula	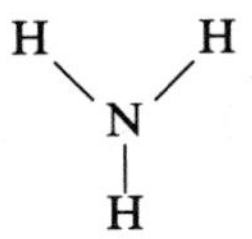	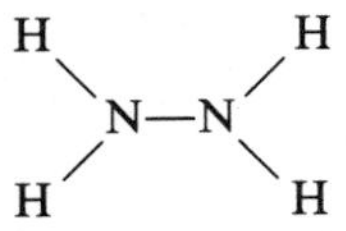	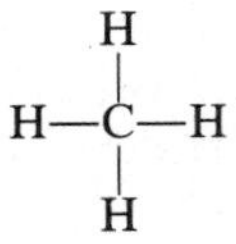	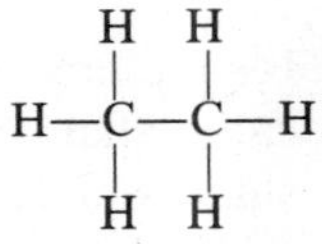
electron-dot formula	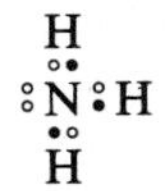	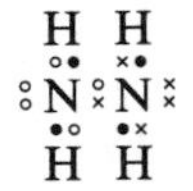	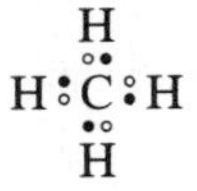	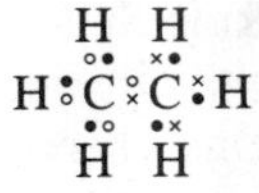
oxidation numbers	H = +1 N = −3	H = +1 N = −2	H = +1 C = −4	H = +1 C = −3
model of molecule		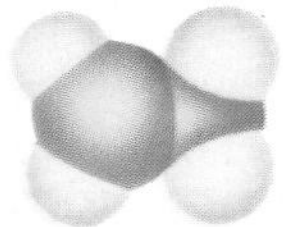	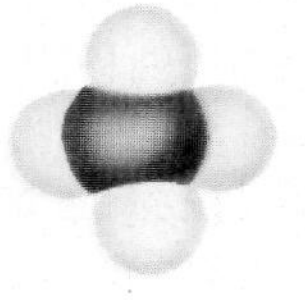	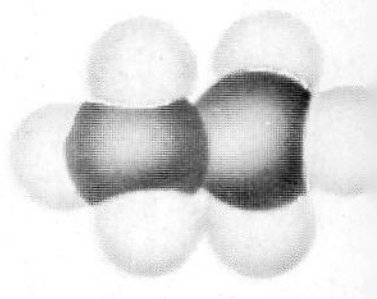

◻ 6.17 Hybridization

In a methane molecule, CH_4, one carbon atom is covalently bonded to four hydrogen atoms. The hydrogen atoms are symmetrically arranged as if at the vertices of a regular tetrahedron with the carbon atom at the center. The carbon-hydrogen bond angles in this molecule are all 109.5°. See Figure 6-11.

In orbital notation, carbon atoms are represented

$$\text{C} \quad \underset{1s}{\downarrow\uparrow} \quad \underset{2s}{\downarrow\uparrow} \quad \underbrace{\uparrow \quad \uparrow \quad \underline{}}_{2p}$$

This notation indicates that the valence electrons should be two $2s$ and two $2p$ electrons. However, when carbon atoms combine, it is believed that one of the $2s$ electrons acquires enough energy to occupy a $2p$ orbital. This structure can be represented

$$\text{C} \quad \underset{1s}{\downarrow\uparrow} \quad \underset{2s}{\uparrow} \quad \underbrace{\uparrow \quad \uparrow \quad \uparrow}_{2p}$$

Thus the bonding electrons of a carbon atom are one $2s$ electron and three $2p$ electrons. A carbon atom, therefore, can form four covalent bonds, as it does with hydrogen atoms in the methane molecule.

Because one of the valence electrons of the carbon atom is a $2s$ electron and the other three are $2p$ electrons, one of the carbon-hydrogen bonds in methane might be expected to be different from the other three. Experimentally, however, this is not the case. All the bonds are equivalent. This difference can be explained by assuming that *hybridization* of the one $2s$ and three $2p$ orbitals occurs. Four equivalent orbitals are produced.

Hybridization is the combining of two or more orbitals of nearly the same energy into new orbitals of equal energy. The hybrid orbitals of the carbon atom are called sp^3 (read "sp-three") orbitals. Hybrid orbitals result from the combination of one s orbital and three p orbitals. In orbital notation, the effect of hybridization can be shown as

$$\text{C} \quad \underset{1s}{\downarrow\uparrow} \quad \underbrace{\uparrow \quad \uparrow \quad \uparrow \quad \uparrow}_{2sp^3}$$

As mentioned, these four sp^3 orbitals point toward the corners of a regular tetrahedron from the carbon atom at their center. This arrangement permits the maximum separation of four orbitals grouped about a given point. This arrangement accounts for the regular tetrahedral shape of methane molecules.

The idea of hybrid tetrahedral orbitals can also account for the observed shape of the ammonia molecule. This is true even though ammonia has only three hydrogen atoms attached to a central nitrogen atom. The electron-dot symbol for a nitrogen

Figure 6-11. In the methane molecule, CH_4, a carbon atom is covalently and symmetrically bonded to four hydrogen atoms. The tetrahedral shape is the result of sp^3 hybridization of the carbon-atom orbitals.

atom is

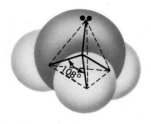

Figure 6-12. The pyramidal shape of the ammonia molecule, NH_3, may be explained by the sp^3 hybridization of nitrogen-atom orbitals.

Imagine that the electrons in the four positions about the symbol are distributed among four equivalent tetrahedral orbitals. This arrangement gives one orbital with a pair of electrons and three orbitals with single electrons that can be shared with the electron from each of three hydrogen atoms. The result is a structure that resembles a pyramid, as shown in Figure 6-12. The three hydrogen atoms form the base of the pyramid. The unshared pair of nitrogen electrons forms the peak. The angles between the **N—H** bonds in ammonia are known to be 108°. This agrees well with the tetrahedral angle of 109.5°.

This idea can be extended to the structure of the water molecule. The electron-dot formula for this molecule is

$$H \overset{\cdot\cdot}{\underset{\cdot\cdot}{O}} \overset{\cdot\cdot}{:}$$
$$H$$

Here there are four tetrahedral hybrid orbitals. Two of these form the oxygen-hydrogen bonds. The other two are each a pair of unshared oxygen electrons. See Figure 6-13. The bond angle in the water molecule is only 105°. The unshared electron pairs on the oxygen atom tend to repel each other more than the shared electrons repel each other. These unequal opposing repulsions make the angle between the shared pairs decrease slightly in size.

Other types of hybridization are described in Chapter 18.

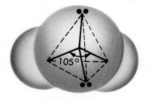

Figure 6-13. The bent shape of the water molecule, H_2O, may be explained by the considerable sp^3 hybridization of oxygen-atom orbitals.

❑ 6.18 Size of molecules

Molecules are very small. It is estimated that if a drop of water could be magnified to the size of the earth, the molecules composing it would be about one meter in diameter. But molecules vary greatly in size. The simple molecules of gases, consisting of one, two, or three atoms, have diameters of about 3×10^{-8} cm. Some virus protein molecules consist of about 7.5×10^5 atoms and have diameters of about 2.3×10^{-6} cm. These molecules have been photographed with an electron microscope. On the angstrom scale, the range of molecular diameters is from 3 Å to 230 Å.

ELECTRONEGATIVITY

❑ 6.19 Electronegativity

In ionic bonding, electrons are *completely transferred* from the outer shells of metallic atoms to the outer shells of nonmetallic atoms. In covalent bonding, electrons are *shared* in the outer shells of the bonded atoms.

If two covalently bonded atoms are alike, their attractions for the shared electrons are equal. The electrons are most probably distributed equally about both atoms. Each atom remains electrically neutral, even though they are bonded together. *A* *covalent bond in which there is an equal attraction for the shared electrons and a resulting balanced distribution of charge is called a **pure**, or **nonpolar, covalent bond**.* If two different atoms are covalently bonded, one atom may attract the shared electron pair more strongly than the other atom does. The electrons are not equally shared but are more closely held by the atom with stronger attraction. This atom is not electrically neutral. Instead it is slightly negative, though not as negative as a singly charged anion. The other atom is left slightly positive, though not as positive as a singly charged cation. *A covalent bond in which there is an unequal attraction for the shared electrons and a resulting unbalanced distribution of charge is called a **polar covalent bond**.* Polar covalent bonds are intermediate in nature between ionic bonds and pure covalent bonds. In ionic bonds, electron transfer is complete. In pure covalent bonds, electron sharing is equal. Polar covalent bonds are part covalent and part ionic in character.

Ionization energy is a measure of the strength with which a neutral atom holds an outer-shell electron. Electron affinity indicates the strength of the attraction between a neutral atom and an additional electron. Linus Pauling (b. 1901) and other chemists studied these two values, together with certain properties of molecules. They derived an arbitrary scale that indicates *the attraction of an atom for the shared electrons forming a bond between it and another atom. This property is called **electronegativity**.* Atoms with high electronegativity have a strong attraction for electrons they share with another atom. Atoms with low electronegativity have a weak attraction for electrons they share with another atom. The relative electronegativities of two atoms give an indication of the type of bonding that can exist between them.

Figure 6-14 gives the electronegativity values of the elements. A study of this chart shows that:

1. Low electronegativity is characteristic of metals. The lower the electronegativity, the more active the metal. Thus, the lowest electronegativities are found at the lower left of the periodic table.

2. High electronegativity is characteristic of nonmetals. Thus, the highest electronegativities are found at the upper right of the periodic table. Fluorine is the most electronegative element. Oxygen is second.

3. Within the numbered groups or families, electronegativity generally decreases with increasing atomic number. In the transition element groups, there is usually only a slight variation.

4. Electronegativity increases within a period or series through the middle of the periodic table. It decreases slightly in the remaining metals and then increases usually to a maximum in Group VII or VIII.

2.1
H
1

																VIII

| | | | | | | | | | | | | | | | | He |
| | | | | | | | | | | | | | | | | 2 |

I	II											III	IV	V	VI	VII	
1.0	1.5											2.0	2.5	3.0	3.5	4.0	
Li	**Be**											**B**	**C**	**N**	**O**	**F**	**Ne**
3	4											5	6	7	8	9	10
0.9	1.2											1.5	1.8	2.1	2.5	3.0	
Na	**Mg**											**Al**	**Si**	**P**	**S**	**Cl**	**Ar**
11	12											13	14	15	16	17	18
0.8	1.0	1.3	1.5	1.6	1.6	1.5	1.8	1.8	1.8	1.9	1.6	1.6	1.8	2.0	2.4	2.8	3.0
K	**Ca**	**Sc**	**Ti**	**V**	**Cr**	**Mn**	**Fe**	**Co**	**Ni**	**Cu**	**Zn**	**Ga**	**Ge**	**As**	**Se**	**Br**	**Kr**
19	20	21	22	23	24	25	26	27	28	29	30	31	32	33	34	35	36
0.8	1.0	1.2	1.4	1.6	1.8	1.9	2.2	2.2	2.2	1.9	1.7	1.7	1.8	1.9	2.1	2.5	2.6
Rb	**Sr**	**Y**	**Zr**	**Nb**	**Mo**	**Tc**	**Ru**	**Rh**	**Pd**	**Ag**	**Cd**	**In**	**Sn**	**Sb**	**Te**	**I**	**Xe**
37	38	39	40	41	42	43	44	45	46	47	48	49	50	51	52	53	54
0.7	0.9	1.2	1.3	1.5	1.7	1.9	2.2	2.2	2.2	2.4	1.9	1.8	1.8	1.9	2.0	2.2	2.4
Cs	**Ba**	**Lu**	**Hf**	**Ta**	**W**	**Re**	**Os**	**Ir**	**Pt**	**Au**	**Hg**	**Tl**	**Pb**	**Bi**	**Po**	**At**	**Rn**
55	56	71	72	73	74	75	76	77	78	79	80	81	82	83	84	85	86
0.7	0.9																
Fr	**Ra**	**Lr**	**Unq**	**Unp**	**Unh**	**Uns**											
87	88	103	104	105	106	107											

1.1	1.1	1.1	1.1	1.1	1.1	1.1	1.1	1.1	1.1	1.1	1.1	1.1	1.1
La	**Ce**	**Pr**	**Nd**	**Pm**	**Sm**	**Eu**	**Gd**	**Tb**	**Dy**	**Ho**	**Er**	**Tm**	**Yb**
57	58	59	60	61	62	63	64	65	66	67	68	69	70
1.1	1.3	1.5	1.7	1.3	1.3	1.3	1.3	1.3	1.3	1.3	1.3	1.3	1.3
Ac	**Th**	**Pa**	**U**	**Np**	**Pu**	**Am**	**Cm**	**Bk**	**Cf**	**Es**	**Fm**	**Md**	**No**
89	90	91	92	93	94	95	96	97	98	99	100	101	102

Figure 6-14. Periodic table showing the electronegativities of the elements on an arbitrary scale.

☐ 6.20 Electronegativity difference and chemical bonding

The electronegativity difference between two elements is related to the percentage of ionic character of a single bond between atoms of the two elements. Table 6-6 gives values for this useful approximate relationship.

Bonds with more than 50% ionic character are considered to be largely ionic. Thus, the bonds between metallic elements and the distinctly nonmetallic elements are largely ionic. Sodium chloride, NaCl, with an electronegativity difference of $3.0 - 0.9 = 2.1$, is a compound with ionic bonds. Similarly, $CaBr_2$ and BaO are examples of compounds with ionic bonds. ($CaBr_2$: $2.8 - 1.0 = 1.8$; BaO: $3.5 - 0.9 = 2.6$)

Bonds with less than 50% ionic character are considered to be largely covalent. Below 5% ionic character, a bond is considered nonpolar covalent. Between 5% and 50% ionic character, a bond is considered polar covalent. The nonmetallic elements have rather similar electronegativity values. So the bonding between nonmetallic elements is largely covalent. The hydrogen-oxygen bonds in water, with an electronegativity difference of $3.5 - 2.1 = 1.4$, are 39% ionic. Thus they are polar covalent bonds, with the oxygen being somewhat negative and the hydrogen being somewhat positive.

Bonds between like atoms are found in molecules of elements such as oxygen or chlorine. These bonds have no ionic character since the electronegativity difference is zero. (O_2: $3.5 - 3.5 = 0$; Cl_2: $3.0 - 3.0 = 0$)

Chemical bonds have been classed as ionic bonds or covalent bonds. But it is apparent that these classifications are not clear and distinct. On the periodic table, the type of bonding gradually changes. Bonds are essentially ionic between the active metals of Groups I and II and oxygen or the halogens. But they are essentially covalent between metalloids and nonmetals as well as between two nonmetals. A third type of bonding, metallic bonding, occurs between atoms of metals. It will be described in Chapter 12.

The noble gases have electron configurations that are chemically very stable. It is possible, however, to produce compounds in which xenon is bonded to fluorine, chlorine, oxygen, or nitrogen. Compounds of krypton or radon with fluorine are also known.

The sixth rule for assigning oxidation numbers can now be introduced.

Rule 6: *In combinations involving nonmetals, the oxidation number of the less electronegative element is positive, and that of the more electronegative element is negative.*

Rule 6 leads to two further exceptions to the rules as already stated. First, hydrogen forms some ionic compounds with very active metals such as lithium and sodium. In these compounds, the hydrogen atom gains an electron from the metal and forms a *hydride* ion, H^-. In hydrides the oxidation number of hydrogen is -1. Second, in compounds with fluorine, oxygen is the less electronegative element. In such compounds, therefore, oxygen must have a positive oxidation number $+2$.

☐ 6.21 Molecular polarity

If all the bonds in a molecule are nonpolar, the valence electrons are equally shared by the bonding atoms. Thus, there is a uniform distribution of electrons on the exterior of the molecule. This uniform distribution occurs regardless of the number of bonds and their direction in space. A molecule with such characteristics is a *nonpolar molecule*. Molecules such as H_2, Cl_2, O_2, N_2, CH_4, and C_2H_6 are nonpolar because all of the bonds in each molecule are nonpolar.

Diatomic molecules like HCl and HBr have only one bond and it is a polar bond. These molecules have one somewhat more negative end and a somewhat less negative end. On the more negative end, the electron density (probability of finding electrons) is greater than on the less negative end. Molecules with such unbalanced electron distributions are *polar molecules*. Because polar molecules have two regions of different electric charge, they are called *dipolar molecules*, or simply *dipoles*.

Table 6-6
RELATIONSHIP BETWEEN ELECTRONEGATIVITY DIFFERENCE AND IONIC CHARACTER

Electro-negativity difference		Percentage of ionic character
0.2	nonpolar	1
0.4	covalent bond	4
0.6		9
0.8		15
1.0	polar	22
1.2	covalent	30
1.4	bond	39
1.6		47
1.8		55
2.0		63
2.2		70
2.4	ionic	76
2.6	bond	82
2.8		86
3.0		89
3.2		92

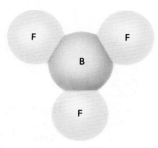

Boron trifluoride molecule

Figure 6-15. Even though the boron-fluorine bonds are polar bonds, their symmetrical arrangement in the molecule explains why boron trifluoride molecules are nonpolar.

A model of a carbon dioxide molecule is shown in Figure 17.12.

RESONANCE

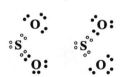

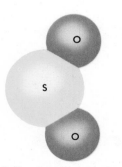

Sulfur dioxide molecule

Figure 6-16. A model that shows the arrangement of atoms in sulfur dioxide molecules.

If a molecule has more than one polar bond, the molecule as a whole may be nonpolar or polar depending on the arrangement in space of the bonds in the molecule. If the polar bonds in a molecule are all alike, the polarity of the molecule as a whole depends only on the arrangement in space of the bonds. Thus, water molecules are polar owing to a bent structure.

$$O$$
$$H \quad \quad H$$

But carbon dioxide is nonpolar due to a linear structure.

$$O=C=O$$

Triangular boron trifluoride molecules

are nonpolar, but pyramidal ammonia molecules are polar.

$$N$$
$$H \quad | \quad H$$
$$H$$

◻ 6.22 Resonance

If an attempt is made to draw an electron-dot formula for the molecular compound sulfur dioxide, the result is that two formulas may be written. Each formula gives all three atoms in the molecule an octet. These are shown in the margin at left.

From these formulas, it might be suspected that the two sulfur-oxygen bonds in the molecule are different. Experimental evidence indicates, however, that these bonds are identical. Hence, neither of the formulas can be correct. Unfortunately, *bond identity cannot be satisfactorily represented by any single formula using the electron-dot notation system and keeping the octet rule.* To describe such situations a concept called *resonance* is used.

Sulfur dioxide molecules may be considered to have a structure intermediate between the two electron-dot structures given. In this sense, the electron arrangement in the molecules is a *resonance hybrid* of the written structures. The term "resonance" is not really very accurate in this connection. It encourages the wrong idea that the structure of the molecule switches from one electron-dot formula to the other and that a pair of electrons is sometimes part of one bond and sometimes part of the other.

Sulfur dioxide molecules have only one real structure. The properties of a resonance hybrid do not switch from those of one electron-dot structure to those of the other. The properties are definite and are characteristic of the hybrid structure. The concept of resonance is an attempt to make up for deficiencies in writing the electron-dot structures of certain molecules. Difficulties occur when the electron-pair and electron-octet rules are used to write the structures of these molecules. The difficulties lie in the method of writing formulas, not in the molecules that are represented.

◘ 6.23 Polyatomic ions

Some covalently bonded groups of atoms act like single atoms in forming ions. These charged groups of covalently bonded atoms are called *polyatomic* (many-atomed) *ions*. Some common polyatomic ions are the sulfate ion, SO_4^{--}, the nitrate ion, NO_3^-, and the phosphate ion, PO_4^{---}. The bonds within these polyatomic ions are largely covalent. When combined, the groups of atoms have an excess of electrons and thus are negative ions. A common positive polyatomic ion, the ammonium ion, NH_4^+, is produced when a molecule of ammonia, NH_3, acquires a proton. Electron-dot representations of these polyatomic ions are shown in the margin at right.

There are some covalent bonds in which both electrons that form the bond between two atoms come from only one of the bonded atoms. Each of the electron-dot formulas shown here has at least one such bond. In the ammonium ion, for example, three of the covalent nitrogen-hydrogen bonds consist of one shared electron from nitrogen and one shared electron from hydrogen. The other covalent nitrogen-hydrogen bond consists of two electrons supplied by a nitrogen atom only. A hydrogen ion (proton) can thus bond at this position and produce the single net positive charge of the NH_4^+ ion.

Looking at the structure another way, there are eleven protons in the ammonium ion (seven in the nitrogen nucleus and one in each of four hydrogen nuclei). There are only ten electrons (two $1s$ electrons of the nitrogen atom, and eight valence electrons shown). With eleven protons and only ten electrons, an ammonium ion has a net charge of $+1$.

Figure 6-17. Models showing the arrangement of atoms in four common polyatomic ions.

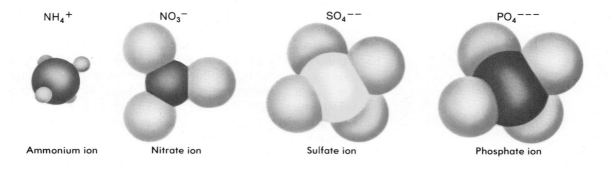

NH₄⁺   NO₃⁻   SO₄⁻⁻   PO₄⁻⁻⁻

Ammonium ion   Nitrate ion   Sulfate ion   Phosphate ion

Rule 7: *The algebraic sum of the oxidation numbers of the atoms in the formula of a polyatomic ion is equal to its charge.*

In an ammonium ion, the oxidation number of hydrogen is +1 (Rules 4 and 6). But the algebraic sum of the oxidation numbers must equal +1 (Rule 7). Using x as the oxidation number of nitrogen:

$$\overset{x\ +1}{NH_4{}^+}$$

$$x + 4(+1) = +1 \quad \text{and} \quad x = -3$$

The bonding, charges, and oxidation numbers of the elements in the other polyatomic ions can be examined in similar fashion. An electron represented by x is acquired by the ion from another element through electron transfer.

The electron-dot formula shown for the nitrate ion is only one of several possible formulas that can be written. Nitrate ions have a resonance-hybrid structure.

◻ 6.24 More about particles of matter

Free and isolated atoms are rarely found in nature. Instead, atoms of most elements combine with one another at ordinary temperatures and form larger structural particles. Notable exceptions are the noble elements: helium, neon, argon, krypton, xenon, and radon. The atoms of these noble gases do not combine with each other and form larger particles. There is no distinction, therefore, between the atoms and molecules of these gases. A molecule of helium, **He,** is monatomic.

The atoms of some elements combine naturally and form pairs that exist as simple diatomic molecules. Atmospheric oxygen and nitrogen are two examples. Their molecules are represented as O_2 and N_2, respectively. Observe that O_2 means two atoms of oxygen are bonded together to form one oxygen molecule. On the other hand, **2O** means two separate unbonded oxygen atoms. The expression $3O_2$ means three molecules of oxygen, each of which consists of two oxygen atoms bonded together. The other elemental gases, hydrogen, fluorine, and chlorine, also exist as diatomic molecules, H_2, F_2, and Cl_2, respectively. The nonmetal bromine, a liquid at ordinary temperatures, exists as diatomic molecules, Br_2. Iodine forms molecular crystals in which each molecular particle is diatomic, I_2.

Other elements may form groups consisting of a larger number of atoms. Phosphorus may form molecules consisting of four atoms, written P_4. Sulfur molecules may be eight-atom particles, or S_8. The metallic elements generally exhibit crystalline structures. Their atoms are closely packed in regular patterns that show no simple molecular units. Each individual crystal is considered a single giant molecule.

Some compounds have distinct unit structures composed of simple molecules. Water is a familiar example. Water molecules consist of two hydrogen atoms and one oxygen atom, $\mathbf{H_2O}$. The expression $\mathbf{2H_2O}$ represents two molecules of water, each containing two atoms of hydrogen and one atom of oxygen. Similarly, $\mathbf{5H_2O}$ signifies five molecules of water. When no other coefficient (the number before the formula) is used, it is understood that the coefficient is 1. Molecules of compounds range from a minimum of two atoms to large numbers of atoms.

Some substances show complex unit structures formed by groups of molecules or molecular aggregates. Still others have no molecular organization at all. Ordinary table salt, sodium chloride, consists of sodium and chloride ions distributed in a regular crystalline lattice pattern that is continuous to each face of the salt crystal. Simple molecules of sodium chloride do not exist except in the vapor state at very high temperatures. In general, *a coefficient of a symbol or formula gives the number of particles whose composition is given by the symbol or formula; a subscript gives the number of atoms of a particular kind in the particle.*

6.25 Summary of oxidation-number rules

1. The oxidation number of an atom of a free element is zero.

2. The oxidation number of a monatomic ion is equal to its charge.

3. The algebraic sum of the oxidation numbers of the atoms in the formula of a compound is zero.

4. In compounds, the oxidation number of hydrogen is +1, *except* in metallic hydrides, where its oxidation number is −1.

5. In compounds, the oxidation number of oxygen is −2, *except* in peroxides, where its oxidation number is −1. In compounds with fluorine, oxygen is the less electronegative element and has a positive oxidation number, +2.

6. In combinations involving nonmetals, the oxidation number of the less electronegative element is positive, and that of the more electronegative element is negative.

7. The algebraic sum of the oxidation numbers of the atoms in the formula of a polyatomic ion is equal to its charge.

SUMMARY

There is a relationship between the structure of an atom and the number of other atoms that combine with it. The electrons in an incomplete outer shell of an atom are known as valence electrons. In forming chemical compounds from the elements, valence electrons are usually either transferred from the outer shell of one atom to the outer shell of another atom or shared among the outer shells of the combining atoms. This transfer or sharing of electrons produces chemical bonds. Electron transfer results in ionic bonding while electron sharing produces covalent bonding. The process of electron transfer is always exothermic; electron sharing is usually exothermic. Bond energy is the energy required to break chemical bonds and form neutral atoms.

A chemical formula is a shorthand method of using chemical symbols to represent the composition of a substance. An empirical formula indicates the simplest whole-number ratio of the kinds of atoms in a compound. A molecule is the smallest chemical unit of a substance that is capable of stable independent existence. A molecule is also the neutral particle that results from the covalent bonding of atoms. A formula that indicates the actual composition of a molecule is called a molecular formula.

The oxidation state of an element is represented by a positive or negative number called an oxidation number. A chemical reaction in which an element attains a more positive oxidation state is called oxidation. The particle whose oxidation state becomes more positive is said to be oxidized. A chemical reaction in which an element attains a more negative oxidation state is called reduction. The particle whose oxidation state becomes more negative is said to be reduced. The substance that is oxidized is the reducing agent. The substance that is reduced is the oxidizing agent.

Positive ions are called cations; they are smaller than the atoms from which they are formed. Negative ions are called anions; they are larger than the atoms from which they are formed.

Hybridization is the combining of two or more orbitals of nearly the same energy into new orbitals of equal energy. Some molecular shapes can be explained by the hybridization of orbitals.

A covalent bond in which there is an equal attraction for the shared electrons and a resulting balanced distribution of charge is called a pure, or nonpolar, covalent bond. A covalent bond in which there is an unequal attraction for the shared electrons and a resulting unbalanced distribution of charge is called a polar covalent bond. The attraction of an atom for the shared electrons forming a bond between it and another atom is called electronegativity. Electronegativity difference between atoms accounts for the different kinds of bonds.

Molecules with a uniform exterior electron distribution are nonpolar molecules. Molecules with unbalanced exterior electron distributions are polar molecules, or dipoles.

The concept of resonance is used to explain the structure of a molecule whose bond characteristics cannot be described adequately by a single electron-dot formula.

Some covalently bonded groups of atoms act like single atoms in forming ions. They are called polyatomic ions.

VOCABULARY

anion	electron-dot formula	molecule	polyatomic ion
bond energy	electronegativity	monatomic	reducing agent
cation	empirical formula	nonpolar covalent bond	reduction
chemical formula	hybridization	oxidation	resonance
covalent bond	ionic bond	oxidation number	structural formula
diatomic	kernel	oxidizing agent	valence electron
dipole	molecular formula	polar covalent bond	

QUESTIONS

Group A

1. (*a*) What part of the atom is involved in the production of a chemical bond? (*b*) How are such bonds formed?
2. (*a*) What are the types of chemical bonding?

(*b*) What particles result from each type of bonding?

3. (*a*) What kind of outer electron shell does an atom usually attain when it combines with other atoms? (*b*) Explain why this electron

structure is chemically stable.

4. Which type of energy changes can occur (a) in electron transfer? (b) in electron sharing?

5. (a) What is a chemical formula? (b) Distinguish between an empirical formula and a molecular formula.

6. Which type of formula is used to represent the composition of (a) an ionic compound? (b) a covalent compound?

7. Draw an electron-dot symbol for (a) a potassium atom; (b) a potassium ion.

8. Draw an electron-dot symbol for (a) a sulfur atom; (b) a sulfide ion.

9. Using electron-dot symbols, represent a compound of potassium and sulfur.

10. (a) State the general definition for oxidation; (b) for reduction.

11. (a) Why is a substance that undergoes oxidation a reducing agent? (b) Why is a substance that undergoes reduction an oxidizing agent?

12. Explain: A barium atom is larger than a calcium atom.

13. Explain: A bromide ion is larger than a chloride ion.

14. For a fluorine molecule, draw: (a) its orbital notation; (b) its electron-dot formula; (c) its molecular formula.

15. Distinguish between an atom and a molecule.

16. What is the difference between a symbol and a formula?

17. (a) From a comparison of the bond energies of H_2, N_2, O_2, and Cl_2, which is the most stable molecule? (b) Which is the least stable molecule?

18. What is electronegativity?

19. What electronegativity difference is there between atoms that form (a) ionic bonds; (b) polar covalent bonds; (c) bonds with no ionic character?

20. Assuming chemical union between the following pairs, indicate in each case which element would have the positive oxidation number: (a) hydrogen-sodium; (b) chlorine-fluorine; (c) chlorine-oxygen; (d) hydrogen-lithium; (e) bromine-hydrogen.

21. What is the oxidation number of each element in the following compounds: (a) MnO_2, a dioxide; (b) H_3PO_4; (c) HNO_3; (d) P_4O_{10}; (e) Na^+OH^-?

22. (a) What gaseous elements have diatomic molecules? (b) By what symbol or formula is each represented?

23. (a) What gaseous elements have monatomic molecules? (b) By what symbol or formula is each represented?

24. How many atoms of each element are represented by the following formulas: sugar, $C_{12}H_{22}O_{11}$; sand, SiO_2; salt, NaCl; hydrogen peroxide, H_2O_2; soap, $C_{17}H_{35}COONa$?

25. What does each of the following represent? (a) Ar; (b) $4N_2$; (c) HI; (d) $6H_2SO_4$; (e) $3Cu$; (f) $2K^+Br^-$; (g) CO; (h) Co.

Group B

26. Draw the orbital notation for (a) a calcium atom; (b) a calcium ion.

27. Draw the orbital notation for (a) a fluorine atom; (b) a fluoride ion.

28. Using orbital notation, show how an ionic compound of calcium and fluorine is formed.

29. Explain why a calcium atom is smaller than a potassium atom.

30. Explain why a sulfide ion is larger than a chloride ion.

31. For a hydrogen bromide molecule, HBr, draw: (a) its orbital notation; (b) its electron-dot formula.

32. Hydrogen and sulfur form a simple molecular compound. Using both orbital notation and electron-dot notation, show how such a compound can be represented. Then determine its probable molecular formula.

33. (a) From a consideration of the electron-dot notation of phosphorus, what is the shape of a PH_3 molecule? (b) Consider sulfur and H_2S in similar fashion.

34. For each of the following bonds give the percent ionic character and indicate whether the bond is largely ionic, polar covalent, or pure covalent. (a) K—Br; (b) C—O; (c) Na—O; (d) C—H; (e) Br—Br.

35. What is the oxidation number of manganese in (a) potassium permanganate, $K^+MnO_4^-$; (b) manganese(II) sulfate, $Mn^{++}SO_4^{--}$?

(c) If manganese(II) sulfate is one of the products of a reaction in which potassium permanganate was one of the reactants, what kind of change has manganese undergone? (d) What name is given to manganese in this change?

36. What is the oxidation number of (a) iron in $Fe^{++}SO_4^{--}$ and in $Fe^{+++}Cl^-_3$? (b) chromium in Cr_2O_3, $K^+_2CrO_4^{--}$, and $K^+_2Cr_2O_7^{--}$?

37. The four oxygen acids of chlorine are hypochlorous acid, $HClO$; chlorous acid, $HClO_2$; chloric acid, $HClO_3$; and perchloric acid, $HClO_4$. What is the oxidation number of chlorine in each acid of the series?

38. What is the oxidation number of each element in the following polyatomic ions? (a) SO_4^{--}; (b) SO_3^{--}; (c) NO_2^-; (d) CO_3^{--}; (e) CrO_4^{--}

39. Oxygen atoms form a triatomic molecule, O_3, called ozone. (a) Draw an electron-dot formula for this molecule that satisfies the octet rule. (b) Is this the only formula you can draw for this molecule that satisfies the octet rule? (c) What is the explanation of the actual structure of an ozone molecule?

40. Classify each of the following as ionic crystal, polar covalent molecule, or nonpolar covalent molecule. (a) $MgCl_2$; (b) CF_4, consisting of a central carbon atom and four symmetrically arranged fluorine atoms; (c) HBr; (d) SO_2, consisting of an oxygen atom, a sulfur atom, and a second oxygen atom arranged in a bent molecule; (e) P_4.

◖ PROBLEMS

Group A

1. From bond-energy data, determine whether the energy change in this reaction is exothermic or endothermic. What is the amount of the energy change?

$\frac{1}{2}$ **mole** H_2 + $\frac{1}{2}$ **mole** Br_2 → **1 mole HBr**

2. From bond-energy data, determine the kind and amount of energy change for the reaction

1 mole H_2 + $\frac{1}{2}$ **mole** O_2 → **1 mole** H_2O

Group B

3. Calculate the energy change for the reaction

1 mole Mg + 2 moles Br →
1 mole $Mg^{++}Br^-_2$

As described in Section 6.6, this reaction may be assumed to consist of three separate reactions.

1 mole Mg + energy →
1 mole Mg^{++} **+ 2 moles** e^-

The energy required for this reaction is the sum of the ionization energies for removing the first and second electrons from a magnesium atom. Obtain energy data from Chapter 5.

2 moles Br + 2 moles e^- →
2 moles Br^- **+ energy**

The energy released is the electron affinity of *two* moles of bromine atoms. Obtain energy data from Chapter 5.

1 mole Mg^{++} **+ 2 moles** Br^- →
1 mole $Mg^{++}Br^-_2$ **+ 587 kcal**

Set up these three equations in suitable form and do the required calculations. Is the overall reaction exothermic or endothermic?

4. From bond-energy data, determine the kind and amount of energy change for the reaction

1 mole H_2 + **1 mole** O_2 → **1 mole** H_2O_2

Assume four reaction steps: (1) breaking bonds in H_2 molecules; (2) breaking bonds in O_2 molecules; (3) combining of H atoms and O atoms into H—O groups; (4) combining of H—O groups into H_2O_2 molecules by forming O—O bonds between them.

5. From bond-energy data, determine the kind and amount of the energy change for the reaction

1 mole N_2 + **2 moles** H_2 →
1 mole N_2H_4 **(hydrazine)**

Chemical Composition

Almost every area of human endeavor has its system of characters, signs, or symbols. In the English language, the twenty-six letters of the alphabet are used to express millions of ideas. In mathematics, ten digits are sufficient for representing extremely small or very large quantities. In music, only a few symbols are needed to record the thousands of sounds in a symphony. The symbols of writers, mathematicians, and musicians all have this in common: They are a shorthand way of conveying information. If a writer didn't have letters to represent sounds, expressing words and ideas would be impossible. If a mathematician had no system for symbolizing quantity, day-to-day transactions would require counting each and every item that changes hands. A great work of art such as a symphony could not be preserved if musicians didn't have a means of transcribing its sounds on paper. In chemistry, the symbols of the elements are the alphabet of the chemist. Knowing these symbols and the rules for combining them can lead to knowledge and adventure.

☐ 7.1 Common ions and their charges

The formula of a compound is useful only if it correctly represents the composition of the substance. The composition of a compound is determined by chemical analysis. Its formula is then derived from the analysis data by applying concepts from atomic theory and chemical bonding. This procedure for determining the formulas of compounds is discussed in Section 7.12.

It is possible to write the formulas of many common compounds without composition data from chemical analyses. For ionic compounds, this is done by using the positively and negatively charged ions that constitute these compounds. A list of common ions and their charges is presented in Table 7-1. To become proficient in writing the formulas of compounds correctly, the ions and their charges listed in this table should be memorized.

Observe that, with the exception of ammonium ions and mercury(I) ions, all positively charged ions listed in Table 7-1 are monatomic. They have the same names as the elements from which they are derived. In some cases the positive or negative charge on a monatomic ion is directly related to the position of the element in the periodic table. The elements of Groups I, II, and VII are examples.

Recall that atoms of the Group I metallic elements are characterized by the presence of a single, unpaired *s* electron in the outer shell. First ionization energies in this group are low; second ionization energies are much higher. This suggests that the single *s* electron is removed with relative ease from a Group I atom,

In this chapter you will gain an understanding of:

- **writing chemical formulas**
- **naming compounds from their formulas**
- **molecular and empirical formulas**
- **formula and molecular weights**
- **the calculation of percentage composition of a compound**
- **the relationship between atomic theory, law of definite composition, law of multiple proportions, and percentage composition**
- **the mole concept**
- **the determination of empirical and molecular formulas**

The formula of a compound represents the relative number of atoms of each element present.

Representative ionization energies are listed in Table 5-2.

Table 7-1
COMMON IONS AND THEIR CHARGES

+1	+2	+3
ammonium, NH_4^+	barium, Ba^{++}	aluminum, Al^{+++}
copper(I), Cu^+	calcium, Ca^{++}	chromium(III), Cr^{+++}
potassium, K^+	copper(II), Cu^{++}	iron(III), Fe^{+++}
silver, Ag^+	iron(II), Fe^{++}	
sodium, Na^+	lead(II), Pb^{++}	
	magnesium, Mg^{++}	
	mercury(I), Hg_2^{++}	
	mercury(II), Hg^{++}	
	nickel(II), Ni^{++}	
	zinc, Zn^{++}	

−1	−2	−3
acetate, $C_2H_3O_2^-$	carbonate, CO_3^{--}	phosphate, PO_4^{---}
bromide, Br^-	chromate, CrO_4^{--}	
chlorate, ClO_3^-	dichromate, $Cr_2O_7^{--}$	
chloride, Cl^-	oxide, O^{--}	
fluoride, F^-	peroxide, O_2^{--}	
hydrogen carbonate, HCO_3^-	sulfate, SO_4^{--}	
hydrogen sulfate, HSO_4^-	sulfide, S^{--}	
hydroxide, OH^-	sulfite, SO_3^{--}	
iodide, I^-		
nitrate, NO_3^-		
nitrite, NO_2^-		

leaving a + 1 monatomic ion with the stable electron configuration of the preceding noble gas.

Atoms of the Group II metallic elements have two paired electrons in the outer shell. Both first and second ionization energies are relatively low; third ionization energies are much higher. With the loss of its two outer-shell electrons, a Group II element forms a + 2 monatomic ion with the stable electron configuration of the preceding noble gas.

Review electron affinity in Section 5.9.

Atoms of the Group VII nonmetallic elements have seven outer-shell electrons and high positive electron affinity. The acquisition of an electron by a Group VII atom results in a − 1 monatomic ion with the stable configuration of the following noble gas.

The atoms of some metallic elements form ions in more than one oxidation state. For example, copper forms Cu^+ and Cu^{++} ions. The name of each copper ion includes its oxidation number as a Roman numeral in parentheses. The copper(I) ion is simply called the "copper-one" ion and is represented by Cu^+. The copper(II) ion is called the "copper-two" ion and is represented by Cu^{++}. This Roman numeral notation is not used with metals that form ions in only a single oxidation state.

An older system for distinguishing the metallic ions of an element formed in different oxidation states is still in limited use. By means of an appropriate suffix, the oxidation states are identified as a lower or higher state. The suffix *-ous* is used for the lower state and *-ic* for the higher state.

If the symbol for the element is derived from its Latin name, the Latin root may be used. For example, Fe, the symbol for iron, is derived from the Latin *ferrum*. The iron(II) ion, Fe^{++}, becomes the ferr*ous* ion. The iron(III) ion, Fe^{+++}, becomes the ferr*ic* ion. This older system for naming metallic ions is not used in this book. However, some common name equivalents are listed in Table 7-2 for comparison purposes.

Many of the common negative ions in Table 7-1 are polyatomic, as is the positive ammonium ion. They are covalently bonded groups of atoms that form ions just as single atoms do. It will be helpful to review polyatomic ions and their electron-dot configurations in Section 6.23. Refer also to the table inside the front cover or to Appendix Table 6 for a more extensive list of common ions and their charges.

Table 7-2
METALLIC ION NAME EQUIVALENTS

Old system		New system	
chromic	Cr^{+++}	chromium(III)	Cr^{+++}
cobaltous	Co^{++}	cobalt(II)	Co^{++}
cobaltic	Co^{+++}	cobalt(III)	Co^{+++}
ferrous	Fe^{++}	iron(II)	Fe^{++}
ferric	Fe^{+++}	iron(III)	Fe^{+++}
cuprous	Cu^{+}	copper(I)	Cu^{+}
cupric	Cu^{++}	copper(II)	Cu^{++}
mercurous	Hg^{+}	mercury(I)	Hg_2^{++}
mercuric	Hg^{++}	mercury(II)	Hg^{++}
plumbous	Pb^{++}	lead(II)	Pb^{++}
plumbic	Pb^{++++}	lead(IV)	Pb^{++++}
stannous	Sn^{++}	tin(II)	Sn^{++}
stannic	Sn^{++++}	tin(IV)	Sn^{++++}

☐ 7.2 Writing chemical formulas

As stated above, the formulas for many *ionic* compounds can easily be derived from the table of ions and their charges. It is not necessary to become involved with the details of atomic structure and chemical bonding to do this. The first step in writing such a formula is to recognize the positive and negative ions named in the compound. Using this information, the ion notations (including their charges) are written in the order named. Then the number of each kind of ion is adjusted as required to provide *total* positive and negative ionic charges of equal magnitudes. This procedure is called the *ion-charge* method of writing formulas. Its use depends on a compound having been named systematically on the basis of its composition. The following examples illustrate the ion-charge procedure.

Sodium chloride consists of positive sodium ions and negative chloride ions. The sodium ion is represented by Na^{+}, and the chloride ion is represented by Cl^{-}. When writing formulas for ionic compounds, *the total charge of the first (positive) part of the compound must be equal and opposite to the total charge of the second (negative) part of the compound*. The total charge for an ion in the formula is the product of the charge of the ion and the number of that ion taken. For the sodium chloride example, the charge of one sodium ion is equal and opposite to the charge of one chloride ion. The formula for sodium chloride is simply *NaCl,* indicating that there is one of each kind of ion represented in the formula.

The formula for *calcium chloride* is derived in the same manner. The calcium ion is represented by Ca^{++}, and the chloride ion is Cl^{-}. The total charge of the negative part of the compound must be equal to that of the positive part. Thus, two chloride ions are needed with one calcium ion. Observe that one

Figure 7-1. Jöns Jakob Berzelius introduced letter symbols for elements early in the nineteenth century. He conducted meticulous chemical analyses that resulted in the first systematic determination of atomic weights.

Polyatomic ions are covalent structures with an electric charge. Review Section 6.23.

calcium ion has a charge of $+2$, one chloride ion has a charge of -1, and the total charge of two chloride ions is -2. The formula is written as $CaCl_2$. The subscript $_2$ indicates that the composition of calcium chloride is two chloride ions per calcium ion. No subscript is required with Ca since only one Ca^{++} is represented in the formula $CaCl_2$. When no subscript is written in the formula, the subscript $_1$ is understood.

The compound named *iron(III) oxide* consists of iron(III) ions, Fe^{+++}, and oxide ions, O^{--}. The total positive charge and total negative charge represented in the formula for iron(III) oxide must be equal. The lowest common multiple of 3 (Fe^{+++}) and 2 (O^{--}) is 6. The formula must indicate a total positive charge of $+6$ and a total negative charge of -6. Therefore, 2 Fe^{+++} ions and 3 O^{--} ions are required in the formula. Iron(III) oxide has the formula $Fe^{+++}_2O^{--}_3$, or simply Fe_2O_3. Conversely, if the oxide ion represents oxygen atoms in the -2 oxidation state, the formula Fe_2O_3 must signify that iron ions present are in the $+3$ oxidation state.

What is the formula for *aluminum bromide?* The aluminum ion is Al^{+++} and the bromide ion is Br^-. Three Br^- ions are needed to balance the positive charge of one Al^{+++} ion. The formula is $AlBr_3$.

Observe that this ion-charge method of writing formulas yields empirical formulas. Recall that an empirical formula shows the simplest whole-number ratio of atoms in a compound.

☐ 7.3 Writing the formulas for other compounds

The formula for *lead(II) sulfate* is easy to write. The lead(II) ion is Pb^{++}, the sulfate ion is SO_4^{--}, and the charges are equal and opposite. Thus the empirical formula for lead(II) sulfate has just one Pb^{++} ion and one SO_4^{--} ion, $PbSO_4$.

In the formula for *magnesium hydroxide,* the magnesium ion is Mg^{++} and the hydroxide ion, a polyatomic ion, is OH^-. Two OH^- ions are required for the negative charge to be equal and opposite to the positive charge of one magnesium ion. More than one polyatomic ion must be represented in the formula. When writing the formula for magnesium hydroxide, parentheses are used to enclose the two-atomed hydroxide ion that is to be taken twice. Then the subscript $_2$ is written outside the parentheses, $(OH)_2$. This clearly shows that the *entire* OH^- ion is taken twice. The complete formula for magnesium hydroxide is $Mg(OH)_2$, not $MgOH_2$. This incorrect formula, $MgOH_2$, represents one oxygen atom and two hydrogen atoms. *Parentheses are not used when only one polyatomic ion is required in a formula.* For example, the formula for *potassium hydroxide,* KOH, represents one K^+ ion and one OH^- ion. The parentheses would serve no purpose in this formula.

As another example, consider the formula for *lead(II) acetate*. The lead(II) ion is Pb^{++} and the acetate ion is the polyatomic $C_2H_3O_2^-$. For each lead ion, two acetate ions are required in the formula. Following the scheme used in writing the formula for magnesium hydroxide, the formula for lead(II) acetate becomes $Pb(C_2H_3O_2)_2$. Observe that the *two* $C_2H_3O_2^-$ ions required are represented by $(C_2H_3O_2)_2$.

Ammonium sulfate has two polyatomic ions in its formula. The ammonium ion is NH_4^+, and the sulfate ion is SO_4^{--}. In order to achieve total equality of $+$ and $-$ charges, two NH_4^+ ions are required with one SO_4^{--} ion. Of course, two ammonium ions are represented in the formula by enclosing the NH_4^+ ion in parentheses with a subscript $_2$ outside. The formula is then written as $(NH_4)_2SO_4$.

Finally, consider the formula for *tin(IV) chromate*. (The metallic ions formed by atoms of tin are listed in the table inside the front cover and in Appendix Table 6.) The tin(IV) ion is Sn^{++++}, and the chromate ion is CrO_4^{--}. Again, the total positive and negative charges represented in the formula must be equal. Because the positive charge is supplied in units of 4 as Sn^{++++} and the negative charge is supplied in units of 2 as CrO_4^{--}, the equal-charge requirement is satisfied with a ratio of Sn^{++++} ions to CrO_4^{--} ions of $2:4$. The formula can be written as $Sn_2(CrO_4)_4$. However, an empirical formula requires the smallest whole-number ratio of constituent units. Since the ratio $2:4 = 1:2$, the smallest whole-number ratio of Sn^{++++} ions to CrO_4^{--} ions in the tin(IV) chromate is $1:2$. The formula is correctly written as $Sn(CrO_4)_2$.

It must be recognized that the ion-charge method has limitations. A formula can give no more information than that required to write it. It is possible to write the formula for a compound and then learn that such a compound does not exist! On the other hand, there are many covalent compounds that *do* exist but whose formulas cannot be written using the ion-charge method.

If a metallic atom forms more than one ion, a Roman numeral is used in the name of the ion to identify its oxidation state.

◻ 7.4 Naming compounds from their formulas

The names of many chemical compounds consist of two words: the name of the first part of the formula and the name of the second part. $BaSO_4$ is called barium sulfate (Ba^{++} represents the barium ion; SO_4^{--} represents the sulfate ion). $FeCl_3$ is the formula for iron(III) chloride. Notice that there are two possible oxidation states for iron. One is iron(II), with an oxidation number of $+2$; the other is iron(III), with an oxidation number of $+3$. There are 3 chloride ions associated with one iron ion in the formula $FeCl_3$. Therefore, the iron ion has a charge of $+++$, and the compound is *iron(III) chloride*. $FeCl_2$ is *iron(II) chloride*.

A Roman numeral used in the name of a metallic ion does not appear in the formula of a compound containing the ion.

Table 7-3
NITROGEN-OXYGEN SERIES OF BINARY COMPOUNDS

Formula	Name
N_2O	dinitrogen monoxide
NO	nitrogen monoxide
N_2O_3	dinitrogen trioxide
NO_2	nitrogen dioxide
N_2O_5	dinitrogen pentoxide

The names of binary compounds have -ide *endings.*

The use of Roman numerals to indicate oxidation states does not always provide simple and useful names for compounds. The system is commonly used with ionic compounds in which the metallic ion has different possible oxidation states. Another system, using Greek numeral prefixes, is used for certain binary covalent compounds. *Binary compounds are those that consist of only two elements.* Some elements form more than one covalent compound with another element. For example, there are two co-valent compounds of sulfur and oxygen, SO_2 and SO_3. Nitrogen forms a series of five different compounds with oxygen. The formulas and corresponding names of this series are given in Table 7-3. The names of these compounds must provide a way of distinguishing between them. Covalent binary compounds are named by the following steps.

1. The first word of the name is made up of (*a*) a prefix indicating the number of atoms of the first element appearing in the formula, if more than one; and (*b*) the name of the first element in the formula.

2. The second word of the name is made up of (*a*) a prefix indicating the number of atoms of the second element appearing in the formula, if more than one compound of these two elements exists; (*b*) the root of the name of the second element; and (*c*) the suffix *-ide,* which means that *only* the two elements named are present.

Carbon monoxide is written CO. Only one atom of the first element appears in the formula, so no prefix is used with the first word. It consists only of the name of the first element, *carbon.* The prefix *mon-* is used in the second word of the name because only one atom of oxygen appears in this formula, but more than one compound of carbon and oxygen exists. *Ox-* is the root of the name of the element oxygen. It is followed by the suffix *-ide.*

In a similar manner, CO_2 is *carbon dioxide.* The prefix *di-* indicates the presence of two oxygen atoms in the compound. The prefix indicating three is *tri-;* four is *tetra-;* and five is *pent-* or *penta-.* These prefixes can be used with both the first and second words in the name. Some examples of the use of Greek numerical prefixes are: $SbCl_3$, *antimony trichloride;* CCl_4, *carbon tetra-chloride;* and As_2S_5, *diarsenic pentasulfide.*

A few negative polyatomic ions have names with an *-ide* suffix. The hydroxide ion, OH^-, and cyanide ion, CN^-, are examples. Compounds formed with either of these polyatomic ions obviously are not binary. Similarly, compounds formed with the positive ammonium ion, $NH_4{}^+$, are not binary. All binary compounds end in *-ide,* but not all compounds with *-ide* endings are binary. For example, NaOH, $Ca(CN)_2$, and NH_4Cl have names that end in *-ide,* but they are not binary compounds.

1. Write the formulas for the following compounds: (*a*) sodium chromate, (*b*) magnesium bromide, (*c*) nickel(II) nitrate, (*d*) calcium phosphate, (*e*) mercury(I) sulfate.
   ans. (*a*) Na_2CrO_4,   (*b*) $MgBr_2$,   (*c*) $Ni(NO_3)_2$, (*d*) $Ca_3(PO_4)_2$,   (*e*) Hg_2SO_4.
2. Name the following compounds: (*a*) AgI, (*b*) $Cu(OH)_2$, (*c*) $Pb(C_2H_3O_2)_2$, (*d*) $(NH_4)_2S$, (*e*) FeO.
   ans. (*a*) silver iodide, (*b*) copper(II) hydroxide, (*c*) lead(II) acetate, (*d*) ammonium sulfide, (*e*) iron(II) oxide.

PRACTICE PROBLEMS

❏ 7.5 Significance of chemical formulas

You have learned to write formulas for many chemical compounds by using your knowledge of the charges of the ions composing them. When it is known that a substance exists as simple molecules, its formula represents one molecule of the substance. Such a formula is known as a ***molecular formula.***

The molecular structure of some substances is not known. Other substances have no simple molecular structure. For these substances, the formula represents (1) the elements in the substances and (2) the simplest whole-number ratio of the atoms of these elements. In these cases, the formula is called an ***empirical,*** or simplest, ***formula.***

From Section 6.20, you learned that the character of the chemical bonds between elements in a compound is related to the electronegativity difference between these elements. Table 6-6 shows that the ionic character of the bond increases with electronegativity difference, and that the change-over region from covalent to ionic bond is indistinct and somewhat arbitrary. From these observations, you can reasonably assume that nonmetal-nonmetal compounds are molecular, and their formulas are molecular formulas. Similarly, metal-nonmetal compounds are essentially ionic, and their formulas are empirical. When no specific information about the structure of a compound is available, you can use this loose guideline to decide whether the formula is a molecular formula or an empirical formula.

The chemical formula of a compound reveals important information about the compound. For example, hydrogen sulfide has the molecular formula H_2S. It has a nonmetal-nonmetal composition. The formula shows that each molecule of hydrogen sulfide is composed of *two atoms of hydrogen and one atom of sulfur.*

The atomic weight of hydrogen is 1.0 and the atomic weight of sulfur is 32.1. Hence this molecular formula signifies that the *formula weight of hydrogen sulfide is 34.1.*

An empirical formula gives the simplest whole-number ratio of the atoms of constituent elements in a compound.

Observe that the molecular formula of H_2S is also its empirical formula.

$$
\begin{array}{l}
\underline{\begin{array}{l}
2 \text{ atoms H} \times \text{atomic weight } 1.0 = 2.0 \\
1 \text{ atom } S \times \text{atomic weight } 32.1 = 32.1
\end{array}} \\
\text{formula weight } H_2S = 34.1
\end{array}
$$

*The **formula weight** of any compound is the sum of the atomic weights of all of the atoms represented in the formula.*

The compound sodium chloride has the empirical formula NaCl. It is a crystalline solid that has no molecular structure but is composed of an orderly arrangement of sodium and chloride ions. This empirical formula indicates the relative number of atoms (as ions) of each element present in the compound. It shows that there are equal numbers of Na^+ ions and Cl^- ions in any quantity of NaCl. The atomic weight of sodium is 23.0 and that of chlorine is 35.5. Hence the empirical formula denotes a formula weight for sodium chloride of 23.0 + 35.5, or 58.5.

◻ 7.6 Molecular weight

You have learned that a molecular formula represents one molecule of a substance. The formula H_2S is a molecular formula. It represents one molecule of hydrogen sulfide. The formula weight, 34.1, is then the relative weight of *one molecule* of hydrogen sulfide. *The formula weight of a molecular substance is its **molecular weight**.*

In the strictest sense, it is not correct to use the "molecular weight" for a nonmolecular substance. Sodium chloride, for example, is represented by an empirical formula. Empirical formulas have "formula weights." The term *formula weight* is a more general term than *molecular weight* and is therefore preferred. In elementary chemical calculations the distinction is not important.

◻ 7.7 Formula weight of a compound

Formula weight is the sum of the atomic weights of all the atoms represented in a formula.

To find the total weight of all the members of your chemistry class, you must add the weights of the individual members of the class. Similarly, to find the formula weight of any substance for which a formula is given, you must add the atomic weights of all the atoms represented in the formula. Consider the formula for cane sugar, $C_{12}H_{22}O_{11}$, as an example. The approximate atomic weights found inside the front cover and in Appendix Table 5 can be used.

Number of atoms	Atomic weight	Total weight
12 of C	12.0	$12 \times 12.0 = 144.0$
22 of H	1.0	$22 \times 1.0 = 22.0$
11 of O	16.0	$11 \times 16.0 = 176.0$
	formula weight (molecular weight) =	342.0

Molecular weights are formula weights of molecular substances.

The formula for calcium hydroxide is $Ca(OH)_2$. The subscript $_2$ following the parentheses indicates that there are two polyatomic hydroxide ions per calcium ion. Thus, the formula

$Ca(OH)_2$ includes atomic weights of one calcium atom, two oxygen atoms, and two hydrogen atoms.

Number of atoms	Atomic weight	Total weight
1 of Ca	40.1	1 × 40.1 = 40.1
2 of O	16.0	2 × 16.0 = 32.0
2 of H	1.0	2 × 1.0 = 2.0
		formula weight = 74.1

The atomic weights of the elements are relative weights based on an atom of carbon-12 that has an assigned value of exactly 12. In the quantitative study of chemical reactions, the atomic weights and formula weights indicate the relative quantities of elements and compounds that combine or react. These quantities can be expressed in any desired units. Thus, atomic weights, formulas, and formula weights are important in chemical calculations.

Atomic weights apply to monatomic ions and atoms alike.

☐ 7.8 Percentage composition of a compound

Frequently it is important to know the composition of a compound in terms of the *mass percentage* of each element of which the compound is made. You may want to know the percentage of iron in the compound iron(III) oxide. Or, you may want to know the percentage of oxygen in potassium chlorate. This knowledge enables you to determine the amount of potassium chlorate needed to supply enough oxygen for a laboratory experiment.

The chemical formula for a compound can be used directly to determine its formula weight. This is done by adding the atomic weights of all the atoms represented. The formula weight represents *all*, or 100 percent, of the composition of the substance as indicated by the formula. The part of the formula weight contributed by each element represented in the formula is the product of the atomic weight of that element × the number of atoms of that element. The fractional part due to each element is

$$\frac{\text{(atomic weight} \times \text{number of atoms) of the element}}{\text{formula weight of the compound}}$$

The percentage of each element present in the compound is therefore a fractional part of 100 percent of the compound.

$$\frac{\text{(atomic weight} \times \text{number of atoms) of the element}}{\text{formula weight of the compound}} \times 100\% \text{ of the compound}$$

The mass percentage of an element in a compound can be expressed as

$$\frac{\text{(atomic weight} \times \text{number of atoms) element}}{\text{formula weight of compound}} \times 100\% \text{ compound} = \% \text{ element}$$

Figure 7-2. Students determining the composition of a compound in a laboratory experiment.

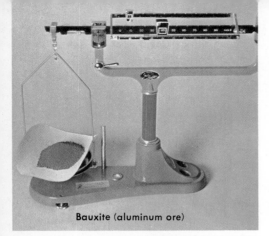

Bauxite (aluminum ore)

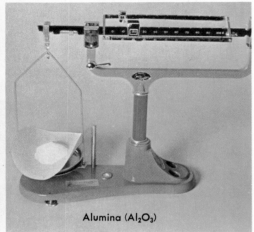

Alumina (Al₂O₃)

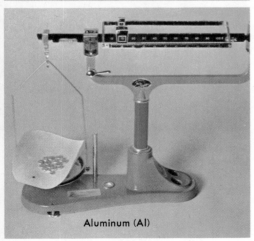

Aluminum (Al)

Figure 7-3. A supply of bauxite is 50.0% aluminum oxide, Al_2O_3. Assuming all the available Al is extracted in the recovery process, how many kg of metallic Al are produced by processing 1.00 metric ton (see Table 1-3) of bauxite?

Consider the compound iron(III) oxide. The formula is Fe_2O_3. What is the percentage of each of the elements in this compound?

    1. Formula weight of Fe_2O_3

$$\text{total atomic weight Fe} = 2 \times 55.8 = 111.6$$
$$\underline{\text{total atomic weight O} \ = 3 \times 16.0 = \ \ \ 48.0}$$
$$\text{formula weight } Fe_2O_3 = 159.6$$

    2. Percentage of Fe

$$\frac{\text{total atomic weight Fe}}{\text{formula weight } Fe_2O_3} \times 100\% \ Fe_2O_3 = \% \ Fe$$

Using three significant figures,

$$\frac{112 \ Fe}{16\bar{0} \ Fe_2O_3} \times 100\% \ Fe_2O_3 = 70.0\% \ Fe$$

    3. Percentage of O

$$\frac{\text{total atomic weight O}}{\text{formula weight } Fe_2O_3} \times 100\% \ Fe_2O_3 = \% \ O$$

$$\frac{48.0 \ O}{16\bar{0} \ Fe_2O_3} \times 100\% \ Fe_2O_3 = 30.0\% \ O$$

Of course, since there is no third element present, the percentage of oxygen is $100.0\% - 70.0\% = 30.0\%$.

    Observe that the formulas Fe_2O_3 in step 2 cancel, leaving the symbol Fe in the result. In step 3, the formulas Fe_2O_3 cancel, leaving the symbol O in the result. The symbols remaining are the ones expected for each of these answers. Many errors in the solutions to problems in chemistry can be avoided by consistently labeling each quantity properly and solving the expression for both the numerical result and the unit that is a part of the result.

    As a second example, the percentage composition of a crystallized form of sodium carbonate, $Na_2CO_3 \cdot 10H_2O$, will be determined. The raised dot indicates that the crystals contain 10 molecules of water of crystallization for each 2 Na^+ ions or for each CO_3^{--} ion present.

    1. Formula weight $Na_2CO_3 \cdot 10H_2O$

2 Na	$2 \times 23.0 =$	46.0
1 C	$1 \times 12.0 =$	12.0
3 O	$3 \times 16.0 =$	48.0
10H₂O $\begin{cases} 20 \text{ H} \\ 10 \text{ O} \end{cases}$	$\begin{matrix} 20 \times 1.0 = 2\bar{0} \\ 10 \times 16.0 = 16\bar{0} \end{matrix} \Big\}$	$18\bar{0}$

$$\text{formula weight} = 286$$

    2. Percentage of Na

$$\frac{46.0 \ Na}{286 \ Na_2CO_3 \cdot 10H_2O} \times 100\% \ Na_2CO_3 \cdot 10H_2O = 16.1\% \ Na$$

3. Percentage of C

$$\frac{12.0 \text{ C}}{286 \text{ Na}_2\text{CO}_3 \cdot 10\text{H}_2\text{O}} \times 100\% \text{ Na}_2\text{CO}_3 \cdot 10\text{H}_2\text{O} = 4.2\% \text{ C}$$

4. Percentage of O (in CO_3^{--} ion)

$$\frac{48.0 \text{ O}}{286 \text{ Na}_2\text{CO}_3 \cdot 10\text{H}_2\text{O}} \times 100\% \text{ Na}_2\text{CO}_3 \cdot 10\text{H}_2\text{O} = 16.8\% \text{ O}$$

5. Percentage of H_2O

$$\frac{180 \text{ H}_2\text{O}}{286 \text{ Na}_2\text{CO}_3 \cdot 10\text{H}_2\text{O}} \times 100\% \text{ Na}_2\text{CO}_3 \cdot 10\text{H}_2\text{O} = 62.9\% \text{ H}_2\text{O}$$

Approximate atomic weights usually have no more than two or three significant figures. The result is not improved by carrying out the computations beyond the precision of the data. Thus the sum of the mass percentages may only approximate 100%.

◻ 7.9 Law of definite composition and the atomic theory

The law of definite composition (Section 2.9) states, in effect, that the percentage composition of a chemical compound is constant. This characteristic of constant composition of chemical compounds depends upon two facts: (1) the relative mass of the atoms of an element is constant, and (2) the proportion in which atoms are present in a compound is constant. The idea that, under most conditions, atomic weights are constant is basic to the atomic theory. For practical purposes, the atomic weight used for an element is the average relative mass of the naturally occurring mixture of its isotopes. (This fact was discussed in Section 3.15.) For example, the average relative mass (atomic weight) of the hydrogen atom is 1.0079. That of the chlorine atom is 35.453.

The atomic theory explains how atoms combine in a constant proportion by mass. Individual atoms can lose, gain, or share only a definite number of electrons. Therefore, the mass of one element that can combine with a given mass of another element is limited. In forming hydrogen chloride, for example, only one hydrogen atom can combine with one chlorine atom. One hydrogen atom can share only 1 electron. One chlorine atom has room for only 1 electron to complete its octet of 3rd-energy-level electrons. So the ratio of these two atoms that combine can only be 1:1. It cannot be 1:2, or 3:2, or any other ratio. Consequently, a molecule of hydrogen chloride always consists of one atom of hydrogen, atomic weight 1.0079, and one atom of chlorine, atomic weight 35.453. The molecule has a molecular weight of 36.461.

Furthermore, hydrogen chloride always contains $\frac{1.0079}{36.461}$ parts by mass of hydrogen, or 2.7643% hydrogen, and $\frac{35.453}{36.461}$ parts by mass of chlorine, or 97.235% chlorine.

The law of definite composition in its present form may not hold rigorously for certain metallic sulfides and oxides under all reaction conditions.

Elements in compounds are combined in simple whole-number ratios.

A

B

Figure 7-4. Compounds formed by the same two elements combined in different proportions may have very different chemical properties. In (A), water, H_2O, is unreactive with the green felt. In (B), hydrogen peroxide, H_2O_2, bleaches the green dye in the felt.

☐ 7.10 Law of multiple proportions

It is not uncommon in chemistry for two or more compounds to be composed of the same two elements. Hydrogen and oxygen form a series of two compounds, water (H_2O) and hydrogen peroxide (H_2O_2). The constituent elements, hydrogen and oxygen, are present in each of these two compounds in unvarying but different *mass* proportions.

For water, the composition is approximately 1 part hydrogen to 8 parts oxygen. For hydrogen peroxide, the composition is 1 part hydrogen to 16 parts oxygen. Considering quantities of these two compounds *that have the same masses of hydrogen,* the relative masses of the second element (oxygen) are related *as a ratio of small whole numbers.*

Consider, for example,

$$H_2O \quad \text{1 g of H} \quad \text{and} \quad \text{8 g of O}$$
$$H_2O_2 \quad \text{1 g of H} \quad \text{and} \quad \text{16 g of O}$$

The *masses of hydrogen* in this series, 1 g and 1 g, are in the constant ratio of 1:1. The *masses of oxygen,* 8 g and 16 g, are in the simple whole-number ratio of 1:2. Now observe that the ratio of *atoms of hydrogen* in the series of two compounds is 1:1, whereas the ratio of *atoms of oxygen* is 1:2.

Iron and chlorine also form a series of two compounds that exhibit similar simple whole-number relationships. Consider

$$FeCl_2 \quad \text{56 g of Fe} \quad \text{and} \quad \text{71 g of Cl}$$
$$FeCl_3 \quad \text{56 g of Fe} \quad \text{and} \quad \text{106.5 g of Cl}$$

The *masses of iron* in this series, 56 g and 56 g, are in the constant ratio of 1:1. The *masses of chlorine,* 71 g and 106.5 g, are in the simple whole-number ratio of 2:3. Again observe that the ratio of *atoms of iron* in the series is 1:1, whereas the ratio of *atoms of chlorine* is 2:3. The **law of multiple proportions** describes such series of compounds. *If two or more different compounds composed of the same two elements are analyzed, the masses of the second element combined with a fixed mass of the first element can be expressed as a ratio of small whole numbers.*

This law was first proposed by John Dalton in connection with his atomic theory. He recognized the possibility that two kinds of atoms could combine in more than one way and in more than one proportion. But only whole atoms could be involved in such combinations. Therefore, Dalton reasoned, the masses of the second atom combined with fixed masses of the first atom would have to be in the ratio of small whole numbers. This ratio is the same as the ratio of the actual numbers of atoms of the second element combined with a fixed number of atoms of the first element. The information summarized in the law of multiple proportions is one of the strongest supports for the atomic theory.

Today scientists recognize two facts that support the law of multiple proportions. (1) Some elements exist in more than one oxidation state. (2) Some elements combine in more than one way with another element. Iron can exist in compounds as iron(II) ions with an oxidation number of +2 or as iron(III) ions with an oxidation number of +3. You have seen that iron and chlorine combine to form two different compounds: $FeCl_2$, iron(II) chloride, and $FeCl_3$, iron(III) chloride. The ratio of the numbers of atoms of chlorine combined with a single atom of iron is 2:3. As recognized by Dalton, the relative numbers of atoms that combine is proportional to the masses that combine. Therefore, the ratio of the masses of chlorine combined with a fixed mass of iron in these two compounds is also 2:3.

Analysis of the composition and molecular structure of water and hydrogen peroxide leads to these electron-dot formulas:

$$H \overset{\cdot\cdot}{\underset{\overset{\cdot\cdot}{H}}{\text{O}}}: \qquad\qquad :\overset{\overset{\text{H}}{\circ\circ}}{\underset{\cdot\cdot}{\text{O}}}:\overset{\cdot\cdot}{\underset{\overset{\cdot\cdot}{H}}{\text{O}}}:$$

water   hydrogen peroxide

These two formulas represent the two ways in which hydrogen and oxygen atoms combine. Each molecule of water contains 2 hydrogen atoms combined with only 1 oxygen atom. Each molecule of hydrogen peroxide contains 2 hydrogen atoms combined with 2 oxygen atoms. The numbers of atoms combined are proportional to the masses combined. So the ratio of the masses of oxygen combined with the same mass of hydrogen in these two compounds is 1:2, a ratio of small whole numbers.

1. Based on the constant number of 2 atoms of nitrogen, express the ratios of oxygen atoms through the binary nitrogen-oxygen series.   *ans.* N = 2:2:2:2:2; O = 1:2:3:4:5
2. Recognizing that the oxidation state of oxygen through the series is −2, assign oxidation numbers to nitrogen in each compound of the series.
   ans. O: −2 −2 −2 −2 −2; N: +1 +2 +3 +4 +5
3. Research the properties of the nitrogen-oxygen series to determine which member is (*a*) called "laughing gas" and (*b*) a major air pollutant.   *ans.* (*a*) compound with 63.6% N; (*b*) compound with 30.4% N

PRACTICE PROBLEMS

(Refer to Table 7-3)

◻ 7.11 Mole concept

Imagine that all the people on the earth were assigned the task of counting the molecules in a tablespoon of water. If each person counted at the rate of one molecule per second, it would take approximately 8×10^6 years to complete the project. The number of molecules involved staggers the imagination!

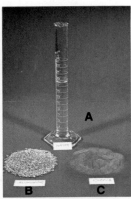

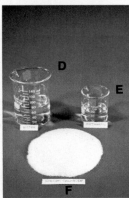

Figure 7-5. A comparison of mole quantities of several substances: (a) 1 mole (18.0 g) of H_2O; (b) 1 mole (27.0 g) of Al; (c) 1 mole (63.5 g) of Cu; (d) 4 moles (72.0 g) of H_2O; (e) 1 mole (32.0 g) of CH_3OH (methanol); and (f) 1 mole (58.5 g) of NaCl.

Fortunately, chemists are not ordinarily faced with the problem of weighing out a certain number of molecules of a compound or atoms of an element. They do frequently need to weigh out equal numbers of atoms or molecules of different substances. A knowledge of the atomic weights of the elements allows this to be done very simply.

In Sections 3.14 and 3.15, four important quantitative definitions were recognized.

1. The number of carbon-12 atoms in the defined quantity of exactly 12 grams of this nuclide is the *Avogadro number,* 6.02×10^{23}.

2. The amount of substance containing the Avogadro number of any kind of chemical unit is called a *mole* of that substance.

3. The mass in grams of one mole of naturally occurring atoms of an element is the *gram-atomic weight* of the element.

4. The numerical portion of the gram-atomic weight of an element is the *atomic weight* of the element.

It is evident from these definitions that 12 g of carbon (one gram-atomic weight) consists of 1 mole of carbon atoms, the Avogadro number of atoms. Similarly, 1.0 g of hydrogen (one gram-atomic weight) consists of 1 mole of hydrogen atoms, the Avogadro number of atoms. These two quantities, 12 g of carbon and 1.0 g of hydrogen, contain the same number of atoms. Thus, any given masses of carbon and hydrogen that are in the ratio of 12:1 (the ratio of their atomic weights) must also have the same number of atoms.

To obtain 5.0 moles of oxygen atoms, 5.0×16 g $= 8\bar{0}$ g of oxygen must be measured. To obtain 5.0 moles of sulfur atoms, 5.0×32 g $= 160$ g of sulfur must be measured. These two quantities, $8\bar{0}$ g of oxygen and 160 g of sulfur, contain the same number of atoms. Observe that the ratio of these masses equals the ratio of the atomic weights of the elements

$$\frac{8\bar{0} \text{ g}}{160 \text{ g}} = \frac{16}{32} = \frac{1}{2}$$

Using similar logic and the atomic weights of other elements, the following important generalization can be recognized: *If the mass quantities of two elements are in the same ratio as their atomic weights, they contain the same number of atoms.* Recall that quantities of substances are measured in gram (mass) units. These masses of substances are sometimes referred to as "weights" because "weighing" methods are used to determine them. However, you should remember that quantities measured in gram units are, in fact, mass quantities. Atomic weights that express the average relative masses of atoms of different elements are most useful when they are expressed in gram units. *The **gram-atomic weight** of an element is the mass of one mole of atoms of that element.* Thus, the mass of one mole of O atoms is 16 g of oxygen, of one mole of S atoms is 32 g of sulfur, and of one mole of Fe atoms is 56 g of iron.

The mole concept is extended to include the molecules of molecular substances. Oxygen, O_2, is one of several elemental gases composed of *diatomic molecules.* One mole of O_2 molecules consists of two moles of O atoms. Two moles of O atoms have a mass of 2×16 g $= 32$ g. Consequently, one mole of O_2 molecules must have this same mass of 32 g. This value is the molecular weight of O_2, 32, expressed in gram units. *The mass of a molecular substance expressed in grams equal to its molecular weight is its* **gram-molecular weight.** An extension of this logic leads to the observation that one mole of H_2 molecules has a mass of 2.0 g, and one mole of Cl_2 molecules has a mass of 71.0 g. Thus, *the gram-molecular weight of a diatomic molecular element is the mass of one mole of molecules of that element.* Observe that one mole of O atoms has a mass of 16 g, but one mole of O_2 molecules has a mass of 32 g. Also observe that 16 g of O atoms, 32 g of O_2 molecules, 1.0 g of H atoms, 2.0 g of H_2 molecules, 35.5 g of Cl atoms, and 71.0 g of Cl_2 molecules all consist of the same number of *particles—* atoms or molecules, as the case may be.

One mole of H_2O molecules contains two moles of H atoms and one mole of O atoms. Two moles of H atoms has a mass of 2.0 g; one mole of O atoms has a mass of 16 g. Thus, by addition, one mole of H_2O molecules has a mass of 18 g. This mass is the gram-molecular weight of water. One mole of methane, CH_4, contains one mole of C atoms and four moles of H atoms. One mole of C atoms has a mass of 12 g; four moles of H atoms has a mass of 4 g. One mole of CH_4 molecules has a mass, then, of 16 g, its gram-molecular weight. From these examples, it is evident that the *gram-molecular weight of a molecular substance*

Gram-molecular weight is the gram-formula weight of a molecular substance.

Table 7-4
MASS-MOLE RELATIONSHIPS

---

1 gross = 144 objects

If you compare	
144 erasers @ 10.0 g each = 1440 g	The masses of the gross-quantity packages are different because the mass of each kind of object is different. However, the ratios between the masses of the packages, 1440 g: 720 g: 43200 g, are the same as the ratios between the masses of the individual objects, 10.0 g: 5.0 g: 300 g, since each package contains the same number of objects.
144 pencils @ 5.0 g each = 720 g	
144 tablets @ 300 g each = 43200 g	

1 mole = 6.02×10^{23} particles

If you compare	
6.02×10^{23} helium atoms = 4.0 g	The mass of the mole varies just as the mass of the gross varies. It depends upon what the particles are. However, the ratios between the masses of the moles are the same as the ratios between the masses of the individual particles since each mole contains the same number of particles.
6.02×10^{23} hydrogen molecules = 2.0 g	
6.02×10^{23} water molecules = 18.0 g	
6.02×10^{23} NaCl formula units = 58.5 g	

is the mass of one mole of molecules of the substance. There is the same number of molecules in 32 g of O_2, 18 g of H_2O, and 16 g of CH_4. One-mole quantities of all molecular substances contain the same number of molecules, the Avogadro number, 6.02×10^{23} molecules. It follows that *any mass quantities* of oxygen, water, and methane that are in the ratio 32:18:16 *contain equal numbers of molecules.*

The mole concept is also extended to include ionic substances that are expressed by empirical formulas. For example, the *gram-formula weight* (formula weight in grams) of sodium chloride is 23.0 g + 35.5 g = 58.5 g. One mole of sodium atoms (as Na^+ ions) has a mass of 23.0 g; one mole of chlorine atoms (as Cl^- ions) has a mass of 35.5 g. Thus, 58.5 g is the mass of one mole of sodium chloride. One mole of sodium chloride contains one mole of Na^+ ions *and* one mole of Cl^- ions.

The symbol for an element not only represents one atom of the element, but also the mass of one mole of atoms of that element. A formula for a diatomic molecule of an element represents one molecule of that element. The formula also represents the mass of one mole of these molecules. Similarly, the formula for a compound represents the mass of one mole of that compound as well as its composition. These mole relationships are summarized in Table 7-5.

Gram-formula weights are formula weights expressed in grams.

The simplest whole-number ratio of the atoms of different elements in a compound provides its empirical formula.

☐ 7.12 Determining the empirical formula of a compound

The empirical formula for a compound consists of the symbols for the constituent elements in their smallest whole-number ratio. In Section 7.8 you learned how to determine the percentage composition of a compound from its formula. You will now learn how to determine the formula for a compound from its percentage composition, obtained experimentally by chemical analysis.

This is the method by which most empirical formulas are originally determined. A compound is analyzed to identify the elements present and to determine their mass ratios or the percentage composition. The empirical formula is then calculated from this information. By knowing the mass per mole of atoms (gram-atomic weight) of each element, the mass ratios are reduced to atom ratios.

Edward W. Morley (1838–1923) of Western Reserve University found that 1.0000 part by mass of hydrogen combines with 7.9396 parts by mass of oxygen to form 8.9396 parts by mass of water vapor. Every 8.9396 parts of water formed requires 1.0000 part of hydrogen and 7.9396 parts of oxygen. Thus, water consists of

$$\frac{\text{1.0000 part H}}{\text{8.9396 parts water}} \times 100\% \text{ water} = 11.186\% \text{ hydrogen}$$

Figure 7-6. Edward W. Morley was a skillful chemical analyst. His very precise determinations of the densities of oxygen and hydrogen and of the mass ratio in which they combine, published in 1895, were the results of 12 years of research.

Table 7-5
THE MOLE CONCEPT

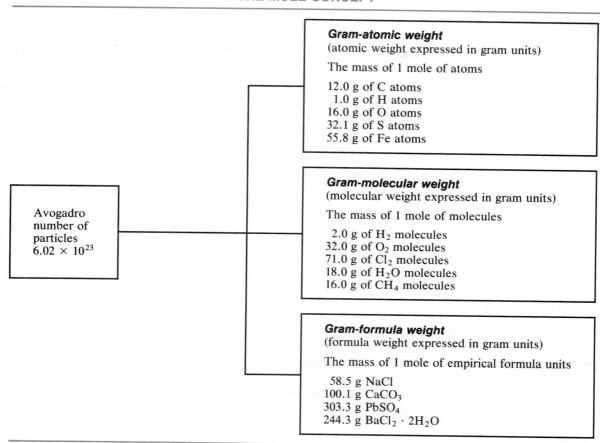

Gram-atomic weight
(atomic weight expressed in gram units)

The mass of 1 mole of atoms

12.0 g of C atoms
1.0 g of H atoms
16.0 g of O atoms
32.1 g of S atoms
55.8 g of Fe atoms

Gram-molecular weight
(molecular weight expressed in gram units)

The mass of 1 mole of molecules

2.0 g of H_2 molecules
32.0 g of O_2 molecules
71.0 g of Cl_2 molecules
18.0 g of H_2O molecules
16.0 g of CH_4 molecules

Gram-formula weight
(formula weight expressed in gram units)

The mass of 1 mole of empirical formula units

58.5 g NaCl
100.1 g $CaCO_3$
303.3 g $PbSO_4$
244.3 g $BaCl_2 \cdot 2H_2O$

Avogadro number of particles 6.02×10^{23}

and

$$\frac{7.9396 \text{ parts O}}{8.9396 \text{ parts water}} \times 100\% \text{ water} = 88.814\% \text{ oxygen}$$

From these data the relative number of atoms of hydrogen and oxygen in water is easily determined. This is done by comparing the mass percentages of the elements or their actual masses by analysis to their respective gram-atomic weights (masses per mole of atoms).

$$\frac{\text{mass of the element}}{\text{mass of 1 mole of atoms of the element}} = \text{moles of atoms of an element}$$

1. From percentage composition data. The simplest way to think of percentage composition is in terms of *parts per hundred.* Morley's experiments show that (rounding to 3 significant figures) 11.2% of water is hydrogen and 88.8% is oxygen. In other words,

100.0 parts of water consists of 11.2 parts hydrogen and 88.8 parts oxygen. Similarly, there are 11.2 g of hydrogen and 88.8 g of oxygen per 100.0 g of water. How many moles of hydrogen and oxygen atoms are present in 100.0 g of water?

$$H: \quad \frac{11.2 \text{ g H}}{1.01 \text{ g/mole}} = 11.1 \text{ moles H}$$

$$O: \quad \frac{88.8 \text{ g O}}{16.0 \text{ g/mole}} = 5.55 \text{ moles O}$$

Recall that 1 mole of atoms of one element is the same number of atoms as 1 mole of atoms of any other element (the Avogadro number). Therefore, the relative number of atoms is

$$H \;:\; O = 11.1 \;:\; 5.55$$

2. From relative mass data. Because approximate atomic weights are used, Morley's relative masses are rounded off to 1.00 part hydrogen and 7.94 parts oxygen in 8.94 parts water. Accordingly, each 8.94-g quantity of water produced requires 1.00 g of hydrogen and 7.94 g of oxygen. As before, the numbers of moles of hydrogen and oxygen atoms in 8.94 g of water are determined and then reduced to the relative number of atoms of each constituent element.

$$H: \quad \frac{1.00 \text{ g H}}{1.01 \text{ g/mole}} = 0.990 \text{ mole H}$$

$$O: \quad \frac{7.94 \text{ g O}}{16.0 \text{ g/mole}} = 0.496 \text{ mole O}$$

The relative number of atoms is

$$H \;:\; O = 0.990 \;:\; 0.496$$

From these calculations, the empirical formula of water can be written as

$$H_{11.1}O_{5.55} \quad \text{or} \quad H_{0.990}O_{0.496}$$

To find an empirical formula:
1. *Convert gram ratio to mole ratio.*
2. *Adjust mole ratio to simplest whole-number ratio.*

Both formulas show the correct ratio of hydrogen atoms to oxygen atoms in the compound water. However, according to the atomic theory, only whole atoms combine chemically. These atom ratios must be converted to their simplest whole-number values. This is accomplished by dividing each ratio by its smaller term, shown as

$$
\begin{array}{ccc}
H & : & O \\[4pt]
\dfrac{11.1}{5.55} & : & \dfrac{5.55}{5.55} \\[8pt]
2.00 & : & 1.00
\end{array}
$$

and

$$\begin{array}{ccc} \textbf{H} & \textbf{:} & \textbf{O} \\[4pt] \dfrac{0.990}{0.496} & \textbf{:} & \dfrac{0.496}{0.496} \\[6pt] 2.00 & \textbf{:} & 1.00 \end{array}$$

The empirical formula for water is, therefore, H_2O.

Sometimes the operation just performed does not yield a simple whole-number ratio. In such instances the simplest whole-number ratio can be found by expressing the result as fractions and clearing. **CAUTION:** In some problems, dividing by the smallest term may result in such ratios as $1:2.01$, $1:2.98$, or $1:3.99$. In such situations, do not attempt to clear the fractions; simply round off to 2, 3, or 4, respectively. The whole-number ratios are then $1:2$, $1:3$, and $1:4$. These operations are illustrated in the Sample Problems that follow.

 SAMPLE PROBLEM

A compound is found by analysis to contain 75.0% carbon and 25.0% hydrogen. What is the empirical formula?

 SOLUTION

Since the compound is 75.0% carbon (75.0 parts/100.0), 75.0 g per 100.0 g is carbon. Similarly 25.0 g per 100.0 g of the compound is hydrogen. The number of moles of atoms of each element in 100.0 g of the compound is determined by the following expression:

$$\frac{\text{mass of the element}}{\text{mass of 1 mole of atoms of the element}} = \text{moles of atoms of an element}$$

C: $\qquad\qquad\qquad \dfrac{75.0 \text{ g C}}{12.0 \text{ g/mole}} = \textbf{6.25 moles C}$

H: $\qquad\qquad\qquad \dfrac{25.0 \text{ g H}}{1.01 \text{ g/mole}} = \textbf{24.8 moles H}$

Relative number of atoms: $\quad$ C:H $= 6.25:24.8$

Smallest ratio of atoms: $\dfrac{6.25}{6.25} : \dfrac{24.8}{6.25} = 1:4$

$$\text{Empirical formula} = CH_4$$

◐ | **SAMPLE PROBLEM**

A compound contains carbon, 81.7%, and hydrogen, 18.3%. Find the empirical formula.

◐ | **SOLUTION**

Each 100.0-g quantity of the compound contains 81.7 g of carbon and 18.3 g of hydrogen, as shown by the percentage composition.

$$\frac{\text{mass of the element}}{\text{mass of 1 mole of atoms of the element}} = \text{moles of atoms of an element}$$

C: $\qquad \dfrac{81.7 \text{ g C}}{12.0 \text{ g/mole}} = 6.81 \text{ moles C}$

H: $\qquad \dfrac{18.3 \text{ g H}}{1.01 \text{ g/mole}} = 18.1 \text{ moles H}$

Relative number of atoms: C:H = 6.81:18.1

Smallest ratio of atoms: $\dfrac{6.81}{6.81}$: $\dfrac{18.1}{6.81}$ = 1:2.66

Simplest whole number ratio: $1:2.66 = 1:2\frac{2}{3} = \frac{3}{3}:\frac{8}{3} = 3:8$

Empirical formula = C_3H_8

◐ | **SAMPLE PROBLEM**

The decomposition of 11.47 g of a compound of copper and oxygen yields 9.16 g of copper. What is the empirical formula for the compound?

◐ | **SOLUTION**

Since the compound is composed of only copper and oxygen, the mass of oxygen removed in the decomposition process must be

$$11.47 \text{ g} - 9.16 \text{ g} = 2.31 \text{ g oxygen}$$

$$\frac{\text{mass of the element}}{\text{mass of 1 mole of atoms of the element}} = \text{moles of atoms of an element}$$

Cu: $\qquad \dfrac{9.16 \text{ g Cu}}{63.5 \text{ g/mole}} = 0.144 \text{ mole Cu}$

O: $\qquad \dfrac{2.31 \text{ g O}}{16.0 \text{ g/mole}} = 0.144 \text{ mole O}$

Relative number of atoms: Cu:O = 0.144:0.144

Smallest ratio of atoms: 1:1

Empirical formula = CuO

1. A 100-g sample of a compound is found by analysis to contain 39.3 g of sodium and 60.7 g of chlorine. Find its empirical formula.   *ans*. NaCl
2. Analysis: hydrogen, 2.77%; chlorine, 97.3%. What is the empirical formula?   *ans*. HCl
3. Analysis: hydrogen, 5.92%; sulfur, 94.1%. What is the empirical formula?   *ans*. H_2S
4. Analysis: calcium, 20.0%; bromine, 80.0%. What is the empirical formula?   *ans*. $CaBr_2$
5. Analysis: nitrogen, 9.66%; hydrogen, 2.79%; iodine, 87.6%. Find the empirical formula.   *ans*. NH_4I

❏ 7.13 Finding the molecular formula   •

The analysis of a substance enables you to determine its empirical formula. This simplest formula may or may not be the molecular formula. You calculated the empirical formula for the gas methane as CH_4. Any multiple of CH_4, such as C_2H_8, C_3H_{12}, or C_nH_{4n}, represents the same ratio of carbon and hydrogen atoms. How then can the correct molecular formula be determined?

It is not possible to decide which is the true formula unless the molecular weight of the substance has been determined. Some substances lend themselves to known methods of determining molecular weights and some do not. These methods will be discussed in Chapters 11 and 13. But if the molecular weight is known, it is a simple matter to decide which multiple of the empirical formula is the molecular formula.

The correct multiple of the empirical formula can be represented by the subscript $_x$. Then

Molecular weight must be known before a molecular formula can be determined.

(empirical formula)$_x$ = molecular formula

and (empirical formula weight)$_x$ can be equated to the known molecular weight.

(empirical formula weight)$_x$ = molecular weight

In the case of methane, the molecular weight is known to be 16.0. The equation is

$$(CH_4 \text{ weight})_x = 16.0$$

$$[12.0 + 4(1.0)]_x = 16.0$$

$$x = 1$$

molecular formula = $(CH_4)_1$ or CH_4

Molecular weight is a whole-number multiple of the empirical formula weight.

Hence the empirical formula for methane is also the molecular formula. You have seen that this is also true in the case of water. For another example, see the Sample Problem that follows.

SAMPLE PROBLEM

Hydrogen peroxide is found by analysis to consist of 5.9% hydrogen and 94.1% oxygen. Its molecular weight is determined to be 34.0. What is the correct formula?

SOLUTION

1. The empirical formula, determined from the analysis by the method described in Section 7.12, is

$$HO$$

2. The molecular formula determined from the empirical formula and molecular weight is

$$(HO \text{ weight})_x = 34.0$$

$$(1.0 + 16.0)_x = 34.0$$

$$x = 2$$

$$\text{molecular formula} = (HO)_2 \text{ or } H_2O_2$$

SUMMARY

The formulas for common ionic compounds can be written using the ion-charge method. The ion notations are written in the order used in the name of the compound. The number of each kind of ion is then adjusted to make the total positive and negative ionic charges equal.

The names of ionic compounds include the names of the constituent ions. If the metallic ion present has different possible oxidation states, Roman numerals are added to the name of the ion to indicate the oxidation state. A system of prefixes is used in the names of covalent compounds when an element forms more than one compound with another element. For binary compounds, the *-ide* ending means that only two elements are present.

The gram-atomic weights of elements and the gram-formula weights of compounds represent the mass of a mole of these substances.

The percentage composition of a compound can be calculated if the formula is known. Conversely, the empirical formula can be calculated if the composition of a compound is known. Furthermore, if the compound is molecular and its molecular weight is known, the molecular formula can be determined.

VOCABULARY

binary compounds
formula weight
gram-atomic weight
gram-formula weight

gram-molecular weight
law of multiple proportions
molecular weight
percentage composition

◖ QUESTIONS

Group A

1. What is the full significance of the molecular formula for ammonia, NH_3?
2. Why is *formula weight* a more general term than *molecular weight?*
3. What is the symbol and charge of (a) sodium ion; (b) copper(I) ion; (c) iron(III) ion; (d) nickel(II) ion; (e) lead(II) ion; (f) iron(II) ion; (g) chloride ion; (h) oxide ion; (i) sulfide ion; (j) iodide ion; (k) copper(II) ion; (l) potassium ion; (m) silver ion; (n) mercury(I) ion.
4. What are the names and charges of these polyatomic ions: (a) NH_4; (b) SO_4; (c) NO_3; (d) CO_3; (e) $C_2H_3O_2$; (f) Cr_2O_7; (g) ClO_3; (h) HSO_4; (i) OH; (j) NO_2.
5. What is the symbol or formula and charge of (a) hydrogen carbonate ion; (b) bromide ion; (c) chromate ion; (d) sulfite ion; (e) phosphate ion; (f) peroxide ion; (g) magnesium ion; (h) zinc ion; (i) barium ion; (j) fluoride ion.
6. Write formulas for (a) barium chloride; (b) calcium oxide; (c) magnesium sulfate; (d) silver bromide; (e) zinc carbonate.
7. Name these compounds: (a) $NaHCO_3$; (b) K_2O_2; (c) $HgCl_2$; (d) $Fe(OH)_3$; (e) $Ni(C_2H_3O_2)_2$.
8. Write the formulas for these compounds: (a) ammonium nitrate; (b) aluminum sulfide; (c) copper(II) hydroxide; (d) lead(II) phosphate; (e) iron(III) sulfate.
9. Name these compounds: (a) $CuCl_2$; (b) CaS; (c) $KHSO_4$; (d) $NaNO_2$; (e) $Ni_3(PO_4)_2$.
10. Write the formulas for these compounds: (a) chromium(III) fluoride; (b) nickel(II) chlorate; (c) potassium hydrogen carbonate; (d) calcium chromate; (e) mercury(II) iodide.
11. Name these compounds: (a) Na_2O_2; (b) NH_4NO_2; (c) $Mg_3(PO_4)_2$; (d) $FeSO_4$; (e) Ag_2CO_3; (f) Na_2O; (g) Hg_2Cl_2; (h) $HgCl_2$; (i) H_2O_2.
12. Write the formulas for (a) sodium hydrogen sulfate; (b) lead(II) chromate; (c) copper(I) chloride; (d) mercury(I) nitrate; (e) iron(II) oxide.
13. Name the following: (a) K_2SO_4; (b) $BaCr_2O_7$; (c) $Cr(OH)_3$; (d) $PbBr_2$; (e) HgI_2.
14. What is the formula for (a) aluminum hydroxide; (b) copper(I) oxide; (c) ammonium sulfide; (d) lead(II) acetate; (e) iron(III) bromide?
15. Write the formulas for (a) magnesium hydrogen carbonate; (b) silver sulfide; (c) potassium sulfite; (d) chromium(III) sulfate; (e) sodium phosphate.

Group B

16. How are percentage composition, the law of definite composition, and the atomic theory related?
17. How is the law of multiple proportions related to the atomic theory?
18. Write the names for these compounds according to the system for naming binary compounds: (a) SO_3; (b) $SiCl_4$; (c) PBr_3; (d) As_2O_5; (e) PbO.
19. Write the formulas for these compounds: (a) sulfur dioxide; (b) bismuth trichloride; (c) manganese dioxide; (d) arsenic pentaiodide; (e) carbon tetraiodide.
20. Name these compounds: (a) CO; (b) CO_2; (c) CBr_4; (d) N_2O_3; (e) N_2O_5.

◖ PROBLEMS

Group A

1. What is the formula weight of hydrazine, N_2H_4?
2. Find the formula weight of sulfuric acid, H_2SO_4.
3. Dextrose, or grape sugar, has the formula $C_6H_{12}O_6$. Determine its formula weight.
4. Find the formula weight of ethyl alcohol, C_2H_5OH.
5. Calcium phosphate has the formula $Ca_3(PO_4)_2$. Determine the formula weight.

6. Crystallized magnesium sulfate, or Epsom salts, has the formula $MgSO_4 \cdot 7H_2O$. What is its formula weight?

7. Determine the formula weight for each of these compounds: (a) HNO_3; (b) $NaOH$; (c) HgO; (d) $CuSO_4 \cdot 5H_2O$; (e) $HC_2H_3O_2$; (f) $MgBr_2$; (g) Al_2S_3; (h) $Ca(NO_3)_2$; (i) $Fe_2(Cr_2O_7)_3$; (j) $KMnO_4$.

8. Vinegar contains acetic acid, $HC_2H_3O_2$. Find its percentage composition.

9. All baking powders contain sodium hydrogen carbonate, $NaHCO_3$. Calculate its percentage composition.

10. What is the percentage composition of a soap having the formula $C_{17}H_{35}COONa$?

11. What is the percentage composition of each of these compounds: (a) SO_2; (b) $Ca(OH)_2$; (c) $Ca(H_2PO_4)_2 \cdot H_2O$; (d) $MgSO_4 \cdot 7H_2O$?

12. Which of these compounds contains the highest percentage of nitrogen: (a) $Ca(NO_3)_2$; (b) $CaCN_2$; or (c) $(NH_4)_2SO_4$?

13. A strip of pure copper, mass 6.356 g, is heated with oxygen to form a compound of copper and oxygen, mass 7.956 g. What is the compound's percentage composition?

14. Calculate the mass of (a) 1.00 mole of chlorine atoms; (b) 5.00 moles of nitrogen atoms; (c) 3.00 moles of bromine molecules; (d) 6.00 moles of hydrogen chloride; (e) 10.0 moles of magnesium sulfate; (f) 2.50 moles of potassium iodide; (g) 0.500 mole of silver nitrate; (h) 0.100 mole of sodium chloride.

15. You are given 25.0 g of (a) CaO; (b) $Na_2CO_3 \cdot 10H_2O$; (c) $BaCl_2 \cdot 2H_2O$; (d) $(NH_4)_2SO_4$; (e) $Fe(NO_3)_3 \cdot 6H_2O$; (f) $Al_2(SO_4)_3 \cdot 18H_2O$; (g) K_2CrO_4. How many moles of each do you have?

16. How many moles of iron can be recovered from 1.000 metric ton (1000 kg) of Fe_3O_4?

17. Cinnabar, an ore of mercury, has the formula HgS. Calculate the number of moles of mercury recovered from 1.00 kg of cinnabar.

18. Calculate the percentage of copper in each of these minerals: cuprite, Cu_2O; malachite, $CuCO_3 \cdot Cu(OH)_2$; and cubanite, $CuFe_2S_4$.

19. Calculate the percentage of CaO in $CaCO_3$.

20. Calculate the percentage of H_2O in $CuSO_4 \cdot 5H_2O$.

Group B

21. One compound of platinum and chlorine is known to consist of 42.1% chlorine. Another consists of 26.7% chlorine. What are the two empirical formulas?

22. What is the empirical formula for silver fluoride, which is 85% silver?

23. What is the percentage composition of the drug Chloromycetin, $C_{11}H_{12}N_2O_5Cl_2$?

24. Analysis: phosphorus, 43.67%; oxygen, 56.33%. What is the empirical formula?

25. Analysis: potassium, 24.58%; manganese, 34.81%; oxygen, 40.50%. What is the empirical formula?

26. Calculate the empirical formula for a compound having 37.70% sodium, 22.95% silicon, and 39.34% oxygen.

27. A compound has the composition: Na, 28.05%; C, 29.26%; H, 3.66%; O, 39.02%. What is the empirical formula?

28. The analysis of a compound shows the following: nitrogen, 21.20%; hydrogen, 6.06%; sulfur, 24.30%; oxygen, 48.45%. Find the simplest formula.

29. A compound has this composition: potassium, 44.82%; sulfur, 18.39%; oxygen, 36.79%. Determine its empirical formula.

30. A compound has the following composition: calcium, 24.7%; hydrogen, 1.2%; carbon, 14.8%; oxygen, 59.3%. What is its empirical formula?

31. An oxide of iron has the following composition: Fe = 72.4%, O = 27.6%. Determine its empirical formula.

32. The analysis of a gas reveals this composition: C, 92.3%; H, 7.7%. Its molecular weight is 26.0. What is the molecular formula?

33. Analysis of a compound reveals this composition: 80% C and 20% H. Its molecular weight is 30.0. What is its molecular formula?

34. By analysis, a compound is found to be 76.0% iodine and 24.0% oxygen. Its molecular weight is 334. (a) Determine the molecular formula. (b) What is the oxidation state of iodine in this iodine-oxygen compound?

35. The percentages by mass of carbon in its two oxides are 42.8% and 27.3%. Use these data to illustrate the law of multiple proportions.

Equations and Mass Relationships

The 1700's was a period of upheaval in the Western world. The British colonies in America were fighting for independence, while in France the storming of the Bastille ended the reign of Louis XVI. A new order was established in the sciences also; alchemy became the science of chemistry. Credit for this liberation belongs to one man above all others, Antoine Lavoisier. A French nobleman with a keen interest in science, Lavoisier appreciated the important role measurement plays in understanding the natural world. When studying chemical reactions, Lavoisier was careful to measure the quantities of the reactants and the products. So doing, he discovered one of the most important laws in chemistry: The weight of the products of a chemical reaction is no more, or no less, then the weight of the initial substances. Using this law, he and other chemists changed the way in which matter was studied.

◻ 8.1 Writing equations

The most useful way of representing the chemical changes that occur during chemical reactions is by writing *chemical equations*. A **balanced chemical equation** is a concise, symbolized expression for a chemical reaction. It is a *quantitative* statement which indicates the proportionate number of moles of each chemical species that enters into the reaction and is formed by the reaction.

The first step in writing chemical equations involves describing the basic facts of the reaction systems in *word equations*.

1. Word equations. This verbal equation is a brief statement that gives the names of the chemical species involved in the reaction. In a reaction system, the chemical species that react are called the *reactants*, and the species that are formed are called the *products*. The word equation does not give the *quantities* of reactants used or products formed. Thus, a word equation has only *qualitative*, or descriptive, significance.

Experiments show that the combustion of hydrogen, whether in air or in an atmosphere of pure oxygen, produces water as the only combustion product. The word equation for this combustion reaction is

hydrogen + oxygen → water

The arrow (→) in this expression is the "yields" sign. It conveys the information that a chemical reaction occurs. It is read, "*react to yield,*" or just "*yields.*" The word equation is ordinarily read, "*hydrogen and oxygen react to yield water,*"

CHEMICAL EQUATIONS

In this chapter you will gain an understanding of:

- **the difference between word equations and formula equations in terms of the information each provides**
- **the significance of balanced chemical equations**
- **the procedure in writing balanced chemical equations**
- **the four general types of chemical reactions**
- **the activity series of the elements and its use in predicting reactions and completing equations**
- **stoichiometry and the solution of mass-mass problems by the mole method**

Chemical equations are the means by which chemists represent chemical reactions.

Figure 8-1. A mixture of zinc and iodine reacts chemically under favorable conditions to form zinc iodide. The reaction is represented by the chemical equation $Zn + I_2 \rightarrow ZnI_2$.

The balanced formula equation is commonly referred to as the chemical equation.

$$2H_2 + O_2 \rightarrow 2H_2O$$

2 molecules hydrogen	+	1 molecule oxygen	→	2 molecules water
2 moles hydrogen	+	1 mole oxygen	→	2 moles water
4 grams hydrogen	+	32 grams oxygen	→	36 grams water
any mass quantity of hydrogen	+	mass of oxygen in ratio 8:1 with mass of hydrogen	→	mass of water in ratio 9:1 with mass of hydrogen

Figure 8-2. The chemical equation is a symbolized expression of a chemical reaction that indicates the proportionate number of quantity units of each chemical species in the reaction system.

or simply, *"hydrogen and oxygen yield water."* The word equation signifies that hydrogen and oxygen react chemically to form water. Thus, it briefly states an experimental fact. It does not specify the conditions under which the reaction occurs, the relative quantities of hydrogen and oxygen used, and the relative quantity of water formed.

2. Formula equations. Suppose you replace the names of the reactants, hydrogen and oxygen, and the name of the product, water, with their respective formulas. The equation becomes

$$H_2 + O_2 \rightarrow H_2O \quad \textbf{(not balanced)}$$

The law of conservation of matter and energy is fundamental in science. From this law a very useful generalization results: *In ordinary chemical reactions, the total mass of the reacting substances is equal to the total mass of the products formed.* This statement may be referred to as **the law of conservation of atoms.**

By adjusting for the relative quantities of reactants and products as found by experiment, the equation can be written as a *balanced formula equation.* This equation agrees with the law of conservation of atoms.

$$2H_2 + O_2 \rightarrow 2H_2O$$

This agreement is verified by comparing the total number of atoms of hydrogen and oxygen on the left side of the reaction sign ($\rightarrow$) to their respective totals on the right. Two molecules of hydrogen contains 4 atoms of hydrogen; two molecules of water also contains 4 hydrogen atoms. One molecule of oxygen contains 2 atoms of oxygen; two molecules of water also contains 2 oxygen atoms. Thus a chemical equation is similar to an algebraic equation. They both express equalities. *Until it is balanced, a chemical equation cannot express a chemical equality and is not a valid equation.* The yields sign ($\rightarrow$) has the meaning of an equals sign ($=$). In addition, the yields sign indicates the direction in which the reaction proceeds.

3. Significance of equations. This chemical equation now signifies much more than a word equation. It tells you

(*a*) the relative proportions of the reactants, hydrogen and oxygen, and the product, water, and

(*b*) that **2 molecules** of hydrogen react with **1 molecule** of oxygen to form **2 molecules** of water.

Most importantly, because one mole of a molecular substance contains the Avogadro number of molecules, the equation tells you

(*c*) that **2 moles** of hydrogen molecules reacts with **1 mole** of oxygen molecules to form **2 moles** of water molecules.

Because the mass of one mole of a molecular substance is its gram-molecular weight, the equation tells you

(*d*) that **4 g** of hydrogen reacts with **32 g** of oxygen to form **36 g** of water.

Furthermore, since these are proportionate, the equation tells you

(*e*) that any masses of hydrogen and oxygen that are in the ratio of **1:8,** respectively, and that react to form water yield a mass of water that is related to the masses of hydrogen and oxygen as **1:8:9.**

Finally, in any equation the equality exists in both directions. If $x + y = z$, then $z = x + y$. Therefore, the equation tells you

(*f*) that the decomposition of **2 moles** of water yields **2 moles** of hydrogen and **1 mole** of oxygen.

From these six statements it is clear that balanced formula equations have quantitative significance. These chemical equations represent experimentally established facts about reactions. They indicate the identities and relative quantities of reactants and products in a chemical reaction system. However, equations reveal nothing about the mechanisms by which the reactants become restructured into the products.

It is possible to write an equation for a reaction that does not occur. For example, gold and oxygen *do not* react directly to form gold(III) oxide, Au_2O_3. Yet an equation for the nonreaction can be written and balanced to conform with the law of conservation of atoms. Even though the equation is properly written and balanced, it is invalid because it is contrary to known facts.

Quantitative information relates to the measured quantities of reactants and products in a reaction system.

◻ 8.2 Factors in equation writing

A chemical equation has no value unless it is accurate in every detail. Three factors must be considered in writing a balanced equation.

1. The equation must represent the facts. If you are to write the equation for a reaction, you need to know the facts concerning the reaction. You need to know all the reactants and all the products. The chemist relies upon analysis for these facts.

2. The equation must include the symbols and formulas for all elements and compounds that are used as reactants and formed as products. You must know these symbols and formulas and be sure that they are correctly written. The elements that exist as diatomic molecules are oxygen, hydrogen, nitrogen, fluorine, chlorine, bromine, and iodine. These elements are listed in Table 8-1 for review purposes. Other elements are usually considered to be monatomic (one-atomed) structures. Your knowledge of the oxidation states of the elements and the ion-charge method of writing correct formulas will enable you to satisfy this requirement for correct symbols and formulas.

Table 8-1
ELEMENTS WITH DIATOMIC MOLECULES

Element	Symbol	Atomic number	Molecular formula	Structural formula	Phase at room temperature
hydrogen	H	1	H_2	H—H	gas
nitrogen	N	7	N_2	N≡N	gas
oxygen	O	8	O_2	O=O	gas
fluorine	F	9	F_2	F—F	gas
chlorine	Cl	17	Cl_2	Cl—Cl	gas
bromine	Br	35	Br_2	Br—Br	liquid
iodine	I	53	I_2	I—I	solid

3. *The law of conservation of atoms must be satisfied.* There must be the same number of atoms of each species represented on each side of the equation. A new species of atom cannot be represented on the product side and no species of atom can disappear from the reactant side. These are the *balancing requirements*. They are met by adjusting the *coefficients* of the formulas of reactants and products. You must adjust these coefficients to the *smallest possible whole numbers* that satisfy the law of conservation of atoms.

Balanced equations have
1. *the chemical facts.*
2. *correct formulas.*
3. *atoms conserved.*

☐ 8.3 Procedure in writing equations

To write the chemical equation that represents a chemical reaction, you must proceed in steps that satisfy the three factors in equation writing identified in Section 8.2.

1. *Represent the facts.*

2. *Write correct formulas for compounds balanced as to oxidation number or ion charge.* (Formulas for elemental substances with diatomic molecules must also be correctly written.)

3. *Balance the equation according to the law of conservation of atoms.*

Consider the chemical reactions that follow and write the chemical equation for each reaction described. When an electric current is passed through water made slightly conductive, the elements hydrogen and oxygen are formed as decomposition products. First represent the facts by the word equation. Then write and balance the formula equation for this reaction.

Step 1: What are the facts? The only reactant is water and the only products are hydrogen and oxygen. The word equation is

water → hydrogen + oxygen

Now substitute the formulas for these substances.

$$H_2O \rightarrow H_2 + O_2 \quad \textbf{(not balanced)}$$

Step 2: Are the formulas correctly written? The oxidation number of hydrogen is +1 and of oxygen −2. Thus the for-

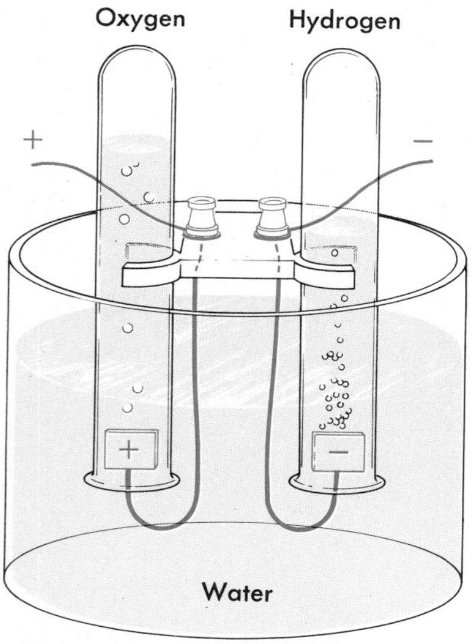

Oxygen   Hydrogen

Figure 8-3. The decomposition of water to hydrogen and oxygen by means of an electric current. Hydrogen is collected at the negative electrode, and oxygen is collected at the positive electrode.

mula for water is correctly written as H_2O. Both hydrogen and oxygen exist in the free state as diatomic molecules; their molecular formulas are correctly written as H_2 and O_2.

Step 3: Is the equation balanced as to atoms? On the left, 1 molecule of water is represented. It consists of 2 hydrogen atoms and 1 oxygen atom. On the right of the yields sign ($\rightarrow$), 1 molecule of hydrogen consisting of 2 atoms and 1 molecule of oxygen consisting of 2 atoms are represented. However, *there is only 1 atom of oxygen on the left.* How can this difference be reconciled? A subscript $_2$ may *not* be added to the oxygen of the water formula since this subscript would change a formula that is now correctly written. *Once the formulas of the substances in the equation are written correctly, their subscripts must not be changed.* This rule applies because the number of atoms in a molecule is an established experimental fact. However, the number of molecules or moles of a substance in an equation can be changed by changing the coefficient.

Change coefficients, not subscripts, to balance atoms in an equation.

Suppose the number of water molecules is increased to 2. This change can be made by placing the coefficient 2 ahead of the formula H_2O, making it $2H_2O$. Now the equation shows 2 molecules of water, each having 1 oxygen atom. This change gives the necessary 2 atoms of oxygen on the left.

$$2H_2O \rightarrow H_2 + O_2 \quad \textbf{(not balanced)}$$

Two molecules of water have a total of 4 atoms of hydrogen. The right side of the equation must now be adjusted to represent 4 atoms of hydrogen. This is accomplished by placing the coefficient 2 ahead of the hydrogen molecule, making it $2H_2$. There is now a total of 4 atoms of hydrogen represented on the right. The equation reads

$$2H_2O \rightarrow 2H_2 + O_2$$

The same number of atoms of each element is represented on both sides of the equation. Furthermore, the equation has the lowest possible whole-number ratio of coefficients. Thus the equation is balanced.

To indicate the physical phases of the various species in the reaction (the reactant, water, to the left of the yields sign and the products, hydrogen and oxygen, to the right), the balanced equation is written

$$2H_2O(l) \rightarrow 2H_2(g) + O_2(g)$$

The abbreviations commonly used in this way are (s) solid, (l) liquid, (g) gas, and (aq) water solution. In this text, the abbreviations are used when they contribute to a better understanding of the reaction represented by the equation.

Phase symbols in an equation are
(s) = solid
(l) = liquid
(g) = gas
(aq) = water solution

When sulfur burns in oxygen (or in air) it combines with the oxygen gas to form sulfur dioxide gas. These reaction

Figure 8-4. Sulfur burns in oxygen to form sulfur dioxide gas.

Dispense with the word-equation step when you no longer need it as the initial expression of the facts.

CAUTION: *All formulas in the equation must be correctly written* **before** *the atom-balancing step is undertaken.*

facts can be written as

$$\text{sulfur} + \text{oxygen} \rightarrow \text{sulfur dioxide}$$

or

$$S(s) + O_2(g) \rightarrow SO_2(g)$$

Molecular oxygen is diatomic and is represented as O_2. The binary name "sulfur dioxide" indicates that its formula is SO_2. All formulas are correctly written. The number of atoms of sulfur and of oxygen are the same on both sides of the equation. No further adjustments are required; the equation is balanced.

Oxygen can be prepared in the laboratory by heating mercury(II) oxide. The facts are: when solid mercury(II) oxide is heated, it yields liquid metallic mercury and oxygen gas.

$$\text{mercury(II) oxide} \rightarrow \text{mercury} + \text{oxygen}$$

By substituting the proper symbols and formulas, the word equation becomes

$$HgO \rightarrow Hg + O_2 \quad \text{(not balanced)}$$

Mercury(II) has an oxidation number of $+2$ and oxygen has an oxidation number of -2. The formula of mercury(II) oxide is correct as written. However, the equation is not balanced. Two molecules of HgO must decompose to yield the 2 atoms of the diatomic oxygen molecule. After making this adjustment, 2 additional atoms of mercury must also appear on the right. The balanced equation, including the phase of each species, is

$$2HgO(s) \rightarrow 2Hg(l) + O_2(g)$$

Zinc reacts with hydrochloric acid (a water solution of hydrogen chloride gas). The reaction produces hydrogen gas and a solution of zinc chloride. These facts can be represented by

$$\text{zinc} + \text{hydrochloric acid} \rightarrow \text{zinc chloride} + \text{hydrogen}$$

Or the facts can be represented directly by the initial formula equation

$$Zn + HCl \rightarrow ZnCl_2 + H_2 \quad \text{(not balanced)}$$

This equation shows 1 hydrogen atom on the left and 2 on the right. Hydrogen atoms are balanced by representing 2 molecules of hydrogen chloride as 2HCl. Note that this change also gives 2 chlorine atoms on the left, which balance the 2 on the right. The balanced equation is

$$Zn(s) + 2HCl(aq) \rightarrow ZnCl_2(aq) + H_2(g)$$

Do not become discouraged if equations cause you some initial difficulty. Common mistakes made by students while learning the equation-balancing technique are (1) neglecting to verify the correctness of each formula in the "facts" equation and (2) altering a correctly written formula in an attempt to establish the required number of atoms for a balanced equation. Keep in mind that once a formula is correctly written, *subscripts cannot be added, deleted, or changed.* Formulas must be written correctly *before* proceeding with the final atom-balancing step. As you continue your study of chemistry and gain experience in the laboratory, the equations that now seem difficult will become easy.

This next reaction occurs in one step of a water-purification process. Aluminum sulfate and calcium hydroxide are added to water containing unwanted suspended matter. The two substances react in water to produce two insoluble products, aluminum hydroxide and calcium sulfate. These products settle out, taking the suspended matter with them.

The two *reactants* are aluminum sulfate and calcium hydroxide. Their respective formulas (by ion-charge balancing) are $Al_2(SO_4)_3$ and $Ca(OH)_2$. The two *products* of the reaction are aluminum hydroxide, $Al(OH)_3$, and calcium sulfate, $CaSO_4$. Having determined the correct formula for each species involved in the reaction, the word equation can be omitted and the initial "facts" equation can be written directly.

$$Al_2(SO_4)_3 + Ca(OH)_2 \rightarrow Al(OH)_3 + CaSO_4 \quad \text{(not balanced)}$$

The next step is to balance the equation. On the left, the formula $Al_2(SO_4)_3$ represents 2 Al atoms. On the right, 2 Al atoms are realized by placing the coefficient 2 in front of $Al(OH)_3$. The equation now reads

$$Al_2(SO_4)_3 + Ca(OH)_2 \rightarrow 2Al(OH)_3 + CaSO_4 \quad \text{(not balanced)}$$

Three polyatomic SO_4^{--} ions are indicated on the left. Therefore the coefficient 3 is placed in front of $CaSO_4$. The equation now reads

$$Al_2(SO_4)_3 + Ca(OH)_2 \rightarrow 2Al(OH)_3 + 3CaSO_4 \quad \text{(not balanced)}$$

Next observe that there must be 3 Ca atoms on the left to balance the 3 Ca atoms now on the right. The coefficient 3 is placed in front of $Ca(OH)_2$. This coefficient also gives 6 OH^- ions on the left which balance the 6 OH^- ions on the right. The equation is now balanced.

$$Al_2(SO_4)_3 + 3Ca(OH)_2 \rightarrow 2Al(OH)_3(s) + 3CaSO_4(s)$$

The (s) notations indicate that both products are insoluble. They leave the reaction environment as *precipitates*.

CAUTION: *Do not attempt to balance atoms until* after *all formulas have been written correctly.*

In summary, to write chemical equations correctly you need to

1. know the symbols of the common elements;
2. know the usual oxidation numbers or ionic charges of the common elements and polyatomic ions;
3. know the facts relating to the reaction for which an equation is to be written;
4. assure that all formulas are correctly written before attempting to balance the equation;
5. balance the equation for atoms of all elements represented so that the lowest possible ratio of whole-number coefficients results.

PRACTICE PROBLEMS

Write the balanced equations for the following reactions:

1. zinc + chlorine → zinc chloride   *ans.* $Zn + Cl_2 \rightarrow ZnCl_2$
2. sodium bromide + chlorine → sodium chloride + bromine
ans. $2NaBr + Cl_2 \rightarrow 2NaCl + Br_2$
3. sodium hydrogen carbonate → sodium carbonate + water + carbon dioxide   *ans.* $2NaHCO_3 \rightarrow Na_2CO_3 + H_2O + CO_2$
4. ammonium chloride + calcium hydroxide → calcium chloride + ammonia (NH_3) + water   *ans.* $2NH_4Cl + Ca(OH)_2 \rightarrow CaCl_2 + 2NH_3 + 2H_2O$
5. calcium hydroxide + carbon dioxide → calcium carbonate + water   *ans.* $Ca(OH)_2 + CO_2 \rightarrow CaCO_3 + H_2O$
6. potassium hydroxide + carbon dioxide → potassium hydrogen carbonate   *ans.* $KOH + CO_2 \rightarrow KHCO_3$
7. hydrogen sulfide + lead(II) chloride → hydrogen chloride + lead(II) sulfide   *ans.* $H_2S + PbCl_2 \rightarrow 2HCl + PbS$
8. ammonia (NH_3) + hydrogen sulfide → ammonium sulfide
ans. $2NH_3 + H_2S \rightarrow (NH_4)_2S$

◻ 8.4 General types of chemical reactions

There are several different ways of classifying chemical reactions. No single scheme is entirely satisfactory. In elementary chemistry, it is helpful to recognize reactions that fall into the four categories given below. Later you will learn other ways in which chemical reactions can be classified. The four main types of reactions are:

Composition reactions are also called synthesis reactions.

1. *Composition reactions,* in which two or more substances combine to form a more complex substance. Composition reactions have the general form

$$A + X \rightarrow AX$$

Examples:
Iron and sulfur combine to form iron(II) sulfide.

$$Fe + S \rightarrow FeS$$

Magnesium burns in air (combines with oxygen) to form magnesium oxide. This combustion is shown in Figure 8-5.

$$2Mg + O_2 \rightarrow 2MgO$$

Water and sulfur trioxide combine to form hydrogen sulfate (sulfuric acid).

$$H_2O + SO_3 \rightarrow H_2SO_4$$

2. Decomposition reactions are the reverse of the first type. Here one substance breaks down to form two or more simpler substances. Decomposition reactions have the general form

$$AX \rightarrow A + X$$

Examples:
Water is decomposed, yielding hydrogen and oxygen.

$$2H_2O \rightarrow 2H_2(g) + O_2(g)$$

When heated, potassium chlorate decomposes, yielding potassium chloride and oxygen.

$$2KClO_3 \rightarrow 2KCl + 3O_2(g)$$

Mercury(II) oxide decomposes when heated. The products are metallic mercury and oxygen. See Figure 8-6.

$$2HgO \rightarrow 2Hg + O_2(g)$$

3. Replacement reactions, in which one substance is replaced in its compound by another substance. Replacement reactions have the general form

$$A + \overset{\frown}{BX} \rightarrow AX + B$$

or

$$Y + \overset{\frown}{BX} \rightarrow BY + X$$

Examples:
Iron replaces copper in a solution of copper(II) sulfate, yielding iron(II) sulfate and copper.

$$Fe + CuSO_4 \rightarrow FeSO_4 + Cu(s)$$

The Fe atom loses 2 electrons to the Cu^{++} ion and replaces it in the solution as an Fe^{++} ion. The Cu^{++} ion gains 2 electrons and leaves the solution as a Cu atom.

Copper replaces silver in a solution of silver nitrate, and copper(II) nitrate and silver are the products.

$$Cu + 2AgNO_3 \rightarrow Cu(NO_3)_2 + 2Ag(s)$$

$2Mg(s) + O_2(g) \rightarrow 2MgO(s)$

Figure 8-5. A composition reaction. Magnesium metal burns in air to form magnesium oxide.

Reactants in composition reactions aren't always elements.

Products of decomposition reactions aren't always elements.

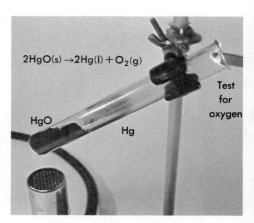

$2HgO(s) \rightarrow 2Hg(l) + O_2(g)$

Test for oxygen

HgO

Hg

Figure 8-6. A decomposition reaction. With mild heating, mercury(II) oxide decomposes to metallic mercury and oxygen gas.

$Cu(s) + 2AgNO_3(aq) \rightarrow Cu(NO_3)_2(aq) + 2Ag(s)$

Figure 8-7. A replacement reaction. Copper atoms replace silver ions from an aqueous solution of silver nitrate.

The Cu atom loses 2 electrons, 1 to each of the 2 Ag^+ ions, and replaces them in the solution as a Cu^{++} ion. The 2 Ag^+ ions gain one electron each and leave the solution as Ag atoms.

This reaction is shown in Figure 8-7. Silver nitrate solutions are colorless; copper(II) nitrate solutions are blue. Observe the color of the solution and the spongy deposit of silver on the copper strip in the beaker on the right.

Chlorine replaces iodine in a solution of potassium iodide, yielding potassium chloride and iodine.

$$Cl_2 + 2KI \rightarrow 2KCl + I_2$$

In this replacement reaction, the iodide ion, I^-, loses an electron to a chlorine atom. The I^- ion becomes an I atom; iodine remains in solution as I_2 molecules. The Cl atom becomes a chloride ion, Cl^-. Potassium ions, K^+, do not participate in the replacement reaction.

In these first three types of reactions (composition, decomposition, and replacement), some change in the sharing of electrons occurs, or there is a transfer of electrons from one atom to another. Usually, but not always, there are changes in oxidation states.

4. *Ionic reactions* involve no transfer of electrons. Instead, ions in solution combine to form a product that leaves the reaction environment. Ionic reactions may have the general form

$$A^+(aq) + B^-(aq) \rightarrow AB$$

Examples:

A solution of sodium chloride, containing sodium ions and chloride ions, is added to a solution of silver nitrate, containing silver ions and nitrate ions. A reaction occurs between the silver ions and chloride ions. A white precipitate of silver chloride is formed.

$$Ag^+(aq) + Cl^-(aq) \rightarrow Ag^+Cl^-(s)$$

Aqueous ions that do not participate in an ionic reaction are called "spectator ions."

The sodium ions and nitrate ions do not participate in the reaction but remain in solution as aqueous ions. By evaporating the water, they can be recovered as ionic crystals of sodium nitrate. The sodium ions and silver ions can be regarded as having exchanged places. For this reason, ionic reactions are sometimes referred to as *exchange* reactions.

Formula equations can be written for ionic reactions to identify the substances used as sources of the participating ions. These equations have the general form

$$AX + BY \rightarrow AY + BX$$

In this sense, the ionic reaction just described is written

$$NaCl + AgNO_3 \rightarrow NaNO_3 + AgCl(s)$$

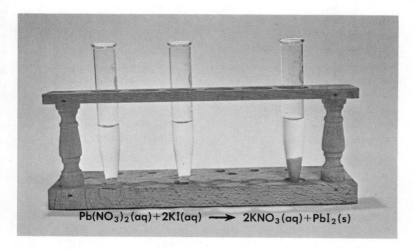

$$Pb(NO_3)_2(aq) + 2KI(aq) \longrightarrow 2KNO_3(aq) + PbI_2(s)$$

Figure 8-8. An ionic reaction. When aqueous potassium iodide is added to an aqueous solution of lead(II) nitrate, lead(II) iodide is precipitated.

When a solution of potassium iodide is added to a solution of lead(II) nitrate, insoluble lead(II) iodide separates as a yellow precipitate. See Figure 8-8. The potassium ions and nitrate ions remain in solution and do not participate in the ionic reaction. The net equation is

$$Pb^{++}(aq) + 2I^-(aq) \rightarrow PbI_2(s)$$

In order for an ionic reaction to occur, a product must be formed that separates ions from the reaction environment (the solution). The product may be a solid precipitate, an insoluble gas, or a new molecular species (water).

Use the solubility table, Appendix Table 12, to help determine whether a proposed ionic reaction occurs.

◻ 8.5 Six kinds of decomposition reactions

You have learned that the first step in writing a balanced equation is to represent the facts about the reaction. You must know what substances react and what products are formed. In this connection, it can be helpful to recognize general reaction patterns among chemically similar substances.

For example, many metallic carbonates have a similar reaction pattern when heated. They decompose into the corresponding metallic oxide and carbon dioxide gas. When this reaction pattern is known, equations can be written for the decomposition of several different metallic carbonates. Other patterns are evident in decomposition and replacement reactions.

Decomposition reactions are promoted by heat or electricity. The kinds generally recognized are:

1. Metallic carbonates, when heated, form metallic oxides and carbon dioxide. When heated, calcium carbonate, $CaCO_3$, forms calcium oxide, CaO. Carbon dioxide, CO_2, is given off as a gas.

$$CaCO_3 \rightarrow CaO + CO_2(g)$$

Ammonium carbonate, $(NH_4)_2CO_3$, because of the nonmetallic nature of the ammonium ion, decomposes in a special manner. The equation for this reaction is

$$(NH_4)_2CO_3 \rightarrow 2NH_3(g) + H_2O(g) + CO_2(g)$$

Ammonia, steam, and carbon dioxide are produced.

2. Many metallic hydroxides, when heated, decompose into metallic oxides and water. If calcium hydroxide, $Ca(OH)_2$, is strongly heated, steam is given off and calcium oxide, CaO, remains.

$$Ca(OH)_2 \rightarrow CaO + H_2O(g)$$

Sodium hydroxide and potassium hydroxide are common exceptions to this rule.

3. Metallic chlorates, when heated, decompose into metallic chlorides and oxygen. This is the type of reaction used to prepare oxygen from potassium chlorate.

$$2KClO_3 \rightarrow 2KCl + 3O_2(g)$$

Knowing these general decomposition reaction patterns helps you predict the decomposition products of other similar reactions.

4. Some acids, when heated, decompose into nonmetallic oxides and water. Acids may be formed by the composition reaction of certain nonmetallic oxides and water. The reactions described below involve the reverse process—the decomposition of the acid. Carbonic acid yields water and carbon dioxide gas.

$$H_2CO_3 \rightarrow H_2O + CO_2(g)$$

Sulfurous acid yields water and sulfur dioxide gas.

$$H_2SO_3 \rightarrow H_2O + SO_2(g)$$

The two reactions above take place quite readily at room temperature. The following reaction occurs at elevated temperatures.

$$H_2SO_4 \rightarrow H_2O + SO_3(g)$$

5. Some oxides, when heated, decompose. Most oxides are very stable compounds. There are only a few that decompose on heating. Two such reactions are

$$2HgO \rightarrow 2Hg + O_2(g)$$

$$2PbO_2 \rightarrow 2PbO + O_2(g)$$

Important reaction conditions are sometimes shown above or below the yields sign in a chemical equation.

6. Some decomposition reactions are produced by an electric current. The following reactions are typical.

$$2H_2O \xrightarrow{\text{(electricity)}} 2H_2(g) + O_2(g)$$

$$2NaCl \xrightarrow{\text{(electricity)}} 2Na + Cl_2(g)$$

The separation of a compound into simpler substances by an electric current is called **electrolysis**.

☐ 8.6 Four kinds of replacement reactions

The quantities of energy involved in replacement reactions are generally smaller than those in composition and decomposition reactions. The possibility of reaction depends on the relative activities of the elements involved. An experimentally derived *activity series,* as in Table 8-2 (Section 8.8), is generally useful for writing replacement reactions. Four kinds of replacement reactions are considered here.

1. Replacement of a metal in a compound by a more active metal. One reaction of this type involves zinc and a solution of copper(II) sulfate, $CuSO_4$. Zinc replaces the copper in the solution. This reaction indicates that zinc is a more active metal than copper.

Figure 8-9. Zinc is a more active metal than copper and replaces copper in the aqueous copper(II) sulfate solution.

$$Zn + CuSO_4 \rightarrow ZnSO_4 + Cu(s)$$

2. Replacement of hydrogen in water by metals. The very active metals, such as potassium, calcium, and sodium, react vigorously with water. They replace half the hydrogen to form metallic hydroxides. The reaction represented by the following equation is typical.

$$Ca + 2H_2O \rightarrow Ca(OH)_2 + H_2(g)$$

At elevated temperatures less active metals, such as magnesium, zinc, and iron, react with water (steam) to replace hydrogen. Because of the high temperature involved, oxides rather than hydroxides are formed. Metals less active than iron do not react measurably with water.

3. Replacement of hydrogen in acids by metals. Many metals react with certain acids, such as hydrochloric acid and dilute sulfuric acid. These metals replace hydrogen in the acids to form the corresponding metallic compounds. This method is commonly used for the laboratory preparation of hydrogen, in which sulfuric acid reacts with zinc.

Refer to the activity series when determining whether a proposed replacement reaction occurs.

$$Zn + H_2SO_4 \rightarrow ZnSO_4 + H_2(g)$$

4. Replacement of halogens. The halogens are the elements in Group VII of the periodic table. These elements are fluorine, chlorine, bromine, and iodine. Experiments show that fluorine is the most active halogen; it replaces the other three halogens in their compounds. Chlorine replaces bromine and iodine in their compounds. Bromine replaces only iodine. The replacement by chlorine of bromide ions in a potassium bromide solution is an example of the halogen replacement reaction.

$$Cl_2 + 2KBr \rightarrow 2KCl + Br_2$$

Chlorine replaces iodide ions, forming the corresponding chloride.

$$Cl_2 + 2NaI \rightarrow 2NaCl + I_2$$

Bromine replaces iodide ions, but not as vigorously as chlorine does.

$$Br_2 + 2KI \rightarrow 2KBr + I_2$$

☐ 8.7 Many reactions are reversible

Frequently, the products of a chemical reaction can react to produce substantial amounts of the original reactants. Hydrogen can be used as a reducing agent to separate certain metals from their oxides. If dry hydrogen gas is passed over hot magnetic iron oxide, iron and steam are produced.

$$4H_2 + Fe_3O_4 \rightarrow 3Fe + 4H_2O(g)$$

If the procedure is reversed and steam is passed over hot iron, magnetic iron oxide and hydrogen are formed.

$$3Fe + 4H_2O \rightarrow Fe_3O_4 + 4H_2(g)$$

Such reactions are said to be reversible. Reversible reactions are identified by two yields signs pointing in opposite directions ($\leftrightarrows$).

$$3Fe + 4H_2O \leftrightarrows Fe_3O_4 + 4H_2$$

Conditions may be such that both reactions occur at the same time. That is, if none of the products leaves the field of action, they may react to form the original reactants. Under such circumstances, an equilibrium (state of balance) may develop with the two opposing reactions proceeding at equal rates. After equilibrium is reached, the quantities of all the reactants remain constant. The subject of equilibrium reactions is discussed in Chapter 21.

☐ 8.8 The activity series of the elements

In general, the ease with which the atoms of a metal lose electrons determines the ease with which the metal forms compounds. In the replacement reaction

$$A + BX \rightarrow AX + B$$

metal **A** gives up electrons to metal **B** and replaces it. Thus metal **A** is shown to be more active than metal **B**. If metal **B** is immersed in a solution of the compound **AX**, metal **B** does not replace metal **A**. Atoms of a more active metal lose electrons to positively charged ions of a less active metal under proper reaction conditions. Similarly, atoms of more active nonmetals acquire electrons from negatively charged ions of less active nonmetals.

Zinc, being a more active metal than copper, replaces copper from a copper(II) sulfate solution. This replacement reaction is described in Section 8.6 and is shown in Figure 8-9.

$$Zn + Cu^{++}SO_4^{--} \rightarrow Zn^{++}SO_4^{--} + Cu$$

Each Zn atom loses two electrons to a Cu^{++} ion to form a Zn^{++} ion.

$$Zn \rightarrow Zn^{++} + 2e^-$$

Each Cu^{++} ion that gains two electrons forms a Cu atom.

$$Cu^{++} + 2e^- \rightarrow Cu$$

Observe that SO_4^{--} ions do not participate in this replacement reaction. The net equation is

$$Zn(s) + Cu^{++}(aq) \rightarrow Zn^{++}(aq) + Cu(s)$$

When copper is placed in a solution of zinc sulfate, no reaction is observed. Copper is a less active metal than zinc and does not replace zinc from a solution of a zinc compound.

Many spontaneous chemical reactions can be carried out in such a way that electric energy is given off. From a study of such reactions, chemists are able to devise an activity series of elements that helps predict the course of replacement reactions. Some composition and decomposition reactions can likewise be predicted with the aid of an activity series. The series presented in Table 8-2 lists important common elements in descending order of their metallic and nonmetallic activities.

The relative positions of the elements in the activity series support the application of some of the following generalizations to appropriate composition, decomposition, and replacement reactions.

1. Each element in the list displaces from a compound any of the elements below it. The larger the interval between elements in the series, the more vigorous the replacement reaction.

2. All metals above hydrogen displace hydrogen from hydrochloric acid or dilute sulfuric acid.

3. Metals above magnesium vigorously displace hydrogen from water. Magnesium displaces hydrogen from steam.

4. Metals above silver combine directly with oxygen; those near the top do so rapidly.

5. Metals below mercury form oxides only indirectly.

6. Oxides of metals below mercury decompose with mild heating.

7. Oxides of metals below chromium easily undergo reduction to metals by heating with hydrogen.

8. Oxides of metals above iron resist reduction by heating with hydrogen.

9. Elements near the top of the series are never found free in nature.

10. Elements near the bottom of the series are often found free in nature.

Table 8-2
ACTIVITY SERIES OF THE ELEMENTS

Metals	*Nonmetals*
lithium	fluorine
potassium	chlorine
calcium	bromine
sodium	iodine
magnesium	
aluminum	
zinc	
chromium	
iron	Decreasing
nickel	activity
tin	
lead	
HYDROGEN	
copper	
mercury	
silver	
platinum	
gold	

MASS RELATIONSHIPS

❑ 8.9 Stoichiometry

The determination of empirical formulas for compounds is always the result of experimentation. Empirical formulas are derived from the relative numbers of moles of atoms or ions of the elements present in compounds. Therefore, the empirical formulas indicate the relative numbers of atoms or ions present. An empirical formula reveals nothing about the nature of the association of these particles or whether a substance actually exists in simple molecular units. Nevertheless, empirical formulas are very useful in calculations involving the combining and reacting relationships among substances.

The branch of chemistry that deals with the numerical relationships of elements and compounds and the mathematical proportions of reactants and products in chemical reactions is known as **stoichiometry** (stoy-key-*om*-eh-tree). The determinations of percentage composition of compounds and of empirical formulas are discussed in Chapter 7. The calculations for these determinations are based upon *stoichiometric relationships.* You are now ready to learn to solve stoichiometric problems involving the mass relations of reactants and products in chemical reactions. To do this, you will need an understanding of the mole concept and some skill in writing and balancing chemical equations. The concept of mole volumes of gases is introduced in Chapter 11. This concept will enable you to use simple computations to solve a great number of problems involving mass and volume relationships of gaseous reactants and products. These simple mass and volume relationships exist only for gases.

❑ 8.10 Mole relationships of reactants and products

When carbon burns in the oxygen of the air, carbon dioxide, a covalent molecular gas, is produced.

$$C + O_2 \rightarrow CO_2(g)$$

The balanced equation indicates the mole proportions of the reactants and products. It also gives the composition of each substance in terms of the kinds of elements and the relative number of each kind of atom present. Thus the equation signifies that 1 mole of carbon atoms combines with 1 mole of oxygen molecules to yield 1 mole of carbon dioxide molecules. This may be indicated as follows:

$$
\begin{array}{ccccc}
C & + & O_2 & \rightarrow & CO_2(g) \\
\text{1 mole} & & \text{1 mole} & & \text{1 mole} \\
= 12.0 \text{ g} & & = 32.0 \text{ g} & & = 44.0 \text{ g}
\end{array}
$$

The mole proportions of reacting substances and products convert readily to equivalent mass quantities, as shown above. An equation is used in this way to determine the mass of one substance that reacts with, or is produced from, a definite mass of another. This is one of the common problems chemists are called upon to solve.

◻ 8.11 Mole method of solving mass–mass problems

The mole concept is both important and practical in chemistry. Here is an example of its use in solving a typical mass-mass problem.

Suppose you want to determine the mass of calcium oxide produced by heating 50.0 g of calcium carbonate. Observe that the mass of the reactant is given and the mass of a product is required. From the data given in the problem and the facts known concerning this reaction, you can *set up the problem*. This can be done in four steps.

Step 1: Write the balanced equation.

Step 2: Show the problem specifications: what is given and what is required. To do this, write the mass of calcium carbonate, 50.0 g, above the formula $CaCO_3$. Let X represent the unknown mass of calcium oxide produced, and place it above the formula CaO.

Step 3: Show the mole proportions established by the balanced equation. This is done by writing under each substance in the problem the number of *moles* indicated by the equation.

Step 4: Determine the mass of 1 mole of each substance involved in the problem. These masses are written below the equation setup. The problem is now ready to be solved.

A balanced equation is required for a correct problem solution.

$$\begin{array}{llll}
Step\ 2: & 50.0\ g & X & \\
Step\ 1: & CaCO_3 \rightarrow & CaO\ + & CO_2(g) \\
Step\ 3: & 1\ mole & 1\ mole &
\end{array}$$

$$\begin{array}{ll}
Step\ 4: & 1\ mole\ CaCO_3 = 100.1\ g \\
& 1\ mole\ CaO\quad =\ \ 56.1\ g
\end{array}$$

The number of moles of $CaCO_3$ *given in the problem* is found by multiplying the given mass of $CaCO_3$, 50.0 g, by the fraction $\dfrac{mole}{100.1\ g}$, or

$$50.0\ g\ CaCO_3 \times \frac{mole}{100.1\ g} = moles\ CaCO_3$$

The balanced equation indicates that for each mole of $CaCO_3$ decomposed, 1 mole of CaO is produced. So from the given mass of $CaCO_3$ you can produce

$$50.0\ g\ CaCO_3 \times \frac{mole}{100.1\ g} \times \frac{1\ mole\ CaO}{1\ mole\ CaCO_3} = moles\ CaO$$

To determine the mass of CaO produced, multiply by the mass of 1 mole of CaO.

$$50.0 \text{ g CaCO}_3 \times \frac{\text{mole}}{100.1 \text{ g}} \times \frac{1 \text{ mole CaO}}{1 \text{ mole CaCO}_3} \times \frac{56.1 \text{ g}}{\text{mole}} = \text{g CaO}$$

It is always prudent to *estimate* the answer to a problem before starting the computations. A simple units-operation check of the solution setup will reveal the answer unit and the correctness of the setup. For this problem, the unit operations indicate a result in g CaO. Thus the problem solution is set up correctly. A numerical estimate indicates an answer of approximately 30 ($\frac{1}{2} \times 1 \times$ about 60). The problem solution can now be expected to yield a reliable answer of approximately 30 g CaO.

$$X = 50.0 \text{ g CaCO}_3 \times \frac{\text{mole}}{100.1 \text{ g}} \times \frac{1 \text{ mole CaO}}{1 \text{ mole CaCO}_3} \times \frac{56.1 \text{ g}}{\text{mole}}$$
$$X = 28.0 \text{ g CaO}$$

The calculated result, 28.0 g CaO, is in good agreement with the estimated value of approximately 30 g CaO. This mass–mass problem-solving technique is further illustrated in the following Sample Problems.

SAMPLE PROBLEM

How many grams of potassium chlorate must be decomposed to yield 30.0 g of oxygen?

SOLUTION

First, set up the problem by writing the balanced equation. *Second,* write the specifications of the problem above the equation. *Third,* write the number of moles of each specified substance under its formula. And *fourth,* calculate the mass/mole of each of the specified substances. Let **X** represent the mass of potassium chlorate decomposed.

Step 2:   **X**   **30.0 g**
Step 1: $2KClO_3 \rightarrow 2KCl + 3O_2(g)$
Step 3:   **2 moles**   **3 moles**

Step 4:   **1 mole $KClO_3$ = 122.6 g**
          1 mole O_2 =   32.0 g

$$X = \underbrace{30.0 \text{ g O}_2 \times \frac{\text{mole}}{32.0 \text{ g}}}_{\substack{\text{Operation 1} \\ \text{gives expression} \\ \text{for moles} \\ O_2 \text{ given}}} \times \underbrace{\frac{2 \text{ moles KClO}_3}{3 \text{ moles O}_2}}_{\substack{\text{Operation 2} \\ \text{gives expression} \\ \text{for moles} \\ KClO_3 \text{ required}}} \times \underbrace{\frac{122.6 \text{ g}}{\text{mole}}}_{\substack{\text{Operation 3} \\ \text{gives expression} \\ \text{for grams} \\ KClO_3 \text{ required}}} = \underbrace{76.6 \text{ g KClO}_3}_{\substack{\text{Operation 4} \\ \text{involves unit} \\ \text{check, estimate of} \\ \text{answer, and} \\ \text{arithmetic} \\ \text{operations}}}$$

SAMPLE PROBLEM

(*a*) How many grams of oxygen are required to oxidize $14\overline{0}$ g of iron to iron(III) oxide? (*b*) How many moles of iron(III) oxide are produced?

SOLUTION

The problem setup for Parts (*a*) and (*b*) is

Step 2:	$14\overline{0}$ g	X	Y
Step 1:	4Fe	+ $3O_2$(g) →	$2Fe_2O_3$
Step 3:	4 moles	3 moles	2 moles

Step 4:   1 mole Fe = 55.8 g
          1 mole O_2 = 32.0 g

The solution setup for Part (*a*) is

$$X = 14\overline{0} \text{ g Fe} \times \frac{\text{mole}}{55.8 \text{ g}} \times \frac{3 \text{ moles } O_2}{4 \text{ moles Fe}} \times \frac{32.0 \text{ g}}{\text{mole}} = 60.2 \text{ g } O_2$$

The solution setup for Part (*b*) is

$$Y = 14\overline{0} \text{ g Fe} \times \frac{\text{mole}}{55.8 \text{ g}} \times \frac{2 \text{ moles } Fe_2O_3}{4 \text{ moles Fe}} = 1.25 \text{ moles } Fe_2O_3$$

PRACTICE PROBLEMS

Use factor-label techniques and maintain the proper numbers of significant figures in all calculations.

1. An excess of chlorine gas is bubbled into an aqueous solution containing 4.65 g of potassium bromide. (*a*) What mole quantity of molecular bromine is produced? (*b*) What is the mass of this mole quantity of bromine?
   ans. (*a*) 0.0195 mole Br_2 (*b*) 3.12 g Br_2
2. When magnesium burns in air, it combines with oxygen to form magnesium oxide. (*a*) What mass of oxygen combines with 10.0 g of magnesium in this reaction? (*b*) What mass of magnesium oxide is produced?
   ans. (*a*) 6.58 g O_2 (*b*) 16.6 g MgO

SUMMARY

A chemical equation is a concise, symbolized statement of a chemical reaction. Useful quantitative information about a reaction is provided by a balanced formula equation.

Three conditions must be met in a balanced equation. (1) The equation must represent the

facts of the reaction, the substances that react and the products formed. (2) The symbols or formulas for all reactants and products must be written correctly. (3) The law of conservation of atoms must be satisfied.

In some chemical reactions, changes occur in

the sharing of electrons or electrons are transferred from one reactant to another. In other reactions, aqueous ions combine to form a product that separates from the reaction environment. Chemical reactions may be separated into four main types: (1) composition; (2) decomposition; (3) replacement; and (4) ionic.

The numerical relationships of elements and compounds, and the proportions of reactants and products, in chemical reactions are called stoichiometry. Problems dealing with mass relationships of the reactants and products in chemical reactions are stoichiometric problems. Solutions of stoichiometric problems are based on the fact that balanced equations establish the quantitative relationships among reactants and products. The quantities in these equations are expressed in moles.

 VOCABULARY

activity series	product	stoichiometry
balanced chemical equation	qualitative	synthesis
electrolysis	quantitative	word equation
law of conservation of atoms	reactant	

EQUATIONS

Group A

Write balanced chemical equations for these reactions and identify the type of reaction. *Do not write in this book.*

1. zinc + sulfur → zinc sulfide.
2. potassium chloride + silver nitrate → silver chloride(s) + potassium nitrate.
3. calcium oxide + water → calcium hydroxide.
4. sodium hydroxide + hydrochloric acid (HCl) → sodium chloride + water.
5. magnesium bromide + chlorine → magnesium chloride + bromine.
6. sodium chloride + sulfuric acid (H_2SO_4) → sodium sulfate + hydrogen chloride(g).
7. aluminum + iron(III) oxide → aluminum oxide + iron.
8. ammonium nitrite → nitrogen(g) + water.
9. silver nitrate + nickel → nickel(II) nitrate + silver(s).
10. hydrogen + nitrogen → ammonia (NH_3)(g).

Complete the word equation and write the balanced chemical equation. Give a reason for the product(s) in each case. Consult the activity series in Table 8-2, and solubilities in Appendix Table 12, as necessary.

Composition reactions:
11. sodium + iodine →
12. calcium + oxygen →
13. hydrogen + chlorine →

Decomposition reactions:
14. nickel(II) chlorate →
15. barium carbonate →
16. zinc hydroxide →

Replacement reactions:
17. aluminum + sulfuric acid →
18. potassium iodide + chlorine →
19. iron + copper(II) nitrate → iron(II) nitrate +

Ionic reactions:
20. silver nitrate + zinc chloride →
21. copper(II) hydroxide + acetic acid ($HC_2H_3O_2$) →
22. iron(II) sulfate + ammonium sulfide →

Group B

Where the word equation is complete, write and balance the chemical equation. Where the word equation is incomplete, complete it, write and balance the formula equation, tell the type of reaction, and give a reason for the product(s).

23. barium chloride + sodium sulfate →
24. calcium + hydrochloric acid →
25. iron(II) sulfide + hydrochloric acid → hydrogen sulfide(g) +
26. zinc chloride + ammonium sulfide →
27. ammonia + oxygen → nitric acid (HNO_3) + water.
28. magnesium + nitric acid →
29. potassium + water →
30. sodium iodide + bromine →
31. silver + sulfur →
32. sodium chlorate →
33. carbon + steam (H_2O) → carbon monoxide(g) + hydrogen(g).
34. zinc + lead(II) acetate →
35. iron(III) hydroxide →
36. iron(III) oxide + carbon monoxide → iron + carbon dioxide(g).
37. lead(II) acetate + hydrogen sulfide →
38. aluminum bromide + chlorine →
39. magnesium carbonate →
40. iron(III) chloride + sodium hydroxide →
41. calcium oxide + diphosphorus pentoxide → calcium phosphate.
42. chromium + oxygen →
43. sodium + water →
44. calcium carbonate + hydrochloric acid →
45. calcium hydroxide + phosphoric acid (H_3PO_4) →
46. sodium carbonate + nitric acid →
47. aluminum hydroxide + sulfuric acid →
48. sodium sulfite + sulfuric acid →
49. copper + sulfuric acid → copper(II) sulfate + water + sulfur dioxide(g).
50. calcium hydroxide + ammonium sulfate → calcium sulfate + water + ammonia(g).

◖ PROBLEMS

Group A

1. A mass of 25.0 g of mercury(II) oxide is decomposed by heating. The reaction is $2HgO \rightarrow 2Hg + O_2$. (*a*) How many moles of mercury(II) oxide are decomposed? (*b*) How many moles of oxygen are prepared? (*c*) How many grams of oxygen are prepared?

2. A mass of 25.0 g of potassium chlorate is decomposed by heating. (*a*) How many moles of potassium chlorate are decomposed? (*b*) How many moles of oxygen are prepared? (*c*) How many grams of oxygen can be prepared?

3. A quantity of zinc reacts with sulfuric acid to produce 0.10 g of hydrogen. (*a*) How many moles of hydrogen are produced? (*b*) How many moles of zinc are required? (*c*) How many grams of zinc are required?

4. Sodium chloride reacts with 10.0 g of silver nitrate in water solution. (*a*) How many moles of silver nitrate react? (*b*) How many moles of sodium chloride are required? (*c*) How many grams of sodium chloride are required?

5. (*a*) How many moles of silver chloride are precipitated in the reaction of Problem 4? (*b*) How many grams of silver chloride is this?

6. In a reaction between sulfur and oxygen, 80.0 g of sulfur dioxide is formed. How many grams of sulfur were burned?

7. How many grams of hydrogen are required to completely convert 25 g of hot magnetic iron oxide (Fe_3O_4) to elemental iron? Steam is the other product of the reaction.

8. How many grams of copper(II) oxide can be formed by oxidizing 1.00 kg of copper?

9. What mass of silver in g is precipitated when 40.0 g of copper reacts with an excess of silver nitrate in solution?

10. Suppose 10.0 g of iron(II) sulfide is reacted with an excess of hydrochloric acid. How many grams of hydrogen sulfide gas are produced?

Group B

11. An excess of sulfuric acid reacts with $15\overline{0}$ g of barium peroxide. (*a*) How many moles of hydrogen peroxide are produced? (*b*) How many moles of barium sulfate?

12. Approximately 130 g of zinc was added to a solution containing $10\overline{0}$ g of HCl. After the action ceased, 41 g of zinc remained. How many moles of hydrogen were produced?

13. A mixture of 10.0 g of powdered iron and 10.0 g of sulfur is heated to its reaction temperature in an open crucible. (*a*) How many grams of iron(II) sulfide are formed? (*b*) The reactant in excess is oxidized. How many grams of its oxide are formed?

14. What mass in grams of calcium hydroxide can be produced from 1.00 kg of limestone, calcium carbonate? (Decomposition of calcium carbonate with heat yields calcium oxide and carbon dioxide. Calcium hydroxide is formed by the reaction of calcium oxide and water.)

15. How many grams of air are required to complete the combustion of 93 g of phosphorus to diphosphorus pentoxide, assuming the air to be 23% oxygen by mass?

16. How many metric tons of carbon dioxide can be produced from the combustion of 1.00 metric ton $(100\overline{0}$ kg) of coke that is $9\overline{0}\%$ carbon?

17. (*a*) What mass of H_2SO_4 in grams is required in a reaction with an excess of aluminum to produce 0.50 mole of aluminum sulfate? (*b*) How many moles of hydrogen are also produced?

18. A certain rocket uses butane, C_4H_{10}, as fuel. How many kilograms of liquid oxygen should be carried for the complete combustion of each 1.00 kg of butane to carbon dioxide and water vapor?

19. When 45 g of ethane gas, C_2H_6, is burned completely in air, cabon dioxide and water vapor are formed. (*a*) How many moles of carbon dioxide are produced? (*b*) How many moles of water are produced?

20. (*a*) How many grams of sodium sulfate are produced in the reaction between $15\overline{0}$ g of sulfuric acid and an excess of sodium chloride? (*b*) How many grams of sodium chloride are used? (*c*) How many grams of hydrogen chloride are also produced?

Two Important Gases: Oxygen and Hydrogen

How fire fascinated people throughout history! The sixteenth-century physician Paracelsus speculated that wood burned because it contained sulfur. A century and a half later, the German alchemist Johann Joachim Becher proposed that still another substance was responsible for combustion. Phlogiston, *from the Greek "to set on fire," was a constituent of matter responsible for burning. Becher pictured combustion as a process in which phlogiston detached itself from a sample of matter. This detachment accounted for the flame and heat that accompanied burning. The weight of the sample, he claimed, would naturally be less after combustion. Becher's phlogiston theory at first seemed to be a good explanation of this little-understood process. One hundred years later, however, carefully conducted laboratory experiments by Lavoisier, Priestley, and Scheele were to disprove the theory of phlogiston.*

9.1 Introduction

Thus far your study of chemistry has been concerned mostly with the theory of atomic structure and its explanation of the nature of elements and compounds. You have learned about common types of chemical reactions. The writing of chemical formulas and equations has been explained. Some calculations involving formulas and equations have been described, and you have had problems for practice. Now a more detailed description of gases, liquids, and solids than that given in Chapter 1 will be presented. But before gases in general are considered, two important gaseous elements, oxygen and hydrogen, will be studied.

9.2 Occurrence of oxygen

Oxygen, atomic number 8, has several characteristics that make it a very important element. It is the most abundant element in the earth's crust. In fact, it is estimated that even if the composition of the entire earth is considered, there are more oxygen atoms in the earth, the waters on the earth, and the atmosphere surrounding the earth than atoms of any other single element. After hydrogen and helium, oxygen atoms rank third in abundance in the known universe. Oxygen is necessary for the support of plant and animal life. Oxygen combines with all other elements except the lower-atomic-weight noble gases.

About one fifth of the earth's atmosphere by volume is oxygen. Animals living in water get their oxygen from the small amount that is dissolved in water. Oxygen in the air and oxygen

In this chapter you will gain an understanding of:

- **the occurrence and discovery of oxygen**
- **the preparation, properties, and uses of oxygen**
- **the preparation, properties, and uses of ozone**
- **the difference between oxygen and ozone**
- **the preparation, properties, and uses of hydrogen**
- **the isotopes of hydrogen**

OXYGEN

Gases, liquids, and solids are described in Section 1.8.

You may wish to review the explanation of the earth's composition in Section 2.7.

Figure 9-1. Free oxygen comprises about one fifth of the earth's atmosphere by volume. Combined oxygen is abundant in water and in the rocks of the earth's crust.

In this reaction, for each $\overset{+4}{Mn}$ that is reduced to $\overset{+2}{Mn}$, an $\overset{-2}{O}$ is oxidized to $\overset{0}{O}$.

The decomposition of mercury(II) oxide is shown in Figure 8-6.

Figure 9-2. Karl Wilhelm Scheele, a Swedish pharmacist, prepared oxygen and studied some of its properties in 1771.

that is dissolved in water are examples of *free oxygen*. As the free element, oxygen consists of diatomic covalent molecules, O_2.

Oxygen that has united with other elements in compounds is called *combined oxygen*. Combined oxygen is much more plentiful than free oxygen. Water contains almost 89% oxygen by mass in combination with hydrogen. Such minerals as clay, sand, and limestone contain a large percentage of combined oxygen. Oxygen is one of the elements present in most of the rocks and minerals of the earth's crust.

❏ 9.3 Discovery of oxygen

The discovery of oxygen is related to the work of three eighteenth-century scientists. Karl Wilhelm Scheele (*shay*-luh) (1742–1786), a Swedish pharmacist, prepared oxygen in 1771 by heating manganese dioxide with concentrated sulfuric acid.

$$2MnO_2 + 2H_2SO_4 \rightarrow 2MnSO_4 + 2H_2O + O_2(g)$$

Scheele carried out experiments with oxygen which proved to him that oxygen was different from other known gases. He also identified oxygen as that part of the air involved in combustion and oxidation of metals. However, it was not until 1776 that the announcement of Scheele's discovery was published.

Meanwhile, Joseph Priestley (1733–1804), an English clergyman and scientist, prepared oxygen in 1774 by using a lens to focus the sun's rays on mercury(II) oxide. When this powdery red oxide is heated strongly, it decomposes. Oxygen gas is evolved and liquid mercury remains.

$$2HgO \rightarrow 2Hg + O_2(g)$$

Priestley was delighted to find that a candle would flare up and continue to burn brightly in oxygen. Upon inhaling some of the gas, Priestley observed that he felt peculiarly light and easy for some time. News of Priestley's work was published in 1775.

In late 1774, the French chemist Antoine-Laurent Lavoisier (1743–1794) privately learned of both Scheele's and Priestley's discoveries. Between 1772 and 1786, Lavoisier carried out many combustion experiments in which he made careful mass measurements. From these experiments he concluded that oxygen is an element and a component of the atmosphere. He also discovered that when substances burn in air or oxygen they gain mass because of the oxygen with which they combine. These observations brought about a reevaluation of the phlogiston theory and its eventual abandonment.

Oxygen was given its name by Lavoisier. Scheele and Priestley are considered codiscoverers of this element.

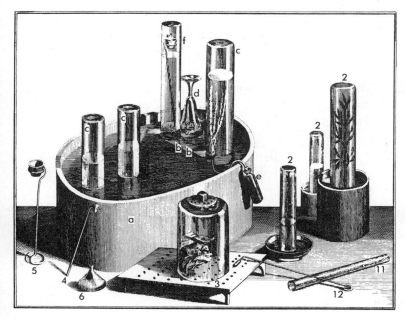

Figure 9-3. Some of the laboratory apparatus used by Priestley in his experiments on the properties of gases. The pneumatic trough *a* is fitted with a shelf *bb*. The trough is filled with water. Two collecting jars *c* and *c* stand in the water. A gas is being produced by a chemical reaction in the generator bottle *e* and delivered through tubing into a jar *c* on the shelf of the trough. An inverted glass *d* contains a mouse breathing a confined gas. Jar *f* contains a cup mounted on a wire stand, also shown as *5*. A growing plant is surrounded by a gas in large jar *2*. Compare this equipment with that which you use for collecting and testing gases.

◻ 9.4 Preparation of oxygen

1. By the decomposition of hydrogen peroxide. This is a safe and convenient laboratory method of preparing oxygen. A dilute (6%) solution of hydrogen peroxide in water decomposes very slowly at room temperature. But manganese dioxide may be used as a catalyst to increase the rate of decomposition. If hydrogen peroxide solution is allowed to react drop by drop with manganese dioxide powder at room temperature, the hydrogen peroxide decomposes rapidly and smoothly. See Figure 9-5. Oxygen gas is given off and water is formed.

$$2H_2O_2 \rightarrow 2H_2O(l) + O_2(g)$$

The oxygen gas produced in the flask passes through the delivery tube into a water-filled inverted bottle. As the oxygen rises in the bottle, it displaces the water. This method of collecting gases is known as *water displacement*. It is used for gases that are not very soluble in water.

2. By adding water to sodium peroxide. Sodium peroxide, Na_2O_2, is prepared by burning sodium in air. If water is allowed to drop onto sodium peroxide in a generator like that shown in Figure 9-5, oxygen is liberated.

$$2Na_2O_2 + 2H_2O \rightarrow 4NaOH + O_2(g)$$

This is another convenient laboratory method for preparing small quantities of oxygen since it does not require heat. **CAUTION:** *The sodium hydroxide solution that is formed must be disposed of carefully. It can burn the skin and destroy certain textile fibers.*

Figure 9-4. Lavoisier's great contributions to chemistry involved extending and interpreting the experiments of others, such as Scheele and Priestley (co-discoverers of oxygen) and Cavendish (discoverer of hydrogen). Lavoisier used logical procedures, repeated and refined experiments, and made mass and volume measurements. Then he worked out reasonable explanations of what he observed.

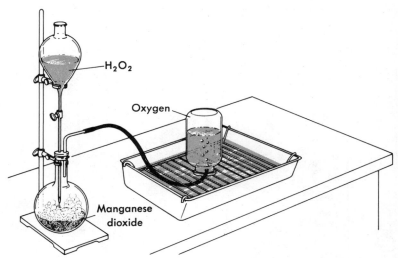

H₂O₂

Oxygen

Manganese dioxide

Figure 9-5. Oxygen may be prepared in the laboratory by the catalytic decomposition of hydrogen peroxide. Manganese dioxide is used as the catalyst. Oxygen is collected by water displacement. This same generator setup may be used for preparing oxygen by the action of water (placed in the dropping funnel) on sodium peroxide (placed in the flask).

Decomposition of metallic chlorates, as a type of decomposition reaction, is explained in Section 8.5(3).

A catalyst is a substance or combination of substances that alters the rate of a chemical reaction without itself being permanently changed. The purpose and use of catalysts are described in Section 2.13(5).

3. *By heating potassium chlorate.* Potassium chlorate is a white, crystalline solid. When this compound is heated, it decomposes. Oxygen is given off and potassium chloride is left as a residue.

$$2KClO_3 \rightarrow 2KCl + 3O_2(g)$$

Manganese dioxide is usually mixed with the potassium chlorate in this laboratory preparation. It acts as a catalyst by lowering the decomposition temperature of potassium chlorate.

Figure 9-6 shows the laboratory set-up for the generation of oxygen from potassium chlorate and the collection of oxygen by water displacement. **CAUTION:** *The decomposition of potassium chlorate is dangerous. It should be carried out with only*

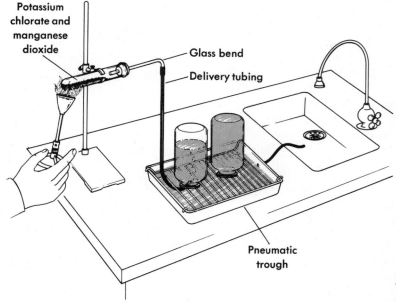

Potassium chlorate and manganese dioxide

Glass bend

Delivery tubing

Pneumatic trough

Figure 9-6. An alternate, though very hazardous, method of preparing oxygen in the laboratory is the decomposition of potassium chlorate. Manganese dioxide is used as a catalyst to lower the decomposition temperature.

*small quantities of reagent-grade chemicals. Carefully as-
sembled, inspected, and well-shielded equipment should be used
under close supervision. Potassium chlorate is extremely dangerous when mixed with combustible materials.*

4. *By the electrolysis of water.* Figure 9-7 represents a laboratory apparatus in which water may be decomposed by an electric current. During the electrolysis of water, a direct current
is passed through the water. Oxygen gas collects at the positive
terminal and hydrogen gas at the negative terminal. Sulfuric
acid is added to make the water a better conductor of electricity.

$$2H_2O \rightarrow 2H_2(g) + O_2(g)$$

Large quantities of electric energy are needed to decompose
the water. Industrially, this method yields oxygen of the highest
purity. The hydrogen, which is produced along with it, is sold as
a by-product.

5. *From liquid air.* This is the common industrial method for
preparing oxygen. Air liquefies when compressed greatly while
being cooled to a very low temperature ($-200\ °C$). The liquid
air that results consists largely of oxygen and nitrogen. Oxygen
is separated from nitrogen on the basis of the boiling point difference between them. Liquid nitrogen boils at $-195.8\ °C$, or
about thirteen degrees lower than liquid oxygen at $-183.0\ °C$. If
liquid air is permitted to stand, the nitrogen soon boils away
and leaves nearly pure liquid oxygen. The oxygen which then
boils away is pure enough for industrial purposes. In 1979 the
commercial production of oxygen in the United States was over
32 million metric tons. Oxygen ranked fourth, after sulfuric acid,
lime, and ammonia, in tonnage produced.

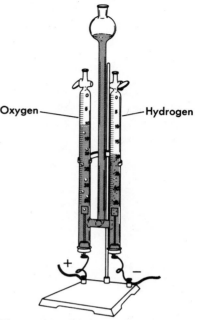

Figure 9-7. Water may be decomposed by electrolysis into its constituent elements, oxygen and
hydrogen.

◻ 9.5 Physical properties of oxygen

Pure oxygen is a colorless, odorless, tasteless gas. It is slightly
denser than air. At 0 °C and one atmosphere pressure, one liter
of oxygen has a mass of 1.43 g. Under the same conditions, one
liter of air has a mass of 1.29 g. Oxygen is slightly soluble in
water. The colder the water is, the more oxygen it can dissolve.
About five liters of oxygen can be dissolved in 100 liters of water
at 0 °C, but only three liters at 20 °C.

Any gas can be converted into a liquid if it is simultaneously
compressed under a high enough pressure and cooled sufficiently.
Liquid oxygen is pale-blue in color and boils at $-183.0\ °C$. It is
attracted by a magnet, which leads chemists to believe that there
are unpaired electrons in an oxygen molecule. Thus the electron-
dot formula for an oxygen molecule is sometimes written as

rather than

Table 9-1
PROPERTIES OF OXYGEN

atomic number	8
atomic weight	15.9994
electron configuration	2, 6
oxidation numbers	$-2, -1, +2$
melting point	$-218.4\ °C$
boiling point	$-183.0\ °C$
density, 0 °C, 1 atm	1.429 g/L
atom radius	0.70 Å
ion radius, O⁻⁻	1.40 Å

Further cooling of liquid oxygen results in its freezing to a pale-blue crystalline solid at $-218.4\,°C$.

◻ 9.6 Chemical properties of oxygen

Oxygen is one of the most active elements. Oxygen combines with other elements to form compounds called *oxides*. *An **oxide** is a compound consisting of oxygen and usually one other element; in oxides, the oxidation number of oxygen is -2.* When oxides are formed by direct combination of the elements, the reaction is exothermic. Generally, oxides are very stable compounds. Pure oxygen is much more active than air.

Oxygen reacts with the metals of Groups I and II. High temperatures are required to start reactions with the lower-atomic-weight metals lithium, sodium, potassium, magnesium, and calcium. The higher-atomic-weight metals rubidium, cesium, strontium, and barium, on the other hand, react spontaneously at room temperature. The electronegativity difference between oxygen and each of these metals is large. The oxygen compounds formed are ionic compounds.

Lithium reacts with oxygen to form lithium oxide.

$$4Li + O_2 \rightarrow 2Li^+_2O^{--}(s)$$

Depending on conditions, sodium reacts with oxygen to form sodium oxide or sodium peroxide. Heating sodium with dry oxygen at $180\,°C$ yields sodium oxide.

$$4Na + O_2 \xrightarrow{180\,°C} 2Na^+_2O^{--}(s)$$

Combustion of sodium in oxygen yields sodium peroxide.

$$2Na + O_2 \rightarrow Na^+_2O_2^{--}(s)$$

The combustion of potassium, rubidium, and cesium in oxygen yields the peroxides.

The Group II metals react with oxygen under the temperature conditions stated above to yield oxides. The reaction with barium is typical.

$$2Ba + O_2 \rightarrow 2Ba^{++}O^{--}(s)$$

The reactions of nonmetals and oxygen generally occur at the high temperatures of combustion. The electronegativity difference between oxygen and the nonmetals is small. The resulting oxides contain covalent bonds and exist as molecules. The following reactions are examples of this type of oxide formation.

$$S + O_2 \rightarrow SO_2(g)$$
$$C + O_2 \rightarrow CO_2(g)$$
$$2H_2 + O_2 \rightarrow 2H_2O(l)$$

The composition reaction of magnesium burning in the oxygen of the air is shown in Figure 8-5.

The burning of sulfur in oxygen is shown in Figure 8-4.

Reactions between oxygen and metals other than those of Groups I and II may occur slowly at room temperature. They will occur, sometimes quite rapidly, if the temperature is raised. The electronegativity difference between oxygen and these metals is of intermediate value, from about 0.8 to 1.8.

Iron at room temperature and in the presence of moisture unites slowly with oxygen. The resulting product is iron(III) oxide, commonly called rust.

$$4Fe + 3O_2 \rightarrow 2Fe_2O_3(s)$$

A strand of steel picture wire or a small bundle of steel wool, heated red hot and plunged into pure oxygen, burns brilliantly and gives off bright sparks. Molten drops of Fe_3O_4, another oxide of iron, are formed in this reaction but quickly solidify as they cool.

$$3Fe + 2O_2 \rightarrow Fe_3O_4(s)$$

Such metals as tin, lead, copper, and zinc unite with oxygen to form oxides. These reactions occur slowly when the elements are cold, but more rapidly when they are heated. Oxides of metals such as gold and platinum are formed only at high temperatures. The oxides of metals of intermediate electronegativity difference usually have structures that are more complex than those of ionic compounds or simple molecular compounds.

Figure 9-8. Iron burns brilliantly in pure oxygen to form the iron oxide Fe_3O_4.

The detailed explanation of the structures of solids is given in Chapter 12.

◻ 9.7 The test for oxygen

A blazing splint continues to burn in air, but it burns more vigorously in pure oxygen. A glowing splint, lowered into a bottle of pure oxygen, bursts into flame immediately. If a glowing splint, lowered into a bottle of colorless, odorless gas, bursts into flame, the gas *is* oxygen. This test is commonly used to identify oxygen.

◻ 9.8 Uses of oxygen

1. As an essential for life. In higher-order animals, oxygen enters the lungs with the inhaled air. It diffuses through thin membranes of the lungs into the bloodstream, from which it passes into the tissues and fluids of the body.

Fish and other animals that breathe by gills get their oxygen from air that is dissolved in the water.

All plants, except some of the simplest bacteria, also require oxygen.

2. In the iron and steel industry. This is the most important industrial use of oxygen. Oxygen is used in large quantities in the basic-oxygen method of making steel. It is also used for removing surface impurities from steel slabs and for welding and

Figure 9-9. During steel making in a basic-oxygen furnace, impurities are burned off by directing a stream of oxygen from above into the molten metal.

The basic-oxygen method of steel production is described in Chapter 26.

The operation of oxyacetylene torches is explained in Chapters 18 and 19.

cutting steel. Welding and cutting iron and steel are done using oxygen-acetylene torches.

3. For producing chemical compounds. Depending on the proportion of oxygen used, the temperature, and the selection of catalyst, different products are formed when pure oxygen reacts with coal, natural gas, or liquid fuels. Sometimes a mixture of hydrogen and carbon monoxide results. This mixture can be used to make synthetic gasoline, methanol, or ammonia. Under other conditions, partially oxygenated carbon and hydrogen compounds are formed. They can be used to make detergents, synthetic rubber, or compounds used as antifreeze.

4. For medical treatment. Pure oxygen or air to which more oxygen has been added is sometimes given to persons suffering from pneumonia or other diseases. It is also administered to persons who may be too weak to inhale a normal quantity of air because of heart attacks. Small portable oxygen tanks are used as the oxygen supply for active persons with chronic lung disease.

In cases of asphyxiation from inhaling smoke or suffocating gases, from apparent drowning, or from electric shock, oxygen may be administered by using a resuscitator.

5. For water and sewage treatment. Sunlight and oxygen are excellent agents for destroying harmful bacteria. Fountains, cascades, and other aerating devices are used to purify water supplies. By exposing water to air, disease bacteria are destroyed, and the water becomes tastier for drinking.

In sewage disposal plants, sewage is exposed to air in order to increase the amount of dissolved oxygen and thus speed up the purification process. Sometimes oxygen is added to sewage to purify it even faster.

6. For rocket propulsion. Liquid oxygen is used in many rockets and missiles. The fuel may be a kerosene-like liquid or liquid hydrogen. For the very rapid burning needed to propel rockets, oxygen must be supplied in large quantities. Oxygen is needed whether the rocket is moving through the earth's atmosphere or in interplanetary space.

Figure 9-10. Portable oxygen equipment is used for emergency treatment of patients whose breathing may have been impaired.

Figure 9-11. The liquid effluent from a sewage processing plant is treated with oxygen by sprinkling it into the air over rocks.

9.9 Occurrence of ozone

A peculiar odor in the air is often noticed after lightning has flashed nearby. This odor is due to the presence of ozone, O_3, another form of elemental oxygen. Electric discharges through the air, such as sparks from electric machinery or lightning flashes, convert some of the oxygen of the air into ozone.

The ultraviolet rays from the sun change some of the oxygen in the upper atmosphere into ozone. In the stratosphere, between 15 km and 50 km above the earth, ozone occurs to the extent of 5 to 10 parts per million. The greatest concentration of ozone is found at an altitude of about 25 km.

The absorption of ultraviolet rays by this upper-atmosphere layer of ozone protects the earth's surface from most of the sun's ultraviolet radiation. The sun's ultraviolet radiation is one cause of human skin cancer. Too much ultraviolet radiation can cause increased sunburning, skin aging, and eye damage. It can also damage crops, cause cancer in livestock, produce changes in the climate, and bring about environmental changes that would upset the balance between both the water and land systems of plants and animals.

9.10 Preparation of ozone

Ozone is commonly produced by passing oxygen through an ozone generator like that shown in Figure 9-13. This device consists of glass tubes that are partially covered with layers of metal foil. The inner layers of metal foil are connected to one terminal of an induction coil or static electricity machine. The outer layers are connected to the other terminal. The discharge of electricity from one layer to the other provides the energy that converts some of the oxygen passing through the generator to ozone.

In converting oxygen to ozone, energy is absorbed. The preparation of ozone from oxygen is an endothermic reaction. Ozone, therefore, has a higher energy content than oxygen. Ozone is less stable and more active than oxygen. Three molecules of oxygen form two molecules of ozone. This is because oxygen, O_2, has 2 atoms per molecule, while ozone, O_3, has 3 atoms per molecule.

$$3O_2 + \text{energy} \rightarrow 2O_3(g)$$

9.11 The difference between oxygen and ozone

Several chemical elements exist in two or more different forms. Oxygen is one of these elements. Other elements such as carbon, sulfur, and phosphorus also occur in different forms. *The existence of an element in two or more forms in the same physical phase is known as **allotropy**.* The different forms of such elements are called *allotropes*.

OZONE

Figure 9-12. The satellite launched by this rocket in 1979 is used to measure the amount of ozone at various latitudes from a circular orbit nearly 400 miles above the earth.

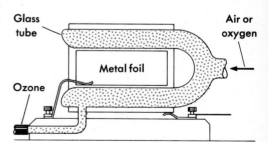

Figure 9-13. An ozone generator. Some of the oxygen passing through the generator is converted to ozone by the electric discharge from one metal-foil layer to the other.

Another reason for allotropy is described in Section 17.3.

Oxygen molecule

Ozone molecule

Figure 9-14. Oxygen molecules consist of two atoms of oxygen. Ozone molecules consist of three atoms of oxygen. Oxygen and ozone are allotropes.

You may wish to review how resonance explains the structure of sulfur dioxide molecules, Section 6.22.

Bond energy is the energy required to break chemical bonds. See Sections 6.9 and 6.11.

Ordinary oxygen and ozone are allotropes of the element oxygen. Allotropes are generally given different names: in this case, oxygen and ozone. One reason for allotropy is that an element has two or more kinds of molecules, each with different numbers of atoms. Thus, oxygen's allotropy is due to the existence of oxygen molecules, O_2, and ozone molecules, O_3.

◻ 9.12 The structure of ozone molecules

Ozone molecules are bent molecules with electron-dot formulas similar to those of sulfur dioxide. The angle between the two oxygen-oxygen bonds is about 117°.

Experimental evidence shows that there is no difference between the two oxygen-oxygen bonds in the ozone molecule. Each bond has a length of 1.28 Å. Thus, the concept of resonance must be used to describe ozone's molecular structure. The electron arrangement in the ozone molecule is a resonance hybrid of the electron-dot formulas written above. Each oxygen-oxygen bond in the molecule is intermediate in properties between single and double covalent bonds.

The oxygen-oxygen bond energy in the ozone molecule is 72 kcal/mole; it is 118 kcal/mole in the oxygen molecule. This bond energy difference means that the oxygen-oxygen bonds in the ozone molecule are weaker than the oxygen-oxygen bond in the oxygen molecule. This bond energy difference is not unexpected. Even though the bonded atoms are the same kind, the bonds in the ozone molecule are longer, 1.28 Å, than those in the oxygen molecule, 1.21 Å.

◻ 9.13 The properties of ozone

Ozone is a poisonous, blue gas with an irritating and pungent odor. It is denser than oxygen and much more soluble in water.

Table 9-2
PHYSICAL PROPERTIES OF OXYGEN AND OZONE

Allotrope	Molecular formula	Color	Odor	Density, 0 °C, 1 atm (g/L)	Melting point (° C)	Boiling point (° C)	Solubility in water, 0 °C (cm³/100 cm³ H_2O)
oxygen	O_2	colorless	odorless	1.429	−218.4	−183.0	4.89
ozone	O_3	blue	pungent, irritating	2.144	−192.7	−111.9	49

Some physical properties of oxygen and ozone are compared in Table 9-2. Because ozone molecules have more energy than oxygen molecules, ozone is one of the most vigorous oxidizing agents known. It destroys bacteria and it causes many colors to fade rapidly.

The presence of ozone in amounts over 0.25 part per million in the cabin atmosphere of jet airplanes that fly long distances in the stratosphere can cause chest pain, coughing, headache, and eye irritation. The amount of ozone in airplanes can be reduced by special charcoal filters.

◻ 9.14 Several important uses of ozone

The uses of ozone are applications of its oxidizing properties. Ozone destroys bacteria, fungi, and algae. Ozone has been used for many years as an excellent water-purifying agent. In concentrations of less than one part per million, it completely sterilizes and deodorizes water, as well as removes certain objectionable impurities such as iron and manganese compounds. Ozone may be used to disinfect sewage. Ozone is also used in producing metal oxides, in bleaching wet paper pulp and wet textile fibers, and in preparing some complex compounds containing carbon, hydrogen, and oxygen.

Figure 9-15. In this water treatment plant in Newport, Rhode Island, ozone is being generated for use in purifying and decolorizing the drinking water supply.

◻ 9.15 Occurrence of hydrogen

Hydrogen is a gas at ordinary temperatures. It ranks ninth in abundance by mass among the chemical elements in the earth's surface environment. In the known universe, however, there are more atoms of hydrogen than of any other chemical element. On the earth, hydrogen is usually combined with other elements in a variety of compounds. There are more compounds of hydrogen than of any other element. Free, or elemental, hydrogen exists as covalent diatomic molecules, H_2. Free hydrogen is not common on earth because of its flammability.

Very small traces of elemental hydrogen, probably derived from volcanoes and coal mines, do exist in the air. However, these amounts are so small that hydrogen is not listed as one of the important gases of the atmosphere. Tremendous quantities of elemental hydrogen occur in the sun and the stars. One ninth of water by mass is combined hydrogen, and all acids contain this element. Hydrogen is a constituent of nearly all plant and animal tissues. Fuels such as natural gas, wood, coal, and oil contain hydrogen compounds.

◻ 9.16 Early history of hydrogen

In the seventeenth century it was observed that a combustible gas was produced when sulfuric acid reacted with iron. The

HYDROGEN

English scientist Henry Cavendish (1731–1810) is usually credited with the discovery of hydrogen because in 1766 he prepared a quantity of the gas and observed its properties. Cavendish observed that hydrogen burns. He called the gas "inflammable air." In 1783, he showed that water is the only product formed when hydrogen burns in air. That same year Lavoisier suggested the name *hydrogen,* a word derived from two Greek words meaning "water producer."

☐ 9.17 Preparation of hydrogen

Replacement reactions of this type are explained in Section 8.6(3). The activity series appears in Table 8-2.

1. From acids by replacement. This is the usual laboratory method of preparing hydrogen. All acids contain hydrogen, which may be displaced by reaction with metals that are above hydrogen in the activity series. Several different acids and metals can be used. For example, iron, zinc, or magnesium will react with either hydrochloric acid or sulfuric acid to produce hydrogen. The rate at which hydrogen is given off in such reactions depends upon several factors: the amount of metal surface exposed to the acid; the temperature; the strength and kind of acid used; the kind of metal used; and the purity of the metal.

Figure 9-16 shows one type of apparatus commonly used for the laboratory preparation of hydrogen. Zinc is put into the generator bottle and either dilute sulfuric or hydrochloric acid is then added through the funnel tube. The hydrogen is collected by water displacement. The equations for the chemical reactions of zinc with sulfuric acid, H_2SO_4, and hydrochloric acid, HCl, are

$$Zn + H_2SO_4 \rightarrow ZnSO_4 + H_2(g)$$

$$Zn + 2HCl \rightarrow ZnCl_2 + H_2(g)$$

If the formulas of the acids are compared with the formulas of the zinc compounds produced, it can easily be seen that an atom of zinc has replaced two atoms of hydrogen. The zinc sulfate or zinc

Figure 9-16. Laboratory setup for the preparation of hydrogen. Any metal more active than hydrogen can be used to replace the hydrogen from any one of many acids. The metal is put in the wide-mouth generator bottle, and the acid is added through the funnel tube. Hydrogen is collected by water displacement.

chloride products are dissolved in the excess water in the generator. Either can be recovered as a white solid by evaporating the water.

2. From water by replacement. Sodium is a silvery metal, soft enough to easily be cut with a knife, and of low enough density to float on water. It reacts vigorously with water and displaces hydrogen from it. Each sodium atom replaces one of the hydrogen atoms in a molecule of water. To show this reaction more clearly, the formula for water is written as HOH, instead of the usual H_2O.

Replacement of hydrogen in water by metals is described in Section 8.6(2).

$$2Na + 2HOH \rightarrow 2NaOH + H_2(g)$$

This equation shows that each water molecule has had *one* of its hydrogen atoms replaced by a sodium atom. The sodium hydroxide produced can be recovered as a white, crystalline solid if the excess water is evaporated.

Potassium is a metal similar to sodium. It is below sodium in Group I in the periodic table and is more active. It displaces hydrogen from water so vigorously that the heat of the reaction ignites the hydrogen.

Figure 24-2 is a photo showing the reaction of potassium and water.

$$2K + 2HOH \rightarrow 2KOH + H_2(g)$$

Magnesium reacts slowly with *boiling* water. Calcium, in the same family as magnesium but more reactive, replaces hydrogen from cold water.

$$Ca + 2HOH \rightarrow Ca(OH)_2 + H_2(g)$$

At a high temperature, iron displaces hydrogen from steam. This iron-steam reaction is the only one of the water-replacement methods of preparing hydrogen described that is used commercially. All the other methods are laboratory methods.

3. From water by electrolysis. In the electrolysis of water, hydrogen as well as oxygen is produced. Commercially, if oxygen is the main product, hydrogen becomes a useful by-product. This method is used in the United States for producing pure hydrogen wherever cheap electricity is available. It is also a laboratory method of preparing hydrogen.

4. From hydrocarbons. Hydrocarbons are compounds of hydrogen and carbon, commonly derived from petroleum or natural gas. If a hydrocarbon such as methane, CH_4, reacts with steam in the presence of a nickel catalyst at a temperature of about 850 °C, hydrogen and carbon monoxide are produced.

$$CH_4 + H_2O \rightarrow CO(g) + 3H_2(g)$$

When this mixture of gaseous products is cooled and compressed, the carbon monoxide liquefies. The remaining hydrogen gas is then compressed into steel cylinders. This is the principal commercial method of producing hydrogen.

5. *From water by hot carbon.* This is another commercial method of producing hydrogen. When steam is passed over red-hot coal or coke, a mixture of gases called *water gas* is formed. It consists mainly of hydrogen and carbon monoxide. The equation for the reaction is

$$C + H_2O \rightarrow CO(g) + H_2(g)$$

Frequently, the carbon monoxide is converted to carbon dioxide by passing the water gas with additional steam over a catalyst, such as iron oxide, at a temperature below 500 °C.

$$CO + H_2O \rightarrow CO_2(g) + H_2(g)$$

Additional hydrogen is produced from the steam, and the resulting carbon dioxide is separated by dissolving it in water under moderate pressure.

◻ 9.18 Physical properties of hydrogen

Hydrogen gas is colorless, odorless, and tasteless. It is the gas of lowest density. Its density is only one fourteenth that of air. One liter of hydrogen at 0 °C under one atmosphere pressure has a mass of 0.0899 gram. It is less soluble than oxygen in water. Because of its low solubility, hydrogen is collected in the laboratory by water displacement.

In 1898, the Scotch chemist and physicist James Dewar (1842–1923) succeeded in converting hydrogen into a liquid by simultaneously cooling the gas to a very low temperature and applying very high pressure. Liquid hydrogen is clear and colorless, and only one fourteenth as dense as water. Thus, liquid hydrogen is the liquid of lowest density, with a mass of only about 70 grams per liter. Under atmospheric pressure, liquid hydrogen boils at −252.9 °C. When a part of the liquid is evaporated, the remainder freezes to an icelike solid. Its melting point is −259.1 °C. Solid hydrogen is also the solid of lowest density, having a mass of about 80 grams per liter.

Hydrogen is *adsorbed* on certain metals such as platinum and palladium. **Adsorption** *is an acquisition of one substance by the surface of another.* Heat is evolved when adsorption occurs. During adsorption, widely separated gas molecules are brought much closer together. This process causes the molecules to give up energy, which appears as heat. Finely divided platinum can adsorb hydrogen so rapidly that the heat given off may ignite the hydrogen.

Hydrogen, as a gas, a liquid, or a solid, is a nonconductor of electricity under usual conditions. The elements, other than hydrogen, that have a single valence electron are metals. Metals have the general property of being conductors of electricity. Scientists believe that it is possible, under very high pressure, to convert hydrogen into a solid having metallic properties.

Table 9-3
PROPERTIES
OF HYDROGEN

atomic number	1
atomic weight	1.0079
electron configuration	1
oxidation numbers	+1, −1
melting point	−259.1 °C
boiling point	−252.9 °C
density, 0 °C, 1 atm	0.0899 g/L
atom radius	0.32 Å
ion radius, H^-	1.53 Å

Do not confuse ad*sorption with* ab*sorption. Absorption is the soaking up of one substance through the entire mass of another.*

☐ 9.19 Chemical properties of hydrogen

1. Reactions with nonmetals. The electronegativity of hydrogen, 2.1, is equal to or less than the electronegativity of other nonmetals. Consequently, hydrogen reacts with nonmetals to form molecular compounds. The polarity of the covalent bonds in these compounds depends on the electronegativity of the nonmetal. The bonds range in polarity from the almost nonpolar H—C bond to the highly polar H—F bond.

Hydrogen burns in air or oxygen with a very hot, pale blue, and nearly invisible flame. Water is the only product. See Figure 9-17.

$$2H_2 + O_2 \rightarrow 2H_2O(g)$$

Hydrogen does not support combustion. If a bottle of hydrogen is held mouth downward while a blazing splint is thrust slowly upward into the bottle, the hydrogen ignites and burns at the mouth of the bottle. But the splint does not burn in the atmosphere of hydrogen inside the bottle. See Figure 9-18.

Hydrogen is not a very active element at ordinary temperatures. A mixture of hydrogen and oxygen must be heated to 800 °C or ignited at a lower temperature by an electric spark to make the gases combine. Then they combine explosively to form water.

Hydrogen and chlorine do not combine when they are mixed in the dark. But in the presence of direct sunlight, they unite explosively to form hydrogen chloride. A jet of hydrogen will burn in chlorine. The equation for these chemical changes is the same.

$$H_2 + Cl_2 \rightarrow 2HCl(g)$$

Under suitable conditions, hydrogen can unite with nitrogen to form ammonia, NH_3, a very important compound.

$$3H_2 + N_2 \rightarrow 2NH_3(g)$$

Electronegativity data are given in Figure 6-14 and Table 6-6.

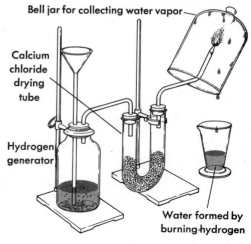

Figure 9-17. Hydrogen is produced by the action of a metal and dilute acid in the generator. The gas then passes through a drying tube filled with calcium chloride, $CaCl_2$. Here the water vapor carried over with the hydrogen from the generator is removed. The dry hydrogen burns at the jet tip in the air-filled bell jar. The water vapor formed during combustion condenses on the cool walls of the bell jar and drops into the collecting vessel. When hydrogen is burned in air, water is the only product.

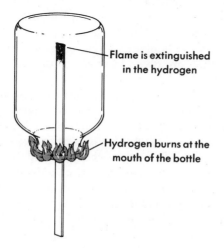

Figure 9-18. When a blazing splint is thrust upward into a bottle of hydrogen, the hydrogen is ignited and burns at the mouth of the bottle. The splint does not burn inside the bottle in an atmosphere of hydrogen. Hydrogen does not support combustion.

2. Reactions with metals. Hydrogen reacts with many non-transition metals to form binary compounds called *hydrides*. In these compounds hydrogen is the more electronegative element. The hydrides of Group I metals and of the Group II metals calcium, strontium, and barium are ionic compounds. At room temperature they are white crystalline solids. In these compounds, hydrogen is present as the H^-, hydride ion, and has an oxidation number of -1. Metallic hydrides can be produced by heating the metal in an atmosphere of hydrogen.

$$2Na + H_2 \rightarrow 2Na^+H^-(s)$$

$$Ba + H_2 \rightarrow Ba^{++}H^-_2(s)$$

The formation of iron-titanium hydride is a safe way to store large quantities of hydrogen in a small volume at ordinary temperatures.

◻ 9.20 The test for hydrogen

Suppose you are given a colorless gas to identify. You suspect it might be hydrogen. If the gas burns in air and forms water, you know that hydrogen is present. If the gas burns in air or oxygen with a nearly colorless flame, and water is the *only* product, then the gas *is* hydrogen.

◻ 9.21 Uses of hydrogen

1. For making hydrogen compounds. Ninety percent of elemental hydrogen produced today is used for preparing two useful hydrogen compounds, ammonia and methanol. Ammonia, NH_3, is made by direct union of nitrogen and hydrogen. Ammonia is then used as the starting point for making fertilizers, explosives, dyestuffs, and many other important compounds. Methanol, CH_3OH, which is used as a solvent and for preparing other compounds, is made from hydrogen and carbon monoxide.

Increasing quantities of hydrogen chloride, HCl, are being prepared by direct combination of hydrogen and chlorine. Hydrogen chloride is then dissolved in water to produce hydrochloric acid.

2. In petroleum refining. Hydrogen is used in refining thick, sulfur-containing crude oil. The addition of hydrogen makes the oil more liquid and removes the sulfur. These changes improve the oil's quality as a fuel. Sulfur is also removed from low-boiling petroleum products by reaction with hydrogen.

3. For solidifying oils. Millions of pounds of cottonseed oil are changed each year from liquid oil to solid or semisolid fat by hydrogenation. Finely divided nickel is the catalyst used in this reaction. Some of the molecules in the liquid oil combine with hydrogen atoms to produce a substance that is solid at room tem-

Hydrogenation: chemical addition of hydrogen to a material.

perature but still a liquid at body temperature. Most vegetable shortenings found on the market today are examples of such hydrogenated oil.

Peanut, corn, soybean, and coconut oil are also hardened by hydrogenation to make margarine. Some fish oils lose their offensive odor when hydrogenated and thus become suitable for making soap. Lard is sometimes hydrogenated to produce a whiter, firmer product.

4. As a reducing agent. Hydrogen can remove oxygen from the oxides of some metals such as copper, tin, lead, zinc, and iron. Hydrogen could be used as a reducing agent to separate these metals from their oxide ores. More often, however, carbon in the form of coke is used as the reducing agent because it is usually less expensive and more convenient.

Some metals must be worked in an atmosphere free of oxygen, called a *reducing atmosphere*. A reducing atmosphere prevents the unwanted reaction of the metal with oxygen at the high temperatures needed for the processes. Tungsten, a metal that is used for making the filaments of electric lamps, is worked in a reducing atmosphere. By surrounding the tungsten with hydrogen in a closed furnace, the oxidation of the metal is prevented.

5. As a fuel. Nearly all fuels contain hydrogen, either free or combined with other elements. Coal gas and oil gas contain hydrogen in quantity. Methane, CH_4, is a major component of natural gas. Hydrogen is used as a fuel for the oxyhydrogen torch. Pure hydrogen makes an excellent fuel but is somewhat more expensive than other available gaseous fuels.

◻ 9.22 Deuterium

Deuterium (described in Section 3.6) was discovered and named in 1931 by scientists at Columbia University headed by Harold C. Urey (1893–1981). In addition to its occurrence on the earth, deuterium exists in the atmosphere of Jupiter, in our sun, in distant stars and nebulae, and in interstellar space. The discoveries of deuterium in space were made by ultraviolet spectroscopes and radio telescopes from the earth's surface or from aboard earth satellites. By studying the relative amounts of protium (hydrogen-1) atoms and deuterium atoms in our galaxy, scientists hope to learn more about the origin and nature of the universe.

Protium atoms consist of a proton nucleus and an orbital electron. Deuterium atoms have a proton and a neutron in the nucleus, and an orbital electron. Consequently, deuterium atoms have a mass about double that of protium atoms. This mass difference between hydrogen isotopes is proportionally larger than between isotopes of any other element. The mass difference is related to differences in physical properties. See Table 9-4.

Models showing the structures of protium and deuterium are shown in Figure 3-4.

Table 9-4
PHYSICAL PROPERTIES OF PROTIUM AND DEUTERIUM

Isotope	Symbol	Atomic mass	Molecular formula	Melting point (°C)	Boiling point (°C)	Density of liquid (g/L)
protium	H	1.007825	H_2	−259.1	−252.9	0.0709 (−252.7 °C)
deuterium	D	2.01410	D_2	−254.6	−249.7	0.169 (−250.9 °C)

The separation of deuterium oxide from water by electrolysis is described in Section 12.20.

Differences in chemical properties of most isotopes are so slight that they are not usually considered. But because of the significant mass difference between its isotopes, this is not true for hydrogen. Protium and deuterium react the same way and form similar compounds. But the rates of their reactions are different. Reactions of deuterium and deuterium compounds are generally much slower than those of protium and protium compounds. This rate difference makes possible the electrolytic separation of deuterium oxide from water.

SUMMARY

Oxygen, the earth's most abundant element, is found in the air, in water, and in the earth's crust. Scheele and Priestley are codiscoverers of oxygen. Oxygen was shown by Lavoisier to be an element, and was named by him. Oxygen can be prepared in the laboratory by decomposing hydrogen peroxide, adding water to sodium peroxide, heating potassium chlorate, and electrolyzing water. Commercially, oxygen is produced from liquid air or by electrolyzing water.

Oxygen is a colorless, odorless, tasteless gas which is slightly denser than air and slightly soluble in water. Liquid oxygen is slightly attracted by a magnet. Oxygen is an active element that combines with other elements to form oxides. An oxide is a compound consisting of oxygen and usually one other element; in oxides the oxidation number of oxygen is −2. Oxygen does not burn, but supports combustion.

Oxygen is necessary for life. It is used extensively in the iron and steel industry and for producing many chemical compounds. Patients who have difficulty breathing are sometimes administered oxygen. Oxygen aids in the purification of water and sewage. It is used to support the combustion of fuels in rockets and missiles.

Ozone is a more active form of oxygen that is produced by electric discharge. It exists naturally in the stratosphere, where it shields the earth from much of the sun's ultraviolet radiation.

The existence of an element in two or more forms in the same physical phase is known as allotropy. The different forms of such elements are allotropes. Oxygen, O_2, and ozone, O_3, are allotropes of the element oxygen. The structure of the ozone molecule is a resonance hybrid of two different structures. Ozone is a vigorous oxidizing agent. It is used in water and sewage purification, for producing metal oxides, for bleaching, and in preparing chemical compounds.

Hydrogen is the most abundant element in the universe. It is found in water, acids, living tissues, and many fuels. It was discovered by Cavendish and named by Lavoisier. In the laboratory, hydrogen is prepared from acids by replacement, from water by replacement, and from water by electrolysis. Industrially, hydrogen is prepared from hydrocarbons, from water by hot carbon, and from water by electrolysis.

Hydrogen is a colorless, odorless, tasteless gas that has the lowest density of any material known. It is very slightly soluble in water. Platinum and palladium adsorb hydrogen. Adsorption is an acquisition of one substance by the surface of another. It is believed that at very low temperatures and extremely high pressures, solid hydrogen can acquire metallic properties.

Hydrogen burns with a very hot flame that is nearly invisible. Hydrogen does not support combustion. Hydrogen is not active at ordinary temperatures. A mixture of hydrogen and oxygen, when ignited, produces an explosion and water vapor is the only product. Hydrogen and chlorine react to form hydrogen chloride. Hydrogen and nitrogen can be made to react; ammonia is the product. Hydrogen reacts with many nontransition metals to form hydrides.

Hydrogen is used for making hydrogen compounds, principally ammonia and methanol. It is used in petroleum refining, for solidifying oils, as a reducing agent, and as a fuel.

Deuterium, the hydrogen isotope with mass number 2, has different physical properties from protium, hydrogen-1. Chemically it reacts more slowly than protium. This is the result of the proportionally great mass difference between the two isotopes.

◖ | VOCABULARY

adsorption
allotropy
combined oxygen

deuterium
free oxygen
hydride

oxide
ozone
reducing atmosphere

◖ | QUESTIONS

Group A

1. (a) Distinguish between *free* oxygen and *combined* oxygen. (b) What are the most abundant sources of each on the earth?
2. Describe (a) Scheele's discovery of oxygen; (b) Priestley's discovery of oxygen.
3. (a) What is a catalyst? (b) What is its purpose in the preparation of oxygen from hydrogen peroxide? (c) What is its purpose in the preparation of oxygen from potassium chlorate?
4. Why is it possible to collect oxygen by water displacement?
5. (a) When liquid air is permitted to stand, which gas boils away first? (b) Why?
6. What are the physical properties of oxygen gas?
7. What is an *oxide?*
8. How do you test a colorless, odorless, tasteless gas to determine whether it is oxygen or not?
9. How is oxygen used in the iron and steel industry?
10. What chemical property of oxygen makes it useful in water and sewage purification?
11. (a) Where does ozone occur naturally? (b) How does this affect life on the earth's surface?
12. (a) What is allotropy? (b) In what way does the element oxygen exhibit allotropy?
13. What chemical property of ozone determines its uses?
14. Describe the abundance of free and combined hydrogen on the earth.
15. In the explorable universe, which is more abundant, oxygen or hydrogen?
16. (a) What substances are used for the usual laboratory preparation of hydrogen? (b) What products are formed?
17. Give five physical properties of hydrogen.
18. Distinguish between *adsorption* and *absorption.*

19. (*a*) Does hydrogen support combustion ? (*b*) What simple laboratory test can you use to demonstrate this?
20. How do you test a colorless, odorless, tasteless gas to determine whether it is hydrogen or not?
21. For what purpose is most elemental hydrogen used commercially?
22. (*a*) What is a reducing atmosphere? (*b*) Why is it useful?

Group B
23. Lavoisier did not discover any new substances. He did not design any new laboratory apparatus. He did not develop any better preparation methods. Yet Lavoisier is recognized as one of the greatest eighteenth-century chemists. Why?
24. (*a*) Write balanced formula equations for each of the four laboratory methods of preparing oxygen. (*b*) Assign oxidation numbers to each oxygen atom in these equations. (*c*) For each equation, determine whether the oxygen was oxidized, reduced, or both.
25. Why do chemists believe there are unpaired electrons in an oxygen molecule?
26. Write balanced formula equations for the following reactions: (*a*) Potassium burns in oxygen and yields the ionic compound potassium peroxide. (*b*) Calcium reacts with oxygen and yields the ionic compound calcium oxide. (*c*) Nitrogen reacts with oxygen and forms the covalent compound nitrogen monoxide.
27. Oxygen and fluorine combine indirectly and form OF_2. Is this compound an oxide? Give a reason for your answer.
28. Why is air enriched with oxygen helpful to persons with lung or heart disease?
29. Compare the energy content and activity of oxygen molecules and ozone molecules.
30. Describe the bonding in the ozone molecule.

31. Why is Cavendish credited with the discovery of hydrogen, even though the gas had been known much earlier?
32. What factors determine the rate at which hydrogen is evolved from hydrochloric acid by reaction with coarse iron filings?
33. (*a*) From its position in the periodic table, would you expect cesium to react with water more or less vigorously than potassium? (*b*) Why?
34. Write the balanced chemical equation for the principal commercial method of producing hydrogen.
35. In the reaction of steam on hot coke for producing water gas, which substance is (*a*) the oxidizing agent; (*b*) the reducing agent; (*c*) the substance oxidized; (*d*) the substance reduced?
36. What physical property change of hydrogen can be used to determine the conditions under which hydrogen can be changed from its usual nonmetallic properties to those of metals?
37. (*a*) What product is formed when hydrogen combines with chlorine? (*b*) with nitrogen? (*c*) What type of bond does hydrogen form with these two elements? (*d*) Of what type of particle do these compounds consist?
38. (*a*) What product is formed when hydrogen combines with potassium? (*b*) with strontium? (*c*) What type of bond does hydrogen form with these two elements? (*d*) Of what type of particle do these compounds consist?
39. Tin(II) oxide reacts with hydrogen to form tin and water vapor. In this reaction, which substance is (*a*) the oxidizing agent; (*b*) the reducing agent; (*c*) oxidized; (*d*) reduced?
40. (*a*) Protium atoms and deuterium atoms are both classed as hydrogen atoms, yet they have different physical properties. Why? (*b*) In what way are their chemical properties different?

The Gas Laws

The history of civilization records the existence of several families of geniuses. An exceptional example is the Bachs. In eight generations, the Bach family produced at least twenty-five eminent musicians. What the Bachs were to music, the Bernoullis were to science. As mathematicians, physicists, botanists, chemists, and astronomers, the Bernoullis have greatly enriched our store of scientific knowledge. Nearly two hundred years ago, Daniel Bernoulli set forth the fundamental principles of fluid behavior in his now famous book, Hydrodynamica. *Assuming that gases consist of "very minute corpuscles," "practically infinite in number," "driven hither and thither with a very rapid motion," Bernoulli explained why gases exert pressure, take the shape of their containers, and expand when heated. Describing heat as "an increasing internal motion of the particles," Bernoulli was not only giving an explanation for this expansion, but also saying that heat is a form of energy — energy possessed by particles in motion.*

◻ 10.1 Kinetic theory

In Chapter 1, matter was described as existing in three physical phases—gas, liquid, and solid. In later chapters, it was explained that the particles making up various substances are atoms, molecules, or ions. A physical model will now be used to help you understand the properties of gases, liquids, and solids. This model explains the properties in terms of (1) the forces between the particles of matter, and (2) the energy these particles possess. This useful model is the *kinetic theory.*

Most of the data in support of the kinetic theory comes from indirect observation. It is almost impossible to observe the behavior of individual particles of matter. However, scientists can observe the behavior of large groups of particles. From the results of these observations, they can describe the average behavior of the particles under study.

The three basic assumptions of the *kinetic theory* are:

1. Matter is composed of very tiny particles. The chemical properties of the particles of matter depend on their composition. Their physical properties depend on the forces they exert on each other and the distance separating them.

2. The particles of matter are in continual motion. Their average kinetic energy (energy of motion) depends on temperature.

3. The total kinetic energy of colliding particles remains constant. When individual particles collide, some lose energy while others gain energy. But there is no overall energy loss. Collisions of this type are said to be *elastic* collisions.

In this chapter you will gain an understanding of:

- the three basic assumptions of the kinetic theory
- the properties of gases
- the attractive forces between gas molecules
- the dependency of gas volume on temperature and pressure
- the Kelvin temperature scale
- Boyle's law and Charles' law
- solving problems involving calculation of new volume, temperature, or pressure

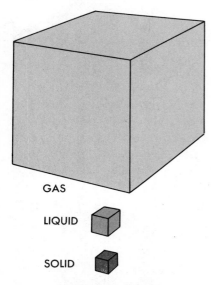

GAS

LIQUID

SOLID

Figure 10-1. The density of many substances in the gaseous phase is about 1/1000 of their density in the liquid and solid phases. This diagram shows the relative volumes of 1.5 g of oxygen as a gas, a liquid, and a solid. The oxygen gas occupies 1050 mL, whereas liquid oxygen occupies 1.3 mL and solid oxygen occupies 1.0 mL.

Figure 10-2. The rate of diffusion of bromine vapor in air. Diffusion has occurred for 2 minutes in the left cylinder. Diffusion has occurred for 20 minutes in the right cylinder.

10.2 Observed properties of gases

A study of gases reveals four characteristic properties:

1. Expansion. A gas does not have a definite shape or a definite volume. It completely fills any container in which it is confined. For example, the shape and volume of the air in balloons of various sizes and shapes, in automobile tires, and in air mattresses are determined by the container.

2. Pressure. When a toy balloon is inflated, it becomes larger because the pressure on its inside surface is increased. If the air is allowed to escape, the balloon becomes smaller because the pressure is decreased. Raising the temperature of the air in the balloon by warming it causes the balloon to become larger. This observation indicates that pressure increases with an increase in temperature. As the balloon cools, its size decreases because the pressure decreases.

3. Low density. The density of a gas is about $\frac{1}{1000}$ of the density of the same substance in the liquid or solid phase. The densities of gaseous, liquid, and solid oxygen and hydrogen are typical data. Oxygen gas has a density of 1.429 g/L (0.001429 g/mL) at 0 °C and 1 atmosphere pressure. Liquid oxygen has a density of 1.149 g/mL at −183 °C, and solid oxygen has a density of 1.426 g/mL at −252.5 °C. Hydrogen gas has a density of 0.0899 g/L (0.0000899 g/mL) at 0 °C and 1 atmosphere pressure. Liquid hydrogen has a density of 0.0708 g/mL at −253 °C. Solid hydrogen has a density of 0.0706 g/mL at −262 °C. See Figure 10-1.

4. Diffusion. If the stopper is removed from a container of ammonia, the irritating effects of this gas on the eyes, nose, and throat soon become evident throughout the room. When the chemistry class makes the foul-odored hydrogen sulfide gas in the laboratory, objections may come from other students and teachers in all parts of the building. This process of spreading out spontaneously (without additional help) to occupy a space uniformly is characteristic of all gases. It is known as *diffusion.* See Figure 10-2.

10.3 Kinetic-theory description of a gas

According to the kinetic theory, a gas consists of very small independent particles that move at random in space and experience elastic collisions. This theoretical description is of an imaginary gas called the **ideal gas.**

The particles of substances that are gases at room temperature are molecules. Some of these molecules consist of a single atom (He, Ne, Ar). Many consist of two atoms (O_2, H_2, HCl, etc.). Others consist of several atoms (NH_3, CH_4, C_2H_2, etc.). Matter in the gaseous phase occupies a volume of the order of 1000 times that which it occupies in the liquid or solid phase. Thus, molecules of gases are much farther apart than those of liquids or solids. This difference accounts for the much lower density of gases as compared to solids or liquids. Even so, 1 mL of a gas at 0 °C and 1 atmosphere pressure contains about 3×10^{19} molecules. Many ordinary molecules have diameters of the order of 4 Å, or 4×10^{-10} m. In gases, these molecules are widely separated. They are, on an average, about 4×10^{-9} m (or about 10 diameters) apart at 0 °C and 1 atmosphere pressure. The kinetic energy of the molecules of a gas (except near its condensing temperature) overcomes the attractive forces between them. The molecules of a gas are essentially independent particles. These molecules travel in random directions at high speed. This speed is of the order of 10^3 m/s at 0 °C and is independent of the pressure. At this speed, molecules of a gas travel about 10^{-7} m before colliding with other gas molecules or with the walls of the container. Because gas molecules collide and exchange energy, their speeds will vary. They undergo about 5×10^9 collisions per second.

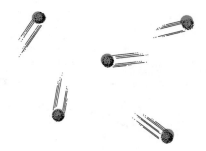

Figure 10-3. Molecules of a gas are widely separated and move rapidly.

The expansion and diffusion of gases are both explained by the fact that gas molecules are essentially independent particles. They move through space until they strike other gas molecules or the walls of the container. A gas moves very rapidly into an evacuated container. Gaseous diffusion is slowed down, but not prevented, by the presence of other gases. The rate of diffusion of one gas through another depends on three properties of the intermingling gas molecules:

1. Speed,

2. Diameter,

3. Attractive force.

Hydrogen diffuses rapidly because hydrogen molecules are smaller and move about with greater speed than the larger, heavier molecules of other gases at the same temperature. The diffusion of hydrogen can be demonstrated by placing a bottle filled with hydrogen above another bottle filled with air, as shown in Figure 10-4. After a few minutes, the mouth of each bottle is held in the flame of a laboratory burner. The resulting explosions show that the hydrogen molecules moved so that there were some in both bottles.

Even if two gases are separated by a porous barrier, such as a membrane or an unglazed porcelain cup, diffusion takes place through the pores. See Figure 10-5. An unglazed porcelain cup is closed by a rubber stopper through which a piece of glass tubing has been inserted. When a large beaker filled with hydrogen is placed over the porcelain cup, hydrogen molecules diffuse into the cup faster than the molecules of the gases in air diffuse out of the cup and into the beaker. This creates a pressure in the cup that forces gas out the end of the tube.

Gas pressure results from many billions of moving molecules continuously hitting the walls of the container. If the num-

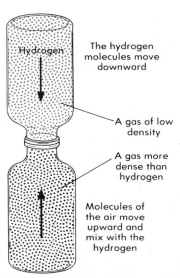

The hydrogen molecules move downward

A gas of low density

A gas more dense than hydrogen

Molecules of the air move upward and mix with the hydrogen

Figure 10-4. Even though hydrogen is less dense than air, hydrogen diffuses downward and air upward.

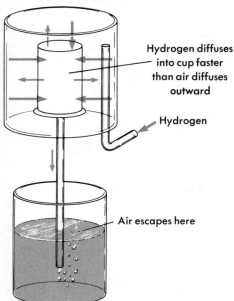

Figure 10-5. Because hydrogen diffuses into the cup faster than air diffuses outward, the net pressure in the cup increases, forcing gas bubbles out of the tube.

ber of molecules within the container is increased, the number that strike any area of the inside surface increases. Therefore, the pressure on the inside surface increases. If the temperature of the gas is raised, the molecules on an average have more kinetic energy. They move more rapidly and collide more energetically with the walls of the container. These more frequent and more energetic collisions with the container walls increase the pressure. The pressure drops when the number of molecules is decreased or the temperature is lowered.

Figure 10-6 shows the distribution of molecular speeds in a gas at two different temperatures. From these graphs two conclusions can be drawn:

1. All molecules of a gas do not have the same speed.

2. An increase in temperature increases the average rate at which gas molecules move.

The kinetic energy of a molecule is related to its speed by the equation

$$E_k = \tfrac{1}{2}mv^2$$

where E_k is the kinetic energy of the molecule, m is its mass, and v is its speed. Since the molecules of a gas do not all have the same speed, they will not all have the same kinetic energy. Since the average molecular speed varies with the temperature, the average kinetic energy of the molecules of a gas varies with the temperature. Thus, the temperature of a gas provides an indication of the average kinetic energy of the molecules. The higher the temperature, the higher the average kinetic energy. The lower the temperature, the lower the average kinetic energy.

☐ 10.4 Attractive forces between gas molecules

The lowest temperature at which a substance can exist as a gas at atmospheric pressure is the *condensation temperature* of the gas. At this temperature, the kinetic energy of the gas particles is not sufficient to overcome the forces of attraction between the particles. The gas condenses to a liquid. The kinetic theory states that the temperature of a substance is a measure of the kinetic energy of its particles. So a study of condensation temperatures of various substances should provide an idea of the magnitude (size) of the forces of attraction between particles of matter. Table 10-1 gives selected condensation temperatures.

Substances such as H_2, O_2, and CH_4 (methane) consist of low-molecular-weight nonpolar covalent molecules. They can exist as gases at very low temperatures. Evidently the attractive forces between such molecules in the gaseous phase are very small. More complex substances such as CCl_4 and C_6H_6 (benzene) have condensation temperatures somewhat above room temperature. They have higher-molecular-weight non-

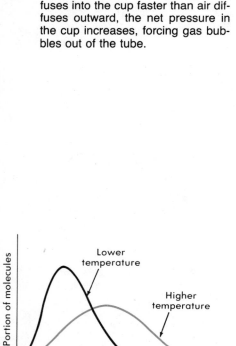

Figure 10-6. Molecular speed distribution in a gas at different temperatures.

polar molecules. The forces of attraction between such molecules must be greater than those between similar molecules that are less complex.

Ammonia (NH_3) and H_2O consist of polar covalent molecules. Notice that their molecular weights are low and their molecular structures are simple. Even so, their condensation temperatures are considerably above those of nonpolar molecules of the same molecular weight.

The condensation temperatures of ionic compounds such as sodium chloride, covalent network substances such as diamond, and metals are all very high. Evidently the attractive forces between particles of such substances are very strong. The nature of these forces will be described in Chapter 12.

The attractive forces between molecules are called *van der Waals forces*. These forces are important only when molecules are very close together. Hence van der Waals forces are not important in gases unless the gas molecules are under very high pressure or are at a temperature near their condensation temperature. Van der Waals forces are of two types. One type, called *dispersion interaction,* exists between all molecules. The other type, called *dipole-dipole attraction,* exists between polar molecules only.

The strength of dispersion interaction depends on the number of electrons in a molecule and the tightness with which the electrons are held. The greater the number of electrons and the less tightly they are bound, the more powerful is the attractive force of dispersion interaction. This effect can be observed most easily between nonpolar molecules, where dispersion interaction is the only type of attractive force. Thus, for nonpolar molecules in general, the higher the molecular weight, the higher the condensation temperature. This generalization can be observed in Table 10-1. Compare the condensation temperatures of oxygen, hydrogen, and methane with those of carbon tetrachloride and benzene. The energy associated with dispersion interaction is only a few tenths of a kilocalorie per mole.

Dipole-dipole attraction is the attraction between the oppositely charged portions of neighboring polar molecules. Remember from Section 6.21 that polar molecules are sometimes called dipoles. Dipole-dipole attractive forces as well as dispersion interaction forces act between polar molecules. This combination of forces accounts for the much higher condensation temperatures of polar molecules as compared to nonpolar molecules of similar complexity. For example, methane, ammonia, and water have comparable molecular weights. Yet the condensation temperature of ammonia is about 130 C° higher than that of methane. The condensation temperature of water is over 130 C° higher than that of ammonia. The energy associated with dipole-dipole attraction can be as high as 6 kilocalories per mole.

Table 10-1
CONDENSATION TEMPERATURES OF REPRESENTATIVE SUBSTANCES

Type of substance	Substance	Condensation temperature (1 atm, °C)
nonpolar covalent molecular	H_2	−253
	O_2	−183
	CH_4	−164
	CCl_4	77
	C_6H_6	80
polar covalent molecular	NH_3	−33
	H_2O	100
ionic	NaCl	1413
	MgF_2	2239
covalent network	$(SiO_2)_x$	2230
	C_x (diamond)	4200
metallic	Hg	357
	Cu	2567
	Fe	2750
	W	5660

Johannes Diderik van der Waals (1837–1923) was a Dutch scientist who helped explain the differences in physical properties between real gases and the ideal gas.

Specific temperatures are expressed in °C. Temperature intervals are expressed in C°.

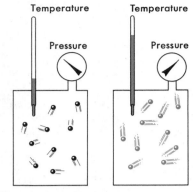

Figure 10-7. At constant volume, as the temperature of a gas increases, the pressure it exerts increases.

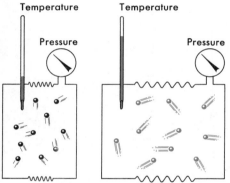

Figure 10-8. At constant pressure, as the temperature of a gas increases, the volume it occupies increases.

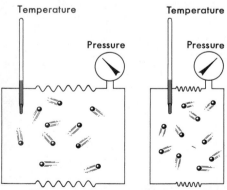

Figure 10-9. At constant temperature, as the volume of a gas decreases, the pressure it exerts increases.

☐ 10.5 Dependence of gas volume on temperature and pressure

A given number of molecules can occupy widely different volumes. The expression "a liter of air" means little unless the temperature and pressure at which it is measured are known. A liter of air can be compressed to a few milliliters in volume. It can also expand to fill an auditorium. Steel cylinders containing oxygen and hydrogen are widely used in industry. They have an internal volume of about 55 liters. When such cylinders are returned "empty," they still contain about 55 liters of gas, although when they were delivered "full" they may have had 100 times as many molecules of the gas compressed within the cylinder.

You have learned that the temperature of a gas is an indication of the average kinetic energy of its molecules. The higher the temperature of a gas, the more kinetic energy its molecules have, and the more rapidly they move about. The pressure that a gas exerts on the walls of its container is the result of the collisions of gas molecules with the walls. Gas molecules that have more kinetic energy (because they are at a higher temperature) undergo more frequent and energetic collisions with the walls. If the volume of one mole of gas molecules remains constant, the pressure exerted by the gas increases as its temperature is raised. It follows that the pressure exerted by one mole of gas molecules decreases as the temperature is lowered. This relationship is shown in Figure 10-7.

Furthermore, if the pressure exerted by one mole of gas molecules is to remain the same as the temperature increases, the volume that the gas occupies must increase. Since the molecules move faster at higher temperatures, they strike the walls of the container more frequently and with more force. Suppose the area of the wall is increased. Then the force of collisions on a unit area of the wall can remain the same as at the lower temperature, and the pressure will remain the same. The area that the molecules strike can be enlarged by enlarging the volume of the container. On the other hand, if the pressure remains constant and the temperature decreases, the volume that one mole of gas molecules occupies must decrease. See Figure 10-8.

Finally, suppose the temperature of one mole of gas molecules remains constant. Then the pressure exerted by the gas becomes greater as the volume that the gas occupies becomes smaller. And similarly, the pressure exerted by one mole of gas molecules is less if the volume available to the gas is larger. See Figure 10-9. In light of these consequences, the kinetic theory satisfactorily explains how gas volumes are related to the temperature and pressure of the gas. Accordingly, both temperature and pressure must be considered when measuring the volume of a gas.

☐ 10.6 Standard temperature and pressure

As explained in Section 10.5, the volume of a gas depends greatly on temperature and pressure. For this reason, it is very helpful to have a standard temperature and a standard pressure for use in measuring or comparing gas volumes. *Standard temperature is defined as exactly zero degrees Celsius.* It is the temperature of melting ice. This temperature was selected because pure water is widely available and the melting temperature of ice is not significantly affected by pressure changes. *Standard pressure is defined as the pressure exerted by a column of mercury exactly 760 millimeters high.* This value is used as the standard pressure because it is the average atmospheric pressure at sea level. Temperatures are easily measured with an accurate thermometer. The pressure of a gas in simple gas experiments can be determined from a properly corrected barometer reading. Standard temperature and pressure are commonly abbreviated as STP.

☐ 10.7 Variation of gas volume with pressure: Boyle's law

If a rubber ball filled with air is squeezed, the volume of the gas inside is decreased. But the gas expands again when the pressure is released. The English chemist and physicist Robert Boyle (1627–1691) was the first scientist to make careful measurements showing the relationship between pressures and volumes of gases. The results of these and later experiments by other scientists established that the pressure on a gas and its volume are inversely proportional. Doubling the pressure on a gas reduces its volume by one-half. Reducing the pressure on a gas to one-third enables it to expand and occupy a volume three times as great. This relationship has been formulated into a law that bears Boyle's name. *Boyle's law* is stated: *The volume of a definite quantity of dry gas is inversely proportional to the pressure, provided the temperature remains constant.*

This law is expressed mathematically as

$$\frac{V}{V'} = \frac{p'}{p}$$

V is the original volume, V' the new volume, p the original pressure, and p' the new pressure. Solving the expression for V', Boyle's law takes the form:

$$V' = V \frac{p}{p'}$$

☐ 10.8 Using Boyle's law

Suppose 40.0 mL of hydrogen gas, collected when the barometer reading is $74\overline{0}$ mm, stands until the barometric pressure has risen to $75\overline{0}$ mm. If the temperature is unchanged, the volume

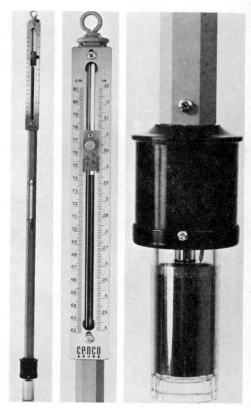

Figure 10-10. A barometer is used to measure atmospheric pressure. Left, a laboratory mercurial barometer. Center, a close-up of the top of the mercury column showing the height-measuring scales. Right, the adjustable reservoir with indicator pin for setting the height of the mercury level exposed to the atmosphere.

Robert Boyle is considered to be the founder of modern chemistry because (1) he recognized that chemistry is a worthwhile field of learning and not just a branch of medicine or alchemy; (2) he introduced careful experimentation into chemistry; and (3) he defined an element as something that could be combined with other elements to form compounds but could not itself be decomposed—a definition that held for over 200 years.

If you need to review inverse proportion, see Section 1.22.

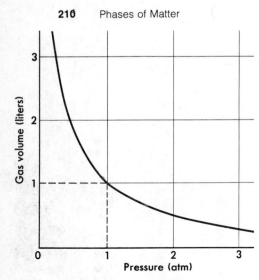

Figure 10-11. The variation of volume with pressure at constant temperature of 1 liter of an ideal gas measured at 1 atmosphere pressure. $pV = constant$.

of gas becomes smaller because of the increased pressure. The new gas volume is measured as 39.5 mL.

Using Boyle's law, the new volume resulting from the pressure change can be calculated without actually experiencing the pressure change. The new volume V' is p/p', or $74\bar{0}$ mm/$75\bar{0}$ mm of the original volume V, 40.0 mL. Substituting this value in the Boyle's law formula, the new volume is calculated as

$$V' = Vp/p'$$
$$V' = 40.0 \text{ mL} \times 74\bar{0} \text{ mm}/75\bar{0} \text{ mm}$$
$$V' = 39.5 \text{ mL}$$

Later, if the pressure falls to $72\bar{0}$ mm, the new gas volume V' is calculated as

$$V' = 40.0 \text{ mL} \times 74\bar{0} \text{ mm}/72\bar{0} \text{ mm}$$
$$V' = 41.1 \text{ mL}$$

The following Sample Problem gives another example of Boyle's law.

SAMPLE PROBLEM

A $20\bar{0}$-mL sample of hydrogen is collected when the pressure is $80\bar{0}$ mm of mercury. What volume will the gas occupy at $76\bar{0}$ mm pressure?

SOLUTION

$$V' = Vp/p'$$
$$V'_{76\bar{0}mm} = 20\bar{0} \text{ mL} \times 80\bar{0} \text{ mm}/76\bar{0} \text{ mm}$$
$$V'_{76\bar{0}mm} = 211 \text{ mL}$$

PRACTICE PROBLEM

Oxygen, 19.0 mL, is collected at a pressure of $73\bar{0}$ mm. What is its volume at $76\bar{0}$ mm pressure?   *ans.* $V'_{76\bar{0} \text{ mm}} = 18.2$ mL

10.9 Variation of gas volume with temperature

Bread dough rises when put in a hot oven. The increase in temperature causes the bubbles of carbon dioxide gas within the dough to expand. The rather large increase in the volume of the dough during baking shows that the gas must expand considerably as the temperature increases. In fact, gases expand many times as much per degree rise in temperature as do liquids and solids.

Jacques Charles (1746–1823), a French scientist, was the first to make careful measurements of the changes in volume of gases with changes in temperature. His experiments revealed that:

1. All gases expand or contract at the same rate with changes in temperature, provided the pressure is unchanged.

2. The change in volume amounts to $\frac{1}{273}$ of the original volume at 0 °C for each Celsius degree the temperature is changed.

You may start with a definite volume of a gas at 0 °C and experiment by heating it. Just as the whole of anything may be considered as made up of two halves, $\frac{2}{2}$, or three thirds, $\frac{3}{3}$, so this volume can be considered as $\frac{273}{273}$. If the gas is warmed one Celsius degree, it expands $\frac{1}{273}$ of its original volume. Its new volume is $\frac{274}{273}$. In the same manner, the gas expands $\frac{100}{273}$ when it is heated $10\overline{0}$ C°. Such expansion, added to the original volume, makes the new volume $\frac{373}{273}$. Any gas warmed 273 Celsius degrees expands $\frac{273}{273}$. That is, its volume is doubled, as represented by the fraction $\frac{546}{273}$.

A gas whose volume is measured at 0 °C contracts by $\frac{1}{273}$ of this volume if it is cooled 1 C°. Its new volume is $\frac{272}{273}$ of its original volume. Cooling the gas to $-10\overline{0}$ °C reduces the volume by $\frac{100}{273}$. In other words, the gas shrinks to $\frac{173}{273}$ of its original volume. At this rate, if the gas were cooled to -273 °C, it would lose $\frac{273}{273}$ of its volume. Its new volume would be zero. Such a situation cannot occur, however, because all gases become liquids before such a low temperature is reached. This rate of contraction with cooling applies only to gases.

❏ 10.10 Kelvin temperature scale

In Section 1.15 the Celsius temperature scale was described. This scale is based on the *triple point* of water. The **triple point** *of pure water is that single temperature and pressure condition at which water exists in all three phases at equilibrium.* On the Celsius scale, the triple point of water has a temperature of 0.01 °C.

From measuring the variation of gas volume with temperature at low pressures, scientists believe that -273.15 °C is the lowest possible temperature. At this temperature a body would have lost all the heat that it is possible for it to lose. Scientists

You may wish to review Section 1.15.

Table 10-2
COMPARISON OF TEMPERATURES ON THE KELVIN AND CELSIUS SCALES

Celsius scale (°C)	Kelvin scale (°K)
100°	373°
50°	323°
20°	293°
5°	278°
4°	277°
3°	276°
2°	275°
1°	274°
0°	273°
−100°	173°
−273°	0°

have come very close to this lowest possible temperature, but theoretically it is impossible to reach. The interval between the lowest possible temperature, −273.15 °C, and the triple-point temperature of water, 0.01 °C, is 273.16 C°.

The physicist Sir William Thomson (1824–1907), better known by his title Lord Kelvin, invented the Kelvin temperature scale. A Kelvin degree is the same temperature interval as a Celsius degree. But 0 °K is the lowest possible temperature, −273.15 °C. The temperature of the triple point of water is 273.16 °K. The lowest possible temperature, 0 °K, is frequently called *absolute zero*. Temperatures measured on the Kelvin scale are often called *absolute temperatures*.

The normal freezing point of water is 0.01 C° lower than the triple-point temperature of water. On the Celsius scale the normal freezing point of water is 0.00 °C. Recall that a Kelvin degree is the same temperature interval as a Celsius degree. So the normal freezing point of water is also 0.01 K° lower than the triple-point temperature of water, 273.16 °K, or 273.15 °K. Thus, 0.00 °C = 273.15 °K. In many calculations, 273.15 °K is rounded off to 273 °K. Table 10-2 will help you compare Kelvin and Celsius temperatures.

Kelvin temperature = Celsius temperature + 273 °

In Section 10.3, you learned that the temperature of a gas provides an indication of the average kinetic energy of the molecules. Since the Kelvin scale starts at what is believed to be the lowest possible temperature, the average kinetic energy of the molecules of a gas is directly proportional to the Kelvin temperature of the gas.

☐ 10.11 Charles' law

Thermometers are not graduated (marked) to give Kelvin-scale readings. But use of the Kelvin scale does give results that correspond with actual volume changes observed in gases. In problems dealing with changes in gas volumes as temperatures vary, the Kelvin scale eliminates the use of zero and of negative numbers. Using the Kelvin temperature scale, *Charles' law* can be stated: *The volume of a definite quantity of dry gas varies directly with the Kelvin temperature, provided the pressure remains constant.*

Charles' law may be expressed mathematically as

$$\frac{V}{V'} = \frac{T}{T'}$$

where V is the original volume, V' the new volume, T the original *Kelvin* temperature, and T' the new *Kelvin* temperature. Solving

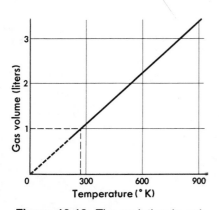

Figure 10-12. The variation in volume with Kelvin temperature at constant pressure of 1 liter of an ideal gas measured at 273 °K. V/T = constant.

the expression for V',

If you need to review direct proportion, see Section 1.22.

$$V' = V \frac{T'}{T}$$

The Sample Problem below illustrates the use of this formula.

SAMPLE PROBLEM

A 50.0-mL volume of gas is measured at $2\overline{0}$ °C. If the pressure remains unchanged, what will be the volume of the gas at $\overline{0}$ °C?

SOLUTION

Change the Celsius temperatures to Kelvin temperatures:

$$2\overline{0} \text{ °C} + 273 \text{ °} = 293 \text{ °K}; \overline{0} \text{ °C} + 273 \text{ °} = 273 \text{ °K}$$
$$V' = VT'/T$$
$$V'_{\overline{0}\text{ °C}} = 50.0 \text{ mL} \times 273 \text{ °K}/293 \text{ °K}$$
$$V'_{\overline{0}\text{ °C}} = 46.6 \text{ mL}$$

| PRACTICE PROBLEMS

1. A 50.0-mL volume of gas is measured at $2\overline{0}$ °C. If the pressure remains unchanged, what will be the volume of the gas at $4\overline{0}$ °C?   *ans.* $V'_{4\overline{0}\text{ °C}}$ = 53.4 mL

2. A gas volume, 149 mL, is measured at 25 °C. What is the gas volume at $\overline{0}$ °C if the pressure does not change? *ans.* $V'_{\overline{0}\text{ °C}}$ = 136 mL

☐ 10.12 Use of Boyle's and Charles' laws combined

Calculation of the new volume of a gas when both temperature and pressure are changed involves no new principles. The new volume is the same whether the changes in temperature and pressure are done together or in either order. The original volume is first multiplied by a ratio of the pressures. In this way the new volume corrected for pressure alone is determined. Then this answer is multiplied by a ratio of the Kelvin temperatures. This gives the new volume corrected for both pressure and temperature. Expressed mathematically,

$$V' = V \times \frac{p}{p'} \times \frac{T'}{T}$$

The following Sample Problem illustrates the use of this formula. You will find it much easier to solve gas-law problems if you use logarithms, a slide rule, or a calculator in making your calculations.

SAMPLE PROBLEM

A gas measures 25.0 mL at $2\overline{0}$ °C and 735 mm pressure. What will be its volume at 15 °C and $75\overline{0}$ mm pressure?

SOLUTION

$$2\overline{0}\,°C = 293\,°K;\ 15\,°C = 288\,°K$$

$$V' = V \times p/p' \times T'/T$$

$$V'_{15\,°C,\ 75\overline{0}\ mm} = 25.0\ mL \times 735\ mm/75\overline{0}\ mm \times 288\,°K/293\,°K$$

$$V'_{15\,°C,\ 75\overline{0}\ mm} = 24.1\ mL$$

PRACTICE PROBLEM

A gas occupies 37.5 mL at 27 °C and $72\overline{0}$ mm pressure. What will be its volume at 12 °C and $75\overline{0}$ mm pressure?

ans. $V'_{12\,°C,\ 75\overline{0}\ mm} = 34.2\ mL$

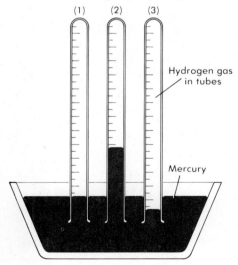

Figure 10-13. In (1) the pressure of the hydrogen is the same as that of the atmosphere. In (2) the pressure of the hydrogen is less than that of the atmosphere. In (3) the pressure of the hydrogen is greater than that of the atmosphere.

10.13 Pressure of a gas collected by displacement of mercury

You have learned how gas volume varies with pressure and temperature changes. But no practical laboratory methods of making the necessary measurements have as yet been considered. These laboratory operations will now be explained. In the laboratory, a gas may be collected and its volume measured by using a long graduated tube closed at one end. This tube is called a *eudiometer* (you-dee-*om*-eh-ter), Figure 10-13.

Suppose some hydrogen is delivered into a eudiometer that was previously filled with mercury. As hydrogen enters the tube, it bubbles to the top and pushes the mercury down. Suppose enough hydrogen is added to make the level of the mercury inside the tube the same as the level of the mercury in the bowl, as in (1), Figure 10-13. *When these two levels are the same, the pressure of the hydrogen is the same as that of the atmosphere.* This pressure can be found by reading a barometer. The volume of hydrogen is read from the graduations (markings) on the eudiometer.

Suppose, however, that not enough hydrogen is delivered into the eudiometer to make the mercury levels the same even when the eudiometer rests on the bottom of the bowl of mercury. Then the mercury level inside the tube is above the level outside the tube, as in (2), Figure 10-13. The pressure of the gas inside the tube is less than the pressure of the air outside. Otherwise, the enclosed gas would push the mercury down to the same level as that outside the tube. To determine the pressure of the hydrogen, the difference between the levels of the mercury inside and outside the tube must be *subtracted* from the barometer reading. The gas volume is read, as before, from the eudiometer graduations.

Suppose enough hydrogen is delivered into the eudiometer to force the mercury level inside the tube below the outside level. Then the pressure of the gas inside the tube is greater than the pressure of the air outside, as in (3), Figure 10-13. To determine the pressure of the gas in this case, the difference between the levels of the mercury inside and outside the tube must be *added* to the barometer reading. To make this measurement and that of the gas volume directly would not be practical, since mercury is not transparent. It is easier to raise the eudiometer in the bowl of mercury until the mercury levels inside and outside the tube are the same. Then the gas pressure inside will be the same as that read on the barometer. The volume of hydrogen can now be read from the graduations on the eudiometer. See the following Sample Problem.

◖ **SAMPLE PROBLEM**

What is the pressure of the gas in a eudiometer (gas-measuring tube) when the mercury level in the tube is 14 mm higher than that outside? The barometer reads 735 mm.

◖ **SOLUTION**

Since the mercury level inside is higher than that outside, the pressure of the gas in the eudiometer must be less than atmospheric pressure. Accordingly, the difference in levels is subtracted from the barometric pressure to obtain the pressure of the gas,

735 mm − 14 mm = 721 mm, the pressure of the gas

◖ | SAMPLE PROBLEM

The volume of oxygen in a eudiometer is 37.0 mL. The mercury level inside the tube is 25.0 mm higher than that outside. The barometer reading is 742.0 mm. The temperature is 24 °C. What will be the volume of the oxygen at STP?

◖ | SOLUTION

Note: When STP conditions are involved, 0 °C and 760 mm are considered exact quantities. No bars are required over the zeros. These terms have no effect on the number of significant figures in the calculated result.

1. Correction for difference in levels:

$$742.0 \text{ mm} - 25.0 \text{ mm} = 717.0 \text{ mm}$$

2. Conversion of Celsius temperatures to Kelvin temperatures:

$$24 \text{ °C} + 273 \text{ °} = 297 \text{ °K}; \; 0 \text{ °C} + 273 \text{ °} = 273 \text{ °K}$$

3. Correction for change in pressure and temperature:

$$V' = V \times p/p' \times T'/T$$
$$V'_{STP} = 37.0 \text{ mL} \times 717.0 \text{ mm}/760 \text{ mm} \times 273 \text{ °K}/297 \text{ °K}$$
$$V'_{STP} = 32.1 \text{ mL}$$

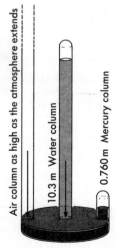

Figure 10-14. The pressure of the atmosphere supports a column of water 13.5 times as high as the column of mercury it supports.

◻ 10.14 Pressure of a gas collected by water displacement

In elementary work, gases are usually collected by water displacement rather than by mercury displacement. (Mercury is very expensive and poisonous.) Water is $\frac{1}{13.5}$ as dense as mercury. Therefore, a given gas pressure will support a column of water 13.5 times as high as an equivalent column of mercury (Figure 10-14). When a gas is collected by water displacement, pressure corrections are made just as with mercury displacement. *But a difference in water levels must first be divided by 13.5 to convert it to its equivalent height in terms of a column of mercury.*

In advanced work, gases are often collected by mercury displacement. The advantage of this method is that mercury does not evaporate measurably at room temperatures. When a gas is bubbled through water, however, the collected gas always has some water vapor mixed with it. Water vapor, like other gases, exerts pressure. Since the gas pressure is the result of the collision of the various gas molecules with the walls of the container, *the total pressure of the mixture of gases* (the collected gas and the water vapor) *is the sum of their partial pressures.* This is a statement of **Dalton's law of partial pressures.** The partial pressure is the pressure each gas would exert if it alone were present. The partial pressure of the water vapor, called *water vapor pressure,* depends only on the temperature of the water. Appendix Table 8 gives the pressure of water vapor at different water temperatures. *To determine the partial pressure of the dry gas* (unmixed with water vapor), *the vapor pressure of water at the given temperature is subtracted from the total pressure of the gas within the tube.*

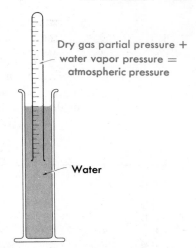

Figure 10-15. Because the liquid levels inside and outside this eudiometer are the same, the sum of the partial pressures of the confined gas and water vapor equals atmospheric pressure. To determine the dry gas pressure, the water vapor pressure must be subtracted from the atmospheric pressure.

SAMPLE PROBLEM

Oxygen is collected in a eudiometer by water displacement. The water level inside the tube is 27.0 mm higher than that outside. The temperature is 25.0 °C. The barometric pressure is 741.0 mm. What is the partial pressure of the dry oxygen in the eudiometer?

SOLUTION

To convert the difference in water levels to an equivalent difference in mercury levels, the difference in water levels is divided by 13.5.

27.0 mm ÷ 13.5 = 2.0 mm, the equivalent difference in mercury levels

Since the level inside the tube is higher than that outside, the difference in levels must be subtracted from the barometric pressure.

741.0 mm − 2.0 mm = 739.0 mm

Appendix Table 8 indicates that the water vapor pressure at 25.0 °C is 23.8 mm. To correct for the water vapor pressure, this pressure must be subtracted from the pressure corrected for difference in levels.

739.0 mm − 23.8 mm = 715.2 mm, the partial pressure of the dry oxygen

SAMPLE PROBLEM

A gas-measuring tube contains 38.4 mL of air collected by water displacement at a temperature of 20.0 °C. The water level inside the eudiometer is 139 mm higher than that outside. The barometer reading is 740.0 mm. Calculate the volume of dry air at STP. (See Figure 10-16.)

SOLUTION

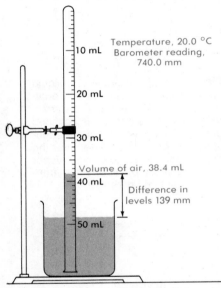

Temperature, 20.0 °C
Barometer reading, 740.0 mm

Volume of air, 38.4 mL

Difference in levels 139 mm

Figure 10-16. Laboratory setup for a gas-volume conversion problem.

PRACTICE PROBLEM

Note that in this problem the barometric pressure is measured to the nearest 0.1 mm, while the water level difference is measured to the nearest unit millimeter.

1. Correction for difference in levels:

139 mm ÷ 13.5 = 10.3 mm

Since the water level inside is higher than that outside, the correction must be subtracted from the barometric pressure.

740.0 mm − 10.3 mm = 729.7 mm

2. Correction for water vapor pressure: Appendix Table 8 indicates that the water vapor pressure at 20.0 °C is 17.5 mm. This correction is subtracted:

729.7 mm − 17.5 mm = 712.2 mm

3. Correction for pressure and temperature changes:

$$V' = V \times p/p' \times T'/T$$
$$V'_{STP} = 38.4 \text{ mL} \times 712.2 \text{ mm}/760 \text{ mm} \times 273 \text{ °K}/293 \text{ °K}$$
$$V'_{STP} = 33.5 \text{ mL}$$

A volume of oxygen, 23.6 mL, is collected by water displacement at 24.0 °C. The water level inside the eudiometer is 49.6 mm higher than that outside. The barometer reading is 735.0 mm. What is the volume of dry oxygen at STP?

ans. $p = 708.9$ mm; $V'_{STP} = 20.2$ mL

◻ 10.15 Behavior of real gases

Boyle's and Charles' laws describe the behavior of the *ideal gas*. Real gases consist of molecules of finite size that do exert forces on each other. These forces affect the behavior of the molecules. But at temperatures near room temperature and at pressures of less than a few atmospheres, real gases conform closely to the behavior of an ideal gas. Under these conditions of temperature and pressure, the spaces separating the molecules are large enough so that the size of the molecules and forces between them have little effect.

Boyle's law applies to real gases with a fairly high degree of accuracy. But it does not apply to gases under very high pressure. Under such pressures the molecules are close enough together to attract each other, and the gas is almost at its condensation point.

Charles' law holds for real gases with considerable accuracy, except at low temperature. Under this condition, gas molecules move more slowly and molecular attraction exerts a greater influence. Thus, Charles' law does not apply at temperatures near the point at which a gas condenses into a liquid.

◖ SUMMARY

The kinetic theory helps explain the properties of gases, liquids, and solids in terms of the forces between the particles of matter and the energy these particles possess. The three basic assumptions of the kinetic theory are: (1) matter is composed of very tiny particles; (2) the particles of matter are in continual motion; and (3) the total kinetic energy of colliding particles remains constant.

Gases have four characteristic properties: expansion, pressure, low density, and diffusion. These may be explained by describing the motion of the widely spaced particles in a gas.

The attractive forces between molecules are van der Waals forces. These are of two types: dispersion interaction, which exists between all molecules; and dipole-dipole attraction, which exists between polar molecules only.

If the volume that a certain number of gas molecules occupies remains constant, the pressure exerted by the gas increases as its temperature increases. If the pressure exerted by this number of gas molecules remains the same as the temperature is increased, the volume that the gas occupies increases. If the temperature of these gas molecules remains constant, the pressure exerted by the gas increases if its volume becomes smaller. Gas volumes are related to the temperature and pressure of the gas.

Standard temperature is zero degrees Celsius. Standard pressure is the pressure exerted by a column of mercury exactly 760 millimeters high. The temperature of a gas is measured by means of a thermometer, and its pressure is measured by using a barometer. When a gas is collected over water, some water vapor becomes mixed with the gas. The amount of pressure due to water vapor varies according to the temperature.

Boyle's law: The volume of a definite quantity of dry gas is inversely proportional to the pressure, provided the temperature remains constant. Jacques Charles found that all gases expand or contract at the same rate. Gases expand $\frac{1}{273}$ of the volume at 0 °C for each Celsius degree the temperature is raised. The lowest possible temperature is -273 °C. The Kelvin temperature scale has its 0 °K reading at -273 °C. The readings on the Kelvin scale are 273 degrees higher than on the Celsius scale. Charles' law: The volume of a definite quantity of dry gas varies directly with the Kelvin temperature, provided the pressure remains constant. Boyle's law and Charles' law may be combined in the formula $V' = V \times p/p' \times T'/T$.

◖ VOCABULARY

absolute zero	diffusion	Kelvin scale
Boyle's law	dipole-dipole attraction	kinetic theory
Charles' law	dispersion interaction	STP
condensation temperature	elastic collision	triple point
Dalton's law of partial pressures	ideal gas	van der Waals forces

◖ | **QUESTIONS**

Group A

1. What are the three basic assumptions of the kinetic theory?
2. Why does the pressure of a gas in a closed vessel remain constant indefinitely under constant conditions?
3. (*a*) What is the relationship between the temperature of a gas and the kinetic energy of its molecules? (*b*) Do gas molecules all have exactly the same kinetic energy at the same temperature? Explain.
4. (*a*) What is the condensation temperature of a gas? (*b*) What occurs at this temperature? (*c*) Explain in terms of the kinetic theory.
5. What two types of attractive forces may exist between the molecules of molecular substances? Explain each.
6. Why is the term "a cubic meter of air" unsatisfactory?
7. (*a*) What is standard temperature? (*b*) What is standard pressure?
8. State both Boyle's law and Charles' law (*a*) in words; (*b*) mathematically.
9. (*a*) What is the Celsius temperature corresponding to 0 °K? (*b*) How does any Celsius temperature compare with the corresponding Kelvin temperature?
10. If some hydrogen gas is enclosed in a eudiometer, in what ways will its pressure compare with that of the air in the room?

Group B

11. In terms of the kinetic theory explain these properties of a gas: (*a*) expansion; (*b*) pressure; (*c*) low density; (*d*) diffusion.
12. If it is assumed that the molecules of a solid or a liquid are in contact with each other but those of a gas are about 10 diameters apart, why is the volume occupied by a gas about 1000 times that of the solid or liquid?
13. Compare the strength of the attractive forces between the particles of nonpolar covalent molecular substances and polar covalent molecular substances as indicated by their condensation temperatures.
14. Compare the strength of the attractive forces between the particles of molecular substances and the particles of ionic, covalent network, and metallic substances, as indicated by their condensation temperatures.
15. At constant volume, how is the pressure exerted by a gas related to the Kelvin temperature?
16. At constant pressure, how is the volume occupied by a gas related to the Kelvin temperature?
17. At constant temperature, how is the volume occupied by a gas related to its pressure?
18. (*a*) What is meant by the vapor pressure of water? (*b*) What effect does it have on the observed pressure of a gas collected by water displacement? (*c*) How is the observed pressure corrected to obtain the partial pressure of the dry gas?
19. What corrections are applied to the barometer reading: (*a*) gas collected by displacement of mercury, level inside the eudiometer the same as that outside; (*b*) gas collected by displacement of mercury, level inside eudiometer higher than that outside; (*c*) gas collected by displacement of water, level inside eudiometer same as that outside; (*d*) gas collected by displacement of water, level inside eudiometer higher than that outside?
20. Boyle's and Charles' laws describe the behavior of the ideal gas. Under what conditions do they describe the behavior of real gases?

◖ | **PROBLEMS**

Group A

Use cancellation whenever possible.

1. Some oxygen occupies $25\overline{0}$ mL when its pressure is $72\overline{0}$ mm. How many milliliters will it occupy when its pressure is $75\overline{0}$ mm?
2. A gas collected when the pressure is $80\overline{0}$ mm

has a volume of 38$\overline{0}$ mL. What volume, in milliliters, will the gas occupy at standard pressure?

3. A gas has a volume of 10$\overline{0}$ mL when the pressure is 735 mm. How many milliliters will the gas occupy at 70$\overline{0}$ mm pressure?

4. A gas has a volume of 240.0 mL at 70.0 cm pressure. What pressure, in centimeters of mercury, is needed to reduce the volume to 60.0 mL?

5. Convert the following temperatures to Kelvin scale: (*a*) 2$\overline{0}$ °C; (*b*) 85 °C; (*c*) −15 °C; (*d*) −19$\overline{0}$ °C.

6. Given 90.0 mL of hydrogen gas collected when the temperature is 27 °C, how many milliliters will the hydrogen occupy at 42 °C?

7. A gas has a volume of 18$\overline{0}$ mL when its temperature is 43 °C. What change in Celsius temperature reduces its volume to 135 mL?

8. A gas measures 50$\overline{0}$ mL at a temperature of −23 °C. What will be its volume in milliliters at 23 °C?

9. A sample of gas occupies 50.0 L at 27 °C. What will be the volume of the gas in liters at standard temperature?

10. Convert to standard conditions: 2280 mL of gas measured at 3$\overline{0}$ °C and 808 mm pressure.

11. Convert to standard conditions: 1000 mL of gas at −23 °C and 70$\overline{0}$ mm pressure.

12. Convert to standard conditions: 1520 mL of gas at −33 °C and 72$\overline{0}$ mm pressure.

13. A gas collected when the temperature is 27 °C and the pressure is 80.0 cm measures 50$\overline{0}$ mL. Calculate the volume in milliliters at −3 °C and 75.0 cm pressure.

14. Given 10$\overline{0}$ mL of gas measured at 17 °C and 38$\overline{0}$ mm pressure, what volume, in milliliters, will the gas occupy at 307 °C and 50$\overline{0}$ mm pressure?

Use logarithms, a slide rule, or a calculator, as directed by your instructor.

Group B

15. Hydrogen, 35.0 mL, was collected in a eudiometer by displacement of mercury. The mercury level inside the eudiometer was 4$\overline{0}$ mm higher than that outside. The temperature was 25 °C and the barometric pressure was 740.0 mm. Convert the volume of hydrogen to STP.

16. A gas collected by displacement of mercury in an inverted graduated cylinder occupies 60.0 mL. The mercury level inside the cylinder is 25 mm higher than that outside; temperature, 2$\overline{0}$ °C; barometer reading, 715 mm. Convert the volume of gas to STP.

17. Hydrogen is collected by water displacement in a eudiometer. Gas volume, 25.0 mL; liquid levels inside and outside the eudiometer are the same; temperature, 17 °C; barometer reading, 720.0 mm. Convert the volume to that of dry gas at STP.

18. Some nitrogen is collected by displacement of water in a gas-measuring tube. Gas volume, 45.0 mL; liquid levels inside and outside the tube are the same; temperature, 23 °C; barometer reading, 732.0 mm. Convert the volume to that of dry gas at STP.

19. A volume of 50.0 mL of oxygen is collected by water displacement. The water level inside the eudiometer is 65 mm higher than that outside. Temperature, 25 °C; barometer reading, 727.0 mm. Convert the volume to that of dry gas at STP.

20. At 18 °C and 745.0 mm barometric pressure, 12.0 mL of hydrogen is collected by water displacement. The liquid level inside the gas-measuring tube is 95 mm higher than that outside. Convert the volume to that of dry gas at STP.

21. The density of carbon dioxide at STP is 1.98 g/L. What is the mass of exactly one liter of the gas, if the pressure increases by 4$\overline{0}$ mm of mercury?

22. The density of oxygen at STP is 1.43 g/L. Find the mass of exactly one liter of oxygen at a temperature of 39 °C, if the pressure remains unchanged.

23. The density of nitrogen is 1.25 g/L at STP. Find the mass of exactly one liter of nitrogen at a temperature of 27 °C and at a pressure of 90.0 cm of mercury.

24. A gas measures 40$\overline{0}$ mL at a temperature of 25 °C, under a pressure of 80$\overline{0}$ mm. To what Celsius temperature must the gas be cooled, if its volume is to be reduced to 35$\overline{0}$ mL when the pressure falls to 74$\overline{0}$ mm?

careers
careers
careers
careers
careers

You are experiencing chemistry as a course of study, a body of knowledge. For many people, chemistry is the foundation upon which they have built their life's work. The people pictured here are applying the principles and concepts of chemistry in their daily work: as research chemists, biochemists, organic chemists, industrial chemists, environmental chemists, agricultural chemists, laboratory technicians, and teachers. Their efforts will increase our understanding of the world, bring us new and exciting products, provide important solutions to current problems, and supply the research and technology vital to our future progress.

Molecular Composition of Gases

The sun is a gigantic ball of nothing but gases, yet its energy state provides light, heat, and other forms of energy to the nine planets of our solar system. The earth, too, has gaseous structure — the gases of our atmosphere. Although we cannot see it, this gaseous envelope is as important for human survival as is the sun. Not only does it provide the gases needed to support life, it also distributes the heat from the sun, protects us from harmful cosmic radiation, reflects radio waves, and supports the flight of birds and planes. From our very first cry to our last breath, air with its component gases figures prominently during our lives. We are indeed creatures dependent on air.

◻ 11.1 Law of combining volumes of gases

In Chapter 2, you learned that the observations made by Proust led to the law of definite composition. Applying this law to his investigation of the masses of combining substances, Dalton developed the atomic theory. Meanwhile, the Swedish chemist Berzelius was improving methods of chemical analysis. And at this same time, the French chemist Joseph Louis Gay-Lussac (1778–1850) was experimenting with gaseous substances. He was particularly interested in measuring and comparing the volumes of gases that react with each other. He also measured and compared the volumes of any gaseous products.

Gay-Lussac investigated the reaction between hydrogen and oxygen. He observed that when the volumes of reactants and products were measured at the same temperature and pressure, 2 liters of hydrogen reacted with 1 liter of oxygen to form 2 liters of water vapor.

2 liters hydrogen + 1 liter oxygen → 2 liters water vapor

This equation can be written in a more general form to show the simple relationship between the volumes of the reactants and the volume of the product.

2 volumes hydrogen + 1 volume oxygen → 2 volumes water vapor

Gay-Lussac also found that 1 liter of hydrogen combined with 1 liter of chlorine to form 2 liters of hydrogen chloride gas.

1 volume hydrogen + 1 volume chlorine → 2 volumes hydrogen chloride

In this chapter you will gain an understanding of:

- **Gay-Lussac's law of combining volumes of gases**
- **the relationship between Gay-Lussac's law, Avogadro's principle, and the molecular composition of gases**
- **the molar volume of a gas**
- **solving chemical problems involving gases**
- **the distinction between real gases and the ideal gas**

From a third experiment, Gay-Lussac discovered that 1 liter of hydrogen chloride combined with 1 liter of ammonia to produce a white powder. No hydrogen chloride or ammonia remained.

1 volume hydrogen chloride + 1 volume ammonia → ammonium chloride(s)

Another French chemist, Claude Louis Berthollet (1748–1822), recognized a similar relationship in experiments with hydrogen and nitrogen. He found that 3 liters of hydrogen always combined with 1 liter of nitrogen to form 2 liters of ammonia.

3 volumes hydrogen + 1 volume nitrogen → 2 volumes ammonia

In 1808, Gay-Lussac summarized the results of these experiments and stated the principle that bears his name. *Gay-Lussac's law of combining volumes of gases states: Under the same conditions of temperature and pressure, the volumes of reacting gases and of their gaseous products are expressed in ratios of small whole numbers.*

Proust had demonstrated the definite proportion of elements in a compound. Dalton's atomic theory had explained this regularity in the composition of substances. However, Dalton had pictured an atom of one element combining with an atom of another element to form a single particle of the product. He could not explain why *one* volume of hydrogen reacted with *one* volume of chlorine to form *two* volumes of hydrogen chloride gas. To explain this volume relationship in terms of Dalton's theory would require that atoms be subdivided. Dalton had described the atoms of elements as "ultimate particles" not capable of subdivision. Here was a disagreement between Dalton's theory and Gay-Lussac's observations. Was there an explanation to resolve the difficulty?

☐ 11.2 Avogadro's principle

In 1811, Avogadro proposed a possible explanation for Gay-Lussac's simple ratios of combining gases. This explanation was to become one of the basic principles of chemistry, although its importance was not understood until after Avogadro's death.

Avogadro's explanation was that *equal volumes of all gases, under the same conditions of temperature and pressure, contain the same number of molecules.* Avogadro decided upon this believable explanation after studying the behavior of gases. He immediately saw its application to Gay-Lussac's volume ratios.

Avogadro further reasoned that the numbers of molecules of all gases, as reactants and products, *must be in the same ratio as their respective gas volumes.* Thus the composition of water vapor

2 volumes hydrogen   +   1 volume oxygen   →   2 volumes water vapor

could be represented as 2 molecules of hydrogen combining with 1 molecule of oxygen to produce 2 molecules of water vapor.

2 molecules hydrogen + 1 molecule oxygen → 2 molecules water vapor   (Equation 1)

Avogadro reasoned that the oxygen molecules must somehow be equally divided between the two molecules of water vapor formed. *Thus, each molecule of oxygen must consist of **at least** two identical parts (atoms).* Avogadro did not reject the atoms of Dalton. He merely stated that they did not exist as independent, basic particles. Instead, they were grouped into molecules that consisted of two identical parts. The simplest such molecule would, of course, contain two atoms.

Avogadro's reasoning applied equally well to the combining volumes in the composition of hydrogen chloride gas.

1 volume hydrogen   +   1 volume chlorine   →   2 volumes hydrogen chloride

1 molecule hydrogen + 1 molecule chlorine → 2 molecules hydrogen chloride   (Equation 2)

Each molecule of hydrogen must consist of two identical parts. After the reaction one of these parts is found in each of the two molecules of hydrogen chloride. Likewise, each chlorine molecule must consist of two identical parts. One of these parts is found in each of the two molecules of hydrogen chloride.

By Avogadro's explanation, the simplest molecules of hydrogen, oxygen, and chlorine each contain two atoms. The simplest possible molecule of water contains two atoms of hydrogen and one atom of oxygen. The simplest molecule of hydrogen chloride contains one atom of hydrogen and one atom of chlorine.

The correctness of Avogadro's explanation is so well recognized today that it has become known as *Avogadro's principle*. It is supported by the kinetic theory of gases. Chemists use it widely in determining molecular weights and molecular formulas.

☐ 11.3 Molecules of active gaseous elements are diatomic

By applying Avogadro's principle to Gay-Lussac's law of combining volumes of gases, the simplest possible makeup of elemental gases can be determined. But whether the simplest structure of an elemental gas is the correct one must be known. To do this, the molecular formula for the product of each composition reaction described so far must be determined. In Sections 7.12 and 7.13, empirical and molecular formulas were discussed. You will recall that an empirical formula can be determined from percentage composition data obtained by chemical analysis. The molecular formula can then be calculated if the molecular weight is known. The molecular weights of gases can be determined from their densities. The molecular weights of solids and liquids that exist as molecules can be found by measuring the freezing or boiling temperatures of their solutions.

Chemists have analyzed hydrogen chloride gas and, with the aid of atomic weights, have determined its empirical formula to be HCl. The molecular formula could be the same as the empirical formula, or it could be any multiple of the empirical formula such as H_2Cl_2, H_3Cl_3, etc. To decide which formula is correct, chemists must experimentally determine the molecular weight. By measuring the density of hydrogen chloride, they have found its molecular weight to be 36.5. So the molecular formula must be HCl. The weight of one atom of hydrogen is 1.0 and the weight of one atom of chlorine is 35.5, giving a calculated molecular weight of 36.5. Any other multiple of the empirical formula gives a calculated molecular weight that is too high compared to the molecular weight determined experimentally. Thus, a molecule of hydrogen chloride contains *only one* atom of hydrogen and *only one* atom of chlorine.

Equation 2 in Section 11.2 indicates that two molecules of hydrogen chloride (2HCl) are formed from one molecule of hydrogen and one molecule of chlorine. But 2HCl contains two atoms of hydrogen. These two hydrogen atoms must have been provided by the one molecule of hydrogen reactant. Therefore this molecule must be a two-atomed, or *diatomic,* molecule, H_2. Similarly, 2HCl contains two atoms of chlorine which must have been provided by the one molecule of chlorine reactant. This chlorine molecule must therefore be a diatomic molecule, Cl_2. The equation can be correctly written as

$$H_2 + Cl_2 \rightarrow 2HCl$$

Similarly, oxygen molecules are proved to be diatomic because H_2O is the known molecular formula of water vapor.

$$2H_2 + O_2 \rightarrow 2H_2O$$

One additional gaseous reaction deserves examination. Berthollet found that *3 volumes* of hydrogen combined with *1 volume* of nitrogen to form *2 volumes* of ammonia. By Avogadro's prin-

Figure 11-1. As HCl is known to be the correct molecular formula for hydrogen chloride gas, the molecules of hydrogen and chlorine are proved to be diatomic.

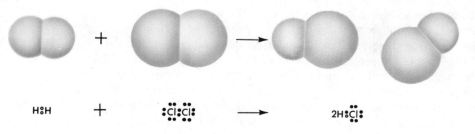

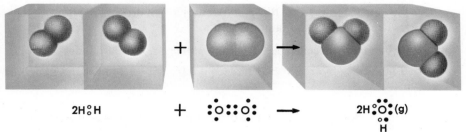

$2H \overset{\circ}{\circ} H$ $+$:$\overset{\bullet\bullet}{O}$::$\overset{\bullet\bullet}{O}$: $\longrightarrow$ $2H \overset{\bullet\bullet}{\underset{\bullet\bullet}{O}} (g)$
$\qquad\qquad\qquad\qquad\qquad\qquad\qquad\qquad\qquad\qquad H$

ciple, *3 molecules* of hydrogen combine with *1 molecule* of nitrogen to form *2 molecules* of ammonia. Analysis of ammonia reveals that it is composed of 82% nitrogen and 18% hydrogen. The atomic weights of nitrogen and hydrogen are 14 and 1.0, respectively. The molecular weight of ammonia is known from gas density measurements to be 17.0. Therefore, the molecular formula is determined as follows:

Figure 11-2. The correct molecular formula for water vapor is H_2O. Applying Avogadro's principle to the gas volumes observed by Gay-Lussac shows that hydrogen and oxygen molecules are diatomic.

At this point, you may wish to review the calculations explained in Sections 7.12 and 7.13.

$$N: \quad \frac{82 \text{ g N}}{14 \text{ g/mole}} = 5.9 \text{ moles N}$$

$$H: \quad \frac{18 \text{ g H}}{1.0 \text{ g/mole}} = 18 \text{ moles H}$$

$$N:H = \frac{5.9}{5.9} : \frac{18}{5.9} = 1.0 : 3.0$$

Empirical formula $= NH_3$
Molecular formula $= (NH_3)_x$
and $(NH_3 \text{ weight})_x = 17.0$
thus $\qquad\qquad x = 1$
Molecular formula $= NH_3$

Since each molecule of NH_3 contains 1 nitrogen atom, the 2 molecules of NH_3 produced must contain a total of 2 nitrogen atoms. Therefore, 2 nitrogen atoms must come from the 1 molecule of nitrogen reactant. Again the 2 molecules of NH_3 produced must contain a total of 6 hydrogen atoms. Therefore, these 6 atoms

Figure 11-3. Application of Avogadro's principle to Gay-Lussac's combining volumes shows that molecules of elemental gas reactants are diatomic.

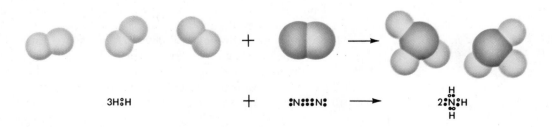

$3H \overset{\circ}{\circ} H$ $+$:N:::N: $\longrightarrow$ $2 \overset{H}{\underset{H}{N}} \overset{\bullet\bullet}{\circ} H$

must come from the 3 molecules of hydrogen reactant. These relations can be summarized as:

3 volumes hydrogen + 1 volume nitrogen → 2 volumes ammonia

3 molecules hydrogen + 1 molecule nitrogen → 2 molecules ammonia

$$3H_2 \quad + \quad N_2 \quad \rightarrow \quad 2NH_3$$

Both nitrogen and hydrogen molecules are diatomic.

◘ 11.4 Molecules of the noble gases are monatomic

By using the methods described in the preceding sections, it can be shown that the molecules of all *ordinary* gaseous elements contain *two* atoms. Other methods have shown that the *noble* gaseous elements, such as helium and neon, have only *one* atom to each molecule. None of these methods applies to solids and may not even apply to the vapors of certain elements that are liquid or solid at room temperature. For example, at high temperatures the molecules of mercury and iodine vapors are known to consist of only one atom each.

Particles of matter are described in Section 6.24.

◘ 11.5 Molar volume of a gas

Oxygen gas consists of diatomic molecules. One mole of O_2 contains the Avogadro number of molecules (6.02×10^{23}) and has a mass of 31.9988 g. One mole of H_2 contains the same number of molecules and has a mass of 2.016 g. Helium is a monatomic gas. One mole of **He** contains the Avogadro number of monatomic molecules and has a mass of 4.003 g. One-mole quantities of all molecular substances contain the Avogadro number of molecules.

The Avogadro number and the mole are explained in Section 3.14.

The volume occupied by one mole (or by one gram-molecular weight) of a gas at STP is called its **molar volume**. Since moles of gases all have the same numbers of molecules, Avogadro's principle indicates that they must occupy equal volumes under the same conditions of temperature and pressure. *The molar volumes of all gases are equal under the same conditions.* This has great practical significance in chemistry. You will now see how the molar volume of gases can be determined.

Recall from Section 10.6 that STP means standard temperature and pressure.

The densities of gases represent the masses of *equal numbers* of their respective molecules measured at STP. Since different gases have different densities, the mass of an *individual molecule* of one gas must be different from the mass of an individual molecule of a different gas.

Density is defined in Section 1.7 as mass per unit volume.

The density of hydrogen is 0.0899 g/L, measured at STP. A mole of hydrogen, or 1 g-mol wt of hydrogen, has a mass of 2.016 g. (G-mol wt is an abbreviation for gram-molecular weight.) Since 0.0899 g of H_2 occupies 1 L volume at STP, what volume will 2.016 g of H_2 occupy under the same conditions? The molar volume expressed in liters bears the same relation to 1 L as 2.016 g bears to 0.0899 g. This proportionality can be expressed as follows:

$$\frac{\text{molar volume of } H_2}{1 \text{ L}} = \frac{2.016 \text{ g}}{0.0899 \text{ g}}$$

Solving for molar volume,

$$\text{molar volume of } H_2 = \frac{2.016 \text{ g} \times 1 \text{ L}}{0.0899 \text{ g}}$$

$$\text{molar volume of } H_2 = 22.4 \text{ L}$$

The density of oxygen is 1.43 g/L. A mole of oxygen has a mass of 31.9988 g. Following the reasoning in the case of hydrogen, the molar volume of O_2 is

$$\frac{\text{molar volume of } O_2}{1 \text{ L}} = \frac{32.0 \text{ g}}{1.43 \text{ g}}$$

$$\text{molar volume of } O_2 = \frac{32.0 \text{ g} \times 1 \text{ L}}{1.43 \text{ g}}$$

$$\text{molar volume of } O_2 = 22.4 \text{ L}$$

Computations with data on other gases would yield similar results. However, it is clear from Avogadro's principle that this is unnecessary. The proportion used above can be generalized to read as follows:

$$\frac{1 \text{ molar volume}}{1 \text{ L}} = \frac{\text{g-mol wt}}{\text{mass of 1 L}}$$

Transposing terms,

$$\frac{\text{mass of 1 L}}{1 \text{ L}} = \frac{\text{g-mol wt}}{1 \text{ molar volume}}$$

But

$$\frac{\text{mass of 1 L}}{1 \text{ L}} = \text{density } (D) \text{ of a gas}$$

and

$$1 \text{ molar volume} = 22.4 \text{ L}$$

So

$$D \text{ (of a gas)} = \frac{\text{g-mol wt}}{22.4 \text{ L}}$$

and

$$\text{g-mol wt} = D \times 22.4 \text{ L}$$

Thus, the *gram-molecular weight* (mass in grams of one mole) *of a gaseous substance is the mass, in grams, of 22.4 liters of the gas measured at STP.* In other words, it is simply the density of the gas multiplied by the constant 22.4 L. Similarly, the density

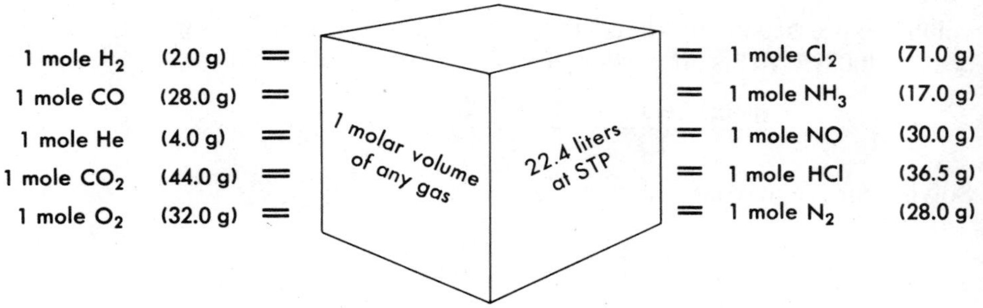

1 mole H_2 (2.0 g) $=$
1 mole CO (28.0 g) $=$
1 mole He (4.0 g) $=$
1 mole CO_2 (44.0 g) $=$
1 mole O_2 (32.0 g) $=$

1 molar volume of any gas *22.4 liters at STP*

$=$ 1 mole Cl_2 (71.0 g)
$=$ 1 mole NH_3 (17.0 g)
$=$ 1 mole NO (30.0 g)
$=$ 1 mole HCl (36.5 g)
$=$ 1 mole N_2 (28.0 g)

Figure 11-4. At STP, 22.4 liters of all gases have the same number of molecules, and the mass of each volume in grams is numerically equal to its molecular weight.

of a gas can be found by dividing its gram-molecular weight by the constant, 22.4 L.

If the molecular formula for a gas is known, its density can be determined directly from the formula. For example, the mass of one mole of SO_2 is 64.1 g. Thus

$$D_{SO_2} = \frac{64.1 \text{ g}}{22.4 \text{ L}} = 2.86 \text{ g/L at STP}$$

PRACTICE PROBLEMS

1. What is the density of CO_2 at STP?
   ans. $D_{CO_2} = 1.96$ g/L at STP
2. What is the mass of $25\overline{0}$ mL CO_2 at STP?
   ans. $D = m/V$, $m = 0.490$ g
3. What is the volume of 15.0 g CO_2 at STP? *ans.* $V = 7.65$ L
4. What is the molecular weight of a gas that has a density of 1.34 g/L at STP? *ans.* mol wt = 30.0

◘ 11.6 Molecular weights of gases determined experimentally

The molecular weights of gases, or of the vapors of substances that vaporize without decomposition, can be determined by the *molar-volume method*.

It is generally impractical in the laboratory to directly weigh a molar volume (22.4 L) of a gas or vapor at STP. Indeed, some substances otherwise suitable for this method are liquids or even solids at STP conditions. Fortunately, it is not necessary to weigh a full molar volume of a gas or vapor to find its molecular weight. Any quantity of a gas or vapor that can be weighed to determine its mass precisely can be used. Its volume can be measured under any suitable conditions of temperature and pressure. This volume is then converted to STP and the mass of 22.4 L is calculated. The Sample Problem shows how this experimental method is used to determine molecular weight.

Conversion of a gas volume at given conditions to STP is explained in Section 10.14.

◘ | SAMPLE PROBLEM

A gas sample, mass 0.350 g, is collected by water displacement at $2\overline{0}$ °C and $75\overline{0}$ mm pressure. Its volume is $15\overline{0}$ mL. What is the molecular weight of the gas?

SOLUTION

Correction for water vapor pressure: From Appendix Table 8, the water vapor pressure at $20\,°C$ is 17.5 mm. This water vapor pressure is subtracted from the barometric pressure to obtain the pressure of the dry gas.

$$750 \text{ mm} - 17.5 \text{ mm} = 732 \text{ mm}$$

Conversion of Celsius temperatures to Kelvin temperatures:

$$20\,°C + 273\,° = 293\,°K; \; 0\,°C + 273\,° = 273\,°K$$

Correction for pressure and temperature changes:

$$V' = V \times p/p' \times T'/T$$

$$V'_{STP} = 150 \text{ mL} \times \frac{732 \text{ mm}}{760 \text{ mm}} \times \frac{273\,°K}{293\,°K}$$

$$V'_{STP} = 135 \text{ mL, or } 0.135 \text{ L}$$

The quantity of 0.350 g per 0.135 L at STP is an expression of the density of the gas and can be substituted for it. Thus

$$\text{g-mol wt} = D \times 22.4 \text{ L}$$

$$\text{g-mol wt} = \frac{0.350 \text{ g}}{0.135 \text{ L}} \times 22.4 \text{ L}$$

$$\text{g-mol wt} = 58.1 \text{ g}$$

$$\text{mol wt} = 58.1$$

The volume occupied by a known mass of a gas under any conditions of temperature and pressure can be calculated also if the molecular formula of the gas is known. The molecular formula provides the mass of 1 mole of the gas. One mole of any gas occupies the molar volume, 22.4 L, at STP. By proportion, the volume of the known mass of the gas at STP can be determined. Then by applying the gas laws, the volume at any temperature and pressure can be computed. See the following Sample Problem.

SAMPLE PROBLEM

What is the volume of 10 g of carbon dioxide gas, CO_2, at $20\,°C$ and 740 mm?

SOLUTION

The formula CO_2 indicates that the molecular weight is 44. Now 44 g (1 mole) of CO_2 occupies 22.4 L (1 molar volume) at STP. The volume occupied by 10 g will be represented as X.

$$\frac{44 \text{ g}}{22.4 \text{ L}} = \frac{10 \text{ g}}{X}$$

Solving for X,

$$X = 1\bar{0}\ g \times \frac{22.4\ L}{44\ g} = 5.1\ L,\ at\ STP$$

Correction for pressure and temperature changes:

$$V' = V \times p/p' \times T'/T$$

$$V'_{20\ °C,\,740\ mm} = 5.1\ L \times \frac{760\ mm}{740\ mm} \times \frac{293\ °K}{273\ °K}$$

$$V'_{20\ °C,\,740\ mm} = 5.6\ L$$

❏ 11.7 Chemical problems involving gases

As shown in Section 8.1, the equation for a chemical reaction expresses quantities of reactants and products in *moles*. The numerical coefficients in the balanced equation indicate the number of moles of each substance.

Frequently, a reactant or a product of a reaction is a gas. Indeed in certain reactions, *all* reactants and products may be gaseous. Avogadro's principle indicates that single moles of all such gases have the same volume under the same conditions of temperature and pressure. At STP, a mole of any gas occupies 1 molar volume, 22.4 L. *Consequently, the mole relationships in the equation are also the volume relationships of gases.*

Ideal-gas laws and real-gas behavior are described in Section 10.15.

Remember that the behavior of real gases is not described exactly by the ideal gas laws. Calculations that involve the molar volume as 22.4 L can give only approximately correct answers.

There are two general types of problems that involve chemical equations and the volumes of gases.

1. Gas volume–gas volume problems. In these problems, a certain *volume of a gas* reactant or product is given. The *volume of another gas* reactant or product is required.

2. Mass–gas volume problems. Here a certain *mass* of a reactant or product is given and the *volume of a gas* reactant or product is required, or vice versa.

❏ 11.8 Gas volume–gas volume problems

The *volume* of one *gaseous substance* is given in gas volume–gas volume problems. In this type of problem, you are asked to determine the *volume* of another *gaseous substance* involved in the chemical action. Recall that single moles of all gases at the same temperature and pressure occupy the same volume. Thus, in a balanced equation, the volumes of gases are proportional to the number of moles shown by the numerical coefficients. To illustrate,

$$2CO(g) + O_2(g) \rightarrow 2CO_2(g)$$

| 2 moles | 1 mole | 2 moles |
| 2 volumes | 1 volume | 2 volumes |

The balanced equation signifies that 2 moles of CO reacts with 1 mole of O_2 to produce 2 moles of CO_2. From Avogadro's principle, 2 volumes (liters, milliliters, etc.) of carbon monoxide reacts with 1 volume (liter, milliliter, etc.) of oxygen to produce 2 volumes (liters, milliliters, etc.) of carbon dioxide. (In this relationship it is assumed, of course, that the temperature and pressure of all three gases are the same.) Thus, 10 liters of CO would require 5 liters of O_2 for complete combustion and would produce 10 liters of CO_2. The volume relationship is 2 : 1 : 2 under the same conditions of temperature and pressure.

Since the above reaction is exothermic, the gas that is produced expands because of the rise in temperature. The volume relations apply only after the temperature of the gaseous product has been lowered to that of the reactants at the beginning of the reaction.

The conditions of temperature and pressure must be known in order to determine which substances exist as gases. Whenever the conditions are not stated, they are assumed to be standard. Consider the complete combustion of methane.

$$CH_4(g) \ + \ 2O_2(g) \ \rightarrow \ CO_2(g) \ + 2H_2O(l)$$

1 mole	2 moles	1 mole	2 moles
1 volume	2 volumes	1 volume	

The formula for water is followed by the symbol (l) because water is a liquid at temperatures under $100\,°C$. Assume that the volumes of the gaseous reactants are measured under ordinary room conditions. If so, water cannot be included in the volume ratio. But the reactants, methane and oxygen, and the product, carbon dioxide, are gases. Their volume relationship is seen to be 1 : 2 : 1.

Gas volume–gas volume problems are very simple to solve. The problem setup is similar to that of mass–mass problems (see Section 8.11). However, it is not necessary to use atomic weights to convert moles of the specified gases to their respective masses as represented in the equation. Once set up, most gas volume–gas volume problems can be solved by inspection. The following example shows how these problems are commonly solved.

Suppose you wish to know the volume of hydrogen that combines with 4.0 L of nitrogen to form ammonia gas. The problem is set up this way:

$$\begin{matrix} X & 4.0\,L & Y \\ 3H_2(g) \ + & N_2(g) \ \rightarrow & 2NH_3(g) \\ 3\text{ moles} & 1\text{ mole} & 2\text{ moles} \end{matrix}$$

The equation shows that H_2 and N_2 combine in the ratio of 3 moles to 1 mole. From Avogadro's principle, these gases must combine in the ratio of 3 volumes to 1 volume. Thus, 4.0 liters of nitrogen requires 12 liters of hydrogen for complete reaction.

Mathematically, the problem can be set up

$$X = 4.0 \text{ L } N_2 \times \frac{3 \text{ moles } H_2}{1 \text{ mole } N_2}$$

Solving,

$$X = 12 \text{ L } H_2$$

Since the equation shows that 2 moles of NH_3 is produced, it is apparent by inspection that 8.0 L of NH_3 is formed from 4.0 L of N_2.

$$Y = 4.0 \text{ L } N_2 \times \frac{2 \text{ moles } NH_3}{1 \text{ mole } N_2}$$

$$Y = 8.0 \text{ L } NH_3$$

See the following Sample Problem.

◖ SAMPLE PROBLEM

Assuming air to be 21.0% oxygen by volume: (*a*) How many liters of air must enter a carburetor to complete the combustion of 60.0 L of octane vapor? (*b*) How many liters of carbon dioxide are formed? (All gases are measured at the same temperature and pressure.)

◖ SOLUTION

Octane has the formula C_8H_{18}. Its complete combustion produces carbon dioxide and water. Note that it is only the *oxygen* of the air that reacts with octane. Therefore it is necessary to first determine the volume of oxygen required. Let X be this volume and Y the volume of CO_2 formed. The problem setup is

$$
\begin{array}{cccc}
\textbf{60.0 L} & \textbf{X} & \textbf{Y} & \\
2C_8H_{18}(g) + & 25O_2(g) \rightarrow & 16CO_2(g) + & 18H_2O(l) \\
\textbf{2 moles} & \textbf{25 moles} & \textbf{16 moles} &
\end{array}
$$

(*a*) Solving

$$X = 60.0 \text{ L } C_8H_{18} \times \frac{25 \text{ moles } O_2}{2 \text{ moles } C_8H_{18}}$$

$$X = 75\overline{0} \text{ L } O_2$$

Now $75\overline{0}$ L of O_2 is 21.0% of the air required. So

$$\text{air required} = 75\overline{0} \text{ L} \times \frac{100\%}{21.0\%} = 3570 \text{ L}$$

(*b*) Solving as before,

$$Y = 60.0 \text{ L } C_8H_{18} \times \frac{16 \text{ moles } CO_2}{2 \text{ moles } C_8H_{18}}$$

$$Y = 48\overline{0} \text{ L } CO_2$$

Reminder: Because this is a gas volume–gas volume problem, the volumes of air and CO_2 computed are those that would be measured at the temperature and pressure of the octane vapor prior to its combustion. Under such conditions, the water product would be a liquid. Thus its quantity is not considered in solving the problem.

◻ 11.9 Mass–gas volume problems

This type of problem involves the relation between the *volume of gas* and the *mass* of another substance in a reaction. In some cases, the mass of the substance is given and the volume of the gas is required. In others, the volume of the gas is given and the mass of the substance is required.

As an illustration, suppose you wish to determine how many grams of calcium carbonate, $CaCO_3$, must be decomposed to produce 4.00 L of carbon dioxide, CO_2, at STP. The problem setup is

$$\begin{array}{ccc} \text{X} & & \text{4.00 L} \\ \text{CaCO}_3(\text{s}) \rightarrow \text{CaO(s)} & + & \text{CO}_2(\text{g}) \\ \text{1 mole} & & \text{1 mole} \end{array}$$

$$\text{1 mole CaCO}_3 = 10\overline{0}\text{ g}$$
$$\text{1 mole CO}_2 = 22.4\text{ L}$$

Observe that the molar volume (22.4 L) is used in place of the mass/mole (44 g/mole) of CO_2. This is possible because each mole of gas occupies 22.4 L at STP (*and only at STP*). The problem can now be solved by the method used for mass–mass problems.

The volume of CO_2 multiplied by the fraction $\dfrac{\text{mole}}{22.4\text{ L}}$ will indicate the number of moles of CO_2 given (operation 1):

$$\textbf{4.00 L CO}_2 \times \frac{\textbf{mole}}{\textbf{22.4 L}} = \textbf{number of moles CO}_2$$

Then, after operations 2, 3, and 4 of the solution of a mass–mass problem,

$$\textbf{X} = \textbf{4.00 } \cancel{\textbf{L}} \cancel{\textbf{CO}_2} \times \frac{\cancel{\textbf{mole}}}{\textbf{22.4 } \cancel{\textbf{L}}} \times \frac{\textbf{1 } \cancel{\textbf{mole}} \textbf{ CaCO}_3}{\textbf{1 } \cancel{\textbf{mole}} \cancel{\textbf{CO}_2}} \times \frac{\textbf{10}\overline{\textbf{0}}\textbf{ g}}{\cancel{\textbf{mole}}} = \textbf{17.9 g CaCO}_3$$

The four operations in solving mass–mass problems are explained in Section 8.11.
1. *Determine the number of moles of the substance given.*
2. *Determine the number of moles of the substance whose mass is required.*
3. *Determine the mass of the substance required.*
4. *Check the units; estimate the answer. Perform the arithmetic operations and compare the calculated result with the estimated one.*

PRACTICE PROBLEMS

1. How many liters of CO_2 at STP can be produced by the decomposition of 25.0 g of $CaCO_3$?

   ans. $\text{X} = 25.0 \cancel{\text{ g CaCO}_3} \times \dfrac{\text{mole}}{10\overline{0} \cancel{\text{ g}}} \times \dfrac{\text{1 } \cancel{\text{mole}} \text{ CO}_2}{\text{1 } \cancel{\text{mole CaCO}_3}} \times \dfrac{22.4\text{L}}{\cancel{\text{mole}}} = 5.60\text{ L CO}_2$

2. How many liters of H_2 at STP can be produced by the reaction of 2.30 g Na and excess H_2O?   *ans.* $\text{X} = 1.12\text{ L H}_2$

3. How many grams of Na are needed to react with H_2O and liberate 500 mL H_2 at STP?   *ans.* $\text{X} = 5.15\text{ g Na}$

☐ 11.10 Gases not measured at STP

Gases are seldom measured under standard conditions of temperature and pressure. But *only* gas volumes under standard conditions can be placed in a proportion with the molar volume of 22.4 L. Therefore, *gas reactants measured under conditions other than STP must first be corrected to STP before proceeding with mass–gas volume calculations*. These corrections are performed in agreement with the gas laws in Chapter 10.

For example, suppose that the gas in question is a *product* whose volume is to be measured under conditions other than STP. *You must first calculate the volume at STP from the chemical equation.* Then convert this volume at STP to the required conditions of temperature and pressure by proper application of the gas laws.

Gas volume–gas volume calculations do not require STP corrections since volumes of gases are related to moles rather than to molar volumes. Thus, in gas volume–gas volume problems, it is necessary only that all measurements of gas volumes be made at the same temperature and pressure.

☐ 11.11 Gases collected by water displacement

The volume of any gas in a mass–gas volume problem is calculated under STP conditions and must be corrected for any other specified conditions of temperature and pressure. If this gas is collected by water displacement, the vapor pressure of the water must be taken into account. The partial pressure of the gas is the difference between the measured pressure and the partial pressure exerted by water vapor at the specified temperature.

This type of calculation is explained in Section 10.14.

Suppose that a gaseous product is collected by water displacement. The volume of this product is to be determined at 29 °C and 752 mm pressure by a mass–gas volume calculation. The volume at STP is computed from an appropriate chemical equation. The vapor pressure of water at 29 °C is found in the tables to be $\overline{30}$ mm. Thus

$$V'_{29°C,\,752\,mm} = V_{STP} \times \frac{760 \text{ mm}}{(752 - \overline{30}) \text{ mm}} \times \frac{302 °K}{273 °K}$$

See the Sample Problem that follows.

◖ SAMPLE PROBLEM

What volume of oxygen, collected by water displacement at $2\overline{0}$ °C and 750.0 mm pressure, can be obtained by the decomposition of 175 g of potassium chlorate?

◙ | **SOLUTION**

A mass is given and a gas volume is required. The volume of the gas at STP is first found from the chemical equation. The problem setup is as follows:

$$\underset{\text{2 moles}}{\overset{175 \text{ g}}{2KClO_3(s)}} \rightarrow 2KCl(s) + \underset{\text{3 moles}}{\overset{X}{3O_2(g)}}$$

This type of problem setup is described in Section 11.9.

$$1 \text{ mole } KClO_3 = 122.6 \text{ g}$$
$$1 \text{ mole } O_2 = 22.4 \text{ L}$$

Solution by moles

$$X = 175 \text{ g } KClO_3 \times \frac{\text{mole}}{122.6 \text{ g}} \times \frac{3 \text{ moles } O_2}{2 \text{ moles } KClO_3} \times \frac{22.4 \text{ L}}{\text{mole}}$$

$$X = 48.0 \text{ L } O_2 \text{ at STP}$$

The vapor pressure of water at $2\overline{0}$ °C is found to be 17.5 mm.
Correction for change in pressure and temperature:

$$V' = V \times p/p' \times T'/T$$

$$V'_{2\overline{0}\,°C,\,750.0\,\text{mm}} = 48.0 \text{ L} \times \frac{760 \text{ mm}}{(750.0 - 17.5) \text{ mm}} \times \frac{293 \text{ °K}}{273 \text{ °K}}$$

$$V'_{2\overline{0}\,°C,\,750.0\,\text{mm}} = 53.5 \text{ L}$$

▢ 11.12 The gas constant

From Avogadro's principle you know that the volume of a mole is the same for all gases under the same conditions of temperature and pressure. The volume of any gas is directly proportional to the number of moles (n) of the gas, if pressure and temperature are constant. The $\propto$ means "varies directly as."

Direct and inverse proportions are explained in Section 1.22.

$$V \propto n \quad (p \text{ and } T \text{ constant})$$

From Boyle's law you know that the volume of a gas is inversely proportional to the pressure applied to it if the quantity of gas (number of moles of gas) and temperature are constant. The inverse relationship is shown by placing the pressure in the denominator.

$$V \propto \frac{1}{p} \quad (n \text{ and } T \text{ constant})$$

Similarly, from Charles' law you know that the volume of a gas is directly proportional to the Kelvin temperature if the pressure and quantity of gas remain constant.

$$V \propto T \quad (p \text{ and } n \text{ constant})$$

Thus,

$$V \propto n \times \frac{1}{p} \times T$$

By inserting a proportionality constant R of suitable dimensions, this proportion can be restated as an equation.

$$V = nR \left(\frac{1}{p}\right) T$$

or

$$pV = nRT$$

The proportionality constant R is known as the *gas constant*. When the quantity of gas is expressed in moles, R has the same value for all gases. Usually the gas volume V is expressed in *liters*, the quantity n in *moles*, the temperature T in *degrees Kelvin*, and the pressure p in *atmospheres* (abbreviated atm). Of course, the standard pressure of 760 mm is *1 atmosphere*. So

$$\frac{\text{pressure in mm Hg}}{760 \text{ mm Hg/atm}} = \text{pressure in atm}$$

The dimensional units of the gas constant R can be determined from the ideal-gas equation as follows:

$$pV = nRT$$

Solving for R,

$$R = \frac{pV}{nT}$$

Using the units stated,

$$R = \frac{\text{atm} \times \text{L}}{\text{moles} \times \text{°K}}$$

Thus R must have the dimensions L *atm/mole* $°K$.

Careful measurements of the density of oxygen at low pressures yield the molar volume of 22.414 L. This is accepted as the accurate molar volume of an ideal gas. It represents the volume occupied by exactly 1 mole of ideal gas under conditions of exactly 1 atm and 273.15 °K. Substituting in the ideal-gas equation and solving the expression for R,

$$R = \frac{pV}{nT} = \frac{1 \text{ atm} \times 22.414 \text{ L}}{1 \text{ mole} \times 273.15 \text{ °K}}$$

$$R = 0.082057 \text{ L atm/mole °K}$$

Suppose the properties of an unknown gas are examined at a temperature of 28 °C and 74$\overline{0}$ mm pressure. It is found that the mass of 1 L is 4.62 g under these conditions. You wish to determine the molecular weight of the gas. This calculation can be made directly by using the gas constant R, 0.0821 L atm/mole °K, and the ideal-gas equation, $pV = nRT$. The use of R in the ideal-gas equation enables moles per liter of gas to be computed.

$$T = 273° + 28 \text{ °C} = 301 \text{ °K}$$

$$V = 1 \text{ L}$$

$$p = \frac{74\overline{0} \text{ mm}}{760 \text{ mm/atm}} = 0.974 \text{ atm}$$

$$pV = nRT$$

Solving for n moles,

$$n = \frac{pV}{RT}$$

$$n = \frac{0.974 \text{ atm} \times 1 \text{ L}}{\dfrac{0.0821 \text{ L atm}}{\text{mole °K}} \times 301 \text{ °K}}$$

$$n = \frac{0.974 \text{ mole}}{0.0821 \times 301} = 0.0394 \text{ mole}$$

This calculation shows that the experimental mass of 1 L of the gas, 4.62 g, is 0.0394 mole.

Since 0.0394 mole has a mass of 4.62 g, the mass of 1 mole is

$$1 \text{ mole} \times \frac{4.62 \text{ g}}{0.0394 \text{ mole}} = 117 \text{ g}$$

Therefore, the molecular weight of the gas is 117.

The ideal-gas equation simplifies the solution of mass–gas volume problems under nonstandard conditions. The number of moles of gas required is calculated by the mole method. This result can then be substituted in the ideal-gas equation, together with the pressure and temperature conditions. The gas volume is then calculated directly. Similarly, if the volume of a gas under nonstandard temperature and pressure conditions is known, the ideal-gas equation can be used to calculate the *number of moles* of the gas. This quantity can then be used to complete the solution of a gas volume–mass problem by the mole method.

PRACTICE PROBLEMS

1. What volume does 0.0200 mole H_2 occupy at 0.821 atm pressure and $30\overline{0}$ °K?   *ans.* $V = 0.600$ L
2. Some oxygen, $75\overline{0}$ mL, is measured at 25 °C and $72\overline{0}$ mm pressure. How many moles is this?   *ans.* $n = 0.0290$ mole

◻ 11.13 Real gases and the ideal gas

Precise experiments involving molar volumes of gases show that all gases vary slightly from the ideal-gas characteristics assigned to them by the gas laws and Avogadro's principle. This does not mean that the laws are only approximately true. Rather, it indicates that real gases do not behave as ideal gases over wide ranges of temperature and pressure. They act most like ideal gases at low pressures and high temperatures.

The behavior of real gases is described earlier in Section 10.15.

Two factors contribute to the difference between the behavior of real gases and the equations for an ideal gas:

1. Compression of a gas is *limited* by the fact that the molecules themselves occupy space, even though the volume of the molecules is extremely small.

2. Compression of a gas is *aided* by the fact that van der Waals (attractive) forces, however weak, do exist between the molecules.

Only when these two opposing tendencies within the gas balance exactly will the gas respond as an ideal gas.

For most gases, deviations from ideal-gas performance through ordinary ranges of temperature and pressure do not exceed two percent.

When expressed to five significant figures, the molar volume of an ideal gas is 22.414 L. Gases such as ammonia and chlorine, which at ordinary temperatures are not far above their condensation points, show rather marked deviations from 22.4 L as the molar volume. The molar volumes of ammonia and chlorine, measured at standard conditions, are 22.09 L and 22.06 L, respectively. Gases such as oxygen and nitrogen, which have low condensation points, behave more nearly as ideal gases under ordinary conditions. The molar volumes of both oxygen and nitrogen at standard conditions are 22.39 L.

◖ SUMMARY

According to Gay-Lussac's law, under the same conditions of temperature and pressure, the volumes of reacting gases may be expressed in a ratio of small whole numbers. If a product is a gas, its volume under the same conditions has a simple whole-number relationship to the volumes of the reacting gases.

Avogadro suggested that equal volumes of all gases, under similar conditions of temperature and pressure, contain the same number of molecules. He applied this idea to Gay-Lussac's volume ratios and obtained the ratios of the numbers of reacting molecules. Avogadro's principle, together with Gay-Lussac's law and molecular-weight data, can be used to show that molecules of the active elemental gases are diatomic.

The volume occupied by one mole of a gas at STP is called the molar volume of the gas. Molar volumes of all gases are equal and are found experimentally to be 22.4 liters at STP. This relationship provides a simple experimental method for determining the molecular weights of gases and of other molecular substances that can be

vaporized without undergoing decomposition.

There are two general types of problems involving gas volumes: gas volume–gas volume problems and mass–gas volume problems. Both types are based on an application of Avogadro's principle.

When gas volumes are measured under conditions other than STP, they must be adjusted to STP before being placed in a calculation with the molar volume, 22.4 liters. Calculations from chemical equations yield gas volumes at standard temperature and pressure. If gas volumes at other conditions are required, conversion is made using the gas laws.

The gas laws can be developed into a useful equation involving a gas constant. This equation enables certain calculations with gas measurements to be made easily.

An ideal gas conforms exactly to the gas laws and Avogadro's principle. Real gases deviate slightly from the behavior of the ideal gas except when the responsible molecular characteristics balance out.

◖ VOCABULARY

Avogadro's principle   law of combining volumes   molar volume
ideal gas equation   of gases   real gas

◖ PROBLEMS

*In the absence of stated conditions of tempera-
ture and pressure, assume gases at STP.*

Group A

1. Calculate the density of hydrogen chloride gas, HCl, at STP to three significant figures.

2. What is the density of hydrogen sulfide, H_2S, at STP, calculated to three significant figures?

3. What is the mass in grams of 1.00 L of methane gas, CH_4, at STP?

4. The mass of 1.00 L of gas at STP is 2.75 g. What is its molecular weight?

5. The mass of 1.00 L of nitrogen at STP is 1.25 g. (a) Calculate the molecular weight of nitrogen from these data. (b) From this calculated molecular weight, determine the number of atoms in a molecule of nitrogen.

6. Hydrogen is the gas of lowest density. What is the mass in grams of $30\overline{0}$ mL of hydrogen at STP?

7. At standard conditions, 225 mL of a gas has a mass of 0.6428 g. Calculate the molecular weight of the gas from these data.

8. What is the mass in grams of $75\overline{0}$ mL of CO_2 at STP?

9. If the mass of $25\overline{0}$ mL of methane is 0.179 g at STP, what is its molecular weight?

10. The compounds HBr, PH_3, and N_2O are all gaseous at room temperature. (a) Calculate their molecular weights to 3 significant figures. (b) What is the density of each?

11. Find the mass in grams of 4.00 L of N_2, NH_3, and C_2H_2.

12. How many liters of hydrogen and of nitrogen are required to produce $2\overline{0}$ L of ammonia gas?

13. Carbon monoxide burns in oxygen and forms carbon dioxide. (a) How many liters of carbon dioxide are produced when 15 L of carbon monoxide burns? (b) How many liters of oxygen are required?

14. Acetylene gas, C_2H_2, burns in oxygen and forms carbon dioxide and water vapor. (a) How many liters of oxygen are needed to burn 25.0 L of acetylene? (b) How many liters of carbon dioxide are formed?

15. Ethane gas, C_2H_6, burns in air and produces carbon dioxide and water vapor. (a) How many liters of carbon dioxide are formed when 12 L of ethane is burned? (b) How many moles of water are formed?

16. How many liters of air are required to furnish the oxygen to complete the reaction in Problem 15? (Assume the air to be 21% oxygen by volume.)

17. If $40\overline{0}$ mL of hydrogen and $40\overline{0}$ mL of oxygen are mixed and ignited, (a) what volume of oxygen remains uncombined? (b) What volume of water vapor is formed if all gases are measured at $15\overline{0}$ °C?

18. How many grams of sodium are needed to release 4.0 L of hydrogen from water?

19. (a) How many liters of hydrogen are required to convert 25.0 g of hot copper(II) oxide to metallic copper? (b) How many moles of water are formed?

20. When $13\overline{0}$ g of zinc reacts with $15\overline{0}$ g of HCl, how many liters of hydrogen are formed? (Note: first determine which reactant is in excess.)

21. (a) How many liters of oxygen can be produced by the decomposition of 90.0 g of water? (b) How many liters of hydrogen are produced in the same reaction?

22. (a) How many grams of copper will be produced when hydrogen is passed over 39.75 g of hot copper(II) oxide? (b) How many liters of hydrogen are required?

23. How many liters of hydrogen will be produced by the action of 25 g of calcium metal

and an excess of hydrochloric acid? Calcium chloride is the other product of the reaction.

Group B

24. A compound contains nitrogen, 30.51%; oxygen, 69.49%. The density of the gas is 4.085 g/L. Find (a) its empirical formula; (b) its molecular weight; (c) its molecular formula.

25. It is found that 1.00 L of a certain gas, collected at a pressure of $72\overline{0}$ mm of mercury and a temperature of 27 °C, has a mass of 1.30 g. Calculate its molecular weight.

26. It is found that 1.00 L of nitrogen combines with 1.00 L of oxygen in an electric arc and forms 2.00 L of a gas. By analysis, this gas contains 46.7% nitrogen and 53.3% oxygen. Its density is determined to be 1.34 g/L. (a) Find the empirical formula of the product. (b) What is the molecular formula? (c) Using the information of this problem and the arguments of Avogadro, determine the number of atoms per molecule of nitrogen and oxygen.

27. How many liters will 2.0 g of CS_2 vapor occupy at 756 mm pressure and $5\overline{0}$ °C?

28. A 1.00-L flask filled with a gas at STP is attached to a high vacuum pump and evacuated until the pressure is only 1.00×10^{-4} mm. Assuming no temperature change, how many molecules remain in the flask?

29. A sample of a vapor having a mass of 0.865 g measures 174 mL at $10\overline{0}$ °C and 745 mm. What is the molecular weight?

30. (a) How many liters of sulfur dioxide gas at STP are formed when $5\overline{0}$ g of sulfur burns? (b) What volume will this gas occupy at 25 °C and 745 mm pressure?

31. Hydrogen ($40\overline{0}$ mL) measured at $2\overline{0}$ °C and 740 mm pressure is to be prepared by reacting magnesium with hydrochloric acid. What mass in grams of magnesium is required?

32. How many liters of hydrogen, collected by water displacement at 25 °C and 755.0 mm pressure, can be obtained from 6.0 g of magnesium and an excess of sulfuric acid?

33. What is the mass in grams of 12.0 L of oxygen collected by water displacement at 23 °C and 745.0 mm pressure?

34. A reaction between 5.0 g of aluminum and an excess of dilute sulfuric acid is used as a source of hydrogen gas. What volume of hydrogen is collected by water displacement at $2\overline{0}$ °C and 765 mm pressure? Aluminum sulfate is the other product of the reaction.

35. How many liters of dry air, measured at 29 °C and 744 mm pressure, are required to complete the combustion of 1.00 mole of carbon disulfide, CS_2, to carbon dioxide, CO_2, and sulfur dioxide, SO_2?

36. What is the volume of the mixture of CO_2 and SO_2 produced in the reaction of Problem 35, if measured under the same conditions as the air used in the reaction?

37. Chlorine gas may be generated in the laboratory by a reaction between manganese dioxide and hydrogen chloride. The equation is

$$MnO_2(s) + 4HCl(aq) \rightarrow$$

$$MnCl_2(aq) + 2H_2O(l) + Cl_2(g)$$

(a) How many grams of MnO_2 are required to produce 1.00 L of Cl_2 gas at STP? (b) How many grams of HCl are required?

38. In Problem 37, the HCl is available as a water solution which is 37.4% hydrogen chloride by mass. The solution has a density of 1.189 g/mL. What volume of HCl solution (hydrochloric acid) must be supplied to the reaction?

39. How many grams of charcoal, 90.0% carbon, must be burned to produce $10\overline{0}$ L of CO_2 measured at $2\overline{0}$ °C and 747 mm pressure?

40. How many grams of chlorine gas are contained in a 5.00-L flask at $2\overline{0}$ °C and 600 mm pressure?

41. What temperature must be maintained to insure that a 2.50-L flask containing 0.100 mole of a certain gas will show a continuous pressure of 745 mm?

42. From the ideal-gas equation, $pV = nRT$, and the density of a gas defined as the mass per unit volume, $D = m/V$, prove that the density of a gas at STP is directly proportional to its molecular weight.

43. At 12.0 °C and $74\overline{0}$ mm, 1.07 L of a gas has a mass of 1.98 g. Calculate the molecular weight of the gas from the ideal-gas equation.

Liquids–Solids–Water

Water is a sculptor. *Rivers etch the landscape, rains level the mountains, and the ebb and flow of seas and oceans give shape and boundaries to the vast continents.* Water is a source of life. *Thirsty fields wait for the arrival of the spring rains. The oceans, lakes, and rivers of the world are aquariums alive with an endless variety of creatures. Coursing its way through never-ending channels, the water-rich blood in our bodies bathes the tissues.* Water is a tool. *Churning water and plummeting falls provide forces for turning huge electric dynamos. Networks of waterways provide transportation routes for commerce.* Water is a symbol. *Of life. Of purity, as it washes away imperfections. Of time, with its eternal flow. Water, as sculptor, as vital source, as tool, and as symbol. Water is all these things, and more.*

◻ 12.1 Properties of liquids

All liquids have several easily observed properties in common.

1. Definite volume. A liquid occupies a definite volume; it does not expand and completely fill its container as does a gas. A liquid can have one free surface; its other surfaces must be supported by the container walls.

2. Fluidity. A liquid can be made to flow or can be poured from one container to another. A liquid takes the shape of its container.

3. Noncompressibility. If water at 20 °C is subjected to a pressure of 1000 atmospheres, its volume decreases by only 4%. This behavior of water is typical of all liquids. Even under very high pressure, liquids are compressed only slightly.

4. Diffusion. Suppose you slowly pour some ethanol (ethyl alcohol) down the side of a graduated cylinder already half full of water. If you pour carefully, the alcohol can be made to float on the water. At first, a fairly definite boundary exists between the liquids. However, if you let this system stand, the boundary becomes less and less distinct. Some of the water diffuses into the alcohol while at the same time some of the alcohol diffuses into the water. If the cylinder stands undisturbed for some time, the alcohol and water completely mix.

5. Evaporation. If a liquid is left in an open container, it may gradually disappear. Spontaneously, many liquids slowly change into vapors at room temperature.

LIQUIDS

In this chapter you will gain an understanding of:

- properties and kinetic-theory description of liquids
- physical equilibrium and equilibrium vapor pressure
- Le Chatelier's principle
- properties and kinetic-theory description of solids
- nature of crystals
- structure, properties, and chemical behavior of water
- preparation, properties, and uses of hydrogen peroxide

Phases of matter are first described in Section 1.8.

The basic assumptions of the kinetic theory are listed in Section 10.1.

Densities of gases and liquids are compared in Section 10.2(3).

Figure 12-1. The attractive forces between the particles of a liquid are strong enough so that a liquid has a definite volume but weak enough so that the particles can move with respect to one another.

Van der Waals forces—dispersion interaction and dipole-dipole attraction—are explained in Section 10.4.

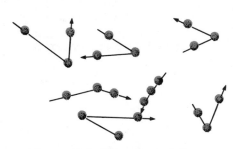

Figure 12-2. This enlarged diagram shows the movement of particles of paint as they are bombarded by invisible molecules of the liquid in which they are suspended.

◻ 12.2 Kinetic-theory description of a liquid

Liquids are denser than gases. This fact indicates that the particles of liquids are much closer together than those of gases. Further, liquids are practically noncompressible. Therefore, the particles of a liquid must be almost as close together as it is possible for them to be. A liquid has a definite volume and can have one free surface. This observation shows that a body of liquid holds together. Consequently, the attractive forces among the particles of a liquid must be much stronger than those among the particles of a gas.

Liquids are fluid and take the shape of their containers. These observations indicate that single particles or groups of particles in a liquid move with respect to one another. The kinetic energy of the liquid particles must be large enough to make this motion possible despite the attractive forces among them. See Figure 12-1.

Substances composed of low-molecular-weight nonpolar molecules are liquids only at temperatures below room temperature. Higher-molecular-weight nonpolar molecular substances can be liquids at room temperature. Hence, the forces of attraction among nonpolar molecules are the relatively weak dispersion interaction forces.

Substances composed of low-molecular-weight polar molecules may be liquids at room temperature. Thus, the attractive force among polar molecules is the stronger combination of dispersion interaction and dipole-dipole attraction forces.

Most metals, ionic compounds, and covalent network substances are liquids only at temperatures well above room temperature. Therefore, it is believed that the attractive forces among the particles of these substances are much stronger than van der Waals forces. Table 12-1 gives the range of temperatures over which examples of each of these kinds of substances exist as liquids.

There is abundant evidence that the particles of liquids are in motion. Very small particles of a solid suspended in water or some other liquid can be viewed through a microscope. They are observed to move about in a random manner. The motion is increased by using smaller particles and higher temperatures. Thus, the observed random motion is believed to be caused by collisions with molecules of the liquid. This is illustrated in Figure 12-2.

Liquid molecules intermingle because of their motion. This movement results in diffusion. The diffusion of liquids is slower than that of gases because the molecules of liquids move more slowly and are closer together. Their movement in a given direction is thereby hindered.

Water and some other liquids, such as perfume, evaporate fairly rapidly. Evaporation occurs when some molecules acquire enough kinetic energy to escape from the surface into the vapor phase. See Figure 12-3. The vapor molecules of liquids in closed containers exert pressure, as do the molecules of all confined gases. This vapor pressure reaches some maximum value depending on the temperature and nature of the substance.

The molecules of the vapors of liquids and solids have properties similar to those of gases. On cooling, gases and vapors may condense and become liquids. With further cooling, they may ultimately become solids.

❏ 12.3 Dynamic equilibrium

Suppose a cover is placed over a container partially filled with a liquid. It appears that evaporation of the liquid continues for a while and then ceases. This apparent situation can be examined in terms of the kinetic theory. The temperature of the liquid is proportional to the average kinetic energy of all the molecules of the liquid. Most of these molecules have energies very close to the average. However, as a result of collisions with other molecules, some have very high energies and a few have very low energies at any given time. The motions of all are random.

Some high-energy molecules near the surface are moving toward the surface. These molecules may overcome the attractive forces of the surface molecules completely and escape, or evaporate. But some of them then collide with molecules of gases in the air or other vapor molecules and rebound into the liquid. As the evaporation continues, the concentration of vapor molecules continues to increase. This causes the chance of collisions of escaping molecules with vapor molecules to increase. Consequently, the number of vapor molecules rebounding into the liquid increases.

Eventually, the number of vapor molecules returning to the liquid equals the number of liquid molecules evaporating. Beyond this point, there will be no *net* increase in the *concentration* of vapor molecules. That is, there will be no change in the number of vapor molecules per unit volume of air above the liquid. But the motions of the molecules do not cease. The two actions, *evaporation* and *condensation, do not cease* either. They merely *continue at equal rates*. An *equilibrium* is reached between the rate of liquid molecules evaporating and the rate of vapor molecules condensing. This *equilibrium* is a dynamic condition in which *opposing changes* occur at *equal rates*. Since this dynamic equilibrium involves only physical changes, it is referred to as **physical equilibrium:** *a dynamic state in which two opposing physical changes occur at equal rates in the same system.*

The evaporation process can be represented as

$$\textbf{liquid + energy} \rightarrow \textbf{vapor}$$

Table 12-1 LIQUID-PHASE TEMPERATURE RANGES OF REPRESENTATIVE SUBSTANCES

Type of substance	Substance	Temperature range of liquid phase (1 atm, °C)
nonpolar covalent molecular	H_2	−259 – −253
	O_2	−218 – −183
	CH_4	−182 – −164
	CCl_4	−23 – 77
	C_6H_6	6 – 80
polar covalent molecular	NH_3	−78 – −33
	H_2O	0 – 100
ionic	NaCl	801 – 1413
	MgF_2	1266 – 2239
covalent network	$(SiO_2)_x$	1610 – 2230
	C_x (diamond)	3700 – 4200
metallic	Hg	−39 – 357
	Cu	1083 – 2567
	Fe	1535 – 2750
	W	3410 – 5660

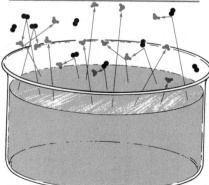

Figure 12-3. Water evaporates because some molecules acquire sufficient kinetic energy to escape from the surface into the vapor phase. Some molecules rebound into the surface after colliding with molecules of gases in the air or with other water vapor molecules.

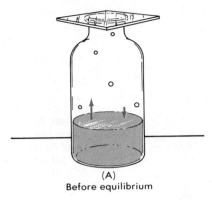

(A)
Before equilibrium

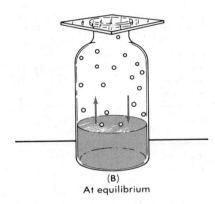

(B)
At equilibrium

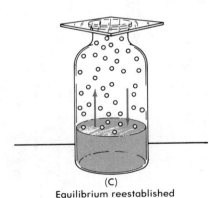

(C)
Equilibrium reestablished
at a higher temperature

Figure 12-4. An example of physical equilibrium and the influence of temperature. The different lengths of the arrows indicate the relative rates of evaporation (up) and condensation (down). The pressure exerted by the vapor molecules at equilibrium is known as the equilibrium vapor pressure of that particular liquid.

Then the condensation process will be

vapor → liquid + energy

The state of dynamic equilibrium occurring in a confined space is

liquid + energy ⇌ vapor

Because of the double "yields" sign in an equation representing an equilibrium reaction, the equation can be read in either direction. The *forward* reaction is represented when the equation is read from *left to right:* liquid + energy → vapor. The *reverse* reaction is represented when the equation is read from *right to left:* vapor → liquid + energy.

☐ 12.4 Equilibrium vapor pressure

The vapor molecules of liquids in closed containers exert pressure, as do the molecules of all confined gases. But when equilibrium is reached, there is no further net change in the system. The concentration of vapor molecules in the space above the liquid surface remains constant. Thus, at equilibrium, there is a vapor pressure characteristic of the liquid present in the system. It is known as the *equilibrium vapor pressure* of the liquid. *Equilibrium vapor pressure is the pressure exerted by a vapor in equilibrium with its liquid.*

What is the effect on a liquid-vapor equilibrium system if the temperature of the liquid is raised? Again, this situation can be examined in terms of the kinetic theory. The rise in temperature means that the average kinetic energy of the liquid molecules has been increased. A relatively larger number of liquid molecules now possess enough energy to escape through the liquid surface. Thus, the rate of evaporation is increased. In this way, the liquid-vapor equilibrium is *disturbed.* The concentration of vapor molecules above the liquid surface is increased. More vapor molecules, in turn, increase the chances of collision with escaping molecules and cause an increase in the rate of condensation. Soon the equilibrium is reestablished but at a *higher equilibrium vapor pressure.* See Figure 12-4.

All liquids have characteristic forces of attraction between their molecules. If the attractive forces are strong, there is less tendency for the liquid to evaporate. The equilibrium vapor pressure of such a liquid is correspondingly low. Glycerol is an example of a liquid with a low equilibrium vapor pressure at room temperature. On the other hand, the attractive forces between liquid molecules may be relatively weak. Then the liquid tends to evaporate readily, with a resulting high equilibrium vapor pressure. Ether is such a liquid. The equilibrium vapor pressure of a liquid depends *only* on the *nature of the liquid and its temperature.*

◻ 12.5 Le Chatelier's principle

In systems that have attained equilibrium, opposing actions occur at equal rates. Any change that alters the rate of either the forward or the reverse action disturbs the equilibrium. It is often possible to displace an equilibrium in a desired direction by changing the equilibrium conditions.

In 1888, the French chemist Henri Louis Le Chatelier (luh-*shah*-teh-lee-ay) (1850–1936) set forth an important principle. This principle is the basis for much of our knowledge of equilibrium. *Le Chatelier's principle* may be stated as follows: *If a system at equilibrium is subjected to a stress, the equilibrium will be displaced in such direction as to relieve the stress.* This principle is a general law that applies to all kinds of dynamic equilibria. It can be applied to the

$$\text{liquid} + \text{energy} \rightleftarrows \text{vapor}$$

system under discussion.

You have already learned something about how the kinetic theory applies to this system. You know that the system may reach equilibrium at a given temperature. If the temperature is then raised, equilibrium can be reestablished, but at a greater vapor concentration. *The rise in temperature is a stress on the system.* According to Le Chatelier's principle, the equilibrium is displaced in the direction that relieves this stress. The equilibrium is displaced in the direction that counteracts the temperature rise; it is displaced in the direction that absorbs energy. In this case, the forward (left-to-right) reaction is endothermic. The forward reaction absorbs heat energy and displaces the equilibrium to the right. This displacement means that the vapor concentration is higher when equilibrium is reestablished. Similarly, Le Chatelier's principle can be applied to a lowering of the temperature of the system at equilibrium. Here, the reverse (right-to-left) reaction is favored. Equilibrium is reestablished at the lower temperature with a reduced vapor concentration. The equilibrium is displaced in the direction that counteracts the temperature decrease; it is displaced in the direction that releases energy. Thus, Le Chatelier's principle is used to predict the dependence of equilibrium vapor pressure on temperature.

Suppose the temperature of the system is kept constant but the volume that the system occupies is altered. This constant-temperature condition means that the vapor pressure at equilibrium remains constant. It also means that the concentration of vapor molecules (density of the vapor) at equilibrium remains constant.

First, the volume that the system occupies is increased. The volume of the liquid cannot change measurably, but the volume of the vapor can. When the volume of the vapor increases at constant temperature, its pressure must drop (Boyle's law). In

Figure 12-5. Henri Louis Le Chatelier, a French mining engineer and chemist, was a brilliant scientist, teacher, writer, and editor. He did work in the science and technology of metals, high-temperature measurement, microscopy, ceramics, cements, chemical mechanics, and the theory of combustion of gases. His important contribution to the understanding of the direction in which a physical or chemical change will occur is now known as Le Chatelier's principle.

order to restore the vapor to its equilibrium concentration, more vapor molecules must be produced. Le Chatelier's principle indicates that the equilibrium must shift to the right, and more liquid must evaporate. Equilibrium is then restored with the same vapor pressure and the same concentration of vapor molecules as before. But with a larger volume of vapor, the actual number of vapor molecules must be greater. The number of liquid molecules is, therefore, necessarily reduced. Energy is required for this evaporation. Since the temperature of the system is kept constant, the system must absorb this needed energy from its surroundings.

If the volume that the system occupies is reduced, the pressure of the vapor increases. To restore equilibrium, this increased pressure must be reduced to the equilibrium vapor pressure at the same temperature. Le Chatelier's principle indicates that some vapor molecules must condense to liquid molecules. The reverse reaction, condensation, is favored. Equilibrium is once again established. This time there are fewer vapor molecules and a greater number of liquid molecules. But the same concentration of vapor molecules exists as before. The energy given off during condensation is transferred by the system to the surroundings in order to maintain the system's constant temperature.

❏ 12.6 Boiling of liquids

You now have some understanding of equilibrium and of the way in which equilibrium vapor pressures arise. You can now apply this knowledge to the phenomenon of *boiling*.

Pressure exerted uniformly on the surface of a confined liquid is transmitted undiminished in every direction throughout the liquid (Pascal's law). Consider a beaker of water being heated over a Bunsen flame, as in Figure 12-6. Vapor bubbles first appear at the bottom of the beaker, where the water is hottest. They diminish in size and disappear completely as they rise into cooler water. According to Pascal's law, atmospheric pressure presses from all directions perpendicular to the surface of the vapor bubble, collapsing it. Only when the equilibrium vapor pressure exerted by the vapor molecules on the liquid at the surface of the bubbles is equal to the atmospheric pressure can the vapor bubble be maintained as it rises through the liquid.

As the temperature of the water increases, the vapor pressure also increases. *Ultimately a temperature is reached at which the equilibrium vapor pressure is equal to the pressure of the atmosphere acting on the surface of the liquid.* At this temperature, the vapor bubbles maintain themselves in the liquid. They present to the liquid a greatly increased liquid-vapor surface. This allows evaporation (a surface phenomenon) to occur at a greatly increased rate. The liquid is said to *boil*. The **boiling point** of a *liquid is the temperature at which the equilibrium vapor pressure*

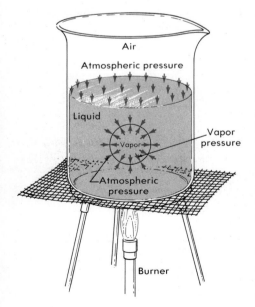

Figure 12-6. A liquid boils when its equilibrium vapor pressure becomes equal to the prevailing atmospheric pressure.

of the liquid is equal to the prevailing atmospheric pressure. If the pressure on the surface of a liquid is increased, the boiling point of the liquid is raised. If the pressure is decreased, the boiling point of the liquid is lowered.

The boiling point of water is exactly 100 °C at *standard atmospheric pressure*. This temperature is known as the *standard (or normal) boiling point of water*. When the boiling points of liquids are given, standard pressure conditions are understood. Ether, which has a high equilibrium vapor pressure, boils at 34.6 °C. The boiling point of glycerol, mentioned earlier (Section 12.4) for its low equilibrium vapor pressure, is 290 °C. See Figure 12-7.

During boiling, the temperature of a liquid remains constant. The temperature of the vapor is the same as that of the liquid. Hence, the kinetic energies of linear motion of liquid and vapor molecules must be the same. But energy must be supplied for boiling to continue. This energy is absorbed by the liquid as it becomes a vapor. The energy separates the molecules in the liquid to the much wider spacing of molecules in the gas. It effects this separation by overcoming the attractive forces between the molecules. Thus, this supplied energy increases the potential energy of the molecules.

The heat energy required to vaporize one mole of liquid at its standard boiling point is its *standard molar heat of vaporization.* Its magnitude is a measure of the degree of attraction between liquid molecules.

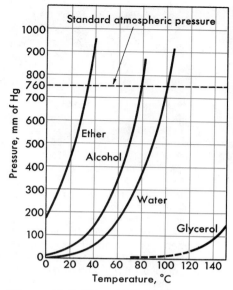

Figure 12-7. The equilibrium vapor pressures of some common liquids as a function of temperature.

It will be helpful at this point to refer to Figure 2-13.

◻ 12.7 Liquefying gases

Michael Faraday (1791–1867) discovered that it is possible to liquefy certain gases by cooling and compressing them at the same time. He used a thick-walled sealed tube of the type shown in Figure 12-8. With this apparatus, Faraday liquefied chlorine, sulfur dioxide, and some other gases. One end of the glass tube containing the chlorine gas was strongly heated. That caused the gas in the heated end of the tube to expand. The expanding gas exerted pressure on the gas in the other end of the tube, which was cooled in a freezing mixture. Cooling and compression in this manner converted the gaseous chlorine into liquid chlorine.

The modern method of liquefying a gas is more complicated. The first step involves compressing the gas and then removing the heat of compression. Compressing a gas always raises its temperature since energy is acquired by the molecules of a gas when work is done to push them closer together. In liquefying gases, the heat of compression is absorbed by a suitable coolant. The gas molecules thereby lose the energy acquired during compression. The compressed gas is cooled to the same temperature that it had before compression. The molecules possess the same kinetic energy they had before compression but are now closer.

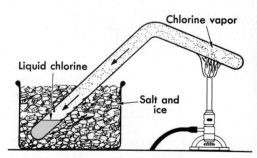

Figure 12-8. By using a tube like the one shown above, Faraday succeeded in liquefying chlorine, sulfur dioxide, and several other gases that have high critical temperatures.

Figure 12-9. Propane, a gaseous fuel, may be used in a trailer for cooking, water heating, space heating, and refrigeration. The supply of propane is contained as a liquid under pressure in metal bottles mounted on the hitching tongue of the trailer.

The second step in liquefying a gas is to permit the cool compressed gas to expand without absorbing external energy. When a compressed gas expands, the molecules lose energy as they do work in spreading apart against the force of molecular attraction. This energy loss by the molecules is observed as a decrease in the temperature of the gas. Remember that the temperature of the compressed gas was that which it had *before* compression. So the *expanded* gas is now at a much lower temperature than originally. By repeating this compression, cooling, and expansion cycle, the temperature of the gas is lowered still further.

Liquefying a gas is the result of a combination of lowered temperature and increased pressure. The increased pressure crowds the gas molecules together. The lowered temperature slows their movement. Ultimately, they are slowed down greatly and crowded together very closely. At this point, the attractive forces between the molecules cause them to condense to a liquid.

Scientists have found that above a certain characteristic temperature it is impossible to liquefy a gas by pressure alone. Above this temperature, the kinetic energy of the molecules is great enough to overcome the attractive forces between them. Thus the gas does not liquefy no matter how great the pressure applied. *The highest temperature at which it is possible to liquefy a gas with any amount of pressure is called its **critical temperature**. The pressure required to liquefy a gas at its critical temperature is called its **critical pressure**. The volume occupied by one mole of a gas under these conditions is called its **critical volume**.* The critical temperature and critical pressure of several common gases are given in Table 12-2.

From these data, it is apparent that two conditions are necessary to liquefy a gas:

1. Its temperature must be lowered to or below its critical temperature.

2. Its pressure must be raised to or above the vapor pressure of the liquefied gas at this temperature.

This combination of conditions enables the attractive forces between the molecules to effect condensation. All gases can be liquefied.

In Section 1.8, a vapor was initially defined as the gaseous phase of a substance that is a solid or liquid at normal temperatures. Now that the meaning of critical temperature has been explained, a vapor can be defined more precisely. *A **vapor** is a gas at a temperature below its critical temperature.*

☐ 12.8 Critical temperature and molecular attraction

The critical temperature of a gas has been defined as the temperature above which it cannot be liquefied no matter how

Table 12-2
CRITICAL TEMPERATURES AND PRESSURES

Gas	Critical temperature (°C)	Critical pressure (atm)
water	374.2	218.3
sulfur dioxide	157.5	77.9
chlorine	144.0	76.1
carbon dioxide	31.0	72.8
oxygen	− 118.4	50.1
nitrogen	− 146.9	33.5
hydrogen	− 239.9	12.8

great the pressure. Thus, the magnitude of the critical temperature of a gas serves as a measure of the attractive forces between its molecules. The higher the critical temperature of a gas, the larger is the attractive force between its molecules. The lower the critical temperature of a gas, the smaller is the attractive force between its molecules.

The high critical temperature of water is shown in Table 12-2. This high critical temperature indicates that the forces of attraction between polar water molecules are very great. In fact, they can cause water vapor to liquefy even at 374 °C. The critical temperature of sulfur dioxide is less than that of water. Thus, the attractive forces between sulfur dioxide molecules must be less than those between water molecules. This difference is expected because sulfur dioxide molecules are less polar than water molecules. Consequently, sulfur dioxide can be condensed to a liquid only below 157 °C.

Attractive forces also exist between nonpolar covalent molecules such as chlorine, carbon dioxide, oxygen, nitrogen, and hydrogen. These attractive forces are dispersion interaction forces. Such forces generally increase with an increase in the complexity of a nonpolar molecule. Thus, the higher the molecular weight of such a molecule, the higher its critical temperature. This phenomenon is clearly illustrated in Table 12-2. Notice the descending order of the critical temperatures of chlorine, carbon dioxide, oxygen, nitrogen, and hydrogen.

◻ 12.9 Properties of solids

SOLIDS

Some of the general properties of solids that can easily be seen are

1. Definite shape. A solid maintains its shape. Unlike liquids and gases, it does not flow under ordinary circumstances. The shape of a solid is independent of its container.

2. Definite volume. All of the surfaces of a solid are free surfaces. Hence, the volume of a solid is also independent of its container.

3. Noncompressibility. The pressures required to decrease the volumes of solids are even greater than those required for liquids. For all practical purposes, solids are noncompressible. Solids such as wood, cork, sponge, etc., may *seem* to be compressible. But remember that these materials are very porous. Compression does not reduce the volume of the solid portion of such substances significantly. It merely reduces the volume of the pores of the solid.

4. Very slow diffusion. Suppose a lead plate and a gold plate are placed in close contact. After several months, particles of gold can be detected in the lead and vice versa. This observation is evidence that diffusion occurs even in solids, although at a *very slow rate*.

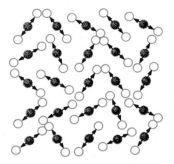

Figure 12-10. The particles of a solid vibrate about fixed equilibrium positions.

As you study this section, it will be helpful to refer again to Figure 2-13.

Figure 12-11. The liquid and solid phases of water make artistic patterns on this window.

5. Crystal formation. Solids may be described as either *crystalline* or *amorphous.* Crystalline solids have a regular arrangement of particles. Amorphous solids have a random particle arrangement.

☐ 12.10 Kinetic-theory description of a solid

Particles of solids are held close together in fixed positions by forces that are stronger than those between particles of liquids. This is how scientists explain the definite shape and volume of a solid as well as its noncompressibility. Whether the particle arrangement is orderly or not determines whether the solid is crystalline or amorphous. The particles of a solid vibrate back and forth weakly about fixed equilibrium positions. Their kinetic energy is related to the extent of this vibratory motion. Their kinetic energy is proportional to the temperature of the solid. At low temperatures, the kinetic energy is small. At higher temperatures, it is larger. Crystal particles vibrate extensively at high temperatures. But there is relatively little diffusion in any solid because the vibration is about fixed positions.

☐ 12.11 Changes of phase involving solids

The physical change of a liquid to a solid is called *freezing,* and involves a loss of energy by the liquid.

$$\text{liquid} \rightarrow \text{solid} + \text{energy}$$

Since this change occurs at constant temperature, the liquid and solid particles must have the same kinetic energy. The energy loss is a loss of *potential* energy. The particles lose potential energy as the forces of attraction do work on them.

The reverse physical change, *melting,* also occurs at constant temperature.

$$\text{solid} + \text{energy} \rightarrow \text{liquid}$$

It involves a gain of potential energy by the particles of the solid as they do work against the attractive forces in becoming liquid particles.

For pure crystalline solids, the temperatures at which these two processes occur coincide. That is, the freezing point and the melting point are the same. For pure water, both processes occur at 0 °C. Ice melts at 0 °C and forms liquid water; water freezes at 0 °C and forms ice. The heat energy required to melt one mole of solid at its melting point is its *molar heat of fusion.*

If ice gradually disappears in a mixture of ice and water, the melting process clearly is proceeding faster than the freezing process. Suppose, however, that the relative amounts of ice and water remain unchanged in the mixture. Then both processes must be proceeding at equal rates and a state of physical equilibrium is indicated.

$$\text{solid} + \text{energy} \rightleftarrows \text{liquid}$$

Not all particles of a solid have the same energy. A surface particle of a solid may acquire sufficient energy to overcome the attractive forces holding it to the body of the solid. Such a particle may escape from the solid and become a vapor particle.

$$\text{solid} + \text{energy} \rightarrow \text{vapor}$$

If a solid is placed in a closed container, vapor particles cannot escape from the system. Eventually they come in contact with the solid and are held by its attractive forces.

$$\text{vapor} \rightarrow \text{solid} + \text{energy}$$

Thus a solid in contact with its vapor can reach an equilibrium.

$$\text{solid} + \text{energy} \rightleftarrows \text{vapor}$$

In such a case, the solid exhibits a characteristic equilibrium vapor pressure. Like that of a liquid, the equilibrium vapor pressure of a solid depends only on the temperature and the substance involved. Some solids like camphor and naphthalene (moth crystals) have fairly high equilibrium vapor pressures. They evaporate noticeably when exposed to air. Solids like carbon dioxide (Dry Ice) and iodine have equilibrium vapor pressures that rise very rapidly as the temperature is raised. The equilibrium vapor pressures of these solids equal atmospheric pressure before the solids melt. In such cases the solids vaporize directly, without passing through the liquid phase. The change of phase from a solid to a vapor is known as *sublimation*.

☐ 12.12 Amorphous solids

The term *amorphous solids* refers to those that appear to have random particle arrangement. Many solids that scientists once thought were amorphous have been found to have a partially crystalline structure. Charcoal is such a solid.

Materials like glass and paraffin are considered amorphous. These materials have the properties of solids. That is, they have definite shape and volume and diffuse slowly. But they do not have the orderly arrangement of particles characteristic of crystals. They also lack sharply defined melting points. In many respects, they resemble liquids that flow very slowly at room temperature.

Amorphous forms of metal alloys have recently been prepared. They are called *metallic glasses*. They are made by *very rapid* cooling of a thin film of melted metal. The cooling occurs so rapidly that the metal atoms do not have time to arrange themselves in a crystal pattern. Metallic glasses may find use in applications based on their unusual nondirectional magnetic

Figure 12-12. A molten iron alloy made into an amorphous metallic glass. The iron alloy is melted in a quartz tube at the left by using radio-frequency currents. Under pressure, the molten metal is squirted through a small opening onto the surface of the rapidly rotating, very cold copper cylinder. A very thin ribbon of metallic glass, shown as the bright yellow streak, is formed and peels off the cylinder. Minute drops of metal thrown from the cylinder produce the small spark streaks.

Figure 12-13. X-ray diffraction photograph of ice. Chemists use X-ray diffraction in their study of crystal structure.

Homogeneous materials, such as crystals, have similar properties throughout.

properties. Some of these applications are in electric transformer cores, in the heads of magnetic tape recorders and players, and in magnetic bubble lattice memories in computer systems.

☐ 12.13 Nature of crystals

Most substances exist as solids in some characteristic crystalline form. *A **crystal** is a homogeneous portion of a substance bounded by plane surfaces making definite angles with each other, giving a regular geometric form.*

Scientists determine the arrangement of particles composing a crystal by mathematical analysis of the crystal's diffraction patterns. These patterns appear clearly on photographs produced when the crystal is illuminated by X rays. An example of an X-ray diffraction photograph is shown in Figure 12-13. Every crystal structure shows a pattern of points that describes the arrangement of its particles. This pattern of points is known as the *crystal lattice*. The smallest portion of the crystal lattice that exhibits the pattern of the lattice structure is called the *unit cell*. The unit cell defines the kind of symmetry to be found throughout a crystalline substance.

The classification of crystals by shape is a part of the science of *crystallography*. Shape classification helps chemists to identify crystals. Any crystal can be placed in one of the seven crystalline systems shown in Figure 12-15.

1. Cubic. The three axes are at right angles, as in a cube, and are of equal length.

2. Tetragonal. The three axes are at right angles to each other, but only the two lateral axes are of equal length.

3. Hexagonal. Three equilateral axes intersect at angles of 60°. A vertical axis of variable length is at right angles to the equilateral axes.

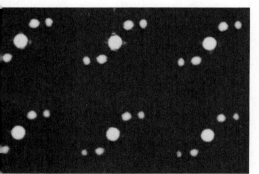

Figure 12-14. Images of atoms in a crystal. By using X rays, a computer, and laser light, an image showing the location and relative sizes of atoms in a crystal can be produced. The one shown in the photograph is of a complex crystal of magnesium bromide tetrahydrofuran, a compound containing magnesium, bromine, carbon, hydrogen, and oxygen. The magnesium atoms are the largest spots. The two next largest dots on opposite sides of the magnesium atoms are oxygen atoms, and the smallest outermost dots are carbon atoms. This image is evidence of the regularity that is characteristic of the structure of crystals.

4. *Trigonal.* There are three equal axes and three equal oblique (not right-angle) intersections.

5. *Orthorhombic.* Three unequal axes are at right angles to each other.

6. *Monoclinic.* There are three unequal axes, with one oblique intersection.

7. *Triclinic.* There are three unequal axes and three unequal oblique intersections.

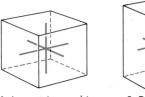
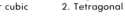

1. Isometric or cubic   2. Tetragonal

Crystals of common salt, NaCl, are cubic. This cubic nature can be seen by sprinkling a little table salt on a black surface and examining the crystals with a magnifying lens. Alum crystals, $K_2SO_4 \cdot Al_2(SO_4)_3 \cdot 24H_2O$, are also cubic, but are formed as *octahedrons* (regular eight-sided solids). An example of a tetragonal crystal is $NiSO_4 \cdot 6H_2O$. Hexagonal crystals are formed by $Na_3PO_4 \cdot 12H_2O$ and $SrCl_2$, while $NaNO_3$ and $CaCO_3$ form trigonal crystals. Both KNO_3 and $AgNO_3$ form orthorhombic crystals. The compounds $KClO_3$ and $BaCl_2 \cdot 2H_2O$ crystallize as monoclinic crystals. Copper(II) sulfate pentahydrate, $CuSO_4 \cdot 5H_2O$, forms blue triclinic crystals.

3. Hexagonal   4. Trigonal

Crystals of many chemical compounds are formed when their solutions evaporate or when their hot, saturated solutions cool. Crystals also form when certain substances change from the liquid to the solid phase and when others change from the gaseous to the solid phase. Most of you are familiar with snowflake crystals. These are formed when water vapor changes directly to the solid phase. Melted sugar, sulfur, and iron form crystals in a similar manner when they change from the liquid to the solid phase. In some cases, crystals grow from the solid phase.

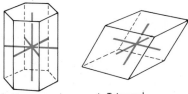

5. Orthorhombic   6. Monoclinic

7. Triclinic

Figure 12-15. Schematic diagram of the seven basic crystal systems. Photos of crystals representing each of the seven basic crystal systems are shown on page 628.

◻ 12.14 Binding forces in crystals

The regularity of crystal structures is their most fascinating feature. When possible, ions or atoms or molecules arrange themselves in positions of least energy. The more opportunity there is for particles to do this during the formation of crystals, the more symmetrical and regular the crystals will be. Thus, the more slowly crystals form, the more closely their shapes approach perfect regularity.

The seven crystalline systems are described in terms related to symmetry. But it is frequently more useful to classify crystals according to the types of lattice structure. Is the crystal lattice *ionic, covalent network, metallic,* or *covalent molecular?* Ionic and covalent molecular crystal lattices represent the two extremes of bonding. Covalent network and metallic crystal lattices are intermediate types. See Table 12-3.

1. *Ionic crystals.* The ionic crystal lattice consists of positive and negative ions arranged in a characteristic regular pattern.

Models of ionic crystals are shown in Figures 6-3 and 6-6.

Table 12-3
MELTING POINTS AND BOILING POINTS
OF REPRESENTATIVE SUBSTANCES

Type of substance	Substance	Melting point (°C)	Boiling point (1 atm, °C)
nonpolar covalent molecular	H_2	−259	−253
	O_2	−218	−183
	CH_4	−182	−164
	CCl_4	−23	77
	C_6H_6	6	80
polar covalent molecular	NH_3	−78	−33
	H_2O	0	100
ionic	NaCl	801	1413
	MgF_2	1266	2239
covalent network	$(SiO_2)_x$	1610	2230
	C_x (diamond)	3700	4200
metallic	Hg	−39	357
	Cu	1083	2567
	Fe	1535	2750
	W	3410	5660

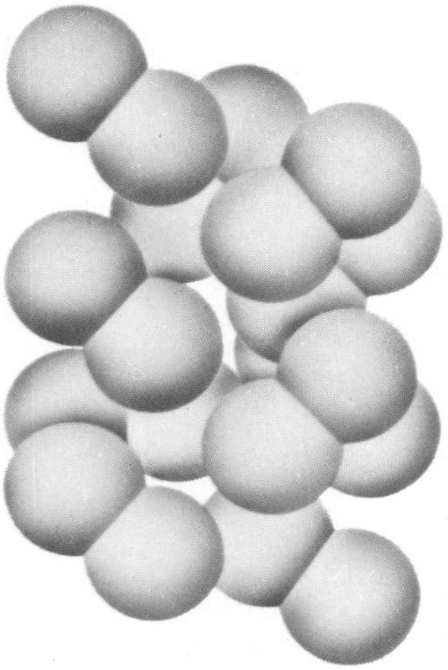

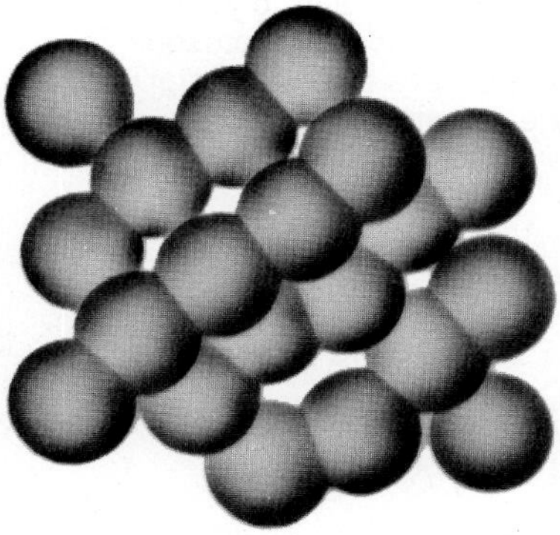

Figure 12-16. Solid iodine (top) forms molecular crystals. Compare its molecular structure with that of diamond (bottom), which forms covalent crystals that may be considered to be giant molecules.

No molecular units are evident within the crystal. The strong binding forces result from the attraction of positive and negative charges. Consequently, ionic crystals are hard and brittle, have rather high melting points, and are good insulators. Generally, ionic crystals result from Group I or Group II metals combining with Group VI or Group VII nonmetals, or the nonmetallic polyatomic ions.

2. Covalent network crystals. The covalent network crystal lattice consists of an array of atoms. Each of the atoms shares electrons with neighboring atoms. The binding forces are strong covalent bonds that extend in fixed directions. The resulting crystals are compact, interlocking, covalent network structures. They may be considered to be giant molecules. They are very hard and brittle, have rather high melting points, and are non-conductors. Diamond, silicon carbide, silicon dioxide, and oxides of transition metals are of this type.

3. Metallic crystals. The metallic crystal lattice consists of positive ions surrounded by a cloud of valence electrons. This cloud is commonly referred to as the *electron "gas."* The binding force is the attraction between the positive ions of the metal and the electron "gas." The valence electrons are donated by the atoms of the metal and belong to the crystal as a whole. These electrons are free to migrate throughout the crystal lattice. This electron mobility explains the high electric conductivity associated with metals. The hardness (resistance to wear) and melting points of metallic crystals vary greatly for different metals. Sodium, iron, tungsten, copper, and silver are typical examples of metallic crystals that have good electric conductivity. But they are quite different in terms of other characteristics, such as hardness and melting point.

4. *Covalent molecular crystals.* The covalent molecular crystal lattice consists of an orderly arrangement of individually distinct molecules. If the molecules are nonpolar, the binding force is the relatively weak dispersion interaction force. If the molecules are polar, both types of van der Waals attractions make up the binding force. The covalent chemical bonds that bind the atoms within the molecules are much stronger than the forces that form the crystal lattice. Thus, molecular crystals have low melting points, are relatively soft, volatile (easily vaporized), and good insulators. Iodine, carbon dioxide, water, and hydrogen form crystals of this type. See Section 12.17 for the discussion of ice crystals.

❏ 12.15 Occurrence of water

On the earth, water is the most abundant and essential liquid. The oceans, rivers, and lakes cover about 75% of the surface of the earth. Significant quantities of water are frozen in glaciers, which cover almost 10% of the land surface. Water vapor is always present in the air, and there are large quantities of underground water.

Water is essential to human, animal, and vegetable life. From 70% to 90% of the weight of living things is water. The chemical reactions of life processes take place in water; water is frequently also a reactant or product of such reactions.

The Viking mission has produced evidence that leads scientists to believe that the planet Mars has an underground layer of ice. The polar regions of Mars are covered with a layer consisting mostly of ice. Studies have revealed that water vapor is present in Jupiter's atmosphere. Photographs and other data obtained by the Voyager spacecraft showed the presence of large amounts of water ice on the surfaces of Europa and Ganymede, two of the moons of Jupiter.

❏ 12.16 Physical properties of water

Pure water is a transparent, odorless, tasteless, and almost colorless liquid. The faint blue or blue-green color of water is apparent only in deep layers.

WATER

Figure 12-17. On May 18, 1979, the Viking 2 lander's camera took this picture of the Martian landscape showing the surface whitened by frozen water.

The expansion that occurs when water freezes is unusual. When most *liquids freeze, they contract.*

Any odor or taste in water is caused by impurities such as dissolved mineral matter, dissolved liquids, or dissolved gases. The strong odor and taste of water from some mineral springs are caused by the presence of such substances in detectable quantity.

Depending on temperature and pressure, water may exist as a vapor, liquid, or solid. Liquid water changes to ice at 0 °C under standard pressure, 760 mm of mercury. As water solidifies, it gives off heat and expands one-ninth in volume. Consequently, ice has a density of about 0.9 g/cm^3. The density of ice increases slightly as ice is cooled below 0 °C. The molar heat of fusion of ice at 0 °C is 1.44 kcal.

When water at 0 °C is warmed, it contracts until its temperature reaches 4 °C. Then water gradually expands as its temperature is raised further. Thus water occupies its minimum volume and has its maximum density at 4 °C. *At its temperature of maximum density, 4 °C, one milliliter of water has a mass of one gram.*

When the pressure on the surface of water is *one atmosphere* (760 mm of mercury), water boils at a temperature of 100 °C. The molar heat of vaporization of water at 100 °C is 9.70 kcal. The steam that is formed by boiling water occupies a much greater volume than the water from which it was formed. When one liter of water at 100 °C is completely boiled away, the steam occupies about 1700 liters at 100 °C and 1 atmosphere pressure.

When water is heated in a closed vessel so that the steam cannot escape, the pressure on the water's surface increases. As a result, the boiling temperature of the water is raised above 100 °C. But suppose that the air and water vapor above the liquid in a closed vessel are partially removed by means of a vacuum pump. Then the pressure is decreased and the water boils at a lower temperature than 100 °C. Pressure cookers are used for cooking food because the higher temperature of the water cooks the food in a shorter time. Vacuum evaporators are used to concentrate milk and sugar solutions. Under reduced pressure, the water boils away at a temperature low enough so that the sugar or milk is not scorched.

❏ 12.17 Structure and properties of water molecules

Water molecules are composed of two atoms of hydrogen and one atom of oxygen joined by polar covalent bonds. Studies of the crystal structure of ice indicate that these atoms are not joined in a straight line. Instead, the molecule is bent, with a structure that can be represented as

The angle between the two hydrogen-oxygen bonds is about 105°. This was explained in Section 6.17 as evidence of considerable sp^3 hybridization of the oxygen-atom orbitals.

Since oxygen is more strongly electronegative than hydrogen, the bonds in a water molecule are polar. The electronegativity difference indicates that H—O bonds have about 39% ionic character. Thus, the electrons are not distributed perfectly uniformly about the molecule. On the average, they are clustered slightly about the oxygen nucleus. This gives the oxygen part of the molecule a partial negative charge and leaves the hydrogen parts with a partial positive charge. Since the polar covalent bonds in this molecule do not lie on the same straight line, the molecule as a whole is polar. Water molecules, being polar, are sometimes called water dipoles.

The polarity of water molecules enables them to be attracted to one another. This mutual attraction causes water molecules to *associate,* or join together into groups of molecules. One slightly positive hydrogen atom of a water molecule may weakly, but effectively, attract the slightly negative oxygen atom of a second water molecule. In this way, one hydrogen serves as a link between the oxygen atoms of two water molecules by sharing electrons with them. This situation is an example of a *hydrogen bond. A **hydrogen bond** is a weak chemical bond between a hydrogen atom in one polar molecule and a very electronegative atom in a second polar molecule.* A hydrogen of the second water molecule may be attracted to the oxygen of a third water molecule, and so on. In this way, a group of molecules is formed. The number of molecules in such a group decreases with an increase in temperature. But there are usually from four to eight molecules per group in liquid water. The formation of molecular groups by hydrogen bonding causes water to be liquid at room temperature. Other substances, such as methane, CH_4, have nonpolar molecules similar in size and mass to water molecules. But these substances do not undergo hydrogen bonding and are gases at room temperature. Hydrogen bonding seems to occur only between hydrogen and highly electronegative, small, nonmetallic atoms such as oxygen, fluorine, and nitrogen.

Ice consists of H_2O molecules arranged in a definite hexagonal structure. They are held together by hydrogen bonds in a rather open hexagonal pattern, as Figure 12-18 illustrates. As heat is applied to ice, the increased energy of the atoms and molecules causes them to vibrate more vigorously. This stretches the hydrogen bonds, and the ice expands as it is heated.

When the melting point of ice is reached, the energy of the atoms and molecules is so great that the rigid open lattice structure of the ice crystals breaks down. The ice turns into water. The hydrogen bonds in water at 0 °C are longer than those in

Figure 12-18. A computer-generated drawing of a portion of an ice crystal. The larger spheres are oxygen atoms. The smaller spheres are hydrogen atoms. The "sticks" represent hydrogen bonds.

Table 12-4
DENSITY OF WATER

Temperature (°C)	Density (g/mL)
0	0.99987
1	0.99993
2	0.99997
3	0.99999
4	1.00000
5	0.99999
6	0.99997
7	0.99993
8	0.99988
9	0.99981
10	0.99973
15	0.99913
20	0.99823
25	0.99707
30	0.99567
40	0.99224
50	0.98807
60	0.98324
70	0.97781
80	0.97183
90	0.96534
100	0.95838

The type of replacement reaction, replacement of hydrogen in water by metals, is described in Section 8.6(2).

The reactions of water with metallic oxides are composition reactions. See Section 8.4(1).

ice. But they are more flexible. Thus, the groups of liquid molecules can crowd together more compactly than can the groups of ice molecules. As a result, H_2O molecules occupy less volume as water than they do as ice. Water is denser than ice.

As water is warmed from 0 °C, two phenomena having opposite effects occur:

1. The breaking down of some hydrogen bonds enables water molecules to crowd closer together.

2. The increased energy of the water molecules causes them to overcome molecular attractions more effectively and spread apart.

Up to 4 °C, the first effect predominates and water increases in density. Above 4 °C, the first phenomenon continues to occur, but the effect of the second becomes much greater. Thus, above 4 °C, the density of water decreases.

Groups of water molecules must absorb enough energy to break up into single molecules before water boils. This energy requirement makes the boiling point of water relatively high. It also makes it necessary to use a large amount of heat to vaporize water at its normal boiling point.

❑ 12.18 Chemical behavior of water

1. Stability of water. Water is a very **stable compound.** *A stable compound is one that does not break up, or decompose, easily.* Mercury(II) oxide, on the other hand, is a rather **unstable compound.** *This means that it does not require much energy to decompose it into its elements.* Water is so stable that it does not decompose a measurable amount until its temperature reaches about 2700 °C. The stability of water is evidence of the strength of the covalent bonds between the oxygen and hydrogen atoms.

2. Behavior with metals. Very active metals such as sodium and potassium react with cold water, setting hydrogen free and forming metallic hydroxide solutions.

$$2Na(s) + 2HOH(l) \rightarrow 2NaOH(aq) + H_2(g)$$

Magnesium reacts with boiling water to form magnesium hydroxide and hydrogen. When heated red hot, iron reacts with steam to form iron oxide and hydrogen. Aluminum and zinc also react with water at high temperatures.

3. Behavior with metallic oxides. The oxides of many metals are insoluble, and water has little or no effect on them. But water does react with the ionic oxides of the very active metals. The oxides of sodium, potassium, calcium, and barium unite with water to form soluble hydroxides. Soluble metallic hydroxides are compounds whose water solutions have *basic* properties. Some basic properties of a solution are a slippery feeling, a bitter taste, and the ability to change red litmus to blue. Calcium hydroxide is formed when water is added to calcium oxide, CaO.

$$CaO(s) + H_2O(l) \rightarrow Ca(OH)_2(s)$$

Compounds such as calcium oxide, CaO, are known as *anhydrides*. The word anhydride means "without water." Since it forms a solution with basic properties when water is added to it, calcium oxide is called a *basic anhydride*. A **basic anhydride** *is the oxide of a metal that unites with water to form a solution having basic properties.*

4. *Behavior with oxides of nonmetals.* The oxides of such nonmetals as carbon, sulfur, and phosphorus are molecular compounds with polar covalent bonds. They unite with water to form a solution with *acidic* properties. Two acidic properties are a sour taste and the ability to turn blue litmus to red. For example, water unites with carbon dioxide to form carbonic acid, H_2CO_3.

The reactions of water with the oxides of nonmetals are also composition reactions, Section 8.4(1).

$$CO_2(g) + H_2O(l) \rightarrow H_2CO_3(aq)$$

Carbon dioxide is an anhydride that, with water, forms a solution having acidic properties. Therefore, it is called an *acid anhydride*. An **acid anhydride** *is the oxide of a nonmetal that unites with water to form a solution having acidic properties.*

5. *Water of crystallization.* In some crystals, many positive ions and a few negative ions are surrounded by a definite number of water molecules. These crystals are formed by evaporating the water from their solutions. This water is called *water of crystallization* or *water of hydration. A crystallized substance that contains water of crystallization is a* **hydrate**. Each hydrate holds a definite proportion of water that is necessary for the formation of its crystal structure. For example, blue crystals of copper(II) sulfate consist of copper(II) ions, sulfate ions, and water molecules. Each copper(II) ion is surrounded by four water molecules. Each sulfate ion is associated with one water molecule. The formula of this substance is written as

$$CuSO_4 \cdot 5H_2O$$

This formula is empirical in two ways:

1. The empirical formula $CuSO_4$ shows the composition of the crystal with respect to copper(II) and sulfate ions.

2. The water of crystallization is shown as the *total* per formula unit of copper(II) sulfate. This total is expressed as $\cdot 5H_2O$. If $CuSO_4 \cdot 5H_2O$ is heated to above 150 °C, the water of crystallization is driven off.

$$CuSO_4 \cdot 5H_2O(s) \rightarrow CuSO_4(s) + 5H_2O(g)$$

The substance that remains is called an **anhydrous compound**. Anhydrous copper(II) sulfate, $CuSO_4$, is a white powder. It

Figure 12-19. Water acts to promote some reactions, as shown when effervescent alkalizing tablets are added to water.

can be prepared by gently heating the blue $CuSO_4 \cdot 5H_2O$ crystals in a test tube. The fact that water turns anhydrous copper(II) sulfate blue can be used as a *test for water*. Other examples of hydrates are the compounds $ZnSO_4 \cdot 7H_2O$, $CoCl_2 \cdot 6H_2O$, and $Na_2CO_3 \cdot 10H_2O$. Some hydrates have two or more forms that are stable over different temperature ranges.

Many other compounds form crystals that do not require water of crystallization. Examples are $NaCl$, KNO_3, and $KClO_3$.

When certain hydrates are exposed to the air, they lose some or all of their molecules of water of crystallization. Sodium carbonate decahydrate crystals, $Na_2CO_3 \cdot 10H_2O$, are an example.

$$Na_2CO_3 \cdot 10H_2O(s) \rightarrow Na_2CO_3 \cdot H_2O(s) + 9H_2O(g)$$

The loss of some or all molecules of water of crystallization when a hydrate is exposed to the air is called **efflorescence**. Efflorescence occurs when the water vapor pressure of the hydrate is greater than the partial pressure of the water vapor in the air surrounding it. The water vapor pressure of hydrates varies greatly. $Na_2CO_3 \cdot 10H_2O$ has a high water vapor pressure and effloresces quite rapidly. $CuSO_4 \cdot 5H_2O$, on the other hand, has a low water vapor pressure. It can be exposed to the air at room temperature without efflorescence taking place.

6. Water promotes many chemical changes. One good example of these changes is the reaction of an effervescent alkalizing tablet, which is a dry mixture. As long as the tablet is kept dry, no chemical action occurs. When the tablet is dropped in water, the substances in the mixture dissolve and react immediately. Bubbles of gas are given off, as shown in Figure 12-19. Mixtures of many other dry substances do not react until water is added. The way water promotes chemical changes will be more fully explained in Unit 5.

◻ 12.19 Deliquescence

Suppose some calcium chloride granules are placed on a watch glass and exposed to moist air for half an hour. The granules become moist and may even form a solution with water from the air. *Certain substances take up water from the air and form solutions. This property is called* **deliquescence**. Deliquescent substances are very soluble in water. Their concentrated solutions have water vapor pressures lower than the normal range of partial pressures of water vapor in the air. Consequently, such substances and their solutions absorb water vapor from the air more rapidly than they give it off. The absorption of water results in a gradual dilution of the solution involved. Absorption and dilution continue until the water vapor pressure of the solution and the partial pressure of water vapor in the surrounding air are equal.

Many insoluble materials such as silk, wool, hair, and tobacco take up water vapor from the air. The water molecules may be held in pores and imperfections of the solid. All such materials, along with deliquescent substances, are classed as *hygroscopic*.

☐ 12.20 Deuterium oxide

Most water molecules are composed of hydrogen atoms with mass number 1 and oxygen atoms with mass number 16. But there are other possible types of water molecules. There are two natural isotopes of hydrogen with mass numbers 1 and 2. There are three natural isotopes of oxygen with mass numbers 16, 17, and 18. The possible combinations of these five nuclides give nine types of water molecules. In liquid water, these molecules are associated most commonly in chains of from four to eight units. In water, there is also a very small proportion of hydronium (H_3O^+) ions, hydroxide ions, and oxide ions. These ions are formed from the various isotopes of hydrogen and oxygen. Thus water is a complex mixture of many kinds of molecules and ions.

Particles other than ordinary water molecules exist in only small traces in a water sample. But one such type of water molecule has been studied rather extensively. This is the *deuterium oxide* molecule, D_2O. The symbol D is used to represent an atom of the isotope of hydrogen with mass number 2. Electrolysis separates D_2O from H_2O. The D_2O molecules are not as readily decomposed by the passage of electric current as are H_2O molecules. Thus, the concentration of D_2O molecules increases as H_2O molecules are decomposed. From 2400 L of water, 83 mL of D_2O that is 99% pure can be obtained.

Deuterium oxide is about 10% denser than ordinary water. It boils at 101.42 °C, freezes at 3.82 °C, and has its maximum density at 11.6 °C. Delicate tests have been devised for detecting deuterium oxide. It has been used as a "tracer" in research work on living organisms. By tracing the course of deuterium oxide molecules through such organisms, scientists have gained new information about certain life processes. Deuterium oxide usually produces harmful effects on living things, particularly when present in high concentrations. The most important use of deuterium oxide is in nuclear reactors. You will learn more about this use of deuterium oxide in Chapter 31.

☐ 12.21 Hydrogen peroxide

In addition to water, H_2O, the elements hydrogen and oxygen form another compound, hydrogen peroxide, H_2O_2. The bond-

Figure 12-20. Calcium chloride, a deliquescent substance, is used to control dust on dirt roads. In the photograph, a solution of calcium chloride is being sprayed on the surface of a dirt road. Some of the water of the solution does evaporate, but the calcium chloride continues to attract sufficient moisture from the air to hold the fine particles of dirt to the road surface.

ing, structure, and oxidation states of the elements in hydrogen peroxide molecules were described in Section 6.15.

A nearly pure water solution of hydrogen peroxide can be prepared in the laboratory by reacting equivalent quantities of a solution of barium peroxide, BaO_2, and ice-cold dilute sulfuric acid, H_2SO_4.

$$BaO_2(aq) + H_2SO_4(aq) \rightarrow H_2O_2(aq) + BaSO_4(s)$$

The $BaSO_4$ is insoluble and can be separated from the H_2O_2 solution by filtration.

The commercial preparation involves the indirect combination of hydrogen and oxygen to form hydrogen peroxide by means of a very complex carbon-hydrogen-oxygen compound, $C_{16}H_{14}O_2$, and a palladium catalyst.

Some physical properties of water and hydrogen peroxide are given in Table 12-5. Pure hydrogen peroxide is a colorless liquid. Hydrogen peroxide solutions have a faint odor similar to that of ozone, but are practically tasteless. Hydrogen peroxide vapor consists of widely separated H_2O_2 molecules, but in the liquid phase the H_2O_2 molecules associate by hydrogen bonding. This accounts for the high boiling point of hydrogen peroxide. Solid H_2O_2 is a compact crystalline substance in which the molecules are held together by hydrogen bonding. Unlike water, when solid H_2O_2 melts it expands (as most substances do). Water is denser than ice, but solid H_2O_2 is denser than liquid H_2O_2.

Hydrogen peroxide decomposes into water and oxygen.

$$2\overset{-1}{H_2O_2} \rightarrow 2\overset{-2}{H_2O} + \overset{0}{O_2}(g)$$

Observe that during this decomposition, for each oxygen atom that is oxidized from $\overset{-1}{O}$ to $\overset{0}{O}$, another oxygen atom is reduced from $\overset{-1}{O}$ to $\overset{-2}{O}$. Thus the decomposition of hydrogen peroxide involves the oxidation and reduction of atoms having the same oxidation state. The rate of this decomposition reaction is in-

The name of this complex carbon-hydrogen-oxygen compound is 2-ethyl-9,10-dihydroxyanthracene. You will be able to understand this name and the structure of this compound after studying Chapters 18 and 19.

Figure 12-21. Hydrogen peroxide is used as a bleaching agent during the production of cotton cloth.

Table 12-5
PHYSICAL PROPERTIES OF WATER AND HYDROGEN PEROXIDE

Property	Water	Hydrogen peroxide
melting point, °C	0.00	−0.41
boiling point, °C	100.0	150.2
density of solid, −20 °C	0.919	1.71
density of liquid, 20 °C	0.998	1.442
heat of fusion, kcal/mole	1.44	2.92

creased by an increase in temperature, an increase in the concentration of the H_2O_2, and the presence of catalysts.

Hydrogen peroxide is used to bleach natural and artificial fibers, to purify gas and liquid waste materials produced by industrial plants, in uranium mining and metal extraction processes, and as a starting material for preparing other compounds in which oxygen has an oxidation number of -1. The 3% solution in water may be used as a mild antiseptic.

Manganese dioxide was used as a catalyst to increase the rate of decomposition of hydrogen peroxide in the laboratory preparation of oxygen, Section 9.4(1).

SUMMARY

All liquids have the properties of definite volume, fluidity, noncompressibility, diffusion, and evaporation. These properties can be explained by the spacing, motion, and attractive forces of molecules of liquids.

Physical equilibrium is a dynamic state in which two opposing physical changes occur at equal rates in the same system. Equilibrium vapor pressure is the pressure exerted by a vapor in equilibrium with its liquid. The equilibrium vapor pressure of a liquid depends on only the nature of the liquid and its temperature. The principle of Le Chatelier is: If a system at equilibrium is subjected to a stress, the equilibrium will be displaced in such a direction as to relieve the stress. Stresses on a physical equilibrium system can be changes in pressure, temperature, and volume. The boiling point of a liquid is the temperature at which the equilibrium vapor pressure of the liquid equals the prevailing atmospheric pressure.

Liquefying a gas requires two steps: (1) compressing the gas and then removing the heat of compression; (2) permitting the cool compressed gas to expand without absorbing external energy. The highest temperature at which it is possible to liquefy a gas with any amount of pressure is called its critical temperature. The pressure required to liquefy a gas at its critical temperature is called its critical pressure. The volume occupied by one mole of a gas under these conditions is called its critical volume. Critical temperature is related to the strength of the attractive forces between molecules. A vapor is a gas at a temperature below its critical temperature.

General properties of solids are definite shape, definite volume, noncompressibility, very slow diffusion, and crystal formation. These properties can also be explained by the spacing, motion, and attractive forces of particles of solids.

Freezing is the physical change of a liquid to a solid. The reverse physical change is melting. The change of phase from a solid to a vapor is known as sublimation.

Amorphous solids are those that appear to have a random particle arrangement. A crystal is a homogeneous portion of a substance bounded by plane surfaces making definite angles with each other, giving a regular geometric form. There are seven crystal systems. Crystalline materials can have ionic, covalent-network, metallic, or covalent-molecular lattice structures.

Water is the most abundant and essential liquid on earth, and water molecules are widespread in the known universe. Pure water is transparent, odorless, tasteless, and almost colorless. Impurities may affect its odor and taste. Water freezes at 0 °C and boils at 100 °C under standard pressure. Water molecules are polar molecules. They are linked by hydrogen bonds into groups of from four to eight molecules in liquid water. A hydrogen bond is a weak chemical bond between a hydrogen atom in one polar molecule and a very electronegative atom in a second polar molecule.

Water is a very stable compound. It reacts with active metals such as sodium and potassium. Steam reacts with red-hot iron. The ionic oxides of very active metals are basic anhydrides, and the covalent oxides of nonmetals are acid anhydrides. Many crystals contain water of crystallization which can be driven off by heat, forming anhydrous compounds. Water promotes many chemical changes.

The loss of some or all molecules of water of crystallization when a hydrate is exposed to the air is called efflorescence. The property of certain substances of taking up water from the air and forming solutions is deliquescence. Insoluble materials that take up water vapor from the air and deliquescent substances are hygroscopic.

Deuterium oxide is used in research work on living organisms and in nuclear reactors.

Hydrogen peroxide is prepared in the laboratory by reacting barium peroxide and sulfuric acid. Commercially it is prepared by the catalytic combination of hydrogen and oxygen. Hydrogen peroxide is a colorless liquid with a faint odor. Hydrogen peroxide molecules associate by hydrogen bonding. The decomposition of hydrogen peroxide involves oxidation and reduction of oxygen atoms in the -1 oxidation state. Because of its oxidizing properties, hydrogen peroxide is used for bleaching and purification processes.

◖ | **VOCABULARY**

acid anhydride	critical temperature	forward reaction	molar heat of
amorphous solid	critical volume	freezing	vaporization
anhydrous	crystal	hydrate	physical equilibrium
basic anhydride	deliquescence	hydrogen bond	reverse reaction
boiling	efflorescence	Le Chatelier's principle	stable compound
boiling point	equilibrium vapor	melting	sublimation
critical pressure	pressure	molar heat of fusion	vapor

◖ | **QUESTIONS**

Group A

1. How does the kinetic theory explain these properties of liquids: (*a*) definite volume; (*b*) fluidity; (*c*) noncompressibility; (*d*) diffusion; (*e*) evaporation?
2. What evidence is there that the particles of a liquid are in constant motion?
3. Describe the conditions prevailing in a system in equilibrium.
4. Would you expect an equilibrium vapor pressure to be reached in the space above a liquid in an open container? Why?
5. Water standing in a covered flask experiences a drop in temperature of 10 C°. How is the liquid-vapor equilibrium disturbed? Explain.
6. What effect does the pressure on a water surface have on the boiling temperature of the water?

7. Define (*a*) critical temperature; (*b*) critical pressure; (*c*) critical volume.
8. What conditions must be met in order for a gas to be liquefied?
9. What term describes a gas (*a*) at a temperature below its critical temperature; (*b*) at a temperature above its critical temperature?
10. How does the kinetic theory explain these properties of solids: (*a*) definite shape; (*b*) definite volume; (*c*) noncompressibility; (*d*) very slow diffusion; (*e*) crystal formation?
11. Compare these crystal systems. (*a*) Cubic and trigonal. (*b*) Tetragonal and orthorhombic. (*c*) Orthorhombic, monoclinic, and triclinic.
12. What are the general properties of solids composed of (*a*) ions; (*b*) molecules; (*c*) atoms in a covalent network structure; (*d*) metal ions in an electron "gas"?

13. Where does water occur?
14. List six physical properties of water.
15. How does the volume of steam compare with the volume of water from which it was produced?
16. (*a*) Write a formula equation for the melting of one mole of ice at 0 °C to water at 0 °C, including the quantity of energy involved. (*b*) Similarly, write an equation for the boiling of one mole of water at 100 °C to steam at 100 °C.
17. Describe the structure of the water molecule, and tell why it is a polar molecule.
18. (*a*) What is a hydrogen bond? (*b*) What effect do the hydrogen bonds in water have on its boiling point?
19. (*a*) What is a stable compound? Give an example. (*b*) What is an unstable compound? Give an example.
20. (*a*) List five metals that react with water. (*b*) Give the conditions under which they react.
21. (*a*) What is an anhydride? (*b*) Distinguish between a basic anhydride and an acid anhydride. (*c*) What type of compound may be an acid anhydride? (*d*) What type of compound may be a basic anhydride?
22. What is the significance of the raised dot in $BaCl_2 \cdot 2H_2O$?
23. Give an example of a chemical change promoted by the presence of water.
24. A package of washing soda, $Na_2CO_3 \cdot 10H_2O$, labeled "one pound" was found to weigh only 14 ounces. Was the packer necessarily dishonest? Explain.
25. (*a*) Explain why anhydrous calcium chloride can be used to keep the air in a basement dry. (*b*) How would you accomplish this?
26. How is deuterium oxide separated from ordinary water?
27. Give some uses for deuterium oxide.
28. (*a*) Describe the structure of the H_2O_2 molecule. (*b*) What is the oxidation state of each atom in the molecule?
29. (*a*) Write a balanced formula equation for the laboratory preparation of hydrogen peroxide. (*b*) What type of reaction is this? (*c*) Why does it go to completion?
30. Give three uses for hydrogen peroxide.

Group B

31. What kinds of particles compose substances that are liquids (*a*) well below room temperature; (*b*) at room temperature; (*c*) well above room temperature?
32. (*a*) Using the curves of Figure 12-7, determine the temperature at which water in an open vessel will boil when the atmospheric pressure is reduced to $60\overline{0}$ mm. (*b*) What is the boiling point of alcohol at this pressure? (*c*) of ether?
33. The system **alcohol(l) + energy ⇆ alcohol(g)** is at equilibrium in a closed container at $5\overline{0}$ °C. What will be the effect of each of the following stresses on the equilibrium? (*a*) Temperature is raised to $6\overline{0}$ °C. (*b*) Volume of container is doubled. (*c*) Barometer rises from $72\overline{0}$ mm to $74\overline{0}$ mm.
34. (*a*) Why does compressing a gas raise its temperature? (*b*) Why does a gas become colder when it is allowed to expand?
35. (*a*) Can carbon dioxide be liquefied at $10\overline{0}$ °C? (*b*) Can chlorine be liquefied at $10\overline{0}$ °C? Explain.
36. (*a*) How does the addition of the molar heat of vaporization affect the energy of the particles of one mole of liquid at its standard boiling point? (*b*) How does the addition of the molar heat of fusion affect the energy of the particles of one mole of a solid at its standard melting point?
37. (*a*) What is a metallic glass? (*b*) For what purposes can metallic glasses be used?
38. A bottle of alum crystals was erroneously labeled "sodium chloride." How could the error be detected at once by an alert chemistry student?
39. Camphor crystals are soft and volatile. Explain.
40. Why is water essential on earth?
41. Explain why ice occupies a greater volume than the water from which it is formed.
42. The system **ice + energy ⇌ water** is at equilibrium at 0 °C in an open vessel. What will be the effect on the system if (*a*) heat is supplied to the system; (*b*) heat is removed from the system; (*c*) the pressure on the system is increased?

43. Explain why water has a point of maximum density at 4 °C.
44. What does the extreme stability of H_2O molecules indicate about the strength of the covalent bonds between the oxygen and hydrogen atoms?
45. Tobacco growers prefer to handle dried tobacco leaves during damp weather. Explain.
46. What particles are present in pure water besides ordinary H_2O molecules?
47. Oxygen has a molecular weight of 32 and boils at −183.0 °C. Hydrogen peroxide has a molecular weight of 34 and yet it boils at 150.2 °C. What explanation can you give for this difference in boiling points?
48. (a) Write a balanced formula equation for the decomposition of hydrogen peroxide. (b) Assign oxidation numbers to each atom. (c) Identify the oxidation reaction. (d) Identify the reduction reaction.

◖ PROBLEMS

Group A

1. A mixture of 50.0 mL of hydrogen and 30.0 mL of oxygen is ignited by an electric spark. What gas remains? What is its volume in milliliters?
2. A mixture of 40.0 mL of oxygen and 120.0 mL of hydrogen is ignited. What gas remains and how many milliliters does it occupy?
3. (a) How many milliliters of hydrogen are needed for complete reaction with 37.5 mL of oxygen? (b) What fraction of a mole of water is produced?
4. A mixture of equal volumes of oxygen and hydrogen has a volume of 100.0 mL. (a) After the mixture is ignited, what gas remains and what is its volume in milliliters? (b) How many millimoles of water are formed?
5. How many grams of hydrogen and oxygen are required to produce 15.0 moles of water?
6. (a) How many grams of BaO_2 are required for reaction with H_2SO_4 to produce 51.0 g of H_2O_2? (b) How many grams of $BaSO_4$ are also formed?
7. (a) The volume of a water molecule is 15 Å^3. From this information, calculate the volume in milliliters one mole of water should occupy. (b) From the gram-molecular weight of water and its density at 4 °C, calculate the volume in milliliters actually occupied by one mole of water. (c) What is the meaning of the difference between these two results?

Group B

8. How many grams of anhydrous sodium carbonate can be obtained by heating $10\overline{0}$ g of $Na_2CO_3 \cdot 10H_2O$?
9. Calculate the percentage of cobalt, chlorine, and water in $CoCl_2 \cdot 6H_2O$.
10. What is the empirical formula of hydrated crystals composed of 56.14% $ZnSO_4$ and 43.86% water?
11. If 124.8 g of copper(II) sulfate crystals is heated to drive off the water of crystallization, the loss of mass is 45.0 g. What is the percentage of water in hydrated copper(II) sulfate?
12. The anhydrous copper(II) sulfate in Problem 11 was found to contain copper, 31.8 g; sulfur, 16.0 g; and oxygen, 32.0 g. What is the empirical formula of hydrated copper(II) sulfate crystals?
13. The density of carbon tetrachloride at 0 °C is 1.600 g/mL. (a) Calculate the volume in milliliters occupied by a molecule of CCl_4. (b) Assuming the molecule to be spherical, calculate its approximate diameter in Å.
14. Obtain from Figure 5-5 the radius of an atom of mercury. (a) Assuming this atom to be spherical, what is its volume in Å^3? (b) If liquid mercury atoms are packed in a cubic array with six nearest neighbors, what is the volume in milliliters of 1.00 mole of liquid mercury?

Solutions

Solutions abound in nature. So much around us exists as blends. The oceans, the atmosphere, and even earth's interior mix together many of the world's innumerable substances. The seas are soups concocted of many ingredients. The air is a smooth blend of many gases. Like an enormous underground furnace, earth's interior smelts together nature's various elements and compounds. In these examples, each solution has a different dissolving medium: for the air, it is a gas; for the seas, a liquid; for the earth, a molten solid. Is there one substance, a universal solvent, capable of dissolving all the riches of these vast domains? The story is told of a teacher who asked his students this question. No one seemed to know the answer. One student, however, boasted that he would find this universal solvent. The teacher, in his wisdom, challenged: "If you do find it, what shall you put it in?"

◻ 13.1 Solutions and suspensions

If a lump of sugar is dropped into a beaker of water, it gradually disappears. The sugar is said to *dissolve* in the water. Careful examination of a drop of this water under a microscope does not reveal the dissolved sugar. If more sugar is added, it also dissolves. However, if this process of adding sugar is continued, a point at which no additional sugar dissolves is finally reached.

The sweet taste of the liquid indicates that the sugar is present in the water. The molecules of sugar have become uniformly distributed among the molecules of water; some degree of sweetness is detected in all parts of the liquid. The mixture of sugar in water is homogeneous throughout. It is an example of a *solution*.

A **solution** is a homogeneous mixture of two or more substances, the composition of which can be varied within characteristic limits. The dissolving medium is called the *solvent;* the substance dissolved is called the *solute*. The simplest solution consists of molecules of a single solute distributed throughout a single solvent. In the example of the sugar-water solution, sugar is the solute and water is the solvent.

Not all substances form true solutions in water. If clay is mixed with water, for example, very little clay actually dissolves. Particles of clay are huge compared to molecules of water. The result is a muddy, heterogeneous mixture called a *suspension*. Because the components of the mixture have different densities, they readily separate into two distinct phases. However, some very small particles, still much larger than water molecules, are kept permanently suspended. They are bombarded from all sides

THE SOLUTION PROCESS

In this chapter you will gain an understanding of:

- **the difference between solutions and suspensions in terms of properties and composition**
- **the selective nature of solvents and how it is related to their molecular structures**
- **solution equilibrium**
- **the effect of temperature and pressure on solubility**
- **the dissolving mechanism and heat of solution**
- **solution concentration in terms of molality**
- **colligative properties of solutions**

Water is the most common solvent.

Figure 13-1. A beam of light used to distinguish a colloidal suspension from a true solution. The jar at the left contains a water solution of sodium chloride. The jar at the right contains a suspension of gelatin in water.

The colloidal state has been called the world of neglected dimensions. It lies between true solutions and coarse suspensions that separate on standing. Colloidal size ranges between ordinary molecular size and a size great enough to be seen through a microscope. Colloidal particles have dimensions ranging from approximately 10 Å to 10,000 Å. Ordinary simple molecules are only a few angstroms in diameter.

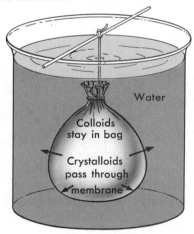

Figure 13-2. Dialysis: An ultrafiltration process for separating ions and molecules of solutions from dispersed particles of colloidal suspensions. The process is based on the difference in their rates of diffusion through a semipermeable membrane.

by water molecules, and this bombardment keeps them from settling out. Such mixtures may appear to be homogeneous, but careful examination shows that they are not true solutions. Mixtures of this type are called *colloidal suspensions*. One simple way of distinguishing between a true solution and a colloidal suspension is shown in Figure 13-1.

The term *colloid* was originally applied to sticky substances such as starch and glue. *Colloids* are substances that, when mixed with water, do not pass through parchment (semipermeable) membranes. In contrast, substances such as sugar and salt form true solutions with water and do pass through parchment membranes. These substances are called *crystalloids*. This distinction is illustrated in Figure 13-2.

Under certain conditions, some substances are nondiffusing and colloidal. Under different conditions, they are crystalloidal in behavior. *The state of subdivision* of a substance, rather than its chemical nature, determines whether it forms a suspension or a true solution when dispersed in a second medium. For example, a colloidal suspension can be formed if sodium ions and chloride ions are brought together in a medium in which sodium chloride is not soluble. Colloidal-sized crystals, each consisting of many sodium ions and chloride ions, are formed in the medium.

A true solution is formed when a solute, as molecules or ions, is dispersed throughout a solvent to form a homogeneous mixture. A true solution consists of a *single phase*. The solute is said to be *soluble* in the solvent. A colloidal suspension, on the other hand, is a *two-phase system*. It has dispersed particles rather than a solute, and a dispersing medium rather than a solvent. The dispersed substance, *internal phase,* is not soluble in the dispersing medium, *external phase.* The system consists of finely divided particles that remain suspended in the medium.

An ionic solid, such as sodium chloride, does not have a simple molecular structure. Instead, it has a crystal lattice composed of ions bound together by the strong electrostatic force of attraction between positive and negative charges. Soluble ionic substances form aqueous solutions that conduct an electric current. Such substances are called **electrolytes**.

Generally, covalent substances that dissolve in water form molecular solutions that do not conduct an electric current. Such substances are called **nonelectrolytes**. Many covalent acids are exceptions. When undissolved, their structures are molecular. However, their aqueous solutions do conduct an electric current. These acids are *electrolytes*.

Solutions of electrolytes have physical properties that are different from solutions of nonelectrolytes. Electrolytes will be considered in detail in Chapters 14 and 15. The remainder of this discussion of the properties of solutions will deal primarily with solutions of nonelectrolytes.

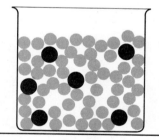

13.2 Types of solutions

Matter can exist as a solid, liquid, or gas, depending upon temperature and pressure. Therefore, nine different types of solutions are possible. These types of solutions are listed in Table 13-1.

All mixtures of gases are solutions because they consist of homogeneous systems of different kinds of molecules. Solutions of solids in liquids are very common. Since water is a liquid at ordinary temperatures, water vapor in air can be thought of as a liquid-in-gas solution. Solutions of gases in solids are rare. An example is the *condensation* of hydrogen on the surfaces of palladium and platinum. This phenomenon, called *adsorption*, approaches the nature of a solution.

Perhaps a more familiar example of adsorption is illustrated in the use of a charcoal gas mask to remove toxic gases from air before it is inhaled. A porous wafer of charcoal presents an unusually large surface area of carbon atoms. These surface carbon atoms attract gas molecules, especially of the polar type. When a mixture of toxic gases and air is passed over the surface of the charcoal, the toxic gas molecules are selectively adsorbed and air passes on through for respiration. Toxic gases are usually complex polar molecules. The air gases, mainly nitrogen and

Figure 13-3. Emulsions are colloidal dispersions of two immiscible liquids. (A) Vinegar is mostly water. When shaken with a salad oil, as in the preparation of a salad dressing, a temporary oil-in-vinegar emulsion is formed. It quickly separates into a layer of oil and a layer of vinegar. (B) Mayonnaise is also an oil-in-vinegar emulsion in which the yolk of eggs, a colloidal material, acts as an emulsifying agent that stabilizes the dispersed oil droplets with a protective film that prevents their coalescence.

Adsorption is a surface phenomenon. See Section 9.18.

Gaseous solution

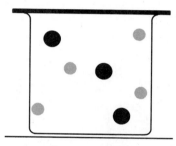

Liquid solution

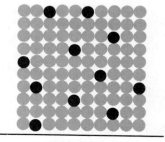

Solid solution

Figure 13-4. Models of solutions.

Table 13-1
TYPES OF SOLUTION

Solute	Solvent	Example
gas	gas	air
gas	liquid	soda water
gas	solid	hydrogen on platinum
liquid	gas	water vapor in air
liquid	liquid	alcohol in water
liquid	solid	mercury in copper
solid	gas	sulfur vapor in air
solid	liquid	sugar in water
solid	solid	copper in nickel

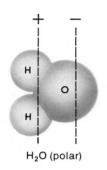

H₂O (polar)

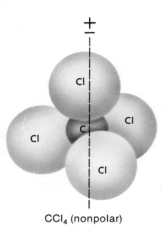

CCl₄ (nonpolar)

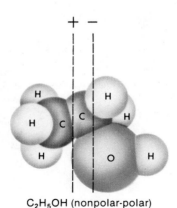

C₂H₅OH (nonpolar-polar)

Figure 13-5. Molecular models of three common solvents. Differences in molecular structure may help to explain why they are selective.

oxygen, are simple nonpolar molecules. Layers of other materials can be added to the charcoal wafer to remove smokes, dusts, mists, carbon monoxide, etc.

Substances that have similarities in their chemical makeup, such as silver and gold or alcohol and water, are apt to form solutions. Two liquids that are mutually soluble in each other in all proportions are said to be *miscible*. Ethanol (ethyl alcohol) and water are miscible in all proportions. Similarly, ether and ethanol are completely miscible. Ether and water, on the other hand, are only slightly miscible. Acetone is completely miscible with water, alcohol, and ether. Solutions of metals are called *alloys*.

☐ 13.3 Solvents are selective

High solubility occurs when solutes and solvents are structurally alike. In a very general sense, the *possibility* of solvent action is increased by a similarity in the composition and structure of substances. Chemists believe that the distribution of electronic forces helps to explain why solvents are *selective*. That is, it may explain why solvents dissolve some substances readily and others only to an insignificant extent.

The water molecule is a polar structure with a distinct negative region (the oxygen atom) and a distinct positive region (the hydrogen atoms). It is frequently referred to as the *water dipole*. The two polar covalent O—H bonds in water form an angle of about 105°. Thus the molecule as a whole is polar and behaves as a dipole (has a negative region and a positive region).

The carbon tetrachloride molecule, CCl₄, contains four polar covalent bonds. Each C—Cl bond is formed by electron sharing between an sp^3 hybrid orbital of the carbon atom and a p orbital of a chlorine atom. The set of four sp^3 orbitals of carbon (see Section 6.17) leads to the regular tetrahedral shape of the CCl₄ molecules, as shown in Figure 13-5. Because of the symmetrical arrangement of the four polar bonds, the molecule is nonpolar. Gasoline-type compounds, though unsymmetrical in bond arrangement, are practically nonpolar because the electronegativity difference between the hydrogen and carbon atoms of which they are composed is small.

If the rough rule that *like dissolves like* is applied to these solvents, water is expected to dissolve polar substances and carbon tetrachloride to dissolve nonpolar substances. Solute crystals composed of polar molecules or ions are held together by strong attractive forces. They are more likely to be attracted away from their solid structures by polar water molecules than by nonpolar solvents. Thus many crystalline solids like sodium chloride and molecular solids like sugar readily dissolve in water. Compounds that are insoluble in water, such as oils and greases, readily dissolve in nonpolar carbon tetrachloride.

Ethanol, C_2H_5OH, is typical of a group of solvents that dissolve both polar and nonpolar substances.

$$\begin{matrix} \mathbf{H} & \mathbf{H} & \\ \overset{\text{\tiny$\bullet\times$}}{\underset{\text{\tiny$\times\bullet$}}{\mathbf{H} \overset{\bullet}{\times} \mathbf{C}}} & \overset{\text{\tiny$\bullet\times$}}{\underset{\text{\tiny$\times\bullet$}}{\overset{\bullet}{\times} \mathbf{C}}} & \overset{\text{\tiny$\circ\circ$}}{\underset{\text{\tiny$\circ\circ$}}{\overset{\circ}{\circ} \mathbf{O} \overset{\circ}{\times} \mathbf{H}}} \\ \mathbf{H} & \mathbf{H} & \end{matrix}$$

There are five essentially nonpolar carbon-hydrogen bonds. There is also one carbon-carbon bond that is completely nonpolar. The carbon-oxygen bond and the hydrogen-oxygen bond are polar. As in water, the oxygen region of an ethanol molecule is more negative than the other regions. Thus an ethanol molecule has some polar character. This may account for the fact that ethanol is a good solvent for some polar and some nonpolar substances. As a solvent, it is intermediate between the strongly polar water molecule and the nonpolar carbon tetrachloride molecule.

A rough rule for solutions: Like dissolves like.

◻ 13.4 Hydrogen bonds and properties of solvents

Electronegativity is the measure of the tendency of an atom in a molecule to attract shared electrons (Section 6.19). Hydrogen atoms form distinctly polar covalent bonds with atoms of such highly electronegative elements as fluorine, oxygen, and nitrogen. The hydrogen end of these polar bonds is unique; it can be thought of as an essentially exposed proton. Shared electrons are more strongly attracted by the highly electronegative atom than by hydrogen. The effect of this unequal sharing is to leave the hydrogen nucleus (a proton) without an electron shield to isolate its positive charge.

Because of the unique character of the hydrogen end of the bond, the polar molecules formed may experience relatively strong intermolecular forces. The positive hydrogen end of one molecule may attract the highly electronegative atom of another molecule strongly enough to form a loose chemical bond. The bond between such molecules is called the *hydrogen bond* (Section 12.17). Although hydrogen bonds between hydrogen and fluorine are stronger, those with oxygen are by far the most common. See Figure 13-6.

Hydrogen bonds are loose chemical bonds.

It is the uniqueness of the polar bonds between atoms of hydrogen and those of highly electronegative elements that accounts for hydrogen bonding between their molecules. All elements that share electrons with highly electronegative elements differ from hydrogen in one significant way. Their atoms have inner-shell electrons that continue to isolate or shield their nuclear charges when the polar bonds are formed. The positive ends of their bonds do not have the unique character of hydrogen in such polar bonds. Their molecules, however polar, do not ex-

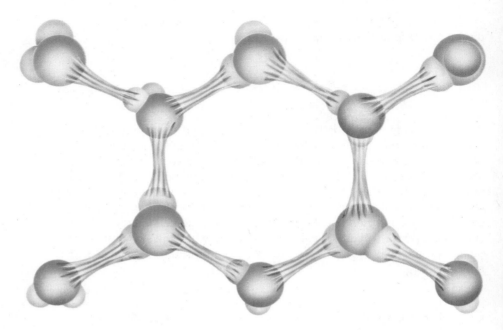

Figure 13-6. Hydrogen bond formation in an ice crystal.

hibit hydrogen-bond behavior. The abnormally high boiling and melting points of water may be attributed in part to hydrogen bonds among water molecules. Also, the formation of hydrogen bonds between a solvent and a solute increases the solubility of the solute. Hydrogen bond formation between water and ethanol molecules may partially explain the complete miscibility of these two substances.

◻ 13.5 Solution equilibrium

The solution process can be thought of as *reversible*. Again consider the lump of sugar dropped into a beaker of water. The sugar molecules that break away from the crystals and enter the water have completely random motions. Some of these molecules come in contact with the undissolved sugar. Here they are attracted by the sugar molecules in the crystal and become part of the crystal structure once more. In this way, the solution process includes the processes of dissolving and crystallizing.

The solution process involves two actions: dissolving and crystallizing.

At first, there are no sugar molecules in solution. The solution process occurs only in the direction of dissolving. Molecules leave the crystal structure and diffuse throughout the water. *As the solution concentration (number of sugar molecules per unit volume of solution) increases, the reverse process begins.* The rate at which the sugar crystals rebuild increases as the concentration of the solution increases. Eventually, if undissolved sugar remains, sugar crystals rebuild as fast as they dissolve.

At this point, the concentration of the solution is the maximum possible under existing conditions. Such a solution is said to be *saturated.* At saturation, solute crystallizes at the same rate as solute dissolves. These opposing processes proceeding at equal rates describe a solution in a state of dynamic *equilibrium.* **Solution equilibrium** *is the physical state in which the opposing processes of dissolving and crystallizing of a solute occur at equal rates. A **saturated solution** is one that contains the maximum proportion of dissolved solute to solvent under existing equilibrium conditions.* What visible evidence is there that the solution shown in Figure 13-7 is saturated?

If more water is added to the sugar solution, it is no longer saturated. It is now described as an *unsaturated* solution. The concentration of solute molecules is decreased and, consequently, the rate of the crystallization process is lowered. In terms of Le Chatelier's principle, this decrease in concentration of solute particles acts as a stress on the equilibrium. The stress is lessened by a decrease in the rate of crystallization. Fewer sugar molecules separate from the solution than enter it; the *same equilibrium concentration* of solute molecules is restored. Solution equilibrium exists when no more solute can be contained in a given quantity of solvent under existing conditions. *The* **solubility** *of a substance is defined as the maximum amount of that substance that can dissolve in a given amount of a solvent under specified conditions.*

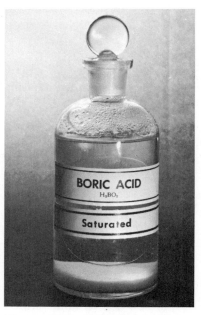

Figure 13-7. A saturated solution contains the equilibrium concentration of solute under existing conditions.

🞏 13.6 Influence of pressure on solubility

All mixtures of gases are homogeneous, and the "solubility" of one gas in another is independent of pressure. The gas laws describe the behavior of mixtures of gases (gas-in-gas solution) just as they do of individual gases.

Figure 13-8. A comparison of the masses of three common solutes that can be dissolved in 10$\overline{0}$ g of water at 0 °C. Convert these quantities to moles of solute per 10$\overline{0}$ g of water and compare them.

100 g of water	100 g of water	100 g of water
4.90 g of potassium dichromate	31.6 g of copper(II) sulfate, pentahydrate	76.7 g of cobalt(II) chloride, hexahydrate

The "fizz" of an opened bottle of carbonated beverage is an example of effervescence.

Ordinary changes in pressure affect the solubilities of liquids or solids in liquid solvents so slightly that they may be entirely neglected. The solubility of gases in liquid solvents, however, always increases significantly with increasing pressure.

Carbonated beverages *effervesce* when poured into an open glass tumbler. At the bottling plant, carbon dioxide gas is forced into solution in the flavored water under a pressure of from 5 to 10 atmospheres, and the gas-in-liquid solution is sealed in the bottles. When the cap is removed, the pressure is reduced to 1 atmosphere, and some of the carbon dioxide escapes from solution as gas bubbles. *This rapid escape of a gas from a liquid in which it is dissolved is known as* **effervescence.**

Equilibrium is a dynamic state; two opposing actions proceed at equal rates.

Solutions of gases in liquids reach equilibrium in about the same way that solids in liquids do. The attractive forces between gas molecules are relatively insignificant, and thus their motions are relatively free. If a gas is in contact with the surface of a liquid, gas molecules can easily enter the liquid surface. As the concentration of dissolved gas molecules increases, some molecules begin to escape from the liquid and reenter the gas phase above the liquid surface. An equilibrium is eventually established between the rates at which gas molecules enter the liquid phase and escape from it. While this equilibrium persists, the concentration of the gas-in-liquid solution remains constant. It is a dynamic equilibrium in which the entering and escaping rates of gas molecules are equal. Thus the solubility of the gas is limited to its equilibrium concentration in the solvent under existing conditions.

If the pressure of the gas above the liquid is increased, gas molecules enter the liquid surface at a higher rate. This tends to relieve the pressure and increase the concentration of dissolved gas molecules. In turn, the increasing solute concentration causes the rate at which gas molecules escape from the liquid surface to increase until the rates are again equal and equilibrium is restored at a higher gas solute concentration.

Henry's law relates gas solubility to pressure.

Again, in terms of Le Chatelier's principle, the increase in gas pressure acts as a stress on the initial equilibrium system. The stress is lessened by a decrease in pressure. Thus the solubility of the gas in the liquid is increased. *The solubility of a gas in a liquid is directly proportional to the pressure of the gas above the liquid.* This is a statement of **Henry's law,** named after the English chemist William Henry (1775–1836).

Gases that react chemically with their liquid solvents are generally more soluble than those that do not form compounds with the solvent molecules. Oxygen, hydrogen, and nitrogen are only slightly soluble in water. Ammonia, carbon dioxide, and sulfur dioxide are more soluble probably because they form the weak monohydrates $NH_3 \cdot H_2O$, $CO_2 \cdot H_2O$, and $SO_2 \cdot H_2O$ with the water solvent. Such gases deviate from Henry's law.

If a mixture of different gases is confined in a space of constant volume and temperature, *each gas exerts the same pressure it would if it alone occupied the space.* The pressure of the mixture as a whole is the *total* of the individual, or *partial,* pressures of the gases composing the mixture. You will recognize this statement as *Dalton's law of partial pressures,* discussed in Section 10.14. The partial pressure of each gas is proportional to the number of molecules of that gas in the mixture.

When a mixture of gases is in contact with a liquid, the solubility of each gas is proportional to its partial pressure. Assuming that the gases in the mixture do not react in any way when in solution, each gas dissolves to the same extent that it would if the other gases were not present.

Air is about 20% oxygen. When air is bubbled through water, only about 20% as much oxygen dissolves as would dissolve if pure oxygen were used at the same pressure. Oxygen remains dissolved in the water because it is in equilibrium with the oxygen in the air above the water. If the oxygen were removed from the air above the water, this equilibrium would be disturbed. By Le Chatelier's principle, the dissolved oxygen would eventually escape from the water. This fact is important when the abundance of life that exists in water is considered.

Chemistry students should know Le Chatelier's principle.

☐ 13.7 Temperature and solubility

1. Gases in liquids. A glass of water drawn from the hot water tap often appears milky. Tiny bubbles of air suspended throughout the water cause this cloudiness. The suspended air was originally *dissolved* in cold water. It was driven out of solution as the water was heated.

Raising the temperature of a gas-in-water solution increases the average speed of its molecules. Molecules of dissolved gas leave the solvent at a faster rate than gas molecules enter the solvent. This lowers the equilibrium concentration of the solute. Thus the solubility of a gas decreases as the temperature of the

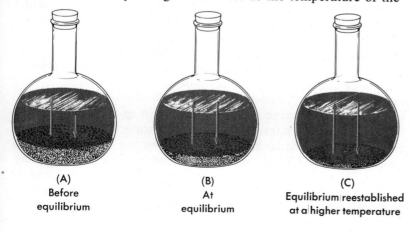

(A)
Before
equilibrium

(B)
At
equilibrium

(C)
Equilibrium reestablished
at a higher temperature

Figure 13-9. An example of solution equilibrium in which the solubility of solute increases with temperature. The different lengths of arrows indicate the relative rates of dissolving (up) and crystallizing (down).

Figure 13-10. Crystals of sugar growing on a string from a super-saturated solution of sugar in water.

Solubility of a solute depends on the temperature of the solvent.

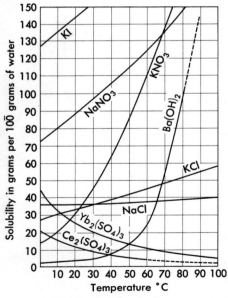

Figure 13-11. Solubility curves. The solubility of a solute is expressed in grams per $10\overline{0}$ grams of solvent at a stated temperature.

solvent increases. Appendix Table 11 shows how the solubility of gases varies with the kind of gas and the temperature.

2. Solids in liquids. An excess of sugar added to water results in an equilibrium between the sugar solute and the undissolved crystals. This equilibrium is characteristic of a saturated solution.

If the solution is warmed, the equilibrium is disturbed and solid sugar dissolves as the temperature of the solution rises. It is evident that the solubility of the sugar in water has increased with the rise in temperature. A new solution equilibrium is eventually reached at the higher solution temperature, where it has a higher equilibrium concentration of solute sugar.

Cooling the solution causes dissolved sugar to separate as crystals. The separation of solute from the solution indicates that solubility diminishes as the temperature falls. No more than the equilibrium concentration of the solute can normally remain in solution. Thus lowering the temperature disturbs the equilibrium, and sugar crystallizes from solution faster than solid crystals dissolve.

When a hot saturated solution of sugar is allowed to cool, the excess solute usually, but not always, separates as expected. If, on cooling, crystallization of the excess solute does not occur, the solution is said to be *supersaturated*. The solution contains a higher concentration of solute than does the saturated solution at the lower temperature. Supersaturation can easily be demonstrated by using a solute that is much more soluble in hot water than in cold water (sodium thiosulfate or sodium acetate, for example). The hot saturated solution is filtered and left undisturbed to cool slowly.

A supersaturated solution is unstable and usually has a strong tendency to reestablish normal equilibrium. A sudden shock or disturbance may cause the excess solute to separate. A small crystal fragment of the solute dropped into the solution (called seeding) starts the crystallizing process instantly.

Many pure liquids can be cooled below their normal freezing points with similar treatment. They are called *supercooled* liquids. As expected, this condition is unstable and the solutes usually show a strong tendency to solidify.

Increasing the temperature usually increases the solubility of solids in liquids. Sometimes, however, the reverse effect is observed. A certain rise in temperature may result in a large increase in solubility in one case, a slight increase in another case, and a definite decrease in still another. For example, the solubility of potassium nitrate in $10\overline{0}$ g of water at 0 °C is about 14 g. Solubility increases to nearly 170 g when the temperature is raised to 80 °C. Under similar circumstances, the solubility of sodium chloride increases only about 2 g. The solubility of cerium sulfate *decreases* nearly 14 g. Typical solubility curves are shown in Figures 13-11 and 13-12. If the solubility curve for cane sugar in water were included, the graph would have to be extended considerably. At 0 °C, 179 g of sugar dissolves in 100 g of water. The solubility increases to 487 g at 100 °C. The solubility of solids depends upon the nature of the solid, the nature of the solvent, and the temperature. Solubility data for various substances in water are given in Table 13-2.

When a solid dissolves in a liquid, the solid may be thought of as changing in phase to something resembling a liquid. Such a change is endothermic; heat is absorbed. Thus the temperature of the solution should be lowered as the solid dissolves. The solubility of the solid should increase as the temperature is raised. Deviations from this normal pattern may indicate some kind of chemical reaction between solute and solvent.

3. Liquids in liquids. Similar logic applies to solutions of liquids in liquids. As no change in phase occurs when such solutions are prepared, small changes in temperature are expected.

A large change in temperature, as in the case of sulfuric acid in water, suggests some type of chemical reaction between solute and solvent. With water as the solvent, this reaction may involve *hydration,* a clustering of water dipoles about the solute particles.

☐ 13.8 Increasing the rate of dissolving

The rate at which a solid dissolves in a liquid depends on the solid and liquid involved. As a rule, the more nearly the solute and solvent are alike in structure, the more readily solution occurs. However, the rate of solution of a solid in a liquid can be increased in three ways.

1. By stirring. The diffusion of solute molecules throughout the solvent occurs rather slowly. Stirring or shaking the mix-

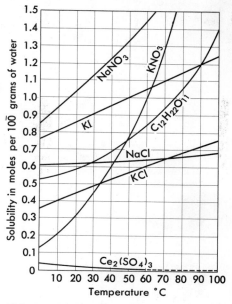

Figure 13-12. Solubility plotted in moles of solute per 100 grams of water as a function of temperature. Compare the relative positions of the curves with those of Figure 13-11.

The most common solutions are solids dissolved in liquids.

Table 13-2
SOLUBILITY OF SOLUTES AS A FUNCTION OF TEMPERATURE
(Grams of solute per 100 grams of H_2O)

Substance	Temperature, °C					
	0°	20°	40°	60°	80°	100°
$AgNO_3$	122	216	311	440	585	733
$Ba(OH)_2$	1.67	3.89	8.22	20.9	101	—
$C_{12}H_{22}O_{11}$	179	204	238	287	362	487
$Ca(OH)_2$	0.189	0.173	0.141	0.121	0.094	0.076
$Ce_2(SO_4)_3$	20.8	10.1	—	3.87	—	—
KCl	28.0	34.2	40.1	45.8	51.3	56.3
KI	128	144	162	176	192	206
KNO_3	13.9	31.6	61.3	116	167	245
Li_2CO_3	1.54	1.33	1.17	1.01	0.85	0.72
NaCl	35.7	35.9	36.4	37.1	38.0	39.2
$NaNO_3$	73	87.6	102	122	148	180
$Yb_2(SO_4)_3$	44.2	$37.5^{10°}$	$17.2^{30°}$	10.4	6.4	4.7
CO_2(gas at SP)	0.335	0.169	0.0973	0.058	—	—
O_2(gas at SP)	0.00694	0.00537	0.00308	0.00227	0.00138	0.0000

ture aids in the dispersion of the solute particles. It does so by bringing fresh portions of the solvent in contact with the undissolved solid.

2. By powdering the solid. Solution action occurs only at the surface of the solid. By grinding the solid into a fine powder, the surface area is greatly increased. Hence, finely powdered solids dissolve much more rapidly than large lumps or crystals of the same substance.

3. By heating the solvent. The rate of dissolving increases with temperature. If heat is applied to a solvent, the molecular activity increases. As a result, the dissolving action is speeded up. At the same time, the solubility of the substance increases if the dissolving process is endothermic.

The first two actions influence the rate of dissolving by increasing the effective contact area between solid and liquid. The third does so by producing a more favorable energy distribution among the particles of the solid. As the temperature is raised, the average kinetic energy of the solute particles is also raised. A larger portion of the particles has enough kinetic energy to overcome the binding forces and leave the surface of the solid.

◻ 13.9 Dissolving mechanisms

The solution process is spontaneous, or self-acting. While the precise manner in which substances enter into solution is not fully understood, some probable mechanisms by which a solid dissolves in a liquid can be examined. At least three energetic actions are assumed to occur in the dissolving process.

1. Solute particles are separated from the solid mass (as a solid changing phase to a liquid). *This action takes up energy.*

2. Solvent particles are moved apart to allow solute particles to enter the liquid environment. *This action also takes up energy.*

3. Solute particles are attracted to solvent particles. *This action gives up energy.*

If dissolving is endothermic, solubility increases with rising temperature.

The first two of these actions are endothermic and the last one is exothermic. If the exothermic action is less than the combined effect of the two endothermic actions, the net change is endothermic. Consequently, the temperature of the solution *decreases* as the solid dissolves. This is the usual pattern for solid-in-liquid solutions. In such cases, heating the solution results in an increase in the solubility of the solid. If the net change is exothermic, the temperature of the solution *increases* as the solid dissolves. Heating such solutions results in a decrease in the solubility of the solid. Refer to Figure 13-11 for examples of dissolving processes that are endothermic and those that are exothermic. The reasons for these effects are discussed in Section 13.10.

If dissolving is exothermic, solubility decreases with rising temperature.

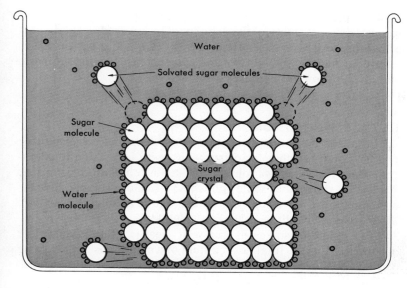

Figure 13-13. A model illustrating a possible mechanism for the dissolving process.

A possible model of the solution process is illustrated in Figure 13-13. Dissolving is aided by the attraction between solute and solvent particles. Solvent molecules move at random; some are attracted to surface molecules of undissolved crystals. As they cluster about these surface molecules, enough energy may be given up to enable solvent molecules to carry off solute molecules. The attraction between unlike molecules of solute and solvent is responsible for this process, which is known as *solvation*. The solute molecules that leave the crystal along with their cluster of solvent molecules are said to be *solvated*. If water is the solvent, the solvation process is known more specifically as *hydration,* and the solute molecules are said to be *hydrated*.

Solvation aids dissolving.

Hydration is solvation in which water is the solvent.

Natural processes generally lead to lower energy states (Section 2.14). Thus an endothermic energy change cannot account for the fact that the dissolving process occurs spontaneously. Perhaps the entropy change in such instances can.

The mixture of solute and solvent particles in a solution represents a more disordered state (higher entropy) than that of the unmixed solid and liquid. Thus, the mixture is more probable than the unmixed states. The favorable entropy change of the dissolving process may cause solution to occur even though the energy change is not toward a lower energy state.

How well is this logic sustained when it is applied to solutions of gases in liquids? The solute is in a more random state as a gas than as a dissolved solute in a liquid. Thus the higher entropy of the gaseous state opposes the dissolving process. For dissolving to occur, the energy change must be favorable (toward a lower state). It also must be great enough to overcome the unfavorable entropy change.

Accordingly, the dissolving process for a gas-in-liquid solu-

Table 13-3
HEATS OF SOLUTION
(kcal/mole solute in 200 moles H_2O)
[(s) = solid, (l) = liquid, (g) = gas at SP]

Substance	Heat of solution
$AgNO_3(s)$	+5.44
$CO_2(g)$	−4.76
$CuSO_4(s)$	−16.20
$CuSO_4 \cdot 5H_2O(s)$	+2.75
$HC_2H_3O_2(l)$	−0.38
$HCl(g)$	−17.74
$HI(g)$	−7.02
$H_2SO_4(l)$	−17.75
$KCl(s)$	+4.20
$KClO_3(s)$	+10.04
$KI(s)$	+5.11
$KNO_3(s)$	+8.52
$KOH(s)$	−13.04
$LiCl(s)$	−8.37
$Li_2CO_3(s)$	−3.06
$MgSO_4 \cdot 7H_2O(s)$	+3.80
$NaCl(s)$	+1.02
$NaNO_3(s)$	+5.03
$NaOH(s)$	−9.94
$Na_2SO_4 \cdot 10H_2O(s)$	+18.76
$NH_3(g)$	−8.28
$NH_4Cl(s)$	+3.88
$NH_4NO_3(s)$	+6.08

Negative heat of solution: Solute solubility decreases with rising temperature.

Positive heat of solution: Solute solubility increases with rising temperature.

tion should be exothermic. If the temperature of the solution is raised, the solubility of the gas should be lowered. Experiments show this to be the case. Heat is evolved when a gas dissolves in water, and the solubility of the gas decreases as the temperature of the solution increases.

☐ 13.10 Heat of solution

From the foregoing discussion, it is clear that no single rule can be stated for changes of solubility with increasing temperature. Gases become less soluble in water as temperature is raised. Table 13-2 shows that some solids become more soluble in water as temperature is raised, others become less soluble, and still others experience little change in solubility.

As a solute dissolves in a solvent, heat is either given off or absorbed. Thus the total heat content of a solution is not the same as that of its separate components. *The difference between the heat content of a solution and the heat contents of its separate components is called the heat of solution.* The heat of solution is a measure of the heat energy absorbed or released as a solution is formed.

$$\text{solute} + \text{solvent} \rightarrow \text{solution} + \text{heat} \quad \text{(exothermic)}$$

or

$$\text{solute} + \text{solvent} + \text{heat} \rightarrow \text{solution} \quad \text{(endothermic)}$$

When the dissolving process is exothermic, the total heat content of the solution is lower than that of its separate components. The solution warms as dissolving proceeds. The heat of solution is said to be *negative*. When the process is endothermic, the heat content of the solution is higher than that of its components. The solution cools as dissolving proceeds and the heat of solution is said to be *positive*.

The dilution of a concentrated solution may cause the release or absorption of heat. Thus the heat of solution of any system depends upon the concentration of the final solution. For this reason, *heat of solution is measured in kilocalories per mole of solute dissolved in a specific number of moles of solvent.* Heats of solution for some common substances are given in Table 13-3. How do these data relate to the solubility information in Table 13-2?

Observe that the change in solubility of a substance with temperature is closely related to its heat of solution. The heat of solution of sodium chloride, for example, is nearly zero. The solubility change of sodium chloride with temperature is also very small.

In a saturated solution with undissolved solute, an equilibrium exists between the dissolving and crystallizing processes.

Consider such a solution of KCl. The symbols (s) and (l) indicate solid and liquid, respectively.

$$KCl(s) + H_2O(l) + heat \rightleftharpoons solution$$

The heat of solution is +4.20 kcal/mole. The dissolving process is endothermic. The crystallizing process must then be exothermic. At equilibrium, the tendency toward lower energy (release of heat) as solute crystallizes just balances the tendency toward higher entropy (greater disorder) as crystals dissolve. Consequently, there is no net driving force in the system.

Suppose the solution is now heated. The increased heat content, as indicated by the rise in temperature, produces a stress on the equilibrium. According to Le Chatelier's principle, the stress is relieved by an increase in the rate of the *endothermic* process by which heat is absorbed. Thus dissolving proceeds faster than crystallizing until the concentration of KCl in solution is increased and the stress is relieved. Equilibrium is again established at a higher solute concentration. Solutes with positive heats of solution ordinarily become more soluble as the temperature of their solutions is raised.

The effect of temperature on saturated solutions of solutes with negative heats of solution is the reverse of the process just described. Here, the dissolving process is exothermic and the crystallizing process is endothermic. A rise in solution temperature disturbs the equilibrium, and the rate of the endothermic (crystallizing) process increases. Solute separates from the solution. Solutes with negative heats of solution ordinarily become less soluble as the temperature of their solutions is raised.

◻ 13.11 Concentration of solutions

The *concentration* of a solution depends upon the relative proportions of solute and solvent. The more solute that is dissolved in a solvent, the more *concentrated* the solution becomes. On the other hand, the more solvent that is added, the more *dilute* the solution becomes.

The terms *dilute* and *concentrated* are qualitative. In order to be of value, the concentrations of solutions must be known quantitatively. Chemists have developed several methods for expressing solution concentrations quantitatively. Three of these methods are introduced in this book. One method expresses solution concentration in terms of the *ratio of solute to solvent*. The other two methods express solution concentration in terms of the *ratio of solute to solution*.

When it is important to know the ratio of solute molecules to solvent molecules in a solution, the concentration is expressed in terms of *molality*. **Molality** is *the concentration of a solution expressed in moles of solute per kilogram of solvent*. The symbol for molality is the small letter *m*.

A

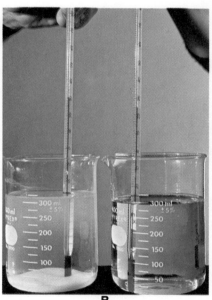

B

Figure 13-14. In (A) the two beakers of water are at the same temperature. In (B) the temperature of the water in the left beaker has been increased by dissolving sodium sulfite.

Table 13-4
CONCENTRATION OF SOLUTIONS IN MOLALITY

Quantity of solute	Quantity of solvent	Mass solute per mole	Conversion to moles solute	Conversion to kg solvent	Moles solute per kg solvent	Molality
18.2 g HCl	$25\overline{0}$ g H_2O	$\dfrac{36.5\text{ g}}{\text{mole}}$	18.2 g HCl $\times \dfrac{\text{mole}}{36.5\text{ g}}$	$25\overline{0}$ g $H_2O \times \dfrac{\text{kg}}{10^3\text{ g}}$	$\dfrac{0.499\text{ mole HCl}}{0.250\text{ kg }H_2O}$	$= 2.00\ m$
2.50 g NH_3	175 g H_2O	$\dfrac{17.0\text{ g}}{\text{mole}}$	2.50 g $NH_3 \times \dfrac{\text{mole}}{17.0\text{ g}}$	175 g $H_2O \times \dfrac{\text{kg}}{10^3\text{ g}}$	$\dfrac{0.147\text{ mole }NH_3}{0.175\text{ kg }H_2O}$	$= 0.840\ m$
15.6 g NaCl	$50\overline{0}$ g H_2O	$\dfrac{58.5\text{ g}}{\text{mole}}$	15.6 g NaCl $\times \dfrac{\text{mole}}{58.5\text{ g}}$	$50\overline{0}$ g $H_2O \times \dfrac{\text{kg}}{10^3\text{ g}}$	$\dfrac{0.267\text{ mole NaCl}}{0.500\text{ kg }H_2O}$	$= 0.533\ m$
12.2 g I_2	$10\overline{0}$ g CCl_4	$\dfrac{254\text{ g}}{\text{mole}}$	12.2 g $I_2 \times \dfrac{\text{mole}}{254\text{ g}}$	$10\overline{0}$ g $CCl_4 \times \dfrac{\text{kg}}{10^3\text{ g}}$	$\dfrac{0.0480\text{ mole }I_2}{0.100\text{ kg }CCl_4}$	$= 0.480\ m$

A 0.1-molal solution contains 0.1 mole of solute per kilogram of solvent.

A *one-molal* (1-*m*) solution contains *one mole of solute per kilogram of solvent*. You will recognize that 0.5 mole of solute dissolved in 0.5 kg of solvent, or 0.25 mole of solute in 0.25 kg of solvent, also gives a 1-*m* solution. A *half-molal* (0.5-*m*) solution contains *one-half mole of solute per kilogram of solvent*. A *two-molal* (2-*m*) solution has *two moles of solute per kilogram of solvent*. Several exercises for expressing the concentration of solutions in terms of molality are given in Table 13-4.

Molal solutions are important to chemists because (for a given solvent) *two solutions of equal molality have the same ratio of solute to solvent molecules*. (A kilogram, 1000 g, of solvent can be expressed in terms of moles since 1000 g ÷ number of grams/mole of solvent = number of moles of solvent.) Molality is preferred for expressing the concentration of solutions in procedures in which temperature changes may occur. The following Sample Problems illustrate calculations involving solution concentrations in molalities.

◖ SAMPLE PROBLEM

How many grams of $AgNO_3$ are needed to prepare a 0.125-*m* solution in $25\overline{0}$ mL of water?

◖ SOLUTION

Molality expresses solution concentration in moles of solute per kilogram of solvent.

$$25\overline{0}\text{ mL }H_2O = 25\overline{0}\text{ g }H_2O$$

The gram-formula weight of $AgNO_3 = 17\overline{0}$ g = mass of 1 mole $AgNO_3$. The

0.125-*m* AgNO$_3$ solution = 0.125 mole AgNO$_3$/kg H$_2$O. The mass of AgNO$_3$ required for 250 g of H$_2$O to give the 0.125-*m* concentration must be determined. Moles of AgNO$_3$ must be converted to grams and grams of H$_2$O to kilograms. This is done by unit cancellations as follows:

$$\frac{0.125 \text{ mole AgNO}_3}{\text{kg H}_2\text{O}} \times \frac{170 \text{ g}}{\text{mole}} \times 250 \text{ g H}_2\text{O} \times \frac{\text{kg}}{10^3 \text{ g}} = 5.31 \text{ g AgNO}_3$$

◖ SAMPLE PROBLEM

A solution contains 17.1 g of sucrose, C$_{12}$H$_{22}$O$_{11}$, dissolved in 125 g of water. Determine the molal concentration.

◖ SOLUTION

The formula weight C$_{12}$H$_{22}$O$_{11}$ = 342. Thus 1 mole has a mass of 342 g. The concentration is 17.1 g sucrose/125 g H$_2$O. To express in terms of molality, grams of sucrose must be converted to moles, and grams of H$_2$O to kilograms, giving moles of sucrose per kilogram of water. This is accomplished by unit cancellations as follows:

$$\frac{17.1 \text{ g C}_{12}\text{H}_{22}\text{O}_{11}}{125 \text{ g H}_2\text{O}} \times \frac{\text{mole}}{342 \text{ g}} \times \frac{10^3 \text{ g}}{\text{kg}} = \frac{0.400 \text{ mole C}_{12}\text{H}_{22}\text{O}_{11}}{\text{kg H}_2\text{O}} = 0.400 \text{ } m$$

PRACTICE PROBLEMS

1. What quantity of methanol, CH$_3$OH, is required to prepare a 0.244-*m* solution in 400 g of water?   *ans.* 3.12 g CH$_3$OH
2. What is the molality of a solution composed of 2.65 g of acetone, (CH$_3$)$_2$CO, dissolved in 200 g of water?
   ans. 0.228 *m*

◻ 13.12 Freezing-point depression of solvents

COLLIGATIVE PROPERTIES OF SOLUTIONS

In the preceding sections the nature of the solution process has been examined in some detail. It should not be surprising to find that the addition of a solute affects certain properties of the solvent.

From experiments involving vapor pressure, it is observed that *at any temperature the vapor pressure of a pure solvent is higher than that of the same solvent containing a nonvolatile solute.* The vapor pressure of a liquid is a measure of the *escaping tendency* of the liquid molecules. Thus the presence of solute particles in solution lowers the escaping tendency of the solvent molecules. This effect is reasonable if the solute particles are thought of as *decreasing the concentration* of solvent molecules.

A solute always lowers the vapor pressure of a liquid solvent.

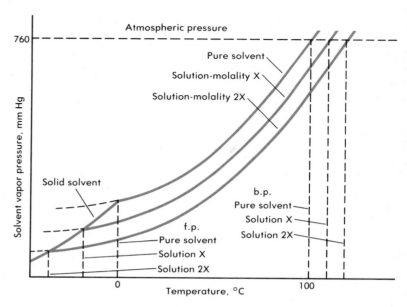

Figure 13-15. Vapor pressure of solvent as a function of temperature plotted for a pure solvent and dilute solutions of molalities X and 2X. Freezing-point depressions and boiling-point elevations are proportional to the molal concentrations of the solutions.

Solutes depress the freezing points of solvents.

Figure 13-15 shows plots of vapor pressure of a solvent as a function of temperature. Curves are shown for the *pure solvent,* for the solvent in a *dilute solution* of molal concentration X, and for the solvent in a *dilute solution* of molal concentration 2X. Observe that at any given temperature *the vapor pressure of the solvent* in the dilute solutions decreases in proportion to the concentration of *solute particles*. This decrease in solvent vapor pressure has the effect of extending the liquid range of the solution. That is, the solution can exist in the liquid phase at both higher and lower temperatures than can the pure solvent. From this observation, what can you conclude about the boiling and freezing points of the solvent in dilute solutions?

Salt water freezes at a lower temperature than fresh water. Sea water is a dilute solution of common salt, NaCl, and many other minerals. Suppose a sample of sea water is cooled enough for freezing to occur. The crystals produced are those of the *pure solvent* itself (in this case, water) and not of the solution. This phenomenon occurs when any dilute solution is cooled enough for solvent freezing to occur. *Solutes lower the freezing point of the solvent in which they are dissolved.* This fact is the basis for the common practice of adding ethylene glycol (permanent antifreeze) to the water in an automobile radiator.

Experiments with many dilute solutions of nonelectrolytes in water show that the *freezing-point depression* of the water is determined by the *number* of solute particles in a given quantity of water, not by the chemical identity of the particles. Dilute solutions of *equal molality,* but which contain different molecular solutes, yield the same freezing-point depression for water. Dilute solutions of different molality give different freezing-point depressions. These facts support the evidence in Figure 13-15 *that the freezing-point depression of the solvent is directly proportional to the molecular concentration of the solute.*

Properties such as vapor pressure and freezing point of a solvent that are influenced by the number but not the chemical identity of particles present are called *colligative properties. A **colligative property** of a system is a property that is determined by the number of particles present in the system but is independent of the properties of the particles themselves.*

Freezing-point depressions of solvents are represented by the symbol ΔT_f and are expressed in Celsius degrees, C°. The Greek letter Δ (delta) signifies "change in." Suppose the freezing point of a quantity of water is lowered from 0.00 °C to −0.36 °C by the addition of a small amount of some molecular solute. The freezing-point depression of the water is 0.36 C°.

Freezing-point depressions are observed for solvents containing volatile solutes as well as nonvolatile solutes.

$$\Delta T_f = 0.36 \text{ C}°$$

The depression of the freezing point of water has been calculated for a 1-molal solution of any molecular solute in water. It has the constant value of 1.86 C°. *This freezing-point depression for a 1-molal water solution is called the **molal freezing-point constant**, K_f, for water.* It is 1.86 C°/molal. Since

$$\text{molality} = \frac{\text{moles solute}}{\text{kg solvent}}$$

K_f has the dimensions $\dfrac{\text{C}°}{\text{mole solute/kg solvent}}$. The molal freezing-point constant for water is

$$K_f = \frac{1.86 \text{ C}°}{\text{molal}} = \frac{1.86 \text{ C}°}{\text{mole solute/kg H}_2\text{O}}$$

According to this value of K_f, a molecular solute added to 1 kg of water should lower the freezing point 1.86 C° per mole of solute dissolved. However, this relation holds experimentally only for dilute solutions. Even a 1-molal solution is concentrated enough so that the freezing-point depression is somewhat less than 1.86 C°. All solvents have their own characteristic molal freezing-point constants. The values of K_f for some common solvents are given in Table 13-5.

The depression of the freezing point of the solvent in a dilute solution of a molecular solute is *directly proportional* to the molal concentration of the solution. *The freezing-point depression, ΔT_f, is equal to the product of the molal freezing-point constant, K_f, of the solvent times the molality, m, of the solution.*

The molal f.p. constant, K_f, for water is 1.86 C°.

$$\Delta T_f \propto m$$

$$\Delta T_f = K_f m$$

When K_f is expressed in C°/(mole solute/kg solvent) and m is

Table 13-5
MOLAL FREEZING-POINT AND BOILING-POINT CONSTANTS

Solvent	Normal f.p. (°C)	Molal f.p. constant, K_f (C°/molal)	Normal b.p. (°C)	Molal b.p. constant, K_b (C°/molal)
acetic acid	16.6	3.90	118.5	3.07
acetone	−94.8	—	56.00	1.71
aniline	−6.1	5.87	184.4	3.22
benzene	5.48	5.12	80.15	2.53
carbon disulfide	−111.5	3.80	46.3	2.34
carbon tetrachloride	−22.96	—	76.50	5.03
ethanol	−114.5	—	78.26	1.22
ether	−116.3	1.79	34.42	2.02
naphthalene	80.2	6.9	218.0	5.65
phenol	40.9	7.27	181.8	3.56
water	0.00	1.86	100.0	0.51

expressed in moles solute/kg solvent, ΔT_f is the freezing-point depression in C°. The following Sample Problems illustrate the use of this expression.

SAMPLE PROBLEM

A solution is prepared in which 17.1 g of sucrose, $C_{12}H_{22}O_{11}$, is dissolved in 200 g of water. What is the freezing-point depression of the solvent?

SOLUTION

The gram-molecular weight of $C_{12}H_{22}O_{11}$ = 342 g. Thus 342 g of sucrose = 1 mole. The mass, 17.1 g of sucrose, must be converted to moles. The mass, 200 g of water, must be converted to kilograms. These conversions are accomplished by familiar unit-cancellation methods.

$$K_f \text{ for water} = \frac{1.86 \text{ C°}}{\text{molal}} = \frac{1.86 \text{ C°}}{\text{mole solute/kg } H_2O}$$

Solving for ΔT_f:

$$\Delta T_f = K_f m$$

$$\Delta T_f = \frac{1.86 \text{ C°}}{\text{mole } C_{12}H_{22}O_{11}/\text{kg } H_2O} \times \frac{17.1 \text{ g } C_{12}H_{22}O_{11}}{200 \text{ g } H_2O} \times \frac{\text{mole}}{342 \text{ g}} \times \frac{10^3 \text{ g}}{\text{kg}}$$

$$\Delta T_f = 0.465 \text{ C°}$$

Observe that the unit-cancellation operations yield the answer unit C°.

$$\Delta T_f = \frac{\text{C°}}{\cancel{\text{mole } C_{12}H_{22}O_{11}/\text{kg } H_2O}} \times \frac{\cancel{\text{g } C_{12}H_{22}O_{11}}}{\cancel{\text{g } H_2O}} \times \frac{\cancel{\text{mole}}}{\cancel{\text{g}}} \times \frac{\cancel{\text{g}}}{\cancel{\text{kg}}}$$

$$\Delta T_f = \text{C°}$$

◀| SAMPLE PROBLEM

A water solution of a nonelectrolyte is found to have a freezing point of −0.23 °C. What is the molal concentration of the solution?

◀| SOLUTION

The normal freezing point of water is 0.00 °C, so the freezing-point depression, ΔT_f, = 0.23 C°.

$$K_f \text{ (water)} = 1.86 \text{ C°/molal}$$

$$\Delta T_f = K_f m$$

Solving for m:

$$m = \frac{\Delta T_f}{K_f} = \frac{0.23 \text{ C°}}{1.86 \text{ C°/molal}} = 0.12 \text{ molal}$$

1. A solution consists of 10.3 g of glucose, $C_6H_{12}O_6$, dissolved in 250 g of water. What is the freezing-point depression of the solvent? *ans.* 0.426 C° 2. In a laboratory experiment the freezing point of a water solution of ethanol, C_2H_5OH, is found to be −0.325 °C. What is the molal concentration of this solution? *ans.* 0.175 *m* 3. A solution is prepared by dissolving 2.69 g of phenol, C_6H_5OH, in 200 g of water. (*a*) Determine the freezing-point depression of the solvent. (*b*) What is the freezing point of the solvent? (*c*) What is the molal concentration of the solution? *ans.* (*a*) 0.266 C°, (*b*) −0.266 °C, (*c*) 0.143 *m*	PRACTICE PROBLEMS

◻ 13.13 Boiling-point elevation of solvents

The boiling point of a liquid is defined in Section 12.6 as the temperature at which the vapor pressure of the liquid is equal to the prevailing atmospheric pressure. A change in either atmospheric pressure or vapor pressure of the liquid will cause a corresponding change in its boiling point. If a nonelectrolyte is dissolved in the liquid, the vapor pressure of the liquid (now the solvent of the solution) is lowered, provided the solute is a nonvolatile substance. From Figure 13-15 it is evident that the boiling point of the solvent is higher than that of the pure liquid alone. Experiments with dilute solutions of nonvolatile solutes have shown *that the boiling-point elevation, ΔT_b, of the solvent is directly proportional to the molecular concentration of the solute.*

Nonvolatile solutes elevate the boiling points of solvents.

When the boiling-point elevation of a 1-molal water solution of a molecular solute is calculated from data derived from dilute solutions at standard pressure, it has the constant value of 0.51 C°. That is, the 1-*m* solution should boil at 100.51 °C at 760 mm

Alcohol and ammonia are examples of volatile solutes in water solutions.

pressure. *This boiling-point elevation of 0.51 C° for a 1-molal water solution is the* **molal boiling-point constant, K_b,** *for water.* It is 0.51 C°/molal. Thus the molal boiling-point constant for water is

$$K_b = \frac{0.51 \; C°}{molal} = \frac{0.51 \; C°}{mole \; solute/kg \; H_2O}$$

Sugar is a nonvolatile solute in water solution.

The actual elevation of the boiling point in concentrated solutions deviates somewhat from that indicated by K_b. Thus its validity as a proportionality constant is limited to dilute solutions. All solvents have their own characteristic molal boiling-point constants. The values of K_b for some common solvents are given in Table 13-5.

Since the elevation of the boiling point of the solvent in a dilute solution of a nonvolatile molecular solute is *directly proportional* to the molal concentration of the solution, the boiling-point elevation, ΔT_b, *is equal to the product of the molal boiling-point constant, K_b, of the solvent times the molality, m, of the solution.*

$$\Delta T_b \propto m$$

$$\Delta T_b = K_b m$$

The molal b.p. constant, K_b, for water is 0.51 C°.

When K_b is expressed in C°/(mole solute/kg solvent) and m is expressed in moles solute/kg solvent, T_b is the boiling-point elevation in C°.

The freezing points and boiling points of solutions of electrolytes are also depressed and elevated. However, they do not follow the simple relationships just described. Such solutes are not molecular, and the generalizations about molecular substances do not hold for them. The behavior of electrolytes in water solution is the subject of Chapter 14.

☐ 13.14 Molecular weights of solutes

The application of the Avogadro principle discussed in Section 11.6 provides a way of determining the molecular weights of gases and volatile liquids. However, molecular weights of substances that decompose instead of vaporizing when heated cannot be determined by this molar-volume method.

The extent to which the freezing point and boiling point of a solution of a molecular solute differ from those of the pure solvent is related to the number of solute molecules in solution and not to their identity. Consequently, the experimental determination of the freezing-point depression or the boiling-point elevation of a solvent enables the molal concentration of that solution to be calculated.

This colligative property of solutions provides a method of determining the molecular weight of a substance that is soluble in water or some other solvent, and that does not react with its solvent. If the empirical formula of the solute has been determined from analysis data, the molecular formula can also be expressed.

The molal freezing-point constants, K_f, and molal boiling-point constants, K_b, are known for many common solvents. If the concentration of a molecular solution in terms of the mass of solute and mass of solvent (for which K_f or K_b is known) is known, the freezing-point depression or boiling-point elevation can be determined. The molecular weight can then be calculated. The freezing-point method is favored in these molecular-weight determinations.

From Section 13.12, recall that

$$\Delta T_f = K_f m$$

$$\text{Molality } m = \frac{\text{moles solute}}{\text{kg solvent}} = \frac{\text{g solute/g-mol wt}}{\text{kg solvent}}$$

Thus,

$$\Delta T_f = K_f \times \frac{\text{g solute/g-mol wt}}{\text{kg solvent}}$$

Solving for gram-molecular weight:

$$\text{g-mol wt} = \frac{K_f \times \text{g solute}}{T_f \times \text{kg solvent}}$$

The following Sample Problem illustrates this method of determining the molecular weight of a solute.

◨ SAMPLE PROBLEM

It is found experimentally that 1.8 g of sulfur dissolved in $10\overline{0}$ g of naphthalene, $C_{10}H_8$, decreases the freezing point of the solvent 0.48 C°. What is the molecular weight of the solute?

◨ SOLUTION

The molal freezing-point constant for naphthalene is 6.9 C°/molal (Table 13-5). Molality is expressed in terms of kilograms of solvent. Therefore, the quantity of naphthalene used must be converted from grams to kilograms, using the factor 10^3 g/kg.

$$\Delta T_f = K_f m$$

$$\text{where } m = \frac{\text{moles solute}}{\text{kg solvent}} = \frac{\text{g solute/g-mol wt}}{\text{kg solvent}}$$

$$\Delta T_f = K_f \times \frac{\text{g solute/g-mol wt}}{\text{kg solvent}}$$

$$\text{g-mol wt} = \frac{K_f \times \text{g solute}}{\Delta T_f \times \text{kg solvent}}$$

$$\text{g-mol wt} = \frac{6.9 \text{ C}^\circ \times 1.8 \text{ g S}}{\text{mole S/kg C}_{10}\text{H}_8 \times 0.48 \text{ C}^\circ \times 100 \text{ g C}_{10}\text{H}_8 \times \text{kg}/10^3 \text{ g}}$$

$$\text{g-mol wt} = 260 \text{ g/mole}$$

$$\text{mol wt} = 260$$

What does this result suggest about the composition of the sulfur molecule?

PRACTICE PROBLEMS

1. When 1.56 g of methanol is dissolved in $20\overline{0}$ g of water, the freezing-point depression of the solvent is 0.453 C°. Determine the molecular weight of the solute.   *ans.* 32.0

2. If 1.84 g of a molecular solute is dissolved in $15\overline{0}$ g of water, the freezing point of the solvent is -0.248 °C. What is the molecular weight of the solute?   *ans.* 92.0

◀ SUMMARY

A solution is a homogeneous mixture made up of two parts, a solute that dissolves and a solvent in which the solute dissolves. Solutes whose water solutions conduct electricity are called electrolytes. Solutes whose water solutions do not conduct are called nonelectrolytes. Solutions are single-phase systems.

Substances whose particles are too large to form solutions but small enough to form permanent suspensions are called colloids. A colloidal suspension is a two-phase system. In colloids, dispersed particles correspond to the solute of a solution, and a dispersing medium corresponds to the solvent of a solution.

The possibility of solubility is increased when substances are alike in composition and structure. The solubility of a solute is increased by hydrogen bonds between solute and solvent particles.

When a solution is in equilibrium, the opposing processes of dissolving and crystallizing occur at equal rates. Solution equilibrium limits the quantity of solute that can dissolve in a given quantity of solvent. Equilibrium is affected by temperature. The solubility of a solute is determined by the equilibrium concentration of solute.

The solubility of a gas in a liquid is affected by pressure in accordance with Henry's law. Gases that react chemically with their liquid solvents are generally more soluble than those that do not. The solubility of a gas decreases as temperature increases. The solubility of most, but not all, solids in liquids increases with temperature.

When the dissolving process is endothermic, the solution cools as dissolving proceeds, and the heat of solution is positive. When the dissolving process is exothermic, the solution warms, and the heat of solution is negative. Heats of solution are expressed in kilocalories per mole of solute dissolved in 200 moles of water.

The concentration of a solution can be expressed in molality as moles of solute per kilogram of solvent. Nonvolatile molecular solutes lower the freezing points and raise the boiling points of their solvents by characteristic amounts determined by the kinds of solvents and the solution concentrations. Each solvent has a specific molal freezing-point depression and molal boiling-point elevation. Specific molal freezing-point depression and molal boiling-point elevation are used to determine molecular weights of soluble substances that cannot be vaporized.

◖ VOCABULARY

alloy	dilute	miscible	solute
boiling-point elevation	effervescence	molal boiling-point constant	solution
colligative property	freezing-point depression	molal freezing-point constant	solution equilibrium
colloid	electrolyte	molality	solvation
colloidal suspension	heat of solution	nonelectrolyte	solvent
concentrated	Henry's law	saturated	supercooled
concentration	hydration	solubility	supersaturated
crystalloid	immiscible	soluble	suspension
			unsaturated

◖ QUESTIONS

Group A

1. Define: (*a*) solution; (*b*) solvent; (*c*) solute.
2. Why are the terms *dilute* and *concentrated* not satisfactory as applied to solutions?
3. (*a*) Name the nine different types of solutions possible. (*b*) Which type is the most common?
4. Why does carbonated water effervesce when drawn from the soda fountain?
5. What action limits the amount of a solute that can dissolve in a given quantity of solvent under fixed conditions?
6. Differentiate between *dissolve* and *melt*.
7. What is the influence of pressure on the solubility of: (*a*) a gas in a liquid; (*b*) a solid in a liquid?
8. What is the influence of temperature on the solubility of: (*a*) a gas in a liquid; (*b*) a solid in a liquid?
9. (*a*) What is the difference between *miscible* and *immiscible*? (*b*) Give an example of each.
10. What is the distinguishing characteristic of *polar* molecules?
11. State three methods of increasing the rate of solution of a solid in a liquid.
12. Explain the expression *saturated solution* in terms of solution equilibrium.
13. Referring to Figure 13-11, what is the solubility of potassium nitrate in water (*a*) at 15 °C? (*b*) at 65 °C?
14. How would you prepare a supersaturated solution of potassium chloride in water?
15. Explain why ethanol (alcohol) is miscible with both ether and water.

Group B

16. Ice cubes made with cold water are usually cloudy while ice cubes made with hot water may be clear. Explain.
17. Alcohol is a nonelectrolyte and is soluble in water, yet a molal solution of alcohol in water does not give the molal boiling-point elevation of water. Explain.
18. (*a*) What determines the amount of oxygen that remains dissolved in water that is at constant temperature and in contact with the atmosphere? (*b*) Explain what would happen if the oxygen were removed from the air above the water.
19. Suppose you wished to make a concentrated solution of copper(II) sulfate in water, using the crystalline hydrate as the solute. How would you hasten the solution process?
20. The carbon tetrachloride molecule contains four polar covalent bonds, yet the molecule as a whole is nonpolar. Explain.
21. How can you explain the fact that alcohol is a solvent for both water and carbon tetrachloride?
22. Why do caps sometimes blow off the tops of ginger ale bottles when they are exposed to direct sunlight for some time?
23. Why is cold water more appropriate than hot water for making a saturated solution of calcium hydroxide?

24. How are the solubility curves like those in Figure 13-11 constructed?

25. Liquid methanol, CH_3OH, and water are miscible in all proportions. When 1 mole of CH_3OH (solute) is mixed with 10 moles of H_2O (solvent), the heat of solution is found to be -1.43 kcal. (*a*) Is the formation of solution accompanied by an increase or decrease in entropy? (State the argument upon which your answer is based.) (*b*) Does the change in entropy favor the separate components or the solution? (*c*) Is the dissolving process endothermic or exothermic? Justify your answer. (*d*) Does the energy change as indicated by the sign of the heat of solution favor the separate components or the solution? (*e*) Are your previous answers consistent with the fact that methanol and water are freely miscible? Explain.

◖ PROBLEMS

Group A

1. How many grams of ethanol, C_2H_5OH, are required to prepare a 0.175-*m* solution in $40\bar{0}$ g of water?

2. Calculate the mass in grams of sucrose, $C_{12}H_{22}O_{11}$, that must be dissolved in $250\bar{0}$ g of water to make up a 0.100-*m* solution.

3. A solution of glucose, $C_6H_{12}O_6$, is prepared by dissolving 6.75 g of the glucose in 325 g of water. What is its molality?

4. What is the molality of a solution containing 46.0 g of glycerol, $C_3H_5(OH)_3$, in $75\bar{0}$ g of water?

5. A solution contains 96.0 g of methanol, CH_3OH, in $350\bar{0}$ g of water. Calculate the molality of the solution.

6. How many grams of water must be added to 90.0 g of glucose, $C_6H_{12}O_6$, to make a 0.250-*m* solution?

7. A 0.400-*m* solution of naphthalene, $C_{10}H_8$, in benzene, C_6H_6, is needed. If 32.0 g of naphthalene is available, how many grams of the benzene must be used?

8. A solution contains 31.0 g of ethylene glycol, $C_2H_4(OH)_2$, in $10\bar{0}$ g of water. What is the molality of the solution?

9. Calculate the molality of a solution containing 0.762 g of I_2 (solute) in $45\bar{0}$ g of CCl_4 (solvent).

10. A solution consists of 15.0 g sucrose, $C_{12}H_{22}O_{11}$, in 150.0 g of water. What is the freezing point of the water?

11. What is the boiling point of the solution described in Problem 10?

12. What is the freezing point of 250 g of water containing 11.25 g of a nonelectrolyte that has a molecular weight of 180?

13. A solution of iodine in benzene is found to have a freezing point of 4.3 °C. What is the molality of the solution?

14. A sucrose-in-water solution raises the boiling point of the solvent to 100.11 °C at standard pressure. Determine the molality of the solution.

Group B

15. The analysis of a compound yields: carbon, 32.0%; hydrogen, 4.0%; oxygen, 64.0%. It is found that 15.0 g of the compound added to 1.00 kg of water lowers the freezing point of the water 0.186 C°. (*a*) Find the empirical formula. (*b*) What is its molecular weight? (*c*) What is its molecular formula?

16. A compound contains: carbon, 40.00%; hydrogen, 6.6%; oxygen, 53.33%. Tests show that 9.0 g of the compound dissolved in $50\bar{0}$ g of water raises the boiling point of the water 0.051 C°. (*a*) Find its empirical formula. (*b*) Find its molecular weight. (*c*) What is its molecular formula?

17. The analysis of a compound shows: carbon, 30.3%; hydrogen, 1.7%; bromine 68%. The substance is soluble in benzene and 10.0 g of it lowers the freezing point of $10\bar{0}$ g of benzene 2.1 C°. (*a*) Find the empirical formula of the solute. (*b*) Determine its molecular weight and (*c*) its molecular formula.

18. Determine the freezing point of an aqueous solution that boils at 100.42 °C at SP.

Ionization

"The universe has a center, the earth, around which the sun, planets, and stars revolve." How ridiculous this statement sounds to us today! Yet at one time it was regarded as absolute truth, "truth" that did not easily yield to contradictory evidence. The victory of reason over superstition required the efforts of many gifted men and women. Galileo Galilei expressed agreement with the Copernican view that the sun, not the earth, was the center of the solar system. For his vehement defense of this theory, Galileo spent his last days in confinement. The Swedish chemist Svante Arrhenius also experienced a taste of the loneliness, humiliation, and despair that the pursuit of truth can sometimes bring. His theory of ionization challenged the accepted theory of how solutions conduct electricity. For his actions, he nearly missed receiving his university degree and chose to leave his homeland to pursue his research. Yet, like Galileo, he stood firm in the knowledge that his theory would someday be accepted as true.

☐ 14.1 Conductivity of solutions

In Section 13.1 water-soluble substances are distinguished as *electrolytes* or *nonelectrolytes* depending on the electric conductivity of their aqueous solutions. Electrolytes form ionic solutions that conduct electric currents. Nonelectrolytes are covalent substances that form molecular solutions that do not conduct electric currents. Exceptions are covalent acids whose aqueous solutions are ionic conductors.

For an aqueous solution to be conductive, its solute must be capable of transporting an electric charge. The neutral molecules of a covalent solute are not charge carriers, and the solution does not conduct. The ions of an ionic solute are charge carriers, and the magnitude of current the solution conducts is related to the solute ion concentration.

The conductivity of a solution can be tested as shown in Figure 14-1. A lamp is connected in the test circuit with an ammeter, a battery (the source of current), a switch, and a pair of electrodes. The electrodes are conductors that make electric contact with the test solution. Observe that the lamp filament is connected in series with the test solution. For a current to be in the lamp filament (and in the meter), the test solution must provide a conducting path between the two electrodes. A nonconducting solution is, in effect, an open switch between the electrodes; thus there can be no current in the circuit.

If the liquid tested is a *good conductor* of electric current, the lamp filament glows brightly when the switch is closed and the meter registers a substantial current in the circuit. For a

In this chapter you will gain an understanding of:

- **the conductivity of solutions in terms of electrolytes and nonelectrolytes**
- **the development of the modern theory of ionization**
- **the dissociation process that occurs when ionic compounds dissolve in water**
- **writing balanced ionic and net ionic equations**
- **the ionization process that occurs when covalent compounds dissolve in water**
- **the hydronium ion and how it is formed**
- **the distinction between strong and weak electrolytes in terms of ionization**
- **the effect of electrolytes on freezing and boiling points of solvents**

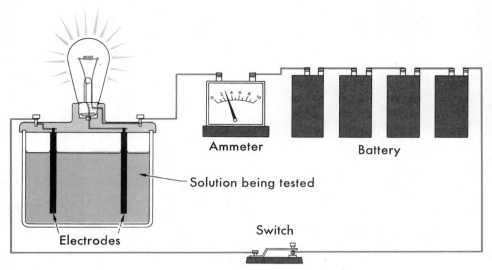

Figure 14-1. An apparatus for testing the conductivity of solutions.

The term pure water *refers to water that contains no other kind of matter.*

Oxidation: toward a more positive oxidation state.
Reduction: toward a more negative oxidation state.

liquid that is only a *moderate conductor,* the lamp is not as bright and the meter registers a smaller current. If a liquid is a *poor conductor,* the lamp does not glow at all and the meter registers only a feeble current.

When pure water is tested, the lamp does not glow and the meter (depending on its sensitivity) may not register a current. Pure water is such a poor conductor that, except in special situations, it may be regarded as a *nonconductor.* Similarly, water solutions of such covalent substances as sugar, alcohol, and glycerol (glycerin) are nonconductors of electricity. These solutes are *nonelectrolytes.*

In general, all solutes whose water solutions conduct an electric current are *electrolytes.* Solutions of electrovalent substances such as sodium chloride, copper(II) sulfate, and potassium nitrate are conductors. These solutes are electrolytes. Hydrogen chloride is one of several covalent compounds whose water solution conducts an electric current. These compounds are also electrolytes.

For an electric current to be conducted through a solution, there must be charged particles (ions) in the solution. These ions must be free to move or migrate through the solution. Chemical reactions by which electric charges enter and leave the solution environment must take place at the two electrodes. Consequently, an oxidation reaction must occur at one electrode and a reduction reaction must occur simultaneously at the other electrode. (Review Section 6.5.) These electrode reactions will be treated in greater detail in Chapter 22.

Ionic compounds can act as conductors of electricity in another way. Any effect that overcomes the attraction between the ions allows them the mobility to conduct an electric current.

In Section 14.5 you will see how water as a solvent provides ion mobility. Heating produces the same effect. If an ionic compound is heated until it melts, or *fuses,* the ions become mobile and can conduct an electric current through the melted substance. Some solid ionic compounds, such as silver nitrate and potassium chlorate, melt at fairly low temperatures. The electric conductivity of such fused salts can be demonstrated easily in the laboratory. Other ionic compounds, such as sodium chloride and potassium fluoride, must be heated to relatively high temperatures before they melt. When melted, they too conduct an electric current.

☐ 14.2 Electrolytes as solutes

The molal freezing-point constant for water, 1.86 C°, is related to the influence of nonelectrolytes in water solution (Section 13.12). *Solutes that are electrolytes have a greater influence on the freezing point of their solvents than solutes that are not electrolytes.* A 0.1-*m* solution of sodium chloride in water lowers the freezing point *nearly twice* as much as a 0.1-*m* solution of sugar. A 0.1-*m* solution of potassium sulfate or calcium chloride lowers the freezing point *nearly three times* as much as a 0.1-*m* solution of sugar. *Electrolytes in water solutions lower the freezing point nearly two, or three, or more times as much as nonelectrolytes in water solutions of the same molality.*

The molal boiling-point constant for water is 0.51 C°. Nonvolatile electrolytes in solution have a greater effect on the boiling point of the solvent than do nonelectrolytes. Dilute sodium chloride solutions have boiling-point elevations *almost twice* those of sugar solutions of equal molality. A 0.1-*m* solution of potassium sulfate shows *almost three times* the rise in boiling point as a 0.1-*m* solution of sugar. *Nonvolatile electrolytes in water solutions raise the boiling point nearly two, or three, or more times as much as nonelectrolytes in water solutions of the same molality.* The observations that freezing-point depressions and boiling-point elevations of electrolytes in aqueous solutions are not exactly two, three, or more times those of nonelectrolytes of the same molalities lead to the development of an important theory of interionic attractions in ionic solutions. This concept is discussed briefly in Section 14.10.

☐ 14.3 Behavior of electrolytes explained

Michael Faraday first used the terms *electrolyte* and *nonelectrolyte* in describing his experiments on the conductivity of solutions. He assumed that ions were formed from molecules in solution by the electric potential difference (voltage) between the electrodes. He concluded that the formation of these ions was what enabled the solution to conduct an electric current.

Figure 14-2. Svante August Arrhenius investigated the nature of solutions that conduct an electric current when he was a graduate student in chemistry at the University of Stockholm. He decided to solve this problem for his doctor's thesis in spite of opposition from his professors. In 1883, at the age of 24, he presented his thesis on "electrolytic dissociation," and his professors gave him a barely passing mark. Twenty years later, he received the Nobel prize in chemistry in recognition of this outstanding contribution to chemistry.

Later experiments showed that electrolytic solutions contained ions regardless of the presence of the charged electrodes.

In 1887, the Swedish chemist Svante Arrhenius (1859–1927) published a report on his study of solutions of electrolytes. In this report (written in 1883), he introduced the original *theory of ionization*. Arrhenius began with an assumption regarding the origin of ions in electrolytic solutions different from that of Faraday. He assumed that charged electrodes were not necessary for ionization, and then described many kinds of properties of electrolytes to show that this assumption was correct. Arrhenius concluded that ions were produced by the *ionization* of molecules of electrolytes in water solution. He considered the ions to be electrically charged. When molecules ionized, they produced both positive ions and negative ions. The solution as a whole contained equal numbers of positive and negative charges. He considered the ionization to be complete only in very dilute solutions. In more concentrated solutions, the ions were in equilibrium with *un-ionized* molecules of the solute.

These assumptions formed the basis of the theory of solutions of electrolytes. As chemists gained a better understanding of crystals and water molecules, some of the original concepts were modified or replaced. It is a great tribute to Arrhenius that his original theory served for so long. Present knowledge of the crystalline structure of ionic compounds was not available to him when, at the age of 24, he wrote his thesis on ionization.

According to the modern theory of ionization, the solvent plays an important part in the solution process. Water is by far the most important solvent. Knowledge of the polar nature of water molecules helps in understanding the solution process. The theory of ionization assumes

1. that electrolytes in solution exist in the form of ions;

2. that an ion is an atom or a group of atoms that carries an electric charge;

3. that in the water solution of an electrolyte, the total positive ionic charge equals the total negative ionic charge.

☐ 14.4 Structure of ionic compounds

A review of Section 6.3 will be helpful at this point.

Ionic compounds result from the transfer of electrons from one kind of atom to another. Thus these compounds are not composed of neutral atoms, but consist of atoms that have lost or gained electrons. Atoms that *gain* electrons in forming the compound become ions with a *negative charge*. Those that lose electrons become ions with a *positive charge*. Atoms lose electric neutrality by forming ions and gain chemical stability by associating with other ions of opposite charge.

The properties of ions are very different from those of the atoms from which they are formed. Such differences accom-

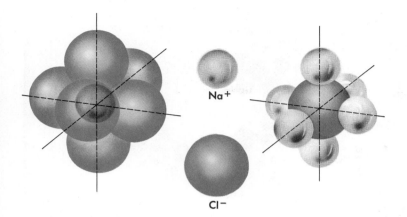

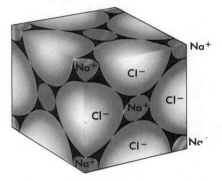

Figure 14-3. The packing of Na^+ and Cl^- ions in the NaCl crystal. In the model on the left, the six Cl^- ions are clustered about one Na^+ ion that cannot be seen here, but whose location is indicated by the dashed outline.

pany changes in electronic structure and the acquisition of charge resulting from the formation of ions. For example, a neutral sodium atom with a single $3s$ electron in the third energy level is different from a sodium ion. The sodium ion does not have the $3s$ electron and thus has one excess positive charge. There is an octet in the second energy level consisting of two $2s$ and six $2p$ electrons.

It is useful to remember that chemical properties are determined chiefly by the outer electron configuration of an atom or an ion. If the outer electron structure changes, the properties change. The loss of the $3s$ electron gives sodium the stable electron configuration of neon. *The charge of a monatomic ion and its oxidation number are the same.* In fact, the charge of the ion determines its oxidation state.

Ionic compounds usually exist as crystals made up of positive and negative ions arranged in a very orderly fashion. The cubic structure of crystalline sodium chloride is shown in Figures 14-3, 14-4, and 14-5. X-ray analysis shows that these crystals are composed of ions. Other ionic compounds crystallize in different patterns. Each has a characteristic lattice structure that depends on the relative size and charge of the ions.

Figure 14-4. The sodium chloride unit cell showing the lattice arrangement of ions in the crystal.

☐ 14.5 Hydration of ions

Suppose a few crystals of sodium chloride are dropped into a beaker of water. The water dipoles exert an attractive force on the ions forming the surfaces of the crystals. The negative oxygen ends of several water dipoles exert an attractive force on a positive sodium ion. Similarly, the positive hydrogen ends of other water dipoles exert an attractive force on a negative chloride ion. These forces weaken the bond by which the sodium and chloride ions are held together in the crystal lattice. The sodium and chloride ions then break away from the crystal lattice. They

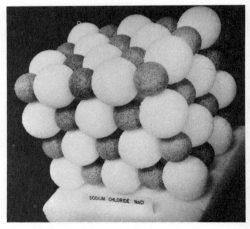

Figure 14-5. Model of a portion of a cubic sodium chloride crystal. The lattice structure is composed of sodium ions and chloride ions. Each ion has six nearest neighbors of opposite charge, the arrangement being repeated in each direction to the edge of the crystal.

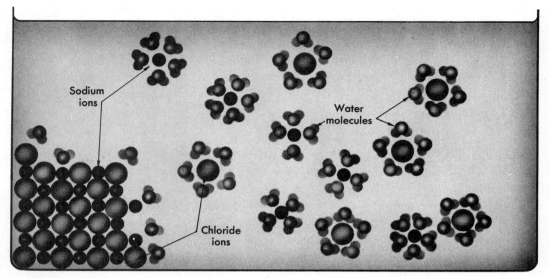

Figure 14-6. When sodium chloride crystals are dissolved in water, the polar water molecules exert attracting forces that weaken the ionic bonds of the crystal. The + end of H_2O dipoles attracts Cl^- ions, and the − end of other H_2O dipoles attracts the Na^+ ions. The process of dissolving occurs as the sodium and chloride ions become hydrated.

diffuse throughout the solution, loosely bonded to the solvent water molecules. See Figure 14-6.

Other sodium and chloride ions are similarly attracted by solvent molecules and diffuse in the solution. In this way, the salt crystal is gradually dissolved and the ions are dispersed throughout the solution. *The separation of ions from the crystals of ionic compounds during the solution process is called* **dissociation**. The dissociation of sodium chloride crystals in water can be represented by use of an ionic equation:

$$Na^+ Cl^- \text{ (solid)} \rightarrow Na^+ \text{ (in water)} + Cl^- \text{ (in water)}$$

Sodium chloride is said to *dissociate* when it is dissolved in water.

You should be familiar with the symbol (s) for "solid." Solutions in water are commonly referred to as "aqueous solutions." In this sense, (aq) means "in water." Thus the dissociation of an ionic compound in water is usually written as

$$Na^+ Cl^- \text{ (s)} \rightarrow Na^+ \text{ (aq)} + Cl^- \text{ (aq)}$$

The number of water dipoles that attach themselves to the ions of the crystal depends largely upon the size and charge of the ion. *This attachment of water molecules to ions of the solute is called* **hydration**. The ions are said to be *hydrated*. The degree of hydration of these ions is somewhat indefinite. Water molecules are interchanged continuously from ion to ion and from ion to solvent.

In certain cases, the water dipoles are not involved in reforming the crystal structure during the evaporation of the solvent. This situation occurs with sodium chloride, whose crystals do not contain water of crystallization. On the other hand, some ions retain a characteristic number of water molecules in re-forming the crystal lattice of their salt in the hydrated form. An example is crystalline copper(II) sulfate, $CuSO_4 \cdot 5H_2O$. Four of the five water molecules are associated with the Cu^{++} ion. The fifth water molecule is associated with the SO_4^{--} ion.

Extensive hydration of the solute ions ties up a large portion of the solvent molecules. This reduces the number of *free* water molecules in the spaces separating hydrated ions of opposite charge. Attraction between ions then becomes stronger, and the crystal begins to form again. Eventually, the tendency for ions to re-form the crystal lattice reaches an *equilibrium* with the tendency for ions to be hydrated. At this point the practical limit of solubility is reached. The solution is saturated under existing conditions.

$$Na^+Cl^-(s) \rightleftarrows Na^+(aq) + Cl^-(aq)$$

Here the tendency toward minimum energy (crystallizing) equals the tendency toward maximum entropy (dissolving).

Many ionic compounds that exist as crystalline solids are very soluble in water. They dissolve and produce solutions with high concentrations of hydrated ions. The following examples are typical.

$$Ca^{++}Cl^-_2(s) \rightarrow Ca^{++}(aq) + 2Cl^-(aq)$$
$$K^+Cl^-(s) \rightarrow K^+(aq) + Cl^-(aq)$$
$$K^+ClO_3^-(s) \rightarrow K^+(aq) + ClO_3^-(aq)$$
$$Ag^+NO_3^-(s) \rightarrow Ag^+(aq) + NO_3^-(aq)$$

When a formula of the type $CaCl_2$ is written ionically, the form $Ca^{++}Cl^-_2$ is used. Observe that the subscript $_2$ is spaced out to mean two Cl^- ions, as in $Ca^{++}(Cl^-)_2$.

Even ionic compounds of very slight solubility in water show measurable dissociation tendencies. Low concentrations of ions are present in water solutions of slightly soluble ionic compounds. Silver chloride, AgCl, is so slightly soluble that it is ordinarily described as being insoluble. However, such "insoluble" compounds precipitate from solutions saturated with respect to their ions, regardless of how low their concentration may be. The dissociation equation for AgCl in aqueous solution is

$$Ag^+Cl^-(s) \rightarrow Ag^+(aq) + Cl^-(aq)$$

Solubility of KCl in water at 20 °C is 4.5 moles/liter.

Both KCl and $AgNO_3$ have been described as very soluble ionic compounds. Their aqueous solutions contain hydrated ions which can be present in very high concentrations. These hydrated particles are $K^+(aq)$ and $Cl^-(aq)$ ions for the KCl solute. They are $Ag^+(aq)$ and $NO_3^-(aq)$ ions for the $AgNO_3$ solute. On the other hand, AgCl is only very slightly soluble in water. Its solubility at 20 °C is 1×10^{-5} mole/liter. This number means that only very low concentrations of both Ag^+ ions and Cl^- ions can be present in the same water solution.

Solubility of $AgNO_3$ in water at 20 °C is 13 moles/liter.

Suppose fairly concentrated solutions of KCl and $AgNO_3$ are mixed. In a single-solution environment there are the four ionic species: K^+(aq), Cl^-(aq), Ag^+(aq), and NO_3^-(aq). However, the concentrations of Ag^+ and Cl^- ions greatly exceed the solubility of AgCl. Excess Ag^+ and Cl^- ions separate from the solution as a *precipitate* of solid AgCl. *The separation of a solid from a solution is called* **precipitation**.

The formula equation for this reaction can be written as

$$KCl + AgNO_3 \rightarrow KNO_3 + AgCl(s)$$

KCl, $AgNO_3$, and KNO_3 are all very soluble in water. Only their aqueous ions are present in the solution environment. A more useful representation is the *ionic equation*,

$$K^+(aq) + Cl^-(aq) + Ag^+(aq) + NO_3^-(aq) \rightarrow K^+(aq) + NO_3^-(aq) + Ag^+Cl^-(s)$$

In this form the equation clearly shows that the K^+(aq) and NO_3^-(aq) ions take no part in the action. Ions that take no part in a chemical reaction are referred to as *"spectator ions."* Suppose these spectator ions are ignored and only the reacting species are retained. The chemical action is then shown most simply by the following *net ionic equation:*

$$Ag^+(aq) + Cl^-(aq) \rightarrow Ag^+Cl^-(s)$$

Sometimes there is no reason to write the complete formula equation or the complete ionic equation for such a reaction. The net ionic equation, which includes only the participating chemical species, may be the most useful way to represent the reaction.

PRACTICE PROBLEMS

For each of the following reactions, write the ionic equation and identify the spectator ions and the insoluble product. From this information, write the net ionic equation. As required, refer to Appendix Table 12 for solubility information.

1. Silver nitrate + ammonium chloride →
   ans. $Ag^+(aq) + Cl^-(aq) \rightarrow Ag^+Cl^-(s)$
2. Iron(III) sulfate + sodium hydroxide →
   ans. $2Fe^{+++}(aq) + 6OH^-(aq) \rightarrow 2Fe^{+++}(OH^-)_3(s)$
3. Zinc nitrate + ammonium sulfide →
   ans. $Zn^{++}(aq) + S^{--}(aq) \rightarrow Zn^{++}S^{--}(s)$
4. Mercury(I) nitrate + iron(II) iodide →
   ans. $Hg_2^{++}(aq) + 2I^-(aq) \rightarrow Hg_2^{++}I^-_2(s)$
5. Lead(II) chloride + potassium chromate →
   ans. $Pb^{++}(aq) + CrO_4^{--}(aq) \rightarrow Pb^{++}CrO_4^{--}(s)$

☐ 14.6 Some covalent compounds ionize

Covalent bonds are formed when two atoms share electrons. The shared electrons move about the nuclei of both atoms joined by the covalent bond. If the two atoms differ in electronegativity, the shared electrons are drawn toward the more electronegative atom. The covalent bond is polar to some degree. The molecule formed by these two atoms is polar covalent with a negative region and a positive region.

When a polar molecule is dissolved in water, the water dipoles exert attractive forces on the oppositely charged regions of the solute molecule. These attractive forces oppose the bonding force within the molecule. If they exceed the bonding force, the covalent bond breaks and the molecule is separated into simpler (charged) fragments. The charged fragments disperse in the solvent as hydrated ions. *The formation of ions from solute molecules by the action of the solvent is called **ionization.***

Factors that favor the ionization of solute molecules are the weakness of their covalent bonds and the ability of the ions formed to associate with the solvent. The tendency for solute molecules to ionize in a suitable solvent is determined by the relative stabilities of the molecules and the separated ions in the solution.

The extent to which covalent solutes ionize varies over a wide range. Some substances are completely ionized in aqueous solutions. Others may be only slightly ionized. This difference among covalent solutes is related to their relative bond strengths and their entropy changes on ionization.

Consider an example of ionization. Hydrogen chloride is one of a series of compounds of hydrogen and a member of the Halogen Family of elements. These elements are fluorine, chlorine, bromine, and iodine. (Refer to Section 5.5.) The compounds, collectively called *hydrogen halides,* are molecular and have single covalent bonds. All are gases and are very soluble in water. Hydrogen chloride, HCl, is the most important hydrogen halide.

As a pure liquid, hydrogen chloride *does not* conduct an electric current. When dissolved in water, the hydrogen chloride solution *does* conduct. Ions are present in the aqueous solution. A solution of hydrogen chloride in a nonpolar solvent such as benzene *does not* conduct. You may conclude that the ions in the aqueous solution result from a chemical reaction between hydrogen chloride molecules and water molecules. The solvent water dipoles are able to overcome the H—Cl bonds and separate the solute molecules into hydrogen ions, H^+, and chloride ions, Cl^-.

Arrhenius believed that the ionization of HCl simply involved the dissociation of solute molecules into H^+ ions and Cl^- ions upon entering the solution. Today chemists recognize that single H^+ ions do not exist as free particles in water solutions. They do, however, show a strong tendency to become hydrated.

The H^+ is a bare hydrogen nucleus that can approach very close to a water molecule. This fact accounts for the strong hydrating effect of water molecules on H^+ ions, which increases the tendency for ionization. Most covalent compounds are non-

The smaller an ion and the higher its charge, the stronger the hydration tendency is likely to be.

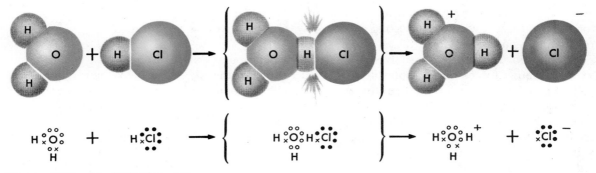

Figure 14-7. An ionization process. Water dipoles react with hydrogen chloride molecules to form hydronium ions and chloride ions.

electrolytes and do not ionize in solution. Those that do ionize are most often hydrogen-containing compounds that can form H^+ ions.

The ionization of HCl in aqueous solution is illustrated with models in Figure 14-7. The ionization reaction is given by the following equation:

$$HCl(g) + H_2O(l) \rightarrow H_3O^+(aq) + Cl^-(aq)$$

Omitting the phase notations for reactants and products, the equation can be written more simply as

$$HCl + H_2O \rightarrow H_3O^+ + Cl^-$$

The H_3O^+ ion is a hydrated proton $(H^+ \cdot H_2O)$ *and is known as the* **hydronium ion.** A model of this ion is shown in Figure 14-8. Because of ionization, a solution of hydrogen chloride in water has distinctly different properties from those of the hydrogen chloride gas. The aqueous solution is given the name *hydrochloric acid.* The properties of acids will be studied in greater detail in Chapter 15.

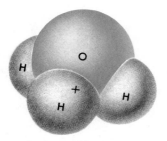

Figure 14-8. A model of the hydronium ion, H_3O^+.

"Proton" as used here refers to the H^+ ion, not to a proton from the nucleus of any of the atoms.

The aluminum halides, binary compounds of aluminum with a halogen, are molecular. The energy required to remove the two $3s$ and one $3p$ electrons from each aluminum atom exceeds the energy available when the elements combine. The bonds are covalent with a partial ionic character.

Aluminum chloride has the structure Al_2Cl_6 in both liquid and vapor phases. A model of this molecule is shown in Figure 14-9. The structure of the solid is less certain but is thought to consist of $AlCl_3$ units. Thus the empirical formula $AlCl_3$ is generally used for this halide.

Aluminum chloride in the liquid phase is a very poor conductor of electricity. In water solution, however, it is a good conductor. This change indicates that ionization occurs during the solution process. The aluminum ion has a strong tendency for hydration. The hydration process provides the energy needed to complete the transfer of three electrons from each aluminum atom to three chlorine atoms. The ionization can be represented

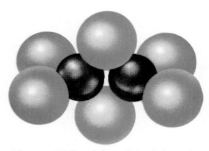

Figure 14-9. A model of the aluminum chloride molecule, Al_2Cl_6, in both the liquid and vapor phases. The solid phase is thought to consist of $AlCl_3$ units. Consequently, the empirical formula $AlCl_3$ is used for this halide.

as follows:

$$Al_2Cl_6 + 12H_2O \rightarrow 2Al(H_2O)_6{}^{+++} + 6Cl^-$$

or, more simply, using the empirical formula

$$AlCl_3 + 6H_2O \rightarrow Al(H_2O)_6{}^{+++} + 3Cl^-$$

Other hydrated aluminum ions probably form at the same time.

⊡ 14.7 Strength of electrolytes

The strength of an electrolyte is determined by the concentration of its ions in solution. Ionic compounds in the solid phase are crystals composed of ions. Their solutions contain the solute only in the form of dispersed hydrated ions. The solutions are said to be completely ionized. Ionic substances, if very soluble in water, can form solutions with high concentrations of ions. Their water solutions are good conductors of electricity. These substances are called *strong electrolytes*.

The single covalent bonds of the hydrogen halide molecules range from the very strong and very polar H—F bond, through the H—Cl and H—Br bonds, to the very weak and slightly polar H—I bond. Even moderately concentrated solutions of HCl, HBr, and HI are essentially completely ionized. They are strong electrolytes. Of these halides, HI has the weakest bonds and is the strongest electrolyte.

Aqueous solutions of hydrogen fluoride, HF, are only slightly ionized. The very strong H—F bond prevents an extensive ionization reaction with the solvent molecules. The concentrations of H_3O^+ ions and F^- ions remain low, and the concentration of HF molecules remains high. Hydrogen fluoride is a *weak electrolyte*. Solutions of weak electrolytes contain low concentrations of ionic species and high concentrations of molecular species.

Acetic acid, a water solution of hydrogen acetate, $HC_2H_3O_2$, is a poor conductor. Its relative merit as a conductor is shown in Figure 14-10. The fact that the solution does conduct slightly indicates that some ionization has occurred. This ionization is shown in the reversible reaction

$$HC_2H_3O_2 + H_2O \rightleftharpoons H_3O^+ + C_2H_3O_2{}^-$$

It must be assumed that the ion concentration is low. A 0.1-m solution of $HC_2H_3O_2$ is approximately 1% ionized; a 0.001-m solution is approximately 15% ionized. Of course, if 1% of the $HC_2H_3O_2$ molecules in solution is present in the form of ions, then 99% is present in the form of covalent molecules. Hydrogen acetate is a weak electrolyte.

Ammonia, NH_3, is a covalent compound and a gas at ordinary temperatures. It is extremely soluble in water and its water solution is a poor conductor. Ammonia ionizes slightly in water solution to give a low concentration of ammonium ions, $NH_4{}^+$, and

(A)

(B)

(C)

Figure 14-10. The brightness of the lamp filament indicates the conductivity of the solution tested. (A) Distilled water is a nonconductor. (B) Dilute acetic acid, a solution of a weak electrolyte, is a poor conductor. (C) Dilute hydrochloric acid, a solution of a strong electrolyte, is a good conductor.

hydroxide ions, OH^-. It is a weak electrolyte. The reaction with water is

$$NH_3(g) + H_2O(l) \rightleftarrows NH_4^+(aq) + OH^-(aq)$$

Ammonia-water solutions are sometimes called *ammonium hydroxide*. This is a traditional name and it may be justified by the fact that many useful properties of aqueous ammonia are those of the few NH_4^+ and OH^- ions present. (A more plausible reason that it is still used might be that all the reagent bottles are now labeled "**AMMONIUM HYDROXIDE**," and no one wants to change the labels.)

The terms *strong* and *weak* must not be confused with the terms *dilute* and *concentrated*. *Strong* and *weak* refer to the *degree of ionization*. *Dilute* and *concentrated* refer to the *amount of solute dissolved in a solvent*. The terms *strong* and *weak* are not precise descriptions of electrolytes. There are many degrees of strength and weakness, and the dividing lines are not clear-cut. The terms *dilute* and *concentrated* can be qualified in a similar way.

☐ 14.8 Ionization of water

The ordinary electric-conductivity test of solutions described in Section 14.1 shows water to be a nonconductor. More sensitive electric-conductivity tests show that pure water has a slight, but measurable, conductivity. It ionizes to the extent of about two molecules in a billion. Even though this concentration of ions is very low, it is important. The slight ionization of water is neglected when dealing with solutes such as hydrogen chloride, which may ionize completely in aqueous solutions.

The ionization of water probably begins with the formation of a hydrogen bond between two water molecules, as shown in Figure 14-11. The ionization products are hydronium ions and hydroxide ions. They are formed by the following reaction:

$$H_2O + H_2O \rightleftarrows H_3O^+ + OH^-$$

In any reaction involving the hydronium ion, the water of hydration is always left behind. This water of hydration is often of

Chemists do not have conclusive evidence that H_3O^+ ions exist in water solution in precisely this form. Some evidence suggests a more aqueous structure such as $H_9O_4^+$ because of hydrogen bonding. When the ion is written H_3O^+, it is with the understanding that additional water molecules might be associated with it.

Figure 14-11. The formation of a hydrogen bond between two water dipoles may be an intermediate step in the ionization of water.

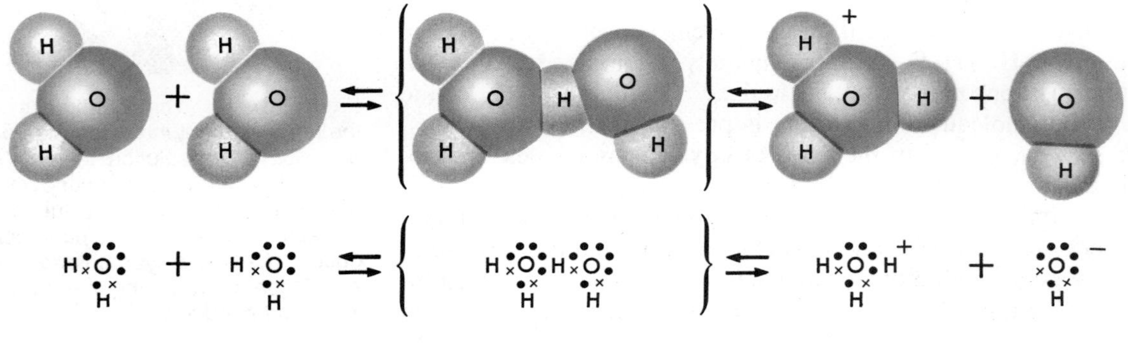

little significance in the reaction process, and the ion can be written more simply as H^+ or $H^+(aq)$. In any case, it is understood that *all ions are hydrated in aqueous solutions*.

☐ 14.9 Electrolytes and the freezing and boiling points of solvents

Molal solutions have a definite ratio of solute particles to solvent molecules (Section 13.11). The depression of the freezing point of a solvent by a solute is directly proportional to the number of particles of solute present. The same reasoning applies to the elevation of the boiling point of a solvent by a nonvolatile solute. Why, then, does one mole of hydrogen chloride dissolved in 1 kg of water lower the freezing point more than one mole of sugar does? Recall that a colligative property of solutions relates the freezing-point depression of a solvent to the number of solute particles present, not to their identity. The greater freezing-point depression is caused by the separation of each molecule of hydrogen chloride that ionizes into *two* particles. This comparison is illustrated in Figure 14-12.

Suppose that, in a concentrated solution, 90 out of every 100 molecules ionize. Then, for every 100 molecules in solution, 190 particles are formed (180 ions and 10 un-ionized molecules). Such a solute lowers the freezing point of its solvent 190/100 = 1.9 times as much as would a solute that does not ionize.

Suppose 100% of the hydrogen chloride molecules were ionized, as in a more dilute solution. The lowering of the freezing point should be double that caused by the solute in a solution of a nonelectrolyte having the same molality.

The following equation assumes the complete ionization of hydrogen sulfate in very dilute solutions.

$$H_2SO_4 + 2H_2O \rightarrow 2H_3O^+ + SO_4^{--}$$

Each molecule of hydrogen sulfate that ionizes completely forms *three ions*. Two are hydronium ions, each with one positive charge. One is a sulfate ion with two negative charges. A very

Figure 14-12. Five sugar molecules provide only five solute particles in solution. Five hydrogen chloride molecules, on the other hand, provide ten solute particles when dissolved in water.

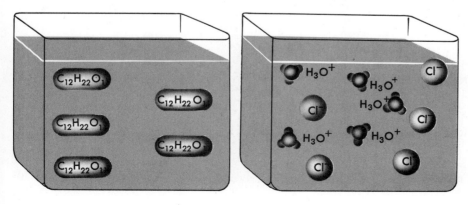

dilute solution of a given molality should, if completely ionized, lower the freezing point of its solvent *three times as much* as a solution of a nonelectrolyte having the same molality. Non-volatile electrolytes in solution raise the boiling points of solvents in a similar way because of their ionization.

Actually, hydrogen sulfate ionizes in aqueous solutions in two steps. The two hydrogen atoms in each molecule are ionized one at a time. In the first step, H_3O^+ ions and HSO_4^- ions are formed. In the second step, the HSO_4^- ions are further ionized to H_3O^+ ions and SO_4^{--} ions. Except in *very* dilute solutions, the second step may be far from complete. The ionization of H_2SO_4 is discussed further in Section 15.3.

Now consider a solution of an ionic substance such as calcium chloride in water. The dissociation equation is

$$Ca^{++}Cl^-{}_2(s) \rightarrow Ca^{++}(aq) + 2Cl^-(aq)$$

One mole of $CaCl_2$ dissociates and provides three times the Avogadro number of solute particles in solution. Recall that one mole of a nonelectrolyte provides one mole of solute particles when completely dissolved in water. An example is one mole of sugar, which provides the Avogadro number of particles. You might expect a $CaCl_2$ solution of a given molality to lower the

Table 14-1
FREEZING-POINT DEPRESSIONS FOR AQUEOUS SOLUTIONS OF IONIC SOLUTES

| *Solute* | *Concentration* | | | | |
| | (in moles solute/kg H_2O) | | | | |
	0.1	0.05	0.01	0.005	0.001

Values are observed molal freezing-point depressions in C° for concentrations indicated.

	0.1	0.05	0.01	0.005	0.001
$2K_f = 2 \times 1.86$ C° $= 3.72$ C°					
$AgNO_3$	3.32	3.42	3.60	—	—
KCl	3.45	3.50	3.61	3.65	3.66
KNO_3	3.31	3.43	3.59	3.64	—
LiCl	3.52	3.55	3.60	3.61	—
$MgSO_4$	2.25	2.42	2.85	3.02	3.38
NH_4Cl	3.40	3.49	3.58	3.62	—
NH_4NO_3	3.40	3.47	3.57	—	—
$3K_f = 3 \times 1.86$ C° $= 5.58$ C°					
$BaCl_2$	4.70	4.80	5.03	5.12	5.30
$Ba(NO_3)_2$	4.25	—	5.01	—	5.39
$CaCl_2$	4.83	4.89	5.11	—	—
$Cd(NO_3)_2$	5.08	—	5.20	5.28	—
$CoCl_2$	4.88	4.92	5.11	5.21	—
K_2SO_4	4.32	4.60	5.01	5.15	5.28
$ZnCl_2$	4.94	—	5.15	5.28	—
$4K_f = 4 \times 1.86$ C° $= 7.44$ C°					
$K_3Fe(CN)_6$	5.30	5.60	6.26	6.53	7.10

freezing point of its solvent three times as much as a nonelectrolyte having the same molality. However, experiments do not confirm this effect except for very dilute solutions. At ordinary concentrations, the freezing-point depressions of ionic solutes are less than those expected from ideal solutions. Table 14-1 gives observed values of freezing-point depressions in Celsius degrees for several ionic solutes at different dilutions of their aqueous solutions. Observe the trend *toward* a whole number multiple of K_f (1.86 C° for water) as the concentrations decrease. This problem is examined in Section 14.10.

◻ 14.10 Apparent degree of ionization

The larger the number of ions in a given volume of a solution, the better it conducts electricity. This fact suggests one way to determine the concentration of ions in a solution. Another way is to measure the lowering of the freezing point caused by an ionized solute in a measured amount of solvent. Suppose a 0.1-*m* solution of sodium chloride were to freeze at −0.372 °C [0° − (2 × 0.186 C°)]. You could assume the solute to be 100% ionized.

Actual measurements, however, give only an *apparent degree of ionization*. You have seen that electrovalent compounds, by the nature of their structure, must be 100% ionic in solution. Experimental results give an apparent degree of ionization somewhat less than 100%. For example, consider the 0.1-*m* solution of sodium chloride referred to above. This solution actually freezes at −0.346 °C, yielding a freezing-point depression of 0.346 C° instead of the predicted value of 0.372 C°. For many years, such differences prevented chemists from deciding whether or not a compound was completely ionized in water solution.

Today it is recognized that attractive forces exist between ions in aqueous solutions. These forces are small compared with those in the crystalline salt. However they do interfere with the movements of the aqueous ions, even in dilute solutions. Only in very dilute solutions is the average distance between ions great enough, and the attraction between ions small enough, for the aqueous solute ions to move freely. Therefore the more dilute the sodium chloride solution, the more nearly the freezing-point depression approaches twice the value for a molecular solute.

These observations are consistent with the Debye-Hückel theory of interionic attraction. This theory accounts quantitatively for the attraction between dissociated ions of ionic solids in dilute water solutions. According to the Debye-Hückel theory, each ion is surrounded on the average by more ions of opposite charge than of like charge. This clustering effect is illustrated in Figure 14-14. The effect is to hinder the movements of an ion. Thus the "ion activity" is less than that expected on the basis

Figure 14-13. Peter J. W. Debye (1884–1966) of Holland had a long and productive career in science. Though primarily a physicist, he made his most lasting and fundamental contributions to physical chemistry. Dr. Debye collaborated with E. Hückel in 1923 to investigate the nature of electrolytes. Together they proposed the Debye-Hückel theory of interionic attraction, which greatly advanced the quantitative understanding of electrolytic solutions. Debye was awarded the Nobel prize in chemistry in 1936 for his research on molecular dipole moments, interatomic distances, X-ray scattering, and the theory of electrolytes. In 1940 he accepted an appointment as professor of chemistry at Cornell University and became an American citizen in 1946.

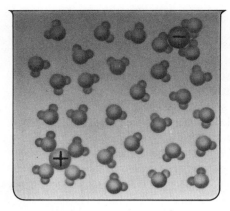 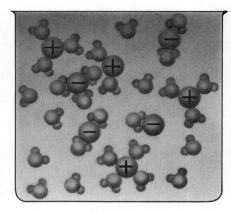

Figure 14-14. The ions in the dilute solution on the left are far apart and act independently. The activity of the ions in the solution on the right is somewhat restricted because of the concentration. Thus the apparent number of ions present may be less than the actual number.

of the number of ions known to be present. Table 14-2 gives the observed freezing-point depressions of aqueous solutions of sodium chloride at various concentrations. The table also shows freezing-point depressions per mole of NaCl calculated from the observed values.

In concentrated solutions, an additional effect on the freezing-point depression may arise from a shortage of solvent molecules. There may not be enough water molecules to hydrate completely all solute ions. In such a case, clusters of ions may act as a single solute unit.

Table 14-2
INFLUENCE OF CONCENTRATION ON FREEZING POINT OF AQUEOUS SOLUTIONS OF NaCl

Concentration of NaCl (m)	Freezing-point depression (C°)	Freezing-point depression/mole NaCl (C°)
0.100	0.346	3.46
0.0100	0.0361	3.61
0.00100	0.00366	3.66
0.000100	0.000372	3.72

SUMMARY

Ions that have mobility and are free to move through a liquid medium are able to conduct electricity. Two electrodes connected to a source of electric current must be in contact with the liquid for conduction to occur through it.

In crystal form, ionic compounds are composed of ions. When fused, their liquid phase consists of ions. They are soluble only in highly polar solvents like water and form solutions that contain ions. Ionic compounds conduct an elec-

tric current only when fused or when dissolved in water. Their ions have mobility in either situation.

The process by which ionic substances are dissolved in water is called dissociation. In dissociation, ions that compose the compounds are torn apart by the hydrating action of the solvent and dissolve as hydrated ions.

Some covalent compounds form solutions that contain ions. As pure liquids covalent compounds do not conduct. The ions are produced by chemical reaction between the solute molecules and the solvent, a process called ionization. Water is the best, but not the only, ionizing agent.

Substances whose water solutions conduct electricity are called electrolytes. Those whose water solutions do not conduct electricity are nonelectrolytes. Electrolytes are strong or weak depending on how well their solutions conduct an electric current. Solutions of strong electrolytes have high concentrations of ions. Those of weak electrolytes have low concentrations of ions. Water ionizes to a very small extent, forming hydronium ions and hydroxide ions in very low concentrations.

Electrolytes affect the freezing and boiling points of solvents to a greater extent than nonelectrolytes. Freezing-point depressions and boiling-point elevations of solvents vary with the number of solute particles in solution. The apparent degree of ionization increases with dilution of an electrolyte in solution. Ionic solutes are composed of ions and consequently are completely dissociated in solution. An apparent degree of ionization less than the actual ion concentration can be explained on the basis of the theory of interionic attraction.

◖ VOCABULARY

Debye-Hückel theory
dissociation
electrolyte
hydrated proton

hydration
hydronium ion
ionic equation
ionization

net ionic equation
precipitation
spectator ion
theory of ionization

◖ QUESTIONS

Group A
1. What is the distinction between an electrolyte and a nonelectrolyte?
2. What effect does the addition of electrolytes have on the boiling points and freezing points of solvents such as water?
3. What theory helps to explain the behavior of electrolytes?
4. What are the important assumptions of this theory?
5. What is an ion?
6. Write the equation for the ionization of water.
7. Explain why the water molecule is a polar molecule.
8. What is the nature of the crystal structure of an ionic compound?
9. How does an atom differ from an ion?
10. How can you account for the stability of an ion?

11. (a) How are water molecules involved in the dissociation of an ionic compound? (b) How can the process be reversed?
12. Why is the dissociation of ionic compounds 100%?
13. Melted potassium chloride conducts an electric current. Explain.
14. Predict the approximate freezing-point depressions for 0.01-m aqueous solutions of the following substances: (a) KI, (b) C_2H_5OH, (c) $Al_2(SO_4)_3$.

Group B
15. (a) Explain how the action of water on a polar compound like hydrogen chloride produces ionization. (b) Showing the part played by the water, write the equation for the ionization of hydrogen chloride in water solution.

16. What is the distinction between dissociation and ionization?
17. Describe the solution equilibrium in a saturated solution of sodium nitrate containing an excess of the crystals.
18. (*a*) What are symmetrical covalent molecules? (*b*) Why don't they ionize?
19. Explain the abnormal freezing-point depression and boiling-point elevation of solvents produced by electrolytes in terms of the theory of ionization.
20. (*a*) Write an equation for the dissociation of calcium chloride. (*b*) What is the theoretical freezing point of a one-molal solution of calcium chloride in water?
21. Describe two ways of measuring the apparent degree of ionization.
22. Why does the measurement of the apparent degree of ionization not coincide with the evidence that ionic compounds are 100% dissociated in solution?
23. How does a concentrated solution of a weak electrolyte differ from a dilute solution of a strong electrolyte?
24. When potassium nitrate is dissolved in water, the dissolving process is endothermic. (*a*) What temperature change does the solution undergo? (*b*) Which is greater, the hydration energy or the lattice energy? (*c*) To what do you attribute the driving force that causes the dissolving process to proceed?
25. (*a*) How is the solubility of potassium nitrate affected by warming the solution discussed in Question 24? (*b*) Apply the principle of Le Chatelier to account for this change in solubility.
26. Suppose 0.1 mole of a substance dissolved in 1 kg of water lowers the freezing point of the water 0.360 C°. (*a*) What can you predict about the nature of the solution? (*b*) What can you conclude about the oxidation numbers of the particles of solute?

Questions 27–30: For each reaction, (1) write the complete ionic equation; (2) identify the spectator ions; (3) write the net ionic equation.

27. Barium bromide + ammonium sulfate →
28. Silver nitrate + magnesium chloride →
29. Manganese(II) sulfate + ammonium sulfide →
30. Zinc iodide + calcium hydroxide →

31. Write the equation for the ionization of hydrogen iodide gas.
32. Write the equation for the ionization of ammonia gas.

◖ PROBLEMS

Group B

1. In a certain experiment it was found that 185 drops of water were required to give a volume of 10.0 mL. (*a*) How many molecules of water are in each drop? (*b*) How many hydronium ions are in each drop? (*c*) How many hydroxide ions are in each drop?
2. How many grams of copper(II) sulfate pentahydrate must be added to 125 g of water to give a 0.0155-*m* solution?
3. Calculate the freezing point of 600 g of water to which 12.0 g of ethyl alcohol, C_2H_5OH, has been added.
4. The composition of a substance was determined by analysis to be 10.1% carbon, 0.846% hydrogen, and 89.1% chlorine. It was found to be soluble in benzene, and when 2.50 g was dissolved in 100 g of benzene, the freezing point of the benzene was 4.41 °C. Determine the molecular formula of the substance.
5. A chemistry student collected 15.0 mL of dry HCl gas at 21.0 °C and 748 mm pressure and then dissolved the gas in 1.00 kg of water. Assuming complete ionization and no interionic attraction, calculate the freezing-point depression of the water.

Acids, Bases, and Salts

Sodium chloride — never has a seasoning given such relish to human affairs! In ancient times its importance probably was not equaled by any other single compound. To ancient civilizations, this crystalline substance was an important commodity. It added flavor to food, kept meat from spoiling, and had medicinal properties. Because of its importance and limited supply, common table salt was highly valued. In fact, Roman soldiers were paid in cakes of salt. Hence from sal, *the Latin word for this vital compound, is derived our word "salary." It is not surprising that salt has come to symbolize many attributes of human behavior. "The salt of youth" was Shakespeare's characterization of the liveliness of this phase of life. "There is salt between us" conveys enduring and devoted friendship. A person with valuable qualities is often described as "worth one's salt." "The salt of the earth" refers to those great human beings who have improved the world by giving of their talents.*

☐ 15.1 The nature of acids

Electrolytes are substances whose aqueous solutions conduct an electric current. Their solutions contain ions. Such substances are historically classified as *acids, bases,* or *salts.* In this sense, **acids** *are substances that react with water to form hydronium ions, H_3O^+.* By this definition, acids are limited to aqueous solutions. **Bases** *are electrolytes that provide hydroxide ions, OH^-, in aqueous solutions.* **Salts** *are ionic compounds of metal–nonmetal composition.* As solids, salts have an ionic crystalline structure; in aqueous solutions, they are dissociated as separate metallic and nonmetallic hydrated ions. Bases and salts are treated in detail beginning with Sections 15.8 and 15.13, respectively.

Acids as a group share a common structural characteristic. When they are ionized in water, their molecules contribute one or more hydrogen ions to the aqueous solution. As might be expected, acids share a common set of properties to varying degrees. All acids have a sour taste. **CAUTION:** *Never use the "taste test" to identify an acid.* The sour taste of lemon juice (citric acid) and cider vinegar (acetic acid) are familiar. Some acids are very corrosive and some are poisonous. All acids contain hydrogen, and some acids liberate hydrogen in reactions with certain metals. The effect of acids on the color of indicators and their neutralization of bases are the concerns of Chapter 16.

Nearly all fruits contain acids, as do many other common foods. Lemons, oranges, and grapefruit contain citric acid. Apples contain malic acid. The souring of milk produces lactic acid. Rancid butter contains butyric acid. The fermentation of hard

ACIDS

In this chapter you will gain an understanding of:

- **the importance of the four major industrial acids**
- **the modern definitions of acids**
- **the properties of aqueous acids**
- **naming binary acids and oxyacids**
- **the modern definitions of bases**
- **the properties of hydroxides protolysis**
- **acid anhydrides and basic anhydrides**
- **conjugate acid–base pairs**
- **the nature and preparation of salts**
- **naming slats**

Review Section 8.8 and Table 8-2.

Indicators are organic dyes that have one color in acidic solutions and another color in basic solutions.

The carboxyl group in organic acids:

cider forms the acetic acid of vinegar. These acids, because of their origin and nature, are called *organic* acids.

All organic acids are covalent (molecular) structures that contain a specific configuration called the carboxyl group (COOH). They are weak acids, being slightly ionized in water solution. To the extent that ionization occurs, the hydrogen atom of the carboxyl group becomes hydrated as an H_3O^+ ion. Organic acids are discussed in Chapter 19.

Acids manufactured from minerals are known as *inorganic* acids, or simply as *mineral* acids. These substances have been known for centuries because their properties are very distinctive. When the term "acid" is used in a very general sense, it usually refers to these compounds. They are the substances historically known as acids; their water solutions are called *aqueous acids*. Mineral acids occupy major roles in the chemical industry. Four mineral acids are among the largest-volume industrial chemicals produced in the United States. Modern definitions of acids give the name "acid" to many substances that are not acids in this traditional sense.

☐ 15.2 Industrial acids

If a manufacturing chemist were asked to name the most important acid, he or she would probably mention *sulfuric acid*. It is a very versatile industrial product. It is used in so many technical and manufacturing processes that the consumption of sulfuric acid is an index to a country's industrialization and prosperity. More sulfuric acid is manufactured in the United States than any other chemical—approximately 38 million metric tons each year.

The second ranking industrial acid is *phosphoric acid* and the third is *nitric acid*. The dominant use of these three acids is in agriculture. More specifically, the production of fertilizers consumes 60% of the sulfuric acid, 80% of the phosphoric acid, and 70% of the nitric acid produced in the United States.

Ranking fourth in importance is *hydrochloric acid*. The gastric secretion in the human stomach is about 0.4% hydrochloric acid. Its industrial uses have little in common with the three acids just mentioned.

Phosphoric acid, H_3PO_4, is a weak acid. It is made by reacting sulfuric acid with phosphate rock, and by burning phosphorus and reacting the oxide with water. Its major uses are in making fertilizers and detergents. It is not as commonly used in the chemistry laboratory as are sulfuric, nitric, and hydrochloric acids. A brief description of each of these three common laboratory acids follows.

1. Sulfuric acid. H_2SO_4 is a dense, oily liquid with a high boiling point. *Concentrated* sulfuric acid contains 95% to 98% sulfuric acid by mass (the balance is water). Its density is 1.84 g/mL.

Common dilute sulfuric acid is made by adding 1 volume of concentrated acid to 6 volumes of water. Its major industrial uses are in refining petroleum and in producing phosphoric acid, cellulose products, and other chemicals.

2. *Nitric acid.* HNO_3 is a volatile liquid. Pure nitric acid is too unstable for commercial use. Concentrated nitric acid, a 70% solution in water, is fairly stable. It has a density of 1.42 g/mL. Common dilute nitric acid is made by adding 1 volume of concentrated acid to 5 volumes of water. A pure solution of nitric acid is colorless. However, it gradually becomes yellow on standing because of slight decomposition that forms brown nitrogen dioxide gas.

$$4HNO_3 \rightarrow 4NO_2 + O_2 + 2H_2O$$

Its major industrial uses are in producing fertilizers, explosives, and other chemicals.

3. *Hydrochloric acid.* HCl, or gaseous hydrogen chloride, is extremely soluble in water. It forms the colorless solution known as hydrochloric acid. Concentrated hydrochloric acid is a water solution containing about 36% hydrogen chloride. Its density is 1.19 g/mL. Common dilute hydrochloric acid is prepared by adding 1 volume of concentrated acid to 4 volumes of water. Such a solution contains approximately 7% hydrogen chloride. Its industrial uses include pickling steel and recovering magnesium.

CAUTION: *Add sulfuric acid to water slowly while stirring. Never add water to acid.*

Pickling: Immersion of iron or steel in an acid solution to remove surface oxides.

☐ 15.3 Aqueous acids

Arrhenius provided a clue to the chemical nature of acids in his *Theory of Ionization.* He believed that acids ionize in water solutions to form hydrogen ions.

The acids just described are essentially covalently bonded structures. They have one element in common, *hydrogen.* Concentrated sulfuric and nitric acids are very poor conductors of electricity because they are only very slightly ionized. Liquid hydrogen chloride is a nonconductor. In dilute water solution, however, each of these substances is highly ionized because of the hydrating action of the water dipoles. Their ionization in water solutions can be represented by the following equations:

$$H_2SO_4 + H_2O \rightarrow H_3O^+ + HSO_4^-$$
$$HNO_3 + H_2O \rightarrow H_3O^+ + NO_3^-$$
$$HCl + H_2O \rightarrow H_3O^+ + Cl^-$$

Hydronium ions, H_3O^+, are present in all of these solutions. It can be assumed that the acid properties of the solutions are due to these H_3O^+ ions.

When a sulfuric acid solution is diluted enough, the ionization of HSO_4^- ions may become appreciable.

$$HSO_4^- + H_2O \rightarrow H_3O^+ + SO_4^{--}$$

Table 15-1

COMMON AQUEOUS ACIDS

Strong acids

$HClO_4$	$\rightleftarrows H^+ + ClO_4^-$
HCl	$\rightleftarrows H^+ + Cl^-$
HNO_3	$\rightleftarrows H^+ + NO_3^-$
H_2SO_4	$\rightleftarrows H^+ + HSO_4^-$

Weak acids

HSO_4^-	$\rightleftarrows H^+ + SO_4^{--}$
H_3PO_4	$\rightleftarrows H^+ + H_2PO_4^-$
HF	$\rightleftarrows H^+ + F^-$
$HC_2H_3O_2$	$\rightleftarrows H^+ + C_2H_3O_2^-$
H_2CO_3	$\rightleftarrows H^+ + HCO_3^-$
H_2S	$\rightleftarrows H^+ + HS^-$
HCN	$\rightleftarrows H^+ + CN^-$
HCO_3^-	$\rightleftarrows H^+ + CO_3^{--}$

The ionization of HSO_4^- ions may be complete in very dilute solutions of sulfuric acid. If so, the equation is written

$$H_2SO_4 + 2H_2O \rightarrow 2H_3O^+ + SO_4^{--}$$

Observe that this equation merely summarizes the two partial ionizations that occur with increasing dilution of the sulfuric acid solution.

(1st stage)	$H_2SO_4 + H_2O$	$\rightarrow H_3O^+ + HSO_4^-$
(2nd stage)	$HSO_4^- + H_2O$	$\rightarrow H_3O^+ + SO_4^{--}$

(summary)	$H_2SO_4 + 2H_2O \rightarrow 2H_3O^+ + SO_4^{--}$	

Acids that ionize completely, or nearly so, in aqueous solution provide high concentrations of hydronium ions. Such concentrations characterize strong acids. Sulfuric, nitric, and hydrochloric acids are strong mineral acids. Substances that produce few hydronium ions in aqueous solution, such as acetic acid and carbonic acid, are weak acids. They ionize slightly in aqueous solution.

◻ 15.4 Modern definitions of acids

The hydronium ion is a hydrated proton. In aqueous solution, it is considered to be in the hydrated form, $H^+ \cdot H_2O$, and is usually represented as H_3O^+. The proton is vigorously hydrated in water because of its small size and high positive charge density.

Chemists have found conclusive evidence that H_3O^+ ions exist in hydrated crystals of perchloric acid (a very strong acid) and in concentrated solutions of strong acids. In dilute aqueous solutions of acids, however, the proton hydration may be more extensive. Physical evidence, such as electric and thermal conductivities, suggests the formula $H^+ \cdot 4H_2O$. This formula corresponds to the ionic species $H_9O_4^+$. A model of the $H_9O_4^+$ ion having the spatial structure of a triagonal pyramid is shown in Figure 15-1.

Other species of the hydrated proton have been suggested for dilute aqueous acid solutions. These species are $H^+ \cdot 2H_2O$ and $H^+ \cdot 3H_2O$, corresponding, respectively, to the species $H_5O_2^+$ and $H_7O_3^+$. Chemists write formulas of this kind only when the degree of hydration is itself the subject of discussion. Otherwise, for simplicity, the hydrated proton in aqueous solutions is written as H^+ (aq) or as the hydronium ion, H_3O^+.

When hydrogen chloride is dissolved in a nonpolar solvent, the solution remains a nonconductor. *This means that protons (hydrogen ions) are not released by molecules such as HCl unless there are molecules or ions present that can accept them.*

Hydrogen chloride dissolved in ammonia transfers protons to the solvent much as it does in water.

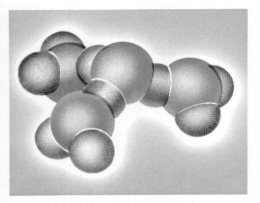

Figure 15-1. A possible model of the $H^+ \cdot 4H_2O$ or $H_9O_4^+$ ion that suggests an H_3O^+ ion with three H_2O molecules attached through hydrogen bonds.

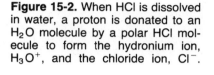

$$H \overset{\bullet\bullet}{\underset{\bullet\bullet}{\overset{\times}{Cl}}} \; + \; H \overset{\circ\circ}{\underset{\times}{O}} \overset{\circ}{\underset{H}{}} \longrightarrow H \overset{\circ\circ}{\underset{\times}{O}} \overset{}{\underset{H}{}} H^+ \; + \; \overset{\bullet\bullet}{\underset{\bullet\bullet}{\overset{\times}{Cl}}} {}^-$$

$$HCl + H_2O \rightarrow H_3O^+ + Cl^-$$
$$HCl + NH_3 \rightarrow NH_4^+ + Cl^-$$

The similarity of these reactions is very clear when electron-dot formulas are used.

$$H \overset{\bullet\bullet}{\underset{\bullet\bullet}{\overset{\times}{Cl}}} \; + \; H \overset{\circ\circ}{\underset{\underset{H}{\times}}{O}} \rightarrow H \overset{\circ\circ}{\underset{\underset{H}{\times}}{O}} H^+ + \; \overset{\bullet\bullet}{\underset{\bullet\bullet}{\overset{}{Cl}}} {}^-$$

$$H \overset{\bullet\bullet}{\underset{\bullet\bullet}{\overset{\times}{Cl}}} \; + \; H \overset{\circ\circ}{\underset{\underset{H}{\times}}{\overset{\circ}{N}}} H \rightarrow H \overset{\overset{H^+}{\circ\circ}}{\underset{\underset{H}{\times}}{\overset{\circ}{N}}} H + \; \overset{\bullet\bullet}{\underset{\bullet\bullet}{\overset{}{Cl}}} {}^-$$

A proton is transferred to the ammonia molecule, forming the *ammonium ion,* just as one is transferred to the water molecule, forming the hydronium ion. See Figures 15-2 and 15-3. In each case, the proton is given up by the hydrogen chloride molecule. This molecule is said to be a *proton donor*. In 1923, the Danish chemist J. N. Brønsted defined all proton donors as acids. According to Brønsted's definition, *an acid is any species (molecule or ion) that gives up protons to another substance*. For example, hydrogen chloride is an acid in this sense even though it does not contain hydrogen ions as a pure substance.

Water is an acid when ammonia is dissolved in it because water molecules donate protons to ammonia molecules.

$$H \overset{\circ\circ}{\underset{\underset{H}{\times}}{\overset{\circ}{N}}} H + H \overset{\bullet\bullet}{\underset{\bullet\times}{\overset{}{O}}} H \rightleftharpoons H \overset{\overset{H^+}{\circ\circ}}{\underset{\underset{H}{\times}}{\overset{\circ}{N}}} H + \; \overset{\bullet\bullet}{\underset{\bullet\bullet}{\overset{}{O}}} H {}^-$$

$$NH_3 + H_2O \rightleftharpoons NH_4^+ + OH^-$$

Johannes Nicolaus Brønsted (1879–1947) spent most of his life as a professor of physical chemistry at the University of Copenhagen. He is recognized for his work on relationships between the forms of energy involved in physical and chemical changes, a method of separating isotopes, the catalytic properties and strengths of acids and bases, and the development of the acid–base theory explained here.

Figure 15-2. When HCl is dissolved in water, a proton is donated to an H_2O molecule by a polar HCl molecule to form the hydronium ion, H_3O^+, and the chloride ion, Cl^-.

Figure 15-3. When HCl is dissolved in ammonia, a proton is donated to an NH_3 molecule by a polar HCl molecule to form the ammonium ion, NH_4^+, and the chloride ion, Cl^-.

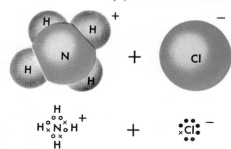

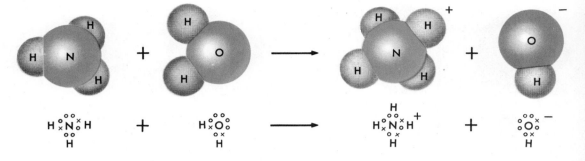

Figure 15-4. When ammonia is dissolved in water, water molecules are the proton donors and ammonia molecules are the proton acceptors.

Furthermore, in water solutions of the strong mineral acids described in Section 15.3, the hydronium ion, H_3O^+, is an acid. The ion is the actual proton donor in reactions involving these solutions. This modern definition of acids can be applied to any molecule or ion capable of donating a proton to another molecule or ion.

☐ 15.5 Properties of aqueous acids

Acids such as hydrochloric, nitric, and sulfuric are quite soluble in water. Their other physical properties differ widely. However, they have many chemical properties in common.

1. Acids donate protons when they react with bases. The many common properties of acids depend on this characteristic behavior. Acids that donate only one proton per molecule are called *monoprotic acids.* Examples are HCl, HNO_3, and $HC_2H_3O_2$. Sulfuric acid, H_2SO_4, and carbonic acid, H_2CO_3, are *diprotic* because they are capable of donating two protons per molecule. Phosphoric acid, H_3PO_4, is *triprotic.*

Relative strengths of aqueous acids are listed in Table 15-5.

2. Acids contain ionizable hydrogen in covalent combination with a nonmetallic element or polyatomic species. The strength of an acid depends upon the *degree* of ionization in water solution, not upon the *amount* of hydrogen in the molecule. Perchloric acid, $HClO_4$, hydrochloric acid, HCl, and nitric acid, HNO_3, are strong acids. They are almost completely ionized in water solutions. Each donates one proton per molecule. Acetic acid, $HC_2H_3O_2$, is a weak acid. It ionizes slightly in water to yield one proton and one acetate ion, $C_2H_3O_2^-$, per ionized molecule.

In Section 15.3, you learned that sulfuric acid ionizes in two stages depending on the amount of dilution:

$$H_2SO_4 + H_2O \rightleftarrows H_3O^+ + HSO_4^-$$
$$HSO_4^- + H_2O \rightleftarrows H_3O^+ + SO_4^{--}$$

The first stage is completed in fairly concentrated solutions. The second stage may be appreciable in more dilute solutions. All stages in the ionization of diprotic and triprotic acids occur in the same solution. Therefore, solutions of H_2SO_4 may contain H_3O^+, HSO_4^-, and SO_4^{--} ions. The concentration of ions formed in the first stage is very much greater than the concentration of ions formed in the second stage.

The rather weak phosphoric acid ionizes in three stages.

$$H_3PO_4 + H_2O \rightleftarrows H_3O^+ + H_2PO_4^-$$

$$H_2PO_4^- + H_2O \rightleftarrows H_3O^+ + HPO_4^{--}$$

$$HPO_4^{--} + H_2O \rightleftarrows H_3O^+ + PO_4^{---}$$

Thus a solution of H_3PO_4 may contain each of the following species: $H_3PO_4, H_3O^+, H_2PO_4^-, HPO_4^{--}$, and PO_4^{---}. As with diprotic acids, the concentration of ions formed in the first stage is very much greater than the concentration of ions formed in the second stage. Similarly, the concentration of ions formed in the second stage is very much greater than the concentration of ions formed in the third stage.

3. Acids have a sour taste. Lemons, grapefruit, and limes are sour. These fruits contain weak acids in solution. A solid acid tastes sour as it dissolves in the saliva to form a water solution. In addition, most laboratory acids are very corrosive (they destroy the skin) and are powerful poisons.

CAUTION: *Never use the "taste test" in the laboratory.*

4. Acids affect indicators. If a drop of an acid solution is placed on a test strip of blue *litmus,* the *blue* color changes to *red*. Litmus is a dye extracted from certain lichens. Other substances are also used as indicators. *Phenolphthalein* (fee-nole-*thall*-een) is *colorless* in the presence of acids. *Methyl orange* turns *red* in acid solutions.

5. Acids neutralize hydroxides. Solutions of an acid and a metallic hydroxide can be mixed in chemically equivalent quantities, in which case each cancels the properties of the other. This process is called *neutralization* and is an example of an ionic reaction. The products of neutralization are a salt and water. The salt is recovered in crystalline form by evaporating the water. The acid and the hydroxide neutralize each other.

Suppose a solution containing 1 mole of NaOH is added to a dilute solution containing 1 mole of HCl. The reaction is represented empirically by the following equation:

$$HCl + NaOH \rightarrow NaCl + H_2O$$

Molecular HCl is ionized in dilute solution. The reactants present are H_3O^+ and Cl^- ions.

$$HCl + H_2O \rightarrow H_3O^+ + Cl^-$$

Ionic NaOH is dissociated in water solution. The reactants in this solution are Na^+ and OH^- ions.

$$Na^+OH^- \rightarrow Na^+ + OH^-$$

The reactants in the separate solutions are present as aqueous ions.

$$H_3O^+ + Cl^- + Na^+ + OH^- \rightarrow Na^+ + Cl^- + 2H_2O$$

The Na^+ and Cl^- ions remain dissociated in the combined solution. They are spectator ions. The ionic species that actually participate in the neutralization reaction are H_3O^+ and OH^-

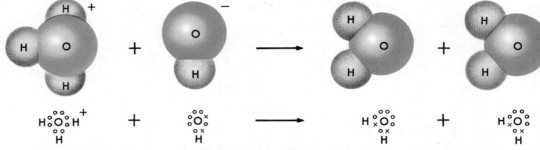

Figure 15-5. In neutralization reactions, hydronium ions and hydroxide ions combine to form essentially un-ionized water molecules.

ions. They form essentially un-ionized water. The net ionic equation is

$$H_3O^+ + OH^- \rightarrow 2H_2O$$

The neutralization reaction between an acid and a base is illustrated with space-filling models in Figure 15-5.

The neutralization reaction is entirely between hydronium ions from the acid and hydroxide ions from the soluble metallic hydroxide. In all neutralizations of very soluble hydroxides by strong acids, the reaction is the same. The nonmetallic ions of the acid and metallic ions of the hydroxide undergo no chemical change. However, you still may prefer to write the complete equation because it shows what pure substances were the original reactants and what salt can be recovered by evaporating the water solvent.

6. Acids react with many metals. Solutions of *nonoxidizing* acids, such as hydrochloric acid and dilute sulfuric acid, react with metals above hydrogen in the replacement series (Table 8-2) to liberate hydrogen gas and form a salt. The replacement reaction between zinc and dilute sulfuric acid is typical.

$$Zn(s) + H_2SO_4(aq) \rightarrow ZnSO_4(aq) + H_2(g)$$

Written ionically,

$$Zn(s) + 2H^+(aq) + SO_4^{--}(aq) \rightarrow Zn^{++}(aq) + SO_4^{--}(aq) + H_2(g)$$

Observe that $SO_4^{--}(aq)$ is a spectator ion. The species actually participating in the reaction are included in the net ionic equation.

$$Zn(s) + 2H^+(aq) \rightarrow Zn^{++}(aq) + H_2(g)$$

Nitric acid and hot, concentrated sulfuric acid are vigorous oxidizing agents. See Section 6.5 for a review of oxidizing and reducing agents.

Upon evaporation of the water solvent, Zn^{++} ions and SO_4^{--} ions separate from solution as crystals of zinc sulfate.

Solutions of *oxidizing* acids, such as nitric acid and hot, concentrated sulfuric acid, react with metals both above and below hydrogen in Table 8-2. These reactions are more complex than the simple replacement example given above. Hot, concentrated sulfuric acid reacts with zinc to form zinc sulfate, hydrogen sulfide gas, and water.

$$4Zn(s) + 5H_2SO_4(aq) \rightarrow 4ZnSO_4(aq) + H_2S(g) + 4H_2O(l)$$

Dilute nitric acid reacts with copper to form copper(II) nitrate, nitrogen monoxide, and water.

$$3Cu(s) + 8HNO_3(aq) \rightarrow 3Cu(NO_3)_2(aq) + 2NO(g) + 4H_2O(l)$$

With concentrated nitric acid, copper forms copper(II) nitrate, nitrogen dioxide, and water.

$$Cu(s) + 4HNO_3(aq) \rightarrow Cu(NO_3)_2(aq) + 2NO_2(g) + 2H_2O(l)$$

7. Acids react with oxides of metals. Salts and water are the products of these reactions. As an example, consider the reaction of copper(II) oxide and sulfuric acid.

$$CuO + H_2SO_4 \rightarrow CuSO_4 + H_2O$$

Written ionically,

$$CuO + 2H^+(aq) + SO_4^{--} \rightarrow Cu^{++} + SO_4^{--} + H_2O$$

The net reaction is

$$CuO + 2H^+(aq) \rightarrow Cu^{++} + H_2O$$

Crystalline $CuSO_4$ is recovered only by evaporating the solvent water.

8. Acids react with carbonates. These reactions produce a salt, water, and carbon dioxide, which is given off.

$$CaCO_3 + 2HCl \rightarrow CaCl_2 + H_2O + CO_2(g)$$

The salt $CaCl_2$ is recovered as a product of the reaction upon evaporation of the solvent water.

This reaction of an acid and a carbonate provides a simple test for carbonates, as with calcium carbonate. Being insoluble in water, calcium carbonate is found in such forms as limestone, marble, and sea shells. A sea shell placed in an acid solution gives the "fizzy" production of CO_2 gas.

☐ 15.6 Naming aqueous acids

Some acids are *binary* compounds. They contain only *two* elements, hydrogen and another nonmetal. Other acids contain oxygen as a third element. They are often referred to as *oxyacids*.

Table 15-2
NAMES OF BINARY ACIDS

Formula	Name of pure substance	Name of acid
HF	hydrogen fluoride	hydrofluoric acid
HCl	hydrogen chloride	hydrochloric acid
HBr	hydrogen bromide	hydrobromic acid
HI	hydrogen iodide	hydriodic acid
H_2S	hydrogen sulfide	hydrosulfuric acid

Figure 15-6. A marble statue, the victim of "acid" rain. When fossil fuels are burned, oxides of nitrogen and (usually) sulfur are released into the atmosphere where they dissolve in moisture to form acidic solutions. These acids react with marble, a form of calcium carbonate, and slowly corrode it.

1. Binary acids. The name of an acid having only two elements begin with the prefix *hydro-*. The root of the name of the nonmetal in combination with hydrogen follows this prefix. The name has the ending *-ic*. This scheme is illustrated by the examples given in Table 15-2. Water solutions of the binary compounds listed are acids known by the names given in the right column.

2. Oxyacids. These acids contain hydrogen, oxygen, and a third element. The formulas and names of the series of oxyacids of chlorine illustrate the general method of naming such acids. The name for the water solution of each oxychlorine acid is shown at the right in the following series.

HClO . . . . hypo-chlor-ous acid
HClO$_2$ . . . . chlor-ous acid
HClO$_3$ . . . . chlor-ic acid
HClO$_4$ . . . . per-chlor-ic acid

In all of these oxyacids, chlorine is the central element. For this reason the root *-chlor-* is used in each case. HClO$_3$ is named *chlor-ic acid*. It contains the chlorate group and no prefix is used. The oxyacid of chlorine that contains *more* oxygen per molecule than chloric acid is called *per-chlor-ic acid*. The prefix *per-* is a contraction of *hyper,* which means *above*. The acid containing *less* oxygen per molecule than chloric acid is called *chlor-ous acid*. The oxyacid of chlorine that contains *still less* oxygen than chlorous acid has the prefix *hypo-*, the root *-chlor-*, and the suffix *-ous*. The prefix *hypo-* means *below*.

To use this scheme, it is only necessary to know the formula and name of one oxyacid in any series. The formula and name of the member of each series that you should memorize are listed below.

HClO$_3$ . . . . chloric acid
HNO$_3$ . . . . nitric acid
HBrO$_3$ . . . . bromic acid
H$_2$SO$_4$ . . . . sulfuric acid
H$_3$PO$_4$ . . . . phosphoric acid

The names of common oxyacids are given in Table 15-3.

15.7 Acid anhydrides

Only fluorine is more electronegative than oxygen. Its compound with oxygen, OF$_2$, is a fluoride rather than an oxide. Other elements form oxides with oxygen. The oxidation number of oxygen in these compounds is −2. Oxides range structurally from ionic to covalent. The more ionic oxides involve the highly electropositive metals on the left side of the periodic table. The oxides formed with nonmetals on the right side of the periodic table are covalent molecular structures.

Table 15-3
NAMES OF OXYACIDS

Formula	Name of acid
HC$_2$H$_3$O$_2$	acetic acid
H$_2$CO$_3$	carbonic acid
HClO	hypochlorous acid
HClO$_2$	chlorous acid
HClO$_3$	chloric acid
HClO$_4$	perchloric acid
HNO$_2$	nitrous acid
HNO$_3$	nitric acid
H$_3$PO$_3$	phosphorous acid
H$_3$PO$_4$	phosphoric acid
H$_2$SO$_3$	sulfurous acid
H$_2$SO$_4$	sulfuric acid

Many of the molecular (nonmetallic) oxides are gases at ordinary temperatures. Examples are carbon monoxide, CO, carbon dioxide, CO_2, and sulfur dioxide, SO_2. Diphosphorus pentoxide, on the other hand, is a solid. The name "diphosphorus pentoxide" is that of the empirical formula P_2O_5. (The molecular formula is now known to be P_4O_{10}.) Most nonmetallic oxides react with water to form *oxyacids*.

All oxyacids contain one or more oxygen-hydrogen (O—H) groups in the covalent structure. They are called *hydroxyl* groups. They are not to be confused with O—H groups existing as OH^- ions whose compounds are called *hydroxides*. The hydroxyl group is arranged in the molecule in such a manner that it may donate a proton. This arrangement gives the molecule its acid character.

Figure 15-7 shows the electron-dot formulas of the four oxyacids of chlorine. Each formula contains the O—H group, not as an ion but as a group covalently bonded to the central Cl atom. Aqueous solutions of these solutes are acidic because the O—H bond is broken during ionization. The O—H group provides the proton donated by the oxychlorine acid molecule.

When carbon dioxide dissolves in water, a very small amount of it reacts chemically with the solvent to form carbonic acid.

$$CO_2 + H_2O \rightleftarrows H_2CO_3$$

These H_2CO_3 molecules can ionize and give the aqueous solution a very low concentration of H_3O^+ ions.

$$H_2CO_3 + H_2O \rightleftarrows H_3O^+ + HCO_3^-$$

The net equation that shows the acid-producing behavior of CO_2 in aqueous solution is

$$CO_2 + 2H_2O \rightleftarrows H_3O^+ + HCO_3^-$$

Carbonic acid and carbon dioxide differ in composition from each other just by a molecule of water. For this reason, carbon dioxide is called the *acid anhydride* of carbonic acid. The name *anhydride* means "without water." *Oxides that react with water to form acids, or that are formed by the removal of water from acids, are known as* **acid anhydrides**.

Binary acids do not contain oxygen and do not have an anhydride form. Thus the reaction between an acid anhydride and water cannot be used to prepare such acids. However, it is an important method of preparing some oxyacids.

Sulfur dioxide is the acid anhydride of sulfurous acid.

$$SO_2 + H_2O \rightleftarrows H_2SO_3$$

Sulfur trioxide is the acid anhydride of sulfuric acid.

$$SO_3 + H_2O \rightleftarrows H_2SO_4$$

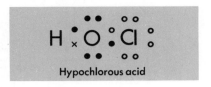
Hypochlorous acid

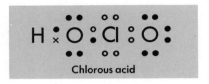
Chlorous acid

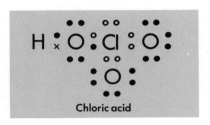
Chloric acid

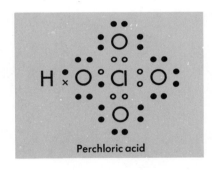
Perchloric acid

Figure 15-7. Electron-dot formulas for the four oxyacids of chlorine.

Acid anhydride: See Section 12.18(4).

Acid anhydrides form oxyacids.

These anhydrides are important in the manufacture of sulfuric acid. Sulfuric acid, because it is cheap and has a high boiling point, can be used in the laboratory to produce several other acids. Although most hydrochloric acid is now produced commercially by other methods, the reaction for producing hydrogen chloride gas is an example.

$$H_2SO_4 + 2NaCl \rightarrow Na_2SO_4 + 2HCl(g)$$

Nitric acid can be produced by the reaction of sulfuric acid with a nitrate. However, this process is not used commercially for preparing HNO_3 because it is more expensive than other processes.

BASES

☐ 15.8 The nature of bases

Several substances long known as bases are commonly found in homes. Household ammonia, an ammonia-water solution, is a familiar cleaning agent. Lye is a commercial grade of sodium hydroxide, NaOH, used for cleaning clogged sink drains. Lime-water is a solution of calcium hydroxide, $Ca(OH)_2$. Milk of magnesia is a suspension of magnesium hydroxide, $Mg(OH)_2$, in water; it is used as an antacid, a laxative, and an antidote for strong acids. All of these hydroxides are *aqueous bases*.

Arrhenius considered a base to be any soluble hydroxide that neutralized an acid when their solutions were mixed. You now know that the only reaction occurring in such a neutralization is between hydronium ions and hydroxide ions. The nonmetal of the acid and the metal of the hydroxide remain in solution as hydrated ions. Hydronium ions combine with hydroxide ions to form water.

$$H_3O^+(aq) + OH^-(aq) \rightarrow 2H_2O(l)$$

Ammonia-water solutions and water solutions of soluble metallic hydroxides are commonly referred to as *aqueous bases*. They are the most useful basic solutions. Aqueous ammonia solutions are traditionally called *ammonium hydroxide*, NH_4OH. This molecular species probably does not exist in water solutions except possibly through the formation of hydrogen bonds between some NH_3 and H_2O molecules. These solutions are more appropriately called ammonia-water solutions, or simply $NH_3(aq)$ (aqueous ammonia). The most common basic solutions used in the laboratory are those of NaOH, KOH, $Ca(OH)_2$, and $NH_3(aq)$. Chemists refer to them as being *alkaline* in their behavior.

In the Brønsted definition, an acid is a *proton donor*. Accordingly, *a base is a proton acceptor*. In this sense, the hydroxide ion, OH^-, is the most common base. However, many other species also combine with protons. The Brønsted use of the term *base* includes all species that accept protons in solution.

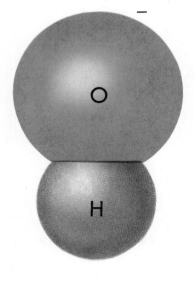

Figure 15-8. A space-filling model of the hydroxide ion and its electron-dot formula. A water molecule is formed when the hydroxide ion accepts a proton.

You know that hydrogen chloride ionizes in water solution as a result of the hydrating action of the solvent dipoles.

$$\underset{\text{acid}}{\text{HCl}} + \underset{\text{base}}{\text{H}_2\text{O}} \rightarrow \underset{\text{acid}}{\overset{\text{weaker}}{\text{H}_3\text{O}^+}} + \underset{\text{base}}{\overset{\text{weaker}}{\text{Cl}^-}}$$

Here the water molecule is the base. It accepts a proton from the HCl molecule, the acid. This reaction forms the H_3O^+ ion, which is a weaker acid than HCl, and the Cl^- ion, which is a weaker base than H_2O. The relative strengths of acids and bases are discussed further in Section 15.12.

Earlier, the neutralization reaction between aqueous solutions of HCl and NaOH were described. Here the H_3O^+ ion acts as the acid since it, and not the HCl molecule, is the proton donor. The OH^- ion is, of course, the proton acceptor or base.

$$\underset{\text{acid}}{\text{H}_3\text{O}^+} + \underset{\text{base}}{\text{OH}^-} \rightarrow \underset{\text{acid}}{\text{H}_2\text{O}} + \underset{\text{base}}{\text{H}_2\text{O}}$$

When HCl gas is dissolved in liquid ammonia, the ammonia acts as the base.

$$\underset{\text{acid}}{\text{HCl}} + \underset{\text{base}}{\text{NH}_3} \rightarrow \underset{\text{acid}}{\text{NH}_4^+} + \underset{\text{base}}{\text{Cl}^-}$$

When NH_3 gas is dissolved in water, the water donates protons and therefore acts as an acid. Ammonia accepts protons and therefore is the base. A low concentration of NH_4^+ ions and OH^- ions is produced in the reversible reaction.

$$\underset{\text{base}}{\text{NH}_3} + \underset{\text{acid}}{\text{H}_2\text{O}} \rightleftarrows \underset{\text{acid}}{\text{NH}_4^+} + \underset{\text{base}}{\text{OH}^-}$$

Suppose open vessels of a saturated aqueous NH_3 solution (concentrated ammonium hydroxide) and a saturated aqueous HCl solution (concentrated hydrochloric acid) are placed near each other. A dense white cloud of NH_4Cl forms above the vessels. This result demonstrates that HCl (the acid) and NH_3 (the base) can react without the intervention of water. See Figure 15-9.

The Brønsted proton-transfer system of acids and bases is more general in scope than the aqueous system of acids and bases. It extends the acid-base concept to reactions in nonaqueous solutions. You will be concerned mainly with aqueous acids and aqueous bases, water solutions of H_3O^+ ions, and water solutions of OH^- ions.

An even more general concept of acids and bases was defined in 1938 by G. N. Lewis, an American chemist. According to the Lewis acid-base system, any species that acts as an *electron-pair acceptor* in a chemical reaction is an *acid*. An *electron-pair donor*

Gilbert Newton Lewis (1875–1946) helped develop the ideas of the electron pair and the octet of electrons, which you have learned in connection with ionic and covalent bonding. He was the first to isolate deuterium. He studied the colors of organic compounds and explained them in terms of excited electron states. He extended Brønsted's ideas of acids and bases.

Figure 15-9. The acid HCl and the base NH_3 react to form the white cloud of NH_4Cl.

is a *base*. The Brønsted system extends the proton transfer concept of acid-base reactions beyond the aqueous system to non-aqueous solutions. The Lewis acid-base system extends the concept of acid-base reactions to some that do not involve proton transfers.

◻ 15.9 Properties of hydroxides

1. Hydroxides of the active metals supply OH^- ions in solution. Sodium and potassium hydroxides are very soluble in water. They are ionic compounds and are, therefore, completely ionized in water solution. Their solutions are *strongly alkaline* because of the high concentration of strongly basic OH^- ions. In speaking of such solutions, chemists often attach the property of the ions to the solution itself. Thus, they may speak of "strongly basic solutions."

$$Na^+OH^- \rightarrow Na^+(aq) + OH^-(aq)$$
$$K^+OH^- \rightarrow K^+(aq) + OH^-(aq)$$

Calcium and strontium hydroxides are also ionic compounds. Thus their water solutions are completely ionized. However, they are only slightly soluble in water and, therefore, only *moderately basic*.

$$Ca^{++}(OH^-)_2 \rightarrow Ca^{++}(aq) + 2OH^-(aq)$$
$$Sr^{++}(OH^-)_2 \rightarrow Sr^{++}(aq) + 2OH^-(aq)$$

The strength of the base depends on the *concentration* of OH^- ions *in solution*. It does not depend on the number of hydroxide ions per mole of the compound.

Ammonia-water solutions are *weakly basic* because they have a low concentration of OH^- ions. Ammonia, NH_3, is not a strong base and thus does not acquire very many protons from water molecules when in solution. Relatively few NH_4^+ ions and OH^- ions are present.

$$NH_3(aq) + H_2O \rightleftharpoons NH_4^+(aq) + OH^-(aq)$$

2. Soluble hydroxides have a bitter taste. Possibly you have tasted limewater and know that it is bitter. Soapsuds also taste bitter because of the presence of hydroxide ions. Strongly basic solutions are very caustic (they chemically burn the skin), and the metallic ions in them are sometimes poisonous.

As with acids, never use the "taste test" in the laboratory.

3. Solutions of hydroxides feel slippery. The very soluble hydroxides, such as sodium hydroxide, attack the skin and can produce severe caustic burns. Dilute solutions have a soapy, slippery feel when rubbed between the thumb and fingers.

4. Soluble hydroxides affect indicators. The basic OH^- ions in solutions of the soluble hydroxides cause *litmus* to turn from *red* to *blue*. This is just the opposite of the color change caused by H_3O^+ ions of acid solutions. In a basic solution, *phenolphthalein* turns *red* and *methyl orange* changes to *yellow*. Many insoluble hydroxides, on the other hand, produce too few hydroxide ions to affect indicators.

5. Hydroxides neutralize acids. The neutralization of HNO_3 by KOH can be represented empirically by the equation

$$KOH + HNO_3 \rightarrow KNO_3 + H_2O$$

Of course, ionic KOH dissociates in water solution and exists as hydrated K^+ ions and OH^- ions.

$$K^+OH^- \rightarrow K^+ + OH^-$$

In water solution, the covalent HNO_3 is ionized and exists as hydrated protons and nitrate ions.

$$HNO_3 + H_2O \rightarrow H_3O^+ + NO_3^-$$

The complete ionic equation for this neutralization reaction is

$$H_3O^+ + NO_3^- + K^+ + OH^- \rightarrow K^+ + NO_3^- + 2H_2O$$

With the removal of the spectator ions, the net ionic equation becomes

$$H_3O^+ + OH^- \rightarrow 2H_2O$$

This represents the only chemical reaction that takes place in the neutralization process. The hydrated K^+ and NO_3^- ions join as ionic crystals of the salt KNO_3 only when the water is evaporated.

6. Hydroxides react with the oxides of nonmetals. Such reactions form salts and sometimes water. For example, sodium hydroxide reacts with carbon dioxide in different ways. The products may be either carbonate *or* hydrogen carbonate ions, depending on the relative quantities of reactants. Two moles of

Common names for sodium hydrogen carbonate, NaHCO₃, are "sodium bicarbonate" and "baking soda."

NaOH per mole of CO_2 forms sodium carbonate, Na_2CO_3, and H_2O.

$$CO_2 + 2NaOH \rightarrow Na_2CO_3 + H_2O$$

One mole of NaOH per mole of CO_2 forms only sodium hydrogen carbonate, $NaHCO_3$.

$$CO_2 + NaOH \rightarrow NaHCO_3$$

The net reactions are

$$CO_2 + 2OH^- \rightarrow CO_3^{--} + H_2O$$

and

$$CO_2 + OH^- \rightarrow HCO_3^-$$

Carbon dioxide is the acid anhydride of carbonic acid. Therefore, these reactions are essentially neutralization reactions between carbonic acid and sodium hydroxide.

7. Certain hydroxides are amphoteric. The metallic hydroxides, except those of the active metals, are practically insoluble in water. They are weakly basic in the presence of strong acids. They are weakly acidic in the presence of strong bases. *Substances that have acidic or basic properties under appropriate conditions are said to be **amphoteric**.* Amphoteric hydroxides, while insoluble in water, are soluble in acids and bases. Aluminum is a metal whose ions form an amphoteric hydroxide. The amphoteric nature of such metallic hydroxides is related to reactions involving hydrated ions.

Amphoteric species can be either acidic or basic.

Aluminum hydroxide separates as a white jelly-like precipitate when hydroxide ions (as NaOH, for example) are added to a solution of a soluble aluminum salt.

$$Al(H_2O)_6^{+++}(aq) + 3OH^-(aq) \rightarrow Al(H_2O)_3(OH)_3(s) + 3H_2O(l)$$

The OH^- ions are strongly basic. They accept protons from three water molecules of each hydrated aluminum ion to form the insoluble hydrated aluminum hydroxide, $Al(H_2O)_3(OH)_3$.

When an excess of the base is added, the high concentration of hydroxide ions causes the aluminum hydroxide precipitate to dissolve. The negative aluminate ions are formed.

$$Al(H_2O)_3(OH)_3(s) + OH^-(aq) \rightarrow Al(H_2O)_2(OH)_4^-(aq) + H_2O(l)$$

The OH^- ion removes a proton from one of the three water molecules in the hydrated aluminum hydroxide structure. Observe the soluble aluminate ion formed has two molecules of water of hydration. In this reaction, the hydrated aluminum hydroxide *acts as an acid in the presence of the strong base.*

The amphoteric aluminum hydroxide also dissolves in an excess of hydronium ions. Hydrated aluminum ions and water are the products.

$$Al(H_2O)_3(OH)_3(s) + 3H_3O^+ \rightarrow Al(H_2O)_6^{+++}(aq) + 3H_2O(l)$$

Table 15-4
SOLUBILITY
OF METALLIC HYDROXIDES

Hydroxide	Solubility (g/100 g H₂O at 20 °C)
soluble (>1 g/100 g H₂O)	
KOH	112
NaOH	109
LiOH	12.8
Ba(OH)₂	3.89
slightly soluble (>0.1 g/100 g H₂O)	
Ca(OH)₂	0.165
insoluble (<0.1 g/100 g H₂O)	
Pb(OH)₂	0.016
Mg(OH)₂	0.0009
Sn(OH)₂	0.0002
Zn(OH)₂	negligible
Cu(OH)₂	negligible
Al(OH)₃	negligible
Cr(OH)₃	negligible
Fe(OH)₃	negligible

This reaction is the reverse of the reaction above in which the hydrated aluminum hydroxide is precipitated. The three hydroxide ions accept protons from the three hydronium ions to form the three water molecules. In this reaction, the hydrated aluminum hydroxide *acts as a base in the presence of the strong acid*. It illustrates proton-transfer reactions, or protolysis, in which protons are transferred from an acid to a base.

The hydroxides of zinc, lead(II), chromium(III), and antimony(III) are other common amphoteric hydroxides. Iron(III) hydroxide is not amphoteric. It is not soluble in an excess of OH^- ions.

In the Brønsted system of acids and bases, water is an amphoteric substance. When a water molecule accepts a proton from hydrogen chloride, it acts as a base. On the other hand, when a water molecule donates a proton to ammonia, it acts as an acid. Indeed, in the slight ionization of water, one water molecule donates a proton to another water molecule. Thus some of the water molecules behave as an acid while others behave as a base.

$$H_2O + H_2O \rightleftarrows H_3O^+ + OH^-$$

Liquid ammonia undergoes a similar ionization, but to a lesser extent than water. Ammonium ions and amide ions, NH_2^-, are formed.

$$NH_3 + NH_3 \rightleftarrows NH_4^+ + NH_2^-$$

Ammonia is therefore amphoteric.

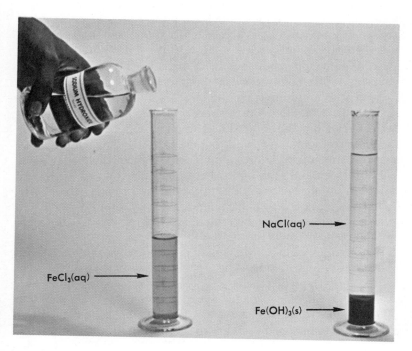

FeCl₃(aq) —→

NaCl(aq) —→

Fe(OH)₃(s) —→

Figure 15-10. The hydroxides of heavy metals are practically insoluble.

☐ 15.10 Basic anhydrides

Oxides of sodium, potassium, calcium, strontium, and barium react vigorously with water. You may have seen a plasterer *slaking* quicklime, CaO, by adding water to it. *Slaked lime,* $Ca(OH)_2$, was being formed.

$$CaO + H_2O \rightarrow Ca(OH)_2$$

Basic anhydrides are oxides of active metals. See Section 12.18(3).

Oxides that react with water to produce solutions containing the basic OH^- ions are called basic anhydrides. The oxides of the active metals are basic anhydrides. (In contrast, acid anhydrides are oxides of nonmetals. They are covalent compounds and have molecular structures. In reactions with water they form oxyacids with one or more O—H groups capable of donating protons. Refer to Section 15.7.)

The oxides of the active metals are ionic in structure. Like other ionic substances, they are solids at room temperature. They contain O^{--} ions. When placed in water, O^{--} ions react with the water to form basic OH^- ions.

$$O^{--} + H_2O \rightarrow 2OH^-$$

If the metallic hydroxide is soluble in water, the solution is basic because of the presence of OH^- ions.

☐ 15.11 Hydroxides and periodic trends

In general, the hydroxides of the active metals are strongly basic. The O—H groups are present as ions and the compounds are usually quite soluble. Other hydroxide compounds may be weakly basic, amphoteric, or acidic. The higher the oxidation state of the atom combined with the O—H group, the more covalent is the bond between this atom and the O—H group. Further, the more covalent the bond, the more difficult it is to remove the OH^- ion. For example, chromium(II) hydroxide is basic, chromium(III) hydroxide is amphoteric, and chromium(VI) forms an oxyacid.

With amphoteric hydroxides, it appears that the O—H bond is as easily broken as the bond between the metal and the O—H group. A strong base acquires a proton by breaking the O—H bond. An acid, on the other hand, donates a proton to the O—H group. In doing so, it breaks the bond between the O—H group and the metal atom.

Hydroxides of atoms having high electronegativity and high oxidation states are acidic. The O—H bond is more easily broken than the bond between the O—H group and the central atom. For example, O_3ClOH is strongly acidic. The chlorine atom is in the +7 oxidation state. It is also the central atom to which three oxygen atoms and one O—H group are bonded. In water solution, the molecule donates a proton from its O—H group to form the negative O_3ClO^- ion.

$$O_3ClOH + H_2O \rightarrow H_3O^+ + O_3ClO^-$$

If the formula is written in the conventional form of acids, O_3ClOH becomes $HClO_4$. You can recognize this formula as *perchloric acid*, an oxyacid. The equation now looks more familiar.

$$HClO_4 + H_2O \rightarrow H_3O^+ + ClO_4^-$$

Figure 15-7 shows the electron-dot configuration from which the formula O_3ClOH is easily recognized.

It may not be apparent from the formula of a substance whether it has acidic or basic properties. You have observed that oxides that react with water form oxygen-hydrogen groups. In general, the oxygen-hydrogen groups formed by ionic oxides (metal oxides) are OH^- ions. Their compounds are hydroxides and their solutions are basic.

Oxygen-hydrogen groups formed by molecular oxides (nonmetal oxides) are not ionic. Instead, they are bonded covalently to another atom in the product molecule. Such groups are identified as hydroxyl groups in Section 15.7. Hydroxyl groups donate protons in aqueous solution. The compounds have acid properties and are oxyacids.

Figure 15-11 shows electron-dot formulas for several molecular substances that contain hydroxyl groups. Their formulas can be written $PO(OH)_3$, $SO_2(OH)_2$, CH_3COOH, and C_2H_5OH. However, none has the basic properties characteristic of OH^- ions in water solution. The first three compounds are oxyacids. This acidic character is recognized by writing their formulas as H_3PO_4, H_2SO_4, and $HC_2H_3O_2$. The fourth compound, ethanol, lacks either acidic or basic properties in aqueous solution. Observe that its formula can be written as HC_2H_5O.

◻ 15.12 Relative strengths of acids and bases

The Brønsted definition of acids and bases provides a basis for the study of protolysis, or proton-transfer reactions. Any molecule or ion capable of donating a proton is considered to be an acid. Any molecule or ion that can accept the proton is a base.

Suppose that an acid (in the Brønsted sense) gives up a proton. The remainder of the acid particle itself is then capable of accepting a proton. Therefore, this remaining particle may be considered to be a base; it is called a *conjugate base*. *A conjugate base is the species that remains after an acid has given up a proton.*

An aqueous solution of sulfuric acid contains H_3O^+ ions and HSO_4^- ions. With further dilution, the HSO_4^- ions may give up protons to H_2O molecules.

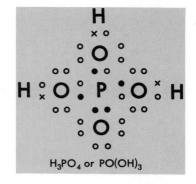

H_3PO_4 or $PO(OH)_3$

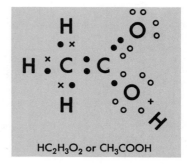

H_2SO_4 or $SO_2(OH)_2$

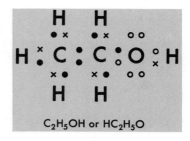

$HC_2H_3O_2$ or CH_3COOH

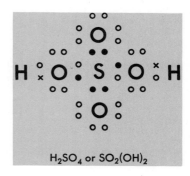

C_2H_5OH or HC_2H_5O

Figure 15-11. Molecular formulas alone will not identify acidic or basic properties.

$$HSO_4^- + H_2O \rightarrow H_3O^+ + SO_4^{--}$$

acid   base   acid   base

Acids have conjugate bases.

The SO_4^{--} ion is the remainder of the HSO_4^- ion after its proton has been removed. It is the conjugate base of the acid HSO_4^-.

The SO_4^{--} ion, as a base, can accept a proton from H_3O^+. When this occurs, the acid HSO_4^- ion is formed.

$$H_3O^+ + SO_4^{--} \rightarrow HSO_4^- + H_2O$$

acid   base   acid   base

Bases have conjugate acids.

The HSO_4^- ion can be called the *conjugate acid* of the base SO_4^{--}. *A conjugate acid is the species formed when a base takes on a proton.* Thus in the example given, the HSO_4^- ion and the SO_4^{--} ion are a *conjugate acid-base pair.*

The H_2O molecule also acts as a base in this reaction. It receives the proton given up by the HSO_4^- ion to form the H_3O^+ ion. Thus the H_3O^+ ion is the conjugate acid of the base H_2O.

Similarly, the acidic H_3O^+ ion gives up a proton to the basic SO_4^{--} ion to form the H_2O molecule. Thus the H_2O molecule is the conjugate base of the H_3O^+ ion. The H_2O molecule and the H_3O^+ ion make up the second conjugate acid-base pair in the reaction.

In the above reaction, each reactant and product is labeled either as an acid or a base. There are two conjugate acid-base pairs.

Conjugate acid-base pair	HSO_4^-	SO_4^{--}
	acid	base
Conjugate acid-base pair	H_2O	H_3O^+
	base	acid

Each acid has one more proton than its conjugate base.

Similar reasoning can be applied to the equation for the initial ionization of H_2SO_4. Here the HSO_4^- ion is the *conjugate base* of H_2SO_4.

$$H_2SO_4 + H_2O \rightarrow H_3O^+ + HSO_4^-$$

acid   base   acid   base

The HSO_4^- ion is *both* the conjugate acid of the base SO_4^{--} and the conjugate base of the acid H_2SO_4. Thus the HSO_4^- ion is amphoteric.

You know that HCl is highly ionized even in concentrated aqueous solutions. The hydrogen chloride molecule gives up protons readily and is therefore a strong acid. It follows that the Cl^- ion, the conjugate base of this acid, has little tendency to retain the proton. It is, consequently, a weak base.

This observation suggests an important statement that follows naturally from the Brønsted definition of acids and bases: *the stronger an acid, the weaker its conjugate base; the stronger a base, the weaker its conjugate acid.*

An aqueous solution of the strong acid $HClO_4$ is highly ionized. The reaction to the right is practically complete even in concentrated solutions.

The stronger the acid, the weaker its conjugate base. The stronger the base, the weaker its conjugate acid.

$$\begin{array}{cccc} \textbf{stronger} & \textbf{stronger} & \textbf{weaker} & \textbf{weaker} \\ HClO_4 \ + & H_2O & \rightleftarrows \ H_3O^+ \ + & ClO_4^- \\ \textbf{acid} & \textbf{base} & \textbf{acid} & \textbf{base} \end{array}$$

The ClO_4^- ion is the conjugate base of $HClO_4$. It is too weak a base to compete successfully with the base H_2O in acquiring a proton. The H_3O^+ ion is the conjugate acid of H_2O. It is too weak an acid to compete successfully with the acid $HClO_4$ in donating a proton. Thus there is little tendency for the reaction to proceed to the left to re-form the $HClO_4$ and H_2O molecules.

Now examine the situation in an aqueous solution of acetic acid.

$$\begin{array}{cccc} \textbf{weaker} & \textbf{weaker} & \textbf{stronger} & \textbf{stronger} \\ HC_2H_3O_2 \ + & H_2O & \rightleftarrows \ H_3O^+ \ + & C_2H_3O_2^- \\ \textbf{acid} & \textbf{base} & \textbf{acid} & \textbf{base} \end{array}$$

The H_3O^+ ion concentration is quite low even in dilute solutions. This fact indicates that $HC_2H_3O_2$ is indeed a weak acid. It does not compete very successfully with H_3O^+ ions in donating protons to a base. The H_2O molecules do not compete very successfully with $C_2H_3O_2^-$ ions in accepting protons. The H_3O^+ ion is the stronger acid and the $C_2H_3O_2^-$ ion is the stronger base. Thus the reaction tends to proceed to the left.

Observe that in each example the stronger acid had the weaker conjugate base and the stronger base had the weaker conjugate acid. Also note that, in each reversible situation, the reaction tended to proceed toward the weaker acid and base.

These observations suggest a second important statement that follows naturally from the Brønsted definition: *Protolysis reactions favor the production of the weaker acid and the weaker base.*

Protolysis occurs when a proton donor and a proton acceptor are brought together in a solution. The extent of this protolysis depends on the relative strengths of the acids and bases involved. For a proton-transfer reaction to approach completion, the reactants must be much stronger as an acid and a base than the products.

Table 15-5 shows the relative strengths of several Brønsted acids and their conjugate bases. Observe that the strongest acid listed, $HClO_4$, has the weakest conjugate base listed, ClO_4^-. The

Table 15-5
RELATIVE STRENGTHS OF ACIDS AND BASES

Acid	Formula	Conjugate base	Formula
perchloric	$HClO_4$	perchlorate ion	ClO_4^-
hydrogen chloride	HCl	chloride ion	Cl^-
nitric	HNO_3	nitrate ion	NO_3^-
sulfuric	H_2SO_4	hydrogen sulfate ion	HSO_4^-
hydronium ion	H_3O^+	water	H_2O
hydrogen sulfate ion	HSO_4^-	sulfate ion	SO_4^{--}
phosphoric	H_3PO_4	dihydrogen phosphate ion	$H_2PO_4^-$
acetic	$HC_2H_3O_2$	acetate ion	$C_2H_3O_2^-$
carbonic	H_2CO_3	hydrogen carbonate ion	HCO_3^-
hydrogen sulfide	H_2S	hydrosulfide ion	HS^-
ammonium ion	NH_4^+	ammonia	NH_3
hydrogen carbonate ion	HCO_3^-	carbonate ion	CO_3^{--}
water	H_2O	hydroxide ion	OH^-
ammonia	NH_3	amide ion	NH_2^-
hydrogen	H_2	hydride ion	H^-

Decreasing Acid Strength (left margin, downward)

Decreasing Base Strength (right margin, downward)

weakest acid, H_2, has the strongest conjugate base, the hydride ion, H^-. A violent protolysis could result from bringing together the strongest acid and the strongest base in certain proportions. Such a reaction would be highly exothermic and very dangerous.

SALTS   ☐ 15.13 Nature of salts

Common table salt, NaCl, is only one of a large class of compounds that chemists refer to as *salts*. The solution of an aqueous acid contains H_3O^+ ions and negatively charged nonmetal ions (anions). These particles result from ionization of the acid in water. The solution of an aqueous base contains positively charged metal ions (cations) and OH^- ions. These particles result from dissociation of the ionic metallic hydroxide in water. A neutralization reaction between two such solutions removes almost all of the H_3O^+ and OH^- ions. They unite to form water, which is only very slightly ionized. The cations of the hydroxide and the anions of the acid are spectator ions. They have no part in the neutralization reaction.

As an example, consider the neutralization reaction between aqueous solutions of HCl and KOH. Aqueous ions are present in the acid solution because of ionization.

$$HCl(g) + H_2O \rightarrow H_3O^+(aq) + Cl^-(aq)$$

Aqueous ions are present in the hydroxide solution because of dissociation.

$$K^+OH^-(s) \rightarrow K^+(aq) + OH^-(aq)$$

Neutralization occurs when the proper quantities of the two solutions are mixed.

$$H_3O^+(aq) + Cl^-(aq) + K^+(aq) + OH^-(aq) \rightarrow K^+(aq) + Cl^-(aq) + 2H_2O$$

Removing all spectator ions, the net equation for the neutralization reaction becomes

$$H_3O^+(aq) + OH^-(aq) \rightarrow 2H_2O$$

As solvent water is evaporated, K^+ cations and Cl^- anions no longer remain separated from each other by water dipoles. They form a characteristic ionic crystalline structure and separate from solution as the *salt* KCl. *A compound composed of the positive ions of an aqueous base and the negative ions of an aqueous acid is called a* ***salt.*** All salts, by this definition, are ionic substances. They vary in solubility in water, but their aqueous solutions are solutions of hydrated ions. Some useful solubility information regarding salts is summarized in Table 15-6.

ROUGH RULES OF SOLUBILITY

soluble:	*>1 g/100 g H_2O*
slightly soluble:	*>0.1 g/100 g H_2O*
insoluble:	*<0.1 g/100 g H_2O*

15.14 Salt-producing reactions

There are several ways of forming salts, but not all of these ways apply to the formation of every salt.

1. Direct union of the elements. Some metals react directly with certain nonmetals to form a salt. For example, burning sodium in an atmosphere of chlorine gas produces sodium chloride.

$$2Na + Cl_2 \rightarrow 2NaCl$$

2. Reaction of a metal with an acid. Many metals replace hydrogen in an aqueous acid to form the corresponding salt. Zinc reacts with hydrochloric acid to form zinc chloride and hydrogen.

$$Zn + 2HCl \rightarrow ZnCl_2 + H_2(g)$$

3. Reaction of a metallic oxide with an aqueous acid. The oxides of some metals react with an acid to form a salt. Magnesium oxide treated with hydrochloric acid forms magnesium chloride and water.

$$MgO + 2HCl \rightarrow MgCl_2 + H_2O$$

Table 15-6
SOLUBILITY OF SALTS

1. Common sodium, potassium, and ammonium compounds are soluble in water.
2. Common nitrates, acetates, and chlorates are soluble.
3. Common chlorides are soluble except silver, mercury(I), and lead. [Lead(II) chloride is soluble in hot water.]
4. Common sulfates are soluble except calcium, barium, strontium, and lead.
5. Common carbonates, phosphates, and silicates are insoluble except sodium, potassium, and ammonium.
6. Common sulfides are insoluble except calcium, barium, strontium, magnesium, sodium, potassium, and ammonium.

If calcium oxide is substituted for magnesium oxide in this reaction, the salt formed is calcium chloride.

$$CaO + 2HCl \rightarrow CaCl_2 + H_2O$$

4. Reaction of a nonmetallic oxide with a base. The oxides of some nonmetals react with a soluble hydroxide to form a salt. Carbon dioxide gas passed into limewater (saturated calcium hydroxide solution) forms insoluble calcium carbonate and water.

$$CO_2 + Ca(OH)_2 \rightarrow CaCO_3(s) + H_2O$$

Additional carbon dioxide converts the calcium carbonate to soluble calcium hydrogen carbonate.

$$CO_2 + H_2O + CaCO_3 \rightarrow Ca(HCO_3)_2$$

The reactions of sulfur dioxide in limewater are similar. Insoluble calcium sulfite, $CaSO_3$, is first formed.

$$SO_2 + Ca(OH)_2 \rightarrow CaSO_3(s) + H_2O$$

When excess sulfur dioxide gas is bubbled through limewater, soluble calcium hydrogen sulfite is formed.

$$SO_2 + H_2O + CaSO_3 \rightarrow Ca(HSO_3)_2$$

5. Acid-base neutralization. When an acid neutralizes a soluble hydroxide, a salt may be recovered from the water solvent. This salt corresponds to the metallic ion of the base and nonmetallic ion of the acid. Many different salts can be prepared by neutralization. An example is the reaction between hydrochloric acid and sodium hydroxide mixed in chemically equivalent quantities. When the solvent water is evaporated, sodium chloride remains.

$$NaOH + HCl \rightarrow NaCl + H_2O$$

6. Ionic reaction. Two salts may be prepared in ionic reactions if one of them is practically insoluble. The equation for the reaction between solutions of sodium sulfate and barium chloride is

$$BaCl_2 + Na_2SO_4 \rightarrow 2NaCl + BaSO_4(s)$$

Since both reactants are dissociated in water solution, the ionic equation is more useful.

$$Ba^{++}(aq) + 2Cl^-(aq) + 2Na^+(aq) + SO_4^{--}(aq) \rightarrow 2Na^+(aq) + 2Cl^-(aq) + BaSO_4(s)$$

In this reaction, barium sulfate is only very slightly soluble and precipitates readily from the solution. Since precipitates always separate from saturated solutions, the solvent water contains a very low saturation concentration of Ba^{++} ions and SO_4^{--} ions in addition to the spectator ions Na^+ and Cl^-. If sodium chloride is recovered by evaporating the solvent water, it will necessarily contain some barium sulfate.

7. Reaction of an acid with a carbonate. A salt can be obtained from this reaction because the other products are water and carbon dioxide gas. If hydrochloric acid is added to a solution of sodium carbonate, the following reaction occurs:

$$2HCl + Na_2CO_3 \rightarrow 2NaCl + H_2O + CO_2(g)$$

Carbon dioxide bubbles out of the solution as a gas. Sodium chloride can be recovered by evaporation.

8. Reaction of a metallic oxide with a nonmetallic oxide. An oxygen-containing salt can be formed by the reaction between a basic oxide and an acidic oxide. Water is not involved in this process. Instead, the dry oxides are mixed and heated. Metallic carbonates and phosphates are typical of the salts produced.

$$MgO + CO_2 \rightarrow MgCO_3$$
$$CaO + CO_2 \rightarrow CaCO_3$$
$$3CaO + P_2O_5 \rightarrow Ca_3(PO_4)_2$$

☐ 15.15 Naming salts

Salts are generally named by combining the names of the ions of which they are composed. For example, the name of $Ba(NO_3)_2$ is *barium nitrate*. By agreement the positive ion, in this case the Ba^{++} ion, is named first. The name of the negative ion, in this case the NO_3^- ion, follows.

Over the years, many difficulties have arisen in the naming of salts. For example, many outdated names of salts have carried over into the present naming system. These old names do not provide for a simple translation from name to formula or from formula to name. In 1940, the International Union of Pure and Applied Chemistry recommended a more logical system for naming inorganic compounds. It is known as the *Stock system,* and it provides the uniformity needed for chemical names.

This text uses the Stock system for naming salts that contain metals *with variable oxidation states.* Several examples of Stock names for salts are given in Table 15-7. Observe that in *double salts* the more electropositive cation is named first. *A double salt is one in which two different kinds of metallic ions are present.*

The names of anions (negative ions) take the same root and prefix as the acid in which they occur. However, the acid ending *-ic* is changed to *-ate,* and the ending *-ous* is changed to *-ite.* Salts derived from binary acids take the ending *-ide.* Table 15-8 shows the names of the anions of salts produced by the reactions of various acids.

Salt anions that are polyatomic and include metallic atoms with variable oxidation states may have rather complex names in the Stock system. For example, polyatomic MnO_4^- anion is the *tetra-*

Table 15-7
SALT NOMENCLATURE

Formula	Stock name
CuCl	copper(I) chloride
CuCl$_2$	copper(II) chloride
FeO	iron(II) oxide
Fe$_2$O$_3$	Iron(III) oxide
Fe$_3$O$_4$	Iron(II, III) oxide
MnCl$_2$	manganese(II) chloride
MnCl$_4$	manganese(IV) chloride
PtO$_2$	platinum(IV) oxide
Cr$_2$(SO$_3$)$_3$	chromium(III) sulfite
CoCO$_3$	cobalt(II) carbonate
Co$_2$(SO$_4$)$_3$	cobalt(III) sulfate
Cu$_2$SO$_4$	copper(I) sulfate
CuSO$_4$	copper(II) sulfate
Fe$_3$(PO$_4$)$_2$	Iron(II) phosphate
Hg(NO$_3$)$_2$	mercury(II) nitrate
KCaPO$_4$	potassium calcium phosphate
NaHCO$_3$	sodium hydrogen carbonate

Alfred Stock (1876–1946), a German chemist, is best known for his work on the hydrides of boron and silicon. For many years, Stock was a victim of chronic mercury poisoning. When he finally recognized its cause, he studied the disease and its dangers and effectively warned others about it.

Table 15-8
ACID–SALT NOMENCLATURE

Formula	Name of acid	Name of salt anion
HF	hydrofluoric	fluoride
HBr	hydrobromic	bromide
HI	hydriodic	iodide
HCl	hydrochloric	chloride
HClO	hypochlorous	hypochlorite
$HClO_2$	chlorous	chlorite
$HClO_3$	chloric	chlorate
$HClO_4$	perchloric	perchlorate
HIO_3	iodic	iodate
H_2MnO_4	manganic	manganate
$HMnO_4$	permanganic	permanganate
H_2S	hydrosulfuric	sulfide
H_2SO_3	sulfurous	sulfite
H_2SO_4	sulfuric	sulfate
HNO_2	nitrous	nitrite
HNO_3	nitric	nitrate
H_2CO_3	carbonic	carbonate
H_3PO_3	phosphorous	phosphite
H_3PO_4	phosphoric	phosphate

oxomanganate(VII) ion in this system. However, its potassium salt, $KMnO_4$, is well known as *potassium permanganate;* it will not likely become *potassium tetraoxomanganate(VII).*

 SUMMARY

Acids and bases are described historically in terms of their water solutions. In this aqueous acid-base system, a substance is an acid if it produces hydronium ions in water solution. Similarly, a substance is a base if it contributes hydroxide ions to its water solution. The properties of acids and bases, their reactions with other substances, and the neutralization reaction between them are the properties of these traditional acids and bases in aqueous solutions.

In the aqueous acid-base system, an acid contains hydrogen which, through ionization in water solution, is transferred as a proton (hydrogen ion) to a water molecule to form the hydronium ion. This aqueous system has been broadened by the Brønsted definition of acids and bases. By this definition, all proton donors are acids and all proton acceptors are bases. The Brønsted proton-transfer system extends the acid-base concept of reactions to nonaqueous solutions. Hydrogen chloride gas is a Brønsted acid when dissolved in ammonia. An HCl molecule donates a proton to an NH_3 molecule. Ammonia is a Brønsted base. It accepts a proton from the HCl molecule.

Other acid-base systems have been defined. The Lewis acid-base system defines an acid as an electron-pair acceptor. A proton-transfer may not necessarily be involved in a Lewis acid-base reaction.

The hydroxides of certain metals in the middle region of the periodic table are amphoteric. They are insoluble in water but dissolve in acidic and basic solutions. Amphoteric hydroxides behave as acids in the presence of strong bases. They behave as bases in the presence of strong acids.

In a proton-transfer reaction, the acid gives up a proton to the base. The species that remains is a base, the conjugate base of the acid donor. The base that accepts the proton in the reaction becomes an acid. It is the conjugate acid of the base. Together they constitute an acid-base pair. The stronger the acid, the weaker is its conjugate base. Proton-transfer reactions tend to produce weaker acids and weaker bases.

Some nonmetallic oxides combine with water to form oxyacids. These oxides are called acid anhydrides. Oxides of active metals react with water to form hydroxides. These oxides are called basic anhydrides.

Salts are compounds composed of the positive ion of an aqueous base and the negative ion of an aqueous acid. They are ionic compounds. Salts vary in their solubility in water; their aqueous solutions are solutions of hydrated ions. Generally, the names of salts follow the Stock system for naming inorganic compounds.

 ## VOCABULARY

acid	conjugate base	litmus	phosphoric acid
acid anhydride	diprotic	methyl orange	pickling
alkaline	double salt	mineral acid	protolysis
amphoteric	electron-pair acceptor	monoprotic	proton acceptor
aqueous	electron-pair donor	neutralization	proton donor
base	hydrochloric acid	nitric acid	salt
basic anhydride	hydronium ion	organic acid	sulfuric acid
binary acid	hydroxide ion	oxyacid	triprotic
conjugate acid	hydroxyl group	phenolphthalein	

QUESTIONS

Group A

1. Name the four most important industrial acids and tell why each is important.
2. What ion is responsible for the acidic properties of aqueous acid solutions?
3. List eight properties that characterize aqueous acids.
4. Why is an acid thought of as a proton donor?
5. (a) What is an acid anhydride? (b) a basic anhydride? (c) Give an example of each.
6. (a) State the rules for naming binary acids. (b) for naming oxyacids.
7. A base is defined as a proton acceptor. How do you interpret this definition?
8. Write the net ionic equation for the neutralization reaction between an acid and a base.

9. List seven properties that characterize hydroxides of active metals.
10. Aluminum hydroxide has basic properties in the presence of a strong acid and acidic properties in the presence of a solution that is strongly basic. What term is used to describe such substances?
11. What composition and structure characterize salts?
12. How are salts named?
13. What method would you use to prepare a small quantity of calcium sulfate quickly and safely in the laboratory? Explain why you chose the method and write the equation.
14. Would barium sulfate be a suitable source of the sulfate ion for an ionic reaction with another salt? Explain.

Group B

15. Explain why a water solution of hydrogen chloride has acidic properties but pure hydrogen chloride does not, in the usual sense.

16. Write the equation for the reaction between zinc and hot, concentrated sulfuric acid (*a*) as an ionic equation and (*b*) as a net ionic equation.

17. Write the equation for the reaction between copper and dilute nitric acid (*a*) as an ionic equation and (*b*) as a net ionic equation.

18. Write the equation for the reaction between copper and concentrated nitric acid (*a*) as an ionic equation and (*b*) as a net ionic equation.

19. (*a*) How can you justify calling hydrogen chloride an acid when it is dissolved in ammonia? (*b*) Write the equation for this reaction.

20. (*a*) Explain how the structure and behavior of water can be interpreted as water behaving like an acid. (*b*) Write an equation that illustrates this behavior using electron-dot formulas.

21. What basic solution would you use (*a*) for cleaning a greasy sink trap? Explain. (*b*) for removing grease spots from clothing? Explain.

22. What basic solutions would you use for neutralizing acid stains on clothing? Explain.

23. Predict the relative solubilities of the following salts in water (as *soluble, slightly soluble,* or *insoluble*): NaCl, $CaCO_3$, $BaSO_4$, $(NH_4)_2S$, $Al(C_2H_3O_2)_3$, Ag_2SO_4, $Pb(NO_3)_2$, Hg_2Cl_2, $Mg_3(PO_4)_2$, CuS.

24. Name the following compounds: (*a*) H_2Se, (*b*) HIO_3, (*c*) $Ga(OH)_3$, (*d*) CsOH, (*e*) $RaBr_2$, (*f*) K_2MnO_4, (*g*) $MgSO_4$, (*h*) $Fe(ClO_4)_2$, (*i*) $KMnO_4$, (*j*) $Cu(IO_3)_2$, (*k*) CaI_2, (*l*) $BaSO_3$, (*m*) NH_4F, (*n*) $AlPO_4$, (*o*) $NaClO_3$.

25. (*a*) When H_2O molecules act as a base, what is its conjugate acid? (*b*) When H_2O molecules act as an acid, what is its conjugate base?

26. (*a*) When NH_3 molecules act as a base, what is its conjugate acid? (*b*) When NH_3 molecules act as an acid, what is its conjugate base?

27. Write the equation for the limited ionization of HF in aqueous solution and identify two conjugate acid-base pairs.

28. Write the equations that show the amphoteric character of HSO_4^- ions.

29. Balance the following equation:

$$Zn(H_2O)_4^{++}(aq) + OH^-(aq) \rightarrow Zn(OH)_2(H_2O)_2(s) + H_2O$$

30. Hydrated zinc hydroxide is insoluble in water but dissolves in an excess of $OH^-(aq)$ ions to form the soluble zincate ion, $Zn(OH)_4^{--}$, and water. Write the balanced net ionic equation.

31. Hydrated zinc hydroxide also dissolves in an excess of H_3O^+ ions to form hydrated zinc ions and water. Write the balanced net ionic equation.

◄ PROBLEMS

Group A

1. Nitric acid can be prepared in the laboratory by the reaction of sodium nitrate with sulfuric acid. Sodium hydrogen sulfate is also formed. (*a*) How many grams of sulfuric acid are required to produce 50.0 g of nitric acid? (*b*) How many grams of sodium hydrogen sulfate are formed?

2. How many liters of carbon dioxide can be collected at 20 °C and 745 mm pressure from a reaction between 25.0 g of calcium carbonate and an excess of hydrochloric acid?

3. How much calcium silicate, $CaSiO_3$, can be prepared by heating a mixture of 75.0 g of calcium oxide and 90.0 g of silicon dioxide?

4. Suppose 75.0 L of dry carbon dioxide gas, measured at 25.0 °C and 755 mm pressure, is available to convert hot calcium oxide to calcium carbonate. (*a*) What quantity of calcium oxide is required? (*b*) What quantity of calcium carbonate is produced?

Acid-Base Titration and pH

Adding a base to an acid or an acid to a base is not only an important laboratory procedure but also an everyday activity. Milk of magnesia soothes the aching stomach that comes from rushing through meals or eating rich foods. This medicine is a base that neutralizes excess acid in the stomach. When farmers add lime to the soil, they do so to ensure optimal acid–base conditions for plant growth. If soil is too acidic, the lime is a perfect base to use for adjusting its pH. Chlorine is added as a disinfectant to the water in swimming pools. Chlorine, however, reacts with water to form acidic compounds that can harm the eyes and skin of swimmers. Chlorinated water must be treated with alkaline compounds that adjust the pH to near-neutral levels. pH is an important quantity in every aspect of life, and acid–base balance an essential operation for controlling it.

◻ 16.1 Molar solutions

In your studies of the influence of solutes on the freezing points and boiling points of solvents (Chapter 13), you learned that the ratio of solute-to-solvent molecules is the significant consideration. The freezing-point depression and boiling-point elevation *of a solvent* are related to the *number* of solute particles dissolved in a given *quantity* of solvent. The concentration of such a solution is expressed in terms of *molality*. Solutions of known molality are prepared when it is important to know the ratio of solute-to-solvent molecules.

Recall that *molality, m,* is an expression of solution concentration in terms of *moles of solute* and *kilograms of solvent*. For example, a 1-molal (1-*m*) solution contains 1 mole of solute per kilogram of solvent. For any given solvent, two solutions of equal molality have the same ratio of solute-to-solvent molecules. Chemists are able to determine molecular weights of many soluble substances by observing the effects of their dilute solutions of known molalities on the freezing points of their solvents.

In the present studies of solutions, the interest is in the quantity of *solute* required to effect a chemical reaction. Because the volume of a solution is easily measured, it can be very convenient to have the quantity of a solute known in terms of a volume of its solution. Using this scheme, solution concentration is expressed in terms of a *known quantity of a solute in a given volume of solution*. When a solution is prepared in this way, any required quantity of solute can be selected by simply measuring out the volume of solution that contains that quantity of solute.

SOLUTION CONCENTRATIONS

In this chapter you will gain an understanding of:

- the difference between solution concentration expressed as molality and molarity
- chemical equivalents of acids, bases, elements, and salts
- solving problems involving equivalents
- normality and normal solutions
- pH in both operational and mathematical terms
- solving problems involving the calculation of pH and H_3O^+ concentration
- acid-base titration and indicators
- solving titration problems involving molar and normal solutions
- expressing solution concentration in terms of molarity and normality

Figure 16-1. A volumetric flask for measuring precise volumes of liquids. When filled to the mark on the neck of the flask with a liquid at the temperature etched on the flask, it contains 500 ± 0.15 mL of the liquid.

Molarity: moles solute per liter solution.

Molality: moles solute per kilogram solution.

If the quantity of solute is stated in *moles* and the volume of solution in *liters,* the concentration of a solution is expressed in *molarity*. The symbol for molarity is *M*. *The **molarity** of a solution is an expression of the number of moles of solute per liter of solution.* A *one-molar* (1-*M*) solution contains *1 mole of solute per liter of solution.* Solutions of the same molarity have the same mole concentration of solutes.

A mole of sodium chloride, NaCl, has a mass of 58.5 g, its gram-formula weight. This quantity of NaCl dissolved in enough water to make exactly 1 liter of solution gives a 1-*M* solution. Half this quantity of NaCl in 1 liter of solution forms a 0.5-*M* solution. Twice this quantity per liter of solution yields a 2-*M* solution.

A *volumetric flask* similar to the one shown in Figure 16-1 is commonly used in preparing solutions of known molarity. A measured quantity of solute is dissolved in a portion of solvent in the flask. Then more solvent is added to fill the flask to the mark on the neck. Thus the quantity of solute and the volume of solution are known, and the molarity of the solution is easily calculated.

As an example, suppose you wish to prepare a 1-*M* solution of potassium chromate. The formula weight of K_2CrO_4 is 194. Thus a mole of K_2CrO_4 has a mass of 194 g. To prepare 1 L of the 1-*M* solution, 194 g of K_2CrO_4 *must be dissolved in enough water to make 1 liter of solution.* To prepare $10\bar{0}$ mL of the 1-*M* solution, 19.4 g of K_2CrO_4 must be dissolved in enough water to make $10\bar{0}$ mL of solution. Similarly, a 0.5-*M* solution requires 0.5 mole (97.0 g) of K_2CrO_4 per liter of solution. A 0.05-*M* solution requires 0.05 mole (9.70 g) of K_2CrO_4 per liter of solution.

Observe that solution *molarity* is based on the *volume of solution.* (Solution *molality,* on the other hand, is based on the *mass of solvent.*) Equal volumes of solutions of the same molarity have equal mole quantities of solutes. Molarity is preferred when volumes of solutions are to be measured. For very dilute solutions, the distinction between the molality and molarity is not significant.

☐ 16.2 Chemical equivalents of acids and bases

Solution concentrations can be expressed in a way that allows *chemically equivalent quantities* of different solutes to be measured very simply. These quantities of solutes are called *equivalents,* equiv. *Equivalents are the quantities of substances that have the same combining capacity in chemical reactions.*

Consider the following equations. They show that 36.5 g (1 mole) of HCl and 49 g (½ mole) of H_2SO_4 are chemically equivalent in neutralization reactions with basic KOH.

$$\text{HCl} \;+\; \text{KOH} \;\rightarrow\; \text{KCl} \;+\; \text{H}_2\text{O}$$
$$\text{1 mole}\quad\text{1 mole} \rightarrow \text{1 mole}\quad\text{1 mole}$$
$$\text{36.5 g}\quad\;\;\text{56 g}$$

$$\text{H}_2\text{SO}_4 + 2\text{KOH} \rightarrow \text{K}_2\text{SO}_4 + 2\text{H}_2\text{O}$$

or,

$$\tfrac{1}{2}H_2SO_4 \ + \ KOH \ \rightarrow \ \tfrac{1}{2}K_2SO_4 \ + \ H_2O$$

$\tfrac{1}{2}$ mole	1 mole	$\tfrac{1}{2}$ mole	1 mole
49 g	56 g		

The equations also reveal that both 36.5 g of HCl and 49 g of H_2SO_4 are chemically equivalent to 56 g (1 mole) of KOH in these neutralization reactions.

Suppose KOH is replaced with $Ca(OH)_2$ in one of the prior reactions. The new equation shows that 37 g (½ mole) of $Ca(OH)_2$ is equivalent to 56 g (1 mole) of KOH.

$$2HCl \ + \ Ca(OH)_2 \rightarrow CaCl_2 \ + \ 2H_2O$$

or,

$$HCl \ + \ \tfrac{1}{2}Ca(OH)_2 \rightarrow \tfrac{1}{2}CaCl_2 \ + \ H_2O$$

1 mole	$\tfrac{1}{2}$ mole	$\tfrac{1}{2}$ mole	1 mole
36.5 g	37 g		

In proton-transfer reactions, *one equivalent of an acid is the quantity, in grams, that supplies one mole of protons*. HCl and H_2SO_4 are the acids in the neutralization reactions just considered. The quantity representing *one equivalent* of each acid in these reactions can be determined as follows:

An acid equivalent donates 1 mole of protons.

$$1 \text{ equiv HCl} = \frac{1 \text{ mole HCl}}{1 \text{ mole } H_3O^+} \times \frac{36.5 \text{ g}}{\text{mole}} = \frac{36.5 \text{ g HCl}}{\text{mole } H_3O^+}$$

$$1 \text{ equiv } H_2SO_4 = \frac{1 \text{ mole } H_2SO_4}{2 \text{ moles } H_3O^+} \times \frac{98 \text{ g}}{\text{mole}} = \frac{49 \text{ g } H_2SO_4}{\text{mole } H_3O^+}$$

One equivalent of a base is the quantity, in grams, that accepts one mole of protons, or supplies one mole of OH^- ions. For KOH and $Ca(OH)_2$ in the above reactions,

A base equivalent accepts 1 mole of protons or supplies 1 mole of OH^- ions.

$$1 \text{ equiv KOH} = \frac{1 \text{ mole KOH}}{1 \text{ mole } OH^-} \times \frac{56 \text{ g}}{\text{mole}} = \frac{56 \text{ g KOH}}{\text{mole } OH^-}$$

$$1 \text{ equiv } Ca(OH)_2 = \frac{1 \text{ mole } Ca(OH)_2}{2 \text{ moles } OH^-} \times \frac{74 \text{ g}}{\text{mole}} = \frac{37 \text{ g } Ca(OH)_2}{\text{mole } OH^-}$$

HCl, HNO_3, and $HC_2H_3O_2$ are monoprotic acids. One mole of each can supply 1 mole of H_3O^+ ions. Therefore, *1 equivalent of a monoprotic acid is the same as 1 mole of the acid.* One mole of a diprotic acid such as H_2SO_4 can supply 2 moles of H_3O^+ ions. Thus, *for complete neutralization, 1 equivalent of a diprotic acid is the same as ½ mole of the acid.* H_3PO_4 is triprotic and can furnish 3 moles of H_3O^+ ions per mole of acid. *When completely neutralized, 1 equivalent of a triprotic acid is the same as ⅓ mole of the acid.*

A diprotic acid has 2 atoms of ionizable hydrogen per molecule.

A triprotic acid has 3 atoms of ionizable hydrogen per molecule.

A similar relationship exists between chemical equivalents and moles of bases. One mole of KOH supplies 1 equivalent of OH^- ions. One mole of $Ca(OH)_2$ supplies 2 equivalents of OH^-

ions. Therefore, 1 equivalent of KOH is the same as 1 mole of KOH, and 1 equivalent of $Ca(OH)_2$ is the same as ½ mole of $Ca(OH)_2$.

In many chemical reactions, a diprotic or triprotic acid is not completely neutralized. In such a case, the number of moles of protons supplied per mole of acid is determined by the reaction it undergoes. For example, suppose a solution containing 1 mole of H_2SO_4 is added to a solution containing 1 mole of NaOH. The salt sodium hydrogen sulfate is then recovered by evaporating the water solvent. Observe that the neutralization of H_2SO_4 is *not* complete.

$$H_2SO_4 + NaOH \rightarrow NaHSO_4 + H_2O$$
$$\text{1 mole} \quad \text{1 mole} \quad \text{1 mole} \quad \text{1 mole}$$
$$\text{98 g} \quad \text{40 g}$$

One mole of H_2SO_4 supplies 1 mole of protons to the base to form an "acid salt" containing HSO_4^- ions. Therefore 1 equivalent of H_2SO_4 is the same as 1 mole of the acid, 98 g, *in this reaction*.

$$1 \text{ equiv } H_2SO_4 = \frac{1 \text{ mole } H_2SO_4}{1 \text{ mole } H_3O^+} \times \frac{98 \text{ g}}{\text{mole}} = \frac{98 \text{ g } H_2SO_4}{\text{mole } H_3O^+}$$

Now, suppose a solution containing 1 mole of H_3PO_4 is added to one containing 1 mole of NaOH. The reaction is

$$H_3PO_4 + NaOH \rightarrow NaH_2PO_4 + H_2O$$
$$\text{1 mole} \quad \text{1 mole} \quad \text{1 mole} \quad \text{1 mole}$$
$$\text{98.0 g} \quad \text{40.0 g}$$

The salt sodium dihydrogen phosphate can be recovered by evaporation. One mole of H_3PO_4 supplies 1 mole of protons to the base to form a salt containing $H_2PO_4^-$ ions. Thus one equivalent of H_3PO_4 is the same as 1 mole of the acid, 98.0 g, *in this reaction*.

An equivalent of H_3PO_4 depends on the reaction.

$$1 \text{ equiv } H_3PO_4 = \frac{1 \text{ mole } H_3PO_4}{1 \text{ mole } H_3O^+} \times \frac{98.0 \text{ g}}{\text{mole}} = \frac{98.0 \text{ g } H_3PO_4}{\text{mole } H_3O^+}$$

Suppose the basic solution in the reaction above contained 2 moles of NaOH. The salt recovered by evaporation would be Na_2HPO_4. One equivalent of H_3PO_4 in this reaction is the same as ½ mole of the acid, 49.0 g. If, in another reaction, the neutralization of the triprotic acid is complete, 1 equivalent of H_3PO_4 is the same as ⅓ mole of the acid, 32.7 g.

◻ 16.3 Chemical equivalents of elements

Now consider a reactant in an electron-transfer reaction. A chemical equivalent of such a reactant is *the quantity, in grams, that supplies or acquires 1 mole of electrons in a chemical reac-*

tion. In the following reaction, a mole of sodium atoms (23 g) loses 1 mole of electrons to form 1 mole of Na^+ ions.

$$Na \rightarrow Na^+ + e^-$$

1 mole   1 mole   1 mole

23 g   23 g

Thus 1 equivalent of sodium is the same as 1 mole of sodium atoms, 23 g.

A mole of calcium atoms ($\overline{40}$ g) supplies 2 moles of electrons when Ca^{++} ions are formed. A mole of aluminum atoms (27 g) supplies 3 moles of electrons when Al^{+++} ions are formed. Thus 1 equivalent of calcium is the mass of ½ mole of calcium atoms, $\overline{20}$ g. One equivalent of aluminum is the mass of ⅓ mole of aluminum atoms, 9.0 g.

$$\tfrac{1}{2}Ca \rightarrow \tfrac{1}{2}Ca^{++} + e^-$$

$\tfrac{1}{2}$ **mole $\tfrac{1}{2}$ mole   1 mole**

$\overline{20}$ g $\overline{20}$ g

and

$$\tfrac{1}{3}Al \rightarrow \tfrac{1}{3}Al^{+++} + e^-$$

$\tfrac{1}{3}$ **mole $\tfrac{1}{3}$ mole   1 mole**

9.0 g   9.0 g

These relationships can be summarized as follows:

$$1 \text{ equiv Na} = \frac{1 \text{ mole Na}}{1 \text{ mole } e^-} \times \frac{23 \text{ g}}{\text{mole}} = \frac{23 \text{ g Na}}{\text{mole } e^-}$$

$$1 \text{ equiv Ca} = \frac{1 \text{ mole Ca}}{2 \text{ moles } e^-} \times \frac{\overline{40} \text{ g}}{\text{mole}} = \frac{\overline{20} \text{ g Ca}}{\text{mole } e^-}$$

$$1 \text{ equiv Al} = \frac{1 \text{ mole Al}}{3 \text{ moles } e^-} \times \frac{27 \text{ g}}{\text{mole}} = \frac{9.0 \text{ g Al}}{\text{mole } e^-}$$

Observe that when Na^+ ions are formed, the numerical *change* in oxidation state for sodium atoms is 1. The change for calcium atoms is 2. For aluminum atoms it is 3. Such numbers can ordinarily be used to determine one equivalent of an element for a given reaction. The mass of 1 mole of atoms of the element (1 g-at wt) is divided by the *change in oxidation state* these atoms undergo in a chemical reaction.

$$1 \text{ equiv Na} = \frac{23 \text{ g}}{1} = 23 \text{ g}$$

$$1 \text{ equiv Ca} = \frac{\overline{40} \text{ g}}{2} = \overline{20} \text{ g}$$

$$1 \text{ equiv Al} = \frac{27 \text{ g}}{3} = 9.0 \text{ g}$$

Oxidizing and reducing agents with several common oxidation states are given special attention in Chapter 22.

□ 16.4 Chemical equivalents of salts

A somewhat similar method can ordinarily be used to find the mass of 1 equivalent of a salt. The mass of 1 mole of the salt is divided by the *total* positive (or negative) ionic charge indicated by its formula. This total positive charge is determined by multiplying the number of cations (shown in the formula of the salt) by the charge on each cation.

$$1 \text{ equiv (salt)} = \frac{\textbf{mass of 1 mole of salt}}{\textbf{total positive charge}}$$

The formula for sodium sulfate is Na_2SO_4, and the mass of 1 mole is 142 g. Each of the two Na^+ ions has a +1 charge. The total positive charge equals 2. (Notice that the total negative charge also equals 2.)

$$1 \text{ equiv } Na_2SO_4 = \frac{142 \text{ g}}{2} = 71.0 \text{ g}$$

One mole of calcium phosphate, $Ca_3(PO_4)_2$, has a mass of $31\overline{0}$ g. Each of the three Ca^{++} ions has a +2 charge. The total positive charge is 6. (Note that the total negative charge is also 6.)

$$1 \text{ equiv } Ca_3(PO_4)_2 = \frac{31\overline{0} \text{ g}}{6} = 51.7 \text{ g}$$

□ 16.5 Normal solutions

Normality: equivalents solute per liter solution.

Solution concentration based on the volume of solution can now be expressed in a second way by stating the quantity of solute in equivalents. This method is called *normality, N. The **normality** of a solution expresses the number of equivalents of solute per liter of solution.* A one-normal (1-*N*) solution contains 1 equivalent of solute *per liter of solution.* For a solution to be 0.25 *N*, it must contain 0.25 equivalent of solute per liter of solution. *Equal volumes of solutions of the same normality are chemically equivalent.* The expressions for solution concentration are summarized in Table 16-1.

Table 16-1
METHODS OF EXPRESSING CONCENTRATION OF SOLUTIONS

Name	Symbol	Solute unit	Solvent unit	Dimensions
molality	*m*	mole	kilogram solvent	$\dfrac{\text{mole solute}}{\text{kg solvent}}$
molarity	*M*	mole	liter solution	$\dfrac{\text{mole solute}}{\text{liter solution}}$
normality	*N*	equivalent	liter solution	$\dfrac{\text{equiv solute}}{\text{liter solution}}$

A mole of the monoprotic hydrogen chloride has a mass of 36.5 g. As a reactant, this quantity of HCl can furnish 1 mole of protons. Thus 1 mole of HCl in 1 liter of aqueous solution provides 1 mole of protons as H_3O^+ ions. The concentration of this solution is 1 N.

Suppose a solution of HCl that can supply 0.100 mole of H_3O^+ ions per liter, a 0.100-N HCl solution, is required. This solution must consist of 3.65 g of HCl dissolved in water and diluted to a 1.00-liter volume. However, *the solute is 3.65 g of anhydrous hydrogen chloride in one liter of solution,* not 3.65 g of the concentrated hydrochloric acid ordinarily found in the laboratory. The volume of concentrated hydrochloric acid containing 3.65 g of hydrogen chloride must be diluted to 1-liter volume. How can this volume of the concentrated HCl solution be determined?

First, the mass percentage of HCl in the concentrated solution and the density of the concentrated solution must be known. This information is printed on the label of the concentrated hydrochloric acid container, as shown in Figure 16-2. Representative values are

Figure 16-2. The manufacturer's label on a reagent bottle provides important analysis information for the chemist.

$$\text{solute HCl} = 37.23\%$$

$$\text{solution density} = 1.19 \text{ g/mL}$$

Thus $10\overline{0}$ g of concentrated solution contains 37.23 g of HCl. Knowing the density of the concentrated solution to be 1.19 g/mL, the mass of HCl per milliliter of concentrated solution can be determined.

$$\frac{37.23 \text{ g HCl}}{10\overline{0} \text{ g conc soln}} \times \frac{1.19 \text{ g}}{\text{mL}} = \frac{0.443 \text{ g HCl}}{\text{mL conc soln}}$$

For 1.00 L of 0.100-N solution, 3.65 g of anhydrous HCl is required, since

$$\frac{0.100 \text{ equiv HCl}}{\text{L}} \times \frac{36.5 \text{ g}}{\text{equiv}} \times 1.00 \text{ L} = 3.65 \text{ g HCl}$$

The mass of HCl per milliliter of concentrated solution and the mass of HCl required are now known. From these data, the volume of concentrated hydrochloric acid solution can be calculated.

$$3.65 \text{ g HCl} \times \frac{\text{mL conc soln}}{0.443 \text{ g HCl}} = 8.24 \text{ mL conc soln}$$

Thus 8.24 mL of concentrated HCl solution diluted to 1.00 L with distilled water gives a 0.100-N solution of HCl.

You have already learned that 1 mole of H_2SO_4 contains 2 equivalents of that substance. A 1-M solution contains 98 g of H_2SO_4 per liter of solution. However, a 1-N solution contains 49 g (98 g ÷ 2) of H_2SO_4 per liter of solution. A 5-N solution contains 245 g (49 g × 5) of H_2SO_4 per liter. Similarly, 0.01-N

Table 16-2
CONCENTRATIONS OF COMMON ACIDS

	(Average values for freshly opened bottles)			
	Acetic	*Hydrochloric*	*Nitric*	*Sulfuric*
formula	$HC_2H_3O_2$	HCl	HNO_3	H_2SO_4
molecular weight	60.03	36.46	63.02	98.08
density of concentrated reagent, g/cm^3	1.06	1.19	1.42	1.84
percentage assay concentrated reagent	99.5	36.0	69.5	96.0
grams active ingredient/mL reagent	1.055	0.426	0.985	1.76
normality of concentrated reagent	17.6	11.7	15.6	35.9
mL concentrated reagent/liter N solution	56.9	85.5	64.0	27.9
molarity of concentrated reagent	17.6	11.7	15.6	17.95
mL concentrated reagent/liter M solution	56.9	85.5	64.0	55.8

H_2SO_4 contains 0.49 g (49 g ÷ 100) of H_2SO_4 per liter of solution. Concentrated sulfuric acid is usually 95%–98% H_2SO_4 and has a density of about 1.84 g/mL. Dilutions to desired normalities are calculated as shown previously for HCl.

Compounds containing water of crystallization present special problems in preparing solutions. For example, crystalline copper(II) sulfate has the empirical formula

$CuSO_4 \cdot 5H_2O$

The formula weight is 249.5. One mole of this hydrate, 249.5 g, contains 1 mole of $CuSO_4$, 159.5 g. This fact must be recognized when moles or equivalents of crystalline hydrates are measured.

A 1-M $CuSO_4$ solution contains 159.5 g of $CuSO_4$ per liter of solution. This 1-M solution is also a 2-N solution because 1 mole of $CuSO_4$ contains 2 equivalents. A 1-N solution requires 79.75 g of $CuSO_4$ per liter. Of course, this solution is 0.5 M.

If a mole of a solute is also 1 equivalent, the molarity and normality of the solution *are the same*. A 1-M HCl solution is also a 1-N solution. If a mole of solute is two equivalents, a 1-M solution is 2 N. A 0.01-M H_2SO_4 solution is therefore 0.02 N. Similarly, a 0.01-M H_3PO_4 solution is 0.03 N if it is completely neutralized. Solutions of equal normality are chemically equivalent, volume for volume.

⌷ 16.6 Ion concentration in water

Water is very weakly ionized by self-ionization, as illustrated in Figure 16-3. This process is sometimes referred to as *autoprotolysis*. The very poor conductivity of pure water results from the slight ionization of water itself. This fact can be demonstrated by testing water that has been highly purified by several different techniques.

Electric conductivity measurements of pure water show

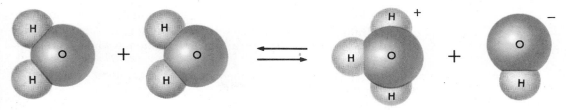

that at 25 °C it is very slightly ionized to H_3O^+ and OH^- ions. Concentrations of these ions in pure water are only

$$\frac{1 \text{ mole } H_3O^+}{10^7 \text{ L } H_2O} \quad \text{and} \quad \frac{1 \text{ mole } OH^-}{10^7 \text{ L } H_2O}$$

One liter of water has a mass of 997 g at 25 °C (1 L = 1000 g at 4 °C). The mass of 1 mole of water is 18.0 g. Using these quantities, 1 liter contains 55.4 moles of water at 25 °C.

$$\frac{997 \text{ g}}{L} \times \frac{1 \text{ mole}}{18.0 \text{ g}} = 55.4 \text{ moles/L}$$

The extent of the ionization can be stated as a percentage if the concentration of H_3O^+ ions (and also OH^- ions) is expressed in moles of ions per mole of water.

$$\frac{1 \text{ mole } H_3O^+}{10^7 \text{ L } H_2O} \times \frac{1 \text{ L}}{55.4 \text{ moles}} = \frac{2 \times 10^{-9} \text{ mole } H_3O^+}{\text{mole } H_2O}$$

This result shows that water is about 0.0000002% ionized at 25 °C.

Pure water is very slightly ionized.

It is more useful to express ion concentration as *moles per liter* than as moles per 10,000,000 liters. This change is accomplished by dividing both terms in the expression "moles per 10^7 liters" by 10^7.

$$\frac{1 \text{ mole } H_3O^+ \div 10^7}{10^7 \text{ L } H_2O \div 10^7} = \frac{10^{-7} \text{ mole } H_3O^+}{L \ H_2O}$$

Thus the concentration of H_3O^+ ions (and OH^- ions) in water at 25 °C is 10^{-7} mole per liter of H_2O.

Chemists use a standard notation to represent concentration in terms of *moles per liter*. The symbol or formula of the particular ion or molecule is enclosed in brackets, [ ]. For example, $[H_3O^+]$ means *hydronium ion concentration in moles per liter*. For the ionic concentrations in water at 25 °C,

$$[H_3O^+] = 10^{-7} \text{ mole/L}$$

and

$$[OH^-] = 10^{-7} \text{ mole/L}$$

or

$$[H_3O^+] = [OH^-] = 10^{-7} \text{ mole/L}$$

Pure water is neutral because $[H_3O^+] = [OH^-]$.

Reminder: 10^{-5} is a larger number than 10^{-7}.

Because the H_3O^+ ion concentration and the OH^- ion concentration are equal, water is neutral. It is neither acidic nor basic. This neutrality prevails in any solution in which $[H_3O^+]$ = $[OH^-]$.

If the H_3O^+ ion concentration in a solution exceeds 10^{-7} mole/liter, the solution is acidic. For example, a solution containing 10^{-5} mole H_3O^+ ion per liter is acidic. If the OH^- ion concentration exceeds 10^{-7} mole per liter, the solution is basic, or alkaline. Thus a solution containing 10^{-4} mole OH^- ion per liter is basic.

In water and dilute solutions $[H_3O^+] \times [OH^-] = 10^{-14} = a$ constant.

It is also true that the *product* of the $[H_3O^+]$ and $[OH^-]$ remains constant in water and dilute aqueous solutions as long as the temperature does not change. Recall that by Le Chatelier's principle, an increase in concentration of either of these ionic species in an aqueous mixture at equilibrium causes a decrease in concentration of the other species. In water and dilute aqueous solutions at 25 °C,

$$[H_3O^+] \times [OH^-] = \text{a constant}$$

$$[H_3O^+][OH^-] = (1 \times 10^{-7} \text{ mole/L})^2$$

$$[H_3O^+][OH^-] = 1 \times 10^{-14} \text{mole}^2/L^2$$

The ionization of water increases as its temperature rises. At 0 °C the product $[H_3O^+][OH^-]$ is 0.11×10^{-14} mole^2 per liter^2. At 60 °C it is 9.6×10^{-14} mole^2 per liter^2.

❑ 16.7 The pH of a solution

The range of solution concentrations encountered by chemists is great. It varies from about $10\ M$ to perhaps $10^{-15}\ M$. However, concentrations of less than $1\ M$ are most commonly used.

As stated above, the product of $[H_3O^+]$ and $[OH^-]$ is a constant at a given temperature. Therefore, if the concentration of either ionic species is known, the concentration of the other species can be determined. For example, the OH^- ion concentration of a 0.01-M NaOH solution is 0.01 or 10^{-2} mole/liter. The H_3O^+ ion concentration of this solution is calculated as follows:

Reminder:
$a^m \times a^n = a^{m+n}$
$10^6 \times 10^3 = 10^{6+3} = 10^9$
$10^5 \times 10^{-2} = 10^{5+(-2)} = 10^3$

$a^m \div a^n = a^{m-n}$
$10^6 \div 10^3 = 10^{6-3} = 10^3$
$10^5 \div 10^{-2} = 10^{5-(-2)} = 10^7$

$$[H_3O^+][OH^-] = 1 \times 10^{-14} \text{ mole}^2/L^2$$

$$[H_3O^+] = \frac{1 \times 10^{-14} \text{ mole}^2/L^2}{[OH^-]}$$

$$[H_3O^+] = \frac{1 \times 10^{-14} \text{ mole}^2/L^2}{1 \times 10^{-2} \text{ mole/L}}$$

$$[H_3O^+] = 1 \times 10^{-12} \text{ mole/L}$$

A Sample Problem follows.

◖ SAMPLE PROBLEM

A 0.0001-*M* solution of HNO_3 has been prepared for a laboratory experiment.
(*a*) Calculate the $[H_3O^+]$ of this solution. (*b*) Calculate the $[OH^-]$.

◖ SOLUTION

(*a*) HNO_3 is a monoprotic acid giving 1 mole of H_3O^+ ions per mole of HNO_3 when completely ionized in aqueous solution.

For 0.0001-*M* aqueous HNO_3

$$[H_3O^+] = 0.0001 \text{ mole/L} = 10^{-4} \text{ mole/L}$$

(*b*) $[H_3O^+][OH^-] = 10^{-14} \text{ mole}^2/L^2$

$$[OH^-] = \frac{10^{-14} \text{ mole}^2/L^2}{[H_3O^+]} = \frac{10^{-14} \text{ mole}^2/L^2}{10^{-4} \text{ mole/L}}$$

$$[OH^-] = 10^{-10} \text{ mole/L}$$

The acidity or alkalinity of a solution can be expressed in terms of its hydronium ion concentration. An $[H_3O^+]$ *higher* than 10^{-7} mole/liter (a *smaller* negative exponent) indicates an acid solution. An $[H_3O^+]$ *lower* than 10^{-7} mole/liter (a *larger* negative exponent) indicates an alkaline solution.

Expressing acidity or alkalinity in this way can become cumbersome, especially in dilute solutions, whether decimal or scientific notations are used. Because it is more convenient, chemists use a quantity called pH to indicate the hydronium ion concentration of a solution.

pH is called the hydronium ion index.

Numerically, the pH of a solution is the common logarithm of the number of liters of solution that contains one mole of H_3O^+ ions. This number of liters of solution is equal to the *reciprocal* of the H_3O^+ ion concentration. This concentration is given in moles of H_3O^+ ions per liter of solution. The reciprocal expression is

$$\frac{1}{[H_3O^+]}$$

*Thus, the **pH of a solution** is defined as the common logarithm of the reciprocal of the hydronium ion concentration. The pH is expressed by the equation*

$$pH = \log \frac{1}{[H_3O^+]}$$

The common logarithm of a number is the power to which 10 must be raised to give the number. Thus 0.0000001 is 10^{-7} and its reciprocal is 10,000,000, or 10^7. The logarithm of 10^7 is 7.

pH of neutral solutions = 7.

Pure water is slightly ionized, and at 25 °C contains 0.0000001 or 10^{-7} mole of H_3O^+ per liter. The pH of water is therefore

$$pH = \log \frac{1}{0.0000001}$$

$$pH = \log \frac{1}{10^{-7}}$$

$$pH = \log 10^7$$

$$pH = 7$$

Suppose the H_3O^+ ion concentration in a solution is *higher* than that in pure water. Then the number of liters required to provide 1 mole of H_3O^+ ions is *smaller*. Consequently, the pH is a *smaller* number than 7. Such a solution is *acidic*. On the other hand, suppose the H_3O^+ ion concentration is *lower than* that in pure water. The pH is then a *larger* number than 7. Such a solution is *basic*.

The range of pH values usually falls between 0 and 14. The pH system is particularly useful in describing the acidity or alkalinity of solutions that are not far from neutral. This includes many food substances and fluids encountered in physiology. The pH of some common substances is given in Table 16-3.

There are two basic types of pH problems that will concern you. They are

1. The calculation of pH when the $[H_3O^+]$ of a solution is known.

2. The calculation of $[H_3O^+]$ when the pH of a solution is known.

These two calculation methods are examined in Sections 16.8 and 16.9.

❑ 16.8 Calculation of pH

In the simplest pH problems, the $[H_3O^+]$ of the solution is an integral power of 10, such as 1 M or 0.01 M. These problems can be solved *by inspection*. The pH equation based on the definition stated in Section 16.7 is

$$pH = \log \frac{1}{[H_3O^+]}$$

Since

$$\log \frac{1}{[H_3O^+]} = -\log [H_3O^+]$$

the first equation can be written in a more useful form to solve for pH.

$$pH = -\log [H_3O^+]$$

In an aqueous solution in which $[H_3O^+] = 10^{-6}$ mole/liter, the pH = 6.

pH of acidic solutions <7.

pH of basic solutions >7.

Table 16-3
APPROXIMATE pH OF SOME COMMON MATERIALS (at 25 °C)

Material	pH
1.0-N HCl	0.1
1.0-N H_2SO_4	0.3
0.1-N HCl	1.1
0.1-N H_2SO_4	1.2
gastric juice	2.0
0.01-N H_2SO_4	2.1
lemons	2.3
vinegar	2.8
0.1-N $HC_2H_3O_2$	2.9
soft drinks	3.0
apples	3.1
grapefruit	3.1
oranges	3.5
cherries	3.6
tomatoes	4.2
bananas	4.6
bread	5.5
potatoes	5.8
rainwater	6.2
milk	6.5
pure water	7.0
eggs	7.8
0.1-N $NaHCO_3$	8.4
seawater	8.5
milk of magnesia	10.5
0.1-N NH_3	11.1
0.1-N Na_2CO_3	11.6
0.1-N NaOH	13.0
1.0-N NaOH	14.0
1.0-N KOH	14.0

Chemical solutions with pH values below 0 and above 14 can be prepared. For example, the pH of 6-M H_2SO_4 is between 0 and -1. The pH of 3-M KOH is near 14.5. However, only common pH values in the 0-14 range will be considered. Observe that the *pH of a solution is the exponent of the hydronium ion concentration with the sign changed*. The following Sample Problems further illustrate this fact.

$$pH = -log[H_3O^+].$$

SAMPLE PROBLEM

Determine the pH of a 0.001-M HCl solution.

SOLUTION

$$pH = -log\ [H_3O^+]$$

$$[H_3O^+] = 0.001\ mole/L = 10^{-3}\ mole/L$$

$$pH = -log\ 10^{-3} = -(-3)$$

$$pH = 3$$

Notice that if the magnitude of the $[H_3O^+] = 10^{-3}$, the pH $= 3$.

SAMPLE PROBLEM

What is the pH of a 0.001-M NaOH solution?

SOLUTION

$$pH = -log\ [H_3O^+]$$

$$[H_3O^+][OH^-] = 10^{-14}\ mole^2/L^2$$

$$[H_3O^+] = \frac{10^{-14}\ mole^2/L^2}{[OH^-]}$$

$$[OH^-] = 0.001\ mole/L = 10^{-3}\ mole/L$$

$$[H_3O^+] = \frac{10^{-14}\ mole^2/L^2}{10^{-3}\ mole/L} = 10^{-11}\ mole/L$$

$$pH = -log\ 10^{-11} = -(-11)$$

$$pH = 11$$

Notice that if the magnitude of the $[H_3O^+] = 10^{-11}$, the pH $= 11$.

The preceding problems have hydronium ion concentrations that are integral powers of ten. They are easily solved by inspec-

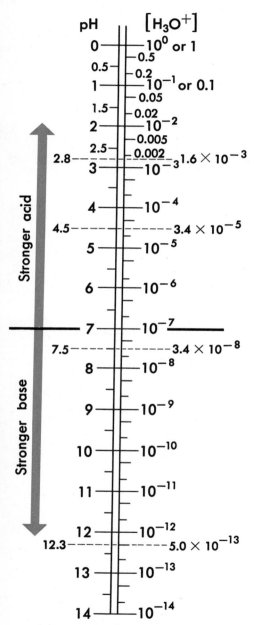

Figure 16-4. A comparison of the numerical pH scale and corresponding hydronium ion concentrations, $[H_3O^+]$.

tion. However, many problems involve hydrogen ion concentrations that are not integral powers of ten. Solving such problems requires some basic knowledge of logarithms and exponents. The common logarithms of numbers are listed in Appendix Table 17. The following brief review of logarithms and the use of the table of logarithms may be helpful at this point.

The common logarithm of a number is the exponent or the power to which 10 must be raised in order to obtain the given number. A logarithm is composed of two parts: the *characteristic*, or integral part; and the *mantissa*, or decimal part. The characteristic of the logarithm of any whole or mixed number is one less than the number of digits to the left of its decimal point. The characteristic of the logarithm of a decimal fraction is always negative and is numerically one greater than the number of zeros immediately to the right of the decimal point. Mantissas are read from tables such as Appendix Table 17. Mantissas are always positive. In determining the mantissa, the decimal point in the original number is ignored since its position is indicated by the characteristic.

Logarithms are exponents and follow the laws of exponents. Specifically, the logarithm of a product equals the sum of the logarithms of the factors.

To find the number whose logarithm is given, determine the digits in the number from the table of mantissas. The characteristic indicates the position of the decimal point.

As the logarithm of a number is the power to which 10 must be raised to give the number, the logarithm of 10^5 is 5 and the logarithm of 10^{-5} is -5. But suppose you require the logarithm of 2.5×10^{-3}. The characteristic of the logarithm of 2.5 is 0, one less than the number of digits to the left of the decimal point. From Appendix Table 17, the mantissa of the logarithm of 2.5 is .40 (to two significant figures). The complete logarithm of 2.5 is 0.40. The logarithm of 10^{-3} is -3. The logarithm of a product is the sum of the logarithms of the factors. Therefore,

$$\log 2.5 \times 10^{-3} = \log 2.5 + \log 10^{-3} = 0.40 + (-3) = -2.60$$

Suppose you must express the number whose logarithm is -9 in scientific notation. The number whose logarithm is -9 is 10^{-9}. Or, stated in another way, the antilog of $(-9) = 10^{-9}$.

Now express the number whose logarithm is -11.30 in scientific notation. The number whose logarithm is -11.30 is $10^{-11.30}$. To convert this expression to scientific notation, the exponent must first be changed to the sum of a positive decimal fraction and a negative whole number:

$$-11.30 = 0.70 + (-12)$$

As the sum of exponents indicates a product:

$$10^{0.70 + (-12)} = 10^{0.70} \times 10^{-12}$$

From Appendix Table 17, 0.70 is the logarithm of 5.0 (to 2 significant figures).

$$10^{0.70} = 5.0$$

$$10^{0.70} \times 10^{-12} = 5.0 \times 10^{-12}$$

The relationship between the pH and $[H_3O^+]$ is shown on the scale of Figure 16-4. This scale can be used to estimate the pH from a known $[H_3O^+]$ value, or the $[H_3O^+]$ from a known pH value. For example, the $[H_3O^+]$ of a solution is 3.4×10^{-5} mole/L. Observe that 3.4×10^{-5} lies between 10^{-4} and 10^{-5} on the $[H_3O^+]$ scale of Figure 16-4. Thus the pH of the solution must be between 4 and 5. The value can be estimated to a second significant figure as 4.5 on the pH scale of Figure 16-4. Calculations are required to obtain a more precise pH value. However, this reliable estimate of pH helps prevent errors that commonly occur in such calculations. Calculations for this pH value are shown in the following Sample Problem.

SAMPLE PROBLEM

What is the pH of a solution if $[H_3O^+]$ is 3.4×10^{-5} mole/liter?

SOLUTION

$$pH = -\log [H_3O^+]$$

$$pH = -\log (3.4 \times 10^{-5})$$

The logarithm of a product is equal to the sum of the logarithms of each of the factors. Thus,

$$pH = -(\log 3.4 + \log 10^{-5})$$

The log of $10^{-5} = -5$ and, from the table of logarithms (Appendix Table 17), the log of 3.4 is found to be 0.53.

$$pH = -(0.53 - 5)$$

Therefore,

$$pH = 4.47$$

16.9 Calculation of $[H_3O^+]$

The pH of a solution has been calculated knowing its hydronium ion concentration. Now suppose the pH of a solution is known. How can its hydronium ion concentration be determined?

The equation for the pH in terms of the $[H_3O^+]$ is

$$pH = -\log [H_3O^+]$$

Remember that the base of common logarithms is 10. This equation can be restated in terms of $[H_3O^+]$ as follows:

$$\log [H_3O^+] = -pH$$

$$[H_3O^+] = \text{antilog } (-pH)$$

$$[H_3O^+] = 10^{-pH}$$

$[H_3O^+] = antilog(-pH).$

For an aqueous solution in which the pH is 2, the $[H_3O^+]$ is 10^{-2} mole/L. When the pH is 0, the $[H_3O^+]$ is 1 mole/L. Recall that $10^0 = 1$. The following Sample Problem has a pH value that is a positive integer.

SAMPLE PROBLEM

Determine the hydronium ion concentration of an aqueous solution that has a pH of 4.

SOLUTION

$$pH = -\log [H_3O^+]$$

$$\log [H_3O^+] = -pH$$

$$[H_3O^+] = \text{antilog } (-pH) = \text{antilog } (-4)$$

$$\text{antilog } (-4) = 10^{-4}$$

$$[H_3O^+] = 10^{-4} \text{ mole/L}$$

Observe that if the pH = 4, the magnitude of the $[H_3O^+] = 10^{-4}$. The pH value in the following Sample Problem is not an integral number.

SAMPLE PROBLEM

The pH of a solution is found to be 7.52. What is the hydronium ion concentration?

SOLUTION

The $[H_3O^+]$ is the number whose logarithm is -7.52. Therefore the antilog of -7.52 will give the hydronium ion concentration.

$$pH = -\log [H_3O^+]$$

Solving for $[H_3O^+]$

$$\log [H_3O^+] = -pH$$

$$[H_3O^+] = \text{antilog } (-pH)$$

$$[H_3O^+] = \text{antilog } (-7.52)$$

But

$$\text{antilog } (-7.52) = \text{antilog } (0.48 - 8)$$

Thus

$$[H_3O^+] = \text{antilog } (0.48 - 8)$$

$$[H_3O^+] = \text{antilog } (0.48) \times \text{antilog } (-8)$$

The antilog of (0.48) is found from the table of logarithms to be 3.0. The antilog of (-8) is 10^{-8}. Therefore,

$$[H_3O^+] = 3.0 \times 10^{-8} \text{ mole/L}$$

1. What is the pH of an aqueous solution whose $[H_3O^+]$ is 2.7×10^{-4} mole per liter?   *ans.* 3.57
2. The $[H_3O^+]$ of an aqueous solution of a weak acid is 3.54×10^{-5} mole per liter. Find the pH of the solution. *ans.* 4.451
3. The pH of an aqueous solution is measured as 1.5. (*a*) Calculate the $[H_3O^+]$. (*b*) What is the $[OH^-]$ of the solution? *ans.* (*a*) 3.2×10^{-2} mole/L; (*b*) 3.1×10^{-13} mole/L

PRACTICE PROBLEMS

Table 16-4 shows the relationship between the hydronium ion and hydroxide ion concentrations, the product of these concentrations, and the pH for several solutions of typical molarities. Since KOH is a soluble ionic compound, its aqueous solutions are completely ionized. The molarity of each KOH solution indicates directly the $[OH^-]$. The product $[H_3O^+][OH^-]$ is constant, 10^{-14} mole^2 per liter^2 at 25 °C. Therefore, the $[H_3O^+]$ can be calculated. If the $[H_3O^+]$ is known, the pH can be determined as $-\log [H_3O^+]$.

Any aqueous solution of HCl that has a concentration below 1-*M* can be considered to be completely ionized. Thus the molarity of a 0.001-*M* HCl solution indicates directly the $[H_3O^+]$.

Table 16-4
RELATIONSHIP OF $[H_3O^+]$ TO $[OH^-]$ AND pH
(at 25 °C)

Solution	*$[H_3O^+]$*	*$[OH^-]$*	*$[H_3O^+][OH^-]$*	*pH*
0.02-*M* KOH	5.0×10^{-13}	2.0×10^{-2}	1.0×10^{-14}	12.3
0.01-*M* KOH	1.0×10^{-12}	1.0×10^{-2}	1.0×10^{-14}	12.0
pure H_2O	1.0×10^{-7}	1.0×10^{-7}	1.0×10^{-14}	7.0
0.001-*M* HCl	1.0×10^{-3}	1.0×10^{-11}	1.0×10^{-14}	3.0
0.1-*M* $HC_2H_3O_2$	1.3×10^{-3}	7.7×10^{-12}	1.0×10^{-14}	2.9

The weakly ionized $HC_2H_3O_2$ solution presents a different problem. Information about the concentrations of $HC_2H_3O_2$ molecules, H_3O^+ ions, and $C_2H_3O_2^-$ ions in the equilibrium mixture in the aqueous solution may be lacking. However, the hydronium ion concentration can be determined by measuring the pH of the solution experimentally. The $[H_3O^+]$ is then determined as the antilog $(-pH)$.

$$[H_3O^+] = \text{antilog } (-pH)$$

◻ 16.10 The neutralization reaction

In a neutralization reaction, the basic OH^- ion acquires a proton from the H_3O^+ ion to form a molecule of water.

$$H_3O^+ + OH^- \rightarrow 2H_2O$$

In aqueous solutions: if $[H_3O^+]$ increases, $[OH^-]$ decreases.

One mole of H_3O^+ ions (19 g) and 1 mole of OH^- ions (17 g) are chemically equivalent. Neutralization occurs when H_3O^+ ions and OH^- ions are supplied in equal numbers. A liter of water at room temperature has an $[H_3O^+]$ and $[OH^-]$ of 10^{-7} M each. Furthermore, the product $[H_3O^+][OH^-]$ of 10^{-14} mole²/liter² is a constant for water and all dilute aqueous solutions at 25 °C.

In aqueous solutions: if $[OH^-]$ increases, $[H_3O^+]$ decreases.

If 0.1 mole of gaseous HCl is dissolved in the liter of water, the H_3O^+ ion concentration rises to 0.1 or 10^{-1} M. Since the product $[H_3O^+][OH^-]$ remains at 10^{-14}, the $[OH^-]$ obviously must decrease from 10^{-7} to 10^{-13} M. The OH^- ions are removed from solution by combining with H_3O^+ ions to form H_2O molecules. Almost 10^{-7} mole of H_3O^+ ions is also removed in this way. However, this quantity is only a small portion (0.0001%) of the 0.1 mole of H_3O^+ ions present in the liter of solution.

Neutralization:
$H^+(aq) + OH^-(aq) \rightarrow H_2O(l)$

Now suppose 0.1 mole (4 g) of solid NaOH is added to the liter of 0.1-M HCl solution. Imagine, also, that the hydroxide and hydronium ions are somehow temporarily prevented from reacting with each other. The NaOH dissolves and supplies 0.1 mole of OH^- ions to the solution. Both $[H_3O^+]$ and $[OH^-]$ are now high and their product is much greater than the constant value 10^{-14} for the dilute aqueous solution.

Figure 16-5. The neutralization reaction. Hydronium ions and hydroxide ions form very slightly ionized water molecules.

Suppose the chemical reaction is now allowed to begin. The ion-removal reaction will be as before except that this time there are as many OH^- ions as H_3O^+ ions to be removed. H_3O^+ and

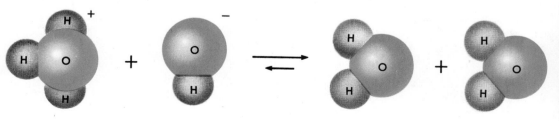

OH$^-$ ions combine until the product [H$_3$O$^+$][OH$^-$] returns to the constant value 10^{-14}, and

$$[\mathbf{H_3O^+}] = [\mathbf{OH^-}] = \mathbf{10^{-7}} \, M$$

The resulting solution is neither acidic nor basic, but is neutral. The process is one in which chemically equivalent quantities of H$_3$O$^+$ ions and OH$^-$ ions combine, a neutralization reaction.

◻ 16.11 Acid-base titration

The above examples should help you understand the nature of the chemical reaction that occurs between acids and bases as a solution of one is progressively added to a solution of the other. This progressive addition of an acid to a base (or a base to an acid) in order to compare their concentrations is called *titration*. *Titration is the controlled addition of the measured amount of a solution of known concentration required to react completely with a measured amount of a solution of unknown concentration.*

Titration provides a sensitive means of determining the relative volumes of acidic and basic solutions that are chemically equivalent. If the concentration of one solution is known, the concentration of the other solution can be calculated. Titration is an important laboratory procedure and is often used in analytical chemistry. See Figure 16-6.

Suppose successive additions of an aqueous base are made to a measured volume of an aqueous acid. Eventually the acid is neutralized. With continued addition of base, the solution becomes distinctly basic. The pH has now changed from a low to a high numerical value. The change in pH occurs slowly at first, then rapidly through the neutral point, and slowly again as the solution becomes basic. Typical pH curves for strong acid–strong base and weak acid–strong base titrations are shown in Figure 16-7.

The very rapid change in pH occurs in the region where equivalent quantities of H$_3$O$^+$ and OH$^-$ ions are present. Any method that shows this abrupt change in pH can be used to detect the *end point,* or *equivalence point,* of the titration.

Many dyes have colors that are sensitive to pH changes. Some change color within the pH range in which an end point occurs. Such dyes may serve as *indicators* in the titration process. Several indicators are listed in Table 16-5.

In order to actually know the concentration of a "known" solution, it is compared to a *standard solution* whose concentration is well established. The known solution is first prepared and its volume is adjusted to the desired concentration. This concentration information is then refined by titrating the solution against a carefully measured quantity of a highly purified compound known as a *primary standard*. The actual concentration

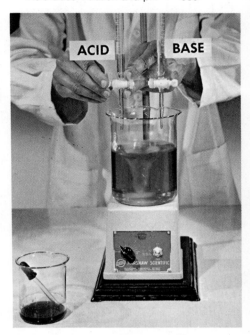

Figure 16-6. An acid-base titration using an indicator for detecting the end point of the reaction and a magnetic stirrer for mixing the reactants during the titration.

End point: the point in a titration at which the reaction is just complete.

Indicators "indicate" pH by their color changes.

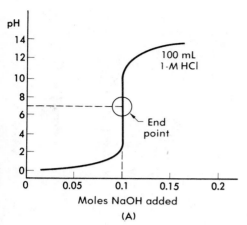

(A)

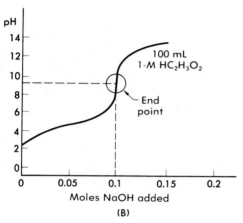

Moles NaOH added

(B)

Figure 16-7. Acid-base titration curves: (A) strong acid–strong base; (B) weak acid–strong base.

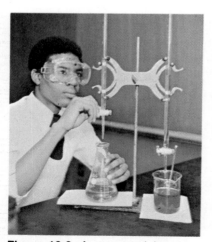

Figure 16-8. A common laboratory titration stand.

of the known solution becomes that established by this standardizing procedure.

☐ 16.12 Titration with molar solutions

Burets like those shown in Figure 16-8 are commonly used in titration to measure solution volumes with good precision. Suppose an aqueous solution of NaOH of unknown concentration is added in successive small amounts to 10.0 mL of 0.01-M aqueous HCl containing a few drops of a suitable indicator until the end point is reached. From the base buret readout it is found that 20.0 mL of the NaOH solution was used. How can these titration data indicate the *molarity* of the basic solution?

The empirical equation for the neutralization reaction is

$$HCl + NaOH \rightarrow NaCl + H_2O$$

The volume and molarity of the HCl solution are known. From these data, the quantity, in moles, of HCl used can be determined.

$$\frac{10.0 \text{ mL}}{1000 \text{ mL/L}} \times \frac{0.01 \text{ mole HCl}}{L} = 0.0001 \text{ mole HCl used}$$

The balanced equation shows that *1 mole* of NaOH is used for *1 mole* of HCl. In other words, NaOH and HCl show chemical equivalence, mole for mole, in the reaction. Therefore, the quantity of NaOH used in the titration is also 0.0001 mole. This quantity was furnished by 20.0 mL of NaOH solution. The molarity of the NaOH solution is obtained as follows:

$$\frac{0.0001 \text{ mole NaOH}}{20.0 \text{ mL}} \times \frac{1000 \text{mL}}{L} = 0.005 \text{ mole NaOH/L}$$

or

$$0.005\text{-}M \text{ NaOH}$$

Suppose the titration is repeated with the same "unknown" NaOH solution, but this time against 10.0 mL of a 0.01-M solution of diprotic H_2SO_4 as the "known" acid solution. When titrated to the end point, the base buret readout shows that 40.0 mL of the NaOH solution was used. The empirical equation for this reaction is

$$H_2SO_4 + 2NaOH \rightarrow Na_2SO_4 + 2H_2O$$

$$\frac{10.0 \text{ mL}}{1000 \text{ mL/L}} \times \frac{0.01 \text{ mole } H_2SO_4}{L} = 0.0001 \text{ mole } H_2SO_4 \text{ used}$$

The equation shows that *2 moles* of NaOH are required for *1 mole* of H_2SO_4. Therefore, 0.0002 mole NaOH is used in the titration as the chemical equivalent of 0.0001 mole H_2SO_4. The molarity of the NaOH solution is obtained as follows:

$$\frac{0.0002 \text{ mole NaOH}}{40.0 \text{ mL}} \times \frac{1000 \text{ mL}}{L} = 0.005 \text{ mole NaOH/L}$$

or

$$\text{0.005-}M \text{ NaOH}$$

To summarize, the molarity of an aqueous base (or acid) of unknown concentration can be determined by titrating against an aqueous acid (or base) of known concentration. The following steps are involved:

1. *Determine moles solute of known solution used in the titration.*
2. *Determine ratio—moles unknown solute/moles known solute—from balanced equation.*
3. *Determine moles solute of unknown solution used in the titration.*
4. *Determine molarity of unknown solution.*

The Sample Problem illustrates the titration process.

◧ SAMPLE PROBLEM

In a titration, 27.4 mL of a standard solution of $Ba(OH)_2$ is added to a 20.0-mL sample of an HCl solution. The concentration of the standard solution is 0.0154 M. What is the molarity of the acid solution?

◧ SOLUTION

The equation for this reaction is

$$\textbf{2HCl} + \textbf{Ba(OH)}_2 \rightarrow \textbf{BaCl}_2 + \textbf{2H}_2\textbf{O}$$

The quantity, in moles, of $Ba(OH)_2$ used in the reaction can be found from the molarity of the standard solution and the volume used.

$$\frac{27.4 \text{ mL}}{1000 \text{ mL/L}} \times \frac{0.0154 \text{ mole Ba(OH)}_2}{L} = 0.000422 \text{ mole Ba(OH)}_2 \text{ used}$$

The equation shows that *2 moles* of HCl are used for *1 mole* of $Ba(OH)_2$. Therefore, 0.000844 mole of HCl is used since this is the chemical equivalent of 0.000422 mole of $Ba(OH)_2$. If 20.0 mL of the unknown solution contains 0.000844 mole of HCl, the concentration is

$$\frac{0.000844 \text{ mole HCl}}{20.0 \text{ mL}} \times \frac{1000 \text{ mL}}{L} = 0.0422 \text{ mole/L}$$

or

$$\text{0.0422-}M \text{ HCl}$$

PRACTICE PROBLEMS

1. A 15.5-mL sample of 0.215-M KOH solution required 21.2 mL of aqueous acetic acid in a titration experiment. Calculate the molarity of the acetic acid solution.   *ans.* 0.157 M
2. By titration, 17.6 mL of aqueous H_2SO_4 just neutralized 27.4 mL of 0.0165-M LiOH solution. What was the molarity of the aqueous acid?   *ans.* 0.0128 M

☐ 16.13 Titration with normal solutions

Chemists sometimes prefer to express solution concentrations in terms of *normality*. The advantage in doing so is that concentrations are expressed directly in terms of equivalents of solute. Solutions of the same normality are chemically equivalent, milliliter for milliliter. Recall that the normality of a given solution is a whole number times its molarity, the factor depending on the substance and the reaction in which it is involved.

A very simple relationship exists between volumes and normalities of solutions used in titration. For example, a titration required 50.0 mL of a 0.100-N solution of NaOH to reach an end point with 10.0 mL of vinegar, a water solution of acetic acid ($HC_2H_3O_2$). The chemical equivalent of $HC_2H_3O_2$ used is the product of the volume of acid solution, V_a, used and its normality, N_a.

$$V_a \times N_a = \textbf{equiv}_a$$

Similarly, the chemical equivalent of NaOH used is the product of the volume of base solution, V_b, used and its normality, N_b.

$$V_b \times N_b = \textbf{equiv}_b$$

At the end point in the titration,

$$\textbf{equiv}_a = \textbf{equiv}_b$$

Therefore,

$$V_aN_a = V_bN_b$$

In this example, the normality of the vinegar, N_a, is to be determined. Solving the above equation for N_a

$$N_a = \frac{V_bN_b}{V_a} = \frac{50.0 \text{ mL} \times 0.100 \text{ } N}{10.0 \text{ mL}}$$

$$N_a = 0.500 \text{ } N$$

In this simple numerical example, it is apparent that 5 times as much base solution was used in the titration as vinegar. Clearly, the vinegar is 5 times more concentrated than the base.

The acidity of vinegar is due to the presence of acetic acid. A 1.0-N acetic acid solution contains 1.0 equivalent per liter of solution. In this case, 1.0 equivalent equals 1.0 mole or $6\overline{0}$ g of $HC_2H_3O_2$ per liter of solution. The 0.50-N solution must contain $3\overline{0}$ g of $HC_2H_3O_2$ per liter. A liter of vinegar has a mass of about 1000 g. Thus, the sample of vinegar used contains 3.0% acetic acid.

NaOH is a strong base and $HC_2H_3O_2$ is a weak acid. The pH curve for this titration, Figure 16-7(B), differs from the curve for a strong acid-strong base titration. The end point occurs at a higher pH because the sodium acetate solution formed in the titration is slightly basic.

Aqueous solutions of some salts may be acidic or basic depending on the composition of the salt. If the anions are sufficiently basic, protons are removed from some water molecules and the $[OH^-]$ increases. If the cations are slightly acidic, protons are donated to some water molecules and the $[H_3O^+]$ increases.

Table 16-5
INDICATOR COLORS

Indicator	Color			Transition interval (pH)
	Acid	Transition	Base	
methyl violet	yellow	aqua	blue	0.0 – 1.6
methyl yellow	red	orange	yellow	2.9 – 4.0
bromphenol blue	yellow	green	blue	3.0 – 4.6
methyl orange	red	orange	yellow	3.2 – 4.4
methyl red	red	buff	yellow	4.8 – 6.0
litmus	red	pink	blue	5.5 – 8.0
bromthymol blue	yellow	green	blue	6.0 – 7.6
phenol red	yellow	orange	red	6.6 – 8.0
phenolphthalein	colorless	pink	red	8.2–10.6
thymolphthalein	colorless	pale blue	blue	9.4–10.6
alizarin yellow	yellow	orange	red	10.0–12.0

◻ 16.14 Indicators in titration

Chemists have a wide choice of indicators for use in titration. They are able to choose one that changes color over the correct pH range for a particular reaction. Why is it not always suitable to use an indicator that changes color at a pH of 7?

Solutions of soluble hydroxides and acids mixed in chemically equivalent quantities are neutral only if both solutes are ionized to the same degree. The purpose of the indicator is to show, by a change in color, that the end point has been reached; that is, to show when equivalent quantities of the two solutes are together. Table 16-5 gives the color changes of several common indicators used in acid-base titrations. The pH range over which an indicator color change occurs is referred to as its *transition interval*. Observe the variations in the transition intervals for the different indicators. The choice of indicator is based on the suitability of its transition interval for a given acid-base reaction.

Figure 16-9. The acid, transition, and base colors of bromthymol blue.

Indicator	Acid color	Transition color	Base color

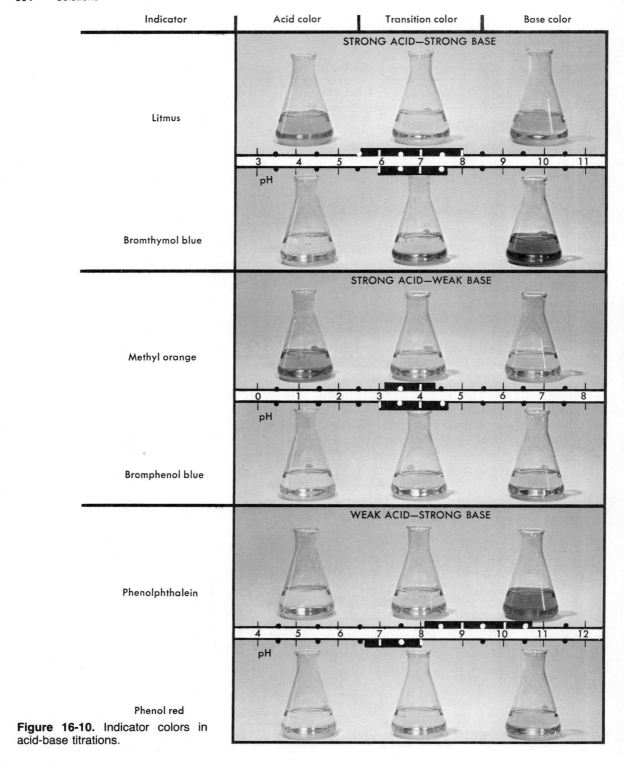

Figure 16-10. Indicator colors in acid-base titrations.

There are four possible types of acid-base combinations. In titration procedures these combinations may have end points occurring in different pH ranges as follows:

1. Strong acid–strong base: pH is about 7. Litmus is a suitable indicator, but the color change is not sharply defined. Bromthymol blue performs more satisfactorily. Its color change is shown in Figure 16-9.

2. Strong acid–weak base: pH is lower than 7. Methyl orange is a suitable indicator.

3. Weak acid–strong base: pH is higher than 7. Phenolphthalein is a suitable indicator.

4. Weak acid–weak base: pH may be either higher or lower than 7, depending on which reactant is stronger. No indicator is very suitable.

☐ 16.15 pH measurements

Indicators used to detect end points in neutralization reactions are organic compounds. They have the characteristics of weak acids. When added to a solution in suitable form and concentration, an indicator gives the solution a characteristic color. If the pH of the solution is changed enough, as in titration, the indicator changes color over a definite pH range, the *transition interval.*

Because indicators are color sensitive to the pH of a solution, they are used to give information about the $[H_3O^+]$ of the solution. The color of un-ionized indicator molecules is different from that of indicator ions. In solutions of high hydronium ion concentration (low pH), the color of the molecular species prevails. Solutions of low hydronium ion concentrations (high pH) have the color of the ionic species. The acid, base, and transition colors of several indicators are shown in Figure 16-10.

An indicator added to different solutions may show the same *transition color.* If so, the solutions are considered to have the same pH. This is the basis for the common *colorimetric* determination of pH. A measured volume of a suitable indicator is added to each solution whose pH is to be determined. The color is then compared with that of the same indicator in solutions of known pH. By careful color comparison, the pH of a solution can be estimated with a precision of about 0.1 pH interval.

End-point determinations in titrations and the pH of solutions can be found in ways other than by the use of indicators. Instrumental methods are generally used by chemists to make rapid titrations and pH determinations. A pH meter, shown in Figure 16-11, provides a convenient way of measuring the pH of a solution. The pH meter measures the voltage difference between a special electrode and a reference electrode placed in the solution. The voltage changes as the H_3O^+ ion concentration of the solution changes. In an acid-base titration, a large change in voltage

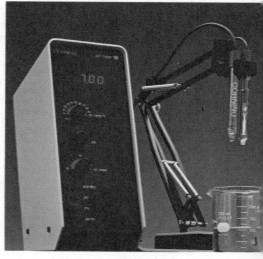

Figure 16-11. A modern pH meter.

occurs when equivalent quantities of the two reactants are present in the solution. This voltage change is related to the sharp color change of an indicator near the end point of the titration process.

SUMMARY

Solution concentrations are expressed in terms of molality, molarity, or normality. Molar solutions are prepared using moles of solute per liter of solution. Normal solutions are prepared using chemical equivalents of solute per liter of solution.

Chemical equivalents of substances have the same combining capacities in reactions. One equivalent of an acid supplies one mole of protons. One equivalent of a base supplies one mole of OH^- ions or accepts one mole of protons. For diprotic and triprotic acids, the reactions they undergo determine their chemical equivalencies.

Water is weakly ionized by autoprotolysis. At 25 °C, the hydronium ion concentration and hydroxide ion concentration are each 10^{-7} mole/liter. The product of these ion concentrations remains constant at 10^{-14} mole^2/liter^2 for water and aqueous solutions as long as the temperature remains at 25 °C. The ionization of water increases slightly with a rise in temperature.

The pH scale is used to indicate the hydronium ion concentration in aqueous solutions. Numerically, the pH of a solution is the common logarithm of the number of liters that contain one mole of H_3O^+ ions. Since this number of liters is the reciprocal of the H_3O^+ ion concentration of the solution, the pH is also the common logarithm of the reciprocal of the hydronium ion concentration. If the hydronium ion concentration of a solution is known, the pH can be calculated. Conversely, the hydronium ion concentration can be calculated if the pH of a solution is known. The pH of pure water and neutral aqueous solutions is 7. Acidic solutions have pH values lower than 7. Basic solutions have pH values higher than 7.

The concentrations of acids and bases are compared by a technique called titration. A solution of a base (or acid) of unknown concentration is added to a solution of an acid (or base) of known concentration until equal chemical equivalents of acid and base are present in the solution. An acid-base indicator is used to show when the end point in the titration is reached. Knowing the concentration of one solution and the volumes of both solutions used to reach the end point, the concentration of the other solution can be calculated.

Indicators change color over characteristic short pH ranges called their transition intervals. The end point is reached at a pH of about 7 for titrations of strong acids and strong bases. Indicators with transition intervals around a pH of 7 are used. Indicators with transition intervals below a pH of 7 are used in titration of strong acids and weak bases. Weak acid–strong base titrations require indicators with transition intervals above a pH of 7.

VOCABULARY

antilog	common logarithm	molarity	titration
autoprotolysis	end point	normality	transition color
[ ]	equivalents	pH	transition interval
characteristic	indicator	primary standard	volumetric flask
colorimetric determination of pH	mantissa	standard solution	

QUESTIONS

Group A

1. Distinguish between solution concentrations expressed in terms of molality and molarity.
2. (a) What determines the mass of 1 equivalent of an acid? (b) of a base?
3. How many grams are in 1 equivalent of each of the following? (a) $Ca(NO_3)_2$ (b) Zn (c) HCO_3^- (d) KCl (e) Li (f) H_3O^+ (g) $ZnSO_4$ (h) OH^- (i) $HC_2H_3O_2$ (j) $Al_2(SO_4)_3$.
4. Determine the number of equivalents per mole of each of the following: (a) H_2O (b) $HClO_4$ (c) $Sr(NO_3)_2$ (d) $AuCl_3$ (e) $Mg(OH)_2$ (f) HF (g) $NaC_2H_3O_2$ (h) K_2SO_4 (i) $CaCl_2$ (j) Bi.
5. Write the equations that show the partial and complete ionization of sulfuric acid.
6. What is the conjugate base for the HCO_3^- ion?
7. Explain the meaning of the notation $[NH_4^+]$.
8. (a) Explain the meaning of pH. (b) What is the usual range of the pH scale?
9. In a certain aqueous solution, the hydronium ion concentration is 1×10^{-3} mole per liter. (a) What is the pH of the solution? (b) What is the hydroxide ion concentration?
10. (a) Explain why neither bromphenol blue nor methyl orange is a suitable indicator for the titration of 0.02-N acetic acid with sodium hydroxide. (b) Name two indicators that are suitable for this titration.

Group B

11. Hydrogen chloride, HCl, has 1 equivalent of hydrogen per mole and hydrogen phosphate, H_3PO_4, has 3 equivalents of hydrogen per mole. Yet hydrochloric acid is described as a *strong* acid and phosphoric acid as a *weak* acid. Explain.
12. (a) How would you test the soil in your lawn or garden to find out whether it is acidic or basic? (b) If you find it to be acidic, what can be added to it to remedy the condition?
13. Test your saliva with litmus paper. (a) Is the saliva acidic or alkaline? (b) Do you think that a toothpaste is likely to be acidic or basic? Test some of them.
14. In a neutralization reaction between hydrochloric acid and potassium hydroxide, the K^+ ion and the Cl^- ion are called *spectator ions*. (a) Explain. (b) How could the potassium chloride be recovered?
15. What indicator would you use to show the end point of the neutralization reaction described in Question 14? Explain why you selected this particular indicator for the neutralization reaction.
16. How many moles of sodium hydroxide are needed for the complete neutralization of (a) 1 mole of hydrochloric acid? (b) 1 mole of sulfuric acid? (c) 1 mole of phosphoric acid? (d) Write the equation for each reaction.
17. (a) What mass of calcium hydroxide is required to prepare 1.0 liter of 0.010-N solution? (b) to prepare 1.0 liter of 0.010-M solution?
18. (a) What volume of water contains a mole of H_3O^+ ions? (b) How many equivalents of hydronium ions is this? (c) How many grams of H_3O^+ ion? (d) What is the mole-concentration of OH^- ion in this volume of water? (e) How many equivalents of hydroxide ions is this? (f) How many grams of OH^- ion?
19. What is the normality of (a) a 0.0040-M solution of copper(II) chloride? (b) a 0.15-M solution of potassium hydroxide? (c) a 2-M solution of sulfuric acid?
20. What is the molarity of (a) a 0.006-N solution of hydroiodic acid? (b) a 0.0036-N solution of aluminum sulfate? (c) a 0.030-N solution of barium hydroxide?

◖ PROBLEMS

Group A

1. (a) How many grams of sodium hydroxide are required to neutralize 54.75 g of hydrogen chloride in water solution? (b) How many moles of each reactant are involved in the reaction?

2. What quantity of potassium nitrate would you add to 500 g of water to prepare a 0.250-M solution?

3. How many grams of sugar, $C_{12}H_{22}O_{11}$, are contained in 50.0 mL of an 0.800-M solution?

4. What is the molarity of a solution containing 49.0 g of H_2SO_4 in 3.00 L of solution?

5. What is the molarity of a $CuBr_2$ solution that contains 446 g of solute in 5.00 L of solution?

6. How many grams of NaCl are required to make 250 mL of 0.500-M solution?

7. How many grams of $Al_2(SO_4)_3 \cdot 18\ H_2O$ are required to make 800 mL of 0.300-M solution?

8. Calculate the mass of one equivalent of (a) K; (b) Ca; (c) NaCl; (d) $CuSO_4$; (e) $Na_2CO_3 \cdot 10H_2O$; (f) $FeCl_3 \cdot 6H_2O$.

9. What is the normality of a solution that contains 4.0 g of Na_2SO_4 per liter of solution?

10. Calculate the normality of a solution containing 710 g of $Al(NO_3)_3$ in 15.0 L of solution?

11. How many grams of $CuSO_4 \cdot 5H_2O$ will be needed to make up 500 mL of 0.100-N solution?

12. How many grams of $FeCl_3 \cdot 6H_2O$ are needed to prepare 200 mL of 0.500-N solution?

13. (a) What is the pH of a 0.01-M solution of HCl, assuming complete ionization? (b) What is the $[OH^-]$ of a 0.01-M solution of sodium hydroxide? (c) What is the pH of this solution?

14. How many milliliters of a 0.150-N solution of a metallic hydroxide are required to neutralize 30.0 mL of a 0.500-N solution of an acid?

15. A chemistry student finds that it takes 34 mL of a 0.50-N acid solution to neutralize 10 mL of a sample of household ammonia. What is the normality of the ammonia-water solution?

Group B

16. How many solute molecules are contained in each milliliter of a 0.1-M solution of a nonelectrolyte?

17. An excess of zinc reacts with 400 mL of hydrochloric acid, and 2.55 L of H_2 gas is collected over water at 20 °C and 745.0 mm. What is the molarity of the acid?

18. Concentrated hydrochloric acid has a density of 1.19 g/mL and contains 37.2% HCl by mass. How many milliliters of concentrated hydrochloric acid are required to prepare (a) 1.00 L of 1.00-M HCl solution; (b) 2.00 L of 3.00-M HCl solution; (c) 5.00 L of 0.100-N HCl solution; (d) 250 mL of 0.200-N HCl solution?

19. The stockroom supply of concentrated sulfuric acid is 95.0% H_2SO_4 by mass and has a density of 1.84 g/mL. How many milliliters of concentrated sulfuric acid are needed to prepare (a) 2.50 L of 0.500-M H_2SO_4 solution; (b) 100 mL of 0.250-M H_2SO_4 solution; (c) 1.00 L of 1.00-N H_2SO_4 solution; (d) 3.00 L of 0.200-N H_2SO_4 solution?

20. In a laboratory titration, 15.0 mL of 0.275-M H_2SO_4 solution neutralizes 20.0 mL of NaOH solution. What is the molarity of the NaOH solution?

21. Suppose a 10.0-mL sample of vinegar is diluted to 100 mL with distilled water and titrated against 0.100-M sodium hydroxide solution. From the burets, 30.0 mL of the diluted vinegar and 25.0 mL of the solution of the base were withdrawn. What percentage of acetic acid, $HC_2H_3O_2$, does the vinegar contain?

22. A solution is determined experimentally to have a pH of 2.9. (a) Find the $[H_3O^+]$. (b) What is the $[OH^-]$?

23. Find the pH of a 0.02-M LiOH solution.

24. What is the pH of a 0.054-M solution of HCl?

25. Suppose 25.0 mL of 0.150-M NaOH and 50.0 mL of 0.100-M HCl solutions are mixed. What is the pH of the resulting solution?

Carbon and Its Oxides

A little more than 150 years ago, the laws of chemistry and physics were believed to apply to some, but not all, forms of matter. Unlike minerals, living organisms are able to reproduce, grow, and adapt to changes in their surroundings. Organic compounds, as substances derived from organisms were called, must be the products of mysterious and unknowable forces. Scientists spoke of a vital force, a force possessed by all organic matter that governed the behavior of living substances but could not be duplicated by chemists in the laboratory. Yet there were skeptics, such as Friedrich Wöhler, who maintained that the laws of nature should apply to all matter in the universe. He attempted to synthesize organic substances and in 1828, after many trials, finally synthesized urea, a major waste product of animals, from ammonium cyanate, an inorganic substance. Now the gap between organic and inorganic was bridged. The laws of chemistry were found to apply as much to the living as to the nonliving world.

◻ 17.1 Abundance and importance of carbon

Charcoal and soot are forms of carbon that have been known from earliest times. But the elemental nature of carbon, its occurrence in charcoal, and its existence as diamond and graphite were not discovered until the late eighteenth century.

Carbon ranks about seventeenth in abundance by weight among the elements in the earth's crust. In importance, carbon ranks far higher. Carbon is present in body tissue and in the foods you eat. It is found in coal, petroleum, natural gas, limestone, and in all living things. In addition to its natural occurrence, chemists have synthesized hundreds of thousands of carbon compounds in the laboratory.

The study of carbon compounds is so important that it forms a separate branch of chemistry called *organic chemistry*. Originally, organic chemistry was defined as the study of materials derived from living organisms. Inorganic chemistry was the study of materials derived from mineral sources. Chemists have known for over a century that this is not a clear distinction. Many substances identical to those produced in living things can also be made from mineral materials. As a result, ***organic chemistry*** *today includes the study of carbon compounds whether or not they are produced by living organisms.*

In most substances containing carbon, the carbon is present in the *combined* form. It is usually united with hydrogen, or with hydrogen and oxygen. In this chapter, carbon in its *free* or *uncombined* forms will first be described. Then carbon dioxide and carbon monoxide will be considered.

CARBON

In this chapter you will gain an understanding of:

- **the structure and properties of carbon atoms**
- **allotropy and the allotropic forms of carbon**
- **the properties and uses of the amorphous forms of carbon**
- **the physical and chemical properties of carbon dioxide and carbon monoxide**
- **the structure, preparation, and uses of carbon dioxide and carbon monoxide**

Figure 17-1. Coal is an important source of carbon and carbon compounds.

Hybridization is explained in Section 6.17.

Allotropy occurs for either of two reasons: (1) An element has two or more kinds of molecules, each with different numbers of atoms, which exist in the same phase; or (2) an element has two or more different arrangements of atoms or molecules in a crystal.

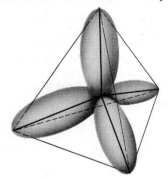

Figure 17-2. In sp^3 hybridization, the four covalent bonds of a carbon atom are directed in space toward the four vertices of a regular tetrahedron. The nucleus of the atom is at the center of the tetrahedron.

☐ 17.2 Characteristics of carbon atoms

Carbon is the element with atomic number 6 and electron configuration $1s^2 2s^2 2p^2$. On the periodic table, it is in the second period, midway between the active metal lithium and the active nonmetal fluorine. The two $1s$ electrons are tightly bound to the nucleus. The two $2s$ electrons and the two $2p$ electrons are the valence electrons. Carbon atoms show a very strong tendency to share electrons and form covalent bonds. This electron sharing usually has the effect of producing a stable outer-shell octet about a carbon atom. Having four valence electrons makes it possible for a carbon atom to form four covalent bonds. These bonds are directed in space toward the four vertices of a regular tetrahedron. This arrangement of carbon valence bonds is explained by sp^3 hybridization. The nucleus of the atom is at the center of the tetrahedron. See Figure 17-2.

The property of forming covalent bonds is so strong in carbon atoms that they join readily with other elements. They also link together with other carbon atoms in chains, rings, plates, and networks. Depending on the number of atoms and the way they are bonded together, each molecule thus formed is a unique carbon compound. The variety of ways in which carbon atoms can be linked explains why there are several times as many carbon compounds as noncarbon compounds.

☐ 17.3 Allotropic forms of carbon

In Section 9.11, the allotropic forms of the element oxygen—oxygen molecules, O_2, and ozone molecules, O_3—were described. Allotropy was defined as the existence of an element in two or more forms in the same physical phase. The reason for oxygen's allotropy is the existence of two kinds of molecules, each with different numbers of atoms.

Carbon occurs in two solid allotropic forms. *Diamond* is a hard crystalline form. *Graphite* is a soft, grayish-black crystalline form. The reason for carbon's allotropy is the existence of two different arrangements of atoms in a crystal.

When substances that contain combined carbon are decomposed by heat, they leave black residues. These residues are sometimes collectively called *amorphous carbon* because they seem to have no definite crystalline shape. Examples of amorphous carbon are *coke, charcoal, boneblack,* and *carbon black.* Studies of the structures of these substances have been made by X-ray scattering. These studies reveal that the various forms of so-called amorphous carbon actually contain regions in which the carbon atoms are arranged in an orderly way. In carbon black, for example, the carbon atoms are arranged somewhat as they are in a layer of graphite.

◻ 17.4 Diamond

The most famous diamond mines in the world are located in South Africa. Diamonds in this region usually occur in the shafts of extinct volcanoes. It is believed that they were formed slowly under extreme heat and pressure. Diamonds, as they are mined, do not have the shape or sparkle of gem stones. The art of cutting and polishing gives them their brilliant appearance.

Synthetic diamonds are chemically identical to natural diamonds but are produced in the laboratory. They are prepared by subjecting graphite and a metal that acts as solvent and catalyst to extremely high pressure (55,000 atm) and high temperature (2000 °C) for nearly a day.

Diamond is the hardest material. It is the densest form of carbon, about 3.5 times as dense as water. Both the hardness (resistance to wear) and density are explained by its structure. Figure 17-3 shows that carbon atoms in diamond are covalently bonded in a strong, compact fashion. The distances between the carbon nuclei are 1.54 Å. Note that each carbon atom is tetrahedrally oriented to its four nearest neighbors. This type of structure gives the crystal a great deal of strength in all three dimensions.

The rigidity of its structure gives diamond its hardness. The compactness, resulting from the small distances between nuclei, gives diamond its high density. The covalent network structure of diamond accounts for its extremely high melting point, about 3700 °C. Since all the valence electrons are used in forming covalent bonds, none can migrate. This explains why diamond is a nonconductor of electricity. Because of its extreme hardness, diamond is used for cutting, drilling, and grinding. A diamond is used as a long-lasting phonograph needle.

Diamond is the best conductor of heat. A perfect single diamond crystal conducts heat more than five times better than silver or copper. Silver and copper are the best metallic conductors. In diamond, heat is conducted by the transfer of energy of vibration from one carbon atom to the next. In a perfect single diamond crystal, this process is very efficient. The carbon atoms have a small mass. The forces binding the atoms together are strong and can easily transfer vibratory motion from one atom to another. The combination of nonconduction of electricity and excellent heat conduction may make diamond useful in semiconductor devices.

Diamond is insoluble in ordinary solvents. In 1772, the French chemist Lavoisier burned a clear diamond in pure oxygen and obtained carbon dioxide as a product. This experiment proved to him that diamond contains carbon. The English chemist Smithson Tennant repeated the experiment in 1797. He weighed the diamond and the carbon dioxide it produced. The mass of carbon dioxide showed that diamond is pure carbon.

Figure 17-3. The crystal structure of diamond. In the diamond structure, each carbon atom is bonded to four tetrahedrally oriented carbon atoms.

A solvent is a dissolving medium; a catalyst is a substance that increases the rate of a chemical reaction without itself being permanently changed.

Smithson Tennant (1761–1815) was the discoverer of the transition elements osmium, atomic number 76, and iridium, atomic number 77. He discovered these in impure platinum.

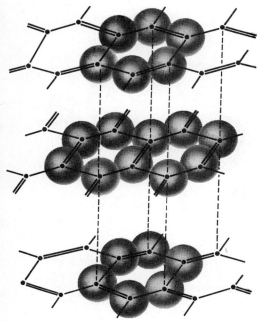

Figure 17-4. The crystal structure of graphite. Within each layer, each carbon atom is bonded to three other carbon atoms 120° apart. The distance between the layers has been exaggerated in order to show the structure of each layer more clearly.

Resonance is explained in Section 6.22.

☐ **17.5 Graphite**

Natural graphite deposits are found throughout the world. The major producers are the Republic of Korea, Austria, North Korea, and the Soviet Union.

More than 70% of the graphite used in the United States is synthetic graphite. Most of this synthetic graphite is produced from petroleum coke. The process involves heating petroleum coke to about 2800 °C in special furnaces.

Graphite is nearly as remarkable for its softness as diamond is for its hardness. It is easily crumbled and has a greasy feel. Graphite crystals are hexagonal (six-sided) in cross section, with a density of about 2.26 g/cm^3. Although graphite is a nonmetal, it is a fairly good conductor of electricity.

The structure of graphite readily explains these properties. The carbon atoms in graphite are arranged in layers of thin hexagonal plates, as shown in Figure 17-4. The distance between the centers of adjacent carbon atoms within a layer is 1.42 Å. This distance is less than the distance between adjacent carbon atoms in diamond. However, the distance between the centers of atoms in adjacent layers is 3.35 Å.

Figure 17-4 shows the bonding within a layer of graphite. Each carbon atom in a layer is bonded to only three other carbon atoms in that layer. This bonding consists of single and double covalent bonds between carbon atoms. When represented in this fashion, three *different* equivalent patterns appear. In each of these, some carbon-carbon bonds are single and others are double. There is, however, no experimental evidence that the bonds in a layer of graphite are of these two distinct types. On the contrary, the evidence indicates that the bonds are all the same. The layers of graphite have a resonance structure in which the carbon-carbon bonds are intermediate in character between single and double bonds. Each layer in graphite is a strongly bonded covalent network structure. As with diamond, this structure gives graphite a very high melting point, about 3600 °C. The strong bonds between the carbon atoms within a layer make graphite difficult to pull apart in the direction of the layer. As a result, carbon fibers, in which the carbon is in the form of graphite, are very strong.

The layers of carbon atoms in graphite are too far apart for the formation of covalent bonds between them. They are held together by weak dispersion interaction forces. These forces result from electron motion within the layers. The weak attraction between layers accounts for the softness of graphite and its greasy feel as one layer slides over another.

On the average, the carbon atoms in graphite are farther apart than they are in diamond, so graphite has a lower density. The mobile electrons in each carbon-atom layer make graphite a fairly good conductor of electricity. Like diamond, graphite does not dissolve in any ordinary solvent. Similarly, it forms carbon dioxide when burned in oxygen.

☐ 17.6 Uses of graphite

The largest single use of natural graphite is for coating the molds used in metal casting. It is also used to increase the carbon content of steel and to make clay-graphite crucibles in which steel and other metals are melted. All of these applications take advantage of the very high melting point of graphite. Graphite is a very good lubricant. It is sometimes mixed with petroleum jelly or motor oil to form graphite lubricants. It can be used for lubricating machine parts that operate at temperatures too high for the usual petroleum lubricants. Graphite leaves a gray streak or mark when it is drawn across a sheet of paper. In making "lead" pencils, graphite is powdered, mixed with clay, and then formed into sticks. The hardness of a pencil depends upon the relative amount of clay that is used.

The most important use of synthetic graphite is in electrodes for electric-arc steelmaking furnaces. Synthetic graphite electrodes are also used in the electrolysis of salt water for making chlorine and sodium hydroxide. Graphite does not react with acids, bases, and organic and inorganic solvents. These properties make it useful in equipment for a variety of processes in the food, chemical, and petroleum industries. Graphite is also used in nuclear reactors.

If certain synthetic fibers are combined with plastic resins and heated under pressure, they become carbon fibers. As mentioned in Section 17.5, the form of carbon in these fibers is graphite. Carbon fibers are less dense than steel but are stronger and stiffer. They are used in aircraft floor decking and wing flaps, and in weather and communication satellites. In sporting goods, carbon fibers are used to make golf club shafts, tennis rackets, fishing rods, and bicycle frames.

☐ 17.7 Coal

Coal is a solid, rocklike material that burns readily. It contains at least 50% carbon and varying amounts of moisture, volatile (easily vaporized) materials, and noncombustible mineral matter (ash).

Geologists believe that coal was formed about 3×10^8 years ago during the carboniferous age. At that time plants grew more luxuriantly than they do today. Possibly there was more carbon dioxide in the atmosphere and it stimulated the growth of vegetation. Tree ferns, giant club mosses, and other forms of vegetation growing in swamps supplied the material for the coal deposits.

Peat bogs were probably formed first. Extensive peat bogs are found in Pennsylvania, Michigan, Wisconsin, and other states.

Figure 17-5. Carbon fiber "tail bullet" sub-assembly prior to fastening to the Challenger 600 aircraft.

Figure 17-6. The luxuriant growth of vegetation during the carboniferous age is the source of our coal deposits today.

Table 17-1
ANALYSIS OF PEAT AND REPRESENTATIVE COALS

	Peat	Lignite	Subbituminous	Bituminous	Anthracite
carbon, %		37.4	51.0	74.5	86.4
hydrogen, %		7.4	6.2	5.2	2.7
oxygen, %		48.4	34.5	9.2	3.6
nitrogen, %		0.7	1.0	1.5	0.9
sulfur, %	0.1	0.6	0.3	0.9	0.6
moisture, %	66.9	43.0	25.9	2.8	2.2
ash, %	4.8	5.5	6.9	8.8	5.9
energy value, kcal/kg	1680	3488	4784	7441	7683

The bogs contain mosses, sedges, and other forms of vegetation that have undergone partial decomposition in swampy land in almost complete absence of air. Peat burns with a smoky flame, and its heat content is rather low. Peat contains a high percentage of moisture. In the United States, peat is used mainly as a soil conditioner, not as fuel. Comparative data for peat and representative samples of coal are given in Table 17-1.

In some areas, upheavals of parts of the earth's crust buried thick masses of vegetable matter. Once buried, this material was subjected to increased temperatures and pressures over many millions of years. At a fairly early stage in these changes, lignite was formed. Lignite is sometimes called brown coal because of its brownish-black color. It is common in some of the western states, as the map in Figure 17-7 shows. Lignite burns with a smoky flame, and while its heat content is higher than

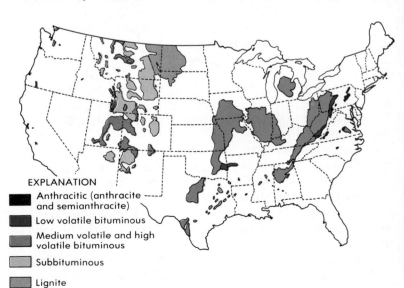

EXPLANATION

Anthracitic (anthracite and semianthracite)

Low volatile bituminous

Medium volatile and high volatile bituminous

Subbituminous

Lignite

Figure 17-7. The various forms of coal are widely distributed in the United States.

that of peat, it is still significantly below that of the other coals. The moisture content of lignite is high.

Subbituminous coal, which is found extensively in Wyoming and other western states, may be considered the next stage of coal formation. The percentage of carbon is higher than in lignite and the moisture content is lower. Subbituminous coal also has a higher heat content than lignite. It can be used for industrial heating, as in electric generating stations.

Bituminous coal appears to have been subjected to greater heat and pressure. The percentage of carbon is high; the moisture content is low. Bituminous coal has a high heat content. It is widely distributed throughout the Appalachian region, the Midwest, and the Rocky Mountain states. Bituminous coal is used for home and industrial heating and for making coke and other coal by-products.

Anthracite is believed to have been subjected to greater temperatures and pressures than the other forms of coal. Anthracite contains the least amount of volatile matter of all coals. It has the highest percentage of carbon. Most anthracite is found in Pennsylvania.

Coal is our most plentiful source of energy. The amount of coal in the United States that can be recovered using known techniques is presently estimated to be about 2×10^{11} metric tons. The total amount of coal mined each year is about 7×10^8 metric tons. Three-fourths of this coal is used to generate electricity.

◻ 17.8 Destructive distillation

Suppose a complex carbon-containing material, such as wood or bituminous coal, is *heated in a closed container without access to air or oxygen. The complex material decomposes into simpler substances.* This process is known as *destructive distillation.* Coke, charcoal, and boneblack are prepared by destructive distillation of coal, wood, and bones, respectively.

◻ 17.9 Coke

When bituminous coal is heated in a hard-glass test tube, a gas that is flammable escapes. This gas burns readily if mixed with air and ignited. Also, a tarlike liquid condenses on the upper walls of the tube. If the heating is continued until all the volatile material is driven off, coke is left as a residue.

Commercially, coke is prepared by destructive distillation of bituminous coal in by-product coke ovens. The volatile products are separated into *coal gas, ammonia,* and *coal tar.* Coal gas can be used as a fuel. Ammonia is used in making fertilizers. Coal tar can be separated by distillation into many useful materials. These materials are used to make drugs, dyes, and ex-

Figure 17-8. Coke is produced by the destructive distillation of bituminous coal in by-product coke ovens. Here the red-hot coke is being discharged from an oven into a waiting railroad car.

Figure 17-9. Charcoal filters are used to absorb ozone from the cabin atmosphere of jet airplanes that make long flights in the stratosphere.

Adsorption is defined in Section 9.18 and further explained in Section 13.2.

plosives. The black pitch that remains after distillation of coal tar is used to surface roads.

About 60,000,000 tons of coke are produced each year in the United States. Coke is a gray, porous solid that is harder and denser than charcoal. It burns with little flame, has a high heat content, and is a valuable fuel.

Coke is an excellent reducing agent. It is widely used in obtaining the metals from the ores of iron, tin, copper, and zinc. These ores are either oxides or are converted into oxides. Coke readily reduces the metals in these oxides. It also has great structural strength and is free from volatile impurities.

☐ 17.10 Charcoal

Destructive distillation of wood yields several gases that can be burned. It also produces methanol (wood alcohol), acetic acid, and other volatile products. The residue that remains is charcoal. Charcoal is prepared commercially by heating wood in *retorts*. These are closed containers in which substances are distilled or decomposed by heat. The burnable gases that result provide supplementary fuel. The other volatile products may be condensed and sold as by-products.

Charcoal is a porous, black, brittle solid. It is odorless and tasteless. It is denser than water, but it often adsorbs enough gas to make it float on water. This ability to *adsorb* a large quantity of gas is the most remarkable physical property of charcoal. One cubic centimeter of freshly prepared willow charcoal adsorbs about 90 cubic centimeters of ammonia gas. Charcoal has been used to adsorb toxic waste products from the blood of persons suffering from liver failure. It is also used to remove ozone from the cabin atmosphere of jet airplanes.

At ordinary temperatures, charcoal is inactive and insoluble in all ordinary solvents. It is a good reducing agent because it unites with oxygen at a high temperature. Charcoal is also a good fuel, but it is more expensive than other common fuels.

☐ 17.11 Boneblack

Animal charcoal, or *boneblack,* is produced by the destructive distillation of bones. The by-products of the process include bone oil and pyridine. These products may be added to ethanol (ethyl alcohol) to make it unfit for drinking. Boneblack usually contains calcium phosphate as an impurity. This can be removed by treating the boneblack with an acid.

☐ 17.12 Activated carbon

Activated carbon is a form of carbon that is prepared in a way that gives it a very large internal surface area. This large surface area makes activated carbon useful for the adsorption of liquid or gaseous substances. Activated carbon can be made from a variety of carbon-containing materials. Such a material is first destructively distilled. The carbon produced is treated with steam or carbon dioxide at about 100 °C. These two processes produce a very porous form of carbon. This porosity creates a very large internal surface area. The surface area of a portion of activated carbon may be as high as 2000 m^2/g, most of the area being internal.

Activated carbon used for adsorption of gases must have a small pore structure. Coconut and other nut shells are the best sources of this type of activated carbon. Gas-adsorbent activated carbon is used in gas masks. It is also used for the recovery of volatile solvent vapors and the removal of impurities from gases in industrial processes. This form of activated carbon can remove odors from the air circulated by large air conditioning systems in offices, restaurants, and theaters.

Activated carbon used for adsorption from the liquid phase comes from both animal and vegetable sources. Boneblack was first used for this purpose, but now such activated carbon is also made from coal, peat, and wood. Inorganic impurities are removed from activated carbon that is to be used in processing food or chemical products. Acids such as dilute hydrochloric or sulfuric react with these impurities to form soluble products that are washed away with water. Liquid-adsorbent activated carbon is used in the refining of cane sugar, beet sugar, and corn syrup. It is also used in municipal and industrial water treatment to adsorb harmful materials as well as impurities that would give the water an objectionable odor and taste.

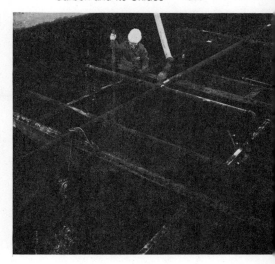

Figure 17-10. Activated carbon is used to remove objectionable color, odor, and impurities from water to be used in public water supplies. Here a workman is measuring the thickness of the activated carbon layer in a filter tank in a water-treatment plant.

☐ 17.13 Other forms of amorphous carbon

Finely divided particles of carbon are set free when liquid or gaseous fuels composed of carbon and hydrogen are burned in an insufficient supply of air. These particles are commonly called *soot*. Soot is an example of the form of amorphous carbon called *carbon black*. Commercially, the production of carbon black involves making soot under carefully controlled conditions.

The most important method of making carbon black is called the *furnace process*. The furnace is made of materials that have high melting points, such as fire brick. In making carbon black, three materials are introduced into the furnace:

1. A spray of liquid fuel or the gaseous fuel vapor.
2. An additional fuel, such as petroleum-refinery gas, which is the fuel gas produced when petroleum is refined.
3. Air, as a source of oxygen.

The supply of oxygen is so low that the fuels are only partially burned in the furnace. But enough fuel burns to provide the energy needed for decomposing the rest of the fuel. The carbon black is collected from the combustion products.

Over 90% of all carbon black produced is used in natural and synthetic rubber. It adds bulk to the rubber and acts as a reinforcing agent. Most of this rubber is used in tires. Carbon black helps to preserve the rubber and makes the tire wear longer. The second largest use of carbon black is in printer's ink. Other uses are in paints, phonograph records, carbon paper, and in coloring plastics and synthetic fibers.

An oil residue remains after the refining of crude petroleum. When destructively distilled, this residue produces a form of amorphous carbon called *petroleum coke*. Rods of petroleum coke are converted to synthetic graphite for use as electrodes. Such electrodes are used as the positive electrodes in dry cells. They also are used in the production of aluminum by electrolysis.

CARBON DIOXIDE

☐ 17.14 Occurrence

Carbon dioxide comprises only about 0.03% of the earth's atmosphere by volume. But it is a very important component of the air. The water of rivers, lakes, and oceans contains about 60 times as much dissolved carbon dioxide as the atmosphere. Both the decay of organic matter and the burning of fossil fuels produce carbon dioxide. So do the respiration processes of living things.

The amount of carbon dioxide in the earth's atmosphere is slowly increasing. It is believed this increase is produced by the burning of carbon-containing fuels and the destruction of forests throughout the world. An increase in the amount of carbon dioxide in the atmosphere enables more of the sun's heat to be held by the earth. This increased heat absorption could eventually raise the average earth temperature enough to change local conditions for growing crops and cause the polar ice caps to melt and the ocean levels to rise.

Carbon dioxide is somewhat denser than air. It sometimes gathers in relatively large amounts in low-lying areas such as bogs, swamps, and marshes. It may also collect in mines, caves, and caverns. Some natural gases contain significant amounts of carbon dioxide.

The atmosphere of the planet Venus is 97% carbon dioxide by volume, with an atmospheric pressure 90 times that on the earth. On Mars, carbon dioxide is also the most abundant component of the atmosphere. It is 95% by volume of the Martian atmosphere. But the atmospheric pressure on Mars is only about $\frac{1}{135}$ of that on the earth.

☐ 17.15 Preparation of carbon dioxide

1. By burning material that contains the element carbon. Carbon dioxide is one of the products of the complete combustion in oxygen or air of any material that contains carbon. If air is used, the carbon dioxide prepared in this way is mixed with other gases. But if these gases do not interfere with the intended use of the carbon dioxide, this method is by far the cheapest and easiest.

$$C \text{ (combined)} + O_2 \rightarrow CO_2$$

2. *By reaction of steam and natural gas.* Natural gas is usually a mixture of several gaseous compounds of carbon and hydrogen. The principal component of natural gas is methane, CH_4. Methane undergoes a series of reactions with steam in the presence of metallic oxide catalysts at temperatures between 500 °C and 1000 °C. The end products of these reactions are carbon dioxide and hydrogen. The equation for the overall reaction is

$$CH_4 + 2H_2O \rightarrow 4H_2 + CO_2$$

The primary purpose of this reaction is the preparation of hydrogen for making synthetic ammonia. The carbon dioxide is a by-product. The carbon dioxide is separated from the hydrogen by dissolving the carbon dioxide in cold water under high pressure.

3. *By fermentation of molasses.* The enzymes of *zymase* are produced by yeast. They catalyze the fermentation of the sugar, $C_6H_{12}O_6$, in molasses. This fermentation produces ethanol (ethyl alcohol) and carbon dioxide. While the process is complex, the overall reaction is

$$C_6H_{12}O_6\,(aq) \rightarrow 2C_2H_5OH(aq) + 2CO_2\,(g)$$

This equation represents a method by which some industrial alcohol is produced. The process is also an important source of carbon dioxide.

4. *By heating a carbonate.* When calcium carbonate (as limestone, marble, or shells) is heated strongly, calcium oxide and carbon dioxide are the products.

$$CaCO_3 \rightarrow CaO + CO_2$$

Calcium oxide, known as *quicklime,* is used for making plaster and mortar. The carbon dioxide is a by-product.

5. *By the action of an acid on a carbonate.* This is the usual laboratory method of preparing carbon dioxide. The gas-generating bottle in Figure 17-11 contains a few pieces of marble, $CaCO_3$. If dilute hydrochloric acid is poured through the funnel tube, carbon dioxide is given off rapidly. Calcium chloride may be recovered from the solution in the bottle.

This reaction proceeds in two stages. *First,* the marble and hydrochloric acid undergo an exchange reaction:

$$CaCO_3\,(s) + 2HCl(aq) \rightarrow CaCl_2\,(aq) + H_2CO_3\,(aq)$$

Second, carbonic acid is unstable and decomposes:

$$H_2CO_3\,(aq) \rightarrow H_2O(l) + CO_2\,(g)$$

Figure 17-11. Carbon dioxide is prepared in the laboratory by the reaction of dilute hydrochloric acid on marble chips, calcium carbonate. Carbon dioxide is collected by water displacement.

The equation that summarizes these two reactions is

$$CaCO_3(s) + 2HCl(aq) \rightarrow CaCl_2(aq) + H_2O(l) + CO_2(g)$$

Even though carbon dioxide is soluble in water, it may be collected by water displacement if it is generated rapidly. It may also be collected by displacement of air. In this case, the receiver must be kept *mouth upward* because carbon dioxide is denser than air.

This reaction is an example of the general reaction of an acid and a carbonate. Almost any acid may be used, even a weak one such as the acetic acid in vinegar. Almost any carbonate may also be used, provided its cation does not have an interfering reaction with the anion of the acid. The ionic equation for the reaction is

$$CO_3{}^{--} + 2H_3O^+ \rightarrow 3H_2O + CO_2(g)$$

6. *By respiration and decay.* This process is a natural method of preparing carbon dioxide. The foods you eat contain compounds of carbon. Oxygen from the air you inhale is used in oxidizing this food. This oxidation supplies energy to maintain body temperature, move muscles, synthesize new compounds in the body, and transmit nerve impulses. Carbon dioxide, which you exhale into the air, is one of the products of this oxidation. All living things give off carbon dioxide during respiration.

When plants and animals die, decay begins and carbon dioxide is produced. This gas eventually finds its way into the surrounding air, or becomes dissolved in surface or underground streams.

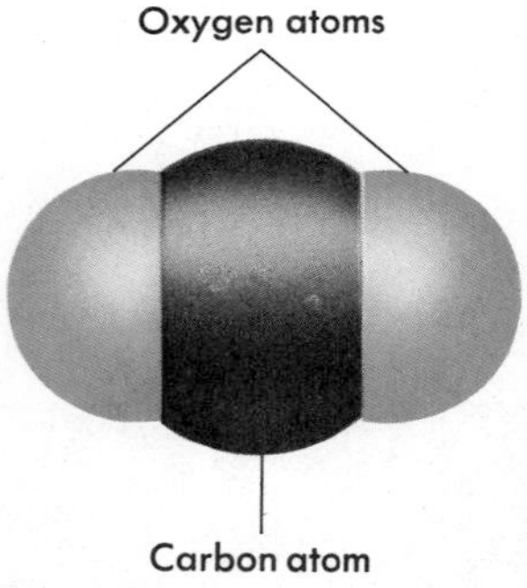

☐ 17.16 Structure of carbon dioxide molecules

Carbon dioxide molecules are linear, with the two oxygen atoms bonded on opposite sides of the carbon atom. See Figure 17-12. The carbon-oxygen bonds in the molecule are somewhat polar. This polarity is explained by the electronegativity difference between carbon and oxygen. However, the arrangement of these bonds, exactly opposite one another, causes the molecule to be nonpolar.

Considering the electron-dot symbols for carbon and oxygen, carbon dioxide molecules might be assigned the electron-dot formula

$$\overset{..}{\underset{..}{:}}O::C::\overset{..}{\underset{..}{O}}:$$

However, this formula is not strictly accurate. The carbon-oxygen bond distance predicted by it is larger than that actually found in carbon dioxide molecules. Carbon dioxide molecules are believed to be *resonance hybrids of four electron-dot structures.* Each of these structures, which are shown at the left, contributes about equally to the actual structure. Such a resonance hybrid has the carbon-oxygen bond distance and energy that are actually observed for carbon dioxide molecules.

Oxygen atoms

Carbon atom

Figure 17-12. A carbon dioxide molecule is linear and consists of one carbon atom and two oxygen atoms.

$$\left\{ \begin{array}{ll} :\overset{..}{\underset{..}{O}}::C::\overset{..}{\underset{..}{O}}: & {}^-:\overset{..}{\underset{..}{O}}:C:::O:{}^+ \\[2em] :\overset{..}{\underset{..}{O}}::C::\overset{..}{\underset{..}{O}}: & {}^+:O:::C:\overset{..}{\underset{..}{O}}:{}^- \end{array} \right\}$$

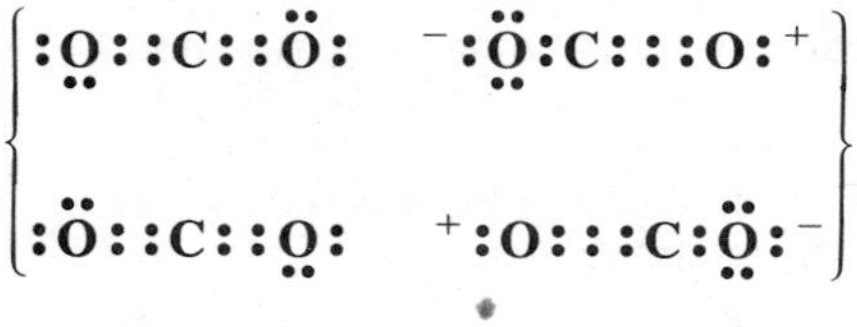

☐ 17.17 Physical properties of carbon dioxide

Carbon dioxide is a gas at room temperature. This fact supports the theory that it has a simple, nonpolar molecular structure. Carbon dioxide is colorless with a faintly irritating odor and a slightly sour taste. The molecular weight of carbon dioxide is 44. Thus, its density is about 1.5 times that of air at the same temperature and pressure. The large, heavy molecules of carbon dioxide gas move more slowly than the smaller, lighter molecules of gaseous oxygen or hydrogen. Because of its high density and slow rate of diffusion, carbon dioxide can be poured from one vessel to another.

At high pressures, the molecules of a gas are much closer together than they are at a pressure of one atmosphere. At room temperature and a pressure of about 70 atmospheres, molecules of carbon dioxide attract each other strongly enough to condense to a liquid. If this liquid is permitted to evaporate rapidly under atmospheric pressure, part of it changes into a gas. This process absorbs heat from the remaining liquid, which is thus cooled until it solidifies in the form called *Dry Ice*.

Solid carbon dioxide has a high vapor pressure. Many molecules of solid carbon dioxide possess enough energy to escape from the surface of the solid into the air. The vapor pressure of solid carbon dioxide equals atmospheric pressure at −78.5 °C. As a result, solid carbon dioxide under atmospheric pressure sublimes (changes directly from a solid to a gas) at this temperature. Liquid carbon dioxide does not exist at atmospheric pressure. It can exist only at low temperatures with pressures higher than 5 atmospheres.

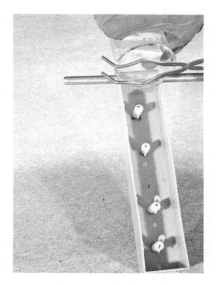

Figure 17-13. Carbon dioxide can be poured down this stair of candles because of its high density and slow rate of diffusion. The candles are extinguished because carbon dioxide does not support combustion.

Carbon dioxide has a critical temperature of 31.0 °C and a critical pressure of 72.8 atm (Section 12.7). The liquid carbon dioxide in a fire extinguisher is under a pressure of 60 atm.

☐ 17.18 Chemical properties of carbon dioxide

Carbon dioxide is a stable gas. It neither burns nor supports combustion. However, burning magnesium is hot enough to decompose carbon dioxide. A piece of burning magnesium ribbon continues to burn in a bottle of the gas. The magnesium unites vigorously with the oxygen set free by the decomposition. Carbon is produced, as shown by a coating of soot on the inside of the bottle.

$$2Mg(s) + CO_2(g) \rightarrow 2MgO(s) + C(s)$$

Carbon dioxide dissolves readily in cold water. A few of the dissolved molecules also unite with the water to form carbonic acid. Carbon dioxide is therefore the acid anhydride of carbonic acid.

$$H_2O + CO_2 \rightleftharpoons H_2CO_3$$

An acid anhydride is the compound formed by removal of water from an acid.

Almost all of the H_2CO_3 molecules ionize. Carbonic acid exists in water solution principally as ions.

$$H_2O + H_2CO_3 \rightleftharpoons H_3O^+ + HCO_3^-$$

$$H_2O + HCO_3^- \rightleftharpoons H_3O^+ + CO_3^{--}$$

Carbonic acid is a weak acid because of the slight reaction between CO_2 and H_2O, even though the few H_2CO_3 molecules formed ionize extensively. Carbonic acid is easily decomposed by heat since CO_2 is less soluble at higher temperatures. The reduction of the concentration of CO_2 in the water causes all the equilibria to shift to the left. This shift further decreases the H_2CO_3 and H_3O^+ concentrations.

When carbon dioxide is passed into a water solution of a hydroxide, it reacts to form a carbonate.

$$CO_2 + 2OH^- \rightarrow CO_3^{--} + H_2O$$

If the positive ion of the hydroxide forms an insoluble carbonate, it is precipitated when carbon dioxide passes through the hydroxide solution.

A *test for carbon dioxide* is to bubble the gas through a saturated solution of $Ca(OH)_2$, called limewater. A precipitate of white calcium carbonate indicates the presence of carbon dioxide.

$$Ca^{++} + 2OH^- + CO_2 \rightarrow Ca^{++}CO_3^{--}(s) + H_2O$$

If excess carbon dioxide gas is bubbled through the solution, the precipitate disappears. It does so because the excess carbon dioxide reacts with the precipitate and water to form soluble calcium hydrogen carbonate.

$$Ca^{++}CO_3^{--} + H_2O + CO_2 \rightarrow Ca^{++} + 2HCO_3^-$$

As stated earlier (Section 17.14), normal air contains about 0.03% carbon dioxide by volume. The air in a crowded, poorly ventilated room may contain as much as 1% carbon dioxide by volume. A concentration of from about 0.1% to 1% brings on a feeling of drowsiness and a headache. Concentrations of 8% to 10% or more cause death from lack of oxygen.

☐ 17.19 Uses of carbon dioxide

1. It is necessary for photosynthesis. **Photosynthesis means** *"putting together by means of light."* It is a complex process by which green plants manufacture carbohydrates with the aid of sunlight. *Chlorophyll,* the green coloring matter of plants, acts as a catalyst. Carbon dioxide from the air and water from the soil are the raw materials. Glucose, a simple sugar, $C_6H_{12}O_6$, is one of the products. The following simplified equation gives only the *reactants* and the *final products.*

$$6CO_2 + 12H_2O \rightarrow C_6H_{12}O_6 + 6O_2 + 6H_2O$$

The sugar may then be converted into a great variety of other plant products. The oxygen is given off to the atmosphere. Photosynthesis and the various other natural and artificial methods of producing atmospheric carbon dioxide comprise the *oxygen–carbon dioxide cycle.*

2. Carbon dioxide is used as a refrigerant. The most important commercial use of carbon dioxide is as a refrigerant for producing and storing frozen foods. Carbon dioxide vapor can be liquefied and carbon dioxide liquid can be made to evaporate at the required low temperatures (below −20 °C) by simply changing the pressure. These properties, coupled with the chemical stability of carbon dioxide, make it a good refrigerant for large installations in food and industrial plants. Nearly half of the carbon dioxide used commercially is used for refrigeration.

A small amount of solid carbon dioxide, Dry Ice, is used as a refrigerant. It is convenient because it has a very low temperature and sublimes at atmospheric pressure. The temperature of Dry Ice is so low that it *must never be handled with bare hands* because serious frostbite can result.

3. Carbonated beverages contain carbon dioxide in solution. Soft drinks are carbonated by forcing the gas into the beverages under pressure. When the bottles are opened, the excess pressure is released. Bubbles of carbon dioxide then escape rapidly from the liquid. The carbonation of beverages accounts for one-fourth of the commercial use of carbon dioxide.

4. Leavening agents produce carbon dioxide. Yeast is a common leavening agent. It is mixed with the flour and other ingredients used in making dough for bread. The living yeast plants produce enzymes that ferment the starches and sugars in the dough. This fermentation reaction produces ethanol and carbon dioxide. The carbon dioxide forms bubbles in the soft dough, causing it to "rise," or decrease in density. The ethanol is vaporized and driven off during the baking process.

Baking powder differs from baking soda. Baking soda is the compound sodium hydrogen carbonate. Baking powder is not a compound, but a dry *mixture* of compounds. It contains baking soda, which can yield the carbon dioxide. It also contains some powder that forms an acid when water is added. The acid compound varies with the kind of baking powder used. Cornstarch is used in baking powders to keep them dry until they are used.

5. Carbon dioxide is used in fire extinguishers. When the *soda-acid type* of fire extinguisher is inverted, sulfuric acid reacts with sodium hydrogen carbonate solution.

$$2NaHCO_3(aq) + H_2SO_4(aq) \rightarrow Na_2SO_4(aq) + 2H_2O(l) + 2CO_2(g)$$

The pressure of the gas forces a stream of liquid a considerable distance. The carbon dioxide dissolved in the liquid helps put out the fire, but water is the main extinguishing agent.

Liquid carbon dioxide fire extinguishers are very efficient and widely used. When the valve is opened, the nozzle directs a stream of carbon dioxide "snow" against the flame. Such an extinguisher is effective against oil fires. It may also be used around electric switchboards where water would be hazardous.

Figure 17-14. The carbonation of beverages is an important use of carbon dioxide.

Sodium hydrogen carbonate is commonly called baking soda. This is the origin of the word soda *in the expression "soda-acid fire extinguisher."*

Figure 17-15. A liquid carbon dioxide fire extinguisher is effective in putting out oil fires. It cools the burning material and shuts off the supply of oxygen from the atmosphere needed for combustion.

CARBON MONOXIDE

❏ 17.20 The occurrence of carbon monoxide

Carbon monoxide is found in samples of the atmosphere all over the world. The amounts vary from 0.04 ppm over the South Pacific Ocean to 360 ppm at street level in a crowded city on a calm day. (Ppm means parts per million. 1 ppm = 0.0001%.) A safe amount of carbon monoxide is somewhat under 50 ppm.

In congested areas, the carbon monoxide in the air comes mainly from incompletely burned fuels. The sources range from the chimney gases of improperly fired coal-burning furnaces to the exhaust gases from automobile engines. In the United States, as much as 90% of the people-caused carbon monoxide in the air may come from gasoline engines. Decaying plants and live algae add significant amounts of carbon monoxide to the air. It has been estimated that the oceans may release up to 85% as much carbon monoxide to the air as incompletely burned fuels do.

Specialists estimate that the carbon monoxide produced on a given day remains in the air for about one to three months. Research is being carried out to determine what happens to carbon monoxide in the air, since no worldwide increase in its concentration has yet been detected. One explanation under study is that certain soil fungi convert carbon monoxide in the air to carbon dioxide. Another possible explanation is that carbon monoxide reacts with OH groups in the lower stratosphere to form carbon dioxide and hydrogen.

Traces of carbon monoxide have been found in the atmospheres of Venus, Mars, and Jupiter. Carbon monoxide is widespread in the interstellar gas clouds of our galaxy, especially in regions where stars are being formed. Carbon monoxide has also been detected in galaxies besides our own.

❏ 17.21 Preparation of carbon monoxide

1. By reducing carbon dioxide. If carbon dioxide comes into contact with white-hot carbon or coke, it is reduced to carbon monoxide.

$$CO_2(g) + C(s) \rightarrow 2CO(g)$$

2. By action of steam on hot coke. Passing steam over white-hot coke produces a mixture called *water gas*. This mixture consists mainly of carbon monoxide and hydrogen. This industrial method produces both carbon monoxide and hydrogen for use as fuel gases or as a synthesis gas for making organic compounds.

$$C(s) + H_2O(g) \rightarrow CO(g) + H_2(g)$$

The two gases can be separated by cooling and compression. This process liquefies the carbon monoxide but not the hydrogen. This reaction is fundamental to the production of fuel gases from coal. It may be carried out above ground in reacting vessels or below ground by burning damp seams of coal or lignite in air or oxygen forced down from the surface.

3. By decomposing formic acid. This decomposition reaction is the usual laboratory method for preparing carbon monoxide. Formic acid, HCOOH, is introduced one drop at a time into hot, concentrated sulfuric acid. Carbon monoxide is produced as each drop strikes the hot acid. See Figure 17-16. Concentrated sulfuric acid is an excellent dehydrating agent. It removes a molecule of water from each molecule of formic acid, leaving carbon monoxide, CO.

$$\text{HCOOH(l)} \xrightarrow{\text{H}_2\text{SO}_4} \text{H}_2\text{O(l)} + \text{CO(g)}$$

CAUTION: *When using this method, be sure the connections are tight so that the carbon monoxide does not escape.* It is preferable to prepare carbon monoxide in a hood.

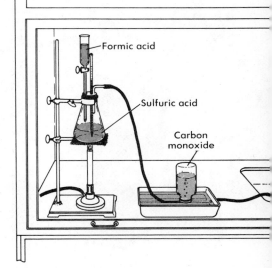

Figure 17-16. Carbon monoxide can be prepared in the laboratory by decomposing formic acid with hot, concentrated sulfuric acid.

☐ 17.22 Structure of the carbon monoxide molecule

Carbon monoxide molecules consist of one carbon atom and one oxygen atom covalently bonded. See Figure 17-17. The distance between the nuclei is 1.13 Å. The molecule is slightly polar, with *the carbon atom somewhat negative*. In order to account for these properties, the carbon monoxide molecule is believed to be a resonance hybrid of the four structures shown at the right. Unlike carbon dioxide, however, these four structures do not contribute equally. The hybrid is estimated to be 10 percent $^+$:C:Ö:$^-$, 20 percent each :C::Ö: and :C::O:, and 50 percent $^-$:C:::O:$^+$. The electronegativity difference discussed in Chapter 6 indicates that the oxygen in carbon monoxide would be negative. However, you must remember that those data apply only to *single* bonds between elements. The structure of carbon monoxide is complicated. Carbon monoxide's stability at ordinary temperatures is explained by the effect of the high percentage of triple-bonded structure. It also gives the carbon atom the slight negative charge in the polar molecule.

$$\left\{ \begin{array}{ll} ^+\text{:C:Ö:}^- & \text{:C::Ö:} \\ \text{:C::O:} & ^-\text{:C:::O:}^+ \end{array} \right\}$$

☐ 17.23 Physical properties of carbon monoxide

Carbon monoxide is a colorless, odorless, tasteless gas. It is slightly less dense than air and only slightly soluble in water. Carbon monoxide has a low critical temperature, −140.23 °C, and a high critical pressure, 34.53 atm (atmospheres). These data indicate that the attractive forces between carbon monoxide molecules are low. Consequently, carbon monoxide is not easily liquefied. Neither is it readily adsorbed by charcoal. However, charcoal can be treated with certain metallic oxides that oxidize carbon monoxide to carbon dioxide. Gas masks containing treated charcoal protect wearers against carbon monoxide con-

Oxygen atom

Carbon atom

Figure 17-17. A carbon monoxide molecule is a slightly polar molecule consisting of one carbon atom and one oxygen atom.

Figure 17-18. A firefighter wearing a self-contained breathing apparatus. This equipment furnishes air from the cylinder worn on the back through a hose to the face mask. With this equipment a firefighter can work safely in an atmosphere containing carbon monoxide.

centrations up to 2%. In atmospheres containing more than 2% carbon monoxide, a self-contained breathing apparatus is needed. This equipment, often used by fire fighters, furnishes air from a cylinder of compressed air to the wearer through a mask.

☐ 17.24 Chemical properties and uses of carbon monoxide

1. As a reducing agent. Carbon monoxide is used in the production of iron, copper, and other metals from their oxides.

$$Fe_2O_3(s) + 3CO(g) \rightarrow 2Fe(s) + 3CO_2(g)$$

2. As a fuel. Carbon monoxide burns with a blue flame. Many fuel gases contain carbon monoxide mixed with other gases that can be burned. Coal gas and water gas always contain some carbon monoxide.

3. For synthesizing organic compounds. Methanol, CH_3OH, is made from carbon monoxide and hydrogen under pressure. A mixture of oxides of copper, zinc, and chromium is used as a catalyst.

$$CO + 2H_2 \rightarrow CH_3OH$$

Carbon monoxide is also used in the synthesis of many other organic compounds.

☐ 17.25 The action of carbon monoxide on the human body

Carbon monoxide is poisonous because it unites very readily with *hemoglobin* molecules. Hemoglobin molecules in red blood cells serve as an oxygen carrier in the body's circulatory system. The attraction of hemoglobin for carbon monoxide is about 300 times greater than for oxygen. If carbon monoxide unites with hemoglobin, the hemoglobin is not available for carrying oxygen. When this happens, cells that need a lot of oxygen function less efficiently. Such cells are found in the heart, the skeletal muscles, and the central nervous system. Low levels of carbon monoxide thus impair a person's vision and reflexes. When persons breathe a large enough amount of carbon monoxide, they collapse because of oxygen starvation.

As stated earlier, Section 17.20, the safe level of carbon monoxide in the air is less than 50 ppm (parts per million). A person breathing air with as little as one part of carbon monoxide per thousand parts of air (1000 ppm) experiences nausea and headache in less than one hour. One part of carbon monoxide in one hundred parts of air (10,000 ppm) may prove fatal in as little as ten minutes.

To repeat: Carbon monoxide is colorless, odorless, tasteless, and induces drowsiness before actual collapse and death. Therefore, *extreme care must be taken to see that it does not contaminate the air in closed areas.* If a coal-burning furnace is not properly operated, carbon monoxide may escape and mix with the air in living or sleeping rooms. An unvented gas heater (one without a chimney to the outside) is also a potential source of carbon monoxide in a home. Carbon monoxide is a component of some fuel gases. Leaking gas lines are dangerous because of the poisonous nature of the gas as well as the fire hazard. Carbon monoxide is present in the exhaust of internal combustion engines. Therefore, the engine of an automobile should never be left running in a closed garage. Similarly, an automobile should not be kept running to provide heat in a car parked with the windows closed. The smoke from burning tobacco contains up to 200 ppm of carbon monoxide. The blood of those who smoke contains several times the amount of hemoglobin-carbon monoxide found in the blood of nonsmokers.

SUMMARY

In combined form, carbon occurs in all living things. Foods, fuels, and carbonates contain combined carbon. In addition, hundreds of thousands of carbon compounds have been synthesized. Organic chemistry is the study of carbon compounds.

A carbon atom, with four valence electrons, forms covalent bonds with atoms of other elements or with other carbon atoms. Carbon atoms can link together in chains, rings, plates, and networks. The variety of ways in which carbon atoms can be linked accounts for the tremendous number of carbon compounds.

Uncombined carbon occurs in the crystalline allotropic forms, graphite and diamond. Amorphous carbon includes coke, charcoal, boneblack, carbon black, and petroleum coke. The forms of amorphous carbon seem to have no definite shape, but contain regions in which the carbon atoms are arranged in an orderly way.

Diamond is the hardest substance known. Diamonds are used as gems, and for cutting, drilling, and grinding very hard substances. Graphite is a soft solid that is a conductor of electricity. It is used in metallurgy, in electrodes, as a lubricant, and for making "lead" pencils.

Coal is a solid, rocklike material that burns readily. It was formed from buried vegetation by decomposition under heat and pressure. Peat, lignite, subbituminous coal, bituminous coal, and anthracite are successive stages in coal formation. Coal is our most plentiful source of energy.

Coke, charcoal, and boneblack are prepared by the destructive distillation of coal, wood, and bones, respectively. Coke is used as a metallurgical reducing agent, while charcoal and boneblack are excellent adsorbents.

Activated carbon is a form of carbon having a very large internal surface area. The large surface area makes activated carbon useful for the adsorption of liquids and gases. It is used as a deodorizer, a decolorizer, and in gas masks.

Carbon black is produced by the incomplete combustion of fuels composed of carbon and hydrogen. It is used in automobile tires, printer's ink, paints, and plastics. Petroleum coke is used to make synthetic graphite electrodes.

At ordinary temperatures all forms of carbon are inactive, but at higher temperatures they react with oxygen to form carbon dioxide.

Carbon dioxide is present in the air, although only in small amounts, as a result of decay, combustion, and the respiration of living things. The amount of carbon dioxide in the air is slowly increasing and may ultimately affect climatic conditions. Carbon dioxide can be prepared by burning carbon or its compounds, by reacting steam and natural gas, by fermenting molasses, by heating a carbonate, by the action of an acid on a carbonate, and by respiration and decay.

Carbon dioxide is a dense, colorless gas that is moderately soluble in water. Its water solution is carbonic acid. Carbon dioxide does not burn or support combustion.

Carbon dioxide is used by plants during photosynthesis, as a refrigerant, in carbonated beverages, as a leavening agent, and in fire extinguishers.

Carbon monoxide can be prepared by reducing carbon dioxide, by the action of steam on hot coke, and by decomposing formic acid. Carbon monoxide is a colorless, odorless, tasteless gas that is exceedingly poisonous. It burns with a blue flame.

Carbon monoxide is used as a reducing agent in the production of iron, copper, and other metals from their ores. It is also a fuel. Large quantities of carbon monoxide are used for synthesizing organic compounds.

The exhaust gases from internal combustion engines always contain some carbon monoxide. So does tobacco smoke. Carbon monoxide unites with the hemoglobin of the blood and reduces the blood's oxygen-carrying capacity. The presence of small amounts of carbon monoxide in the blood impairs the function of body cells. In large amounts, it can cause death by oxygen starvation.

 VOCABULARY

amorphous carbon	charcoal	diamond	lignite
anthracite	chlorophyll	Dry Ice	organic chemistry
bituminous coal	coal	fermentation	peat
boneblack	coke	graphite	photosynthesis
carbon black	destructive distillation	leavening agent	subbituminous coal

QUESTIONS

Group A

1. (a) Why is the study of carbon compounds a separate branch of chemistry? (b) What is this branch of chemistry called?
2. What is the orientation of the four covalent bonds of a carbon atom in sp^3 hybridization?
3. What property of carbon atoms makes possible the large number of carbon compounds?
4. (a) What is *allotropy*? (b) What are the allotropic forms of carbon? (c) Why is amorphous carbon not considered to be a third allotropic form of carbon?
5. Why are diamonds useful in industry?
6. Explain why diamond is an excellent conductor of heat but a nonconductor of electricity.
7. Graphite is soft, yet carbon fibers in which the carbon is in the form of graphite are very strong. Explain.
8. Using valence-bond structures for graphite layers, show how the structure of graphite illustrates resonance.
9. Give several reasons why graphite is used as a lubricant.
10. (a) What is coal? (b) How do geologists believe coal was formed?
11. (a) In what sequence were the various types of coal probably formed? (b) What probably accounts for this sequence?
12. (a) What is *destructive distillation?* (b) Is it really destructive? Explain.
13. Why does a form of carbon such as charcoal or coke remain after the destructive distillation of bituminous coal or wood?
14. What is *adsorption?*
15. Why is boneblack a relatively impure form of carbon?
16. What physical characteristic of activated carbon makes it a useful adsorbent?

17. What are the two successive steps in the preparation of activated carbon?
18. What is the most important use of carbon black?
19. What use is made of petroleum coke?
20. Why is carbon dioxide an important component of the atmosphere even though it occurs to only 0.03% by volume?
21. (a) What change is occurring in the amount of carbon dioxide in the earth's atmosphere? (b) What are the probable causes?
22. What is the probable effect on the earth's climate of the change in the amount of carbon dioxide in the atmosphere?
23. (a) Name the four commercial methods for preparing carbon dioxide. (b) What is the usual laboratory method? (c) Write balanced chemical equations for these methods.
24. What is the function of an enzyme?
25. What difficulties are experienced when collecting carbon dioxide (a) by water displacement; (b) by air displacement?
26. What are the chemical properties of carbon dioxide?
27. (a) How is carbonic acid produced? (b) Is it a strong or a weak acid? Explain.
28. What is the test for carbon dioxide?
29. What are the two parts of the oxygen-carbon dioxide cycle?
30. (a) What is the source of carbon dioxide in most leavening agents? (b) How is it released?
31. (a) Write a balanced formula equation for the reaction that occurs in the discharging of a soda-acid fire extinguisher. (b) Write the ionic and net ionic equations.
32. How does a liquid carbon-dioxide fire extinguisher put out fires?
33. What are the sources of carbon monoxide contamination in the atmosphere?
34. What is the function of sulfuric acid in the preparation of carbon monoxide from formic acid?
35. By comparing their molecular weights, arrange oxygen, hydrogen, carbon dioxide, and carbon monoxide in order of increasing density.
36. What are three uses of carbon monoxide?

Group B

37. Explain why carbon atoms usually do not form ionic bonds with other elements.
38. Show how the carbon atom illustrates hybridization in the formation of sp^3 orbitals.
39. (a) What are the two reasons for allotropy? (b) Which of these reasons is illustrated by the allotropic forms of carbon?
40. What proof is there that diamond is pure carbon?
41. Diamond is very hard and is a nonconductor of electricity. Graphite is soft and is a conductor of electricity. Diamond is more dense than graphite. Both withstand very high temperatures without melting. Explain how these properties are related to the similarities and differences in the structures of diamond and graphite.
42. (a) What uses does natural graphite find in metallurgy? (b) What property of graphite makes these uses possible?
43. (a) What is the most important use for synthetic graphite? (b) What property of graphite makes this use possible?
44. As coal formation progresses from peat to anthracite, what variation occurs in (a) moisture content; (b) carbon content; (c) oxygen content; (d) heat content?
45. When coke is used as a reducing agent, what is oxidized?
46. Powdered charcoal, copper(II) oxide, and manganese dioxide are all black substances. How could you identify each?
47. For what purposes might activated carbon be used in a large dry-cleaning plant?
48. (a) What materials are used in producing carbon black? (b) What is their function?
49. Why is it so difficult to remove stains made by printer's ink?
50. Write a net ionic equation for the reaction between calcium carbonate and hydrochloric acid that produces carbon dioxide.
51. Write a net ionic equation for the reaction between sodium carbonate and sulfuric acid.
52. What property of a solid determines whether it will sublime or melt when heated?
53. Does magnesium ribbon actually burn in carbon dioxide? Explain.

54. Show by means of ionic equations that the reaction between carbon dioxide and aqueous sodium hydroxide may be considered a hydronium ion-hydroxide ion neutralization reaction.

55. Show by means of ionic equations that the reaction that serves as a test for carbon dioxide may be considered a neutralization reaction combined with a precipitation.

56. When a bottle of limewater is left unstoppered, a white ring is formed on the inside at the surface of the liquid. Explain its cause, and tell how it can be removed.

57. The usefulness of carbon dioxide as a refrigerant depends on what (a) physical property; (b) chemical property?

58. Distinguish between baking soda and baking powder.

59. The reaction for the preparation of water gas is endothermic. Applying Le Chatelier's principle, what temperature and pressure conditions would favor the forward reaction?

60. Explain why carbon dioxide molecules are nonpolar while carbon monoxide molecules are polar.

61. Why are both carbon dioxide and carbon monoxide gases at room temperature when water, with a lower molecular weight, exists as a liquid?

62. Both carbon dioxide and carbon monoxide will produce asphyxiation. Explain the difference in their action on the body.

PROBLEMS

Group A

1. What is the percentage composition of formic acid, HCOOH?

2. (a) How many moles of iron(III) oxide can be reduced by the carbon in 2.00 moles of carbon monoxide, according to the equation: $Fe_2O_3 + 3CO \rightarrow 2Fe + 3CO_2$? (b) How many moles of iron are produced? (c) How many moles of carbon dioxide are produced?

3. How many grams of carbon monoxide are needed to react with 12.2 g of zinc oxide to produce elemental zinc? $ZnO + CO \rightarrow Zn + CO_2$

4. In Problem 3, (a) how many grams of zinc are produced? (b) What is the volume in liters at STP of the carbon dioxide produced?

5. How many grams of H_2SO_4 are required for the reaction with 1.00 kg of sodium hydrogen carbonate in a soda-acid fire extinguisher? $2NaHCO_3 + H_2SO_4 \rightarrow Na_2SO_4 + 2H_2O + 2CO_2$

6. Calculate the number of liters of carbon dioxide at STP given off during the discharge of the fire extinguisher of Problem 5.

Group B

7. How many grams of carbon monoxide can be obtained by the dehydration of $23\overline{0}$ g of formic acid by sulfuric acid?

8. How many liters of dry carbon monoxide are produced in Problem 7 if the temperature is 27 °C and the pressure is $75\overline{0}$ mm?

9. How many liters of carbon dioxide result from the combustion of carbon monoxide in Problem 8 if the product is restored to 27 °C and $75\overline{0}$ mm pressure?

10. How many grams of calcium carbonate are needed to prepare 2.50 L of dry carbon dioxide at 17 °C and $74\overline{0}$ mm pressure by the reaction between calcium carbonate and hydrochloric acid?

11. How many milliliters of concentrated hydrochloric acid must be diluted with water to provide the HCl needed for the reaction of Problem 10? Concentrated hydrochloric acid is 38.0% HCl by weight and has a density of 1.20 g/mL.

12. A gaseous compound contains 52.9% carbon and 47.1% oxygen. One volume of this gas reacts with two volumes of oxygen and yields three volumes of carbon dioxide. Knowing that oxygen molecules are diatomic, determine the molecular formula of this compound.

Hydrocarbons

Organic chemistry is the study of compounds of carbon. Why should this single element have a separate branch of chemistry devoted to its study? The carbon atom is unique. It can link together with other carbon atoms by forming single, double, or triple covalent bonds. Carbon atoms can bond together to form long straight or branched chains, rings, plates, and networks. Depending on the number and arrangement of atoms involved, each molecule thus formed constitutes a unique compound of carbon. Thus the number of possible carbon compounds seems to be limitless. Carbon is the element that forms the complex and infinitely large molecules characteristic of living matter. It is no wonder that carbon should be the basis of the chemistry of life. With their understanding of carbon's unique properties, chemists have gone further than nature in building many more carbon compounds. In so doing, they have expanded the science of organic chemistry, once considered the chemistry of living things only, to include all carbon compounds.

☐ 18.1 Abundance of carbon compounds

The number of possible carbon compounds is almost unlimited. Over 3,000,000 are known and about 100,000 new ones are isolated or synthesized each year. Why are there so many carbon compounds and how do they differ from noncarbon compounds? These questions will be answered in this section and in Section 18.4. Then you will learn about natural gas and petroleum, sources of many simple organic compounds. Most of these simple organic compounds are **hydrocarbons,** *compounds composed only of carbon and hydrogen.* You will next find out what specific hydrocarbons occur in natural gas and petroleum, and how these compounds can be changed into other fundamental hydrocarbon compounds. Since the known supply of petroleum in the earth is rapidly being used up, some possible substitutes for petroleum as a source of organic compounds must be considered. In Chapter 19, you will read about a variety of organic compounds derived from hydrocarbons which are important in everyday life.

There are two reasons why there are so many carbon compounds:

1. Carbon atoms link together by means of covalent bonds. In Section 17.2, you learned how carbon atoms readily form covalent bonds with other carbon atoms. This makes possible the existence of molecules in which thousands of carbon atoms are bonded one to another. The molecules of some organic compounds are principally long carbon-atom chains with carbon-atom groups attached. Other carbon-compound molecules have carbon atoms linked together in rings. Still others may consist of several such rings joined together. Not only are carbon atoms

AN INTRODUCTION TO ORGANIC COMPOUNDS

In this chapter you will gain an understanding of:

- **the abundance of carbon compounds**
- **structural formulas for simple organic compounds**
- **isomers**
- **hydrocarbons: structures, sources, and reactions**
- **nature of petroleum and petroleum substitutes**
- **natural and synthetic rubber**

Figure 18-1. The first oil well in the United States was drilled in 1859 near Titusville, Pennsylvania, by Edwin Drake.

linked by single covalent bonds, but they are sometimes linked by double or triple covalent bonds.

2. The same atoms may be arranged in several different ways. One of the substances in petroleum is a hydrocarbon called *octane*. Its molecular formula is C_8H_{18}. A molecule of octane consists of 8 carbon atoms and 18 hydrogen atoms. A carbon atom may form four single covalent bonds while a hydrogen atom forms only one single covalent bond. The straight-chain electron-dot structure for an octane molecule is written like this:

$$H : \overset{\overset{H}{..}}{\underset{\underset{H}{..}}{C}} : \overset{\overset{H}{..}}{\underset{\underset{H}{..}}{C}} : \overset{\overset{H}{..}}{\underset{\underset{H}{..}}{C}} : \overset{\overset{H}{..}}{\underset{\underset{H}{..}}{C}} : \overset{\overset{H}{..}}{\underset{\underset{H}{..}}{C}} : \overset{\overset{H}{..}}{\underset{\underset{H}{..}}{C}} : \overset{\overset{H}{..}}{\underset{\underset{H}{..}}{C}} : \overset{\overset{H}{..}}{\underset{\underset{H}{..}}{C}} : H$$

But there are other ways in which these same atoms can be arranged. For instance, here are three branched-chain formulas:

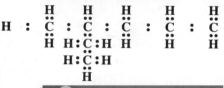

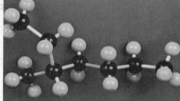

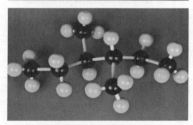

All of these formulas represent arrangements of 8 carbon atoms and 18 hydrogen atoms. Each carbon atom shares four electrons and each hydrogen atom shares one electron. In addition to these four structures for octane, there are 14 others, making a total of 18 possible structures for octane. Each of these 18 structures has the same molecular formula. However, the different arrangements of the atoms in the molecules give each molecule slightly different properties. Thus, each of these molecular arrangements represents a separate chemical compound. *Compounds having the same molecular formula but different structures are called isomers.*

Figure 18-2. Models of the molecules of the four isomers of octane, whose electron-dot structures are given above in the text. Match each model with its electron-dot formula.

◻ 18.2 Structural formulas for organic compounds

The formula H_2SO_4 for sulfuric acid gives enough information for most purposes in inorganic chemistry. But a molecular formula such as C_8H_{18} is not at all satisfactory in organic chemistry. It has already been noted that there are 18 different isomers of this compound. In order to indicate clearly a particular isomer, the organic chemist uses a **structural formula**. *Such a formula not only indicates what kinds of atoms and how many of each but also* *shows how they are arranged in the molecule.* Electron-dot formulas have been used to illustrate the isomers of octane. However, for routine equation work such formulas are tedious to draw. Organic chemists often substitute a dash (—) for the pair of shared electrons forming a covalent bond. Using the dash, the straight-chain structural formula for octane can be represented

$$\begin{array}{c}
\text{H}\ \ \text{H}\ \ \text{H}\ \ \text{H}\ \ \text{H}\ \ \text{H}\ \ \text{H}\ \ \text{H} \\
|\ \ \ |\ \ \ |\ \ \ |\ \ \ |\ \ \ |\ \ \ |\ \ \ | \\
\text{H}-\text{C}-\text{C}-\text{C}-\text{C}-\text{C}-\text{C}-\text{C}-\text{C}-\text{H} \\
|\ \ \ |\ \ \ |\ \ \ |\ \ \ |\ \ \ |\ \ \ |\ \ \ | \\
\text{H}\ \ \text{H}\ \ \text{H}\ \ \text{H}\ \ \text{H}\ \ \text{H}\ \ \text{H}\ \ \text{H}
\end{array}$$

When structural formulas are written, there must be no dangling bonds. Each dash must represent an electron pair that forms the covalent bond linking two atoms.

For practice, on a separate sheet of paper, write the structural formulas for the three branched-chain isomers of octane given in Section 18.1.

☐ 18.3 Determination of an organic structural formula

There are two different organic compounds that consist of carbon, 52.2%, hydrogen, 13.0%, and oxygen, 34.8%. They have the same molecular weight, 46, and thus are isomers. One compound is a colorless liquid that boils at 78 °C. The other is a colorless gas that condenses to a liquid at −25 °C under one atmosphere pressure. Each has its own distinctive odor. How can their structural formulas be determined?

From the percentage composition, you can calculate the empirical formula by the method described in Section 7.12. The empirical formula is C_2H_6O. Since this empirical formula has a formula weight of 46, it must also be the molecular formula of each compound. From what you have already learned about bonding, there are only two ways in which two carbon atoms, six hydrogen atoms, and a single oxygen atom can combine:

$$\begin{array}{cc}
\begin{array}{c}
\text{H}\ \ \text{H} \\
|\ \ \ | \\
\text{H}-\text{C}-\text{C}-\text{O}-\text{H} \\
|\ \ \ | \\
\text{H}\ \ \text{H}
\end{array}
&
\begin{array}{c}
\text{H}\ \ \ \ \ \ \text{H} \\
|\ \ \ \ \ \ \ \ | \\
\text{H}-\text{C}-\text{O}-\text{C}-\text{H} \\
|\ \ \ \ \ \ \ \ | \\
\text{H}\ \ \ \ \ \ \text{H}
\end{array}
\end{array}$$

| Structure A | Structure B |

Now the problem is to match these structures to the two compounds. If each compound is tested for reaction with metallic sodium, only the liquid reacts. In the reaction, hydrogen is given off. The amount of hydrogen given off is equal to one-sixth of the hydrogen that the compound contains. This evidence indicates that in the molecules of the liquid, one of the six hydrogen atoms is bonded differently from the others. Structure *A* is indicated.

Next you discover that the liquid reacts with phosphorus trichloride and gives a product with the molecular formula C_2H_5Cl. In this reaction, chlorine has replaced both a hydro-

$$H-\overset{\overset{\displaystyle H}{|}}{C}-\overset{\overset{\displaystyle H}{|}}{C}-Cl$$

Note that structural formulas

such as $H-\overset{\overset{\displaystyle H}{|}}{\underset{\underset{\displaystyle H}{|}}{C}}-\overset{\overset{\displaystyle H}{|}}{\underset{\underset{\displaystyle Cl}{|}}{C}}-H$ *and*

$H-\overset{\overset{\displaystyle Cl}{|}}{\underset{\underset{\displaystyle H}{|}}{C}}-\overset{\overset{\displaystyle H}{|}}{\underset{\underset{\displaystyle H}{|}}{C}}-H$ *are the same as*

the one given above.

The approximate rule that "like dissolves like" is explained in Section 13.3.

gen atom and an oxygen atom. Only one structural formula for C_2H_5Cl can be written, as shown in the margin at left. You may assume that the chlorine atom occupies the same position as the oxygen and hydrogen atoms that it replaced. Structure *A* is again indicated. You might continue further, because much more evidence can be found to indicate that the liquid does indeed have Structure *A*. This liquid substance is ethanol, or ethyl alcohol. The gaseous substance has the other structural formula and is called dimethyl ether.

Methods similar to those just described can be used to determine the structural formulas of other simple organic compounds. Complicated molecules are generally broken down into simpler molecules. From the structures of these simpler molecules, the structure of the complex molecule can be determined. Sometimes simple molecules of known structure are combined to produce a complex molecule. A comparison of chemical and physical properties of compounds of unknown structure with those of known structure is sometimes helpful.

◻ 18.4 Differences between organic and inorganic compounds

The basic laws of chemistry are the same for organic and inorganic compounds. However, the behavior of organic compounds is somewhat different from that of inorganic compounds. Some of the most important differences are:

1. Most organic compounds do not dissolve in water. The majority of inorganic compounds do dissolve more or less readily in water. Organic compounds generally dissolve in such organic liquids as alcohol, chloroform, ether, carbon disulfide, or carbon tetrachloride.

2. Organic compounds are decomposed by heat more easily than most inorganic compounds. The decomposition (charring) of sugar when it is heated moderately is familiar. Such charring on heating is often a test for organic substances. By contrast, many inorganic compounds, such as common salt (sodium chloride), can be vaporized at a red heat without decomposition.

3. Organic reactions generally proceed at much slower rates. Such reactions often require hours or even days for completion. However, organic reactions in living cells may take place with great speed. Most inorganic reactions occur almost as soon as solutions of the reactants are brought together.

4. Organic reactions are greatly affected by reaction conditions. Many inorganic reactions follow well-known patterns. This makes it possible for you to learn about many inorganic reactions by studying the general types of reactions explained in Chapter 8. There are some general types of organic reactions, too. But changing the temperature, pressure, or the nature of a catalyst can alter the identity of the products formed. The same organic reactants can form different products, depending on reaction conditions.

5. Organic compounds exist as molecules consisting of atoms joined by covalent bonds. Many inorganic compounds have ionic bonds.

CAUTION: *Many organic compounds are **flammable** and **poisonous**. Some organic reactions are rapid and highly exothermic. A student should not perform any experiments with organic compounds without detailed laboratory directions, and then only with adequate ventilation and other safety precautions, and under the supervision of an experienced instructor.*

☐ 18.5 Natural gas and petroleum

Natural gas is a mixture of hydrocarbon gases and vapors found in porous formations in the earth's crust. Natural gas is mostly methane, CH_4. Frequently natural gas occurs with petroleum, or crude oil. Petroleum is a complex mixture of hydrocarbons. This hydrocarbon mixture varies greatly in composition from place to place. The hydrocarbon molecules in petroleum contain from one to more than 50 carbon atoms.

Natural gas and petroleum were probably formed by the decay of plants and animals living millions of years ago. Because of changes in the earth's surface, these plant and animal residues were trapped in rock formations where they slowly decomposed in the absence of atmospheric oxygen.

Natural gas and petroleum are the most common sources of energy. But, more importantly, they are a source of hydrocarbon chemical raw materials that is rapidly being used up. Discoveries of new sources of natural gas and petroleum in the United States are not keeping pace with the amounts being consumed. Estimates of the world petroleum situation indicate that demand will probably exceed available supplies within ten to twenty years.

☐ 18.6 The processing of natural gas

Up to about 97% of natural gas is methane, CH_4. Mixed with the methane are other hydrocarbons whose molecules contain between two and seven carbon atoms. These different hydrocarbons have different boiling points and can be separated on this basis. This method of separation is called *fractional distillation*. The separation of nitrogen from oxygen in liquid air is an example of this method.

The hydrocarbons having 3 or 4 carbon atoms per molecule are sometimes separated and used as "bottled gas" for fuel. The hydrocarbons having 5 to 7 carbon atoms per molecule are liquids at ordinary temperature. Their vapors can be condensed and used as a solvent or in gasoline.

HYDROCARBON SERIES

Figure 18-3. The search for new sources of petroleum continues beneath off-shore waters.

The separation of nitrogen from oxygen in liquid air is described in Section 9.4(5).

Fractional distillation is a method of separating the components of a mixture on the basis of differences in their boiling points.

☐ 18.7 The refining of petroleum

Petroleum is refined by separating crude oil into portions with properties suitable for certain uses. The method used is fractional distillation. No attempt is made to separate the petroleum into individual hydrocarbons. Instead, portions that distill between certain temperature ranges are collected in separate receivers. Table 18-1 summarizes the characteristics of the portions obtained from the fractional distillation of petroleum.

Petroleum refining is carried out in a *pipe still* and a *fractionating tower*. See Figure 18-4. The crude oil is heated to about 370 °C in the pipe still. At this temperature, nearly all the components of the crude oil are vaporized. The hot vapors are then discharged into the fractionating tower at a point near its base. Here, the portions with the highest condensation temperatures condense and are drawn off to collecting vessels. Portions with lower condensation temperatures continue to rise in the tower. As they rise, they are gradually cooled. In this way, the various portions reach their condensation temperatures at different levels. As they condense, the liquids collect in shallow troughs that line the inside of the tower. Pipes lead off the overflow of condensed liquids from the troughs. The gasoline fraction, together with the more volatile portions of the petroleum, passes as a gas from the top of the tower. The gasoline fraction is then liquefied in separate condensers. The uncondensed gases may be piped to the refinery. The liquid and gaseous fractions are subjected to other reactions or processes depending on what products are required.

Table 18-1
SUMMARY OF FRACTIONAL DISTILLATION OF PETROLEUM

Portion	No. of C atoms per molecule	Boiling point range (°C)	Uses
gas	C_1 to C_5	−161–30	fuel; making carbon black, hydrogen, gasoline by alkylation
petroleum ether	C_5 to C_7	20–100	solvent; dry cleaning
gasoline	C_5 to C_{12}	30–200	motor fuel
kerosene	C_{12} to C_{16}	175–275	fuel
fuel oil Diesel oil	C_{15} to C_{18}	250–400	furnace fuel; Diesel engine fuel; cracking
lubricating oils greases petroleum jelly	C_{16}	350	lubrication
paraffin wax	C_{20}	melts 52–57	candles; waterproofing; home canning
pitch tar		residue	road construction
petroleum coke		residue	electrodes

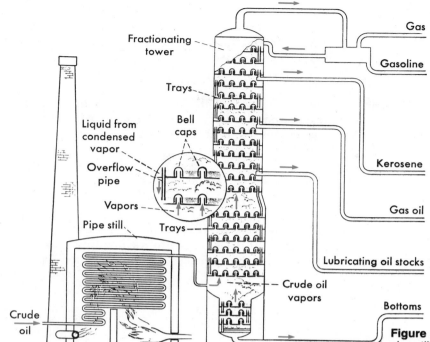

Figure 18-4. A cross section of a pipe still and fractionating tower used in refining petroleum.

☐ 18.8 Classification of hydrocarbons

Compounds composed of only the two elements hydrogen and carbon are called *hydrocarbons*. The hydrocarbons are studied first because they are the basic structures from which other organic compounds are derived. Hydrocarbons are grouped into several different series of compounds. These groupings are based mainly on the type of bonding between carbon atoms.

1. The *alkanes* (al-*kaynes*) are straight-chain or branched-chain hydrocarbons. Their carbon atoms are connected by *single* covalent bonds only:

$$H-\underset{\underset{H}{|}}{\overset{\overset{H}{|}}{C}}-\underset{\underset{H}{|}}{\overset{\overset{H}{|}}{C}}-H$$

Alkanes are the most abundant hydrocarbons in natural gas and petroleum.

2. The *alkenes* (al-*keens*) are straight- or branched-chain hydrocarbons in which two carbon atoms in each molecule are connected by a *double* covalent bond:

$$\underset{H}{\overset{H}{\diagdown}}C=C\underset{H}{\overset{H}{\diagup}}$$

Figure 18-5. A petroleum refinery. The building with the tall chimney is the pipe still. The tower-like structure is a fractionating tower.

3. The *alkynes* (al-*kynes*) are straight- or branched-chain hydrocarbons in which two carbon atoms in each molecule are connected by a *triple* covalent bond:

$$H—C≡C—H$$

4. The *alkadienes* (al-kah-*dy*-eens) are straight- or branched-chain hydrocarbons that have *two double* covalent bonds between carbon atoms in each molecule:

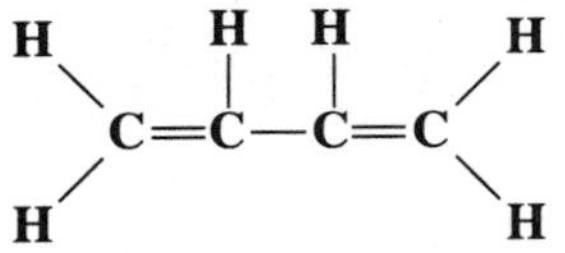

5. The *aromatic hydrocarbons* have resonance structures. These structures are sometimes represented by alternate single and double covalent bonds in six-membered carbon *rings:*

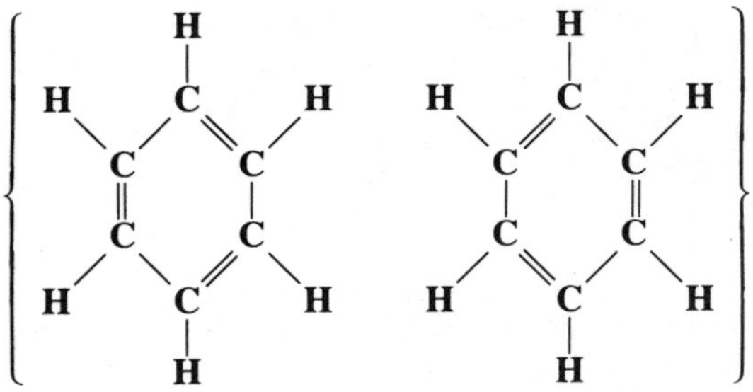

Petroleum from most sources contains some aromatic hydrocarbons. The amount varies from a few percent to as high as 40%.

◘ 18.9 The alkane series

This series of organic compounds is sometimes called the *paraffin series* because paraffin wax is a mixture of hydrocarbons of this series. The word *paraffin* means *little attraction.* Compared to the other hydrocarbon series, the alkanes have low chemical reactivity. This stability results from their single covalent bonds. Because they have only single covalent bonds in each molecule, the alkanes are known as *saturated hydrocarbons.* Saturated bonding occurs when each carbon atom in the molecule forms four single covalent bonds with other atoms.

Table 18-2 lists a few members of the alkane series. The names of the first four members of this series follow no system. However, beginning with pentane, the first part of each name is a Greek or Latin numerical prefix. This prefix indicates the number of carbon atoms. The name of each member ends in *-ane,* the same as the name of the series. The letter prefix "*n*" for "normal" indicates the straight-chain isomer.

If you examine the formulas for successive alkanes, you will

Table 18-2
SOME MEMBERS OF THE ALKANE SERIES

Name	Formula	Melting point (°C)	Boiling point (°C)
methane	CH_4	−182	−161
ethane	C_2H_6	−183	−89
propane	C_3H_8	−190	−44
n-butane	C_4H_{10}	−138	0
2-methylpropane	C_4H_{10}	−160	−12
n-pentane	C_5H_{12}	−130	36
2-methylbutane	C_5H_{12}	−160	28
2,2-dimethylpropane	C_5H_{12}	−20	10
n-hexane	C_6H_{14}	−95	68
n-heptane	C_7H_{16}	−91	98
n-octane	C_8H_{18}	−56	126
n-nonane	C_9H_{20}	−51	151
n-decane	$C_{10}H_{22}$	−30	174
***			
n-eicosane	$C_{20}H_{42}$	37	343
***			
n-hexacontane	$C_{60}H_{122}$	99	

see a clear pattern. Each member of the series differs from the preceding one by the group CH_2,

Compounds that differ in this fashion belong to a *homologous series*. **A homologous series is one in which adjacent members differ by a constant unit.** It is not necessary to remember the formulas for all members of a homologous series. A general formula, such as C_nH_{2n+2} for the alkanes, can be derived. Suppose a member of this series has 30 carbon atoms in its molecules. To find the number of hydrogen atoms, multiply 30 by 2, then add 2. The formula is $C_{30}H_{62}$.

☐ 18.10 Structures of the lower alkanes

Each of the first three alkanes can have only *one* molecular structure. The formulas for these structures are

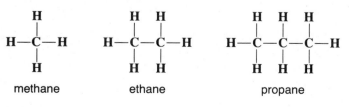

methane   ethane   propane

methane

ethane

propane

Figure 18-6. Models of molecules of the first three members of the alkane series of hydrocarbons.

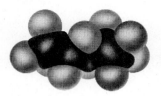

n-butane

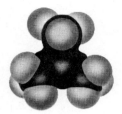

2-methylpropane

Figure 18-7. Models of molecules of the two isomers of butane.

Butane, the alkane with four carbon atoms and ten hydrogen atoms, has *two* isomers. The straight-chain molecule is named *n*-butane (*n* for *normal*). The branched-chain molecule is named 2-methylpropane. Their melting and boiling points are given in Table 18-2.

n-butane

2-methylpropane

The name 2-methylpropane is derived from the structure of the molecule. The longest continuous carbon chain in the molecule is three carbon atoms long, as in propane. One hydrogen atom attached to the second carbon atom in propane is replaced by the CH_3— group. This is a *substitution group*. It is called the *methyl group*. H—C—H is methane with one of the hydrogen atoms removed. The carbon atoms in the main chain of the molecule are numbered. This numbering begins at the end of the molecule that gives the carbon atoms with substitution groups the smallest numbers. Thus in the name **2-methylpropane,** the *2* refers to the number of the carbon atom on which there is a substitution. *Methyl* is the substituting group. *Propane* is the parent hydrocarbon.

There are *three* possible pentanes (C_5H_{12}): *n*-pentane, 2-methylbutane, and 2,2-dimethylpropane. Their melting and boiling points are given in Table 18-2. Their structural formulas are

n-pentane

2-methylbutane

2,2-dimethylpropane

Why is the name **2-methylbutane** used rather than 3-methylbutane?

In the name **2,2-dimethylpropane,** the *2,2* refers to the position of both substitutions. The prefix *dimethyl* shows that the *two* substitutions are both *methyl* groups. *Propane* is the parent hydrocarbon.

Just as the CH_3— group derived from methane is the *methyl* group, C_2H_5— derived from ethane is the *ethyl* group. C_3H_7— derived from propane is the *propyl* group. C_4H_9— derived from butane is the *butyl* group. C_5H_{11}— is usually called the *amyl* group rather than the pentyl group. Other groups are given names following the general rule of dropping the *-ane* suffix and adding *-yl*. Any such group derived from an *alkane* is an *alkyl* group. The symbol **R**— is frequently used to represent an *alkyl* group in a formula.

◻ 18.11 Preparation of the alkanes

Alkanes are generally found in petroleum and natural gas. It is fairly easy to separate the lower members of the alkane series individually from petroleum and natural gas by fractional distillation. However, the alkanes with higher boiling points are usually separated into mixtures with similar boiling points.

Methane is a colorless, nearly odorless gas that forms about 90% of natural gas. Pure methane can be separated from the other components of natural gas. Chemists sometimes prepare small amounts of methane in the laboratory by heating soda lime (which contains sodium hydroxide) with sodium acetate.

$$NaC_2H_3O_2(s) + NaOH(s) \rightarrow CH_4(g) + Na_2CO_3(s)$$

Ethane is a colorless gas that occurs in natural gas and is a product of petroleum refining. It has a higher melting point and boiling point than methane. These properties are related to ethane's higher molecular weight.

Methane and ethane are minor components of the atmosphere of the planet Jupiter. Some gaseous methane is present around Saturn, and it is abundant about Uranus and Neptune. Solid methane has been detected on the surface of Pluto. Methane has also been found in interstellar space.

Figure 18-8. A small quantity of methane can be prepared in the laboratory by heating a mixture of sodium acetate and soda lime. Methane is collected by water displacement.

◻ 18.12 Reactions of the alkanes

1. Combustion. Because the alkanes make up a large proportion of our gaseous and liquid fuels, their most important reaction is combustion. Methane burns with a bluish flame.

$$CH_4 + 2O_2 \rightarrow CO_2 + 2H_2O$$

Ethane and other alkanes also burn in air to form carbon dioxide and water vapor.

$$2C_2H_6 + 7O_2 \rightarrow 4CO_2 + 6H_2O$$

2. Substitution. The alkanes react with halogens such as chlorine or bromine. In such reactions, one or more atoms of a halogen are substituted for one or more atoms of hydrogen. Therefore, the products are called *substitution products*.

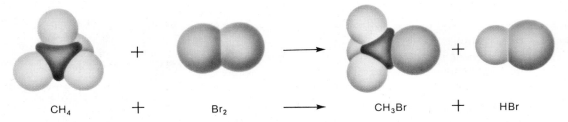

CH_4 + Br_2 ⟶ CH_3Br + HBr

Figure 18-9. Methane and bromine undergo a substitution reaction.

$$H—\overset{\displaystyle H}{\underset{\displaystyle H}{C}}—H + Br_2 \rightarrow H—\overset{\displaystyle H}{\underset{\displaystyle H}{C}}—Br + HBr$$

By supplying additional molecules of the halogen, a halogen atom can be substituted for each of the hydrogen atoms. Carbon tetrachloride, chloroform, and Teflon are examples of halogen-substituted alkanes.

3. Preparation of hydrogen. Propane reacts with steam in the presence of a nickel catalyst at a temperature of about 850 °C.

$$C_3H_8 + 6H_2O \rightarrow 3CO_2 + 10H_2$$

To separate the carbon dioxide from the hydrogen, the carbon dioxide under pressure is dissolved in water.

Compare this reaction with the ones in Sections 9.17(4) and 17.15(2).

◘ 18.13 Alkene series

The alkenes, sometimes called the *olefin series,* are distinguished by a double covalent bond between two carbon atoms. Thus, the simplest alkene must have two carbon atoms. Its structural formula is

$$\overset{\displaystyle H}{\underset{\displaystyle H}{\diagdown}}C{=}C\overset{\displaystyle H}{\underset{\displaystyle H}{\diagup}}$$

Its name is ethene. The name of an alkene comes from the name of the alkane with the same number of carbon atoms. Simply substitute the suffix *-ene* for the suffix *-ane*. Since eth*ane* is the alk*ane* with two carbon atoms, the alk*ene* with two carbon atoms is named eth*ene*. (This substance is also commonly called *ethylene*.) The general formula for the alkenes is C_nH_{2n}.

In 1979, ethene ranked sixth in production behind sulfuric acid, lime, ammonia, oxygen, and nitrogen. The amount produced in the United States was more than 13 million metric tons.

Ethene is the hydrocarbon commercially produced in greatest quantity in the United States. It is also the organic chemical industry's most important starting material.

◘ 18.14 Preparations of alkenes

1. Cracking alkanes. The commercial method of producing alkenes is by *cracking* petroleum. **Cracking is a process by which** *complex organic molecules are broken up into simpler molecules. This process involves the action of heat, or the action of heat and a catalyst.*

Cracking that uses heat alone is known as *thermal cracking*. During cracking, alkanes decompose in several ways that produce a variety of alkenes. A simple example is the thermal cracking of propane, which proceeds in either of two ways in nearly equal proportions.

$$C_3H_8 \xrightarrow{460\,°C} C_3H_6 + H_2$$

$$C_3H_8 \xrightarrow{460\,°C} C_2H_4 + CH_4$$

Alkenes (especially ethene), smaller alkanes, and hydrogen are typical products of the thermal cracking of alkanes. They can be separated, purified, and used as starting materials for making other organic compounds.

The cracking process that involves heat and a catalyst is *catalytic cracking*. The high-boiling fractions from petroleum distillation are catalytically cracked to produce smaller, lower-boiling hydrocarbons useful in gasoline. The catalysts used are mostly oxides of silicon and aluminum. The cracking reactions produce smaller alkanes and alkenes with highly branched structures. Aromatic hydrocarbons are also formed.

2. Dehydration of alcohols. Ethene can be prepared in the laboratory by dehydrating (removing water from) ethyl alcohol. Hot concentrated sulfuric acid is used as the dehydrating agent.

$$C_2H_5OH \xrightarrow[170\,°C]{H_2SO_4} C_2H_4 + H_2O$$

Important reaction conditions are sometimes written near the yields sign.

☐ 18.15 Reactions of alkenes

1. Addition. An organic compound that has one or more double or triple covalent bonds in each molecule is said to be *unsaturated*. It is chemically possible to add other atoms directly to such molecules to form molecules of a new compound. For example, hydrogen atoms can be added to an alkene in the presence of a finely divided nickel catalyst. This reaction produces the corresponding alkane. Breaking the carbon-carbon double bond provides two new bond positions for the hydrogen atoms.

Halogen atoms can be added readily to alkene molecules. For example, two bromine atoms added directly to ethene form 1,2-dibromoethane.

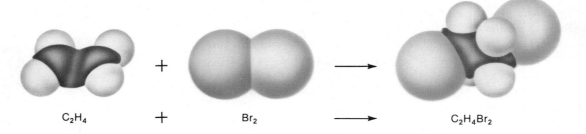

C_2H_4 + Br_2 ⟶ $C_2H_4Br_2$

Figure 18-10. Ethene and bromine undergo an addition reaction.

As the double bond between the carbon atoms breaks, there is one bond position available for each bromine atom.

The name of the product is 1,2-dibromoethane. The basic part of the name, *ethane,* is that of the related alkane with two carbon atoms. *Dibromo-* refers to the two bromine atoms that have been substituted for hydrogen atoms in ethane. *1,2-* means that one bromine atom is bonded to the first carbon atom and the other is bonded to the second carbon atom. An isomer, 1,1-dibromoethane, has the formula

A molecule of a hydrogen halide, such as hydrogen bromide, can be added to an alkene molecule. What is the name of the product?

2. Polymerization. Molecules of ethene join together, or *polymerize,* at about 15 °C and 20 atmospheres pressure in the presence of a catalyst. The resulting large molecules have molecular weights of about 30,000. This polymerized material is called *polyethylene.* It is made up of many single units called *monomers.*

Many monomers join together to make the *polymer* (many units). Polyethylene is used in film for packaging, in electric insulation, in a variety of containers, and in tubing.

3. Alkylation. In alkylation, gaseous alkanes and alkenes are combined. For example, isobutene and isobutane combine in the presence of a sulfuric acid or anhydrous hydrogen fluoride catalyst. The result is a highly branched octane, 2,2,4-trimethylpentane, an important component of gasoline.

4. Combustion. The alkenes burn in oxygen. For example,

$$C_2H_4 + 3O_2 \rightarrow 2CO_2 + 2H_2O$$

◻ 18.16 Alkyne series

The alkynes are distinguished by a triple covalent bond between two carbon atoms. This series is sometimes called the *acetylene series* because the simplest alkyne has the common name *acetylene*. It has two carbon atoms, with the formula

$$H{-}C{\equiv}C{-}H$$

The names of the alk*ynes* are derived from the names of the alk*anes* that have the same number of carbon atoms. The suffix *-yne* is substituted for *-ane*. Hence the chemical name for acetylene, the simplest alkyne, is *ethyne*. The general formula for the alkynes is C_nH_{2n-2}.

Ethyne, C_2H_2, is a minor component of the atmosphere of Jupiter. Ethyne molecules have also been detected in interstellar space.

◻ 18.17 Preparations of ethyne

1. From calcium carbide. Ethyne, a colorless gas, can be prepared by the action of water on calcium carbide, CaC_2. Calcium carbide is made from limestone, $CaCO_3$, in a series of operations. First, the limestone is heated in a kiln (oven). CaO is produced.

$$CaCO_3(s) \rightarrow CaO(s) + CO_2(g)$$

The calcium oxide is then heated with coke at 2000 °C in an electric resistance furnace.

$$CaO(s) + 3C(s) \rightarrow CaC_2(s) + CO(g)$$

Calcium carbide is an ionic compound with the electron-dot structure

$$Ca^{++}$$
$$^-{\overset{x}{\underset{x}{:}}}C{\overset{o}{\underset{o}{:}}}{\overset{o}{\underset{o}{:}}}C{\overset{o}{\underset{x}{:}}}^-$$

When it reacts with water, hydrogen replaces the calcium in the calcium carbide structure. The bonding of hydrogen and carbon in ethyne is covalent.

$$CaC_2(s) + 2H_2O(l) \rightarrow C_2H_2(g) + Ca(OH)_2(aq)$$

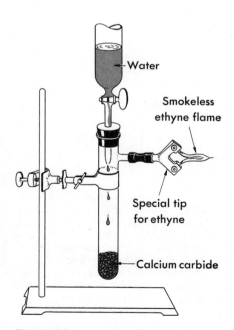

Figure 18-11. A convenient method of preparing a small quantity of ethyne (acetylene) in the laboratory by the action of water on calcium carbide.

The preparation of ethyne from calcium carbide is both a commercial and laboratory method.

2. By partial oxidation of methane. This is an alternate commercial preparation of ethyne. Methane can be partially oxidized under controlled conditions to yield ethyne, carbon monoxide, and hydrogen.

$$6CH_4 + O_2 \xrightarrow{\text{1500 °C}} 2C_2H_2 + 2CO + 10H_2$$

The preparation of methanol from carbon monoxide and hydrogen is described in Section 17.24(3).

The source of the methane is petroleum refining. The carbon monoxide and some of the hydrogen can be used to produce methanol. The balance of the hydrogen can be used as a fuel to maintain the temperature required for the reaction.

☐ 18.18 Reactions of ethyne

1. Combustion. Ethyne burns in air with a very smoky flame. Carbon, carbon dioxide, and water vapor are the products of combustion. With special burners, the combustion to carbon dioxide and water vapor is complete.

$$2C_2H_2 + 5O_2 \rightarrow 4CO_2 + 2H_2O$$

The oxyacetylene welding torch burns ethyne in the presence of oxygen.

2. Halogen addition. Ethyne is more unsaturated than ethene because of the triple bond. It is chemically possible to add two molecules of bromine to an ethyne molecule to form 1,1,2,2-tetrabromoethane.

$$H-C\equiv C-H + 2Br_2 \rightarrow H-\overset{\overset{\displaystyle Br}{|}}{\underset{\underset{\displaystyle Br}{|}}{C}}-\overset{\overset{\displaystyle Br}{|}}{\underset{\underset{\displaystyle Br}{|}}{C}}-H$$

You have now learned three related words: monomer, dimer, and polymer. Monomer means one unit of a compound that can undergo polymerization. Dimer means a polymer formed from two units of a monomer. Polymer means a compound consisting of many repeating structural units.

3. Dimerization. Two molecules of ethyne may combine and form the *dimer* (two units), vinylacetylene. This dimerization is brought about by passing ethyne through a water solution of copper(I) chloride and ammonium chloride. The solution acts as a catalyst.

$$2H-C\equiv C-H \xrightarrow[\text{NH}_4\text{Cl}]{\text{Cu}_2\text{Cl}_2} \overset{\displaystyle H}{\underset{\displaystyle H}{>}}C=\overset{\overset{\displaystyle H}{|}}{C}-C\equiv C-H$$

vinylacetylene

The $CH_2=CH-$ group is the *vinyl* group. Vinylacetylene is the basic raw material for producing Neoprene, a synthetic rubber.

☐ 18.19 Butadiene: an important alkadiene

Alkadienes have two double covalent bonds in each molecule. The *-ene* suffix indicates a double bond. The *-diene* suffix indicates two double bonds. The names of the alkadienes are derived in much the same way as those of the other hydrocarbon series. Butadiene must, therefore, have four carbon atoms and contain two double bonds in each molecule.

$$
\begin{array}{c}
H \quad\quad H \;\; H \quad\quad H \\
\diagdown \quad\quad | \;\; | \quad\quad \diagup \\
C = C - C = C \\
\diagup \quad\quad\quad\quad\quad \diagdown \\
H \quad\quad\quad\quad\quad H
\end{array}
$$

Actually, this structure is 1,3-butadiene, since the double bonds follow the first and third carbon atoms. However, 1,2-butadiene, its isomer, is so uncommon that 1,3-butadiene is usually called simply butadiene.

Butadiene is prepared by cracking petroleum fractions containing butane. It is used in the manufacture of *SBR* rubber, the most common type of synthetic rubber.

☐ 18.20 The aromatic hydrocarbons

The aromatic hydrocarbons are generally obtained from coal tar and petroleum. Benzene, the best known aromatic hydrocarbon, has the molecular formula C_6H_6. It may be represented by the following resonance formula, in which the two structures contribute equally.

benzene, C_6H_6

toluene, C_7H_8

The bonds in benzene are neither single bonds nor double bonds. Instead, each bond is a *resonance hybrid bond*. All the carbon-carbon bonds in the molecule are the same. As a result, benzene and other aromatic hydrocarbons are not as unsaturated as the alkenes.

Because of the resonance structure of benzene, the benzene ring is sometimes abbreviated as

The C_6H_5- group derived from benzene is called the *phenyl* group.

naphthalene, $C_{10}H_8$

anthracene, $C_{14}H_{10}$

Figure 18-12. Molecular models of common aromatic hydrocarbons.

Exposure to benzene can result in the destruction of the bone marrow's ability to make blood cells. It may also cause leukemia.

Benzene is produced commercially from petroleum. It is a flammable liquid that is used as a solvent. Benzene is used in manufacturing many other chemicals, including dyes, drugs, and explosives. Benzene has a strong, yet fairly pleasant, aromatic odor. It is less dense than water and only very slightly soluble in water. *Benzene is poisonous.* The vapors are harmful to breathe and are very flammable. *It is now recommended that benzene not be used in school laboratories.*

❑ 18.21 Reactions of benzene

1. Halogenation. Benzene reacts with bromine in the presence of iron to form the substitution product bromobenzene, or phenyl bromide.

Further treatment causes the successive substitution of other bromine atoms for hydrogen atoms. With complete substitution, hexabromobenzene is produced.

2. Nitration. Nitrobenzene is produced by treating benzene with concentrated nitric and sulfuric acids.

3. Sulfonation. Benzenesulfonic acid is produced at room temperature by treating benzene with fuming sulfuric acid. (Fuming sulfuric acid contains an excess of sulfur trioxide.)

4. Friedel-Crafts reaction. An alkyl group can be introduced into the benzene ring by using an alkyl halide in the presence of anhydrous aluminum chloride.

☐ 18.22 Other aromatic hydrocarbons

Toluene, or methyl benzene, is obtained from petroleum.

Toluene is used to make benzene.

The xylenes or dimethylbenzenes, $C_6H_4(CH_3)_2$, are a mixture of three liquid isomers. The xylenes are used as starting materials for the production of polyester fibers, films, and bottles.

Ethylbenzene is produced by the Friedel-Crafts reaction of benzene and ethene in the presence of hydrogen chloride.

What is the original raw material from which both the benzene and ethene needed for this reaction are derived?

Ethylbenzene is treated with a catalyst of mixed metallic oxides to eliminate hydrogen and produce styrene. Styrene is used along with butadiene in making *SBR* synthetic rubber.

Styrene may be polymerized to polystyrene, a tough, transparent plastic. Polystyrene molecules in this form have molecular weights of about 500,000. Styrofoam, a porous form of polystyrene, is used as a packaging and insulating material and for making throwaway beverage tumblers.

Naphthalene, $C_{10}H_8$, is a coal-tar or petroleum product that crystallizes in white, shining scales. Naphthalene molecules have a structure made up of two benzene rings joined by a common side.

Naphthalene is used as a raw material for the manufacture of some resins and dyes.

Anthracene, $C_{14}H_{10}$, has a structure made up of three benzene rings joined together.

Like naphthalene, anthracene forms a whole series of hydrocarbons. They differ from the compounds related to benzene

Figure 18-13. A technician determining the octane rating of a sample of gasoline.

in that there is more than one ring. Anthracene is obtained commercially from coal tar. It is used in the production of synthetic dyes.

18.23 Octane number of gasoline

Knocking occurs in an automobile engine when the mixture of gasoline vapor and air in the cylinders explodes spontaneously rather than burning at a uniform rate. Knocking causes a loss of power and may harm the engine. It can be prevented by using a gasoline that resists this tendency to explode spontaneously as the temperature and pressure increase within the cylinder.

Air mixtures of gasoline that consists mostly of straight-chain hydrocarbons tend to knock badly in automobiles. Air mixtures of hydrocarbons with branched-chains and rings resist exploding spontaneously as the temperature and pressure in the cylinder increase. Thus, branched-chain and ring hydrocarbons have less tendency to knock than straight-chain hydrocarbons. To improve the antiknock qualities, refiners produce a gasoline mixture that contains a large proportion of branched-chain and ring hydrocarbon molecules.

Certain compounds, when added to gasoline in small amounts, improve the antiknock properties. The best known of these is lead tetraethyl, $Pb(C_2H_5)_4$. The use of lead tetraethyl in gasoline is currently being reduced because it contributes to air pollution.

The octane rating of a gasoline is a number that indicates the tendency of a gasoline to knock in a high-compression engine. The higher the number, the less the tendency of the gasoline to knock. To determine the octane rating, the gasoline is burned in a standard test engine. Its performance in the test engine is compared with a fuel of known octane rating. The fuels used as standards are *n*-heptane and 2,2,4-trimethylpentane, which is also named iso-octane. Iso-octane has excellent antiknock properties. It has an arbitrary octane rating of 100. Normal heptane knocks badly and has a rating of zero. A gasoline with the characteristics of a mixture of 90% iso-octane and 10% *n*-heptane has an octane rating of 90.

Straight-chain alkanes have low octane ratings. Saturated ring-type hydrocarbons have intermediate octane ratings. Highly branched alkanes and aromatic (benzene ring-shaped) hydrocarbons have high octane ratings.

18.24 Petroleum substitutes

It is estimated that about 72% of the energy used in the United States comes from natural gas and petroleum. It is now clearly evident that within only a few decades the known supplies of these important chemical raw materials will be exhausted. Continued wasteful use of natural gas and petroleum as fuels threatens the future supply of these raw materials for other important products. Alternate fuels or sources of energy need to be developed. Energy will have to be used more efficiently as the sources become scarcer.

Coal is by far the most widespread and plentiful fuel remaining in the United States. It is used to supply nearly 20% of our energy. At the present rate of consumption, the amount of recoverable coal in the United States will last at least 2000 years. Both the mining and burning of coal present environmental problems that will have to be resolved. Research on developing large-scale systems of producing fuel gases and petroleum-like liquids from coal is currently underway.

There are two well-known methods by which coal can be converted to fuel gases and petroleum-like liquids. Until now these processes have not been economical in the United States. However, it may now be necessary to develop and adapt one or both of these methods to meet our future needs. The Fischer-Tropsch process starts with the mixture of CO and H_2 formed by reacting steam and hot coke. These gases then react at suitable pressures and temperatures in the presence of a metallic catalyst to form a variety of straight-chain hydrocarbons. The amount of unsaturated products varies with the catalyst used. The Bergius process involves reacting finely powdered coal suspended in oil with hydrogen at very high pressure and high temperature usually in the presence of a metallic catalyst. The complex many-ring compounds in coal are broken down. Liquid hydrocarbons are formed.

Oil shales, found in some western states, are another source of a petroleum-like liquid. In one process, the oil shale is mined and brought to the surface. There it is heated in large ovens to drive out the oil, which is then refined. Another method involves the underground heating and collection of the oil. More research is needed in order to develop economical production methods. Here, too, environmental problems must be resolved.

Nuclear fission, described in Chapter 31, already accounts for the production of about 12% of the electricity in the United States. This, however, is only about 4% of our total energy use. Nuclear fission is a promising source of energy for the next several decades if the environmental and safety problems associated with the location and operation of nuclear power plants can be quickly resolved.

Research into ways to obtain large quantities of energy from underground steam, the sun, ocean water temperature differences, nuclear fusion, and biomass is currently being conducted. Practical results, however, may be many years away. Here, too, environmental and safety problems must be considered.

Figure 18-14. Oil shale, found in some western states, is heated to drive out a petroleum-like liquid that can be refined to make fuel and lubricating oil.

The only commercial-sized plants currently using this process are in South Africa.

These processes provided aviation and other fuels for Germany during World War II.

The remaining energy used in the United States, about 4% of the total, is furnished mostly by water power.

Biomass is the collective term for living materials, or matter derived from living things, that could be used to provide energy. It includes wood and agricultural products and their wastes, algae, animal wastes, sewage, etc.

RUBBER

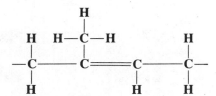

Figure 18-15. Radial automobile tires are made from a mixture, half of which is natural rubber and half synthetic rubber.

☐ 18.25 Nature of rubber

Rubber is an elastic hydrocarbon material obtained from rubber trees. Each tree daily yields about one ounce of a milky fluid called *latex*. Latex contains about 35% rubber in colloidal suspension. When formic acid is added to latex, the rubber separates out as a curd-like mass. After being washed and dried, it is shipped to market as large sheets of crude rubber.

The simplest formula for rubber is $(C_5H_8)_x$. The structural formula for a single C_5H_8 unit is thought to be the one shown in the margin. The C_5H_8 unit is a monomer of rubber. The "*x*" is believed to be a large number. Thus, rubber is a polymer made up of a large number of C_5H_8 units. The units are joined in a zigzag chain. This arrangement accounts for the elasticity of rubber.

☐ 18.26 Compounding of rubber

For commercial processing, raw rubber is mixed with a number of other materials in large batches. The ingredients in these batches vary according to the products to be made. Sulfur, however, is always one of the ingredients. Automobile tires contain considerable amounts of carbon black. This substance adds to the bulk and increases the wearing qualities of the tires.

After mixing, the product is shaped either in a mold or from thin sheets. The whole mass is then vulcanized. *Vulcanization involves heating the rubber mixture to a definite temperature for a definite time*. It gives the article a permanent shape, makes the rubber more elastic, and causes it to lose its sticky qualities. The changes that occur during vulcanization are many and complex. It is believed, however, that the sulfur atoms form bonds between adjacent rubber molecules. Organic catalysts are added to speed the process. Other organic chemicals are added to reduce the effect of oxygen from the air. This treatment slows the aging process that makes the rubber become hard and brittle.

☐ 18.27 Neoprene, a synthetic rubber

About the year 1910, scientists first produced hydrocarbon synthetic rubber by polymerizing isoprene, C_5H_8. This synthetic product cost too much and was inferior to natural rubber from plantations in the East Indies. In 1931, a successful synthetic rubber called *neoprene* appeared on the market.

Hydrogen chloride adds to vinylacetylene to yield chloroprene:

The dimerization of ethyne to form vinylacetylene is described in Section 18.18(3). From what materials can ethyne be prepared?

$$H_2C{=}CH{-}C{\equiv}C{-}H + HCl \rightarrow H_2C{=}CH{-}CCl{=}CH_2$$

vinylacetylene   chloroprene

The catalytic polymerization of chloroprene yields the neoprene unit:

$$
\begin{array}{c}
H Cl H H \\
| | | | \\
-C-C=C-C- \\
| | \\
H H
\end{array}
$$

Oils and greases cause natural rubber to swell and rot. They have little effect on neoprene. Hence, neoprene is used in gasoline delivery hoses and in other objects that must be flexible while resisting the action of hydrocarbons.

☐ 18.28 *SBR*, a synthetic rubber for tires

SBR, Styrene Butadiene Rubber, is a good all-purpose synthetic rubber. It can replace natural rubber for most purposes. However, radial automobile tires are made from a mixture of about half natural rubber and half synthetic rubber. *SBR* is used for automobile tire treads because it resists wear better than other synthetic rubbers. It is made by churning *butadiene* (Section 18.19) and *styrene* (Section 18.22) together in soapy water. The churning is carried out at 5 °C, using a catalyst. This causes the chemicals to polymerize and form *SBR*. The addition of an acid causes the rubber to separate in curd-like masses, which are washed and dried. A possible structural unit is shown in the following structural formula:

What is the original raw material from which SBR *is derived?*

SBR structural unit

SUMMARY

The number of possible carbon compounds is almost unlimited. There are many carbon compounds because: (1) carbon atoms link together by means of covalent bonds; (2) the same atoms may be arranged in several different ways. Isomers are compounds having the same molecular formula but different structures. Structural formulas indicate what kinds of atoms, how many of each, and how they are arranged in the molecule.

Most organic compounds do not dissolve in water. Organic compounds are decomposed by heat more easily than most inorganic compounds. Organic reactions generally proceed at much slower rates than inorganic reactions. Organic reactions are greatly affected by reaction conditions. Organic compounds exist as molecules consisting of atoms joined by covalent bonds.

Hydrocarbons are compounds composed of

only carbon and hydrogen. Their sources are natural gas and petroleum. Some pure hydrocarbons, but more commonly mixtures of hydrocarbons, are separated from natural gas and petroleum by fractional distillation. Fractional distillation is a method of separating the components of a mixture on the basis of differences in their boiling points.

Hydrocarbons are grouped into different series based mainly on the type of bonding between carbon atoms. (1) Alkanes—straight-chain or branched-chain hydrocarbons with carbon atoms connected by only single covalent bonds. (2) Alkenes—straight- or branched-chain hydrocarbons in which two carbon atoms in each molecule are connected by a double covalent bond. (3) Alkynes—straight- or branched-chain hydrocarbons in which two carbon atoms in each molecule are connected by a triple covalent bond. (4) Alkadienes—straight- or branched-chain hydrocarbons having two double covalent bonds between carbon atoms in each molecule. (5) Aromatic hydrocarbons—resonance structures represented by alternate single and double covalent bonds in six-membered carbon rings.

Alkanes are found in natural gas and petroleum. Alkenes are produced from petroleum by cracking. Cracking is a process by which complex organic molecules are broken up into simpler molecules by the action of heat and sometimes a catalyst. Ethyne, the simplest alkyne, is prepared from calcium carbide or by the partial oxidation of methane from petroleum refining. Butadiene, an alkadiene, is prepared by cracking butane separated from petroleum. Simple aromatic hydrocarbons are obtained from petroleum; more complex aromatic hydrocarbons come from coal tar.

Important types of hydrocarbon reactions: Alkanes—combustion, substitution, cracking. Alkenes—addition, polymerization, alkylation, combustion. Alkynes—combustion, addition, dimerization. Benzene—halogenation, nitration, sulfonation, addition of alkyl groups.

The octane rating of a gasoline is a number that indicates the tendency of a gasoline to knock in a high-compression engine. Straight-chain alkanes have low octane ratings. Saturated ring-type hydrocarbons have intermediate octane ratings. Highly branched alkanes and aromatic hydrocarbons have high octane ratings. Gasoline is a mixture of all these types of hydrocarbons blended in the proportions needed to give the desired octane rating.

Substitutes for natural gas and petroleum can be made from coal. The processes for this conversion are the Fischer-Tropsch process and the Bergius process. Another source of a petroleum-like liquid is oil shale.

Natural rubber is an elastic hydrocarbon material obtained from rubber trees. It is a polymer of a large number of C_5H_8 units joined in a zigzag chain. Rubber is compounded by mixing it with sulfur, sometimes carbon black, and other ingredients. The mixture is vulcanized by heating it to a definite temperature for a definite time. This gives the rubber article a permanent shape, makes it more elastic, and causes it to lose its sticky qualities. Neoprene and *SBR* are two kinds of synthetic rubber.

◀ | VOCABULARY

addition	cracking	knocking	saturated
alkadienes	dimer	monomer	structural formula
alkanes	dimerization	nitration	substitution group
alkenes	Friedel-Crafts reaction	olefin series	sulfonation
alkyl group	halogenation	paraffin series	unsaturated
alkylation	homologous series	petroleum	vinyl group
alkynes	hydrocarbon	polymer	vulcanization
aromatic hydrocarbons	isomer	polymerization	

◖ QUESTIONS

Group A

1. Give two reasons for the existence of so many carbon compounds.
2. What does a dash(—) represent in a structural formula?
3. What information do you obtain from a properly written structural formula?
4. Give five important differences between organic and inorganic compounds.
5. Describe the composition of (*a*) natural gas; (*b*) petroleum.
6. (*a*) What is *fractional distillation*? (*b*) How effective is it in separating the components of petroleum?
7. (*a*) What use is made of the petroleum fraction having 5 to 7 carbon atoms per molecule? (*b*) What use is made of the petroleum fraction that has a boiling point range of 250 °C to 400 °C?
8. What are the general formulas for (*a*) the alkane series; (*b*) the alkene series; (*c*) the alkyne series?
9. A hydrocarbon contains six carbon atoms. Give its empirical formula if it is (*a*) an alkane; (*b*) an alkene; (*c*) an alkyne.
10. Beyond the first four members of the alkane series, how are the hydrocarbons of this series named?
11. What does the formula RH represent?
12. How is methane produced in the laboratory?
13. Write a balanced formula equation for the complete combustion of (*a*) methane; (*b*) ethene; (*c*) ethyne; (*d*) butadiene.
14. Write equations for the step-by-step substitution of each of the hydrogen atoms in methane by bromine.
15. (*a*) What is *cracking*? (*b*) Distinguish between thermal and catalytic cracking.
16. Butene reacts with hydrogen in the presence of a nickel catalyst. Write a structural-formula equation for the reaction.
17. (*a*) What is a monomer? (*b*) a dimer? (*c*) a polymer? (*d*) polymerization?
18. What are two uses for ethyne?
19. What do the terms *saturated* and *unsaturated* mean when applied to hydrocarbons?
20. Why is calcium carbide sold in airtight metal cans?
21. How are naphthalene and anthracene related structurally to benzene?
22. (*a*) What causes knocking in an automobile engine? (*b*) How is gasoline formulated to prevent knocking?
23. What does it mean if a gasoline has an octane rating of 96?
24. How is the oil extracted from oil shale?
25. How is rubber separated out from latex?
26. What probably accounts for the elasticity of rubber?
27. How is rubber compounded?
28. Why are additives used in making rubber goods?
29. What is vulcanization?
30. What advantage does neoprene have over natural rubber?

Group B

31. Why would you expect organic compounds with covalent bonds to be less stable to heat than inorganic compounds with ionic bonds?
32. Compare the action shown in Figure 12-6 with that on a single trough in Figure 18-4.
33. Draw structural formulas for the five isomers of hexane.
34. When burned completely, decane, $C_{10}H_{22}$, forms carbon dioxide and water vapor. Write the chemical equation.
35. Draw the structural formula for 2,2-dichloropropane.
36. Draw structural formulas for three isomers of trichloropentane.
37. The element that appears in the greatest number of compounds is hydrogen. The element forming the second greatest number of compounds is carbon. Why are there more hydrogen compounds than carbon compounds?
38. Write a structural-formula equation for the reaction of 2-methylpropane and

2-methylpropene which produces 2,2,4-tri-methylpentane.

39. Write the structural formula equation for the preparation of vinylacetylene from ethyne.

40. (a) Is it geometrically possible for the four hydrogen atoms attached to the end carbon atoms in the 1,3-butadiene molecule to lie in the same plane? (b) If carbon-hydrogen bonds on adjacent singly bonded carbon atoms tend to repel each other, would it be likely that all six hydrogen atoms lie in the same plane? (c) If they do, what is their relation to the plane of the carbon atoms?

41. For the compound propadiene (a) draw the structural formula; (b) write the electron-dot formula; (c) using tetrahedral carbon atoms, draw the molecule, showing the orientation of the valence bonds; (d) from your drawing, decide whether all the hydrogen atoms lie in the same plane or not.

42. The formulas for the first four members of the benzene series are C_6H_6, C_7H_8, C_8H_{10}, C_9H_{12}. From these formulas, determine the general formula for the benzene series.

43. (a) What is *resonance*? (b) Using structural valence-bond formulas, explain resonance in the benzene molecule. (c) Is a double bond in a benzene molecule the same as a double bond in an ethene molecule?

44. Write equations for the step-by-step substitution of each of the hydrogen atoms in benzene by bromine.

45. Write a structural-formula equation for the preparation of methyl benzene from benzene and methyl chloride by the Friedel-Crafts reaction.

46. Draw (a) the three possible valence-bond structural formulas for naphthalene; (b) the four possible valence-bond structural formulas for anthracene.

47. (a) What are the reactants and products of the Fischer-Tropsch process? (b) Of the Bergius process?

48. (a) What materials are polymerized to produce *SBR*? (b) What is an important use for *SBR*? (c) Why is it used for this purpose?

PROBLEMS

Group A

1. What is the mass in kilograms of 15.0 gallons of gasoline? Assume the gasoline is iso-octane which has a density of 0.692 g/mL.

2. Calculate the percentage composition of butane.

3. What volume of carbon dioxide is produced by the complete combustion of 25.0 L of propane? The volumes of carbon dioxide and of propane are measured under the same conditions.

4. How many grams of calcium carbide are required for the production of 2.0 L of ethyne at STP?

Group B

5. A compound consists of 60.0% carbon, 26.7% oxygen, and 13.3% hydrogen. Its molecular weight is $6\overline{0}$. What are the possible structures for molecules of this compound?

6. Calculate the energy change of the substitution reaction between one mole of methane and one mole of bromine molecules. Use the bond energies given in Table 6-4.

7. A volume of ethene (135 mL) is collected by water displacement at 22 °C and 738 mm pressure. What is the volume of the dry ethene at STP?

8. A compound consists of 93.75% carbon and 6.25% hydrogen. The substance dissolves in benzene and 6.40 g of it lowers the freezing point of $10\overline{0}$ g of benzene 2.55 C°. (a) What is the empirical formula of the compound? (b) What is its molecular weight? (c) What is its molecular formula? See Table 13-5 for necessary data.

Hydrocarbon Substitution Products

Many great scientific achievements have been realized by men and women endowed with the gift of imagination. The deciphering of the ring structure of benzene is such an example. For many years scientists had toiled to unravel the geometry of this important hydrocarbon, when in 1865 the German chemist August Kekulé saw it in a dream. In his reverie: "Again the atoms were before my eyes. Little groups kept modestly in the background. My mind's eye, trained by the observation of similar forms, could now distinguish more complex structures of various kinds. Long chains here and there more firmly joined; all winding and turning with a snake-like motion. Suddenly one of the serpents caught its own tail and the ring thus formed whirled exasperatingly before my eyes. . . ." From his experience, Kekulé advised other scientists. "If we learn to dream, we shall perhaps discover truth."

☐ 19.1 Preparation of alkyl halides

An **alkyl halide** is an alkane in which a halogen atom—fluorine, chlorine, bromine, or iodine—is substituted for a hydrogen atom. Since **R** is often used to represent an alkyl group and **X** any halogen, an alkyl halide can be represented as **RX.**

1. Direct halogenation. In Section 18.12, you learned that the halogens react with alkanes to form substitution products. For example, under suitable conditions halogen atoms can be substituted for each of the four hydrogen atoms in methane. This reaction occurs in four stages.

$$CH_4 + X_2 \rightarrow CH_3X + HX$$

$$CH_3X + X_2 \rightarrow CH_2X_2 + HX$$

$$CH_2X_2 + X_2 \rightarrow CHX_3 + HX$$

$$CHX_3 + X_2 \rightarrow CX_4 + HX$$

2. From alkenes and alkynes. As discussed in Sections 18.15 and 18.18, alkenes and alkynes react with halogens or hydrogen halides to form alkyl halides.

3. From alcohols. Alcohols are alkanes in which the hydroxyl group, **—OH,** has been substituted for hydrogen. Hence, an alcohol has the type formula **ROH.** The reaction of an alcohol with a hydrogen halide, HCl, HBr, or HI, yields the corresponding alkyl halide.

$$ROH + HX \rightarrow RX + H_2O$$

HALOGEN SUBSTITUTION PRODUCTS

In this chapter you will gain an understanding of:

- **the preparation and reactions of alkyl halides**
- **the structure, preparations, and reactions of alcohols**
- **the general structural formulas of ethers, aldehydes, ketones, carboxylic acids, and esters**
- **the preparations and reactions of these organic compounds**
- **the reactions of esterification and saponification**

Many halogenated hydrocarbons are toxic, affecting the liver or the heart muscle. Some are believed to cause cancer.

☐ 19.2 Reactions of the alkyl halides

Alkyl halides react with many molecules and ions. One result of these changes is the substitution of another atom or group of atoms for the halogen atom.

For example, alkyl halides react with water solutions of strong hydroxides to yield alcohols and the halide ion. The hydroxyl group from the hydroxide is substituted for the halogen atom in the alkyl halide.

$$RX + OH^- \rightarrow ROH + X^-$$

The Friedel-Crafts reaction [Section 18.21(4)] is an alkyl halide substitution reaction. Here the phenyl group, C_6H_5—, is substituted for the halogen atom in the alkyl halide.

$$RCl + \bigcirc \xrightarrow{\text{AlCl}_3} \bigcirc^{R} + HCl$$

☐ 19.3 Specific alkyl halides

Tetrachloromethane, CCl_4, is commonly called carbon tetrachloride. It is a colorless, volatile, nonflammable liquid. It is an excellent nonpolar solvent. Carbon tetrachloride is sometimes used for dry-cleaning fabrics, removing grease from metals, and extracting oils from seeds. Its vapors are poisonous. Therefore, *there must be good ventilation when carbon tetrachloride is used.* Its most important use is in the preparation of Freon-type compounds. Carbon tetrachloride is prepared commercially by the direct chlorination of methane.

$$CH_4 + 4Cl_2 \rightarrow CCl_4 + 4HCl$$

Dichlorodifluoromethane, CCl_2F_2, is the most important member of a family of compounds named Freon. It is used as a refrigerant in mechanical refrigerators and air conditioners, and as a bubble-making agent in the manufacture of plastic foams. This particular Freon is an odorless, nontoxic, nonflammable, easily liquefied gas. It is prepared from carbon tetrachloride and hydrofluoric acid with antimony compounds as catalysts.

$$CCl_4 + 2HF \xrightarrow{\text{catalyst}} CCl_2F_2 + 2HCl$$

Freon-type compounds, released into the air, do rise into the stratosphere. There it is believed ultraviolet radiation from the sun decomposes these compounds, releasing free halogen atoms. The free halogen atoms then react with the ozone molecules. By a series of reactions, scientists believe the ozone molecules become oxygen molecules. What happens to the halogen atoms after these reactions is unclear. One theory is that the halogen atoms start the decomposition of more ozone. In this way, a small number of halogen atoms can decompose a large number of ozone

The presence of ozone in the stratosphere and its role in protecting the earth's surface from an excess of ultraviolet radiation from the sun are described in Section 9.9.

molecules. Another theory is that the halogen atoms become combined in a compound with nitrogen and oxygen and do not react with more ozone. A decrease in the concentration of ozone in the stratosphere will allow more potentially harmful ultraviolet radiation to reach the earth. Consequently, the production of Freons has been limited and the use of Freons as propellants in aerosol cans has been discontinued in the United States.

Tetrafluoroethene, C_2F_4, can be polymerized. The product has a structure in which the following unit occurs again and again:

$$\begin{array}{c} \quad F \quad\; F \\ \mid \quad\; \mid \\ -C-C- \\ \mid \quad\; \mid \\ \quad F \quad\; F \end{array}$$

This material is called Teflon. Teflon is a very inactive, flexible substance that is stable up to about 325 °C. It is made into fibers for weaving chemical-resistant fabrics or into rods from which small parts may be formed. Teflon has a very low coefficient of friction. It is useful where heat-resistant, nonlubricated moving parts are needed. It is also used to coat metals and give them a "nonsticking" surface.

1,2-dichloroethane, $ClCH_2CH_2Cl$, commonly called ethylene dichloride, is made by chlorinating ethene, as described in Section 18.15. This liquid is used as a solvent and for making adhesives. Most of it, however, is converted to vinyl chloride.

The vinyl group is $CH_2{=}CH{-}$. See Section 18.18.

$$\begin{array}{c} \;H\;\;H \\ \mid\;\;\;\mid \\ Cl-C-C-Cl \\ \mid\;\;\;\mid \\ \;H\;\;H \end{array} \xrightarrow{\text{heat}} \begin{array}{c} H\qquad\quad H \\ \diagdown\qquad\diagup \\ C{=}C \\ \diagup\qquad\diagdown \\ H\qquad\quad Cl \end{array} + \; HCl$$

Vinyl chloride is then polymerized to form polyvinyl chloride, which has the structural unit

$$\begin{array}{c} \quad H \quad\; H \\ \mid \quad\; \mid \\ -C-C- \\ \mid \quad\; \mid \\ \quad H \quad\; Cl \end{array}$$

Polyvinyl chloride has a molecular weight of about 1,500,000. It is used for plastic pipe, plastic siding for buildings, film, wire insulation, and phonograph records.

ALCOHOLS

☐ 19.4 General preparations of alcohols

Alcohols are alkanes in which one or more *hydroxyl* groups, —OH, has been substituted for a like number of hydrogen atoms. (The covalent bonded hydroxyl group must not be confused with the ionic bonded hydroxide ion.)

1. Hydration of alkenes. Ethene reacts exothermically with concentrated sulfuric acid at room temperature. The sulfuric acid molecule adds to the double bond. One hydrogen atom of the sulfuric acid molecule adds to one carbon. The remainder of the sulfuric acid molecule adds to the other carbon.

$$\underset{H}{\overset{H}{\diagdown}}C=C\underset{H}{\overset{H}{\diagup}} + \underset{H-O}{\overset{H-O}{\diagdown}}S\underset{O}{\overset{O}{\diagup}} \rightarrow H-\underset{H}{\overset{H}{C}}-\underset{H}{\overset{H}{C}}-O-\underset{O}{\overset{O}{S}}-O-H$$

If this mixture is diluted with water, the ethene-sulfuric acid-addition compound reacts to produce C_2H_5OH, called ethanol or ethyl alcohol.

$$H-\underset{H}{\overset{H}{C}}-\underset{H}{\overset{H}{C}}-O-\underset{O}{\overset{O}{S}}-O-H + H-O-H \rightarrow H-\underset{H}{\overset{H}{C}}-\underset{H}{\overset{H}{C}}-O-H + \underset{H-O}{\overset{H-O}{\diagdown}}S\underset{O}{\overset{O}{\diagup}}$$

The overall effect of these two reactions is the addition of water across the ethene double bond.

2. From alkyl halides. You learned in Section 19.2 that alkyl halides react with water solutions of strong hydroxides to yield alcohols.

◻ 19.5 Preparation, properties, and uses of specific alcohols

1. Methanol. Methanol is prepared from carbon monoxide and hydrogen under pressure, using a catalyst. See Section 17.24. Methanol is a colorless liquid with a rather pleasant odor. It has a low density and boils at 64.7 °C. *It is very poisonous, even when used externally.* If taken internally in small quantities, it causes blindness by destroying the cells of the optic nerve. Larger quantities may cause death. Methanol is a good fuel, burning with a hot, smokeless flame. It is used as a solvent and is added to ethanol to make it unfit for drinking. It serves as a starting material for preparing other organic compounds such as formaldehyde and acetic acid. Methanol is also used in automobile gas tank de-icers. The methanol in these products prevents water that has condensed in the tank from freezing there as well as in the gas line and carburetor. It is possible to convert methanol directly into high-octane gasoline by a new catalytic process. But the gasoline produced presently costs much more than that obtained from petroleum.

2. Ethanol. Large quantities of ethanol are produced by hydrating ethene. Another method is fermentation. If yeast is added to a dilute solution of sugar or molasses at room temper-

The depression of the freezing point of solvents by molecular solutes is explained in Section 13.12.

This is another way to produce gasoline from coal. See Section 18.24.

ature, chemical action soon occurs. The yeast plants secrete the enzymes sucrase and zymase. These enzymes act as catalysts in changing the sugar into alcohol and carbon dioxide.

$$C_{12}H_{22}O_{11} + H_2O \rightarrow 4CO_2 + 4C_2H_5OH$$

Both processes are used in producing industrial alcohol. However, hydration of ethene is a less expensive method. Another ethanol-preparation process now being developed involves catalytically reacting methanol with carbon monoxide and hydrogen. By this method, ethanol can be prepared starting with coal rather than petroleum.

Ethanol is a colorless liquid. It has a characteristic odor and a sharp biting taste. It boils at 78 °C, freezes at − 115 °C, and burns with a nearly colorless flame. Ethanol is a good solvent for many organic compounds that are insoluble in water. Accordingly, it is used for making a variety of solutions for medicinal use. Ethanol is also used for making ether and acetaldehyde.

A mixture of 10% ethanol and 90% unleaded gasoline is marketed as *gasohol*. The addition of ethanol to unleaded gasoline is claimed to produce an increase in octane number, a reduction in exhaust pollutants, and a reduction in fuel consumption. However, the evidence is conflicting. If the purpose of this addition is also to reduce consumption of petroleum and coal, the ethanol must be prepared by fermentation of renewable materials such as grains and sugar cane. Also, if energy is to be conserved, the ethanol should yield more energy as fuel than it requires for its preparation. This may be a difficult energy problem to solve.

Ethanol is the alcohol in alcoholic beverages. It affects the central nervous system and can damage the liver. *Denatured alcohol* is a mixture composed principally of ethanol. But other poisonous and nauseating materials have been added to it to make it unfit for beverage purposes. It can still be used for industrial purposes, however.

Molecules of methanol and ethanol have been detected in interstellar space.

3. Ethylene glycol. The compound ethylene glycol, $C_2H_4(OH)_2$, has the structural formula

Figure 19-3. Large quantities of ethanol are produced in this plant by the hydration of ethene. Ethene is an important product of the cracking of petroleum.

In ethylene glycol and other alcohols with more than one hydroxyl group, the hydroxyl groups are usually bonded to different carbon atoms. Two hydroxyl groups attached to the same carbon atom are mostly unstable. They may produce a formyl group (Section 19.8), or a carbonyl group (Section 19.10), and water.

$$\begin{array}{ccc} H & H \\ | & | \\ H-C-C-H \\ | & | \\ O & O \\ | & | \\ H & H \end{array}$$

Ethylene glycol is an alcohol containing two hydroxyl groups. It may be prepared by first catalytically oxidizing ethene to ethene oxide.

$$H—\overset{\displaystyle H}{\underset{}{C}}{=}\overset{\displaystyle H}{\underset{}{C}}—H + \tfrac{1}{2}O_2 \xrightarrow{\text{Ag}} H—\overset{\displaystyle H}{C}\underset{\underset{\displaystyle O}{\diagdown\diagup}}{}\overset{\displaystyle H}{C}—H$$

Then ethene oxide is reacted with water in the presence of an acid to yield ethylene glycol.

$$H—\overset{\displaystyle H}{C}\underset{\underset{\displaystyle O}{\diagdown\diagup}}{}\overset{\displaystyle H}{C}—H + H_2O \xrightarrow{\text{acid}} H—\overset{\displaystyle H}{\underset{\underset{\displaystyle H}{\displaystyle O}}{C}}—\overset{\displaystyle H}{\underset{\underset{\displaystyle H}{\displaystyle O}}{C}}—H$$

Ethylene glycol is used extensively as a "permanent" antifreeze in automobile radiators. Its boiling point is so much higher than that of water that it does not readily evaporate or boil away. Ethylene glycol is also used in the production of one type of polyester fiber and film. Ethylene glycol is poisonous.

4. Glycerol. Glycerol, or glycerin, $C_3H_5(OH)_3$, has the structural formula

$$\begin{array}{c} \overset{\displaystyle H}{|} \\ H—C—O—H \\ | \\ H—C—O—H \\ | \\ H—C—O—H \\ | \\ H \end{array}$$

Hygroscopic materials are described in Section 12.19.

It is a colorless, odorless, slow-flowing liquid with a sweet taste. It has a low vapor pressure and is hygroscopic. It is used in making synthetic resins for paints and in cigarettes to keep the tobacco moist. It is also used in the manufacture of cellophane, nitroglycerin, and some toilet soaps. Glycerol is an ingredient of cosmetics and drugs and is used in many foods and beverages. It is a by-product of soap manufacture. Large quantities of glycerol are synthesized from propene, a product of petroleum cracking.

◻ 19.6 Reactions of alcohols

1. With sodium. Sodium reacts vigorously with ethanol, releasing hydrogen. A second product of the reaction is sodium ethoxide, C_2H_5ONa. This compound is recovered as a white solid after the excess ethanol is evaporated. This reaction is similar to the reaction of sodium with water.

$$2C_2H_5OH + 2Na \rightarrow 2C_2H_5ONa + H_2$$

2. With HX. Alcohols react with concentrated water solutions of hydrogen halides, particularly hydrobromic, HBr, and hydriodic, HI, acids. These reactions produce alkyl halides. Sulfuric acid is used as a dehydrating agent.

$$\textbf{ROH + HBr} \rightarrow \textbf{RBr + H}_2\textbf{O}$$

3. Dehydration. Depending on reaction conditions, ethanol dehydrated by hot concentrated sulfuric acid yields either diethyl ether, $C_2H_5OC_2H_5$, or ethene, C_2H_4.

$$\textbf{2C}_2\textbf{H}_5\textbf{OH} \rightarrow \textbf{C}_2\textbf{H}_5\textbf{OC}_2\textbf{H}_5 + \textbf{H}_2\textbf{O}$$

$$\textbf{C}_2\textbf{H}_5\textbf{OH} \rightarrow \textbf{C}_2\textbf{H}_4 + \textbf{H}_2\textbf{O}$$

4. Oxidation. Alcohols that have the hydroxyl group attached to the end carbon can be oxidized by hot copper (II) oxide. The product of such an oxidation is an aldehyde, RCHO.

$$\textbf{RCH}_2\textbf{OH + CuO} \rightarrow \textbf{RCHO + H}_2\textbf{O + Cu}$$

Low-molecular-weight alcohols are flammable and burn readily in air.

$$\textbf{2CH}_3\textbf{OH + 3O}_2 \rightarrow \textbf{2CO}_2 + \textbf{4H}_2\textbf{O}$$

5. Sulfation of long-chain alcohols. 1-dodecanol, $C_{12}H_{25}OH$, is commonly called lauryl alcohol. It is obtained from coconut oil by hydrogenation and partial decomposition. Lauryl alcohol may be *sulfated* by treatment with sulfuric acid and then neutralized with sodium hydroxide. This process yields sodium lauryl sulfate, $C_{12}H_{25}OSO_2ONa$, a very effective cleaning agent.

$$\textbf{C}_{12}\textbf{H}_{25}\textbf{OH + H}_2\textbf{SO}_4 \rightarrow \textbf{C}_{12}\textbf{H}_{25}\textbf{OSO}_2\textbf{OH + H}_2\textbf{O}$$

$$\textbf{C}_{12}\textbf{H}_{25}\textbf{OSO}_2\textbf{OH + NaOH} \rightarrow \textbf{C}_{12}\textbf{H}_{25}\textbf{OSO}_2\textbf{ONa + H}_2\textbf{O}$$

◻ 19.7 Ethers: organic oxides

ETHERS

Ethers have the general formula **ROR′**. R and R′ represent the same or different alkyl groups. Ethers may be thought of as being structurally similar to water. But both hydrogen atoms have been replaced by alkyl groups. Ethers can be prepared by dehydrating alcohols as described in Section 19.6. Diethyl ether is commonly known as *ether*. It is a volatile, very flammable, colorless liquid of characteristic odor. It can be made by heating ethanol and sulfuric acid to 140 °C.

$$\textbf{2C}_2\textbf{H}_5\textbf{OH} \xrightarrow{\text{H}_2\text{SO}_4} \textbf{C}_2\textbf{H}_5\textbf{OC}_2\textbf{H}_5 + \textbf{H}_2\textbf{O}$$

Ether slows down the operation of the central nervous system; this accounts for its former use as an anesthetic. It is also used as a solvent for fats and oils. Ether molecules have been found in outer space.

One of the methyl butyl ethers, $(CH_3)_3COCH_3$, is used in gasoline to increase the octane rating. It has the advantage of being lead-free. This ether is made by catalytically reacting methanol with 2-methylpropene, a gas produced during petroleum cracking.

ALDEHYDES

☐ 19.8 Preparations of aldehydes

An aldehyde is a compound that has a hydrocarbon group and one or more *formyl* groups, 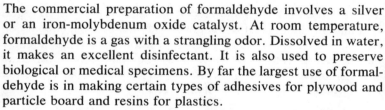 . The general formula for an *aldehyde* is **RCHO**.

The general method of preparing aldehydes was mentioned in Section 19.6. A common process of this type involves passing methanol vapor and a regulated amount of air over heated copper. Formaldehyde, HCHO, is produced.

$$2Cu + O_2 \rightarrow 2CuO$$

$$CH_3OH + CuO \rightarrow HCHO + H_2O + Cu$$

The commercial preparation of formaldehyde involves a silver or an iron-molybdenum oxide catalyst. At room temperature, formaldehyde is a gas with a strangling odor. Dissolved in water, it makes an excellent disinfectant. It is also used to preserve biological or medical specimens. By far the largest use of formaldehyde is in making certain types of adhesives for plywood and particle board and resins for plastics.

Acetaldehyde, CH_3CHO, can be made by the oxidation of ethanol. It is also produced directly from ethene by reacting ethene with oxygen, water, and hydrochloric acid in the presence of a $PdCl_2$-$CuCl_2$ catalyst. Acetaldehyde is a stable liquid used in preparing other organic compounds. Both formaldehyde and acetaldehyde molecules are found in outer space.

☐ 19.9 Reactions of aldehydes

1. Oxidation. The mild oxidation of an aldehyde produces the organic acid having the same number of carbon atoms. The oxidation of acetaldehyde to acetic acid is typical.

$$CH_3CHO + O \text{ (from oxidizing agent)} \rightarrow CH_3COOH$$

2. Fehling's test. Fehling's solution A is copper(II) sulfate solution. Fehling's solution B is sodium hydroxide and sodium tartrate solution. If these are mixed with an aldehyde and heated, the aldehyde is oxidized. The copper(II) ion is reduced to copper(I) and precipitated as brick-red copper(I) oxide.

$$RCHO + 2CuSO_4 + 5NaOH \rightarrow RCOONa + Cu_2O + 2Na_2SO_4 + 3H_2O$$

Figure 19-4. A brick-red precipitate of copper(I) oxide is evidence of a positive Fehling's test.

3. Hydrogen addition. Adding hydrogen to aldehydes in the presence of finely divided nickel or platinum produces alcohols.

$$\mathbf{RCHO + H_2 \xrightarrow{\ Ni\ } RCH_2OH}$$

This reaction is the reverse of the oxidation of alcohols to aldehydes.

☐ 19.10 Preparation and properties of acetone

KETONES

Organic compounds containing the *carbonyl* group, $\diagdown\!C\!=\!O$,

and having the general formula **RCOR**′ are *ketones*.

Ketones can be prepared from alcohols that do *not* have the hydroxyl group attached to an end-carbon atom. For example, acetone, CH_3COCH_3, is prepared by the mild oxidation of 2-propanol, $CH_3CHOHCH_3$. Potassium dichromate, $K_2Cr_2O_7$, in water solution is the oxidizing agent.

Figure 19-5. One of the important uses of acetone is as a solvent in the manufacture of acetate rayon.

Acetone is a colorless, volatile liquid. It is widely used as a solvent in the manufacture of acetate rayon. Storage tanks for ethyne gas are loosely filled with asbestos saturated with acetone. The ethyne dissolves in the acetone and by so doing occupies less volume. This procedure increases the amount of ethyne that can safely be compressed into the tank. Acetone and other ketones are used for cleaning metals, removing stains, and for preparing synthetic organic chemicals. Acetone is a digestive product of untreated diabetics.

☐ 19.11 Preparations of carboxylic acids

CARBOXYLIC ACIDS AND ESTERS

Many organic acids and their salts occur naturally. They are found in sour milk, unripe fruits, rhubarb, sorrel, and other plants. All organic acids contain the *carboxyl* group,

The general formula for a *carboxylic acid* is **RCOOH**.

1. Oxidation of alcohols or aldehydes. The oxidation of alcohols to aldehydes and of aldehydes to carboxylic acids was described in Sections 19.6 and 19.9. Acetic acid can be produced by the catalytic oxidation of acetaldehyde. A new method of preparing very pure acetic acid is by catalytically reacting methanol with carbon monoxide at moderate temperature (175–245 °C) and moderate pressure (15 atm).

$$CH_3OH + CO \xrightarrow{\text{catalyst}} CH_3COOH$$

Concentrated acetic acid is a colorless liquid that is a good solvent for some organic chemicals. It is used for making cellulose acetate, a basic material of many fibers and films.

Cider vinegar is made from apple cider that has fermented to hard cider. The ethanol in hard cider is slowly oxidized by the oxygen of the air. This oxidation produces acetic acid. The reaction is catalyzed by enzymes from certain bacteria.

$$C_2H_5OH + O_2 \rightarrow CH_3COOH + H_2O$$

Vinegar contains from 4% to 6% acetic acid.

2. Formic acid. Formic acid, HCOOH, is prepared from sodium hydroxide solution and carbon monoxide under pressure. This reaction yields sodium formate, HCOONa.

$$NaOH + CO \rightarrow HCOONa$$

If sodium formate is carefully heated with sulfuric acid, formic acid distills off.

$$HCOONa + H_2SO_4 \rightarrow HCOOH + NaHSO_4$$

Formic acid is found in nature in stinging nettle plants and in certain ants. It is also one of the molecules found in outer space. Formic acid is used as an acidifying agent in the textile industry.

Formic acid molecules, as shown in the margin at left, contain two carbon-oxygen bonds. One of them, the double bond, is 1.23 Å long. The other, the single bond, is 1.36 Å long. This evidence supports the idea that these bonds are different. In sodium formate, an ionic compound, the formate ion also has two carbon-oxygen bonds. But these bonds have the same length, 1.27 Å. What explanation is there for this difference? Because the carbon-oxygen bonds in the formate ion are the same length, they should be similar. The formate ion must be a resonance hybrid of two structures, as shown in the margin at left, and have carbon-oxygen bonds midway in character between single and double covalent bonds. The anions of other carboxylic acids have similar resonance hybrid structures.

Resonance is first described in Section 6.22.

19.12 Reactions of carboxylic acids

1. Ionization. This reaction involves the one hydrogen atom bonded to an oxygen atom in the carboxyl group. This hydrogen atom ionizes in water solution, giving carboxylic acids their acid properties. The hydrogen atoms bonded to carbon atoms in these acids *never* ionize in water solution.

$$HCOOH + H_2O \rightleftarrows H_3O^+ + HCOO^-$$

$$CH_3COOH + H_2O \rightleftarrows H_3O^+ + CH_3COO^-$$

These equilibria yield low H_3O^+ ion concentrations. Therefore, carboxylic acids are generally weak acids.

2. *Neutralization.* An organic acid may be neutralized by a hydroxide. A salt is formed in a reaction similar to that of inorganic acids.

$$CH_3COOH + NaOH \rightarrow CH_3COONa + H_2O$$

3. *Esterification.* **An ester is produced when an acid reacts with an alcohol.** Such reactions are called *esterification reactions*. For example, ethyl acetate is the ester formed when ethanol and acetic acid react.

$$CH_3COOH \quad + \quad C_2H_5OH \xrightarrow{H_2SO_4} CH_3COOC_2H_5 \quad + H_2O$$

All such reactions between acids and alcohols are reversible. Achievement of equilibrium is slow and a small amount of sulfuric acid is used as a catalyst. Experiments with alcohols containing oxygen-18 show that the oxygen of the water product comes from the acid.

☐ 19.13 Esters

It is also possible to prepare esters by the reaction of alcohols with inorganic acids. Glyceryl trinitrate, known as nitroglycerin, is an example.

$$C_3H_5(OH)_3 + 3HNO_3 \xrightarrow{H_2SO_4} C_3H_5(NO_3)_3 + 3H_2O$$

Esters give fruits their characteristic flavors and odors. Amyl acetate, $CH_3COOC_5H_{11}$, has an odor somewhat resembling bananas. Commonly called "banana oil," this ester is used as the carrier for some aluminum paints. Ethyl butyrate, $C_3H_7COOC_2H_5$, has an odor and flavor that resemble pineapples. Ripe pineapples contain some of this ester and smaller amounts of other esters.

Esters can be decomposed by hydrolysis into the alcohol and acid from which they were derived. This hydrolysis may occur in the presence of dilute acid or metallic hydroxide solutions.

Figure 19-6. The flavor of pineapples is due mostly to the presence of ethyl butyrate in the juice.

Figure 19-7. The manufacture of soap involves hydrolyzing fats or oils into fatty acids and then reacting this with a very hot sodium hydroxide solution.

◻ 19.14 Saponification

Fats and oils are esters of glycerol and long-carbon-chain acids. The carbon chains of the acids usually contain from 12 to 20 carbon atoms. The structure of a fat or oil can be represented as

$$\begin{array}{c} RCOOCH_2 \\ | \\ R'COOCH \\ | \\ R''COOCH_2 \end{array}$$

R, R', and R'' are saturated or unsaturated long-chain-hydrocarbon groups.

The only difference between a fat and an oil is the physical phase of each at room temperature. Oils are liquids at room temperature, while fats are solids. Long-carbon-chain acids with double bonds produce esters having lower melting points. Hence, oils usually contain more unsaturated hydrocarbon chains than those found in fats.

Saponification is the hydrolysis of a fat using a solution of a strong hydroxide. Alkaline hydrolysis produces the sodium salt of the long-chain carboxylic acid instead of the acid itself.

$$\begin{array}{c} RCOOCH_2 \\ | \\ R'COOCH \\ | \\ R''COOCH_2 \end{array} + 3NaOH \rightarrow RCOONa + R'COONa + R''COONa + C_3H_5(OH)_3$$

Soaps are generally made by hydrolyzing fats and oils with water heated to about 250 °C in a closed container. The water is under a pressure of about 50 atmospheres. At this pressure, water does not boil despite the temperature, which is well above its normal boiling point. The long-chain carboxylic acids thus produced are neutralized with sodium hydroxide. This neutralization yields a mixture of sodium salts that makes up soap.

If the acid chains are unsaturated, a soft soap results. Soaps with hydrocarbon chains of 10 to 12 carbon atoms are soluble in water and produce a large-bubble lather. Soaps containing hydrocarbon chains of 16 to 18 carbon atoms are less soluble in water and give a longer-lasting small-bubble lather. Soap that is a mixture of potassium salts, rather than sodium salts, is generally more soluble in water.

◧ SUMMARY

Hydrocarbon substitution products are those in which an atom such as chlorine or a group such as hydroxyl is substituted for one or more of the hydrogen atoms in a hydrocarbon.

An alkyl halide is an alkane in which a halogen atom is substituted for a hydrogen atom. The general formula for an alkyl halide is RX. Alkyl halides are prepared by the reaction of halogens with alkanes, alkenes, and alkynes, and by the reaction of hydrogen halides with alkenes, alkynes, and alcohols. Many reactions of alkyl halides are substitution reactions. Examples of alkyl halides are carbon tetrachloride, the Freons, Teflon, and vinyl chloride.

Alcohols are alkanes in which one or more hydroxyl groups have been substituted for a like number of hydrogen atoms. The general formula is ROH. They are prepared by the hydration of alkenes and from alkyl halides by substitution. Important alcohols are methanol, ethanol, ethylene glycol, and glycerol. Gasohol is a mixture of 10% ethanol and 90% unleaded gasoline. Alcohols react with sodium and with hydrogen halides. They also undergo dehydration, oxidation, and sulfation reactions.

Ethers are organic oxides with the general formula ROR'. They can be prepared by dehydrating alcohols. Diethyl ether is an example.

Aldehydes have a hydrocarbon group and one or more formyl groups. The general formula is RCHO. They are prepared by the controlled oxidation of alcohols having an hydroxyl group on an end carbon. Formaldehyde and acetaldehyde are examples. Aldehydes undergo oxidation to acids and reduction with hydrogen to alcohols. They give positive Fehling's tests.

Ketones are organic compounds containing the carbonyl group. They have the general formula RCOR'. Ketones are prepared by oxidizing alcohols that do not have the hydroxyl group attached to the end-carbon atom. Acetone is an important ketone.

The general formula for carboxylic acids is RCOOH. They can be prepared by the oxidation of alcohols and aldehydes. Formic acid and acetic acid are familiar examples. Organic acids undergo ionization, neutralization, and esterification reactions. An ester is produced when an acid reacts with an alcohol. The general formula is RCOOR'. Esters give fruits their characteristic flavors and odors. Saponification is the hydrolysis of a fat using a solution of a strong hydroxide, such as sodium hydroxide. The sodium salts produced make up soap.

◀ | VOCABULARY

alcohol	carboxyl group	esterification	hydroxyl group
aldehyde	carboxylic acid	ether	ketone
alkyl halide	denatured alcohol	formyl group	saponification
carbonyl group	ester	gasohol	

◀ | QUESTIONS

Group A

1. What are the general formulas for (*a*) alkyl halides; (*b*) alcohols; (*c*) ethers; (*d*) aldehydes; (*e*) ketones; (*f*) carboxylic acids; (*g*) esters?
2. (*a*) What are the uses of carbon tetrachloride? (*b*) What precautions must be exercised in its use?
3. Draw a structural formula showing the portion of a polymer formed from three molecules of vinyl chloride.
4. How do alcohols differ from inorganic hydroxides?
5. What is the effect of methanol on the body?

6. What advantages are claimed for the addition of ethanol to unleaded gasoline?
7. What property of glycerol makes it useful for keeping tobacco moist?
8. Compare the action of sodium with water and with methanol.
9. How many molecules of oxygen are required for the complete combustion of one molecule of butanol?
10. What are the most important uses for formaldehyde?
11. (*a*) What is Fehling's test? (*b*) What organic group gives a positive Fehling's test?
12. For what purposes is acetone used?

13. (*a*) What is cider vinegar? (*b*) How may it be prepared?

14. (*a*) Oxalic acid is a dicarboxylic acid with the structural formula

$$H-O-\overset{\overset{\displaystyle O}{\|}}{C}-\overset{\overset{\displaystyle O}{\|}}{C}-O-H$$

Write equations for the step-by-step complete ionization of oxalic acid. (*b*) How many moles of potassium hydroxide are required for the complete neutralization of four moles of oxalic acid?

15. What is the source of the hydrogen and oxygen atoms of the water eliminated during an esterification reaction?

16. In what types of reactions mentioned here is sulfuric acid used as a dehydrating agent?

17. (*a*) How are fats and oils alike? (*b*) How do they differ? (*c*) Why do they differ?

18. What is *saponification?*

Group B

19. Draw structural formulas for (*a*) dichloromethane; (*b*) 1,2,3-trihydroxypropane; (*c*) diethyl ether; (*d*) formaldehyde; (*e*) diethylketone; (*f*) acetic acid; (*g*) methyl formate.

20. Write the equations for the preparation of ethyl chloride starting with (*a*) ethane; (*b*) ethene; (*c*) ethanol.

21. Describe the types of alkyl halide substitution reactions given in this chapter.

22. Starting with methane, chlorine, and hydrogen fluoride, show how dichlorodifluoromethane is prepared.

23. What is believed to be the effect of Freon-type compounds in the stratosphere?

24. Using structural formula equations, show how ethanol may be prepared from (*a*) ethene; (*b*) ethyl chloride; (*c*) sugar ($C_{12}H_{22}O_{11}$); (*d*) methanol.

25. On the basis of molecular weight and boiling point, compare the advantages of methanol, ethanol, and ethylene glycol as antifreezes.

26. Write an equation for preparing propyl iodide from propyl alcohol.

27. (*a*) How can propyl ether be prepared from propyl alcohol? (*b*) Write the formula equation for the reaction.

28. What ketone is prepared by the mild oxidation of 2-butanol?

29. Write a formula equation showing the preparation of acetic acid from (*a*) methanol; (*b*) ethanol.

30. (*a*) How do the two carbon-oxygen bonds in formic acid compare? (*b*) How do the two carbon-oxygen bonds in sodium formate compare? (*c*) Account for the difference.

31. Write an equation showing the formation of the ester *n*-butyl acetate.

32. Write a balanced formula equation for the saponification with NaOH of a fat having the formula $(C_{17}H_{35}COO)_3C_3H_5$.

◖ PROBLEMS

Group A

1. Calculate the molecular weight of dichlorodifluoromethane.

2. Sodium hydroxide solution (40.0 mL) exactly neutralizes 35.0 mL of 0.150-*N* formic acid solution. What is the normality of the sodium hydroxide solution?

3. Calculate the number of grams of glycerol that must be dissolved in 0.300 kg of water in order to prepare a 0.400-*m* solution.

4. How many grams of diprotic oxalic acid, $(COOH)_2$, are required to prepare 1.50 L of 0.200-*N* acid?

Group B

5. What is the percentage composition of $C_{12}H_{25}OSO_2ONa$, sodium lauryl sulfate?

6. A compound is found to contain 54.5% carbon, 9.1% hydrogen, and 36.4% oxygen. (*a*) Determine the empirical formula. (*b*) If the molecular weight is 88, what is the molecular formula?

7. The hydronium ion concentration in 0.05-*M* acetic acid is 9.4×10^{-4} mole/L. What is the pH of this solution?

8. What volume of ethanol must be diluted with water to prepare $50\overline{0}$ mL of 0.750-*M* solution? The density of ethanol is 0.789 g/mL.

Reaction Energy and Reaction Kinetics

With the well-ordered arrangement of its heavenly bodies, the universe can be likened to a vast cosmic machine. No machine, however, is perfect. Some of the energy used to run the machine is lost — to friction, to wear and tear, or to some other form of energy not available to do work. The energy required by the planets to orbit the sun is no exception. Each year the planets lose a little of their kinetic energy and are pulled a little closer to the sun; likewise, the sun loses some of its radiant energy and burns less brightly. Scientists have formulated this bleak scenario into one of the most important principles of science, the second law of thermodynamics: Disorder in the universe tends to increase with time. Yet entropy, the name used to describe this disorder, is a statistical quantity and truly cannot tell us how things will be. Perhaps the universe holds deeper truths yet undiscovered by science.

◻ 20.1 Introduction

Chemical equations are often written to represent reactions between different molecular species. The equations show the initial reactants and the final products. They do not show how, during the reaction process, reactant molecules become product molecules. For example, gaseous iodine and hydrogen may react chemically to form gaseous hydrogen iodide. The equation for this reaction is

$$H_2(g) + I_2(g) \rightarrow 2HI(g)$$

This equation makes it easy to visualize molecules of hydrogen and iodine colliding in just the right way and then separating as hydrogen iodide molecules. During the extremely brief encounter, H—H and I—I bonds must be broken, and H—I bonds must be formed.

Chemists are interested in learning how reacting molecules change as a reaction proceeds. New techniques have been developed for studying molecular changes, even those occurring in fast reaction systems. These methods explore the rates of chemical reactions and the pathways along which they occur. The branch of chemistry that is concerned with *reaction rates* and *reaction pathways* is called *chemical kinetics*. The pathway from reactants to products may be a sequence of simple steps called the *reaction mechanism*.

When reaction systems are investigated, the role of energy in the systems is of primary interest. Every substance has a characteristic internal energy because of its structure and physical

In this chapter you will gain an understanding of:

- the term reaction mechanism
- the relationship between the heat of reaction and the terms endothermic and exothermic, and stable and unstable
- solving problems to determine the heat of formation, heat of combustion, and heat of reaction
- writing thermochemical equations for reactions
- the factors that contribute to the driving force of chemical reactions
- the terms free energy, entropy, and enthalpy
- reaction mechanisms and the role of the collision theory
- the difference between activation energy and activated complex
- the five major factors that influence reaction rates
- the reaction rate law

state. Definite quantities of energy are released or absorbed when new substances are formed from reacting substances. Energy changes occur even when products and reactants are both at the same temperature. This energy is related to the breaking and forming of bonds and to the strengths of these bonds.

The first part of this chapter deals with *thermochemistry,* the changes in heat energy that accompany chemical reactions. Later in the chapter, the modern theories of reaction pathways and reaction rates are introduced.

ENERGY OF REACTION

Heat is thermal energy in the process of being added to or removed from a substance.

◻ 20.2 Heat of reaction

Chemical reactions are either exothermic or endothermic processes. During a reaction, a certain amount of chemical binding energy is changed into thermal (internal) energy, or vice versa. Usually the energy change can be measured as heat released or absorbed during the reaction. That is, the energy change can be measured as the *change in heat content* of the substances reacting.

Chemical reactions are generally carried out in open vessels. Volumes may change in such vessels, but pressures remain constant. The heat content of a substance under constant pressure is often called *enthalpy* of the substance. The symbol for enthalpy (and for heat content at constant pressure) is H. If a process is exothermic, the total heat content of the products is *lower* than that of the reactants. The products of an endothermic reaction must have a *higher* heat content than the reactants.

One mole of a substance has a characteristic heat content, just as it has a characteristic mass. The heat content is a measure of the internal energy stored in the substance during its formation. This stored heat content *cannot* be measured *directly.* However, the *change* in heat content that occurs during chemical reaction *can* be measured. This quantity is the heat released during an exothermic change or the heat absorbed during an endothermic change. It is called *heat of reaction. The **heat of reaction** is the quantity of heat released or absorbed during a chemical reaction.*

The heat of reaction is measured when the final state of a system is brought to the same temperature as that of the initial state. Unless otherwise stated, the reaction is assumed to be at 25 °C under standard atmospheric pressure. In addition, each substance is assumed to be in its usual (standard) state at these conditions. For this reason, the phases of reactants and products should be shown along with their formulas in thermochemical equations.

A thermochemical equation includes heat of reaction information.

If a mixture of hydrogen and oxygen is ignited, water is formed and heat energy is released. Because this reaction occurs as an explosion, it is carried out in a special *calorimeter,* as shown in Figure 20-1. Known quantities of reactants are sealed in the reaction chamber, which is immersed in a known quantity of water in an insulated vessel. The heat given off (or absorbed) during the reaction is determined from the temperature change of the known mass of water.

1 kcal of heat is required to change the temperature of 1 kg of water 1 C°.

The quantity of heat given up is proportional to the quantity of water formed in the reaction. No heat is supplied externally, except to ignite the mixture. For this reason, the heat content of the product water must be less than the heat content of the reactants before ignition. The equation for this reaction is ordinarily written as

$$2H_2 + O_2 \rightarrow 2H_2O$$

and the following fact becomes evident: when 2 moles of hydrogen gas at room temperature is burned, 1 mole of oxygen gas is used, and 2 moles of water vapor is formed.

After the product water is brought back to room temperature (the temperature of the initial state), the reaction heat given up by the system is found to be 136.64 kcal. The thermochemical equation can now be written as

$$2H_2(g) + O_2(g) \rightarrow 2H_2O(l) + 136.64 \text{ kcal}$$

The symbols (g), (l), and (s) indicate gas, liquid, and solid phases, respectively.

Heats of reaction are usually expressed in terms of *kilocalories per mole* of substance. From the previous equation, the following equality can be stated.

| heat content of 1 mole of hydrogen gas | + | heat content of $\frac{1}{2}$ mole of oxygen gas | = | heat content of 1 mole of liquid water | + 68.32 kcal |

The thermochemical equation can now indicate the heat of reaction in kcal/mole of product:

$$H_2(g) + \tfrac{1}{2}O_2(g) \rightarrow H_2O(l) + 68.32 \text{ kcal}$$

This equation shows that one mole of the product (liquid) water has a heat content 68.32 kcal *lower* than that of the two gaseous reactants before the reaction occurred. To decompose one mole of water to produce one mole of hydrogen and one-half mole of oxygen, this quantity of energy must be supplied from an external source. The decomposition reaction, which is the reverse of the composition reaction above, is written

$$H_2O(l) + 68.32 \text{ kcal} \rightarrow H_2(g) + \tfrac{1}{2}O_2(g)$$

Here the products, 1 mole of hydrogen and ½ mole of oxygen, have a total heat content 68.32 kcal *higher* than that of the 1 mole of water before the reaction. The two reactions can be represented by the reversible equation

$$H_2(g) + \tfrac{1}{2}O_2(g) \rightleftarrows H_2O(l) + 68.32 \text{ kcal}$$

If the *heat content* of a substance is symbolized by the letter H, then the *change in heat content* can be represented by ΔH.

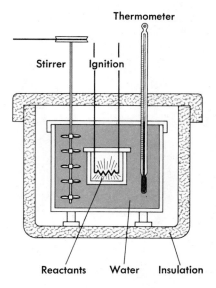

Figure 20-1. Schematic diagram of an ignition calorimeter of the type used for measuring nutritional calories.

The Greek letter Δ (delta) signifies "change in." Thus the change in heat content, ΔH, during a reaction is the difference between the heat content of the products and the heat content of the reactants.

$$\Delta H = \text{heat content of products} - \text{heat content of reactants}$$

Exothermic processes: ΔH is negative.

In this notation scheme, the ΔH for an exothermic reaction has a *negative* sign. Thus, in the preceding reaction

$$\Delta H = -68.32 \text{ kcal/mole}$$

The thermochemical equation·

$$H_2(g) + \tfrac{1}{2}O_2(g) \rightarrow H_2O(l) + 68.32 \text{ kcal}$$

has the same meaning as

Endothermic processes: ΔH is positive.

$$H_2(g) + \tfrac{1}{2}O_2(g) \rightarrow H_2O(l) \qquad \Delta H = -68.32 \text{ kcal}$$

The ΔH for an endothermic reaction is signified by using a *positive* value. This sign convention is an arbitrary one, but it is logical since the heat of reaction is said to be *negative* when the heat content of the system is *decreasing* (exothermic reaction). It is said to be *positive* when the heat content of the system is *increasing* (endothermic reaction). See Figure 20-2.

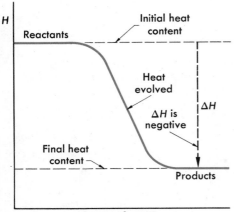

20.3 Heat of formation

Chemical reactions in which elements combine to form compounds are generally exothermic. In these composition reactions the product compounds have lower heat contents than their separate elements, the reactants. The products are also more stable than the uncombined reactants. The formation of water from hydrogen and oxygen illustrates this change in stability.

Elemental hydrogen and oxygen exist as nonpolar diatomic molecules. Water molecules are covalent structures. They are polar because they are bent molecules with an electronegativity difference between the hydrogen and oxygen atoms.

Energy was given up when the single covalent bonds of the diatomic hydrogen and oxygen molecules were originally formed. Therefore, energy is required to break these bonds if the hydrogen and oxygen atoms are to combine. On the other hand, more energy is released when the two polar bonds of the water molecule are formed. Consequently, heat is given off during the composition reaction. The heat of reaction is quite high ($\Delta H = -68.3$ kcal/ mole of water formed), suggesting that water molecules are more stable than hydrogen and oxygen molecules.

The heat released or absorbed in a composition reaction is a useful indicator of product stability. It is referred to as the *heat of formation* of the compound. *The heat of reaction released or absorbed when 1 mole of a compound is formed from its elements*

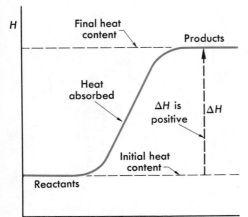

Figure 20-2. Change in heat content during a chemical reaction.

is called the **molar heat of formation** of the compound. By convention, each element in its standard state is said to have a heat content of zero. Then the ΔH during the formation of one mole of a compound from its elements (all in their standard states) is its standard heat of formation. Table 20-1 gives the heats of formation of some common compounds. A more complete list is given in Appendix Table 14.

The sign convention and ΔH notation adopted for heat of reaction apply to heat of formation as well. Heat of formation is merely one category of reaction heats. To distinguish a particular reaction heat as a heat of formation, the more specific notation ΔH_f is used. Heats of formation have negative values for exothermic composition reactions. They have positive values for endothermic composition reactions.

Observe that most of the heats of formation given in Appendix Table 14 are negative. Only a few compounds, such as hydrogen iodide and carbon disulfide, have positive heats of formation.

◻ 20.4 Stability and heat of formation

A large amount of energy is released when a compound with a high negative heat of formation is formed. The same amount of energy is required to decompose such a compound into its sepa-

Table 20-1
HEAT OF FORMATION

ΔH_f = heat of formation of the substance from its elements. All values of ΔH_f are expressed as kcal/mole at 25 °C. Negative values of ΔH_f indicate exothermic reactions. (s) = solid, (l) = liquid, (g) = gas.

Substance	Formula	ΔH_f
ammonia (g)	NH_3	−11.04
barium nitrate (s)	$Ba(NO_3)_2$	−237.06
benzene (l)	C_6H_6	+11.72
calcium chloride (s)	$CaCl_2$	−190.00
carbon (diamond) (s)	C	+0.45
carbon (graphite) (s)	C	0.00
carbon dioxide (g)	CO_2	−94.05
copper(II) sulfate (s)	$CuSO_4$	−184.00
ethyne (acetylene) (g)	C_2H_2	+54.19
hydrogen chloride (g)	HCl	−22.06
water (l)	H_2O	−68.32
nitrogen dioxide (g)	NO_2	+8.09
ozone (g)	O_3	+34.00
sodium chloride (s)	NaCl	−98.23
sulfur dioxide (g)	SO_2	−70.96
zinc sulfate (s)	$ZnSO_4$	−233.88

rate elements. This energy must be supplied to the reaction from an external source. *Such compounds are very stable.* The reactions forming them proceed spontaneously, once they start, and are usually vigorous. Carbon dioxide has a high heat of formation. The ΔH_f of carbon dioxide is -94.05 kcal per mole of gas produced.

Compounds with positive and low negative values of heats of formation are generally unstable. Hydrogen sulfide, H_2S, has a heat of formation of -4.82 kcal per mole. It is not very stable and decomposes when heated. Hydrogen iodide, HI, has a low positive heat of formation, $+6.20$ kcal/mole. It is a colorless gas that decomposes somewhat when stored at room temperature. As it decomposes, violet iodine vapor becomes visible throughout the container of the gas.

The stability of a compound is related to its ΔH_f.

A compound with a high positive heat of formation is very unstable and may react or decompose explosively. For example, ethyne reacts explosively with oxygen. Nitrogen tri-iodide and mercury fulminate decompose explosively. The formation reactions of such compounds store a great deal of energy within them. Mercury fulminate, $HgC_2N_2O_3$, has a heat of formation of $+64$ kcal/mole. Its instability makes it useful as a detonator for explosives.

◻ 20.5 The heat of combustion

Fuels are energy-rich substances.

Fuels, whether for the furnace, automobile, or rocket, are energy-rich substances. The products of their combustion are energy-poor substances. In these combustion reactions the energy yield may be very high. The products of the chemical action may be of little importance compared to the quantity of heat energy given off.

The combustion of 1 mole of pure carbon (graphite) yields 94.05 kcal of heat energy.

$$C(s) + O_2(g) \rightarrow CO_2(g) \qquad \Delta H = -94.05 \text{ kcal}$$

*The heat of reaction released by the complete combustion of 1 mole of a substance is called the **heat of combustion** of the substance.* Observe that the heat of combustion is defined in terms of *1 mole of reactant.* The heat of formation, on the other hand, is defined in terms of *1 mole of product.* The general heat of reaction notation, ΔH, applies to heats of combustion as well. However, the ΔH_c notation may be used to refer specifically to heat of combustion. See Table 20-2.

In some cases, a substance cannot be formed directly from its elements in a rapid composition reaction. The heat of formation of such a compound can be found by using the heats of reaction of a series of related reactions. Heats of combustion are some-

Table 20-2
HEAT OF COMBUSTION

ΔH_c = heat of combustion of the given substance. All values of ΔH_c are expressed as kcal/mole of substance oxidized to H_2O (l) and/or CO_2 (g) at constant pressure and 25 °C. (s) = solid, (l) = liquid, (g) = gas.

Substance	Formula	ΔH_c
hydrogen (g)	H_2	−68.32
carbon (graphite) (s)	C	−94.05
carbon monoxide (g)	CO	−67.64
methane (g)	CH_4	−212.80
ethane (g)	C_2H_6	−372.82
propane (g)	C_3H_8	−530.60
butane (g)	C_4H_{10}	−687.98
pentane (g)	C_5H_{12}	−845.16
hexane (l)	C_6H_{14}	−995.01
heptane (l)	C_7H_{16}	−1151.27
octane (l)	C_8H_{18}	−1307.53
ethene (ethylene) (g)	C_2H_4	−337.23
propene (propylene) (g)	C_3H_6	−491.99
ethyne (acetylene) (g)	C_2H_2	−310.62
benzene (l)	C_6H_6	−780.98
toluene (l)	C_7H_8	−934.50

times useful in these calculations when used according to the following equation:

heat of formation of compound X	=	**sum of heats of formation of products of combustion of compound X**	−	**heat of combustion of compound X**

CO_2 and H_2O are the products of complete combustion of many organic compounds. Their heats of formation are known. The heats of formation of the organic compounds can be calculated indirectly according to the above expression. For example, the heat of combustion, ΔH_c, of methane is determined to be −212.80 kcal/mole.

ΔH_f can be determined indirectly.

$$CH_4 + 2O_2 \rightarrow CO_2 + 2H_2O + 212.80 \text{ kcal}$$

or

$$CH_4 + 2O_2 \rightarrow CO_2 + 2H_2O \quad \Delta H = -212.80 \text{ kcal}$$

The combustion of 1 mole of CH_4 forms 1 mole of CO_2 and 2 moles of H_2O. From Table 20-1, ΔH_f for CO_2 is −94.05 kcal/mole and for H_2O is −68.32 kcal/mole. The heat of formation for methane can be calculated from these data as follows:

$$\Delta H_f(CH_4) = \Delta H_f(CO_2) + 2\Delta H_f(H_2O) - \Delta H_c(CH_4)$$

$$\Delta H_f(CH_4) = -94.05 \frac{kcal}{mole} + 2\left(-68.32 \frac{kcal}{mole}\right) - \left(-212.80 \frac{kcal}{mole}\right)$$

$$\Delta H_f(CH_4) = -17.89 \text{ kcal/mole}$$

CO is formed indirectly.

When carbon is burned in a limited supply of oxygen, carbon monoxide is produced. In this reaction carbon is probably first oxidized to CO_2. Some of the CO_2 may in turn be reduced to CO by hot carbon. The result is an uncertain mixture of the two gases.

$$C(s) + O_2(g) \rightarrow CO_2(g)$$

$$C(s) + CO_2(g) \rightarrow 2CO(g)$$

Because of this uncertainty, the heat of formation of CO cannot be determined by measuring directly the heat given off during the reaction. However, both carbon and carbon monoxide can be burned completely to carbon dioxide. The heat of formation of CO_2 and the heat of combustion of CO are then known (Tables 20-1 and 20-2). From these reaction heats, the heat of formation of CO can be determined by using the equality stated previously.

For the combustion of carbon,

$$C(s) + O_2(g) \rightarrow CO_2(g) + 94.05 \text{ kcal}$$

Thus

$$\Delta H_f \text{ of } (CO_2) = -94.05 \text{ kcal/mole}$$

For the combustion of carbon monoxide,

$$2CO(g) + O_2(g) \rightarrow 2CO_2(g) + 135.28 \text{ kcal}$$

Rewriting this equation for 1 mole of the reactant CO,

Recall that heat of combustion is defined in terms of 1 mole of a reactant.

$$CO(g) + \tfrac{1}{2}O_2(g) \rightarrow CO_2(g) + 67.64 \text{ kcal}$$

Thus

$$\Delta H_c \text{ of } CO = -67.64 \text{ kcal/mole}$$

But

$$\Delta H_f(CO) = \Delta H_f(CO_2) - \Delta H_c(CO)$$

Then, by substitution,

$$\Delta H_f(CO) = -94.05 \text{ kcal/mole} - (-67.64 \text{ kcal/mole})$$

$$\Delta H_f(CO) = -26.41 \text{ kcal/mole}$$

The heat of formation of CO can be added to the heat of combustion of CO to verify the heat of formation of CO_2 determined above.

$$C(s) + \tfrac{1}{2}O_2(g) \rightarrow CO(g) \qquad \Delta H_f = -26.41 \text{ kcal}$$
$$CO(g) + \tfrac{1}{2}O_2(g) \rightarrow CO_2(g) \qquad \Delta H_c = -67.64 \text{ kcal}$$
$$C(s) + O_2(g) \rightarrow CO_2(g) \qquad \Delta H_f = -94.05 \text{ kcal}$$

A thermochemical equation for the formation of CO can now be derived directly from its elements. To do so, the equations for the oxidation of carbon and the reduction of carbon dioxide are combined.

$$C(s) + O_2(g) \rightarrow CO_2(g) \qquad \text{(oxidation of C)}$$
$$C(s) + CO_2(g) \rightarrow 2CO(g) \qquad \text{(reduction of } CO_2)$$
$$2C(s) + O_2(g) \rightarrow 2CO(g) \qquad \text{(net reaction)}$$

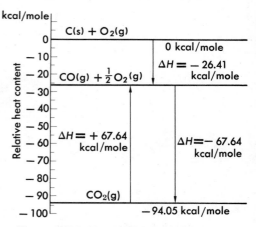

Figure 20-3. Heat of formation diagram for carbon dioxide and carbon monoxide.

Energy is conserved during a chemical reaction; the heat absorbed in decomposing a compound must be equal to the heat released in its formation under the same conditions. Thus, if there is a reason to write the equation for a reaction in reverse form, the sign of ΔH for the reaction must be reversed.

Suppose these principles are applied to the thermochemical equation for the combustion of carbon monoxide:

$$CO(g) + \tfrac{1}{2}O_2(g) \rightarrow CO_2(g) \qquad \Delta H_c = -67.64 \text{ kcal}$$

Writing the reverse of this reaction:

$$CO_2(g) \rightarrow CO(g) + \tfrac{1}{2}O_2(g) \qquad \Delta H_c = +67.64 \text{ kcal}$$

Observe that the sign of ΔH has been reversed to express the change in heat content for a reverse reaction. This principle is actually part of a more general one: *The heat of a given overall reaction is the same regardless of the intermediate steps involved.* The heat of formation of CO calculated from the following equations illustrates this additivity principle.

ΔH for a given overall reaction is independent of the reaction pathway.

$$C(s) + O_2(g) \rightarrow CO_2(g) \qquad \Delta H_f = -94.05 \text{ kcal}$$
$$CO_2(g) \rightarrow CO(g) + \tfrac{1}{2}O_2(g) \qquad \Delta H_c = +67.64 \text{ kcal}$$
$$C(s) + \tfrac{1}{2}O_2(g) \rightarrow CO(g) \qquad \Delta H_f = -26.41 \text{ kcal}$$

Referring to the endothermic reaction between carbon and steam first mentioned in Section 2.15, this "water-gas" reaction occurs spontaneously at the temperature of white-hot carbon. It produces a mixture of CO and H_2 that can be used as a gaseous fuel. What is the thermochemistry of this fuel?

The heat of formation of water is normally expressed in terms of the change in heat content between liquid water at 25 °C and its separate elements at the same temperature. Water vapor must give up 10.52 kcal/mole in order to condense to its liquid phase at 25 °C. This condensation is a physical change.

$$H_2O(g) \rightarrow H_2O(l) + 10.52 \text{ kcal}$$

Thus the steam in the reaction has a higher heat content (and a lower heat of formation) by 10.52 kcal than liquid water.

The following thermochemical equation shows the heat of formation of the product water as a gas from its composition reaction.

$$H_2(g) + \tfrac{1}{2}O_2(g) \rightarrow H_2O(g) + 57.80 \text{ kcal}$$

The complete relationship is shown by the following series of equations.

$$H_2(g) + \tfrac{1}{2}O_2(g) \rightarrow H_2O(g) \qquad \Delta H = -57.80 \text{ kcal}$$
$$H_2O(g) \rightarrow H_2O(l) \qquad \Delta H = -10.52 \text{ kcal}$$
$$\overline{H_2(g) + \tfrac{1}{2}O_2(g) \rightarrow H_2O(l) \qquad \Delta H = -68.32 \text{ kcal}}$$

Experiments have established the quantity of heat absorbed in the water-gas reaction as 31.39 kcal per mole of carbon used. The thermochemical equation is

$$H_2O(g) + C(s) + 31.39 \text{ kcal} \rightarrow CO(g) + H_2(g)$$

The water-gas reaction is endothermic and spontaneous.

The heat of reaction is absorbed; the heat content of the products CO and H_2 is greater than the heat content of the reactants C and H_2O.

When the product gases are burned as fuel, two combustion reactions occur. Carbon dioxide is the product of one and water vapor is the product of the other. Both are familiar reactions shown earlier in this section.

$$CO(g) + \tfrac{1}{2}O_2(g) \rightarrow CO_2(g) + 67.64 \text{ kcal}$$

$$H_2(g) + \tfrac{1}{2}O_2(g) \rightarrow H_2O(g) + 57.80 \text{ kcal}$$

These reactions are exothermic and the heats of combustion, ΔH_c, have negative values.

There are now three thermochemical equations representing the formation of the water gas and its combustion as a fuel. Suppose these equations are arranged in a series. The net additive result is shown below.

$$H_2O(g) + C(s) \rightarrow CO(g) + H_2(g) \qquad \Delta H = +31.39 \text{ kcal}$$
$$CO(g) + \tfrac{1}{2}O_2(g) \rightarrow CO_2(g) \qquad \Delta H = -67.64 \text{ kcal}$$
$$\overline{H_2(g) + \tfrac{1}{2}O_2(g) \rightarrow H_2O(g) \qquad \Delta H = -57.80 \text{ kcal}}$$
$$C(s) + O_2(g) \rightarrow CO_2(g) \qquad \Delta H = -94.05 \text{ kcal}$$

The combined heat of combustion of CO and H_2 is −125.44 kcal. Observe that this value is higher than that of carbon (−94.05 kcal). However, it is higher only by the amount of heat energy put into the first reaction (+31.39 kcal).

☐ 20.6 Bond energy and reaction heat

The change in heat content of a reaction system is related to (1) the change in the number of bonds breaking and forming, and (2) the strengths of these bonds as the reactants form products.

The reaction for the formation of water gas can be used to test this relationship.

The two oxygen-to-hydrogen bonds of each steam molecule must be broken, as must the carbon-to-carbon bonds of the graphite. Carbon-to-oxygen and hydrogen-to-hydrogen bonds must be formed. Recall that energy is absorbed when bonds are broken, and energy is released when bonds are formed.

A possible reaction mechanism for the water-gas reaction in which there is an intermediate stage of free atoms is illustrated in Figure 20-4. Observe that a heat input of 390 kcal is required to break the bonds of 1 mole of graphite and 1 mole of steam. The formation of bonds in the final state releases 358 kcal of heat energy. The net effect is that 32 kcal of heat must be supplied to the system from an external source. This quantity agrees closely with the experimental value of 31.39 kcal of heat input per mole of carbon used.

Figure 20-4. A possible mechanism for the water-gas reaction.

$$C(s) + H_2O(g) + 31.4 \text{ kcal} \longrightarrow CO(g) + H_2(g)$$

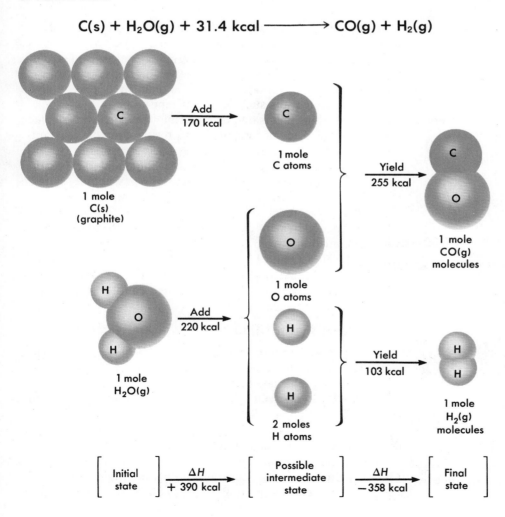

Thermodynamics: the experimental study of the relationship between heat energy and other forms of energy.

In its basic connotation, "state" refers to the "condition" of a substance or system.

Reaction systems that absorb energy are endothermic.

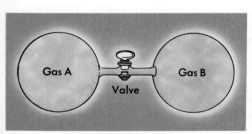

Figure 20-5. The mixing of gases may occur without an energy change.

◻ 20.7 Factors that drive reactions

Whether a reaction occurs and how it occurs are questions that have always concerned chemists. The answers to these questions involve a study of reaction mechanisms and reaction kinetics conducted within the framework of the laws of thermodynamics. This is the realm of *physical chemistry* and *physics*. Here, the concepts that chemists label collectively as the "driving force" of chemical reactions will be examined. Some of these concepts were discussed briefly in Section 2.15.

By observation, it is recognized that most reactions occurring spontaneously in nature are exothermic; they give off energy and lead to lower energy states and more stable structural configurations. The quantity *H*, the energy content of a system, is a function of the state of the system. The drive toward a favorable change in energy content, ΔH, is responsible for this *tendency for processes to occur that lead to the lowest possible energy state.*

If the driving force depended on this energy-change tendency alone, no endothermic reaction could take place spontaneously. One could predict that only exothermic reactions are spontaneous. A great deal of evidence shows that most reactions do release energy. In fact, the greater the quantity of energy given up, the more vigorous such reactions tend to be.

The disturbing fact is that endothermic reactions *do* take place spontaneously. They occur simply as a result of mixing reactants. The production of water gas involves such a reaction. Steam is passed into white-hot coke (impure carbon), and the reaction proceeds spontaneously. It is not driven by any activity outside the reacting system. The process is endothermic: heat is absorbed, and the reaction system cools. Therefore, more heat must be supplied by periodically blowing air into the coke to cause some combustion. From Section 20.5 it is recognized that the product gases, CO and H_2, collectively have a higher heat content than the reactants, steam and carbon. The energy change is positive. This unfavorable energy change cannot be the factor that drives the reaction.

$$H_2O(g) + C(s) \rightarrow CO(g) + H_2(g) \qquad \Delta H = +31.39 \text{ kcal}$$

To see how an endothermic reaction can occur spontaneously, consider a simple physical process that proceeds by and of itself with no energy change. Figure 20-5 shows two identical flasks connected by a valve. One flask is filled with ideal gas **A** and the other with ideal gas **B**. The entire system is at room temperature.

When the valve is opened, the two gases mix until they are distributed evenly throughout the two containers. The gases will remain in this state indefinitely, with no tendency to separate. The temperature remains constant throughout the process. Thus the total heat content cannot have changed to a lower level.

Clearly, the self-mixing process must be caused by a driving force other than the energy-change tendency. What, then, is the driving force for this process?

The concept of *a tendency for processes to occur that lead to the highest possible state of disorder* was discussed briefly in Section 2.15. In general, a system that can go from one state to another without an energy change will adopt the more disordered state, as illustrated in Figure 20-5. There is a quantity *S*, known as *entropy,* which is a function of the state of a system. In the water-gas reaction, the final mixed system of gases represents a more disordered state than the initial pure-gas system. In other words, a favorable entropy change has occurred. The entropy of the mixed-gas system is higher than the entropy of the pure-gas system. The factor that drives the reaction is the *tendency for the disorder (entropy) of the system to increase.*

Entropy describes the state of disorder.

Thus the property of a system that drives the reaction depends on two factors, the tendency toward *lowest energy* and the tendency toward *highest entropy.* A new function of the state of a reaction system has been defined to relate the energy and entropy factors at a given temperature. It is called the *free energy, G,* of the system. It is the function that simultaneously assesses both the energy-change and entropy-change tendencies. In this sense, a reaction system proceeds spontaneously in the way that *lowers its free energy.*

Natural processes tend toward (1) minimum energy and (2) maximum disorder.

The net driving force is called the *free-energy change, ΔG,* of the system. When the energy change and the entropy change oppose each other, the direction of the net driving force is determined by the factor having the larger influence. The free-energy change, ΔG, indicates the quantity of energy that is *free* to perform useful work.

A process is spontaneous in the direction of lower free energy.

At a constant pressure and temperature, *the **free-energy change**, ΔG,* is a property of the reaction system *defined as the difference between the change in heat content, ΔH, and the product of the temperature and the entropy change, $T\Delta S$.*

$$\Delta G = \Delta H - T\Delta S$$

Here ΔG is the change in free energy of the system, ΔH is the change in the heat content, T is the temperature in °K, and ΔS is the change in entropy. (ΔG, ΔH, and the product $T\Delta S$ all have the same dimensions, usually kilocalories per mole. What are the dimensions of ΔS?)

A chemical reaction proceeds spontaneously if it is accompanied by a decrease in free energy. That is, it proceeds spontaneously if the free energy of the products is lower than that of the reactants. In such a case, the *free energy change, ΔG,* in the system is *negative.*

In exothermic reactions ΔH has a negative value. In endothermic reactions its value is positive. From the expression for

ΔG, observe that the more negative ΔH is, the more negative ΔG is likely to be. Reaction systems that change from a high- to a low-energy state tend to proceed spontaneously. Also observe that the more positive ΔS is, the more negative ΔG is likely to be. Thus systems that change from well-ordered states to highly disordered states also tend to proceed spontaneously. Both of these tendencies in a given reaction system are assessed simultaneously in terms of the free-energy change, ΔG.

Spontaneous reaction: ΔG is negative.

In some processes ΔH is negative and ΔS is positive. Here, the process should proceed spontaneously because ΔG is negative regardless of the relative magnitudes of ΔH and ΔS. Processes in which ΔH and ΔS have the same signs are more common. Note that the sign of ΔG can be either positive or negative depending on the temperature T. The temperature of the system is the dominant factor that determines the relative importance of the tendency toward lower energy and the tendency toward higher entropy.

Consider again the water-gas reaction,

$$H_2O(g) + C(s) \rightarrow CO_2(g) + H_2(g) \qquad \Delta H = +31.39 \text{ kcal}$$

Here, a negative free-energy change would require that $T\Delta S$ be positive and greater than 31.39 kcal. This can be so if T is large, or if ΔS is large and positive, or both. Consider first the magnitude and sign of ΔS.

Recall that the solid phase is well-ordered and the gaseous phase is random. One of the reactants, carbon, is a solid and the other, steam, is a gas. However, both products are gases. The change from the orderly solid phase to the random gaseous phase involves an *increase* in entropy. In general, a change from a solid to a gas will proceed with an increase in entropy. If all reactants and products are gases, an increase in the number of product particles increases entropy.

At low temperatures, whether ΔS is positive or negative, the product $T\Delta S$ may be small compared to ΔH. In such cases, the reaction proceeds as the energy change predicts.

Careful measurements show that ΔS for the water-gas reaction is +0.0320 kcal/mole °K at 25 °C (298 °K). Thus

$$T\Delta S = 298 \text{ °K} \times 0.0320 \frac{\text{kcal}}{\text{mole °K}} = 9.54 \frac{\text{kcal}}{\text{mole}}$$

$$\Delta G = \Delta H - T\Delta S = +31.39 \frac{\text{kcal}}{\text{mole}} - 9.54 \frac{\text{kcal}}{\text{mole}}$$

and

$$\Delta G = +21.85 \frac{\text{kcal}}{\text{mole}}$$

Since ΔG has a positive value, the reaction is not spontaneous at 25 °C.

Increases in temperature tend to favor increases in entropy. When ΔS is positive, a high temperature gives $T\Delta S$ a large positive value. Certainly, at a high enough temperature $T\Delta S$ will be larger than ΔH, and ΔG will have a negative value.

The water-gas reaction occurs at the temperature of white-hot carbon, approximately 900 °C. The values of ΔH and ΔS are different at different temperatures. However, if they are assumed to remain about the same at the reaction temperature of 900 °C, an approximate value of ΔG can be calculated for this temperature. Retaining the value of ΔH as +31.39 kcal/mole, $T\Delta S$ is determined at 1173 °K (900 °C) to be

Higher temperature — higher entropy.

$$T\Delta S = 1173 \text{ °K} \times 0.0320 \ \frac{\text{kcal}}{\text{mole °K}} = 37.5 \ \frac{\text{kcal}}{\text{mole}}$$

$$\Delta G = \Delta H - T\Delta S = +31.39 \ \frac{\text{kcal}}{\text{mole}} - 37.5 \ \frac{\text{kcal}}{\text{mole}}$$

$$\Delta G = -6.1 \text{ kcal/mole}$$

The free-energy change for the water-gas reaction is negative at 900 °C, and the reaction is spontaneous at this temperature.

◻ 20.8 Reaction pathways

REACTION MECHANISMS

Chemical reactions involve breaking existing chemical bonds and forming new ones. The relationships and arrangements of atoms in the products of a reaction are different from those in the reactants. Colorless hydrogen gas consists of pairs of hydrogen atoms bonded together as diatomic molecules, H_2. Violet-colored iodine vapor is also diatomic, consisting of pairs of iodine atoms bonded together as I_2 molecules. A chemical reaction between these two gases produces hydrogen iodide, HI, a colorless gas. Hydrogen iodide molecules, in turn, tend to decompose and re-form hydrogen and iodine molecules. The equations for the reactions are

$$H_2(g) + I_2(g) \rightarrow 2HI(g)$$

and

$$2HI(g) \rightarrow H_2(g) + I_2(g)$$

These equations indicate only what molecular species disappear as a result of the reactions and what species are produced. They do not show the pathway by which either reaction proceeds. That is, they do not show the step-by-step sequence of reactions by which the over-all chemical change occurs. Such a sequence, when known, is called the *reaction pathway* or *reaction mechanism*.

A chemical system can usually be examined before the reaction occurs or after the reaction is over. However, such an examination reveals nothing about the pathway by which the action proceeded. See Figure 20-6. For most chemical reactions, only the reactants that disappear and the final products that appear are known. In other words, only the net chemical change is directly observable.

Sometimes chemists are able to devise experiments that reveal a sequence of steps in a reaction pathway. They attempt to learn how the speed of a reaction is affected by various factors. Such factors may include temperature, concentrations of reactants and products, and the effects of catalysts. Radioactive tracer techniques are sometimes helpful.

An overall chemical reaction may proceed in a sequence of simple steps.

A chemical reaction might occur in a single step or in a sequence of steps. Each reaction step is usually a relatively simple process. Complicated chemical reactions take place in a sequence of simple steps. Even a reaction that appears from its balanced equation to be a simple process may actually occur in a sequence of steps.

The reaction between hydrogen gas and bromine vapor to produce hydrogen bromide gas is an example of a *homogeneous reaction*. The reaction system involves a single phase—the gas phase. This reaction system is also an example of a *homogeneous chemical system*. In such a system, all reactants and products in all intermediate steps are in the same phase. The overall chemical equation for this reaction is

$$H_2(g) + Br_2(g) \rightleftarrows 2HBr(g)$$

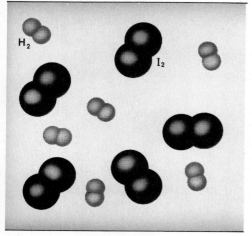

Initial state

It might appear that one hydrogen molecule reacts with one bromine molecule to form the product in a simple, one-step process. However, chemists have found through kinetic studies that the reaction follows a more complex pathway. The initial forward reaction (and the terminating reverse reaction) is

$$Br_2 \rightleftarrows 2Br \qquad (1)$$

This initial step provides bromine atoms that, in turn, initiate a sequence of two steps which can repeat themselves.

$$Br + H_2 \rightleftarrows HBr + H \qquad (2)$$

$$H + Br_2 \rightleftarrows HBr + Br \qquad (3)$$

Observe that the sum of steps 2 and 3 gives the net reaction as shown in the overall equation above.

The equation

$$H_2(g) + I_2(g) \rightleftarrows 2HI(g)$$

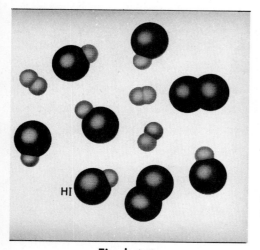

Final state

Figure 20-6. The initial and final states of a mixture of hydrogen gas and iodine vapor which react to form hydrogen iodide gas.

represents another homogeneous chemical system. Figure 20-6 illustrates the initial reactants and final products identified by this equation. For many years chemists thought this reaction was a simple, one-step process. They assumed it involved two molecules, $H_2 + I_2$, in the forward direction and two molecules, HI + HI, in the reverse reaction.

Recent experiments have shown that the reaction $H_2 + I_2$ does not take place. Instead, two possible mechanisms have been proposed. The first has a two-step pathway:

$$I_2 \rightleftarrows 2I \qquad (1)$$

$$2I + H_2 \rightleftarrows 2HI \qquad (2)$$

The second possible mechanism has a three-step pathway:

$$I_2 \rightleftarrows 2I \qquad (1)$$

$$I + H_2 \rightleftarrows H_2I \qquad (2)$$

$$H_2I + I \rightleftarrows 2HI \qquad (3)$$

It appears that, no matter how simple the balanced equation, the reaction pathway may be complicated and difficult to determine. Some chemists feel that simple, one-step reaction mechanisms are unlikely. They suggest that the only simple reactions are those that have not been thoroughly studied.

◻ 20.9 Collision theory

In order for reactions to occur between substances, their particles (molecules, atoms, or ions) must collide. Further, these collisions must result in interactions. Chemists use this *collision theory* to interpret many facts they observe about chemical reactions.

From the kinetic theory you know that the molecules of gases are continuously in random motion. The molecules have kinetic energies ranging from very low to very high values. The energies of the greatest portion are near the average for all the molecules in the system. When the temperature of a gas is raised, the average kinetic energy of the molecules is increased. Therefore, their speed is increased. This relationship is shown in Figure 20-7.

Consider what happens on a molecular scale in one step of a homogeneous reaction system. A good example is the decomposition of hydrogen iodide. The reaction for the first step in the decomposition pathway is

$$HI + HI \rightarrow H_2 + 2I$$

According to the collision theory, the two gas molecules must collide in order to react. Further, they must collide while favorably oriented and with enough energy to disrupt the bonds of the molecules. If they do so, a reshuffling of bonds leads to the formation of the new particle species of the products.

A collision may be too gentle. Here, the distance between the colliding molecules is never small enough to disrupt old bonds

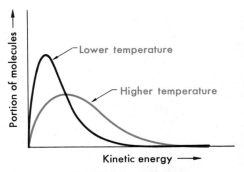

Figure 20-7. Energy distribution among gas molecules at two different temperatures.

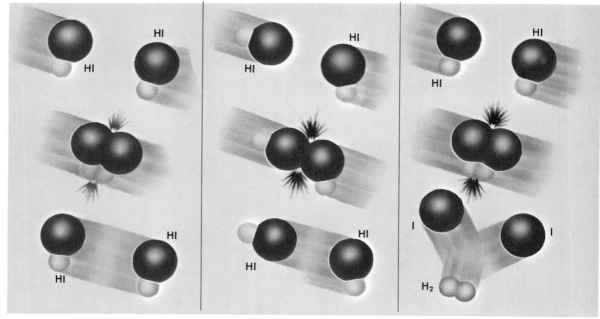

(A) Collision too gentle   (B) Collision in poor orientation   (C) Effective collision

Figure 20-8. Possible collision patterns for HI molecules.

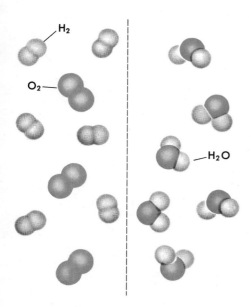

Figure 20-9. A mixture of hydrogen and oxygen molecules will form very stable water molecules when properly activated.

or form new ones. The two molecules simply rebound from each other unchanged. This effect is illustrated in Figure 20-8(A).

Similarly, a collision in which the reactant molecules are poorly oriented has little effect. The distance between certain atoms is never small enough for new bonds to form. The colliding molecules rebound without changing. A poorly oriented collision is shown in Figure 20-8(B).

However, a collision may be suitably oriented and violent enough to cause an interpenetration of the electron clouds of the colliding molecules. Then the distance between the reactant particles *does* become small enough for new bonds to form. See Figure 20-8(C). The minimum energy required to produce this effective collision is called the *activation energy* for the reaction.

Thus collision theory provides two reasons why a collision between reactant molecules may fail to produce a new chemical species. (1) *The collision is not energetic enough to supply the required activation energy.* (2) *The colliding molecules are not oriented in a way that enables them to react with each other.* What then is the reaction pathway of an effective collision that produces a new chemical species?

◻ 20.10 Activation energy

Consider the reaction for the formation of water from the diatomic gases oxygen and hydrogen. The heat of formation is quite high; $\Delta H = -68.3$ kcal/mole at 25 °C. The free energy change is also large; $\Delta G = -56.7$ kcal/mole. Why then do hydrogen and oxygen not combine spontaneously to form water when they are mixed at room temperature?

Hydrogen and oxygen gases exist as diatomic molecules. By some reaction mechanism, the bonds of these molecular species must be broken. Then new bonds between oxygen and hydrogen atoms must be formed. Bond-breaking is an endothermic process and bond-forming is exothermic. Even though the net process is exothermic, it appears that an initial energy "kick" is needed to start the reaction.

It might help to think of the reactants as lying in an energy "trough." They must be lifted from this trough before they can react to form water, even though the energy content of the product is lower than that of the reactants. Once the reaction is started, the energy released is enough to sustain the reaction by activating other molecules. Thus the reaction rate keeps increasing. It is finally limited only by the time required for reactant particles to acquire the energy and make contact.

The energy needed to lift the reactants from the energy trough is called *activation energy*. It is the energy required to loosen bonds in molecules so they can become reactive. Energy from a flame, a spark discharge, or the energy associated with high temperatures or radiations may start reactants along the pathway of reaction. The activation-energy concept is illustrated in Figure 20-10.

The reverse reaction is the decomposition of water molecules. The product water lies in an energy trough deeper than the one from which the reactants were lifted. The water molecules must be lifted from this deeper energy trough before they can decompose to form oxygen and hydrogen. The activation energy needed to start this endothermic reaction is greater than that required for the original exothermic change. The difference equals the amount of energy of reaction, ΔH, released in the original reaction. See Figure 20-11.

This situation can be compared to two mountain valleys separated by a high mountain pass. One valley is lower than the other. Still, to get to it from the upper valley, one must climb over the high pass. The return trip to the upper valley can be made only by climbing over the same high pass again. For this trip, however, one must climb up a greater height since the starting point is lower.

In Figure 20-12, the difference in height of the two valley floors is compared to the energy of reaction, ΔH. Energies E_a and E_a' represent the activation energies of the forward and reverse reactions, respectively. These quantities are compared to the heights of the pass above the high and low valleys.

◻ 20.11 The activated complex

The possession of high motion energy (kinetic energy) does not make molecules unstable. However, when molecules collide,

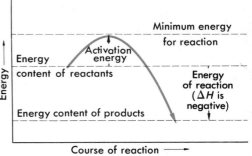

Figure 20-10. Pathway of an exothermic reaction.

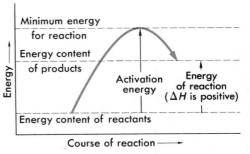

Figure 20-11. Pathway of an endothermic reaction.

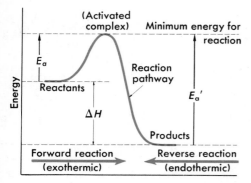

Figure 20-12. Activation energies for the forward reaction E_a and the reverse reaction E_a', and the change in internal energy ΔH in a reversible reaction.

Effective collisions produce transitional complexes.

some of this energy is converted into internal (potential) energy within the colliding molecules. If enough energy is converted, the molecules may be activated.

When particles collide with energy at least equal to the activation energy for the species involved, their interpenetration disrupts existing bonds. New bonds can then form. In the brief interval of bond disruption and bond formation, the *collision complex* is said to be in a *transition state*. Some sort of partial bonding exists in this state. *A transitional structure results from an effective collision. This structure persists while old bonds are breaking and new bonds are forming. It is called the **activated complex**.*

An activated complex is formed when an effective collision raises the internal energies of the reactants to their *minimum-energy-for-reaction level*. See Figure 20-12. Both forward and reverse reactions go through the same activated complex. Suppose a bond is in the process of being broken in the activated complex for the forward reaction. The same bond is in the process of being formed in the activated complex for the reverse reaction. Observe that the activated complex occurs at the maximum energy position along the reaction pathway. In this sense the activated complex defines the activation energy for the system. *Activation energy is the energy required to transform the reactants into the activated complex.*

In its brief existence, the activated complex has partial bonding of both reactant and product. In this state, it may respond to either of two possibilities. (1) It may re-form the original bonds and separate into the reactant particles. (2) It may form new bonds and separate into product particles. Usually the formation of products is just as likely as the formation of reactants. *Do not confuse the activated complex with the intermediate compounds produced at different steps of a reaction mechanism.* The activated complex is a molecular complex in which bonds are in the process of being broken and formed.

A possible configuration of the activated complex in the hydrogen iodide reaction is shown in Figure 20-13. The broken lines represent some sort of partial bonding in the particle. This transitional structure may produce two HI molecules or an H_2 molecule and two I atoms.

Figure 20-14 shows the energy profile for the HI decomposition. Of the 43.8 kcal activation energy, 40.8 kcal is available for excitation of the H_2 and I_2 molecules. Of this amount, 35.5 kcal is used in producing I atoms.

☐ 20.12 Rate-influencing factors

The rates of chemical reactions vary widely. Some reactions are over in an instant, while others take months or years to complete. *The rate of reaction is measured by the amount of reactants*

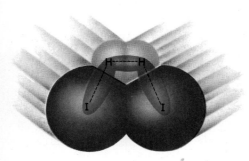

Figure 20-13. Possible activated complex configuration which could form either 2HI or H_2 + 2I.

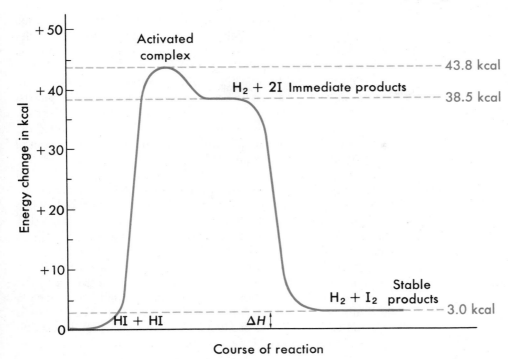

Figure 20-14. An energy profile—experimental results of kinetic studies of hydrogen iodide decomposition.

Reaction rates depend on (1) collision frequency and (2) collision efficiency.

converted to products in a unit of time. Two conditions are necessary for reactions (other than simple decompositions) to occur at all. First, particles must come in contact. Second, this contact must result in interaction. Thus the *rate* of a reaction depends on the *collision frequency* of the reactants and on the *collision efficiency.* (An efficient collision is one with enough energy for activation and in which the reactant molecules are favorably oriented.)

Changing conditions may affect either the frequency of collisions or the collision efficiency. Any such change influences the reaction rate. Five important factors influence the rate of chemical reaction.

1. Nature of the reactants. Hydrogen combines vigorously with chlorine under certain conditions. Under the same conditions it may react only feebly with nitrogen. Sodium and oxygen combine much more rapidly than iron and oxygen under similar conditions. Platinum and oxygen do not combine directly. Atoms, ions, and molecules are the particles of substances that react. Bonds are broken and other bonds are formed in chemical reactions. The rate of reaction depends on the particular bonds involved.

2. Amount of surface. The solution rate for a crystalline solid in water is increased if the crystals are first broken down into small pieces. A cube of solute measuring 1 cm on each edge presents only 6 cm^2 of contact area to the solvent. This same cube when ground to a fine powder might provide a contact area of the order of 10^4 times the original area. Consequently, the solution rate of the powdered solid is greatly increased.

A lump of coal burns slowly when kindled in air. The rate of burning can be increased by breaking the lump into smaller pieces, exposing new surfaces. If the piece of coal is powdered and ignited while suspended in air, it burns explosively. Nickel in large pieces shows no noticeable oxidation in air, but finely powdered nickel reacts vigorously and spectacularly.

Heterogeneous: not uniform throughout.

These reactions between solids and gases are examples of *heterogeneous reactions. Heterogeneous reactions involve reactants in two different phases.* Such reactions can occur only when the two phases are in contact. Thus the amount of surface of a solid (or liquid) reactant is an important *rate* consideration. *Gases* and *dissolved* particles do not have surfaces in the sense just described. *In heterogeneous reactions the reaction rate is proportional to the area of contact of the reacting substances.*

Some chemical reactions between gases actually take place at the walls of the container. Others occur at the surface of a solid or liquid catalyst. If the products are also gases, such a reaction system presents a problem of language. It is a *heterogeneous* reaction because it takes place between two phases. On the other hand, it is a *homogeneous* chemical system because all of the reactants and all of the products are in one phase.

3. Effect of concentration. Suppose a small lump of charcoal is heated in air until combustion begins. If it is then lowered into a bottle of pure oxygen, the reaction proceeds at a much faster rate. A substance that oxidizes in air reacts more vigorously in pure oxygen, as shown in Figure 20-15. The partial pressure of oxygen in air is approximately one-fifth of the total pressure. Pure oxygen at the same pressure as the air has five times the *concentration* of oxygen molecules.

This charcoal oxidation is a heterogeneous reaction system in which one reactant is a gas. Not only does the reaction rate depend on the amount of exposed charcoal surface, *it depends on the concentration of the gas as well.*

Homogeneous reactions may involve reactants in liquid or gaseous solutions. The concentration of gases changes with pressure according to Boyle's law. In liquid solutions, the concentration of reactants changes if either the quantity of solute or the quantity of solvent is changed. Solids and liquids are practically noncompressible. Thus it is not possible to change the concentration of pure solids and pure liquids to any measurable extent.

Reaction rate: effect of concentration of reactants is determined experimentally.

In homogeneous reaction systems, reaction rates depend on the concentration of the reactants. From collision theory, a rate increase might be expected if the concentration of one or more of the reactants is increased. Lowering the concentration should

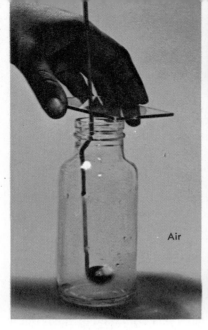
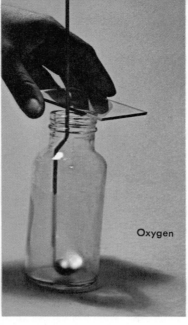

Air   Oxygen

Figure 20-15. Carbon burns faster in oxygen than in air because of the higher concentration of oxygen molecules.

have the opposite effect. However, the specific effect of concentration changes *must be determined experimentally.*

Increasing the concentration of substance **A** in reaction with substance **B** could increase the reaction rate, decrease it, or have no effect on it. The effect depends on the particular reaction. *One cannot tell from the balanced equation for the net reaction how the reaction rate is affected by a change in concentration of reactants.* Chemists account for these differences in behavior in terms of the reaction mechanisms.

Complex chemical reactions may take place in a *series* of simple steps. Instead of a single activated complex, there may be several activated complexes in sequence along the reaction pathway. Of these steps, the one that proceeds at the slowest rate determines the overall reaction rate. When this slowest-rate step can be identified, it is called the *rate-determining step* for the reaction.

4. Effect of temperature. The average kinetic energy of the particles of a substance is proportional to the temperature of the substance. Collision theory explains why a rise in temperature increases the rate of chemical reaction. According to this theory, a decrease in temperature lowers the reaction rate for both exothermic and endothermic reactions.

Reaction rate: slowest step is the rate-determining step.

At room temperature, the rates of many reactions roughly double or triple with a 10 C° rise in temperature. However, this rule must be used with caution. The actual rate increase with a given rise in temperature *must be determined experimentally.*

Large increases in reaction rate are caused partly by the increase in collision frequency of reactant particles. However, for a chemical reaction to occur, the particles must also collide with enough energy to cause them to react. At higher temperatures more particles possess enough energy to form the activated complex when collisions occur. In other words, more particles have the necessary activation energy. Thus a rise in temperature produces an increase in collision energy as well as collision frequency.

5. *Action of catalysts.* Some chemical reactions proceed quite slowly. Frequently their reaction rates can be increased dramatically by the presence of a *catalyst*. A **catalyst** *is a substance or substances that increases the rate of a chemical reaction without itself being permanently consumed.* Catalytic activity is called *catalysis.* Catalysts do not appear among the final products of reactions they accelerate. They may participate in one step along a reaction pathway and be regenerated in a later step. In large-scale and cost-sensitive reaction systems, the catalysts are recovered and reused.

A catalyst that is in the same phase as all the reactants and products in a reaction system is called a *homogeneous catalyst.* When its phase is different from that of the reactants, it is called a *heterogeneous catalyst.* Metals are often used as heterogeneous catalysts. The catalysis of the reaction is promoted by adsorption of reactants on the metal surfaces, which has the effect of increasing the concentration (and therefore the contacts) of the reactants.

Such catalytic actions are hindered by the presence of substances called *inhibitors.* These inhibitors, once referred to as negative catalysts, interfere with the surface chemistry of heterogeneous catalysts and thus *inhibit* and eventually destroy the

Enzymes are biochemical catalysts. Each enzyme accelerates a specific digestive process, thus enabling the chemical reaction to be completed in a few hours. The same uncatalyzed process might require several weeks for completion.

Figure 20-16. Possible difference in potential-energy change along alternate reaction pathways, one catalyzed and the other uncatalyzed.

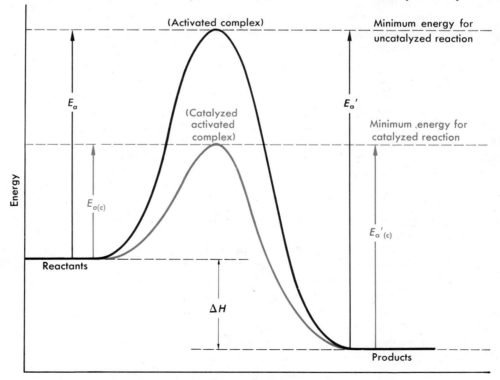

catalytic action. An example is the "poisoning" of metallic oxide catalysts in the catalytic converters of automobile exhaust systems by leaded gasoline.

Chemists believe that a catalyst provides an alternate pathway or reaction mechanism in which the potential energy barrier between reactants and products is lowered. The catalyst may be effective in forming an alternate activated complex that requires a lower activation energy, as suggested in the energy profiles of Figure 20-16.

Catalysts may provide alternate reaction pathways.

☐ 20.13 Reaction rate law

The influence of reactant concentrations on reaction rate in a given chemical system has been mentioned. Measuring this influence is a challenging part of kinetics. Chemists determine the relationship between the rate of a reaction and the concentration of one reactant by first keeping the concentrations of other reactants and the temperature of the system constant. Then the reaction rate is measured for various concentrations of the reactant in question. A series of such experiments reveals how the concentration of each reactant affects the reaction rate.

The following homogeneous reaction is used as an illustration. The reaction is carried out in a vessel of constant volume and at an elevated *constant* temperature.

$$2H_2(g) + 2NO(g) \rightarrow N_2(g) + 2H_2O(g)$$

Here, four moles of reactant gases produces three moles of product gases. Thus the pressure of the system diminishes as the reaction proceeds. The rate of the reaction is determined by measuring the change of pressure in the vessel with time.

Suppose a series of experiments is conducted using the same initial concentration of nitrogen monoxide but different initial concentrations of hydrogen. The initial reaction rate is found to vary directly with the hydrogen concentration. That is, doubling the concentration of H_2 doubles the rate, and tripling the concentration of H_2 triples the rate. Therefore,

$$R \propto [H_2]$$

Here R is the reaction rate and $[H_2]$ is the molecular concentration of hydrogen in moles per liter. The $\propto$ is a proportionality symbol.

Now suppose the same initial concentration of hydrogen is used but the initial concentrations of nitrogen monoxide are varied. The initial reaction rate is found to increase four times when the NO concentration is doubled and nine times when the concentration of NO is tripled. Thus the reaction rate varies directly with the *square* of the nitrogen monoxide concentration.

$$R \propto [NO]^2$$

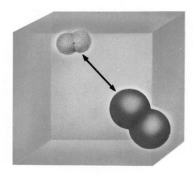

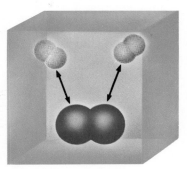

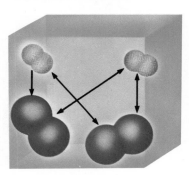

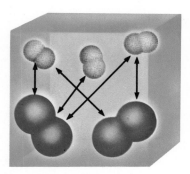

Figure 20-17. Under constant conditions, the collision frequency increases with the concentration of each reactant.

Since R is proportional to $[H_2]$ and to $[NO]^2$, it is proportional to their product.

$$R \propto [H_2][NO]^2$$

By introducing an appropriate proportionality constant k, the expression becomes an equality.

$$R = k[H_2][NO]^2$$

This equation relating the reaction rate and concentrations of reactants is called the *rate law* for the reaction. It is constant for a specific reaction at a given temperature. A rise in temperature causes an increase in the rate of nearly all reactions. Thus the value of k usually increases as the temperature increases.

Collision theory indicates that the number of collisions between particles increases as the concentration of these particles is raised. The reaction rate *for any step* in a reaction pathway is directly proportional to the frequency of collisions between the particles involved. It is also directly proportional to the collision efficiency.

Consider a single step in a reaction pathway. Suppose one molecule of gas **A** collides with one molecule of gas **B** to form two molecules of substance **C**. The equation for the step is

$$A + B \rightarrow 2C$$

One particle of each reactant is involved in each collision. Thus doubling the concentration of either reactant will double the collision frequency. It will also double the reaction rate *for this step*. Therefore, the rate is directly proportional to the concentration of **A** and of **B**. The rate law for the step becomes

$$R = k[A][B]$$

Now suppose the reaction is reversible. In this reverse step, two molecules of **C** must collide to form one molecule of **A** and one of **B**.

$$2C \rightarrow A + B$$

Thus the reaction rate *for this reverse step* is directly proportional to $[C] \times [C]$. The rate law for the step becomes

$$R = k[C]^2$$

A simple relationship *may* exist between the chemical equation *for a step in a reaction pathway* and *the rate law for that step*. Observe that the *power* to which the molar concentration of each reactant or product is raised in the rate laws above corresponds to the coefficient for the reactant or product in the balanced equation.

This relationship *does not always hold*. It holds if the reaction follows a simple one-step pathway. A reaction may proceed in a series of steps, however, and in such reactions *the rate law is simply that for the slowest (rate-determining) step*. Thus the rate law for a reaction must be determined experimentally. *It cannot be written from the balanced equation for the net reaction.*

Again consider the hydrogen–nitrogen monoxide reaction. The balanced equation for the net reaction is

$$2H_2(g) + 2NO(g) \rightarrow N_2(g) + 2H_2O(g)$$

Suppose this reaction occurs in a single step involving a collision between two H_2 molecules and two NO molecules. Doubling the concentration of either reactant should quadruple the collision frequency and the rate. The rate law should then be proportional to $[H_2]^2$ as well as $[NO]^2$. It would take the form

$$R = k[H_2]^2[NO]^2$$

This equation is *not* in agreement with experimental results. Thus the assumed reaction mechanism cannot be correct.

The experimental rate law for the net reaction is actually

$$R = k[H_2][NO]^2$$

Therefore, the reaction pathway must consist of more than one step. The slowest step is rate-determining. The rate law found experimentally for the net reaction is the rate expression of this step.

The general form for a rate law is

$$R = k[A]^n[B]^m \text{-----}$$

Here R is the reaction rate, k is the rate constant, and $[A]$ and $[B]$----- represent the molar concentrations of reactants. The n and m are the respective powers to which the concentrations are raised, *based on experimental data.* Again it should be emphasized that one *cannot* assume that the coefficients in the balanced equation for a net reaction are the exponents in the rate law for the reaction.

The dependence of reaction rate on concentration of reactants was first recognized as a general principle by two Norwegian chemists, Guldberg and Waage, in 1867. It was stated as the **law of mass action:** *the rate of a chemical reaction is directly proportional to the product of the concentrations of reacting substances, each raised to the appropriate power.* This principle is interpreted in terms of the rate law for a chemical system in modern reaction kinetics.

In a rate law, the exponents of reactant concentrations are determined experimentally.

Cato Maximilian Guldberg (1836– 1902) was professor of applied mathematics and technology and Peter Waage (1833–1900) was professor of chemistry at the University of Oslo. They collaborated on the mathematical expression of the law of mass action.

◀ **SUMMARY**

Heat energy is released or absorbed during chemical reactions as the heat of reaction. An exothermic reaction has products with a total heat content lower than that of the reactants. An endothermic reaction has products with a heat content higher than that of the reactants. Inclusion of the heat of reaction information in the chemical equation for a reaction is customary when the energy change is important. Such an equation is called a thermochemical equation.

The heat content of a substance is represented by the letter H and is usually expressed in kilocalories per mole. The change in heat content, the difference between the heat content of products and reactants, is represented as ΔH. For endothermic reactions, ΔH is a positive quantity; for exothermic reactions, it is negative. Changes in heat content in reaction systems are related to changes in the number of bonds breaking and forming, and the strengths of these bonds as reactants form products.

The heat of reaction released or absorbed during the formation of one mole of a compound from its elements is called its heat of formation. The stability of a compound is related to its heat of formation. The heat of reaction released during the complete combustion of one mole of a substance is called its heat of combustion. The heat of formation of a compound not formed directly from its elements may be determined from its heat of combustion and the heats of formation of its combustion products.

The driving force of reaction systems consists of tendencies for processes to occur that lead to lower energy and to higher entropy (state of disorder). The assessment of these two tendencies in a reaction system is expressed in terms of a change in the free energy of the system, ΔG. If the reaction process results in lower free energy, it tends to proceed spontaneously. At low temperatures, the change in heat content toward a lower energy state is the driving force that dominates reaction systems. At high temperatures, the change in entropy toward a higher entropy state dominates reaction systems. Processes that do not proceed spontaneously at low temperatures may become spontaneous at some higher temperature.

A chemical reaction may occur in a sequence of simple steps called the reaction pathway or reaction mechanism. Chemists use the collision theory to help them interpret their observations of reaction processes. According to the collision theory, for reactions to occur, particles must collide and these collisions must result in interactions between the particles. The minimum energy required to produce effective collisions is the activation energy for the reaction. If a collision is energetic enough and the colliding molecules are suitably oriented, an activated complex is formed for a brief interval. It is a molecular complex in which bonds are being broken and formed.

Factors that influence the rate of a chemical reaction are (1) the nature of the reactants, (2) amount of contact area, (3) concentration of reactants, (4) temperature, and (5) catalysis. The rate of a reaction is determined by the amount of reactants converted to products per unit of time. An equation that relates the reaction rate and the concentration of reactants is called the rate law for the reaction. The rate law for a reaction is the rate law for the slowest step in the reaction pathway. This slowest step is the rate-determining step for the reaction. The rate law for a reaction must be determined experimentally. It cannot be written from the balanced equation for the overall reaction.

◖ | VOCABULARY

activated complex	enthalpy	heterogeneous reaction	rate law
activation energy	entropy	homogeneous catalyst	reaction mechanism
bond energy	free energy	homogeneous chemical	reaction pathway
calorimeter	free energy change	system	reaction rate
catalysis	heat of combustion	homogeneous reaction	stable
chemical kinetics	heat of formation	inhibitor	thermochemical equation
collision theory	heat of reaction	law of mass action	thermochemistry
driving force	heterogeneous	molar heat of formation	unstable
	catalyst	rate-determining step	

QUESTIONS

Group A

1. What evidence can be cited to show that a substance has a characteristic internal energy?

2. How does the heat content of the products of a reaction system compare with the heat content of the reactants when the reaction is (*a*) exothermic? (*b*) endothermic?

3. Define the molar heat of formation of a compound.

4. Name two factors that collectively determine the driving force of chemical reactions.

5. What is the basis for assigning a negative value to the change in heat content, ΔH, in an exothermic system?

6. Changes of phase in the direction of the solid phase favor what kind of an entropy change?

7. What is the effect on the entropy of a system when temperature is raised?

8. Define activation energy in terms of the activated complex.

9. In a reversible reaction, how does the activation energy required for the exothermic change compare with the activation energy for the endothermic change?

10. Give two reasons why a collision between reactant molecules may not be effective in producing new chemical species.

11. To what does the term *activated complex* refer?

Group B

12. Considering the structure and physical phase of substances in a reacting system, to what is the energy change in the reaction related?

13. Using the energy profile of Figure 20-14, what is the activation energy for the reaction that produces hydrogen iodide?

14. A compound is found to have a heat of formation ΔH_f of -87.3 kcal/mole. What does this imply about its stability? Explain.

15. Suppose flasks containing two different gases at room temperature are connected so that the gases mix. What kind of evidence would show that they experienced no change in energy content during the mixing?

16. How can the mixing tendency of Question 15 be explained?

17. Explain the circumstances under which an exothermic reaction does not proceed spontaneously.

18. Explain the circumstances under which an endothermic reaction is spontaneous.

19. Referring to Figure 20-12, (*a*) how could you justify calling the reaction pathway the minimum energy pathway for reaction? (*b*) What significance is associated with the maximum energy region of this minimum energy pathway?

20. The balanced equation for a homogeneous reaction between two gases shows that 4 molecules of A react with 1 molecule of B to form 2 molecules of C and 2 molecules of D. $4A + B \rightarrow 2C + 2D$. The simultaneous collision of 4 molecules of one reactant with 1 molecule of the other reactant is extremely improbable. Recognizing this, what would you assume about the nature of the reaction mechanism for this reaction system?

21. Suppose 2 moles of hydrogen gas and 1 mole of iodine vapor are passed simultaneously into a 1-liter flask. The rate law for the forward reaction is $R = k[I_2][H_2]$. What is the effect on the rate of the forward reaction if (*a*) the temperature is increased; (*b*) 1 mole of iodine vapor is added; (*c*) 1 mole of hydrogen is removed; (*d*) the volume of the flask is reduced (assume this is possible); (*e*) a catalyst is introduced into the flask?

22. The decomposition of nitrogen dioxide

$$2NO_2 \rightarrow 2NO + O_2$$

occurs in a two-step sequence at elevated temperatures. The first step is

$$NO_2 \rightarrow NO + O$$

Predict a possible second step which, when combined with the first step, gives the complete reaction.

23. For each of the following reactions, predict

whether the reaction, once started, is likely to proceed rapidly or slowly. State the reason for each prediction.

(a) $H_2(g) + Cl_2(g) \rightarrow 2HCl(g)$

(b) $Ag^+(aq) + Cl^-(aq) \rightarrow AgCl(s)$

(c) $Fe(chunk) + S(l) \rightarrow FeS(s)$

24. What property would you measure in order to determine the reaction rate for the following reaction? Justify your choice.

$$2NO_2(g) \rightarrow N_2O_4(g)$$

25. Ozone decomposes according to the following equation.

$$2O_3 \rightarrow 3O_2$$

The reaction proceeds in two steps. Propose a possible 2-step mechanism.

◖ PROBLEMS

Group A
(Consult Appendix tables for essential thermochemical data.)

1. Write the thermochemical equation for the complete combustion of 1 mole of ethane gas. Then calculate its heat of formation from the heat of reaction and product heats of formation data.
2. Write the thermochemical equation for the complete combustion of 1 mole of ethyne (acetylene) and calculate its heat of formation.
3. Write the thermochemical equation for the complete combustion of 1 mole of benzene and calculate its heat of formation.
4. Using heats of formation data, calculate the heat of combustion of 1 mole of hydrogen gas.
5. Calculate the heat of combustion of 1 mole of sulfur.
6. The heat of formation of ethanol (C_2H_5OH) is -66.36 kcal/mole at 25 °C. Calculate the heat of formation of 1 mole of ethanol.
7. The concentration of reactant A changes from 0.0375 M to 0.0268 M in the reaction time interval 0.0 min–18.0 min. What is the reaction rate during this time interval (a) per minute? (b) per second?

Group B
8. Calculate the heat of formation of $H_2SO_4(l)$ from the ΔH for the combustion of sulfur to $SO_2(g)$, the oxidation of SO_2 to $SO_3(g)$,

and the solution of SO_3 in $H_2O(l)$ to give $H_2SO_4(l)$ at 25 °C.

9. Suppose the following reactants could be used to provide thrust for a rocket engine:

(1) $H_2(g) + \frac{1}{2}O_2(g) \rightarrow H_2O(g)$

(2) $H_2(g) + F_2(g) \rightarrow 2HF(g)$

(a) Calculate the heat of reaction ΔH at 25 °C for each reaction per kilogram of reactants carried aloft.

(b) Since the thrust is greater when the molecular weight of the exhaust gas is lower, which reaction would be preferred on the basis of thrust?

10. A chemical reaction is expressed by the balanced chemical equation

$$A + B \rightarrow C$$

and three reaction rate experiments yield the following data:

Experiment number	Initial [A]	Initial [B]	Initial rate of formation of C
1	0.20 M	0.20 M	2.0×10^{-4} M/min
2	0.20 M	0.40 M	8.0×10^{-4} M/min
3	0.40 M	0.40 M	1.6×10^{-3} M/min

(a) Determine the rate law for the reaction.
(b) Calculate the value of the specific rate constant.
(c) If the initial concentrations of both A and B are 0.30 M, at what initial rate is C formed?

Chemical Equilibrium

MY REPORT TODAY IS ON CHEMISTRY SYMBOLS

THESE ARROWS INDICATE "DIRECTION OF REACTION"... UNLESS YOU'RE A COWBOY.. THEN THEY MEAN, "IF YOU DON'T DUCK, YOU'RE GONNA GET IT IN THE HEAD!"

HA HA HA HA!

OKAY, GETTING BACK TO CHEMISTRY..

☐ 21.1 Reversible reactions

The products formed in a chemical reaction may, in turn, react to re-form the original reactants. The chemical reaction is said to be reversible. All chemical reactions are considered to be reversible under suitable conditions. Theoretically at least, every reaction pathway can be traversed in both directions. Some reverse reactions occur or are driven less easily than others. For example, a temperature near 3000 °C is required for water vapor to decompose into measurable quantities of hydrogen and oxygen. In some cases the conditions for the reverse reactions are not known. An example is the reaction in which potassium chlorate decomposes into oxygen and potassium chloride. Chemists do not know how to reverse this reaction in a single process.

Mercury(II) oxide decomposes when heated strongly.

$$2HgO(s) \rightarrow 2Hg(l) + O_2(g)$$

Mercury and oxygen combine to form mercury(II) oxide when heated gently.

$$2Hg(l) + O_2(g) \rightarrow 2HgO(s)$$

Suppose mercury(II) oxide is heated in a closed container from which neither the mercury nor the oxygen can escape. Once decomposition has begun, the mercury and oxygen released can recombine to form mercury(II) oxide again. Thus both reactions proceed at the same time. Under these conditions, the rate of the composition reaction will eventually equal that of the decomposition reaction. Mercury and oxygen combine to form mercury(II)

In this chapter you will gain an understanding of:

- **the nature of reversible reactions**
- **physical and chemical equilibria**
- **the equilibrium constant and its calculation**
- **factors that disturb equilibrium, and predicting their influence using Le Chatelier's principle**
- **the three conditions that cause an ionic reaction to run to completion**
- **the common ion effect**
- **ionization constants—weak acids and water**
- **hydrolysis of salts: cation and anion hydrolysis**
- **solubility: solubility-product constant, calculating solubilities, predicting precipitates**

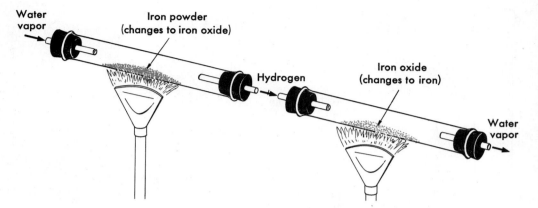

Figure 21-1. A reversible reaction. Water vapor (steam) passed over the hot iron is reduced to hydrogen and the iron is oxidized to iron(II, III) oxide. Hydrogen passed over the hot iron oxide is oxidized to water vapor and the iron oxide is reduced to iron.

Equilibrium: opposing processes proceeding at the same rate.

oxide just as fast as mercury(II) oxide decomposes into mercury and oxygen. The amounts of mercury(II) oxide, mercury, and oxygen can be expected to remain constant as long as these conditions persist. A state of *equilibrium* has been reached between the two chemical reactions. *Both reactions continue, but there is no net change in the composition of the system.* The equilibrium may be written as

$$2HgO(s) \rightleftarrows 2Hg(l) + O_2(g)$$

Chemical equilibrium is a state of balance in which the rates of opposing reactions are exactly equal.

A reaction system in equilibrium shows equal tendencies to proceed in the forward and reverse directions. In Section 20.7, two factors that constitute the driving force for reactions are distinguished: tendency toward higher entropy and tendency toward lower energy. *At equilibrium, the driving force of the energy-change factor is balanced by the driving force of the entropy-change factor.* Under different circumstances, conditions may favor one reaction direction over the other, and a net reaction may result.

⬜ 21.2 Equilibrium, a dynamic state

Equilibrium systems consist of opposing processes occurring at the same time and at the same rate. The evaporation of a liquid in a closed vessel and the condensation of its saturated vapor proceed at equal rates. The resulting equilibrium vapor pressure is a characteristic of the liquid at the prevailing temperature.

If an excess of sugar is placed in water, sugar molecules go into solution. Some of these molecules in turn separate from solution and rejoin the crystals. At saturation, molecules of sugar are crystallizing at the same rate that crystal molecules are dissolving. See Section 12.3.

Solution equilibrium is an example of physical equilibrium.

The above are examples of *physical equilibria*. The opposing physical processes occur at exactly the same rate. *Equilibrium is a dynamic state in which two opposing processes proceed simultaneously at the same rate.*

Electrovalent compounds, such as sodium chloride, are completely ionized in water solution. When an excess of sodium chloride is placed in water, a saturated solution eventually results. The saturated solution is at equilibrium. The rate of association of ions re-forming the crystal equals the rate of dissociation of ions from the crystal. This equilibrium is shown in the ionic equation

$$Na^+Cl^-(s) \rightleftarrows Na^+(aq) + Cl^-(aq)$$

The dynamic character of this equilibrium system is easily demonstrated. Suppose an irregularly shaped crystal of sodium chloride is placed in a saturated solution of the salt. The *shape* of the crystal gradually changes, becoming more regular as time passes. However, the *mass* of the crystal does not change.

Equilibrium is a dynamic state.

Polar compounds, such as acetic acid, are very soluble in water. Molecules of acetic acid in water solution ionize, forming H_3O^+ and $C_2H_3O_2^-$ ions. Pairs of these ions tend to rejoin, forming acetic acid molecules in the solution. This tendency is very strong. Even in fairly dilute solutions, equilibrium is quickly established between un-ionized molecules in solution and their hydrated ions. This system is an example of *ionic equilibrium.* The ionic equilibrium of acetic acid in water solution is represented by the equation

$$HC_2H_3O_2(aq) + H_2O(l) \rightleftarrows H_3O^+(aq) + C_2H_3O_2^-(aq)$$

Many chemical reactions are reversible under ordinary conditions of temperature and concentration. They may reach a state of equilibrium unless at least one of the substances involved escapes or is removed. In some cases, however, the forward reaction is nearly completed before the reverse reaction rate becomes high enough to establish equilibrium. *Here the products of the forward reaction ($\rightarrow$) are favored.* This kind of reaction is referred to as the *reaction to the right* because the convention for writing chemical reactions is that *left-to-right* is forward and *right-to-left* is reverse. In other cases, the forward reaction is barely under way when the rate of the reverse reaction becomes equal to that of the forward reaction, and equilibrium is established. *In these cases, the products of the reverse reaction ($\leftarrow$), the original reactants, are favored.* This kind of reaction is referred to as the *reaction to the left.* In still other cases, both the forward and reverse reactions occur to nearly the same extent before chemical equilibrium is established. *Neither reaction is favored; considerable concentrations of both reactants and products are present at equilibrium.*

An equilibrium established late in the reaction process favors the products of the forward reaction.

An equilibrium established early in the reaction process favors the products of the reverse reaction.

Chemical reactions are ordinarily used to convert available reactants into more desirable products. Chemists try to produce as much of these products as possible from the reactants used. Chemical equilibrium may seriously limit the possibilities of a seemingly useful reaction. In dealing with equilibrium systems, it is important to recognize the conditions that influence reaction rates. Factors that determine the rate of chemical action are discussed in Section 20.12. They are (1) *the nature of the reactants,* (2) *the temperature,* (3) *the presence of a catalyst,* (4) *the surface area,* and (5) *the concentration of reactants.*

In heterogeneous reactions, the chemical reaction takes place at the surfaces where the reactants in different phases meet. Thus the surface area presented by solid and liquid reactants is important in rate considerations. Homogeneous reactions occur between gases and between substances dissolved in liquid solvents. Here the concentration of each reactant is an important rate factor.

Heterogeneous reactions involve two or more phases of matter.

In homogeneous reactions, reactants and products are in the same phase.

☐ 21.3 The equilibrium constant

Many chemical reactions seem likely to yield useful products. After they are started, however, they *appear* to slow down and finally stop without having run to completion. Such reactions are reversible and happen to *reach a state of equilibrium* before the reactants are completely changed into products. Both forward and reverse processes continue at the same rate. The concentrations of products and reactants remain constant.

The time required for reaction systems to reach equilibrium varies widely. It may be a fraction of a second or a great many years, depending on the system and the conditions. Ionic reactions in solution usually reach equilibrium very quickly.

Suppose two substances, **A** and **B**, react to form products **C** and **D,** as in Figure 21-2. In turn, **C** and **D** react to produce **A** and **B.** Under certain conditions, equilibrium occurs in this reversible reaction. This hypothetical equilibrium reaction is represented by the equation

$$A + B \rightleftarrows C + D$$

Initially, the concentrations of **C** and **D** are zero and those of **A** and **B** are maximum. With time, the rate of the forward reaction *decreases* as **A** and **B** are used up. Meanwhile, the rate of the reverse reaction increases as **C** and **D** are formed. As these two reaction rates become equal, equilibrium is established. The individual concentrations of **A, B, C,** and **D** undergo no further change if conditions remain the same.

At equilibrium, the ratio of the product [C] × [D] *to the product* [A] × [B] *has a definite value at a given temperature.* It is known as the **equilibrium constant** of the reaction and is designated by the letter K. Thus,

$$\frac{[C] \times [D]}{[A] \times [B]} = K$$

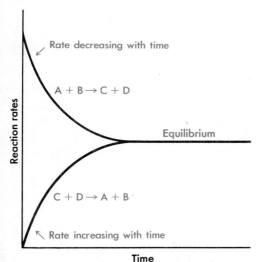

Figure 21-2. Reaction rates for the hypothetical reaction system **A + B ⇄ C + D.** The rate of the forward reaction is represented by curve **A + B.** Curve **C + D** represents the rate of the reverse reaction. At equilibrium, the two rates are equal.

Within the figure:
Rate decreasing with time
A + B → C + D
Equilibrium
C + D → A + B
Rate increasing with time
Reaction rates
Time

Observe that the concentrations of substances on the right side of the chemical equation are given in the numerator. These substances are the *products* of the forward reaction. The concentrations of substances on the left side of the chemical equation are in the denominator. These substances are the *reactants* of the forward reaction. Concentrations of reactants and products are given in *moles per liter*. The constant K is independent of the initial concentrations. It is, however, dependent on the fixed temperature of the system.

Equilibrium constant: K has a unique value for each equilibrium system at a specific temperature.

The value of K for a given equilibrium reaction is important to chemists. It shows them the extent to which the reactants are converted into the products of the reaction. If K is equal to 1, the products of the concentrations in the numerator and denominator have the same value. If the value of K is very small, the forward reaction occurs only very slightly before equilibrium is established. A large value of K indicates an equilibrium in which the original reactants are largely converted to products. The numerical value of K for a particular equilibrium system is obtained experimentally. The chemist must analyze the equilibrium mixture and determine the concentrations of all substances present.

If $K < 1$, reactants of the forward reaction are favored.

If $K > 1$, products of the forward reaction are favored.

Suppose the balanced equation for an equilibrium system has the general form

$$n\text{A} + m\text{B} + \text{-----} \rightleftarrows x\text{C} + y\text{D} + \text{-----}$$

The constant relationship at equilibrium (for this generalized reaction system) becomes

$$K = \frac{[\text{C}]^x[\text{D}]^y\text{-----}}{[\text{A}]^n[\text{B}]^m\text{-----}}$$

*The **equilibrium constant K** is the ratio of the product of the concentrations of substances formed at equilibrium to the product of the concentrations of reacting substances, each concentration being raised to the power that is the coefficient of that substance in the chemical equation.* This equation for K is sometimes referred to as the *chemical equilibrium law* or as the *mass action expression*.

To illustrate, suppose a reaction system at equilibrium is shown by the equation

$$3\text{A} + \text{B} \rightleftarrows 2\text{C} + 3\text{D}$$

The equilibrium constant K is given by the expression

$$K = \frac{[\text{C}]^2[\text{D}]^3}{[\text{A}]^3[\text{B}]}$$

The reaction between H_2 and I_2 in a closed flask at an elevated temperature is easy to follow; the rate at which the violet color of the iodine vapor diminishes is simply observed. Suppose this reaction runs to completion with respect to iodine. If so, the color must disappear entirely since the product, hydrogen iodide, is a colorless gas.

The color does not disappear entirely because the reaction is reversible. Hydrogen iodide decomposes to re-form hydrogen and iodine. The rate of this reverse reaction increases as the concentration of hydrogen iodide builds up. Meanwhile, the concentrations of hydrogen and iodine decrease as they are used up. The rate of the forward reaction decreases accordingly.

As the rates of the opposing reactions become equal, an equilibrium is established. A constant intensity of the violet color indicates that equilibrium exists among hydrogen, iodine, and hydrogen iodide. The net chemical equation for the reaction system at equilibrium is

$$H_2(g) + I_2(g) \rightleftarrows 2HI(g)$$

Thus,

$$K = \frac{[HI]^2}{[H_2][I_2]}$$

Concentrations of substances in an equilibrium system are determined experimentally.

Chemists have carefully measured the concentrations of H_2, I_2, and HI in equilibrium mixtures at various temperatures. In some experiments, the flasks were filled with hydrogen iodide at known pressure. The flasks were held at fixed temperatures until equilibrium was established. In other experiments, hydrogen and iodine were the substances introduced.

Equilibrium constants are computed from experimental data.

Experimental data together with the calculated values for K are listed in Table 21-1. Experiments 1 and 2 began with hydrogen iodide. Experiments 3 and 4 began with hydrogen and iodine. Note the close agreement obtained for numerical values of the equilibrium constant.

The equilibrium constant K for this equilibrium system at 425 °C has the average value of 54.34. This value for K should hold for any system of H_2, I_2, and HI at equilibrium *at this temperature*. If the calculation for K yields a different result, there must be a reason. Either the H_2, I_2, and HI system has not reached equilibrium or the temperature of the system is not 425 °C. The following Sample Problem is a typical example.

Table 21-1
TYPICAL EQUILIBRIUM CONCENTRATIONS OF H_2, I_2, AND HI IN MOLE/LITER AT 425 °C

Exp.	$[H_2]$	$[I_2]$	$[HI]$	$K = \dfrac{[HI]^2}{[H_2][I_2]}$
(1)	0.4953×10^{-3}	0.4953×10^{-3}	3.655×10^{-3}	54.56
(2)	1.141×10^{-3}	1.141×10^{-3}	8.410×10^{-3}	54.33
(3)	3.560×10^{-3}	1.250×10^{-3}	15.59×10^{-3}	54.62
(4)	2.252×10^{-3}	2.336×10^{-3}	16.85×10^{-3}	53.97
			Average	54.34

SAMPLE PROBLEM

An equilibrium mixture of H_2, I_2, and HI gases at 425 °C is determined to consist of 4.5647×10^{-3} mole/liter of H_2, 0.7378×10^{-3} mole/liter of I_2, and 13.544×10^{-3} mole/liter of HI. What is the equilibrium constant for the system at this temperature?

SOLUTION

The balanced equation for the equilibrium system is

$$H_2(g) + I_2(g) \rightleftarrows 2HI(g)$$

$$K = \frac{[HI]^2}{[H_2][I_2]}$$

$$K = \frac{[13.544 \times 10^{-3}]^2}{[4.5647 \times 10^{-3}][0.7378 \times 10^{-3}]} = 54.46$$

This value for K is in close agreement with the average of the four experimental values given in Table 21-1.

The balanced chemical equation for the equilibrium system yields the expression for the equilibrium constant. The data in Table 21-1 show that this expression is an experimental fact. The equilibrium concentrations of reactants and product are determined experimentally. The values of K are calculated from these concentrations. No information concerning the kinetics of the reacting systems is required.

However, you know that an equilibrium system involves forward and reverse reactions proceeding at equal rates. Thus the rate laws for the forward and reverse reactions should yield the same equilibrium constant as does the balanced chemical equation.

Suppose an equilibrium system is expressed by the chemical equation

$$A_2 + B_2 \rightleftarrows 2C$$

Assume that both forward and reverse reactions are simple, one-step processes. The rate law for the forward reaction becomes

$$R_f = k_f[A_2][B_2]$$

The rate law for the reverse reaction becomes

$$R_r = k_r[C]^2$$

Rate law: review Section 20.13.

At equilibrium,

$$R_f = R_r$$

Therefore,

$$k_f[A_2][B_2] = k_r[C]^2$$

Rearranging terms,

$$\frac{k_f}{k_r} = \frac{[C]^2}{[A_2][B_2]} = K$$

The expression is the same as the mass action equation derived from the balanced chemical equation (Section 20.13).

Most reaction mechanisms are complex and proceed by way of a sequence of simple steps. The exponents in the *rate equation* for such a reaction cannot be taken from the balanced equation. They must be determined experimentally.

◻ 21.4 Factors that disturb equilibrium

In systems that have attained chemical equilibrium, opposing reactions are proceeding at equal rates. Any change that alters the rate of either reaction *disturbs the original equilibrium*. The system then seeks a new equilibrium state. By displacing an equilibrium in the desired direction, chemists can often increase production of important industrial chemicals.

Le Chatelier's principle is a "must know."

Le Chatelier's principle (Section 12.5) provides a means of predicting the influence of disturbing factors on equilibrium systems. It may be helpful at this point to restate Le Chatelier's principle: *If a system at equilibrium is subjected to a stress, the equilibrium is displaced in the direction that relieves the stress.* This principle holds for all kinds of dynamic equilibria, physical and ionic as well as chemical. In applying Le Chatelier's principle to chemical equilibrium, three important stresses will be considered.

1. Change in concentration. From collision theory, an increase in the concentration of a reactant causes an increase in collision frequency. Also, a reaction resulting from these collisions should then proceed at a faster rate. Consider the hypothetical reaction

$$A + B \rightleftharpoons C + D$$

A change in concentration of a reactant places a stress on an equilibrium system.

An increase in the concentration of **A** will displace the equilibrium to the *right*. Both **A** and **B** will be used up faster and more of **C** and **D** will be formed. The equilibrium will be reestablished with a lower concentration of **B**. *The equilibrium has shifted in such direction as to reduce the stress caused by the increase in concentration.*

Similarly, an increase in the concentration of **B** drives the reaction to the *right*. An increase in either **C** or **D** displaces the equilibrium to the *left*. A *decrease* in the concentration of either **C** or **D** has the same effect as an *increase* in the concentration of **A** or **B**. That is, it will displace the equilibrium to the *right*.

Changes in concentration have no effect on the value of the equilibrium constant. All concentrations still give the same numerical ratio for the equilibrium constant when equilibrium is reestablished. Thus Le Chatelier's principle leads to the same predictions for changes in concentration as does the equilibrium constant.

2. Change in pressure. A change in pressure can affect only equilibrium systems in which *gases* are involved. According to Le Chatelier's principle, *if the pressure on an equilibrium system is increased, the reaction is driven in the direction that relieves the pressure.*

Pressure changes alter the concentration of gases.

The Haber process for catalytic synthesis of ammonia from its elements illustrates the influence of pressure on an equilibrium system.

$$N_2(g) + 3H_2(g) \rightleftarrows 2NH_3(g)$$

The equation indicates that 4 molecules of the reactant gases form 2 molecules of ammonia gas. Suppose the equilibrium mixture is subjected to an increase in pressure. This pressure can be relieved by the reaction that produces fewer gas molecules and, therefore, a smaller volume. Thus the stress is *lessened* by the formation of ammonia. Equilibrium is displaced toward the right. *High* pressure is desirable in this industrial process. Figure 21-3 shows the effect of pressure on this equilibrium system.

In the Haber process, the ammonia produced is continuously removed by condensation to a liquid. This condensation removes most of the product from the phase in which the reaction occurs. This change in concentration also tends to displace the equilibrium to the right.

Many chemical processes involve heterogeneous reactions in which the reactants and products are in different phases. The *concentrations* in equilibrium systems of pure substances in solid and liquid phases are not changed by adding or removing quantities of such substances. The equilibrium constant expresses a relationship between *relative* concentrations of reactants and products. Therefore, a pure substance in a condensed phase can be removed from the expression for the equilibrium constant; simply substitute the number "1" for its concentration (which remains at unity value in the equilibrium system).

Consider the equilibrium system represented by the equation

$$CaCO_3(s) \rightleftarrows CaO(s) + CO_2(g)$$

Carbon dioxide is the only substance in the system subject to changes in concentration. Since it is a gas, the forward (decom-

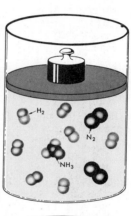

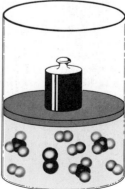

Figure 21-3. Increased pressure results in a higher yield of ammonia because the equilibrium shifts in the direction that produces fewer molecules.

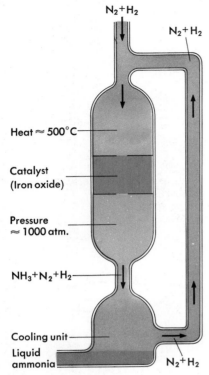

Heat ≈ 500°C

Catalyst
(Iron oxide)

Pressure
≈ 1000 atm.

$NH_3+N_2+H_2$

Cooling unit
Liquid
ammonia

N_2+H_2

Figure 21-4. The Haber process for the production of ammonia. Application of Le Chatelier's principle to the equilibrium system, $N_2(g) + 3H_2(g) \rightleftarrows 2NH_3(g) + 22$ **kcal,** suggests that high pressure and low temperature favor the yield of ammonia. Why, then, is a moderately high temperature used in this process?

In an equilibrium system, one reaction is exothermic and the other reaction is endothermic.

K changes if temperature changes.

position) reaction is favored by a *low* pressure. The expression for the equilibrium constant is

$$K = \frac{[CaO][CO_2]}{[CaCO_3]} = \frac{[1][CO_2]}{[1]} = [CO_2]$$

In the reaction

$$CO(g) + H_2O(g) \rightleftarrows CO_2(g) + H_2(g)$$

there are equal numbers of molecules of gaseous reactants and gaseous products. Pressure change could not produce a shift in equilibrium. Thus *pressure change has no effect* on this equilibrium reaction.

Obviously, an increase in pressure on confined gases has the same effect as an increase in the concentrations of these gases. Recall that changes in concentration have no effect on the value of the equilibrium constant. Thus *changes in pressure do not affect the value of the equilibrium constant.*

3. Change in temperature. Chemical reactions are either exothermic or endothermic. Reversible reactions are exothermic in one direction and endothermic in the other. The effect of changing the temperature of an equilibrium mixture depends on which of the opposing reactions is endothermic.

According to Le Chatelier's principle, *addition* of heat displaces the equilibrium so that heat is absorbed. This favors the *endothermic* reaction. The *removal* of heat favors the *exothermic* reaction. A rise in temperature increases the rate of any reaction. In an equilibrium system, the rates of the opposing reactions are raised *unequally*. Thus *the value of the equilibrium constant for a given system is affected by the temperature.*

The synthesis of ammonia is *exothermic.*

$$N_2(g) + 3H_2(g) \rightleftarrows 2NH_3(g) + 22 \text{ kcal}$$

A high temperature is not desirable as it favors the decomposition of ammonia, the *endothermic* reaction. However, at ordinary temperatures, the forward reaction is too slow to be commercially useful. The temperature used represents a compromise between kinetic and equilibrium requirements. It is high enough that equilibrium is established rapidly but low enough that the equilibrium concentration of ammonia is significant. The reactions of the system are also accelerated by the use of a suitable catalyst. Moderate temperature (about 500 °C) and very high pressure (700–1000 atmospheres) produce a satisfactory yield of ammonia.

The numerical values of equilibrium constants range from very large to very small numbers. You have learned that they are independent of changes in concentrations but not of changes in temperature. The addition of a catalyst accelerates both forward and reverse reactions equally. Therefore, it does not affect

Table 21-2
EQUILIBRIUM CONSTANTS

Equilibrium system	Value of K	Temp. (°C)
$N_2(g) + 3H_2(g) \rightleftharpoons 2NH_3(g)$	2.66×10^{-2}	350°
$N_2(g) + 3H_2(g) \rightleftharpoons 2NH_3(g)$	6.59×10^{-3}	450°
$N_2(g) + 3H_2(g) \rightleftharpoons 2NH_3(g)$	2.37×10^{-3}	727°
$2H_2(g) + S_2(g) \rightleftharpoons 2H_2S(g)$	9.39×10^{-5}	477°
$H_2(g) + CO_2(g) \rightleftharpoons H_2O(g) + CO(g)$	4.40	1727°
$2H_2O(g) \rightleftharpoons 2H_2(g) + O_2(g)$	5.31×10^{-10}	1727°
$2CO(g) + O_2(g) \rightleftharpoons 2CO_2(g)$	2.24×10^{22}	727°
$H_2(g) + I_2(g) \rightleftharpoons 2HI(g)$	66.9	350°
$H_2(g) + I_2(g) \rightleftharpoons 2HI(g)$	54.4	425°
$H_2(g) + I_2(g) \rightleftharpoons 2HI(g)$	45.9	490°
$C(s) + CO_2(g) \rightleftharpoons 2CO(g)$	14.1	1123°
$Cu(s) + 2Ag^+(aq) \rightleftharpoons Cu^{++}(aq) + 2Ag(s)$	2×10^{15}	25°
$I_2(g) \rightleftharpoons 2I(g)$	3.76×10^{-5}	727°
$2O_3(g) \rightleftharpoons 3O_2(g)$	2.54×10^{12}	1727°
$N_2(g) \rightleftharpoons 2N(g)$	1.31×10^{-31}	1000°

the value of K. The time required for a system to reach equilibrium can be reduced dramatically when the system is catalyzed.

Several equilibrium systems are listed in Table 21-2. The table also gives numerical values of the equilibrium constants at various temperatures. A very small K value means that the equilibrium mixture consists mainly of the substances on the left of the equation. If the value of K is large, the equilibrium mixture consists mainly of the substances on the right of the equation.

◻ 21.5 Reactions that run to completion

Many reactions are easily reversible under suitable conditions. A state of equilibrium may be established unless one or more of the products escapes or is removed. An equilibrium reaction may be driven in the preferred direction by applying Le Chatelier's principle.

Some reactions appear to go to completion in the forward direction. No one has found a method of recombining potassium chloride and oxygen directly once potassium chlorate decomposes. Sugar is decomposed into carbon and water by the application of heat. Yet no single-step method of recombining these products is known.

Many compounds are formed by the interaction of ions in solutions. If solutions of two electrolytes are mixed, two pairings of ions are possible. These pairings may or may not occur. If dilute solutions of sodium chloride and potassium bromide are mixed, no reaction occurs. The resulting solution merely contains a mixture of Na^+, K^+, Cl^-, and Br^- ions. Association of ions occurs only if enough water is evaporated to cause crystals to separate from solution. The yield is then a mixture of $NaCl$, KCl, $NaBr$, and KBr.

With some combinations of ions, reactions do occur. *Such reactions appear to run to completion in the sense that the ions are almost completely removed from solution.* Chemists can predict that certain ion reactions will run practically to completion. The extent to which the reacting ions are removed from solution depends on (1) *the solubility of the compound formed* and (2) *the degree of ionization, if the compound is soluble.* Thus a product that *escapes as a gas or is precipitated as a solid, or is only slightly ionized* effectively removes the bulk of the reacting ions from solution. Consider some specific examples of such reactions.

1. Formation of a gas. Unstable substances formed as products of ionic reactions decompose spontaneously. An example is carbonic acid, which yields a gas as a decomposition product.

$$H_2CO_3 \rightarrow H_2O + CO_2(g)$$

Carbonic acid: aqueous solutions called "carbonic acid" are mainly solutions of CO_2 in water. The relatively few H_2CO_3 molecules formed are ionized, making the solution weakly acidic.

Carbonic acid is produced in the reaction between sodium hydrogen carbonate and hydrochloric acid, as shown by the equation

$$NaHCO_3 + HCl \rightarrow NaCl + H_2CO_3$$

The aqueous solution of HCl contains H_3O^+ and Cl^- ions. A careful examination of the reaction mechanism suggests that the HCO_3^- ion, a Brønsted base, acquires a proton from the H_3O^+ ion, a Brønsted acid; Na^+ and Cl^- ions are merely spectator ions. The following equations may be more appropriate for this reaction.

$$H_3O^+ + HCO_3^- \rightarrow H_2O + \cancel{H_2CO_3}$$

$$\cancel{H_2CO_3} \rightarrow H_2O + CO_2(g)$$

or, simply,

$$H_3O^+ + HCO_3^- \rightarrow 2H_2O + CO_2(g)$$

The reaction runs practically to completion because one of the products escapes as a gas. Of course, the sodium ions and chloride ions produce sodium chloride crystals when the water solvent is evaporated.

The reaction between iron(II) sulfide and hydrochloric acid goes practically to completion because a gaseous product escapes. The reaction equation is

$$FeS + 2HCl \rightarrow FeCl_2 + H_2S(g)$$

The net ionic equation is

$$FeS(s) + 2H_3O^+(aq) \rightarrow Fe^{++}(aq) + H_2S(g) + 2H_2O(l)$$

The hydrogen sulfide formed is only moderately soluble and is largely given off as a gas. The iron(II) chloride is formed on evaporation of the water.

2. *Formation of a precipitate.* When solutions of sodium chloride and silver nitrate are mixed, a white precipitate of silver chloride immediately forms.

$$Na^+ + Cl^- + Ag^+ + NO_3^- \rightarrow Na^+ + NO_3^- + Ag^+Cl^- (s)$$

If chemically equivalent amounts of the two solutes are used, Na^+ ions and NO_3^- ions remain in solution in appreciable quantities. All but a meager portion of the Ag^+ ions and Cl^- ions combine and separate from the solution as a precipitate of AgCl. Silver chloride is only very sparingly soluble in water and, like any other substance of either low or high solubility, separates by precipitation from a *saturated solution* of its particles. *The reaction effectively runs to completion because an "insoluble" product is formed.*

The only reaction is between the silver ions and chloride ions. Omitting the spectator ions, Na^+ and NO_3^-, the net ionic equation is simply

$$Ag^+ (aq) + Cl^- (aq) \rightarrow Ag^+Cl^- (s)$$

Crystalline sodium nitrate is recovered by evaporation of the water solvent.

3. *Formation of a slightly ionized product.* Neutralization reactions between H_3O^+ ions from aqueous acids and OH^- ions from aqueous bases result in the formation of water molecules. A reaction between HCl and NaOH illustrates this process. Aqueous HCl supplies H_3O^+ ions and Cl^- ions to the solution, and aqueous NaOH supplies Na^+ ions and OH^- ions. The ionic equation is

$$H_3O^+ + Cl^- + Na^+ + OH^- \rightarrow Na^+ + Cl^- + 2H_2O$$

Neglecting the spectator ions, the net ionic equation is simply

$$H_3O^+ (aq) + OH^- (aq) \rightarrow 2H_2O(l)$$

Water is only slightly ionized and exists almost entirely as covalent molecules. Thus hydronium ions and hydroxide ions are almost entirely removed from the solution. *The reaction effectively runs to completion because the product is only slightly ionized.* Sodium chloride separates on evaporation of the water.

In proton-transfer systems of acids and bases, the H_3O^+ ion is an acid, the OH^- ion a base.

☐ 21.6 Common ion effect

Suppose hydrogen chloride gas is bubbled into a saturated solution of sodium chloride. As the hydrogen chloride dissolves, sodium chloride separates as a precipitate. The mass action principle applies to this example, since chloride ions are *common* to both solutes. The concentration of chloride ions is in-

Common ion effect: add a common ionic species to a saturated solution of a salt and solute precipitates.

creased, while that of sodium ions is not. As sodium chloride crystals form, the concentration of sodium ions in the solution is lowered. Thus increasing the concentration of chloride ions has the effect of decreasing the concentration of sodium ions. This phenomenon is known as the *common ion effect*.

Eventually, the rate of dissociation of sodium chloride crystals equals the rate of association of sodium and chloride ions. An equilibrium then exists.

$$\text{Na}^+\text{Cl}^-(s) \rightleftarrows \text{Na}^+(aq) + \text{Cl}^-(aq)$$

Further additions of hydrogen chloride disturb this equilibrium and drive the reaction to the *left. By forcing the reaction to the left,* more sodium chloride separates. This further reduces the concentration of the sodium ions in solution.

The common ion effect is also observed when *one* ion species of a weak electrolyte is added in excess to a solution. Acetic acid is such an electrolyte. A 0.1-*M* $HC_2H_3O_2$ solution is about 1.4% ionized. The ionic equilibrium is shown by the equation

$$HC_2H_3O_2 + H_2O \rightleftarrows H_3O^+ + C_2H_3O_2^-$$

Common ion effect: add a salt of a weak acid to a solution of the weak acid and the $[H_3O^+]$ decreases.

Sodium acetate, an ionic salt, is completely dissociated in water solution. Small additions of sodium acetate to a solution containing acetic acid greatly increase the acetate ion concentration. The equilibrium shifts in the direction that uses acetate ions. More molecules of acetic acid are formed and the concentration of hydronium ions is reduced. In general, *the addition of a salt with an ion common to the solution of a weak electrolyte reduces the ionization of the electrolyte.* A 0.1-*M* $HC_2H_3O_2$ solution has a pH of 2.9. A solution containing 0.1-*M* concentrations of both acetic acid and sodium acetate has a pH of 4.6.

Common ion effect: add a salt of a weak base to a solution of the weak base and the $[OH^-]$ decreases.

◻ 21.7 Ionization constant of a weak acid

About 1.4% of the solute molecules in a 0.1-*M* acetic acid solution are ionized at room temperature. The remaining 98.6% of the $HC_2H_3O_2$ molecules are un-ionized. Thus the water solution contains three species of particles in equilibrium: $HC_2H_3O_2$ molecules, H_3O^+ ions, and $C_2H_3O_2^-$ ions.

At equilibrium, the *rate* of the forward reaction

$$HC_2H_3O_2 + H_2O \rightarrow H_3O^+ + C_2H_3O_2^-$$

is equal to the *rate* of the reverse reaction

$$HC_2H_3O_2 + H_2O \leftarrow H_3O^+ + C_2H_3O_2^-$$

The equilibrium equation is

$$HC_2H_3O_2 + H_2O \rightleftarrows H_3O^+ + C_2H_3O_2^-$$

The equilibrium constant for this system expresses the *equilibrium ratio of ions to molecules*.

From the equilibrium equation for the ionization of acetic acid,

$$K = \frac{[H_3O^+][C_2H_3O_2^-]}{[HC_2H_3O_2][H_2O]}$$

Water molecules are greatly in excess of acetic acid molecules at the 0.1-M concentration. Without introducing a measurable error, the mole concentration of H_2O molecules can be assumed to remain constant in such a solution. Thus the product $K[H_2O]$ is constant.

Weak acids are slightly ionized in aqueous solution.

$$K[H_2O] = \frac{[H_3O^+][C_2H_3O_2^-]}{[HC_2H_3O_2]}$$

By setting $K[H_2O] = K_a$,

$$K_a = \frac{[H_3O^+][C_2H_3O_2^-]}{[HC_2H_3O_2]}$$

In this expression, K_a is called the *ionization constant* of the weak acid. The concentration of water molecules in pure water and in dilute solutions is about 55 moles per liter. (At 25 °C it is 55.4 moles/liter.) Therefore, the ionization constant of a weak acid, K_a, is about 55 times larger than the equilibrium constant K.

Ionization constant:
$K_a = K[H_2O] = 55.4K$

The equilibrium equation for the typical weak acid **HB** is

$$HB(aq) + H_2O(l) \rightleftarrows H_3O^+(aq) + B^-(aq)$$

From this equation, the expression for K_a can be written in the general form

$$K_a = \frac{[H_3O^+][B^-]}{[HB]}$$

How can the numerical value of the ionization constant K_a for acetic acid at a specific temperature be determined? First, the equilibrium concentrations of H_3O^+ ions, $C_2H_3O_2^-$ ions, and $HC_2H_3O_2$ molecules must be known. The ionization of a molecule of $HC_2H_3O_2$ in water yields one H_3O^+ ion and one $C_2H_3O_2^-$ ion. Therefore, these concentrations can be found experimentally by measuring the pH of the solution.

Suppose that precise measurements in an experiment show the pH of a 0.1000-M solution of acetic acid to be 2.876 at 25 °C. The numerical value of K_a for $HC_2H_3O_2$ at 25 °C can be determined as follows:

$[H_3O^+] = 10^{-pH}$.

$$[H_3O^+] = [C_2H_3O_2^-] = 10^{-2.876}\frac{mole}{liter}$$

$$antilog\,(-2.876) = antilog\,(0.124 - 3) = 1.33 \times 10^{-3}$$

$$[H_3O^+] = [C_2H_3O_2{}^-] = 1.33 \times 10^{-3}$$

$$[HC_2H_3O_2] = 0.1000 - 0.00133 = 0.0987$$

$$K_a = \frac{[H_3O^+][C_2H_3O_2{}^-]}{[HC_2H_3O_2]}$$

$$K_a = \frac{(1.33 \times 10^{-3})^2}{9.87 \times 10^{-2}} = 1.79 \times 10^{-5}$$

K_a changes if temperature changes.

Ionization data and constants for some dilute acetic acid solutions at room temperature are given in Table 21-3.

An increase in temperature causes the equilibrium to shift according to Le Chatelier's principle. Thus K_a has a new value for each temperature. An increase in the concentration of $C_2H_3O_2{}^-$ ions, through the addition of $NaC_2H_3O_2$, also disturbs the equilibrium. This disturbance causes a decrease in $[H_3O^+]$ and an increase in $[HC_2H_3O_2]$. Eventually the equilibrium is reestablished with the same value of K_a. However, there is a higher concentration of un-ionized acetic acid molecules and a lower concentration of H_3O^+ ions. Changes in the hydronium ion concentration and changes in pH go together. In this example, the reduction in $[H_3O^+]$ means an increase in the pH of the solution.

A solution containing both a weak acid and a salt of the acid can react with either an acid or a base. The pH of the solution remains nearly constant even when small additions of acids or bases are present. Suppose an acid is added to a solution of acetic acid and sodium acetate. Acetate ions react with the added hydronium ions to form un-ionized acetic acid molecules.

$$C_2H_3O_2{}^-(aq) + H^+(aq) \rightarrow HC_2H_3O_2(aq)$$

The hydronium-ion concentration and the pH of the solution remain practically unchanged.

Suppose a small amount of a base is added to the solution. The OH^- ions of the base remove hydronium ions as un-ionized water molecules. However, acetic acid molecules ionize and restore the equilibrium concentration of hydronium ions.

$$HC_2H_3O_2(aq) \rightarrow H^+(aq) + C_2H_3O_2{}^-(aq)$$

Table 21-3
IONIZATION CONSTANT OF ACETIC ACID

Molarity	% ionized	$[H_3O^+]$	$[HC_2H_3O_2]$	K_a
0.1000	1.35	0.00135	0.09865	1.85×10^{-5}
0.0500	1.90	0.000950	0.04905	1.84×10^{-5}
0.0100	4.16	0.000416	0.009584	1.81×10^{-5}
0.0050	5.84	0.000292	0.004708	1.81×10^{-5}
0.0010	12.48	0.000125	0.000875	1.78×10^{-5}

The pH of the solution again remains practically unchanged.

A solution of a weak base containing a salt of the base behaves in a similar manner. The hydroxide-ion concentration (and the pH) of the solution remain essentially constant with small additions of acids or bases. Suppose a base is added to an aqueous solution of ammonia that also contains ammonium chloride. Ammonium ions remove the added hydroxide ions as un-ionized water molecules.

$$NH_4^+(aq) + OH^-(aq) \rightarrow NH_3(aq) + H_2O$$

If a small amount of an acid is added to the solution, hydroxide ions from the solution remove the added hydronium ions as un-ionized water molecules. Ammonia molecules in the solution ionize and restore the equilibrium concentration of hydronium ions and the pH of the solution.

$$NH_3(aq) + H_2O \rightarrow NH_4^+(aq) + OH^-(aq)$$

The common ion salt in each of these solutions acts as a "buffer" against significant changes in pH in the solution. The solutions are referred to as *buffered* solutions. They are buffered against changes in pH.

Buffers help stabilize the pH of solutions.

Buffer action has many important applications in chemistry and physiology. Human blood is naturally buffered to maintain a pH of about 7.3. Certain physiological functions require slight variations in pH. However, large changes would lead to serious disturbances of normal body functions or even death.

◻ 21.8 Ionization constant of water

Pure water is a very poor conductor of electricity because it is very slightly ionized. According to the proton-transfer system of acids and bases, some water molecules donate protons, acting as an acid. Other water molecules, which accept these protons, act as a base.

$$H_2O + H_2O \rightleftarrows H_3O^+ + OH^-$$

The degree of ionization is slight. Equilibrium is quickly established with a very low concentration of H_3O^+ and OH^- ions.

Conductivity experiments with very pure water at 25 °C show that the concentrations of H_3O^+ and OH^- ions are both 10^{-7} mole per liter. The expression for the equilibrium constant is

$$K = \frac{[H_3O^+][OH^-]}{[H_2O]^2}$$

A liter of water at 25 °C contains

$$\frac{998 \text{ g}}{18.0 \text{ g/mole}} = 55.4 \text{ moles}$$

This concentration of water molecules remains practically the same in all dilute solutions.

Thus both $[H_2O]^2$ and K in the above equilibrium expression are constants. Their product is the constant K_w, *the ion-product constant for water*. It is equal to the product of the molar concentrations of the H_3O^+ and OH^- ions.

In water and water solutions at 25 °C, $[H_3O^+][OH^-] = 10^{-14}$.

$$K_w = [H_3O^+][OH^-]$$

At 25 °C,

$$K_w = 10^{-7} \times 10^{-7} = 10^{-14}$$

The product, K_w, of the molar concentrations of H_3O^+ and OH^- ions has this constant value not only in pure water but in all water solutions at 25 °C. An acid solution with a pH of 4 has a $[H_3O^+]$ of 10^{-4} mole per liter, and a $[OH^-]$ of 10^{-10} mole per liter. An alkaline solution with a pH of 8 has a $[H_3O^+]$ of 10^{-8} mole per liter, and a $[OH^-]$ of 10^{-6} mole per liter.

$10^{-7} \times 10^{-7} = 10^{-14}$
$10^{-4} \times 10^{-10} = 10^{-14}$
$10^{-8} \times 10^{-6} = 10^{-14}$

◻ 21.9 Hydrolysis of salts

When a salt is dissolved in water, the solution might be expected to be neutral. The aqueous solutions of some salts, such as NaCl and KNO_3 are neutral; their solutions have a pH of 7.

Some other salts form aqueous solutions that are either acidic or basic. As salts, they are completely dissociated in aqueous solution; but unlike salts whose aqueous solutions are neutral, their ions may react chemically with the water solvent. The ions of a salt that do react with the solvent are said to *hydrolyze* in water solution. *Hydrolysis is a reaction between water and ions of a dissolved salt.*

Some ions that do not hydrolyze in aqueous solution: Ba^{++}, Ca^{++}, K^+, Na^+, Cl^-, HSO_4^-, NO_3^-.

Four general categories of salts relating to hydrolysis reactions can be described.

1. Salts of strong acids and strong bases. Recall that a salt is one product of an aqueous acid-base neutralization reaction. The salt consists of the positive ions *(cations)* of the base and the negative ions *(anions)* of the acid. For example,

$$HCl(aq) + NaOH(aq) \rightarrow Na^+Cl^-(aq) + H_2O(l)$$

HCl(aq) is a *strong* acid and NaOH(aq) is a *strong* base. Equivalent quantities of these two reactants yield a neutral aqueous solution of Na^+ and Cl^- ions; the pH of the solution is 7. Neither the Na^+ *cation* (the positive ion of the strong base) nor the Cl^- *anion* (the negative ion of the strong acid) undergoes hydrolysis in water solutions.

Similarly, KNO_3 is the salt of the strong acid HNO_3 and the strong base KOH. Measurements show that the pH of an aqueous KNO_3 solution is always very close to 7. *Neither the cations of a strong base nor the anions of a strong acid hydrolyze appreciably in aqueous solutions.*

2. *Salts of weak acids and strong bases.* Their aqueous solutions are *alkaline.* Anions of the dissolved salt are hydrolyzed in the water solvent and the pH of the solution is *raised,* indicating that the *hydroxide-ion concentration has increased.* Observe that the *anions* of the salt which undergo hydrolysis are the negative ions from the *weak acid.* The *cations* of the salt, the positive ions from the *strong base,* do not hydrolyze appreciably.

3. *Salts of strong acids and weak bases.* Their aqueous solutions are *acidic. Cations* of the dissolved salt are hydrolyzed in the water solvent and the pH of the solution is *lowered,* indicating that the *hydronium-ion concentration has increased.* Observe that in this case the *cations* of the salt which undergo hydrolysis are the positive ions from the *weak base.* The *anions* of the salt, the negative ions from the *strong acid,* do not hydrolyze appreciably.

4. *Salts of weak acids and weak bases.* Both ions of the dissolved salt are hydrolyzed extensively in the water solvent, and the solution can be either neutral, acidic, or basic depending on the salt dissolved.

Salts of weak acids and weak bases form solutions that may be neutral.

If both ions of a salt in aqueous solution are hydrolyzed equally, the solution remains neutral. Ammonium acetate is such a salt. In cases in which both the acid and the base are very weak indeed, the salt may undergo essentially complete decomposition to hydrolysis products. When aluminum sulfide is placed in water, both a precipitate and a gas are formed as hydrolysis products. The reaction is

$$Al_2S_3 + 6H_2O \rightarrow 2Al(OH)_3(s) + 3H_2S(g)$$

Both products are very sparingly soluble in water and are effectively removed from solution.

Hydrolysis often has important effects on the properties of solutions. Sodium carbonate, washing soda, is widely used as a cleaning agent because of the alkaline properties of its water solution. Sodium hydrogen carbonate, baking soda, forms a mildly alkaline solution in water and has many practical uses. Through the study of hydrolysis you can understand why the end point of a neutralization reaction (Section 16.14) can occur at a pH other than 7.

☐ 21.10 Anion hydrolysis

The *cations* of the salt of a weak acid and a strong base do not hydrolyze in water. Only *anion* hydrolysis occurs in an aqueous solution of such a salt. In the Brønsted sense, the anion of the salt is the *conjugate base* (proton acceptor) of the weak acid. These ions are basic enough to remove protons from some water molecules (proton donors) to form OH^- ions. An equilibrium is established in which the net effect of the anion hydrolysis is an

Review Section 15.12.

Salts of weak acids and strong bases form basic solutions.

increase in the hydroxide-ion concentration, [OH$^-$], of the solution. Using the arbitrary symbol B$^-$ for the anion, this hydrolysis reaction is represented by the general anion hydrolysis equation that follows:

$$B^-(aq) + H_2O(l) \rightleftarrows HB(aq) + OH^-(aq)$$

Some anions that hydrolyze in aqueous solutions: $C_2H_3O_2^-$, CO_3^{--}, CN^-, PO_4^{---}, S^{--}.

In the reaction to the right, the anion B$^-$ acquires a proton from the water molecule to form the weak acid HB and the hydroxide ion OH$^-$.

The equilibrium constant for a hydrolysis reaction is called the *hydrolysis constant* K_h. From the general anion hydrolysis equation above, the expression for K_h is

$$K_h = \frac{[HB][OH^-]}{[B^-]}$$

This hydrolysis constant K_h is also expressed by the ratio of the ion-product constant K_w for water to the ionization constant K_a for the weak acid.

$$K_h = \frac{K_w}{K_a}$$

The validity of this expression can be demonstrated in the following way. From Sections 21.7 and 21.8,

$$K_w = [H_3O^+][OH^-] \quad \text{and} \quad K_a = \frac{[H_3O^+][B^-]}{[HB]}$$

Thus,

$$K_h = \frac{K_w}{K_a} = \frac{[H_3O^+][OH^-]}{\frac{[H_3O^+][B^-]}{[HB]}} = \frac{[HB][OH^-]}{[B^-]}$$

Suppose sodium carbonate is dissolved in water and the solution is tested with litmus papers. The solution turns red litmus blue. The solution contains a higher concentration of OH$^-$ ions than pure water and is alkaline.

Sodium ions, Na$^+$, do not undergo hydrolysis in aqueous solution, but carbonate ions, CO_3^{--}, react as a Brønsted base. A CO_3^{--} anion acquires a proton from a water molecule to form the slightly ionized hydrogen carbonate ion, HCO_3^-, and the OH$^-$ ion.

$$CO_3^{--} + H_2O \rightleftarrows HCO_3^- + OH^-$$

Anion hydrolysis: pH > 7, solution alkaline.

The OH$^-$ ion concentration *increases* until equilibrium is established. Consequently, the H$_3$O$^+$ ion concentration *decreases* since the product [H$_3$O$^+$][OH$^-$] remains equal to the ionization constant K_w of water at the temperature of the solution. Thus the pH is *higher* than 7, and the solution is *alkaline*. In general, *salts formed from weak acids and strong bases hydrolyze in water to form alkaline solutions.*

☐ 21.11 Cation hydrolysis

The *anions* of the salt of a strong acid and a weak base do not hydrolyze in water. Only *cation* hydrolysis occurs in an aqueous solution of such a salt.

An aqueous solution of ammonium chloride, NH_4Cl, turns blue litmus paper red. This color change indicates that hydrolysis has occurred and the solution contains an excess of H_3O^+ ions. Chloride ions, the *anions* of the salt, show no noticeable tendency to hydrolyze in aqueous solution. Ammonium ions, the *cations* of the salt, donate protons to water molecules according to the equation

$$NH_4^+ + H_2O \rightleftharpoons H_3O^+ + NH_3$$

Equilibrium is established with an *increased* H_3O^+ ion concentration. The pH is *lower* than 7 and the solution is *acidic*.

Salts of strong acids and weak bases form acidic solutions.

The metallic cations of some salts are hydrated in aqueous solution. These hydrated cations may donate protons to water molecules. Because of this cation hydrolysis, the solution becomes acidic. For example, aluminum chloride forms the hydrated cations

$$Al(H_2O)_6^{+++}$$

Copper(II) sulfate in aqueous solution forms the light-blue hydrated cations

$$Cu(H_2O)_4^{++}$$

Some cations that hydrolyze in water: Al^{+++}, NH_4^+, Cr^{+++}, Cu^{++}, Fe^{+++}, Sn^{++++}.

These ions react with water to form hydronium ions as follows:

$$Al(H_2O)_6^{+++} + H_2O \rightleftharpoons Al(H_2O)_5OH^{++} + H_3O^+$$

$$Cu(H_2O)_4^{++} + H_2O \rightleftharpoons Cu(H_2O)_3OH^+ + H_3O^+$$

Cations such as $Cu(H_2O)_3OH^+$ ions may experience a secondary hydrolysis to a slight extent

$$Cu(H_2O)_3OH^+ + H_2O \rightleftharpoons Cu(H_2O)_2(OH)_2 + H_3O^+$$

Expressions for the hydrolysis constant K_h for cation acids are similar to those of anion bases. In general, *salts formed from strong acids and weak bases hydrolyze in water to form acidic solutions.*

Hydrated copper(II) hydroxide is not very soluble. The scummy appearance of reagent bottles in which copper(II) salt solutions are stored for a long time is caused by the slight secondary hydrolysis of $Cu(H_2O)_3OH^+$ cations. This hydrolysis is aided by the formation of a slightly soluble product.

☐ 21.12 Solubility product

A *saturated* solution contains the maximum amount of solute possible at a given temperature in equilibrium with an undissolved excess of the substance. A saturated solution is *not necessarily* a concentrated solution. The concentration may be high or low, depending on the solubility of the solute.

A rough rule is often used to express solubilities qualita-

Solubility guide:
soluble   > 1.0 g/100 g H_2O
slightly soluble   > 0.1 g/100 g H_2O
insoluble   < 0.1 g/100 g H_2O

tively. By this rule, a substance is said to be *soluble* if the solubility is greater than 1 g per 100 g of water. It is said to be *insoluble* if the solubility is less than 0.1 g per 100 g of water. Solubilities that fall between these limits are described as *slightly soluble*.

"Insoluble" salts are actually very sparingly soluble in water.

Substances usually referred to as insoluble are, in fact, very *sparingly soluble*. An extremely small quantity of such a solute saturates the solution. Equilibrium is established with the undissolved excess remaining in contact with the solution. Equilibria between sparingly soluble solids and their saturated solutions are especially important in analytical chemistry.

You have observed that silver chloride precipitates when Ag^+ and Cl^- ions are placed in the same solution. Silver chloride is so sparingly soluble in water that it is described as insoluble. The solution reaches saturation at a very low concentration of its ions. All Ag^+ and Cl^- ions in excess of this concentration eventually separate as an AgCl precipitate.

The equilibrium principles developed in this chapter apply to all saturated solutions of sparingly soluble salts. Consider the equilibrium system in a saturated solution of silver chloride that contains an excess of the solid salt. The equilibrium equation is

$$AgCl(s) \rightleftarrows Ag^+(aq) + Cl^-(aq)$$

The equilibrium constant is expressed as

$$K = \frac{[Ag^+][Cl^-]}{[AgCl]}$$

Here, [AgCl] refers to concentration of undissolved AgCl.

Because the concentration of a pure substance in the solid or liquid phase remains constant (Section 21.4), adding more solid AgCl to this equilibrium system does not change the *concentration* of the undissolved AgCl present. Thus [AgCl] in the above equation is a constant. By combining the two constants, this equation becomes

$$K[AgCl] = [Ag^+][Cl^-]$$

The product $K[AgCl]$ is also a constant. It is called the *solubility-product constant* K_{sp}.

$$K_{sp} = K[AgCl]$$

Therefore,

$$K_{sp} = [Ag^+][Cl^-]$$

Thus the solubility-product constant K_{sp} of AgCl *is the product of the molar concentrations of its ions in a saturated solution.*

Calcium fluoride is another sparingly soluble salt. The equilibrium system in a saturated CaF_2 solution is given by the equation

$$CaF_2(s) \rightleftarrows Ca^{++}(aq) + 2F^-(aq)$$

The solubility-product constant is given by

$$K_{sp} = [Ca^{++}][F^-]^2$$

Notice how this constant differs from the solubility-product constant for AgCl. For CaF_2, K_{sp} is the product of the molar concentration of Ca^{++} ions and the molar concentration of F^- ions *squared*.

Similar equations apply to any sparingly soluble salt having the general formula M_aX_b. The equilibrium system in a saturated solution is shown by

$$M_aX_b \rightleftarrows aM^{+b} + bX^{-a}$$

The solubility-product constant is expressed by

$$K_{sp} = [M^{+b}]^a[X^{-a}]^b$$

*The **solubility-product constant** of a substance is the product of the molar concentrations of its ions in a saturated solution, each raised to the appropriate power.*

From solubility data listed in Appendix Table 13, 1.94×10^{-4} g of AgCl saturates $10\overline{0}$ g of water at 20 °C. One mole of AgCl has a mass of 143.4 g. Therefore, the saturation concentration (solubility) of AgCl can be expressed in moles per liter.

$$\frac{1.94 \times 10^{-4} \text{ g}}{10.0^2 \text{ g}} \times \frac{10^3 \text{ g}}{L} \times \frac{\text{mole}}{1.434 \times 10^2 \text{ g}} = 1.35 \times 10^{-5} \text{ mole/L}$$

The equilibrium equation is

$$AgCl(aq) \rightleftarrows Ag^+(aq) + Cl^-(aq)$$

Silver chloride dissociates in solution contributing equal numbers of aqueous Ag^+ and Cl^- ions. Therefore, the ion concentrations in the saturated solution are

$$[Ag^+] = 1.35 \times 10^{-5}$$
$$[Cl^-] = 1.35 \times 10^{-5}$$

and

$$K_{sp} = [Ag^+][Cl^-]$$
$$K_{sp} = (1.35 \times 10^{-5})(1.35 \times 10^{-5})$$
$$K_{sp} = (1.35 \times 10^{-5})^2$$
$$K_{sp} = 1.82 \times 10^{-10}$$

This result is the solubility-product constant of AgCl at 20 °C.

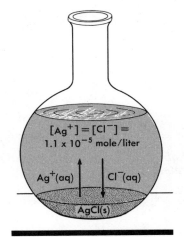

$[Ag^+] = [Cl^-] =$
1.1×10^{-5} mole/liter
$Ag^+(aq)$ $Cl^-(aq)$
AgCl(s)

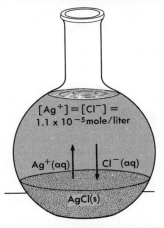

$[Ag^+] = [Cl^-] =$
1.1×10^{-5} mole/liter
$Ag^+(aq)$ $Cl^-(aq)$
AgCl(s)

Figure 21-5. The heterogeneous equilibrium in a saturated solution is not disturbed by the addition of more of the solid phase.

The conversion of solubility in terms of g solute/100 g solvent to mole/liter solution is a factor-label exercise. In very dilute solutions there is no distinction between solution molality and molarity.

From Appendix Table 13, the solubility of CaF_2 at 25 °C is 1.7×10^{-3} g/$10\overline{0}$ g of water. Expressed in moles per liter as before, this concentration becomes 2.2×10^{-4} mole/L.

The equilibrium equation for a saturated solution of CaF_2 is

$$CaF_2 \rightleftarrows Ca^{++} + 2F^-$$

CaF_2 dissociates in solution to yield *twice as many* F^- ions as Ca^{++} ions. The ion concentrations in the saturated solution are

$$[Ca^{++}] = 2.2 \times 10^{-4}$$

$$[F^-] = 2(2.2 \times 10^{-4})$$

and

$$K_{sp} = [Ca^{++}][F^-]^2$$

$$K_{sp} = (2.2 \times 10^{-4})(4.4 \times 10^{-4})^2$$

$$K_{sp} = (2.2 \times 10^{-4})(1.9 \times 10^{-7})$$

$$K_{sp} = 4.2 \times 10^{-11}$$

Thus the solubility-product constant of CaF_2 is 4.2×10^{-11} at 25 °C.

Salts precipitate from their saturated solutions.

If the ion product $[Ca^{++}][F^-]^2$ is *less* than the value for K_{sp} at a particular temperature, the solution is *unsaturated*. If the ion product is *greater* than the value for K_{sp}, CaF_2 precipitates. This precipitation reduces the concentrations of Ca^{++} and F^- ions until equilibrium is established. The solubility equilibrium is then

$$CaF_2(s) \rightleftarrows Ca^{++}(aq) + 2F^-(aq)$$

It is difficult to measure very small concentrations of a solute with precision. For this reason, solubility data from different sources may result in slightly different values of K_{sp} for a substance. Thus calculations of K_{sp} ordinarily should be limited to two significant figures. Representative values of K_{sp} at 25 °C for some sparingly soluble compounds are listed in Table 21-4.

| PRACTICE PROBLEMS

Determine the solubility-product constant, K_{sp}, from solubility data for each of the following substances.
1. Copper(I) chloride. Solubility: 1.08×10^{-2} g/100 g H_2O at 25 °C.   *ans.* 1.19×10^{-6}
2. Lead(II) chloride. Solubility: 1.0 g/$10\overline{0}$ g H_2O at 25 °C. *ans.* 1.86×10^{-4}

▢ 21.13 Calculating solubilities

Solubility-product constants are computed from very careful measurements of solubilities and other solution properties. Once

Table 21-4
SOLUBILITY-PRODUCT CONSTANTS K_{sp} at 25 °C

Salt	Ion product	K_{sp}
$AgC_2H_3O_2$	$[Ag^+][C_2H_3O_2^-]$	2.5×10^{-3}
$AgBr$	$[Ag^+][Br^-]$	5.0×10^{-13}
Ag_2CO_3	$[Ag^+]^2[CO_3^{--}]$	8.1×10^{-12}
$AgCl$	$[Ag^+][Cl^-]$	1.8×10^{-10}
AgI	$[Ag^+][I^-]$	8.3×10^{-17}
Ag_2S	$[Ag^+]^2[S^{--}]$	1.6×10^{-49}
$Al(OH)_3$	$[Al^{+++}][OH^-]^3$	1.3×10^{-33}
$BaCO_3$	$[Ba^{++}][CO_3^{--}]$	1.2×10^{-8}
$BaSO_4$	$[Ba^{++}][SO_4^{--}]$	1.1×10^{-10}
Bi_2S_3	$[Bi^{+++}]^2[S^{--}]^3$	1.0×10^{-97}
CdS	$[Cd^{++}][S^{--}]$	8.0×10^{-27}
$CaCO_3$	$[Ca^{++}][CO_3^{--}]$	1.4×10^{-8}
CaF_2	$[Ca^{++}][F^-]^2$	4.2×10^{-11}
$Ca(OH)_2$	$[Ca^{++}][OH^-]^2$	5.5×10^{-6}
$CaSO_4$	$[Ca^{++}][SO_4^{--}]$	9.1×10^{-6}
CoS	$[Co^{++}][S^{--}]$	3.0×10^{-26}
Co_2S_3	$[Co^{+++}]^2[S^{--}]^3$	2.6×10^{-124}
$CuCl$	$[Cu^+][Cl^-]$	1.2×10^{-6}
Cu_2S	$[Cu^+]^2[S^{--}]$	2.5×10^{-48}
CuS	$[Cu^{++}][S^{--}]$	6.3×10^{-36}
FeS	$[Fe^{++}][S^{--}]$	6.3×10^{-18}
Fe_2S_3	$[Fe^{+++}]^2[S^{--}]^3$	1.4×10^{-85}
$Fe(OH)_3$	$[Fe^{+++}][OH^-]^3$	1.5×10^{-36}
HgS	$[Hg^{++}][S^{--}]$	1.6×10^{-52}
$MgCO_3$	$[Mg^{++}][CO_3^{--}]$	3.5×10^{-8}
$Mg(OH)_2$	$[Mg^{++}][OH^-]^2$	1.5×10^{-11}
MnS	$[Mn^{++}][S^{--}]$	2.5×10^{-13}
NiS	$[Ni^{++}][S^{--}]$	3.2×10^{-19}
$PbCl_2$	$[Pb^{++}][Cl^-]^2$	1.9×10^{-4}
$PbCrO_4$	$[Pb^{++}][CrO_4^{--}]$	2.8×10^{-13}
$PbSO_4$	$[Pb^{++}][SO_4^{--}]$	1.8×10^{-8}
PbS	$[Pb^{++}][S^{--}]$	8.0×10^{-28}
SnS	$[Sn^{++}][S^{--}]$	1.2×10^{-25}
$SrSO_4$	$[Sr^{++}][SO_4^{--}]$	3.2×10^{-7}
ZnS	$[Zn^{++}][S^{--}]$	1.6×10^{-24}

known, the solubility product is very helpful in determining the solubility of a sparingly soluble salt.

Suppose you wish to know how much barium carbonate, $BaCO_3$, can be dissolved in one liter of water at 25 °C. From Table 21-4, K_{sp} for $BaCO_3$ has the numerical value 1.2×10^{-8}.

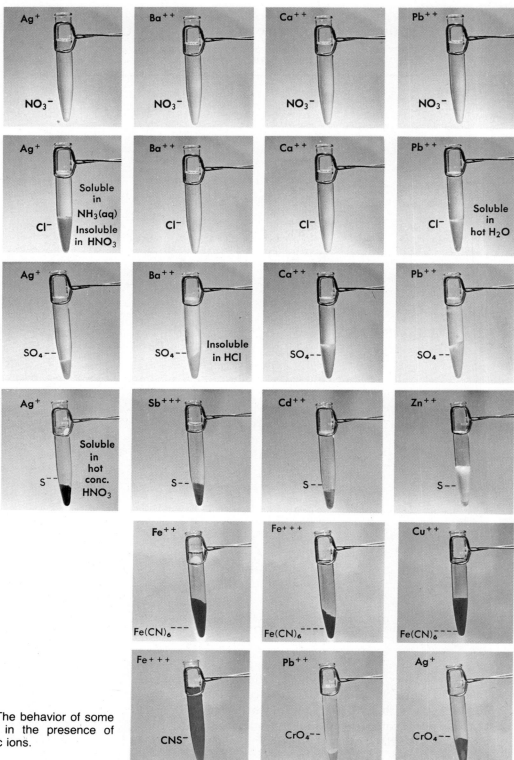

Figure 21-6. The behavior of some negative ions in the presence of certain metallic ions.

The solubility equation is written as follows:

$$BaCO_3(s) \rightleftarrows Ba^{++}(aq) + CO_3^{--}(aq)$$

Knowing the value for K_{sp},

$$K_{sp} = [Ba^{++}][CO_3^{--}] = 1.2 \times 10^{-8}$$

Therefore, $BaCO_3$ dissolves until the product of the molar concentrations of Ba^{++} and CO_3^{--} equals 1.2×10^{-8}.

The solubility equilibrium equation shows that Ba^{++} ions and CO_3^{--} ions enter the solution in equal numbers as the salt dissolves. Thus,

$$[Ba^{++}] = [CO_3^{--}] = [BaCO_3]\,\text{dissolved}$$

$$K_{sp} = 1.2 \times 10^{-8} = [BaCO_3]^2$$

$$[BaCO_3] = \sqrt{1.2 \times 10^{-8}}$$

$$[BaCO_3] = 1.1 \times 10^{-4} \text{ mole/L}$$

The solubility of $BaCO_3$ is 1.1×10^{-4} mole/liter. Thus the solution concentration is 1.1×10^{-4} M for Ba^{++} ions and 1.1×10^{-4} M for CO_3^{--} ions.

$$K_{sp} = [Ba^{++}][CO_3^{--}]$$

PRACTICE PROBLEMS

1. Calculate the concentration of $AgC_2H_3O_2$ in mole/L from the solubility-product constant K_{sp} as listed in Table 21-4. *ans.* 5.0×10^{-2} mole/L
2. Verify that the value for K_{sp} you computed as the answer to Practice Problem Number 1, Section 21.12, yields the concentration of CuCl given in the problem. *ans.* 1.0×10^{-2} g CuCl/100 g H_2O

☐ 21.14 Precipitation calculations

In the example used in Section 21.13, the $BaCO_3$ served as the source of both Ba^{++} and CO_3^{--} ions. Thus the concentrations of the two ions were equal. However, the equilibrium condition does not require the two ion concentrations to be equal. It requires only that the *ion product* $[Ba^{++}][CO_3^{--}]$ *not* exceed the value of K_{sp} for the system.

Suppose unequal quantities of $BaCl_2$ and $CaCO_3$ are added to water. A high concentration of Ba^{++} ions and a low concentration of CO_3^{--} ions might result. If the ion product $[Ba^{++}][CO_3^{--}]$ exceeds the K_{sp} of $BaCO_3$, a precipitate of $BaCO_3$ forms. Precipitation would continue until the ion concentrations decreased to equilibrium values.

The solubility product can be used to predict whether or not a precipitate forms when two solutions are mixed. An illustration of the calculations involved in such a prediction is given in the following Sample Problem.

◨ | **SAMPLE PROBLEM**

Will a precipitate form if 20.0 mL of 0.010-M $BaCl_2$ solution is mixed with 20.0 mL of 0.0050-M Na_2SO_4 solution?

◨ | **SOLUTION**

The two possible new pairings of ions are NaCl and $BaSO_4$. Of these, $BaSO_4$ is a sparingly soluble salt. It will then precipitate from the resulting solution if the ion product $[Ba^{++}][SO_4^{--}]$ exceeds the value of the solubility-product constant K_{sp} for $BaSO_4$. From the table of solubility products (Table 21-4), the K_{sp} is found to be 1.1×10^{-10}

The solubility equilibrium equation is

$$BaSO_4(s) \rightleftarrows Ba^{++}(aq) + SO_4^{--}(aq)$$

and the equilibrium condition is

$$K_{sp} = [Ba^{++}][SO_4^{--}] = 1.1 \times 10^{-10}$$

If the ion product $[Ba^{++}][SO_4^{--}]$ exceeds 1.1×10^{-10}, precipitation of $BaSO_4$ is predicted. Mole quantities of Ba^{++} and SO_4^{--} ions:

$$0.020 \text{ liter} \times \frac{0.010 \text{ mole Ba}^{++}}{\text{liter}} = 0.00020 \text{ mole Ba}^{++}$$

$$0.020 \text{ liter} \times \frac{0.0050 \text{ mole SO}_4^{--}}{\text{liter}} = 0.00010 \text{ mole SO}_4^{--}$$

Total volume of solution containing Ba^{++} and SO_4^{--} ions:

$$0.020 \text{ liter} + 0.020 \text{ liter} = 0.040 \text{ liter}$$

Ba^{++} and SO_4^{--} ion concentrations:

$$\frac{0.00020 \text{ mole Ba}^{++}}{0.040 \text{ liter}} = 5.0 \times 10^{-3} \text{ mole Ba}^{++}/\text{liter}$$

$$\frac{0.00010 \text{ mole SO}_4^{--}}{0.040 \text{ liter}} = 2.5 \times 10^{-3} \text{ mole SO}_4^{--}/\text{liter}$$

Trial value of ion product:

$$[Ba^{++}][SO_4^{--}] = (5.0 \times 10^{-3})(2.5 \times 10^{-3}) = 1.2 \times 10^{-5}$$

The ion product is much greater than $K_{sp}(K_{sp} = 1.1 \times 10^{-10})$, so precipitation occurs.

The solubility-product principle can be very useful when applied to solutions of sparingly soluble substances. It *cannot* be applied to solutions of moderately soluble or very soluble substances. Many solubility-product constants are known only roughly because of difficulties involved in solubility measurements. Sometimes, as with the hydrolysis of an ion in solution, it is necessary to consider two equilibria simultaneously. The solubility product is sensitive to changes in solution temperature to the extent that the solubility of the dissolved substance is affected by such changes.

PRACTICE PROBLEMS

1. Does a precipitate form when $10\bar{0}$ mL of 0.0025-M AgNO$_3$ and $15\bar{0}$ mL of 0.0020-M NaBr solutions are mixed?
   ans. AgBr ion product $= 1.2 \times 10^{-6}$; K_{sp}(AgBr) $= 5.0 \times 10^{-13}$; AgBr precipitates.
2. Does a precipitate form when $2\bar{0}$ mL of 0.038-M Pb(NO$_3$)$_2$ and $3\bar{0}$ mL of 0.018-M KCl solutions are mixed?
   ans. PbCl$_2$ ion product $= 1.8 \times 10^{-6}$; K_{sp}(PbCl$_2$) $= 1.9 \times 10^{-4}$; PbCl$_2$ does not precipitate.

 SUMMARY

Many chemical reactions are reversible. A reaction system in which the forward and reverse reactions occur simultaneously at the same rate is said to be in equilibrium. Both reactions continue, but there is no net change in the composition of the system.

Equilibrium is a dynamic state involving physical as well as chemical processes. At equilibrium, the energy-change and the entropy-change factors are equal. The relative concentrations of reactants and products in a reaction system at equilibrium are expressed in terms of an equilibrium constant. At equilibrium, the ratio of the product of the mole concentrations of substances formed to the product of the mole concentrations of reactants has a definite numerical value at a given temperature. This numerical ratio is the equilibrium constant K. For values of K greater than 1, the products of the forward reaction are favored. For values of K less than 1, the reactants of the forward reaction are favored. The equilibrium constant for an equilibrium system varies only with the system's temperature.

Any change that alters the rate of either the forward or reverse reaction disturbs the equilibrium of the system. The equilibrium is subjected to a stress. According to Le Chatelier's principle, the equilibrium is displaced in the direction that relieves the stress. Only when change in temperature causes the stress is the numerical value of K changed when equilibrium is reestablished. A forward reaction shows little tendency to reach an equilibrium with the reverse reaction when the conditions that encourage each are very different.

The common ion effect is recognized when a solute containing ions like those of a reactant in an equilibrium system is added to the system. Le Chatelier's principle explains the response of the system to the stress caused by the increase in concentration of common ions.

The equilibrium expressions of weak acids can be modified to give an expression for the ionization constant of the acid. This ionization constant is derived from the fact that the equation for the equilibrium constant includes [H$_2$O], which is also a constant. The ionization constant is then set equal to the product of these two constants, $K_a = K$[H$_2$O]. When the equilibrium expression for the slight ionization of water is considered, the ionization constant for water, K_w, becomes $K_w = K$[H$_2$O] = [H$_3$O$^+$][OH$^-$]. At 25 °C, $K_w = 1 \times 10^{-14}$ for water and all aqueous solutions.

When salts are dissolved in water, the resulting solutions are not always neutral. Salts formed from strong bases and weak acids have aqueous solutions that are basic. The anions of the salt act as a base. They acquire protons from water molecules and increase the $[OH^-]$ of the solution. The process is called anion hydrolysis.

Salts formed from strong acids and weak bases have aqueous solutions that are acidic. The cations of the salt act as an acid. They donate protons to water molecules and increase the $[H_3O^+]$ of the solution. This process is called cation hydrolysis.

Salts formed from strong acids and strong bases do not hydrolyze in water and their solutions are neutral. Salts formed from weak acids and weak bases may hydrolyze completely in water solution.

Salts that are usually described as being insoluble in water are, in fact, very sparingly soluble. Their ions form saturated aqueous solutions at extremely low concentrations. Equilibrium is quickly established between undissolved solute and dissolved solute ions. Because the concentration of undissolved salt is constant, the equilibrium expression yields a useful constant, K_{sp}, called the solubility-product constant. The numerical value of K_{sp} is determined by the product of the mole concentrations of solute ions in the saturated solution. Solubility-product constants are very useful in analytical chemistry.

◖ VOCABULARY

anion	dynamic	mass action expression
anion hydrolysis	equilibrium constant	physical equilibrium
buffered solution	hydrolysis	precipitate
cation	hydrolysis constant	reversible reaction
cation hydrolysis	insoluble	slightly soluble
chemical equilibrium	ionic equilibrium	solubility-product constant
chemical equilibrium law	ionization constant	soluble
common ion effect	ionization constant of water	sparingly soluble

◖ QUESTIONS

Group A

1. State three examples of physical equilibrium.
2. Write the ionic equations for three examples of ionic equilibrium.
3. What is wrong with this statement? When equilibrium is reached, the opposing reactions stop.
4. State the law of mass action.
5. A combustion reaction proceeding in air under standard pressure is transferred to an atmosphere of pure oxygen under the same pressure. (*a*) What effect would you observe? (*b*) How can you account for this effect?
6. (*a*) State Le Chatelier's principle. (*b*) To what kinds of equilibria does it apply?

7. (*a*) Name three factors that may disturb, or shift, an equilibrium. (*b*) Which of these affects the value of the equilibrium constant?
8. What are the three conditions under which ionic reactions involving ionic substances may run to completion? Write an equation for each.
9. What are the solubility characteristics of substances involved in solubility equilibrium systems?
10. Define the solubility-product constant.

Group B

11. The reaction between steam and iron is reversible. Steam passed over hot iron pro-

duces magnetic iron oxide (Fe_3O_4) and hydrogen. Hydrogen passed over hot magnetic iron oxide reduces it to iron and forms steam. Suggest a method by which this reversible reaction may be brought to a state of equilibrium.

12. What is the meaning of the term *dynamic* as applied to an equilibrium state?

13. Methanol is produced synthetically as a gas by the reaction between carbon monoxide and hydrogen in the presence of a catalyst, according to the equilibrium reaction: $CO + 2H_2 \rightleftarrows CH_3OH + 24$ kcal. Write the expression for the equilibrium constant of this reaction.

14. How would you propose to regulate the temperature of the equilibrium mixture of CO, H_2, and CH_3OH of Question 13 in order to increase the yield of methanol? Explain.

15. How would you propose to regulate the pressure on the equilibrium mixture of Question 13 in order to increase the yield of methanol? Explain.

16. In the reaction **A** + **B** $\rightleftarrows$ **C**, the concentrations of **A, B,** and **C** in the equilibrium mixture were found to be 2.0, 3.0, and 1.0 moles per liter, respectively. What is the equilibrium constant of this reaction?

17. Write the net ionic equations for the following reactions in water solution. If no visible reaction takes place, write NO REACTION. Omit all *spectator* ions. Show precipitates by (s) and gases by (g). Use solubility data in the Appendix as needed. Use a separate sheet of paper. *Do not write in this book.*

(a) $BaCO_3 + HNO_3 \rightarrow$
(b) $Pb(NO_3)_2 + NaCl \rightarrow$
(c) $CuSO_4 + HCl \rightarrow$
(d) $Ca_3(PO_4)_2 + NaNO_3 \rightarrow$
(e) $Ba(NO_3)_2 + H_2SO_4 \rightarrow$
(f) $FeS + NaCl \rightarrow$
(g) $AgC_2H_3O_2 + HCl \rightarrow$
(h) $Na_3PO_4 + CuSO_4 \rightarrow$
(i) $BaCl_2 + Na_2SO_4 \rightarrow$
(j) $CuO + H_2SO_4 \rightarrow$

18. Explain why the pH of a solution containing both acetic acid and sodium acetate is higher than that of a solution containing the same concentration of acetic acid alone.

19. Referring to Table 21-2, write the expression for the equilibrium constant for each equilibrium system listed.

20. Referring to Table 21-1, explain why $[H_2] = [I_2]$ in the first two experiments.

21. What is the effect of changes in pressure on the $H_2 + I_2 \rightleftarrows 2HI$ equilibrium? Explain.

22. (a) From the development of K_a in Section 21-7, show how you would express an ionization constant K_b for the weak base NH_3. (b) In this case $K_b = 1.8 \times 10^{-5}$. What is the meaning of this numerical value?

23. Given a hydrolysis reaction $B^- + H_2O \rightleftarrows HB + OH^-$, demonstrate that $K_h = K_w/K_a$.

24. The ionization constant K_a for acetic acid is 1.8×10^{-5} at 25 °C. Explain the meaning of this value.

25. Complete the table shown below, using a separate sheet of paper.

pH	[H₃O⁺] (mole/liter)	[OH⁻] (mole/liter)	[H₃O⁺][OH⁻]	Property
0 1 3 5 7 9 11 13 14	$10^{-7} = 0.0000001$	$10^{-7} = 0.0000001$	10^{-14}	Neutral

◀ | **PROBLEMS**

Group A

1. The H_3O^+ ion concentration of a solution is 0.00040 mole per liter. This may be expressed as $[H_3O^+] = 4.0 \times 10^{-4}$ mole per liter. What is the pH of the solution?

2. What is the pH of a 0.002-M solution of HCl? (At this concentration HCl is completely ionized.)

3. Find the pH of a 0.02-M solution of KOH.

4. Given a 250-mL volumetric flask, distilled water, and NaOH, (a) state how you would prepare 250 mL of 0.50-M NaOH solution. (b) What is the normality of the solution?

5. What quantity of copper(II) sulfate pentahydrate is required to prepare 750 mL of 2.00-M solution?

Group B

6. A 0.01000-N solution of acetic acid is found to have a pH of 3.3799 at 18 °C. What is the ionization constant of this weak acid?

7. Ammonia is a weak base and its water solution is slightly basic. The ionization constant for the equilibrium reaction $NH_3 + H_2O \rightleftarrows NH_4^+ + OH^-$ is $K_b = 1.8 \times 10^{-5}$. What is the pH of a 0.50-M NH_3 solution?

(Note: Assume that the change in mole concentration of NH_3 at equilibrium is insignificant.)

8. It was determined by experiment that 1.3×10^{-4} g AgBr could be dissolved in 1.0 L of water at a known temperature to form a saturated solution. What is the K_{sp} for AgBr at that temperature?

9. The solubility of lead(II) bromide was determined experimentally to be 0.86 g per 100 g of water at 20 °C. What is the solubility-product constant for the solute at this temperature?

10. In another experiment a saturated solution of silver carbonate was determined to be 1.26×10^{-4} M. What is the solubility-product constant for silver carbonate at the solution temperature?

11. How many grams of $AgC_2H_3O_2$ can be dissolved in 10.0 liters of water at 25 °C? (Note: The value of K_{sp} for $AgC_2H_3O_2$ can be found in Table 21-4.)

12. If 0.0015 mole of solid $Pb(NO_3)_2$ is added to one liter of 0.0015-M H_2SO_4, (a) what substance might precipitate? (b) will the precipitate form?

Oxidation-Reduction Reactions

Advances in science can be made quite by accident. Electrochemistry, for example, was accidently discovered in the laboratory of the eighteenth-century physiologist Luigi Galvani. When Galvani had attached the legs of dissected frogs to copper and hung these from an iron balcony, he noticed that the frogs' legs twitched when their unattached ends contacted the iron. He attributed these contractions to "animal electricity." His colleague, the physicist Allesandro Volta, however, proposed that the twitching was caused by electricity produced when two dissimilar metals made contact through a salt solution or other conducting medium. Volta tested this theory by connecting a series of two metals, zinc and silver, and separating them with cloth soaked in salt solution. Volta's series of electrochemical cells, called the "voltaic pile," was the forerunner of the modern storage battery. A modified voltaic pile gave scientists a powerful new tool to decompose compounds and analyze their constituent elements.

◻ 22.1 Oxidation and reduction processes

Reactions in which the atoms or ions of an element attain a more positive (or less negative) oxidation state are defined in Section 6.5 as *oxidation processes*. An element species that undergoes a change to a more positive oxidation state is said to be *oxidized*. Reactions in which the atoms or ions of an element attain a more negative (or less positive) oxidation state are defined as *reduction processes*. An element species that undergoes a change to a more negative oxidation state is said to be *reduced*. The rules for assigning oxidation numbers are given in Section 6.25 and summarized in Table 22-1.

1. Oxidation. The combustion of metallic sodium in an atmosphere of chlorine gas illustrates the oxidation process. The product is sodium chloride, and the sodium-chlorine bond is ionic. The formula equation for this reaction is

$$2Na(s) + Cl_2(g) \rightarrow 2NaCl(s)$$

In this reaction each sodium atom loses an electron and becomes a sodium ion.

$$Na \rightarrow Na^+ + e^-$$

The oxidation state of sodium has changed from the 0 state of the atom (Rule 1) to the more positive +1 state of the ion (Rule 2). The sodium atom is said to be *oxidized* to the sodium ion. This change in oxidation state is indicated by the oxidation numbers

In this chapter you will gain an understanding of:

- **the processes of oxidation and reduction**
- **oxidation-reduction reactions**
- **balancing oxidation-reduction equations: oxidation-number method and ion-electron method**
- **oxidizing and reducing agents**
- **electrochemical reactions: electrochemical and electrolytic cells**
- **electrolysis**
- **electrode potentials**

placed above the symbol of the atom and the ion. For each sodium atom,

$$\overset{0}{Na} \rightarrow \overset{+1}{Na^+} + e^-$$

A second example of an oxidation process occurs when hydrogen burns in chlorine to form molecular hydrogen chloride gas. The hydrogen-chlorine bond is covalent. The formula equation for this reaction is

$$H_2(g) + Cl_2(g) \rightarrow 2HCl(g)$$

By Rule 1, the oxidation state of *each* hydrogen atom in the hydrogen molecule is 0. By Rule 4, the oxidation state of the combined hydrogen in the HCl molecule is +1. Because the hydrogen atom has changed from the 0 to the more positive +1 oxidation state, this change is an *oxidation process*.

$$\overset{0}{H_2} + Cl_2 \rightarrow \overset{+1}{2HCl}$$

2. Reduction. How shall the behavior of chlorine be regarded in these reactions with sodium and hydrogen? With sodium, each chlorine atom acquires an electron and becomes a chloride ion. The oxidation state of chlorine changes from the 0 state of the chlorine atom (Rule 1) to the more negative −1 state of the chloride ion (Rule 2). The chlorine atom is *reduced* to the chloride ion. For each chlorine atom,

$$\overset{0}{Cl} + e^- \rightarrow \overset{-1}{Cl^-}$$

Table 22-1
RULES FOR ASSIGNING OXIDATION NUMBERS

---

1. The oxidation number of an atom of a free element is zero.

2. The oxidation number of a monatomic ion is equal to its charge.

3. The algebraic sum of the oxidation numbers of the atoms in the formula of a compound is zero.

4. In compounds, the oxidation number of hydrogen is +1, except in metallic hydrides where it is −1.

5. In compounds, the oxidation number of oxygen is −2. A common exception is in peroxides where it is −1. (In compounds with fluorine, the oxidation number of oxygen is +2.)

6. In combinations of nonmetals, the oxidation number of the less electronegative element is positive and of the more electronegative element is negative.

7. The algebraic sum of the oxidation numbers of the atoms in the formula of a polyatomic ion is equal to its charge.

In the reaction of chlorine with hydrogen, the pair of electrons shared by the hydrogen and chlorine atoms in the hydrogen chloride molecule is not shared equally. Rather, the pair of electrons is more strongly attracted to the chlorine atom because of its higher electronegativity. By Rules 4 and 3, chlorine is assigned an oxidation number of -1. Thus the chlorine atom is changed from the 0 to the -1 oxidation state, a *reduction process*.

$$\overset{0}{H_2} + \overset{-1}{Cl_2} \rightarrow 2HCl$$

Oxidation numbers are assigned to the atoms of covalent molecular species in this arbitrary way to indicate their oxidation states. For the hydrogen chloride molecule, the oxidation number of the hydrogen atom is $+1$ and that of the chlorine atom is -1.

$$\overset{0}{H_2} + \overset{0}{Cl_2} \rightarrow 2\overset{+1\,-1}{HCl}$$

☐ 22.2 Oxidation and reduction occur simultaneously

If *oxidation* occurs during a chemical reaction, then *reduction* must occur simultaneously. Furthermore, the *amount* of oxidation must match the *amount* of reduction. *Any chemical process in which elements undergo a change in oxidation number is an* **oxidation-reduction reaction**. The name is often shortened to "redox" reaction. The processes of oxidation and reduction are *equivalent* in every oxidation-reduction reaction.

Observe that as metallic sodium burns in chlorine gas, *two* sodium atoms are oxidized to Na^+ ions as *one* diatomic chlorine molecule is reduced to *two* Cl^- ions. Elemental sodium and elemental chlorine are chemically equivalent atom for atom and ion for ion.

$$\overset{0}{2Na} \rightarrow 2\overset{+1}{Na^+} + 2e^- \quad \text{(oxidation)}$$

$$\overset{0}{Cl_2} + 2e^- \rightarrow 2\overset{-1}{Cl^-} \quad \text{(reduction)}$$

$$\overset{0}{2Na} + \overset{0}{Cl_2} \rightarrow 2\overset{+1}{Na^+}\overset{-1}{Cl^-} \quad \text{(combined)}$$

Suppose a scheme is devised to recover metallic aluminum from an aluminum salt. In this scheme, sodium atoms are oxidized to Na^+ ions, and Al^{+++} ions are reduced to aluminum atoms. For these oxidation and reduction processes to be equivalent, three Na^+ ions are formed for each Al^{+++} ion reduced.

$$\overset{0}{3Na} \rightarrow 3\overset{+1}{Na^+} + 3e^- \quad \text{(oxidation)}$$

$$\overset{+3}{Al^{+++}} + 3e^- \rightarrow \overset{0}{Al} \quad \text{(reduction)}$$

$$\overset{0}{3Na} + \overset{+3}{Al^{+++}} \rightarrow 3\overset{+1}{Na^+} + \overset{0}{Al} \quad \text{(combined)}$$

Oxidation-reduction reactions are called "redox" reactions.

Powdered antimony

Chlorine

Figure 22-1. The combustion of antimony in chlorine is an oxidation-reduction reaction.

Figure 22-2. As $KMnO_4$ solution is added to an acidic solution of $FeSO_4$, Fe^{++} ions are oxidized to Fe^{+++} ions, and the red MnO_4^- ions are reduced to colorless Mn^{++} ions. When all Fe^{++} ions are oxidized, MnO_4^- ions are no longer reduced to colorless Mn^{++} ions. Thus the first faint appearance of the MnO_4^- color indicates the end point of the titration.

Observe that in the combined equation for each example, both electric charge and atoms are conserved, and that the oxidation and reduction processes are indeed equivalent.

Many of the reactions studied in elementary chemistry involve oxidation-reduction processes. Of the examples considered, the first and second are composition reactions. The third example is a replacement reaction. Not all composition reactions are oxidation-reduction reactions, however. Sulfur dioxide gas, SO_2, dissolves in water to form an acidic solution containing a low concentration of sulfurous acid, H_2SO_3.

$$\overset{+4\ -2}{S\ O_2} + \overset{+1\ -2}{H_2\ O} \rightarrow \overset{+1\ +4\ -2}{H_2\ S\ O_3}$$

Observe that the oxidation states of all elemental species remain unchanged in this composition reaction. It is not an oxidation-reduction reaction.

When a solution of sodium chloride is added to a solution of silver nitrate, an ion-exchange reaction occurs and a white precipitate of silver chloride separates.

$$\overset{+1}{Na^+} + \overset{-1}{Cl^-} + \overset{+1}{Ag^+} + \overset{+5\ -2}{N\ O_3^-} \rightarrow \overset{+1}{Na^+} + \overset{+5\ -2}{N\ O_3^-} + \overset{+1\ -1}{Ag^+Cl^-}\ (s)$$

Or more simply by omitting spectator ions,

$$\overset{+1}{Ag^+}(aq) + \overset{-1}{Cl^-}(aq) \rightarrow \overset{+1\ -1}{Ag^+Cl^-}\ (s)$$

The oxidation state of each species of monatomic ion remains unchanged. This reaction is not an oxidation-reduction reaction.

Oxidation-reduction reactions sometimes involve polyatomic ions. An example is the *permanganate ion*, MnO_4^-, in aqueous potassium permanganate. Under certain conditions this MnO_4^- ion is changed to the *manganese(II) ion*, Mn^{++}. See Figure 22-2. Under other conditions, the MnO_4^- ion is changed to the *manganate ion*, MnO_4^{--}.

When writing the equation for either of these reactions, all changes in elemental oxidation states must be known. The ionic charge alone is of little help if the ion consists of two or more different elements. Assigning the proper oxidation number to each atom present in a polyatomic ion simplifies the task of balancing oxidation-reduction equations. This assignment is accomplished by following the appropriate rules of Table 22-1.

The oxidation state of an atom of an element is 0. This is true whether the atom exists as a free particle or as one of several in a molecule of the element. The oxidation state of each hydrogen atom in the molecule H_2 is 0. It is also 0 for monatomic hydrogen.

The oxidation state of sulfur is 0 in S, S_2, S_4, S_6, and S_8—all of which exist. All atoms in their elemental forms have oxidation numbers of 0. They are written as C, H_2, N_2, Pt, and S_8.

In the following electronic equations, the substances on the left are *oxidized*.

$$\overset{0}{Na} \rightarrow \overset{+1}{Na}{}^+ + e^-$$

$$\overset{0}{Fe} \rightarrow \overset{+2}{Fe}{}^{++} + 2e^-$$

$$\overset{+2}{Fe}{}^{++} \rightarrow \overset{+3}{Fe}{}^{+++} + e^-$$

$$\overset{-1}{2Cl^-} \rightarrow \overset{0}{Cl_2} + 2e^-$$

The number above each symbol is the oxidation number of that particle. (Ionic charges are shown as right superscripts where appropriate.) The difference between oxidation numbers indicates the change in oxidation state. The chloride ion is assigned the oxidation number -1, a *negative* oxidation state. Oxidation results in a *more positive* oxidation number. A change from -1 to 0 is a change to a more positive oxidation number, as is a change from 0 to $+1$, or $+1$ to $+2$.

In the electronic equations that follow, the substances on the left are *reduced*.

$$\overset{+1}{Na}{}^+ + e^- \rightarrow \overset{0}{Na}$$

$$\overset{0}{Cl_2} + 2e^- \rightarrow \overset{-1}{2Cl^-}$$

$$\overset{+3}{Fe}{}^{+++} + e^- \rightarrow \overset{+2}{Fe}{}^{++}$$

$$\overset{+2}{Cu}{}^{++} + 2e^- \rightarrow \overset{0}{Cu}$$

$$\overset{0}{Br_2} + 2e^- \rightarrow \overset{-1}{2Br^-}$$

In the third equation the iron(III) ion, oxidation number $+3$, is reduced to the iron(II) state with oxidation number $+2$. Reduction results in a *more negative* oxidation number. A change from $+3$ to $+2$ is a change to a more negative oxidation number. A change from 0 to -1 is also a change to a more negative oxidation number, as is a change from $+1$ to 0, $+1$ to -1, or -1 to -3.

The oxidation state of each monatomic ion in a binary salt is the same as the ionic charge. In binary covalent compounds, shared electrons are arbitrarily assigned to the more electronegative element.

In the two compounds H_2SO_4 and H_2SO_3, oxygen is assigned the oxidation number -2 and hydrogen $+1$. In the H_2SO_4 molecule, the total contribution of the 4 atoms of oxygen is $4(-2) = -8$. The total contribution of the 2 atoms of hydrogen

Figure 22-3. An oxidation-reduction reaction occurs when a strip of zinc is immersed in an aqueous solution of copper(II) sulfate. What substance is oxidized? What is reduced?

Oxidation numbers are usually placed above the symbols to avoid having them mistaken for ionic charges.

is $2(+1) = +2$. Of course the H_2SO_4 molecule is electrically neutral; therefore the oxidation number of the single sulfur atom must be $+6$. The proper oxidation number can now be placed *above* each symbol in the formula.

$$\overset{+1}{H_2} \overset{+6}{S} \overset{-2}{O_4}$$

$$2(+1) + 1(+6) + 4(-2) = 0$$

In the sulfurous acid molecule, H_2SO_3, the total contribution of oxygen is $3(-2) = -6$. For hydrogen it is $2(+1) = +2$. Thus the oxidation number of the single atom of sulfur must be $+4$.

$$\overset{+1}{H_2} \overset{+4}{S} \overset{-2}{O_3}$$

$$2(+1) + 1(+4) + 3(-2) = 0$$

Suppose these rules are applied to a salt containing a polyatomic ion. Potassium permanganate is made up of potassium ions, K^+, and polyatomic permanganate ions, MnO_4^-. The empirical formula is $KMnO_4$. Oxygen has the oxidation number -2, as before. The total contribution of the 4 oxygen atoms is $4(-2) = -8$. The K^+ ion is assigned the oxidation number that equals its ionic charge, $+1$. The oxidation number of the manganese atom in the polyatomic ion must then be $+7$. The formula showing these oxidation states of the elements can be written

$$\overset{+1}{K^+} [\overset{+7}{Mn}(\overset{-2}{O})_4]^-$$

or more simply,

$$\overset{+1}{K}\overset{+7}{Mn}\overset{-2}{O_4}$$

Manganese has several important oxidation states. This oxidation number, $+7$, represents its highest oxidation state.

◻ 22.3 Balancing oxidation-reduction equations

A principal use of oxidation numbers is in balancing equations for oxidation-reduction reactions. These reactions are recognized by the fact that changes in oxidation states occur among reactants that undergo oxidation or reduction during a chemical reaction. In the equation-balancing process, some accommodation is made for the *conservation of electrons* as well as for the *conservation of atoms*. The use of a pair of electronic equations to achieve electron balance in an oxidation-reduction equation is demonstrated in Section 22.2.

Several methods are used to balance "redox" equations. Two of these methods are illustrated here. The first is the *oxidation-number* or *electron-transfer* method. This basic scheme is simply an extension of the procedure you are now using. The second scheme, the *ion-electron* or *half-reaction* method, is commonly used with ionic equations.

1. Oxidation-number method. In all but the simplest reactions, the electron shift is balanced for the particles oxidized and the particles reduced by balancing the pair of electronic equations that represents this shift. Then the coefficients of all reactants and products are adjusted in the usual way (by inspection) to achieve a balanced equation.

The oxidation-number method of balancing oxidation-reduction equations includes the steps listed below. Observe that Steps 2, 3, and 4 represent additions to the steps you are accustomed to using in equation balancing.

Step 1: Write the skeleton equation for the reaction. To do this, the reactants and products must be known and each represented by the correct formula.

Step 2: Assign oxidation numbers to all elements and determine what is oxidized and what is reduced.

Step 3: Write the electronic equation for the oxidation process and the electronic equation for the reduction process.

Step 4: Adjust the coefficients in both electronic equations so that the number of electrons lost equals the number gained.

Step 5: Place these coefficients in the skeleton equation.

Step 6: Supply the proper coefficients for the rest of the equation to satisfy the conservation of atoms.

Some redox equations are simple enough to be balanced by inspection.

These steps are illustrated by applying them first to a very simple oxidation-reduction reaction that is easily balanced by inspection. Gaseous hydrogen sulfide burns in air to form sulfur dioxide and water. These facts are used to write the skeleton equation.

Step 1:
$$H_2S + O_2 \rightarrow SO_2 + H_2O$$

Oxidation numbers are now assigned. Changes in oxidation numbers indicate that sulfur is oxidized from the -2 state to the $+4$ state; oxygen is reduced from the 0 state to the -2 state. The oxidation number of hydrogen remains the same; it plays no part in the primary action of oxidation-reduction.

Step 2:
$$\overset{+1\ -2}{H_2S} + \overset{0}{O_2} \rightarrow \overset{+4-2}{SO_2} + \overset{+1\ -2}{H_2O}$$

The change in oxidation state of sulfur requires the loss of 6 electrons: $(-2) - (+4) = -6$. The change in oxidation state of oxygen requires the gain of 2 electrons: $(0) - (-2) = +2$. The electronic equations for these two reactions are

Step 3:

$$\overset{-2}{S} \rightarrow \overset{+4}{S} + 6e^- \quad \text{(oxidation)}$$

$$\overset{0}{O} + 2e^- \rightarrow \overset{-2}{O} \quad \text{(reduction)}$$

Free oxygen is diatomic. Thus 4 electrons must be gained during the reduction of a molecule of free oxygen.

$$\overset{0}{O_2} + 4e^- \rightarrow 2\overset{-2}{O}$$

The coefficients of the two electronic equations are now adjusted so that the number of electrons lost in the oxidation of sulfur is equal to the number gained in the reduction of oxygen. The smallest number of electrons common to both equations is 12. To show the gain and loss of 12 electrons in the two equations, the oxidation equation is multiplied by 2, and the reduction equation is multiplied by 3.

Step 4:

$$2\overset{-2}{S} \rightarrow 2\overset{+4}{S} + 12e^-$$

$$3\overset{0}{O_2} + 12e^- \rightarrow 6\overset{-2}{O}$$

Hence the coefficients of H_2S and SO_2 are both 2, and the coefficient of O_2 is 3. Observe that the $6\overset{-2}{O}$ is divided between the two products SO_2 and H_2O. The coefficient 6 is accounted for by the coefficient 2 in front of each formula. These coefficients are transferred to the skeleton equation.

Step 5:

$$2H_2S + 3O_2 \rightarrow 2SO_2 + 2H_2O$$

The coefficients of the equation are adjusted in the usual way to satisfy the law of conservation of atoms. In this case, no further adjustments are needed; the equation is balanced.

Step 6:

$$2H_2S + 3O_2 \rightarrow 2SO_2 + 2H_2O$$

When a redox equation is complex enough that balancing by inspection would be tedious, the redox sequence should be used.

As a second example, an oxidation-reduction equation that is slightly more difficult to balance will be used. This reaction occurs between manganese dioxide and hydrochloric acid. Water, manganese(II) chloride, and chlorine gas are formed. The skeleton equation is

$$\overset{+4 \ -2}{MnO_2} + \overset{+1-1}{HCl} \rightarrow \overset{+1 \ -2}{H_2O} + \overset{+2 \ -1}{MnCl_2} + \overset{0}{Cl_2}$$

Oxidation numbers are assigned to the elements in the reaction. They show that $\overset{+4}{Mn}$ is reduced to $\overset{+2}{Mn}{}^{++}$, and some of the $\overset{-1}{Cl^-}$ is oxidized to $\overset{0}{Cl}$. Hydrogen and oxygen do not take part in the oxidation-reduction reaction. The electronic equations are

$$\overset{-1}{2Cl^-} \rightarrow \overset{0}{Cl_2} + 2e^- \quad \text{(oxidation)}$$

$$\overset{+4}{Mn} + 2e^- \rightarrow \overset{+2}{Mn}{}^{++} \quad \text{(reduction)}$$

The number of electrons lost and gained is the same. The coefficients are transferred to the skeleton equation, which becomes

$$MnO_2 + 2HCl \rightarrow H_2O + MnCl_2 + Cl_2$$

The complete equation can now be balanced by inspection. Two additional molecules of HCl are needed to supply the two Cl^- ions of the $MnCl_2$. This balancing requires 2 molecules of water. These water molecules also account for the 2 oxygen atoms of the MnO_2. The final equation reads

$$MnO_2 + 4HCl \rightarrow 2H_2O + MnCl_2 + Cl_2$$

The equations for both of these examples can be balanced without using electronic equations to balance electron shifts. The step process is now applied to a more complicated oxidation-reduction reaction in the following Sample Problem.

SAMPLE PROBLEM

The oxidation-reduction reaction between hydrochloric acid and potassium permanganate yields water, potassium chloride, manganese(II) chloride, and chlorine gas. Write the balanced equation.

SOLUTION

First, write the skeleton equation. Be careful to show the correct formula for each reactant and each product. Appropriate oxidation numbers are placed above the symbols of the elements.

$$\overset{+1-1}{HCl} + \overset{+1 \; +7 \; -2}{KMnO_4} \rightarrow \overset{+1 \; -2}{H_2O} + \overset{+1-1}{KCl} + \overset{+2 \; -1}{MnCl_2} + \overset{0}{Cl_2}$$

Some chloride ions are oxidized to chlorine atoms. The manganese of the permanganate ions is reduced to manganese(II) ions. Electronic equations for these two reactions are

$$\overset{-1}{2Cl^-} \rightarrow \overset{0}{Cl_2} + 2e^-$$

$$\overset{+7}{Mn} + 5e^- \rightarrow \overset{+2}{Mn}{}^{++}$$

The electron shift must involve an equal number of electrons in these two equations. This number is 10. The first equation is multiplied by 5 and the second by 2.

$$\overset{-1}{10Cl^-} \rightarrow \overset{0}{5Cl_2} + 10e^-$$

$$\overset{+7}{2Mn} + 10e^- \rightarrow \overset{+2}{2Mn^{++}}$$

These coefficients are transferred to the skeleton equation, which becomes

$$10HCl + 2KMnO_4 \rightarrow H_2O + KCl + 2MnCl_2 + 5Cl_2$$

By inspection, $2KMnO_4$ produces $2KCl$ and $8H_2O$. Now $2KCl$ and $2MnCl_2$ call for 6 additional molecules of HCl. The balanced equation becomes

$$16HCl + 2KMnO_4 \rightarrow 8H_2O + 2KCl + 2MnCl_2 + 5Cl_2$$

PRACTICE PROBLEM

A pure solution of nitric acid is colorless but becomes yellow on standing because of slight decomposition that forms brown nitrogen dioxide, oxygen, and water. Balance the redox equation for this decomposition using the oxidation-number method.

ans.
$$\overset{+5\ -2}{HN\,O_3(aq)} \rightarrow \overset{+4}{NO_2(g)} + \overset{0}{O_2(g)} + H_2O(l)$$

$$\overset{+5}{4N} + 4e^- \rightarrow \overset{+4}{4N}$$

$$\overset{-2}{2O} \rightarrow \overset{0}{O_2} + 4e^-$$

$$4HNO_3(aq) \rightarrow 4NO_2(g) + O_2(g) + 2H_2O(l)$$

2. The ion-electron method. In this alternate scheme the participating species are determined as before by assigning oxidation numbers. Separate oxidation and reduction equations are then balanced for both atoms and charge (adjusted for equal numbers of electrons gained and lost) and added together to give a balanced net ionic equation.

To compare the two balancing schemes, suppose the ion-electron method is used to balance the same equation previously used to illustrate the oxidation-number method.

$H^+(aq)$ is equivalent to H_3O^+ for representing the hydronium ion.

Step 1: Write the skeleton equation.

$$HCl(aq) + KMnO_4(aq) \rightarrow H_2O(l) + KCl(aq) + MnCl_2(aq) + Cl_2(g)$$

Step 2: Write the ionic equation.

$$H^+(aq) + Cl^- + K^+ + MnO_4^- \rightarrow H_2O + K^+ + Cl^- + Mn^{++} + 2Cl^- + Cl_2$$

Step 3: Assign oxidation numbers and retain only those species that include an element that changes oxidation state.

$$\overset{-1}{Cl^-} + \overset{+7}{MnO_4^-} \rightarrow \overset{+2}{Mn^{++}} + \overset{0}{Cl_2}$$

Step 4: Write the equation for the reduction.

$$\overset{+7}{MnO_4^-} \rightarrow \overset{+2}{Mn^{++}}$$

Observe from the initial equation that oxygen forms water. Account for the 4 oxygen atoms by adding $4H_2O$ on the right.

$$MnO_4^- \rightarrow Mn^{++} + 4H_2O$$

This addition now requires that $8H^+(aq)$ be added on the left.

$$MnO_4^- + 8H^+(aq) \rightarrow Mn^{++} + 4H_2O$$
$$(-1) \qquad (+8) \qquad (+2) \qquad (0)$$

The equation is now balanced for atoms but not for charge; $5e^-$ must be added on the left side to balance the charge.

$$MnO_4^- + 8H^+(aq) + 5e^- \rightarrow Mn^{++} + 4H_2O$$
$$(-1) \qquad (+8) \qquad (-5) \qquad (+2) \qquad (0)$$

The reduction equation is now balanced for both atoms and charge.

Step 5: Write the equation for the oxidation and balance for atoms.

$$\overset{-1}{2Cl^-} \rightarrow \overset{0}{Cl_2}$$
$$(-2) \qquad (0)$$

To balance charge, $2e^-$ must be added on the right.

$$2Cl^- \rightarrow Cl_2 + 2e^-$$
$$(-2) \qquad (0) \quad (-2)$$

Step 6: Add the balanced reduction equation to the balanced oxidation equation. The reduction equation must be multiplied by 2 and the oxidation equation by 5 so that the number of electrons gained in reduction is equal to that lost in oxidation.

$$2[MnO_4^- + 8H^+(aq) + 5e^- \rightarrow Mn^{++} + 4H_2O]$$
$$5[2Cl^- \rightarrow Cl_2 + 2e^-]$$
$$\overline{2MnO_4^- + 16H^+(aq) + 10Cl^- + 10e^- \rightarrow 2Mn^{++} + 8H_2O + 5Cl_2 + 10e^-}$$

The $10e^-$ cancel, and the ionic equation is balanced.

$$2MnO_4^- + 16H^+(aq) + 10Cl^- \rightarrow 2Mn^{++} + 8H_2O + 5Cl_2$$

Step 7: To write the formula equation, one K^+ ion must be included for each MnO_4^- ion, and six more Cl^- ions must be added so there is one for each $H^+(aq)$ ion. The formula equation is

$$2KMnO_4 + 16HCl \rightarrow 2MnCl_2 + 2KCl + 8H_2O + 5Cl_2$$

PRACTICE PROBLEMS

Balance the equations for the following oxidation-reduction reactions using (*a*) the oxidation-number method and (*b*) the ion-electron method.

1. Copper reacts with hot, concentrated sulfuric acid to form copper(II) sulfate, sulfur dioxide, and water.

ans. (*a*)
$$\overset{+6}{S} + 2e^- \rightarrow \overset{+4}{S}$$

$$\overset{0}{Cu} \rightarrow \overset{+2}{Cu} + 2e^-$$

$$Cu + 2H_2SO_4 \rightarrow CuSO_4 + SO_2 + 2H_2O$$

(*b*) $4H^+(aq) + \overset{+6}{SO_4}^{--} + 2e^- \rightarrow \overset{+4}{SO_2} + 2H_2O$

$$\overset{0}{Cu} \rightarrow \overset{+2}{Cu} + 2e^-$$

$$\overline{Cu + 2H_2SO_4 \rightarrow CuSO_4 + SO_2 + 2H_2O}$$

2. The products of a reaction between nitric acid and potassium iodide are potassium nitrate, iodine, nitrogen monoxide, and water.

ans. (*a*)
$$\overset{+5}{2N} + 6e^- \rightarrow \overset{+2}{2N}$$

$$\overset{-1}{6I} \rightarrow \overset{0}{3I_2} + 6e^-$$

$$8HNO_3 + 6KI \rightarrow 6KNO_3 + 3I_2 + 2NO + 4H_2O$$

(*b*) $8H^+(aq) + \overset{+5}{2NO_3}^- + 6e^- \rightarrow \overset{+2}{2NO} + 4H_2O$

$$\overset{-1}{6I^-} \rightarrow \overset{0}{3I_2} + 6e^-$$

$$\overline{8H^+(aq) + 2NO_3^- + 6I^- \rightarrow 3I_2 + 2NO + 4H_2O}$$

or

$$8HNO_3 + 6KI \rightarrow 6KNO_3 + 3I_2 + 2NO + 4H_2O$$

❏ 22.4 Oxidizing and reducing agents

A strong oxidizing agent easily acquires electrons and becomes a weak reducing agent reluctant to give up electrons.

An *oxidizing agent attains a more negative oxidation state* during an oxidation-reduction reaction. A *reducing agent attains a more positive oxidation state.* These terms are defined in Section 6.5. It follows that the substance oxidized is also the reducing agent, and the substance reduced is the oxidizing agent. An oxidized substance becomes a potential oxidizing agent. Similarly, a reduced substance is a potential reducing agent. Study the oxidation-reduction terms presented in Table 22-2.

A weak oxidizing agent reluctantly accepts electrons and becomes a strong reducing agent that easily gives up electrons.

The relatively large atoms of the Sodium Family of metals make up Group I of the periodic table. These atoms have weak attraction for their valence electrons and form positive ions readily. They are *very active reducing agents.* According to electrochemical measurements, the lithium atom is the most active reducing agent of all the common elements. The lithium ion, on

Table 22-2
OXIDATION-REDUCTION TERMINOLOGY

Term	Change in oxidation number	Change in electron population
oxidation	more positive	loss of electrons
reduction	more negative	gain of electrons
oxidizing agent	more negative	acquires electrons
reducing agent	more positive	supplies electrons
substance oxidized	more positive	loses electrons
substance reduced	more negative	gains electrons

A strong reducing agent easily gives up electrons and becomes a weak oxidizing agent that does not easily acquire electrons.

A weak reducing agent reluctantly gives up electrons and becomes a strong oxidizing agent that easily acquires electrons.

the other hand, is the weakest oxidizing agent of the common ions. The electronegativity scale suggests that Group I metals starting with lithium should become progressively more active reducing agents. Except for lithium, this is true. A possible basis for the unusual activity of lithium is discussed in Chapter 24.

Atoms of the Halogen Family, Group VII of the periodic table, have a strong attraction for electrons. They form negative ions readily and are *very active oxidizing agents*. The fluorine atom is the most highly electronegative atom. It is also the most active oxidizing agent among the elements. Because of its strong attraction for electrons, the fluoride ion is the weakest reducing agent.

In Table 22-3 many familiar substances are arranged according to their activity as oxidizing and reducing agents. The left column shows the relative abilities of some metals to displace other metals from their compounds. Such displacements are oxidation-reduction processes. Zinc, for example, appears above copper. Thus zinc is the more active reducing agent and displaces copper ions from solutions of copper compounds.

$$Zn(s) + Cu^{++}(aq) \rightarrow Zn^{++}(aq) + Cu(s)$$

$$\overset{0}{Zn} \rightarrow \overset{+2}{Zn^{++}} + 2e^- \quad \text{(oxidation)}$$

$$\overset{+2}{Cu^{++}} + 2e^- \rightarrow \overset{0}{Cu} \quad \text{(reduction)}$$

The copper(II) ion, on the other hand, is a more active oxidizing agent than the zinc ion.

Nonmetals and some important ions are included in the series. Any reducing agent is oxidized by the oxidizing agents below it. Observe that F_2 displaces Cl^-, Br^-, and I^- ions from their solutions. Cl_2 displaces Br^- and I^- ions; Br_2 displaces I^- ions.

$$Cl_2 + 2Br^-(aq) \rightarrow 2Cl^-(aq) + Br_2$$

$$\overset{-1}{2Br^-} \rightarrow \overset{0}{Br_2} + 2e^- \quad \text{(oxidation)}$$

$$\overset{0}{Cl_2} + 2e^- \rightarrow \overset{-1}{2Cl^-} \quad \text{(reduction)}$$

Table 22-3
RELATIVE STRENGTH OF OXIDIZING AND REDUCING AGENTS

	Reducing agents	Oxidizing agents	
Strong	Li	Li$^+$	Weak
	K	K$^+$	
	Ca	Ca^{++}	
	Na	Na$^+$	
	Mg	Mg^{++}	
	Al	Al^{+++}	
	Zn	Zn^{++}	
	Cr	Cr^{+++}	
	Fe	Fe^{++}	
	Ni	Ni^{++}	
	Sn	Sn^{++}	
	Pb	Pb^{++}	
	H$_2$	H$_3$O$^+$	
	H$_2$S	S	
	Cu	Cu^{++}	
	I$^-$	I$_2$	
	MnO$_4^{--}$	MnO$_4^-$	
	Fe^{++}	Fe^{+++}	
	Hg	Hg$_2^{++}$	
	Ag	Ag$^+$	
	NO$_2^-$	NO$_3^-$	
	Br$^-$	Br$_2$	
	Mn^{++}	MnO$_2$	
	SO$_2$	H$_2$SO$_4$ (conc)	
	Cr^{+++}	Cr$_2$O$_7^{--}$	
	Cl$^-$	Cl$_2$	
	Mn^{++}	MnO$_4^-$	
Weak	F$^-$	F$_2$	Strong

Permanganate ions, MnO_4^-, and dichromate ions, $Cr_2O_7^{--}$, are important oxidizing agents. They are used mainly in the form of their potassium salts. In neutral or mildly basic solutions, permanganate ions are reduced to MnO_2. If a solution is strongly basic, manganate ions, MnO_4^{--}, are formed. In acid solutions, permanganate ions are reduced to manganese(II) ions, Mn^{++}, and dichromate ions are reduced to chromium(III) ions, Cr^{+++}.

Peroxide ions, O_2^{--}, have a single covalent bond between the two oxygen atoms. The electron-dot formula is

$$\left[:\overset{\cdot\cdot}{\underset{\times\times}{O}} : \overset{\cdot\cdot}{\underset{\times\times}{O}} : \right]^{--}$$

This structure represents an intermediate state of oxidation between free oxygen and oxides. The oxidation number of oxygen in the peroxide form is -1.

Hydrogen peroxide, H_2O_2, decomposes by oxidizing and reducing itself. The products are water and molecular oxygen.

$$\overset{-1}{H_2O_2} + \overset{-1}{H_2O_2} \rightarrow 2\overset{-2}{H_2O} + \overset{0}{O_2}(g)$$

In this decomposition, half of the oxygen in the peroxide is *reduced* to the oxide, forming water, and half is *oxidized* to gaseous oxygen. The process is called *autooxidation*. Impurities in a water solution of hydrogen peroxide may catalyze this process.

Autooxidation: H_2O_2 is both an oxidizing and a reducing agent; it oxidizes and reduces itself.

Oxygen in H_2O_2 is *oxidized* from the -1 to the 0 oxidation state when oxygen is formed. It is *reduced* from the -1 to the -2 state when water is formed. Thus H_2O_2 can be either an oxidizing agent or a reducing agent.

◻ 22.5 Chemical equivalents of oxidizing and reducing agents

In Section 16.2, the chemical equivalent (equiv) of a reactant is described as the *mass of the reactant that loses or acquires the Avogadro number of electrons* in a chemical reaction. If a reactant is oxidized, the mass that loses the Avogadro number of electrons is one equivalent (1 equiv) of that reactant. If a reactant is reduced, the mass that acquires the Avogadro number of electrons is one equivalent of the reactant. Thus 1 equiv of any reducing agent will always react with 1 equiv of any oxidizing agent.

Quantities of reactants are often expressed in terms of chemical equivalents. To do so for oxidizing and reducing agents, *the particular oxidation-reduction reaction must be known.* For example, one atom of iron loses 2 electrons when oxidized to iron(II), Fe^{++}.

$$\overset{0}{Fe} \rightarrow \overset{+2}{Fe}^{++} + 2e^-$$

One mole of iron, 55.8 g, gives up 2 times the Avogadro number of electrons when oxidized to the $+2$ oxidation state. Thus the mass of iron that releases the Avogadro number of electrons in

such a reaction is *one-half mole*. It follows that one equivalent is
55.8 g Fe ÷ 2 = 27.9 g Fe.

One atom of iron loses 3 electrons when oxidized to iron(III),
Fe^{+++}.

$$\overset{0}{Fe} \rightarrow \overset{+3}{Fe}{}^{+++} + 3e^-$$

One mole of iron oxidized to the +3 oxidation state gives up 3
times the Avogadro number of electrons. Thus, one equivalent of
iron oxidized to the +3 state is 55.8 g Fe ÷ 3 = 18.6 g Fe.

Fe^{+++} ions in an iron(III) chloride solution are reduced to
the +2 oxidation state by the addition of a tin(II) chloride solution. The Sn^{++} ions are the reducing agent. Here, one mole of
Fe^{+++} ions acquires one Avogadro number of electrons and is
reduced to Fe^{++} ions. One equivalent of iron in this reaction
is 55.8 g ÷ 1 = 55.8 g. One mole of the reducing agent, Sn^{++}
ions, loses 2 times the Avogadro number of electrons. One equivalent of tin in this reaction is 118.7 g ÷ 2 = 59.35 g. These
relationships are shown clearly in the electronic equations for
this oxidation-reduction reaction.

$$2\overset{+3}{Fe}{}^{+++} + 2e^- \rightarrow 2\overset{+2}{Fe}{}^{++}$$

$$\overset{+2}{Sn}{}^{++} \rightarrow \overset{+4}{Sn}{}^{++++} + 2e^-$$

$$1 \text{ equiv } Fe^{+++} = \frac{2Fe^{+++}}{e^- \text{ gained}} = \frac{2 \times 55.8 \text{ g}}{2} = 55.8 \text{ g}$$

$$1 \text{ equiv } Sn^{++} = \frac{Sn^{++}}{e^- \text{ lost}} = \frac{118.7 \text{ g}}{2} = 59.35 \text{ g}$$

☐ 22.6 Electrochemical reactions

1. Electrochemical cells. Oxidation-reduction reactions involve a transfer of electrons from the substance oxidized to the
substance reduced. If such reactions occur *spontaneously,* they
can be used as sources of electric energy. If the reactants are in
contact, the energy released during the electron transfer is in the
form of heat. If the reactants are placed separately in an electrolytic solution with a conducting wire joining them externally, then
the transfer of electrons takes place through the wire. Such an
arrangement is known as an *electrochemical cell.* The flow of
electrons through the wire is an electric current. Under these
conditions, only part of the energy released during the electron
transfer appears as heat; the rest is available as electric energy.

The dry cell is a common source of electric energy in the laboratory. Small dry cells are familiar as flashlight batteries. A zinc
container serves as the negative electrode, or *cathode.* A carbon
rod serves as the positive electrode, or *anode.* The carbon rod is
surrounded by a mixture of manganese dioxide and powdered car-

The cathode is the electron-rich electrode.

The anode is the electron-poor electrode.

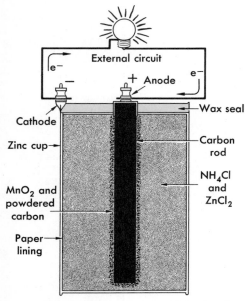

Figure 22-4. In dry cells, zinc is oxidized at the cathode and manganese(IV) is reduced to manganese(III) at the anode.

Figure 22-5. Positively charged copper ions (blue) and negatively charged chromate ions (yellow) in (A) are shown migrating through a gel toward oppositely charged electrodes in (B).

bon. The electrolyte is a moist paste of ammonium chloride containing some zinc chloride. Figure 22-4 shows these parts of the dry cell in a schematic diagram.

When the external circuit is closed, *zinc atoms are oxidized at the cathode.*

$$\overset{0}{Zn} \to \overset{+2}{Zn}^{++} + 2e^-$$

Electrons flow through the external circuit to the carbon anode. If manganese dioxide were not present, hydrogen gas would be formed at the anode by the reduction shown in the following equation.

$$2\overset{+1}{NH_4}^+ + 2e^- \to 2NH_3 + \overset{0}{H_2}(g)$$

However, hydrogen gas is oxidized to water by the manganese dioxide. This explains why *manganese* rather than hydrogen *is actually reduced at the anode.*

$$2\overset{+4}{MnO_2} + 2NH_4^+ + 2e^- \to \overset{+3}{Mn_2O_3} + 2NH_3 + H_2O$$

The ammonia is taken up by Zn^{++} ions, forming complex $Zn(NH_3)_4^{++}$ ions.

2. Electrolytic cells. Some oxidation-reduction reactions *are not spontaneous.* However, such reactions can be forced to occur by means of electric energy. *The process whereby an electric current is used to bring about oxidation-reduction reactions is called* **electrolysis.** Basically, the *electrolytic cell* consists of a pair of electrodes and an electrolyte solution in a suitable container. An electric current supplied by a battery or other direct-current source is connected across the cell. One electrode (the cathode) then becomes negatively charged, and the other (the anode) becomes positively charged.

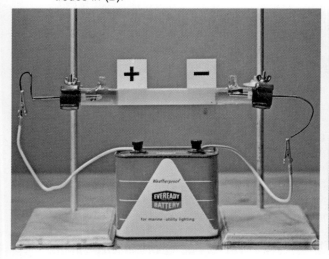

(A)

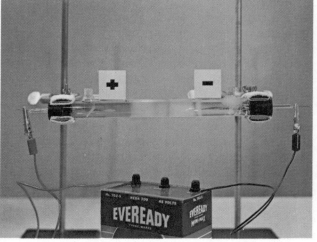

(B)

Ion *migration* in the cell is responsible for the transfer of electric charge. Positively charged ions *migrate* toward the cathode. Negatively charged ions migrate toward the anode. This + and − ion migration is shown in Figure 22-5.

In an electrolytic cell, reduction occurs at the cathode. Electrons are removed from the cathode in this process. Oxidation takes place at the anode, which acquires electrons in the process. The chemical reactions at the electrodes complete the electric circuit between the battery and the cell. The closed-loop path for electric current allows energy to be transferred from the battery to the electrolytic cell. This energy drives the electrode reactions in the cell.

In electrochemical cells, oxidation occurs at the cathode; reduction occurs at the anode. In electrolytic cells, reduction occurs at the cathode; oxidation occurs at the anode.

☐ 22.7 Electrolysis of water

In the decomposition of water by electrolysis, energy is transferred from the energy source to the decomposition products. The reaction is endothermic, and the amount of energy required is 68.32 kcal/mole of water decomposed. The overall reaction is

Review molar heat relationships for water, Section 20.2.

$$2H_2O(l) + 136.64 \text{ kcal} \rightarrow 2H_2(g) + O_2(g)$$

Hydrogen gas is given up at the cathode, and oxygen gas is given up at the anode.

A suitable electrolysis cell is shown in Figure 22-6. It consists of two inert electrodes made of platinum immersed in water. A very small amount of an electrolyte, such as H_2SO_4, is added to provide adequate conductivity. The electrodes are connected to a battery that supplies the electric energy that drives the decomposition reaction forward.

The electric current provided by the battery consists of a flow of electrons. The electrode connected to the negative electrode of the battery acquires an excess of electrons. This electrode becomes the *cathode* of the electrolytic cell. The other electrode is connected to the positive electrode of the battery. It loses electrons to the battery and becomes the *anode* of the electrolytic cell. In a sense, the battery acts as an electron pump by forcing electrons into the cathode of the electrolytic cell and pumping them back from the anode of the cell.

Reduction occurs at the *cathode;* hydrogen gas is the product. If the amount of H_2SO_4 added to improve conductivity is small, its contribution of hydronium ions to the water is also small. At very low hydronium ion concentrations, it is believed that water molecules are reduced by acquiring electrons directly from the cathode.

cathode reaction: (reduction)

$$2\overset{+1}{H_2}O + 2e^- \rightarrow 2OH^- + \overset{0}{H_2}(g)$$

The OH⁻ ion concentration in the solution around the cathode rises.

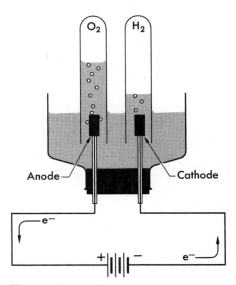

Figure 22-6. The electrolysis of water. In electrolytic cells, reduction occurs at the cathode and oxidation occurs at the anode.

Oxidation occurs at the *anode;* oxygen gas is the product. There are SO_4^{--} ions, OH^- ions, and water molecules in the region about the anode. The OH^- ion concentration is quite low and they are not likely to appear in the anode reaction. The SO_4^{--} ions, also at low concentration, are more difficult to oxidize than water molecules. For these reasons, chemists believe that water molecules are oxidized by giving up electrons directly to the anode.

anode reaction: (oxidation)

$$6H_2\overset{-2}{O} \rightarrow 4H_3O^+ + \overset{0}{O_2}(g) + 4e^-$$

The H_3O^+ ion concentration in the solution around the anode rises.

The overall cell reaction is the sum of the net cathode and anode reactions. The equation for the cathode reaction must be doubled because oxidation and reduction processes are equivalent.

cathode: $4H_2O + 4e^- \rightarrow 4OH^- + 2H_2(g)$
anode: $6H_2O \rightarrow 4H_3O^+ + O_2(g) + 4e^-$

cell: $10H_2O \rightarrow 2H_2(g) + O_2(g) + 4H_3O^+ + 4OH^-$

The solution around the cathode becomes basic because of the production of OH^- ions. The solution around the anode becomes acidic because of the production of H_3O^+ ions. Because of the ordinary mixing tendency in the solution, these ions can be expected to eventually diffuse together and form water. If this neutralization is complete, the net electrolysis reaction is

$$10H_2O \rightarrow 2H_2(g) + O_2(g) + 4H_3O^+ + 4OH^-$$
$$4H_3O^+ + 4OH^- \rightarrow 8H_2O$$

net: $2H_2O \rightarrow 2H_2(g) + O_2(g)$

Reduction at the cathode lowers the oxidation state of hydrogen from +1 to 0; the oxidation state of oxygen at the cathode remains −2. At the anode, oxidation raises the oxidation state of oxygen from −2 to 0; the oxidation state of hydrogen at the anode remains +1.

◻ 22.8 Electrolysis of aqueous salt solutions

The electrode products from the electrolysis of aqueous salt solutions are determined by the relative ease with which the different particles present can be oxidized or reduced. In the case of aqueous NaCl, for example, Na^+ ions are more difficult to reduce at the cathode than H_2O molecules or H_3O^+ ions. Since the solution of NaCl is neutral, the H_3O^+ ion concentration remains very low (10^{-7} mole/liter). Therefore, H_2O molecules are the particles reduced at the cathode.

cathode reaction: (reduction)

$$\overset{+1}{2H_2O} + 2e^- \rightarrow 2OH^- + \overset{0}{H_2}(g)$$

Thus Na^+ ions remain in solution and hydrogen gas is released.

In general, metals that are easily oxidized form ions that are difficult to reduce. That is why hydrogen gas, not sodium metal, is the cathode product above. On the other hand, metals such as copper, silver, and gold are difficult to oxidize and form ions that are easily reduced. Aqueous solutions of their salts give up the metal at the cathode.

The choice for anode reaction in the aqueous NaCl electrolysis lies between Cl^- ions and H_2O molecules. The Cl^- ions are more easily oxidized, so Cl_2 gas is produced at the anode.

Electrolysis of concentrated NaCl solutions yields Cl_2 at the anode.

anode reaction: (oxidation)

$$\overset{-1}{2Cl^-} \rightarrow \overset{0}{Cl_2}(g) + 2e^-$$

Adding the cathode and anode equations gives the net reaction for the cell.

Dilute NaCl solutions may yield both Cl_2 and O_2 at the anode.

net: $2H_2O + 2Cl^- \rightarrow 2OH^- + H_2(g) + Cl_2(g)$

The electrolytic solution gradually changes from aqueous NaCl to aqueous NaOH as the electrolysis continues, as long as the Cl_2 gas is continuously removed from the cell.

Very dilute NaCl solutions yield O_2 at the anode.

Aqueous Br^- ions and I^- ions are oxidized electrolytically in the same way as Cl^- ions. Their solutions give the free halogen at the anode. On the other hand, aqueous solutions of negative ions that do not participate in the oxidation reaction (NO_3^- ions, for example) give O_2 gas at the anode.

◻ 22.9 Electroplating

Note that inactive metals form ions that are more easily reduced than hydrogen. This fact makes possible an electrolytic process called *electroplating*.

An electroplating cell contains a solution of a salt of the plating metal. It has an object to be plated (the cathode) and a piece of the plating metal (the anode). A silverplating cell, illustrated in Figure 22-7, contains a solution of a soluble silver salt and a silver anode. The cathode is the object to be plated. The silver anode is connected to the positive electrode of a battery or other source of direct current. The object to be plated is connected to the negative electrode. *Silver ions are reduced at the cathode of the cell when electrons flow through the circuit.*

$$\overset{+1}{Ag^+} + e^- \rightarrow \overset{0}{Ag}$$

Silver atoms are oxidized at the anode.

$$\overset{0}{Ag} \rightarrow \overset{+1}{Ag^+} + e^-$$

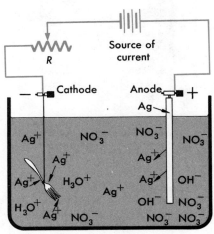

Figure 22-7. An electrolytic cell used for silver plating.

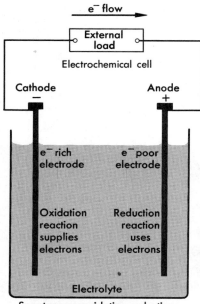

Spontaneous oxidation-reduction
reaction — a source of energy

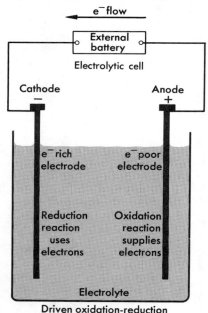

Driven oxidation-reduction
reaction — a user of energy

Figure 22-8. A comparison of electrochemical and electrolytic cells.

Silver ions are removed from the solution at the cathode and deposited as metallic silver. Meanwhile, metallic silver is removed from the anode as ions. This action maintains the Ag^+ ion concentration of the solution. Thus, in effect, silver is transferred from the anode to the cathode of the cell.

In these discussions of electrochemical and electrolytic cells the electrodes have been identified according to their *state of charge*. The negative electrode is referred to as the *cathode* and the positive electrode as the *anode*. These terms agree with modern definitions of such electrodes in physics and electronics. *The electron-rich electrode is the cathode* and *the electron-poor electrode is the anode* in any system of which they are a part.

An older scheme for naming electrodes often used in electrochemistry defines the anode as the electrode at which oxidation occurs and the cathode as the electrode at which reduction occurs. In this system, the names of the electrodes are reversed with respect to their electric charge for electrochemical and electrolytic cells. These cells are compared in Figure 22-8.

◻ 22.10 Lead storage battery

The basic unit of the lead storage battery is a lead(IV) oxide-lead-sulfuric acid cell. The standard twelve-volt automobile battery consists of six of these cells connected in series. As the name implies, the *storage* battery is a *storehouse* of energy. The battery is charged by electric energy from an external source. This electric energy is converted to chemical energy by an oxidation-reduction reaction in which each cell acts as an *electrolytic* cell. While the battery is being discharged, the reverse oxidation-reduction occurs. Chemical energy in the battery is converted to electric energy, and the cells act as *electrochemical* cells.

A fully charged lead storage cell contains an anode of lead(IV) oxide and a cathode of spongy lead. The electrolyte is moderately dilute sulfuric acid. During the *discharging cycle,* the lead at the cathode is oxidized to Pb^{++} ions. Lead(II) sulfate, $PbSO_4$, is formed as a precipitate on the cathode. This oxidation can be summarized as follows:

cathode reaction: (on discharge)

$$\overset{0}{Pb}(s) + H_2O + HSO_4^- \rightarrow \overset{+2}{Pb}SO_4(s) + H_3O^+ + 2e^-$$

At the anode, H_3O^+ ions may be reduced. In turn, they may reduce the PbO_2 to PbO, forming water in the process. Reaction with sulfuric acid then produces lead(II) sulfate and water. Lead(II) sulfate precipitates on the anode. The anode reduction is not fully understood, and the equation for it may oversimplify the actual reaction mechanism. However, this reduction can be summarized as follows:

anode reaction: (on discharge)

$$\overset{+4}{Pb}O_2(s) + HSO_4^- + 3H_3O^+ + 2e^- \rightarrow \overset{+2}{Pb}SO_4(s) + 5H_2O$$

The net oxidation-reduction reaction of the cell during discharge is the sum of the two electrode reactions.

cell reaction: (on discharge)

$$\overset{0}{Pb}(s) + \overset{+4}{Pb}O_2(s) + 2HSO_4^- + 2H_3O^+ \rightarrow 2\overset{+2}{Pb}SO_4(s) + 4H_2O$$

Observe that sulfuric acid is used up and water is formed at both

Figure 22-9. Diagrams illustrating the essential actions in a storage cell.

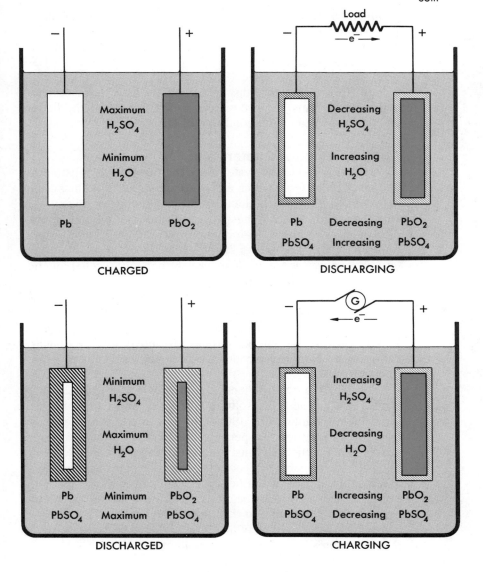

electrodes as the discharging action proceeds. Electrons released by oxidation at the cathode flow through the external circuit to the anode. There, the reduction occurs. This flow of electrons is the electric current. It is capable of delivering energy to devices in the external circuit. *During the discharging cycle, the cell functions as an electrochemical cell.*

When the battery is completely discharged, both electrodes consist of lead(II) sulfate. The electrolyte is diluted because some sulfuric acid has been used up and water has been produced. The cell can be made electrochemically active again by reversing the reaction at each electrode. To recharge the cell, a direct current is supplied from an external source in the opposite direction to the discharging current. *During the charging cycle, the cell functions as an electrolytic cell.* The net reaction is the reverse of the net reaction for the discharge cycle.

During charging, sulfuric acid is formed and water is decomposed. The density of the acid solution increases to about 1.300 g/mL for a fully charged cell. The density decreases during discharge. In a completely discharged cell, it is lowered to about 1.100 g/mL. Thus a measurement of the density of the battery electrolyte indicates the condition of charge.

◻ 22.11 Electrode potentials

Oxidation-reduction systems are the result of two distinct reactions: *oxidation,* in which electrons are supplied to the system, and *reduction,* in which electrons are acquired from the system. In electrochemical cells, these reactions take place at the separate electrodes. The oxidation-reduction reaction is the sum of these two separate reactions. As stated in Section 22.6, oxidation occurs at the negative electrode in an electrochemical cell; reduction occurs at the positive electrode.

As the cell reaction begins, a difference in *electric potential* develops between the electrodes. This potential difference can be measured by a voltmeter connected across the two electrodes. It is a measure of the energy required to move a certain electric charge between the electrodes. Potential difference is measured in *volts.*

Consider the electrochemical cell shown in Figure 22-10. A strip of zinc is placed in a solution of $ZnSO_4$, and a strip of copper is placed in a solution of $CuSO_4$. The two solutions are separated by a porous partition that permits ions to pass but otherwise prevents mixing of the solutions. Such an arrangement is called a *voltaic cell.* It is capable of generating a small electron current in an external circuit connected between the electrodes.

In the two electrode reactions, the zinc electrode acquires a negative charge relative to the copper. The copper electrode becomes positively charged relative to the zinc. This reaction shows that zinc atoms have a stronger tendency to enter the solution as

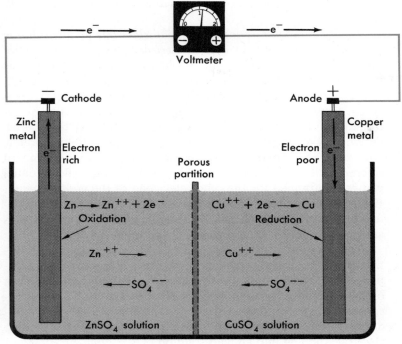

Figure 22-10. A Zn-Cu voltaic cell.

ions than do copper atoms. Zinc is said to be more active, or more easily oxidized, than copper.

The reaction at the surface of the zinc electrode is an oxidation.

$$\overset{0}{Zn}(s) \rightarrow \overset{+2}{Zn^{++}}(aq) + 2e^-$$

The reaction at the surface of the copper electrode is a reduction.

$$\overset{+2}{Cu^{++}}(aq) + 2e^- \rightarrow \overset{0}{Cu}(s)$$

As Zn^{++} ions form, electrons accumulate on the zinc electrode, giving it a negative charge. As Cu atoms form, electrons are removed from the copper electrode, giving it a positive charge. Electrons also flow through the external circuit from the zinc electrode to the copper electrode. Here they replace the electrons removed as Cu^{++} ions undergo reduction to Cu atoms. Thus, in effect, electrons are transferred from Zn atoms through the external circuit to Cu^{++} ions. The overall reaction can be written as

$$Zn + Cu^{++} \rightarrow Zn^{++} + Cu$$

A voltmeter connected across the Cu-Zn voltaic cell measures the potential difference. This difference is about 1.1 volts when the solution concentrations of Zn^{++} and Cu^{++} ions are each 1 m.

A voltaic cell consists of two metal electrodes, each in contact with a solution of its ions. Each of these portions is called a *half-*

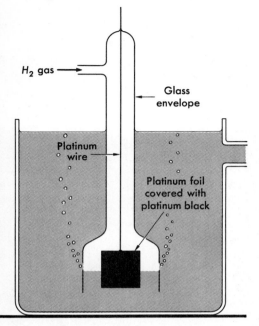

H₂ gas

Glass envelope

Platinum wire

Platinum foil covered with platinum black

Figure 22-11. Hydrogen electrode, the standard reference electrode for measuring electrode potentials.

The hydrogen reference electrode is arbitrarily assigned a standard potential of zero volt.

cell. The reaction taking place at each electrode is called a *half-reaction.*

The potential difference between an electrode and its solution in a half-reaction is known as its **electrode potential.** The sum of the electrode potentials for the two half-reactions roughly equals the potential difference measured across the complete voltaic cell.

The potential difference across a voltaic cell is easily measured. However, there is no way to measure an individual electrode potential. The electrode potential of a half-reaction can be determined by using a *standard half-cell* along with it as a reference electrode. An arbitrary potential is assigned to the standard reference electrode. Relative to this potential, a specific potential can be determined for the other electrode of the complete cell. Electrode potentials are expressed as reduction (or oxidation) potentials. They provide a reliable indication of the tendency of a substance to undergo reduction (or oxidation).

Chemists use a *hydrogen electrode* immersed in a molal solution of H^+ (aq) ions as a standard reference electrode. This practice provides a convenient way to examine the relative tendencies of metals to react with aqueous hydrogen ions (H_3O^+). It is responsible for the activity series of metals listed in Table 8-2. A hydrogen electrode is shown in Figure 22-11. It consists of a platinum electrode dipping into an acid solution of 1-*m* concentration and surrounded by hydrogen gas at 1 atmosphere pressure. This *standard hydrogen electrode is assigned a potential of zero volt.* The half-cell reaction is

$$\overset{0}{H_2}(g) \rightleftarrows 2\overset{+1}{H^+}(aq) + 2e^-$$

To repeat, the potential of the hydrogen electrode is arbitrarily set at zero volt. Therefore, the potential difference across the complete cell is attributed entirely to the electrode of the other half-cell.

Suppose a complete cell consists of a zinc half-cell and a standard hydrogen half-cell, as in Figure 22-12. The potential difference across the cell measures the electrode potential of the zinc electrode relative to the hydrogen electrode (the zero reference electrode). It is found to be −0.76 volt. *The standard electrode potential,* E^0, *of an electrode is given a negative value if this electrode has a negative charge relative to the standard hydrogen electrode.* Electrons flow through the external circuit from the zinc electrode to the hydrogen electrode. There, H^+ (aq) ions are reduced to H_2 gas.

This reaction indicates that the tendency for Zn^{++} ions to be reduced to Zn atoms is 0.76 volt less than the tendency for H^+ (aq) ions to be reduced to H_2. The half-reaction (as a reduction) is

$$\overset{+2}{Zn^{++}} + 2e^- \rightarrow \overset{0}{Zn} \qquad E^0 = -0.76 \text{ v}$$

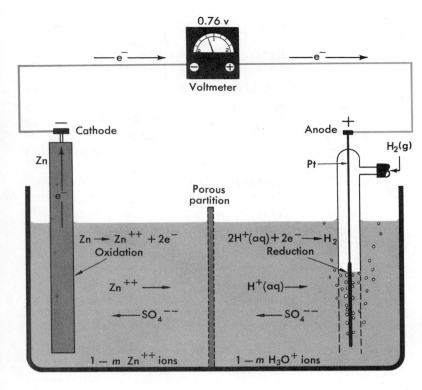

Figure 22-12. The electrode potential of the zinc half-cell is measured by coupling it with a standard hydrogen electrode.

This reaction has less tendency to occur than

$$\overset{+1}{2H^+}(aq) + 2e^- \rightarrow \overset{0}{H_2}(g)$$

by 0.76 volt. This statement also means that the half-reaction (as an oxidation)

$$\overset{0}{Zn} \rightarrow \overset{+2}{Zn^{++}} + 2e^- \qquad E^0 = +0.76 \text{ v}$$

has a greater tendency to occur by 0.76 volt than

$$\overset{0}{H_2}(g) \rightarrow \overset{+1}{2H^+}(aq) + 2e^-$$

Observe that the sign of the electrode potential is reversed when the Zn half-cell reaction is written as an oxidation.

A copper half-cell coupled with the standard hydrogen electrode gives a potential difference measurement of +0.34 volt. This measurement indicates that Cu^{++}(aq) ions are more readily reduced than H^+(aq) ions. *The standard electrode potential, E^0, of an electrode is given a positive value if this electrode has a positive charge relative to the standard hydrogen electrode.* The half-reaction for copper (as a reduction) is

$$\overset{+2}{Cu^{++}} + 2e^- \rightarrow \overset{0}{Cu} \qquad E^0 = +0.34 \text{ v}$$

This reaction has a greater tendency to occur than

$$\overset{+1}{2H^+}(aq) + 2e^- \rightarrow \overset{0}{H_2}(g)$$

by 0.34 volt.

Two observations can be made from these measurements: (1) Zinc has a greater tendency to yield electrons than hydrogen by 0.76 volt. (2) Hydrogen has a greater tendency to yield electrons than copper by 0.34 volt. Taken together, these potentials indicate that zinc has a greater tendency toward oxidation than copper by 1.10 volts (0.76 v + 0.34 v).

How do these electrode potentials apply to the Zn-Cu voltaic cell of Figure 22-10? The potential difference across the complete cell is obtained by adding the electrode potentials of the two half-reactions; the Zn half-reaction is written as an oxidation and the Cu half-reaction as a reduction.

$$\overset{0}{Zn} \rightarrow \overset{+2}{Zn}{}^{++} + 2e^- \qquad E^0 = +0.76 \text{ v}$$

$$\underline{\overset{+2}{Cu}{}^{++} + 2e^- \rightarrow \overset{0}{Cu} \qquad E^0 = +0.34 \text{ v}}$$

$$Zn + Cu^{++} \rightarrow Zn^{++} + Cu \qquad E^0 = +1.10 \text{ v}$$

The positive sign of the potential difference shows that the reaction proceeds spontaneously to the right.

Half-reactions for some common electrodes and their standard electrode potentials are listed in Table 22-4. These reactions are arranged according to their standard electrode potentials, E^0, relative to a standard hydrogen reference electrode. All electrode reactions are written as *reduction reactions* to the right. Electrode potentials are given as *reduction potentials*. Half-reactions with *positive* reduction potentials occur spontaneously to the right as *reduction reactions*. Half-reactions with *negative* reduction potentials occur spontaneously to the left as *oxidation reactions*. When a half-reaction is written as an oxidation reaction, the sign of the electrode potential is changed. The potential then becomes an *oxidation potential*.

The magnitude of the electrode potential measures the tendency of the *reduction half-reaction* to occur as the equation is written in the table. The half-reaction at the top of the column has the *least* tendency toward reduction (adding electrons). Stated in another way, it has the *greatest* tendency to occur as an oxidation (yielding electrons). The half-reaction at the bottom of the column has the *greatest* tendency to occur as a reduction. Thus it has the *least* tendency to occur as an oxidation.

The *lower* a half-reaction is in the column, the *greater* is the tendency for its *reduction reaction* to occur. The *higher* a half-reaction is in the column, the *greater* is the tendency for the *oxidation reaction* to occur. For example, potassium has a large negative electrode potential and a strong tendency to form K^+

Standard electrode potentials describe the relative reaction tendencies of reactants under standardized conditions. As concentrations or temperatures are changed, reaction tendencies change as predicted by Le Chatelier's principle.

ions. Thus, potassium is a strong reducing agent. Fluorine has a large positive electrode potential and a strong tendency to form F^- ions. Fluorine, then, is a strong oxidizing agent. Compare the listings in Table 22-3 with those in Table 22-4.

Table 22-4
STANDARD ELECTRODE POTENTIALS
(as reduction potentials)

Half-reaction	Electrode potential (E^0)
$Li^+ + e^- \rightleftharpoons Li$	-3.04 v
$K^+ + e^- \rightleftharpoons K$	-2.92 v
$Ba^{++} + 2e^- \rightleftharpoons Ba$	-2.90 v
$Ca^{++} + 2e^- \rightleftharpoons Ca$	-2.76 v
$Na^+ + e^- \rightleftharpoons Na$	-2.71 v
$Mg^{++} + 2e^- \rightleftharpoons Mg$	-2.38 v
$Al^{+++} + 3e^- \rightleftharpoons Al$	-1.71 v
$Zn^{++} + 2e^- \rightleftharpoons Zn$	-0.76 v
$Cr^{+++} + 3e^- \rightleftharpoons Cr$	-0.74 v
$S + 2e^- \rightleftharpoons S^{--}$	-0.51 v
$Fe^{++} + 2e^- \rightleftharpoons Fe$	-0.41 v
$Cd^{++} + 2e^- \rightleftharpoons Cd$	-0.40 v
$Co^{++} + 2e^- \rightleftharpoons Co$	-0.28 v
$Ni^{++} + 2e^- \rightleftharpoons Ni$	-0.23 v
$Sn^{++} + 2e^- \rightleftharpoons Sn$	-0.14 v
$Pb^{++} + 2e^- \rightleftharpoons Pb$	-0.13 v
$Fe^{+++} + 3e^- \rightleftharpoons Fe$	-0.04 v
$2H^+(aq) + 2e^- \rightleftharpoons H_2$	0.00 v
$S + 2H^+(aq) + 2e^- \rightleftharpoons H_2S(aq)$	$+0.14$ v
$Cu^{++} + e^- \rightleftharpoons Cu^+$	$+0.16$ v
$Cu^{++} + 2e^- \rightleftharpoons Cu$	$+0.34$ v
$I_2 + 2e^- \rightleftharpoons 2I^-$	$+0.54$ v
$MnO_4^- + e^- \rightleftharpoons MnO_4^{--}$	$+0.56$ v
$Fe^{+++} + e^- \rightleftharpoons Fe^{++}$	$+0.77$ v
$Hg_2^{++} + 2e^- \rightleftharpoons 2Hg$	$+0.80$ v
$Ag^+ + e^- \rightleftharpoons Ag$	$+0.80$ v
$Hg^{++} + 2e^- \rightleftharpoons Hg$	$+0.85$ v
$Br_2 + 2e^- \rightleftharpoons 2Br^-$	$+1.06$ v
$MnO_2 + 4H^+(aq) + 2e^- \rightleftharpoons Mn^{++} + 2H_2O$	$+1.21$ v
$Cr_2O_7^{--} + 14H^+(aq) + 6e^- \rightleftharpoons 2Cr^{+++} + 7H_2O$	$+1.33$ v
$Cl_2 + 2e^- \rightleftharpoons 2Cl^-$	$+1.36$ v
$Au^{+++} + 3e^- \rightleftharpoons Au$	$+1.42$ v
$MnO_4^- + 8H^+(aq) + 5e^- \rightleftharpoons Mn^{++} + 4H_2O$	$+1.49$ v
$F_2 + 2e^- \rightleftharpoons 2F^-$	$+2.87$ v

◖ SUMMARY

The atoms or ions of an element that attain a more positive oxidation state in a chemical reaction are oxidized. Those particles that attain a more negative oxidation state are reduced. The oxidation state of an element is indicated by an oxidation number. Oxidation results in a more positive oxidation number. Reduction results in a more negative oxidation number. Both oxidation and reduction occur simultaneously and in equivalent amounts in redox reactions.

The equations for simple oxidation-reduction reactions can be balanced by inspection. Equations for more complicated oxidation-reduction reactions are more easily balanced if the electrons gained and lost by elements that change oxidation numbers are first made equivalent. These equations can be successfully balanced by following a sequence of steps.

In redox reactions, the substance reduced acts as an oxidizing agent because it acquires electrons from the substance oxidized. The substance oxidized becomes a reducing agent because it supplies the electrons to the substance reduced. A strong oxidizing agent easily acquires electrons and becomes a weak reducing agent reluctant to give up electrons. A strong reducing agent easily gives up electrons and becomes a weak oxidizing agent.

One equivalent of a reactant oxidized or reduced is the quantity that loses or gains one mole (the Avogadro number) of electrons. For a chemical equivalent of a substance involved in a redox reaction to be determined, the particular oxidation-reduction process must be known.

Some oxidation-reduction reactions occur spontaneously and may be used as sources of electric energy when arranged in electrochemical cells. Oxidation-reduction reactions that are not spontaneous can be driven by an external source of electric current. These redox reactions are called electrolysis processes.

The oxidation or reduction reaction between one electrode and its electrolyte in an electrochemical cell is called a half-reaction. The potential difference between the electrode and its solution is called the electrode potential. The electrode potentials of the two half-reactions of a cell indicate roughly the potential difference across the cell.

When measured under standard conditions using a standard hydrogen half-cell as a reference, the measured value is the standard electrode potential of that electrode. These standard electrode potentials indicate the relative strengths of electrode substances as oxidizing and reducing agents.

◖ VOCABULARY

anode	electrolytic cell	positive oxidation state
autooxidation	electron-transfer method	potential difference
cathode	electroplating	redox reaction
charging cycle	half-cell	reducing agent
chemical equivalent	half-reaction method	reduction
conservation of atoms	ion-electron method	standard electrode potential
conservation of electrons	ion migration	storage battery
discharging cycle	negative oxidation state	volt
electrochemical cell	oxidation	voltaic cell
electrode potential	oxidation-reduction reaction	
electrolysis	oxidizing agent	

◀ QUESTIONS

Group A

1. Describe the differences between the processes of oxidation and reduction.
2. Why do oxidation and reduction occur simultaneously?
3. What change in oxidation state do particles that acquire electrons undergo during a chemical action?
4. Which of the following are oxidation-reduction reactions?
   (a) $2Na + Cl_2 \rightarrow 2NaCl$
   (b) $C + O_2 \rightarrow CO_2$
   (c) $2H_2O \rightleftarrows 2H_2 + O_2$
   (d) $NaCl + AgNO_3 \rightarrow AgCl + NaNO_3$
   (e) $NH_3 + HCl \rightarrow NH_4^+ + Cl^-$
   (f) $2KClO_3 \rightarrow 2KCl + 3O_2$
   (g) $H_2 + Cl_2 \rightarrow 2HCl$
   (h) $2H_2 + O_2 \rightarrow 2H_2O$
   (i) $H_2SO_4 + 2KOH \rightarrow K_2SO_4 + 2H_2O$
   (j) $Zn + CuSO_4 \rightarrow ZnSO_4 + Cu$

5. For each oxidation-reduction reaction in Question 4, identify: (a) the substance oxidized; (b) the substance reduced; (c) the oxidizing agent; and (d) the reducing agent.
6. What is the oxidation number of each element in the following compounds?
   (a) $Ca(ClO_3)_2$; (b) Na_2HPO_4; (c) K_2SO_3; (d) H_3PO_3; (e) $Fe(OH)_3$.
7. Assign oxidation numbers to each element in the following compounds: (a) $PbSO_4$; (b) H_2O_2; (c) $K_2Cr_2O_7$; (d) H_2SO_3; (e) $HClO_4$.
8. What constitutes the anode, cathode, and electrolyte of a fully charged lead storage cell?
9. Define (a) electrode potential; (b) half-reaction; (c) half-cell.
10. Why is the standard hydrogen electrode assigned an electrode potential of 0.00 volt?
11. List in proper sequence the six steps involved in balancing oxidation-reduction equations by the oxidation-number method.
12. Complete the first four steps called for in Question 11 for the following:

(a) zinc + hydrochloric acid → zinc chloride + hydrogen.
(b) iron + copper(II) sulfate → iron(II) sulfate + copper.
(c) potassium dichromate + sulfur + water → sulfur dioxide + potassium hydroxide + chromium(III) oxide.
(d) bromine + water → hydrobromic acid + hypobromous acid.

Group B

13. Zinc reacts with sodium chromate in a sodium hydroxide solution to form Na_2ZnO_2, $NaCrO_2$, and H_2O. Balance the redox equation using the oxidation-number method.
14. Balance the following oxidation-reduction equation using the oxidation-number method.
    $K_2Cr_2O_7 + HCl \rightarrow KCl + CrCl_3 + H_2O + Cl_2$.
15. Potassium carbonate and bromine react to form potassium bromide, potassium bromate, and carbon dioxide. Balance the equation using the oxidation-number method.
16. Potassium permanganate, sodium sulfite, and sulfuric acid react to form potassium sulfate, manganese(II) sulfate, sodium sulfate, and water. Balance the equation for this oxidation-reduction reaction using the oxidation-number method.
17. Concentrated nitric acid reacts with copper to form copper(II) nitrate, nitrogen dioxide, and water. Balance the redox reaction using (a) the oxidation-number method, (b) the ion-electron method.
18. Dilute nitric acid reacts with copper to form copper(II) nitrate, nitrogen monoxide, and water. Balance the redox reaction using (a) the oxidation-number method, (b) the ion-electron method.
19. Hot, concentrated sulfuric acid reacts with zinc to form zinc sulfate, hydrogen sulfide, and water. Balance the equation using (a) the oxidation-number method, (b) the ion-electron method.

20. Nitric acid and hydrogen sulfide react to form nitrogen monoxide, sulfur, and water. Balance the equation using (*a*) the oxidation-number method, (*b*) the ion-electron method.

21. Balance the equation for the following redox reaction by the ion-electron method.

    nitric acid + zinc → zinc nitrate + nitrogen monoxide + water

22. Balance the equation for the following redox reaction by the ion-electron method.

    $KMnO_4 + FeSO_4 + H_2SO_4 \rightarrow K_2SO_4 + MnSO_4 + Fe_2(SO_4)_3 + H_2O$.

23. Referring to Table 22-3, the active metals down to magnesium replace hydrogen from water. Magnesium and succeeding metals replace hydrogen from steam. Metals near the bottom of the list do not replace hydrogen from steam. How can the data given in the table help you explain the behavior of these metals?

24. Using data from Table 22-4, write the equations for the half-reactions of a voltaic cell having Cu and Ag electrodes.

25. (*a*) Determine the potential difference across the voltaic cell of Question 24. (*b*) Write the equation for the overall reaction of the cell in the direction that it proceeds spontaneously.

Elements of Period Three

It is hard to imagine a world without glass. This hard, transparent, and amorphous material is used to make windows, lightbulbs, mirrors, eyeglasses, tableware, cookware, and a host of important everyday objects. Brittle when cold, glass softens when heated and when very hot, becomes plastic enough to be blown, rolled, molded, or pressed into any shape. Ordinary glass is composed of the silicates of sodium and calcium. The raw materials are sand, limestone, and sodium carbonate. This soda-lime glass is commonly used to make objects that are not subject to severe conditions, such as extremes of temperature or mechanical stress. Borosilicate or aluminosilicate glass is used to make objects that are exposed to extremes. Pyrex glass, a sodium aluminum borosilicate made by fusing sand, borax, and aluminum oxide, is an example. Extensive research has produced several new kinds of glass with improved strength and flexibility.

☐ 23.1 General appearance

In Chapter 5 you learned how the chemical elements are arranged by atomic number in a periodic table. In such a table, the elements in a given column have similar chemical properties. This chemical similarity is explained by their similar outer-electron arrangements. In going across a row of the periodic table, the properties of the elements vary. The first element is a highly active metal. Metals of decreasing activity come after it. They are followed by metalloids. Nonmetals of increasing activity come next. The last element in a row is a noble gas. This wide variation in chemical properties is explained by the difference in outer-electron arrangements.

In this chapter the elements in Period Three will be discussed. Period Three is a short period containing eight elements. The first three elements are sodium, magnesium, and aluminum. All are silvery metals with a characteristic metallic luster. Sodium is soft enough to be cut easily. Magnesium and aluminum are somewhat harder, but can easily be scratched with a knife. Silicon, the fourth element, is still harder. It is gray with a metallic luster. Because silicon has properties between those of metals and nonmetals, it is classed as a *metalloid*. Phosphorus is the fifth element. It commonly exists as an active, pale yellow, waxy solid or as a more stable red powder. Phosphorus is a nonmetal. The next two elements, sulfur and chlorine, are also nonmetals. Sulfur is a brittle yellow solid, and chlorine is a greenish-yellow gas. Argon, the noble gas of this period, is colorless. Figure 5-4 consists of photographs of samples of the elements of Period Three.

In this chapter you will gain an understanding of:

- the major physical and chemical properties of the elements in Period Three
- the relationship between the variation in atomic structure and the range of properties through Period Three
- electron configurations, ionization energies, and oxidation states of Period Three elements
- the oxides and binary hydrogen compounds of Period Three elements

These elements illustrate the variation in properties that occurs within a period. In later chapters, elements will be considered mainly within their family relationships.

Figure 23-1. The beauty and brilliance of a fireworks display depend on the very rapid combustion of elements such as magnesium, phosphorus, and sulfur.

Metallic crystals are described in Section 12.14(3).

Covalent network crystals are described in Section 12.14(2).

23.2 Structure and physical properties

Table 23-1 gives melting point, boiling point, density, and color data for each element of Period Three.

Because sodium, magnesium, and aluminum are metals, they have certain physical properties in common. Each is a good conductor of heat and electricity, has a silvery luster, and is ductile and malleable. Sodium and aluminum form cubic crystals. Magnesium forms hexagonal crystals. The crystal lattice of each of these elements is made up of metallic ions in an electron "gas" of valence electrons. The good conductivity of these metals is explained by the highly mobile character of their free electrons. Their silvery luster results from free electrons at the crystal surfaces. When light strikes these surfaces, the valence electrons absorb energy and begin to vibrate. These vibrations re-radiate the energy in all directions as light.

The binding force in metallic crystals is the attraction between positive ions and the negative electron "gas" that fills the lattice. This force is exerted equally in all directions. Its magnitude determines the degree of hardness, ductility, and malleability of these metals. The magnitude of this binding force is further indicated by the melting and boiling points of the metals. Sodium is softer and has a lower melting point than magnesium and aluminum. These properties indicate that the forces holding sodium ions in fixed positions in the crystal lattice are weaker than those in magnesium and aluminum. The forces holding the mobile ions together in the liquid phases of these three metals are quite strong. Evidence for this fact is the rather wide temperature range over which the metals are liquids.

Magnesium is denser than sodium, and aluminum is denser than magnesium. The denser elements have heavier, though smaller, atoms than the less dense elements. Besides being heavier, the smaller atoms tend to pack more closely together.

Silicon exists as a covalent network of atoms with a cubic crystal structure. The pattern of atomic arrangement in the silicon

Table 23-1
PHYSICAL PROPERTIES OF ELEMENTS OF PERIOD THREE

Element	Melting point (°C)	Boiling point (°C)	Density (g/cm^3)	Color
sodium	97.8	882.9	0.971	silver
magnesium	649	1090	1.74	silver
aluminum	660.4	2467	2.70	silver
silicon	1410	2355	2.33	gray
phosphorus	44.1 (white)	280	1.82	pale yellow
sulfur	112.8 (rhombic)	444.7	2.07	yellow
chlorine	−101.0	−34.6	3.214 g/L	green-yellow
argon	−189.2	−185.7	1.784 g/L	colorless

crystal is identical to diamond, shown in Figure 17-3. However, the distance between nuclei is greater in silicon, 2.35 Å, than in diamond, 1.54 Å. The electron configuration of carbon is $1s^2 2s^2 2p^2$ and hybridization produces four equivalent sp^3 orbitals. Carbon atoms form four equivalent covalent bonds in the diamond structure. The electron configuration of silicon is similar to carbon, $1s^2 2s^2 2p^6 3s^2 3p^2$. Silicon also undergoes hybridization in the third energy level, forming four equivalent sp^3 orbitals. Silicon, like diamond, has four equivalent covalent bonds. Some of the valence electrons in silicon crystals are free to move. Unlike diamond, which is a nonconductor, silicon has a low electric conductivity.

There is a great difference between the melting points of the two consecutive elements, aluminum and silicon. This difference can be explained on the basis of structure. Aluminum has a metallic structure, while silicon has a covalent network structure. The silicon structure is less compact than that of aluminum. Thus, silicon is less dense than aluminum, even though silicon atoms are smaller and heavier than aluminum atoms.

Phosphorus has the electron configuration $1s^2 2s^2 2p^6 3s^2 3p^3$. With its three half-filled $3p$ orbitals, a phosphorus atom can form three covalent bonds. Elemental white phosphorus exists as separate P_4 molecules. Each atom of a P_4 molecule forms three covalent bonds. See Figure 23-3. White phosphorus has low melting and boiling points and is quite soft. These properties indicate that only weak dispersion interaction forces exist among the P_4 molecules. White phosphorus has no luster. It is a poor conductor of heat and a nonconductor of electricity. These typical properties of nonmetals are explained by their lack of free electrons.

The electron configuration of sulfur is $1s^2 2s^2 2p^6 3s^2 3p^4$. Sulfur atoms have two half-filled $3p$ orbitals and should form two covalent bonds. They do so in elemental sulfur. But, instead of forming a diatomic molecule like oxygen, sulfur atoms form a molecule consisting of eight atoms joined together in a puckered ring. See Figure 23-4. The brittleness and relatively low melting point of sulfur are explained by the weak dispersion interaction forces between S_8 molecules. Sulfur has the common nonmetallic properties: no silvery luster, poor thermal conductivity, and nonconduction of electricity.

You have already learned (Section 6.10) that chlorine exists as diatomic molecules, Cl_2. A single covalent bond joins the two atoms. The dispersion interaction forces between chlorine molecules are very weak. Evidence of this fact is that chlorine is a gas at room temperature.

Argon exists as single atoms because it has no half-filled orbitals to use in bond formation. The dispersion interaction

Figure 23-2. The blue wafers shown in the photo are made of silicon. They are used to make photovoltaic devices, which convert sunlight directly to electricity. The blue color is an anti-reflection coating that increases the amount of sunlight these wafers absorb.

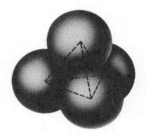

Figure 23-3. The structure of P_4 molecules of phosphorus.

Figure 23-4. The structure of S_8 molecules of sulfur.

Figure 23-5. Argon, which is colorless, is used to produce a blanketing atmosphere around welding sites during the fabrication of structural parts for airplanes.

forces between argon atoms are very weak indeed. This weakness is evident from the very low boiling point of argon.

☐ 23.3 Electron configurations, ionization energies, and oxidation states

Table 23-2 lists the electron configuration, first ionization energy, oxidation states, and atomic radius for each of the Period Three elements.

When ionization energy was first discussed in Section 5.7, you learned that it generally increases across a period because of the increasing nuclear charge. But *decreases* in ionization energy do occur in Period Three at aluminum and again at sulfur. The decrease between magnesium and aluminum is a result of their outer electron arrangements. The outermost electron of aluminum is the first electron in the $3p$ sublevel. The outermost electrons of magnesium occupy the $3s$ sublevel. Less energy is required to remove the $3p$ electron because the $3p$ sublevel has higher energy than the outer $3s$ sublevel. A decrease in ionization energy also occurs between phosphorus and sulfur. It is a result of the pairing of electrons in the $3p$ sublevel that begins in sulfur. The half-filled $3p$ sublevel of phosphorus has three singly occupied orbitals. The $3p$ sublevel in sulfur has one filled and two singly occupied orbitals. The configuration of phosphorus is *more stable* than the configuration of sulfur. In other words, the phosphorus configuration has lower energy. As a result, more energy is required to remove an electron from a phosphorus atom than from a sulfur atom.

The atomic radii decrease gradually across the period. This general decrease is easily explained. Successive electrons enter the same energy level, while the nuclear charge becomes successively greater and pulls the electrons closer to the nucleus.

Table 23-2
ATOMIC STRUCTURE AND RELATED PROPERTIES OF
ELEMENTS OF PERIOD THREE

Element	Electron configuration	First ionization energy (kcal/mole atoms)	Principal oxidation states	Atomic radius (Å)
sodium	$1s^2 2s^2 2p^6 3s^1$	119	$+1$	1.54
magnesium	$1s^2 2s^2 2p^6 3s^2$	176	$+2$	1.36
aluminum	$1s^2 2s^2 2p^6 3s^2 3p^1$	138	$+3$	1.18
silicon	$1s^2 2s^2 2p^6 3s^2 3p^2$	188	$+4$	1.11
phosphorus	$1s^2 2s^2 2p^6 3s^2 3p^3$	242	$+3, +5$	1.06
sulfur	$1s^2 2s^2 2p^6 3s^2 3p^4$	239	$-2, +4, +6$	1.02
chlorine	$1s^2 2s^2 2p^6 3s^2 3p^5$	299	$-1, +5, +7$	0.99
argon	$1s^2 2s^2 2p^6 3s^2 3p^6$	363	0	0.98

The relationship between atomic radius and ionic radius for sodium, magnesium, aluminum, sulfur, and chlorine was described in Section 6.8.

The oxidation states of sodium, $+1$, magnesium, $+2$, and aluminum, $+3$, have been explained in Section 5.8. Sodium has one electron that can be removed at low energy. Magnesium has two and aluminum three such electrons. Silicon atoms undergo sp^3 hybridization and can form four covalent bonds. Its oxidation state is $+4$. Phosphorus, with the electron-dot symbol $\cdot \overset{\displaystyle \cdot}{\underset{\displaystyle \cdot}{P}} \colon$, can add three electrons to each atom to form P^{---} ions, as in the compounds of phosphorus known as phosphides. Here its oxidation number is -3. It is also possible for phosphorus atoms to share three or five electrons in forming covalent compounds. Such sharing gives oxidation numbers of $+3$ or $+5$.

Sulfur, with the electron-dot symbol $\cdot \overset{\displaystyle \cdot\cdot}{\underset{\displaystyle \cdot}{S}} \colon$, can add two electrons to each atom. This electron addition forms sulfide ions, S^{--}, which have oxidation number -2. Sulfur can also share two, four, or six electrons, giving oxidation states of $+2$, $+4$, or $+6$, respectively.

Chlorine, with the electron-dot symbol $\colon \overset{\displaystyle \cdot\cdot}{\underset{\displaystyle \cdot}{Cl}} \colon$, commonly adds one electron to each atom, forming chloride ions. Here chlorine has the oxidation number -1. However, it is also possible for chlorine to share 1, 3, 5, or even all 7 electrons in covalent bonding. In such cases the oxidation numbers are $+1$, $+3$, $+5$, or $+7$, respectively.

Since argon is not yet known to form compounds, it has an oxidation number of zero.

◻ 23.4 Properties of oxides of Period Three elements

The elements of Period Three form a great variety of compounds with oxygen. Sodium, phosphorus, sulfur, and chlorine form two or more oxides. Only one oxide of each element will be described here. See Table 23-3.

Table 23-3
OXIDES OF PERIOD THREE ELEMENTS

Oxide	Melting point (°C)	Boiling point (°C)	Type of compound	Nature of reaction with water
Na_2O	subl. 1275		ionic	forms OH^-
MgO	2852	3600	ionic	forms OH^-
Al_2O_3	2072	2980	ionic	none; hydroxide is amphoteric
SiO_2	1610	2230	covalent network	none
P_4O_{10}	subl. 300	—	molecular	forms H^+ (aq)
SO_2	$-7\underline{3}$	$-1\overline{0}$	molecular	forms H^+ (aq)
Cl_2O	-20	4	molecular	forms H^+ (aq)

Figure 23-6. Aluminum oxide spheres used as a base for the catalysts in automobile emission-control systems.

You may find it helpful to review Section 15.7, acid anhydrides, and Section 15.10, basic anhydrides.

Compare these equations with the more detailed ones given in Section 15.9(7).

Figure 23-7. A close-up view of safety-match sticks passing over the composition dip roll. The match heads contain diantimony trisulfide, glue, and an oxidizing agent. The surface on which the match is to be struck contains red phosphorus, powdered glass, and glue.

Sodium oxide, Na_2O, and magnesium oxide, MgO, are white solids. The reaction of sodium with oxygen usually yields sodium peroxide, Na_2O_2. However, some sodium oxide can be prepared by heating sodium at about 180 °C in a limited amount of dry oxygen. Magnesium oxide is produced by burning magnesium in pure oxygen. Both sodium oxide and magnesium oxide are ionic compounds. Sodium oxide readily dissolves in water and forms a basic solution containing Na^+ and OH^- ions.

$$Na_2O + H_2O \rightarrow 2Na^+ + 2OH^-$$

Magnesium oxide is only slightly soluble in water, but it, too, forms a basic solution.

$$MgO + H_2O \rightarrow Mg^{++} + 2OH^-$$

Aluminum oxide, Al_2O_3, is a white, ionic compound. It can be produced by burning aluminum in pure oxygen. More commonly, it is prepared by heating aluminum hydroxide or the hydrated oxides of aluminum. Because aluminum oxide is virtually insoluble in water, the dehydration reaction is not reversible. Aluminum hydroxide is a white, insoluble, jelly-like substance. It must be prepared indirectly from aluminum oxide. Aluminum hydroxide is amphoteric; it reacts as a base in the presence of hydronium ions and as an acid in the presence of hydroxide ions.

$$Al(OH)_3 + 3H_3O^+ \rightarrow Al(H_2O)_6^{+++}$$

$$Al(OH)_3 + OH^- \rightarrow Al(OH)_4^-$$

Silicon dioxide, SiO_2, exists widely in nature as quartz. White sand is mostly silicon dioxide. Silicon dioxide has a covalent network structure. It consists of silicon atoms tetrahedrally bonded to four oxygen atoms. Each oxygen atom, in turn, is bonded to another silicon atom tetrahedrally bonded to four oxygen atoms. This structure extends indefinitely. All the silicon-oxygen bond distances are equal. The silicon-oxygen bonds are covalent, but with some degree of ionic character.

Silicon dioxide is practically insoluble in water. It acts as an acid in hot, concentrated solutions containing hydroxide ions.

$$SiO_2 + 4OH^- \rightarrow SiO_4^{----} + 2H_2O$$

Silicon dioxide does not react with common acids, but does react with hydrofluoric acid.

$$SiO_2 + 4HF \rightarrow SiF_4(g) + 2H_2O$$

In an abundant supply of oxygen, phosphorus burns and forms diphosphorus pentoxide, P_4O_{10}. (This formula is the correct molecular formula. The name is taken from the corresponding empirical formula, P_2O_5.) P_4O_{10} is a white, molecular solid. It reacts rapidly with water, forming a solution containing phosphoric acid, H_3PO_4.

$$P_4O_{10} + 6H_2O \rightarrow 4H^+(aq) + 4H_2PO_4^-$$

Phosphoric acid is a moderately strong acid. The equilibrium constant for its first ionization is of the order of 10^{-2}.

The explanation of ionization constant of an acid is given in Section 21.7.

Sulfur burns in air or oxygen to form sulfur dioxide, SO_2. This compound is molecular. At room temperature it is a colorless gas with a choking odor. Sulfur dioxide readily dissolves in and reacts with water. This reaction forms a solution containing sulfurous acid, H_2SO_3.

$$SO_2 + H_2O \rightarrow H^+(aq) + HSO_3^-$$

This acid is also moderately strong. The equilibrium constant for its first ionization is of the order of 10^{-2}.

Dichlorine monoxide, Cl_2O, is prepared by the reaction of chlorine with mercury(II) oxide.

$$2Cl_2 + HgO \rightarrow HgCl_2 + Cl_2O$$

This compound is an unstable yellow gas. It reacts with water to give a solution containing hypochlorous acid, HClO.

$$Cl_2O + H_2O \rightarrow 2HClO$$

$$2HClO \rightleftharpoons 2H^+(aq) + 2ClO^-$$

Hypochlorous acid is a very weak acid that exists only in water solution. Its ionization constant is of the order of 10^{-8}.

23.5 Properties of the binary hydrogen compounds of Period Three elements

Each of the elements of Period Three forms at least one binary compound with hydrogen. Silicon, phosphorus, and sulfur each form two or more binary hydrogen compounds. As with the oxides, only one binary hydrogen compound of each Period Three element will be described here. See Table 23-4.

Sodium hydride, NaH, is formed from sodium and hydrogen at moderately high temperatures. It is an ionic compound that crystallizes in a cubic system, as does sodium chloride. The

Figure 23-8. The most important use of elemental sulfur is the manufacture of sulfuric acid. The photo shows a plant in which sulfuric acid is made. Sulfur is first burned to make sulfur dioxide. The sulfur dioxide is catalytically oxidized to sulfur trioxide, which is then hydrated indirectly to sulfuric acid.

Table 23-4
BINARY HYDROGEN COMPOUNDS OF PERIOD THREE ELEMENTS

Compound	Melting point (°C)	Boiling point (°C)	Type of compound	Nature of reaction with water
NaH	d. 800		ionic	forms OH^- + H_2
$(MgH_2)_x$	d. 280		polymeric	forms OH^- + H_2
$(AlH_3)_x$	d. 100		polymeric	forms OH^- + H_2
SiH_4	−185	−112	molecular	forms SiO_2 + H_2
PH_3	−133	−88	molecular	none
H_2S	−86	−61	molecular	forms $H^+(aq)$
HCl	−115	−85	molecular	forms $H^+(aq)$

negative ion in this compound is the hydride ion, H^-. Hydride ions are strong bases. They readily remove protons from water molecules to form hydrogen molecules and hydroxide ions. Sodium hydride reacts vigorously with water, yielding hydrogen gas and hydroxide ions.

$$NaH + H_2O \rightarrow H_2 + Na^+ + OH^-$$

For an inorganic compound, magnesium hydride is relatively new. It was first prepared about 1950.

Magnesium hydride, MgH_2, is a less stable compound than sodium hydride. It can be made directly by heating the elements under high pressure in the presence of magnesium iodide. Complex indirect methods are more satisfactory, however. It is a nonvolatile, colorless solid that reacts violently with water.

$$MgH_2 + 2H_2O \rightarrow Mg(OH)_2 + 2H_2$$

In a vacuum, magnesium hydride is stable to about 300 °C. Above this temperature, it decomposes into its elements. The structure of magnesium hydride is believed to be like that of a polymer. The MgH_2 units are bonded together as $(MgH_2)_x$, in which x is indefinite.

The explanation of a polymer is given in Section 18.15(2).

Aluminum hydride has been known only since the 1940's.

Aluminum hydride, AlH_3, can be made by the action of lithium hydride on aluminum chloride in ether solution.

$$3LiH + AlCl_3 \xrightarrow[\text{solution)}]{\text{(ether}} AlH_3 + 3LiCl$$

Aluminum hydride is a white amorphous solid. Its structure is unknown, but it is probably a polymer $(AlH_3)_x$. It reacts vigorously with water. It is stable in a vacuum up to about 100 °C. At higher temperatures, it decomposes to aluminum and hydrogen.

Monosilane, SiH_4, is a colorless, stable, but readily flammable, gas. It consists of nonpolar covalent molecules. Along with other silicon hydrides, it is produced when magnesium silicide is treated with dilute hydrochloric acid.

$$Mg_2Si + 4H^+(aq) \rightarrow 2Mg^{++} + SiH_4$$

Monosilane reacts very readily with water to yield hydrogen and silicon dioxide.

$$SiH_4 + 2H_2O \rightarrow SiO_2 + 4H_2$$

Recall that the general formula for the alkanes is C_nH_{2n+2}. See Section 18.9.

Other known silicon hydrides are Si_2H_6, Si_3H_8, Si_4H_{10}, Si_5H_{12}, and Si_6H_{14}. Notice the similarity of these formulas to those of the alkanes. These compounds, however, are much more reactive than the alkanes. The reason is that silicon-silicon bonds and silicon-hydrogen bonds are weaker than the carbon-carbon and carbon-hydrogen bonds in the alkanes.

The pyramidal structure of the ammonia molecule is described in Section 6.16.

Phosphine, PH_3, is one of two or three known binary phosphorus-hydrogen compounds. It is a molecular substance in which the atoms are covalently bonded in an ammonia-type structure. At room temperature it is a colorless gas with an unpleasant odor like that of decayed fish. Phosphine is very poisonous and flammable. The simplest method of preparing phosphine is by treating calcium phosphide with water. Phosphine prepared by this method is spontaneously flammable in air because of impurities.

$$Ca_3P_2 + 6H_2O \rightarrow 3Ca(OH)_2 + 2PH_3$$

Phosphine dissolves in water, producing a nearly neutral solution.

Hydrogen sulfide, H_2S, is a colorless, foul-smelling, very poisonous gas. Its odor resembles that of decayed eggs. It is a molecular compound, with slightly polar covalent bonding within the molecule. It is usually prepared in the laboratory by the action of dilute hydrochloric acid on iron(II) sulfide.

$$FeS + 2H^+(aq) \rightarrow Fe^{++} + H_2S$$

Hydrogen sulfide is flammable. The products of combustion are water vapor and sulfur or sulfur dioxide, depending on combustion conditions.

Hydrogen sulfide dissolves in and reacts with water, forming a weakly acid solution of hydrosulfuric acid. The first ionization constant of hydrosulfuric acid is of the order of 10^{-7}.

$$H_2S \rightleftarrows H^+(aq) + HS^-$$

The binary hydrogen compound of chlorine is hydrogen chloride, HCl. This compound is a colorless, sharp-odored, poisonous gas. Hydrogen chloride consists of highly polar covalent molecules. It can be prepared by direct combination of its elements or by heating sodium chloride with moderately concentrated sulfuric acid.

$$H_2 + Cl_2 \rightarrow 2HCl$$

$$NaCl + H_2SO_4 \rightarrow NaHSO_4 + HCl$$

Hydrogen chloride is very soluble in water. It is almost completely ionized by the water, yielding hydronium ions and chloride ions.

$$HCl \rightleftarrows H^+(aq) + Cl^-$$

This solution, called hydrochloric acid, is a strong acid.

SUMMARY

Some physical properties of the Period Three elements are described: hardness, color, melting point, boiling point, density, crystal structure, and conductivity. The chemical properties of the Period Three elements are briefly explained in terms of element type, atomic and molecular structure, and interatomic and intermolecular forces. Their first ionization energies, principal oxidation states, and atomic radii are compared.

The preparation and properties of the oxides and binary hydrogen compounds of the Period Three elements are described and compared. The reactions of these compounds with water are also described and compared.

QUESTIONS

Group A

1. Describe the variation in metallic-nonmetallic properties across Period Three, relating it to the variation in number of outer-shell electrons.

2. (*a*) What physical properties do metals have

in common? (*b*) What physical properties do nonmetals have in common?

3. Describe the nature of the binding force between (*a*) atoms of sodium; (*b*) atoms of silicon; (*c*) atoms of chlorine; (*d*) molecules of chlorine; (*e*) atoms of argon.

4. Even though they are consecutive elements, why is the melting point of silicon so much higher than the melting point of aluminum?

5. What difference is there in the interatomic forces of elements that are malleable and of those that are brittle?

6. Why is the sodium ion so much smaller than the sodium atom?

7. Why is the chloride ion somewhat larger than the chlorine atom?

8. Compare the reactions of Na_2O, SiO_2, and Cl_2O with water.

9. Compare the reactions of NaH, SiH_4, and HCl with water.

10. Why are the silicon hydrides much more reactive than the alkanes?

Group B

11. What accounts for the silvery luster of metals?

12. Why is the density increase between sodium and aluminum proportionally greater than the atomic weight increase?

13. Compare the magnitude of the binding force between atoms of liquid argon and atoms of liquid aluminum.

14. Explain why diamond does not conduct electricity and silicon has a low electric conductivity, when both have the same crystal structure and type of bonding.

15. Phosphorus atoms form three covalent bonds, sulfur atoms form two covalent bonds, and chlorine atoms form one covalent bond; yet phosphorus molecules are tetratomic, sulfur molecules are octatomic, and chlorine molecules are diatomic. Explain.

16. Explain the observed decrease in ionization energy between magnesium and aluminum and between phosphorus and sulfur.

17. (*a*) Draw electron-dot symbols for the elements of Period Three. (*b*) Using these symbols explain how the common oxidation states for each element are attained.

18. Relate electronegativity differences to the type of bonding observed in the (*a*) oxides of the elements of Period Three; (*b*) binary hydrogen compounds of the elements of Period Three.

19. Compare the structure of silicon dioxide with that of elemental silicon.

20. Compare the structures of (*a*) NH_3 and PH_3; (*b*) H_2S and H_2O. In your comparison, include molecular shape and size, and type of bonding.

21. Write the balanced formula equation for the reaction of aluminum hydride and water.

◀ PROBLEMS

Group A

1. What is the mass in grams of a block of aluminum 5.0 cm long, 2.0 cm wide, and 1.5 cm high?

2. How many magnesium atoms are in a length of magnesium ribbon of mass 0.472 g?

3. What is the percentage of phosphorus in P_4O_{10}?

4. What volume of hydrogen at STP is formed by the reaction of 160 mL of gaseous monosilane at STP with water?

5. How many grams of calcium phosphide must react with water to prepare 5.0 g of phosphine?

6. How many liters of SiF_4 at STP can be obtained from 12 g of SiO_2 by reaction with hydrofluoric acid?

Group B

7. A solution of 0.14 g of white phosphorus in 10.0 g of benzene lowers the freezing point of the benzene 0.58 C°. (*a*) Calculate the molecular weight of white phosphorus from these data. (*b*) What is the corresponding molecular formula? See Table 13-5 for additional data.

8. A saturated solution of $Mg(OH)_2$ is approximately 0.000031 *N*. What is its pH?

The Metals of Group I

Life on earth would be impossible without the Group I metals. Sodium and potassium are essential to the proper functioning of nerves. Some of their compounds, such as sodium chloride and potassium iodide, are important nutrients in the diets of humans and animals. Potassium nitrate and sodium chloride are used as food preservatives. Sodium peroxide and potassium hypochlorite are bleaching agents. Lithium finds many uses in metallurgical processes. Its compounds are used in ceramics, welding, drugs, and the synthesis of organic compounds. Alloyed with magnesium, lithium is important in aircraft and spacecraft design because of its high strength-to-weight ratio. Rubidium and cesium are used to remove the last traces of oxygen from electronic tubes and in photoelectric cells. In a phenomenon known as the photoelectric effect, *electrons are ejected very easily from cesium by light falling on the metal.*

☐ 24.1 Structure and properties

The group of elements at the left of the periodic table includes lithium, sodium, potassium, rubidium, cesium, and francium. These elements are all chemically active metals. They are known as the *alkali metals* and also as the Sodium Family of elements. Because of their great chemical reactivity none exists in nature in the elemental state. They are found in natural compounds as monatomic ions with a +1 charge. Sodium and potassium are plentiful, lithium is fairly rare, and rubidium and cesium are rarer still. Francium does not exist as a stable element. Only trace quantities have been produced in certain nuclear reactions.

The Group I elements possess metallic characteristics to a high degree. Each has a silvery luster, is a good conductor of electricity and heat, and is ductile and malleable. These metals are relatively soft and can be cut with a knife. The properties of the Group I metals are related to their characteristic crystalline lattice structures, which are described in Section 12.14(3).

The crystal lattice is made up of metallic ions with a +1 charge. The lattice is built around a body-centered cubic unit cell. In this body-centered structure, each metallic ion is surrounded by eight nearest neighbors at the corners of the cube. A model of the body-centered cubic unit cell is shown in Figure 24-1. Valence electrons form an electron "gas" that permeates the lattice structure. These "free" electrons belong to the solid as a whole. The mobility of the free electrons gives Group I metals their high thermal and electric conductivity. These electrons are responsible for the characteristic silvery luster as well.

In this chapter you will gain an understanding of:

- **the structure and properties of the Group I metals**
- **the occurrence, uses, and compounds of the Group I metals**
- **the Downs cell**
- **the Solvay process**
- **spectroscopy**

The Group I elements form hydroxides whose water solutions are extremely alkaline. This is why the Group I elements are called "alkali metals."

Figure 24-1. Body-centered cubic unit cell.

Ductile: capable of being drawn into a wire.
Malleable: capable of being rolled or pounded into a sheet.

The softness, ductility, and malleability of the alkali metals are explained by the binding force in the metallic crystal lattice. Their low melting points and densities, together with their softness, distinguish these elements from the more familiar common metals. Table 24-1 lists some representative properties of the alkali metals.

The atoms of each element in Group I have a single electron in their outermost shell. Lithium atoms have the electron configuration $1s^2 2s^1$. All other Group I elements have next-to-outermost shells consisting of eight electrons. An ion formed by removing the single valence electron has the stable electron configuration of the preceding noble gas. For example, the sodium ion has the electron configuration $1s^2 2s^2 2p^6$. This matches the configuration of the neon atom. The electron configuration of the potassium ion, $1s^2 2s^2 2p^6 3s^2 3p^6$, matches that of the argon atom.

It is also possible to *add* an electron to a Group I atom to produce an anion having an electron pair in the s orbital of the outermost shell. An example is the Na^- anion which has the electron configuration $1s^2 2s^2 2p^6 3s^2$. Here the oxidation number of sodium is -1. Similar anions of potassium, rubidium, and cesium have also been produced.

☐ 24.2 Chemical activity

Ionization energy measures the tendency of an atom to hold a valence electron.

The very active free metals of the Sodium Family are obtained by reducing the $+1$ ions in their natural compounds. The metals are vigorous reducing agents. They have a weak attraction for their valence electrons. Ionization energy decreases as the atom size increases going down the group. See Table 24-2. This decreasing energy with increasing size shows that it is easier to remove electrons physically from the outer shells of the heavier atoms. However, if you examine the net energy of reactions in which electrons are given up to other elements, you find that the lithium atom is the strongest reducing agent. Although it may be harder to remove an electron from the lithium atom, more energy is given

Table 24-1
PROPERTIES OF GROUP I ELEMENTS

Element	Atomic number	Atomic weight	Electron configuration	Oxida-tion number	Melt-ing point (°C)	Boil-ing point (°C)	Density (g/cm³)	Atomic radius (Å)	Ionic radius (Å)
lithium	3	6.941	2,1	+1	180.5	1347	0.534	1.23	0.68
sodium	11	22.98977	2,8,1	+1	97.8	883	0.971	1.54	0.97
potassium	19	39.0983	2,8,8,1	+1	63.6	774	0.862	2.03	1.33
rubidium	37	85.4678	2,8,18,8,1	+1	38.9	688	1.532	2.16	1.47
cesium	55	132.9054	2,8,18,18,8,1	+1	28.4	678	1.873	2.35	1.67
francium	87	[223]	2,8,18,32,18,8,1	+1	27	677	—	—	—

back by the subsequent interaction of the lithium ion and its surroundings than by the larger alkali-metal ions with their surroundings.

Handling and storing the alkali metals is difficult because of their chemical activity. They are usually stored submerged in kerosene or some other liquid hydrocarbon because they react vigorously with water. See Figure 24-2. In reaction with water, they release hydrogen to form strongly basic hydroxide solutions.

$$2K(s) + 2H_2O(l) \rightarrow 2K^+(aq) + 2OH^-(aq) + H_2(g)$$

All of the ordinary compounds of the alkali metals are ionic, including their hydrides. Only lithium forms the oxide directly with oxygen. Sodium forms the peroxide instead, and the higher metals tend to form superoxides of the form $M^+O_2^-$. However, the ordinary oxides can be prepared indirectly. These oxides are basic anhydrides. They react with water to form the hydroxides.

Nearly all of the compounds of the alkali metals are quite soluble in water. The alkali-metal ions are colorless. They have little tendency to hydrolyze in water solution or to form polyatomic ions.

Compounds of the more important alkali metals are easily identified by *flame tests*. Their compounds impart characteristic colors to a Bunsen flame. Sodium compounds color the flame yellow. Lithium compounds give a flame a red (carmine) color. Potassium colors a flame violet; rubidium and cesium give reddish violet (magenta) flames.

SODIUM

☐ 24.3 Occurrence of sodium

Metallic sodium is never found free in nature. However, compounds containing the Na^+ ion and sodium complexes exist in soil, natural waters, and in plants and animals. Sodium is such a widely distributed element because of the solubility of its compounds that it is almost impossible to find a sodium-free material. Vast quantities of sodium chloride are present in sea water and rock salt deposits. There are important deposits of sodium nitrate in Chile and Peru. The carbonates, sulfates, and borates of sodium are found in dry lake beds.

☐ 24.4 Preparation of sodium

Sir Humphry Davy (1778–1829), an English chemist, first prepared metallic sodium in 1807 by the electrolysis of fused sodium hydroxide. Today sodium is prepared by the electrolysis of fused sodium chloride. An apparatus called the *Downs cell* (see Figure 24-3) is used in this process. Sodium chloride has a high melting point, 801 °C. Calcium chloride is mixed with it to lower the melting point to 580 °C. Liquid sodium is collected under oil.

Table 24-2
IONIZATION ENERGY AND THE SIZE OF ATOMS

Element	Relative size of atoms	Ionization energy (kcal/mole)
Li		124
Na		119
K		$10\overline{0}$
Rb		96.3
Cs		89.8
Fr	—	—

Figure 24-2. Potassium, a Group I metal, like other members of this group reacts vigorously with water. The light for this photograph was produced by dropping a small amount of potassium into a beaker of water.

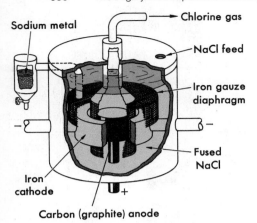

Sodium metal

Chlorine gas

NaCl feed

Iron gauze diaphragm

Fused NaCl

Iron cathode

Carbon (graphite) anode

Figure 24-3. Elemental sodium is produced by the electrolysis of melted sodium chloride in a Downs cell. Chlorine is a valuable by-product.

Chlorine gas is produced simultaneously. This gas is kept separate from the metallic sodium by an iron-gauze diaphragm.

The sodium is recovered by reducing Na^+ ions. This occurs at the cathode of the Downs cell. Each sodium ion acquires an electron from the cathode to form a neutral sodium atom.

$$Na^+ + e^- \rightarrow Na(l)$$

Chloride ions are oxidized at the anode. Each chloride ion loses an electron to the anode to form a neutral chlorine atom.

$$Cl^- \rightarrow Cl + e^-$$

Two chlorine atoms, however, form the diatomic molecule of elemental chlorine gas. The net anode reaction is

$$2Cl^- \rightarrow Cl_2(g) + 2e^-$$

In the overall cell reaction, electron-transfer balance is maintained between the electrodes. Two Na^+ ions are reduced for each Cl_2 molecule formed. The cell reaction can be written

cathode:	$2Na^+ + 2e^- \rightarrow 2Na(l)$
anode:	$2Cl^- \rightarrow Cl_2(g) + 2e^-$
cell:	$2Na^+ + 2Cl^- \rightarrow 2Na(l) + Cl_2(g)$

❏ 24.5 Properties and uses of sodium

Sodium is a silvery-white, lustrous metal that tarnishes rapidly when exposed to air. It is very soft, has a lower density than water, and a low melting point. A pellet of sodium dropped into water melts from the heat of the vigorous exothermic reaction that occurs. This reaction yields hydrogen gas and a strongly basic solution.

$$2Na(s) + 2H_2O \rightarrow 2Na^+(aq) + 2OH^-(aq) + H_2(g)$$

Oxide ion: O^{--}
Peroxide ion: O_2^{--}
Superoxide ion: O_2^-

When exposed to air, sodium unites with oxygen to form sodium peroxide, Na_2O_2. By supplying sodium in excess, some sodium oxide, Na_2O, can be produced along with the bulk product, Na_2O_2. This production of Na_2O is a result of the strong reducing character of sodium atoms. Sodium oxide can also be formed by heating NaOH with sodium.

$$2NaOH + 2Na \rightarrow 2Na_2O + H_2(g)$$

The superoxide of sodium, NaO_2, can be prepared indirectly. Superoxides contain the O_2^- ion having one unpaired electron.

Sodium reacts with all aqueous acids. It burns in an atmosphere of chlorine gas, uniting directly with the chlorine to form sodium chloride.

A flame test of sodium compounds reveals a strong yellow

color characteristic of vaporized sodium atoms. This yellow flame is a common identification test for sodium. See Figure 24-4.

Most of the sodium produced in the United States is used in making tetraethyl lead, an antiknock additive for gasoline. Sodium is used as a heat-transfer agent and in making dyes and other organic compounds. Another use is in sodium vapor lamps.

◻ 24.6 Sodium chloride

Sodium chloride is found in sea water, in salt wells, and in deposits of rock salt. Rock salt is mined in many places in the world.

Pure sodium chloride is not deliquescent. Magnesium chloride is very deliquescent, however, and is usually present in sodium salt as an impurity. This explains why table salt becomes wet and sticky in damp weather. Sodium chloride crystallizes in a cubic pattern. See Figure 24-5.

Sodium chloride is essential in the diets of humans and animals and is present in certain body fluids. Perspiration contains considerable amounts of sodium chloride. People who perspire freely in hot weather often need to increase their salt intake by the use of salt tablets.

Since sodium chloride is the cheapest compound of sodium, it is used as a starting material in making many other sodium compounds. Some sodium compounds are most easily prepared directly from metallic sodium, however. Practically all sodium metal production utilizes sodium chloride as the raw material.

◻ 24.7 Sodium hydroxide

Most commercial sodium hydroxide is produced by electrolysis of an aqueous sodium chloride solution. This electrolysis of aqueous NaCl is somewhat different from that of fused NaCl in the Downs cell. Chlorine gas is produced at the anode, but hydrogen gas (instead of metallic sodium) is produced at the cathode. The solution, meanwhile, becomes aqueous NaOH. Evidence indicates that water molecules acquire electrons from the cathode and are reduced to H_2 gas and OH^- ions.

The cell reaction for the electrolysis of an aqueous NaCl solution is

cathode: $\qquad 2H_2O + 2e^- \rightarrow H_2(g) + 2OH^-(aq)$

anode: $\qquad\qquad 2Cl^- \rightarrow Cl_2(g) + 2e^-$

cell: $\qquad 2H_2O + 2Cl^- \rightarrow H_2(g) + Cl_2(g) + 2OH^-(aq)$

As the Cl^- ion concentration diminishes, the OH^- ion concentration increases. The Na^+ ion concentration remains unchanged during electrolysis. Thus the solution is converted from aqueous NaCl to aqueous NaOH.

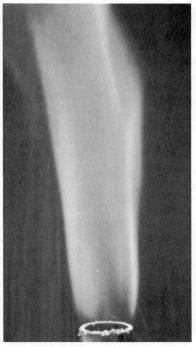

Figure 24-4. Sodium salts impart a strong yellow color to the Bunsen flame. The sodium flame color cannot be seen through cobalt-blue glass. See Figure 24-8.

Figure 24-5. Native crystals of sodium chloride, known as halite, recovered from the Mojave Desert in California.

The 1979 production of sodium hydroxide was over 11 million metric tons. It ranked seventh in amount among chemicals produced in the United States.

Commercial NaOH is called lye or caustic soda.

Sodium hydroxide converts some types of animal and vegetable matter into soluble materials by chemical action. It is very *caustic* and has destructive effects on skin, hair, and wool.

Sodium hydroxide is a white crystalline solid. It is marketed in the form of flakes, pellets, and sticks. It is very deliquescent and dissolves in the water that it removes from the air. It reacts with carbon dioxide from the air, producing sodium carbonate. Its water solution is strongly basic.

Sodium hydroxide reacts with fats, forming soap and glycerol. One of its important uses, therefore, is in making soap. It is also used in the production of rayon, cellulose film, paper pulp, and in petroleum refining.

�‍⃞ 24.8 The Solvay process

Almost all of the sodium carbonate and sodium hydrogen carbonate produced in the world is manufactured by the Solvay process. It was developed in the 1860's by Ernest Solvay (1838–1922), a Belgian industrial chemist. The process is a classic example of efficiency in chemical production. See Figure 24-6.

The raw materials for the Solvay process are common salt, limestone, and coal. The salt is pumped as brine from salt wells. The thermal decomposition of limestone yields the carbon dioxide and calcium oxide needed in the process.

Figure 24-6. A flow diagram of the Solvay process.

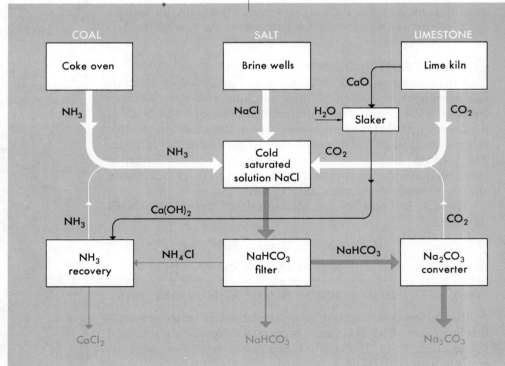

$$CaCO_3(s) \rightarrow CaO(s) + CO_2(g) \qquad \text{(Equation 1)}$$

Coal is converted into coke, gas, coal tar, and ammonia by destructive distillation. The coke and gas are used as fuel in the plant. The ammonia is also used in the process, while the coal tar is sold as a useful by-product.

To begin the process, a cold saturated solution of sodium chloride is further saturated with ammonia and carbon dioxide. The following reactions occur:

$$CO_2(g) + H_2O \rightarrow H_2CO_3$$

$$H_2CO_3 + NH_3(g) \rightarrow NH_4^+(aq) + HCO_3^-(aq)$$

Net: $\quad CO_2(g) + NH_3(g) + H_2O \rightarrow NH_4^+(aq) + HCO_3^-(aq)$

The HCO_3^- ions form in a solution that has a high concentration of Na^+ ions. Since sodium hydrogen carbonate is only slightly soluble in this cold solution, it precipitates.

$$Na^+(aq) + HCO_3^-(aq) \rightarrow NaHCO_3(s)$$

The solution that remains contains NH_4^+ ions and Cl^- ions. The precipitated sodium hydrogen carbonate is filtered and dried. It is either sold as *baking soda* or converted into sodium carbonate by thermal decomposition.

NaHCO$_3$: baking soda
Na$_2$CO$_3$: soda ash
Na$_2$CO$_3$ · 10H$_2$O: washing soda

$$2NaHCO_3(s) \rightarrow Na_2CO_3(s) + H_2O(g) + CO_2(g)$$

The dried sodium carbonate is an important industrial chemical called *soda ash*.

The ammonia used in the process is more valuable than the sodium carbonate or sodium hydrogen carbonate. Hence, it must be recovered and used over again if the process is to be profitable. The calcium oxide from Equation 1 is slaked by adding water. Calcium hydroxide is formed in this reaction.

$$CaO(s) + H_2O(l) \rightarrow Ca(OH)_2(s)$$

The calcium hydroxide is added to the solution containing NH_4^+ ions and Cl^- ions to release the ammonia from the ammonium ion.

$$NH_4^+(aq) + OH^-(aq) \rightarrow NH_3(g) + H_2O$$

The solution now contains mainly Ca^{++} ions and Cl^- ions. Neither of these ions is recycled into the process. As a by-product, calcium chloride has some use as an inexpensive dehydrating agent. The supply generally exceeds the demand, however.

Sodium hydrogen carbonate, as baking soda, is the main ingredient of baking powders. One important industrial use of sodium carbonate is in the production of glass.

The water solution of sodium carbonate is mildly basic because of hydrolysis of CO_3^{--} ions.

$$CO_3^{--} + H_2O \rightleftharpoons HCO_3^- + OH^-$$

Table 24-3
REPRESENTATIVE SODIUM COMPOUNDS

Chemical name	Common name	Formula	Color	Uses
sodium tetraborate, decahydrate	borax	$Na_2B_4O_7 \cdot 10H_2O$	white	as a water softener; in making glass; as a flux
sodium carbonate, decahydrate	washing soda	$Na_2CO_3 \cdot 10H_2O$	white	as a water softener; in glassmaking
sodium hydrogen carbonate	baking soda	$NaHCO_3$	white	as a leavening agent in baking
sodium cyanide	prussiate of soda	$NaCN$	white	to destroy vermin; to extract gold from ores; in silver and gold plating; in case-hardening steel
sodium hydride	(none)	NaH	white	in cleaning scale and rust from steel forgings and castings
sodium nitrate	Chile saltpeter	$NaNO_3$	white, or colorless	as a fertilizer
sodium peroxide	(none)	Na_2O_2	yellowish white	as an oxidizing and bleaching agent; as a source of oxygen
sodium phosphate, decahydrate	TSP	$Na_3PO_4 \cdot 10H_2O$	white	as a cleaning agent; as a water softener
sodium sulfate, decahydrate	Glauber's salt	$Na_2SO_4 \cdot 10H_2O$	white, or colorless	in making glass; as a cathartic in medicine
sodium thiosulfate, pentahydrate	hypo	$Na_2S_2O_3 \cdot 5H_2O$	white, or colorless	as a fixer in photography; as an antichlor
sodium sulfide	(none)	Na_2S	colorless	in the preparation of sulfur dyes; for dyeing cotton; to remove hair from hides

POTASSIUM

24.9 Preparation and properties of potassium

Potassium is abundant in nature and widely distributed, but only in combined form. Great deposits of combined potassium occur in the form of feldspar, a potassium aluminosilicate mineral. This mineral is part of all granitic rocks. It is insoluble and weathers very slowly. Large deposits of potassium chloride, crystallized with magnesium and calcium compounds, are found in Texas and New Mexico. See Figure 24-7. Some potassium compounds are taken from Searles Lake in California.

Potassium was first prepared by Sir Humphry Davy in 1807. His method involved the electrolysis of fused potassium hydroxide. The small annual production today is by the reaction

$$KCl + Na \rightarrow NaCl + K$$

The reaction proceeds to the right and equilibrium is prevented by removing the potassium.

Potassium metal is soft and of low density. It has a silvery luster that quickly tarnishes bluish-gray when exposed to air. Potassium is more active than sodium. It floats on water and reacts with the water so rapidly that the hydrogen gas given off usually ignites.

Potassium imparts a fleeting violet color to a Bunsen flame. The color comes from vaporizing potassium atoms. The presence of sodium, however, masks the violet color of potassium in the flame. Potassium is detected in a mixture of sodium and potassium compounds by observing the colored flame through cobalt-blue glass. This glass filters out the yellow sodium flame color. The violet potassium flame color then shows clearly. A typical potassium flame is shown in Figure 24-8.

◻ 24.10 Compounds of potassium

All common potassium compounds are soluble in water. Potassium hydroxide, prepared by the electrolysis of a solution of potassium chloride, has the typical properties of a strong alkali. Potassium nitrate is made by mixing hot, concentrated solutions of potassium chloride and sodium nitrate.

$$KCl + NaNO_3 \rightarrow KNO_3 + NaCl(s)$$

The solubility curves of Figure 13-11 can be helpful in understanding how potassium nitrate is recovered in this process. Examine the solubility curves of the four possible pairs of ions in the mixed solution. Sodium chloride is the least soluble. It has almost the same solubility over the liquid temperature range of water. Potassium nitrate is much less soluble at low temperature than at high temperature.

The solution is evaporated at high temperature, and sodium chloride first crystallizes. As evaporation continues, sodium chloride continues to separate and the concentration of potassium and nitrate ions increases. The crystallized sodium chloride is removed and the solution is allowed to cool. Very little sodium chloride separates as the solubility remains about the same. Potassium nitrate crystallizes very rapidly as the solution cools. It can be purified by recrystallization.

Sodium compounds are often used instead of potassium compounds because they usually are less expensive. Most glass is made with sodium carbonate, but potassium carbonate yields a more lustrous glass that is preferred for optical uses. Potassium nitrate is not hygroscopic. For this reason, it is used instead of sodium nitrate in making black gunpowder.

There is one very important use of potassium compounds for

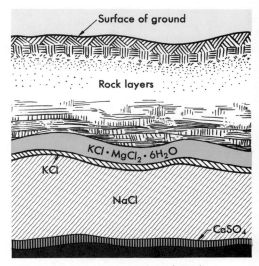

Figure 24-7. A cross section of a salt deposit, showing how the different minerals were deposited as the sea water evaporated.

Figure 24-8. Potassium salts color the Bunsen flame violet. The potassium flame is masked by the presence of sodium salts but is purple when viewed through cobalt-blue glass. Thus the use of cobalt-blue glass permits potassium to be detected by the flame test in a sodium-potassium mixture.

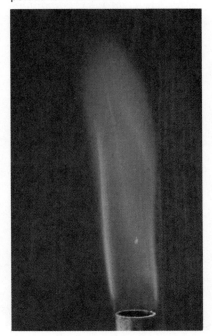

Table 24-4
REPRESENTATIVE POTASSIUM COMPOUNDS

Chemical name	Common name	Formula	Color	Uses
potassium bromide	(none)	KBr	white	as a sedative; in photography
potassium carbonate	potash	K_2CO_3	white	in making glass; in making soap
potassium chlorate	(none)	$KClO_3$	white	as an oxidizing agent; in fireworks; in explosives
potassium chloride	(none)	KCl	white	as a source of potassium; as a fertilizer
potassium hydroxide	caustic potash	KOH	white	in making soft soap; as a battery electrolyte
potassium iodide	(none)	KI	white	in medicine; in iodized salt; in photography
potassium nitrate	saltpeter	KNO_3	white	in black gunpowder; in fireworks; in curing meats
potassium permanganate	(none)	$KMnO_4$	purple	as a germicide; as an oxidizing agent

which there is no substitute. Green plants must have these compounds to grow properly. Therefore, complete chemical fertilizers always contain an appropriate amount of potassium.

SPECTROSCOPY

A spectroscope is an optical instrument that separates the light entering it into its component wavelengths which are then seen as a spectrum.

◻ 24.11 Use of a spectroscope

One type of *spectroscope* consists of a glass prism and a *collimator tube* which focuses a narrow beam of light rays on the prism. It also has a small telescope for examining the light that passes through the prism. When white light passes through a triangular prism, a band of colors called a *continuous spectrum* appears. This effect is caused by the unequal bending of light of different wavelengths as it enters the prism and as it emerges from it. A continuous spectrum is shown in the top band of Figure 24-9.

Examination of a sodium flame by spectroscope reveals a characteristic bright-yellow line. Since this yellow line is always in the same relative place in the spectrum, it identifies sodium. Potassium produces both red and violet spectral lines. The characteristic color lines of several chemical elements are shown in Figure 24-9.

◻ 24.12 Origin of spectral lines

A platinum wire held in a Bunsen flame becomes incandescent and emits white light. When the incandescent wire is viewed through a spectroscope, a continuous spectrum of colors is observed. The energy of the white light is distributed over a continuous range of light frequencies. This range includes the entire visible spectrum. White light is spread out forming a spectrum as it passes through the prism of the spectroscope. Here the light

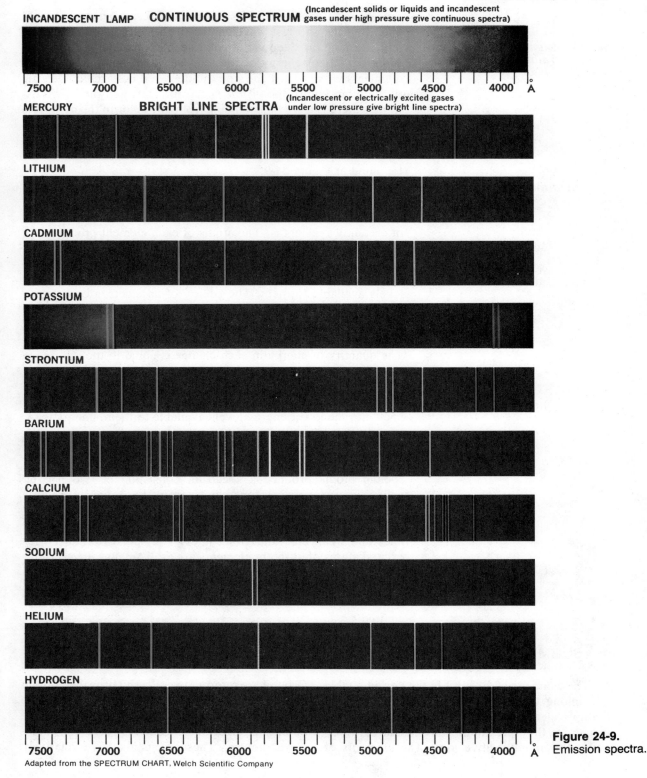

Figure 24-9.
Emission spectra.

Adapted from the SPECTRUM CHART, Welch Scientific Company

The relation between frequency and wavelength of electromagnetic radiation is explained in Section 4.2.

rays of different frequencies are bent different amounts. Light energy of the shortest wavelengths (highest frequencies) is bent most forming the deep violet color seen at one end of the visible spectrum. Light energy of the longest wavelengths (lowest frequencies) is bent least forming the deep red color characteristic of the other end of the visible spectrum. Between these two extremes there is a gradual blending from one color to the next. It is possible to recognize six elementary colors: *red, orange, yellow, green, blue,* and *violet*. In general, incandescent solids and gases under high pressure give continuous spectra. Refer again to the top band in Figure 24-9.

The bright-line spectra of the elements were first described in Section 4.3.

Luminous (glowing) gases and vapors under low pressure give discontinuous spectra called *bright-line spectra*. These spectra consist of narrow lines of color that correspond to the light energy of certain wavelengths. The atoms of each element produce that element's own characteristic line spectra.

Electrons in atoms are restricted to energies of only certain values. In unexcited atoms, electrons occupy the lowest energy levels available to them. The energy of an electron can change only as it moves from one energy level to another. A certain amount of energy is absorbed with each jump to a higher energy level; a certain amount is released with each jump to a lower level. The quantity of energy in each change is equal to the difference between the separate energy levels involved.

When substances are vaporized in a flame, electrons are raised to higher energy levels by heat energy. When these electrons fall back into the lower energy levels available to them, energy is released. The energy released by any substance has wavelengths characteristic of that substance. Different wavelengths produce different spectral lines in the spectroscope. Thus, vaporized sodium atoms produce a spectrum consisting of two narrow yellow lines very close together (seen in the ordinary spectroscope as a single yellow line). Potassium atoms produce two red lines and a violet line. Lithium atoms yield intense red and yellow lines and weak blue and violet lines. The spectra produced by excited atoms of different elements are as distinct as fingerprints.

Bright lines in the visible portion of the spectrum account for the flame coloration produced by certain metals. The color seen is the combination of light energies of the different wavelengths emitted.

◖ SUMMARY

The elements of Group I in the periodic table are among the most chemically active metals. Group I elements do not exist as free elements in nature; they are found only in natural compounds as monopositive ions. The elements of Group I are referred to collectively as the Sodium Family and as the alkali metals.

Group I elements are characterized by a single outer-shell electron added to the preceding noble-gas structure. These elements have relatively low ionization energies. When the outer *s* electron is removed, each alkali-metal ion has the stable electron configuration of a noble gas.

Group I elements are soft, silvery-white metals that are good conductors of heat and electricity. Their structure is a lattice of metallic ions built around a body-centered cubic unit cell. The valence electrons form an electron "gas" that permeates the lattice structure.

The alkali metals form ionic compounds. When combined, they are usually in the +1 oxidation state, but the −1 oxidation state is also possible. Because of their activity, they must be stored in oil or kerosene. They react with water to release hydrogen and form metallic hydroxides that are strongly basic.

Sodium is used in making antiknock gasoline, dyes, and other organic compounds. It is an important reducing agent. Sodium is a heat-transfer agent in certain nuclear reactors. It is prepared by the electrolysis of fused sodium chloride in a Downs cell. Important compounds of sodium are found in nature in great abundance.

The Solvay process is a classic example of efficiency in chemical production. It is used commercially to produce sodium carbonate and sodium hydrogen carbonate. The raw materials are sodium chloride, limestone, and coal.

Potassium is abundant in nature in combined forms. The metal is recovered from potassium chloride by reduction with sodium. Potassium compounds are essential in plant fertilizers. A flame test is used to identify the element. Its common compounds are soluble in water.

Incandescent solids and gases under high pressure give continuous spectra. Luminous gases and vapors under low pressure give bright-line spectra. The atoms of each element produce characteristic bright-line spectra related to electron energy changes in the atoms.

VOCABULARY

alkali metal	continuous spectrum	incandescent	soda ash
baking soda	Downs cell	lye	Solvay process
bright-line spectrum	flame test	peroxide ion	spectroscope
caustic	halite	potash	superoxide ion

QUESTIONS

Group A

1. Describe the electron configuration of the atoms and ions of the elements in Group I.
2. Compare the methods of preparing sodium and potassium.
3. List three uses for metallic sodium.
4. Distinguish between the terms *caustic* and *corrosive*.
5. (*a*) What are the raw materials for the Solvay process? (*b*) What are the products and by-products?
6. (*a*) What is caustic soda? (*b*) washing soda? (*c*) baking soda?
7. Why do molasses and baking soda have a leavening action in cookies?
8. What are the sources of potassium compounds in the United States?
9. (*a*) How are sodium and potassium stored in the laboratory stockroom? (*b*) Why must they be stored in this fashion?
10. Write the ionic equation for the reaction of potassium and water.
11. Describe the flame tests for sodium and potassium.
12. Write three equations to show how sodium carbonate can be produced in the Solvay process.
13. Write three equations for the recovery of ammonia in the Solvay process.
14. (*a*) Describe the metallic crystal lattice of

the alkali metals. (*b*) Describe the unit cell upon which this lattice is built.

Group B

15. Why are the members of the Sodium Family soft, malleable metals with low melting points and low boiling points?
16. Why is NaCl necessary in the diet of many animals and people?
17. Why is sodium chloride used as a starting material for preparing metallic sodium and other compounds of sodium?
18. (*a*) Why are sodium compounds more frequently used than potassium compounds? (*b*) What are the purposes for which sodium compounds cannot be substituted for potassium compounds?
19. What by-product of the Solvay process has such limited use and yet is produced in such quantity that disposal of it is actually a problem to the manufacturers?
20. Why does table salt become sticky in damp weather, although pure sodium chloride is not deliquescent?
21. Explain why potassium has a lower density than sodium, although it consists of heavier atoms.
22. Write the equation for the net reaction that occurs when sodium hydroxide is exposed to the air.
23. In the Solvay process, why does the reaction between sodium chloride and ammonium hydrogen carbonate run to completion?
24. Why does a solution of sodium carbonate in water turn red litmus paper blue?
25. Suppose you had a tremendous quantity of acid that had to be neutralized and that NaOH, KOH, and LiOH were all available at the same price per pound. Which of these three would you use? Why?
26. A 0.1-M solution of $HC_2H_3O_2$ is found to have a pH of 2.9. A solution of 0.1-M $NaC_2H_3O_2$ is added to the acetic acid solution and the pH rises. Explain.

◀ | PROBLEMS

Group A

1. (*a*) How many grams of sulfuric acid in water solution can be neutralized by 10.0 g of sodium hydroxide? (*b*) 10.0 g of potassium hydroxide?
2. If you have 1.00 kg of sodium nitrate and 1.00 kg of potassium chloride, how many kilograms of potassium nitrate can you make by reacting these two substances, assuming that all the potassium nitrate can be recovered?
3. If $Na_2CO_3 \cdot 10H_2O$, crystallized sodium carbonate, sells for 12.5 cents per kilogram, what is anhydrous sodium carbonate worth per kilogram?
4. How many liters of carbon dioxide can be liberated from 50.0 g of each of the following? (*a*) Na_2CO_3; (*b*) $NaHCO_3$; (*c*) K_2CO_3; (*d*) $KHCO_3$.

Group B

5. How many kilograms of sodium chloride are required to produce 1.00 metric ton of anhydrous sodium carbonate?
6. How many cubic meters of carbon dioxide (at STP) are needed in Problem 5?
7. How many cubic meters of carbon dioxide gas must be produced at 150 °C and 745 mm pressure to supply that needed in Problem 6?
8. A load of limestone, analyzed as 92.0% $CaCO_3$, measured 2.72 metric tons. When decomposed by heat in a lime kiln, how many kilograms of calcium oxide are produced?
9. From the reaction of Problem 8, how many liters of carbon dioxide can be stored at 25 °C and 855 mm pressure?
10. A solution is prepared by dissolving 1.1 g NaOH in water and diluting to 50̄0 mL. What is the pH of the solution?

The Metals of Group II

Much of the world is given structure, form, and shape by compounds of calcium. In the organic world, the external skeletons of the crustaceans, the lobster and the crab, often contain calcium. Without such exoskeletons, these shellfish would be unprotected from the immense water pressures at the bottom of the sea. Land animals have internal skeletons that contain calcium. The hard, brittle texture of bone resists the unrelenting pull of gravity. The enormous frames of the giraffe and elephant are constructed from calcium-rich materials. The anatomy of humans starts with the bony foundation provided by apatite, a calcium compound. In the inorganic world, such geological formations as seashores, cliffs, atolls, and caves contain enormous deposits of calcium compounds. Human beings, nature's great imitators, also use calcium compounds as building materials: skyscrapers, roads, and even artworks are compounds of this important metal.

◻ 25.1 The Calcium Family

The elements of Group II of the periodic table are members of the Calcium Family. They are the metals beryllium, magnesium, calcium, strontium, barium, and radium. These elements are also called the *alkaline-earth metals*. Like the alkali metals, they are never found as the free element in nature. The metals must be recovered from their natural compounds. Many of their compounds are insoluble or slightly soluble and are found in the earth's crust. Their carbonates, phosphates, silicates, and sulfates are the most important deposits.

Beryllium and magnesium are commercially important light metals. In their chemical behavior, they resemble the corresponding alkali metals, lithium and sodium. Radium is important because it is radioactive. Radioactivity and other properties of radium are discussed in Chapter 31. The remaining three elements of Group II—calcium, strontium, and barium—have similar properties. They are considered to be typical members of the Calcium Family.

Each alkaline-earth element has two outer-shell electrons beyond the stable configuration of the preceding noble gas. All form doubly charged ions of the M^{++} type. Thus ions of the alkaline-earth metals have stable noble gas structures. Their chemistry, like that of the alkali metals of Group I, is generally uncomplicated.

The attraction between the metal ions and the electron "gas" of the alkaline-earth metal crystals is stronger than in the alkali metals. Therefore, the Calcium Family metals are denser, harder,

In this chapter you will gain an understanding of:

- **the physical and chemical properties of the Group II metals**
- **the major uses of Group II metals**
- **the important compounds of Group II metals**
- **soft water and hard water**
- **methods of softening hard water**

Early chemists used the term "earth" for nonmetallic substances, like the Group II metal oxides, that were practically insoluble in water and unchanged by strong heating. The Group II metal oxides give an "alkaline" reaction with water. Thus these metal oxides have historically been called "alkaline earths," and the metals "alkaline-earth metals."

Group II metals are harder and stronger than Group I metals.

Table 25-1
PROPERTIES OF GROUP II ELEMENTS

Element	Atomic number	Atomic weight	Electron configuration	Oxida-tion number	Melt-ing point (°C)	Boil-ing point (°C)	Density (g/cm³)	Atomic radius (Å)	Ionic radius (Å)
beryllium	4	9.01218	2,2	+2	1280	2970	1.85	0.89	0.35
magnesium	12	24.305	2,8,2	+2	649	1090	1.74	1.36	0.66
calcium	20	40.08	2,8,8,2	+2	839	1484	1.55	1.74	0.99
strontium	38	87.62	2,8,18,8,2	+2	769	1384	2.54	1.91	1.12
barium	56	137.33	2,8,18,18,8,2	+2	725	1640	3.5	1.98	1.34
radium	88	226.0254	2,8,18,32,18,8,2	+2	700	1140	5(?)	2.20	1.43

and have higher melting and boiling points than the corresponding Sodium Family metals.

The atoms and ions of the alkaline-earth metals are smaller than those of the corresponding alkali metals because of their higher nuclear charge. For example, the magnesium ion, Mg^{++}, has the same electron configuration as the sodium ion, Na^+. This configuration is $1s^2 2s^2 2p^6$. However, Mg^{++} has a nuclear charge of $+12$, while Na^+ has a nuclear charge of $+11$. The higher nuclear charge of the Mg^{++} ion attracts electrons more strongly and results in smaller K and L shells. Some properties of Group II metals are listed in Table 25-1.

In Section 24.2 you learned that ionization energies of Group I metals decrease down the group as atomic size increases. This same relationship is seen in Group II. The smaller atoms hold their outer electrons more securely than do the larger atoms.

Metallic character increases down the group.

Recall that ionization energy measures the tendency of an isolated atom to hold a valence electron. The *first* ionization energy relates to the removal of one electron from the neutral atom. The *second* ionization energy is that required to remove an electron from the ion with a $+1$ charge (the atom that has already had one valence electron removed). This second ionization energy is always higher than the first because the particle from which the electron is removed now has a positive charge.

If a third electron were to be removed from a Group II atom, it would come from the stable inner electron configuration (the noble gas structure) of the $+2$ ion. The predicted energy requirement would be much higher. In fact, the energies required for a third level of ionization of alkaline-earth elements are very high. They exceed the energies usually available in chemical reactions. Thus $+2$ ions of these elements are the only ones observed. The first, second, and third ionization energies of the Group II elements are listed in Table 25-2.

The alkaline-earth metals form hydrides, oxides or peroxides, and halides similar to those of the alkali metals. Almost all hy-

Figure 25-1. Fused pellets of beryllium. This metal produces alloys that are extremely elastic.

drides are ionic and contain H⁻ ions. An exception is BeH_2. Binary compounds of beryllium have fairly strong covalent bond character. They react with water to release hydrogen gas and form basic hydroxide solutions. Calcium hydride is often used as a laboratory source of hydrogen.

The oxides of beryllium, magnesium, and calcium have very high melting points. CaO and MgO are used as heat-resistant (refractory) materials. Beryllium oxide is amphoteric and both BeO and MgO are polymeric. All alkaline-earth oxides are more covalent than alkali-metal oxides. Strontium and barium form peroxides with oxygen, probably because of the large size of their ions.

The hydroxides are formed by adding water to the oxides. Except for $Be(OH)_2$, which is amphoteric, the hydroxides dissociate in water solution to yield OH⁻ ions. Hydroxides above barium are only slightly soluble in water, the solubility increasing with the metallic ion's size. Solutions of these hydroxides have low concentrations of OH⁻ ions; they are weakly basic because of the slight solubility in water.

❑ 25.2 Occurrence of magnesium

Magnesium compounds are widely distributed on land and in the sea. Magnesium sulfate is found in the earth's crust in many places. Important deposits occur in the state of Washington and in British Columbia, Canada. A double chloride of potassium and magnesium is mined from the salt deposits of Texas and New Mexico. See Figure 24-7. Sea water contains significant amounts of magnesium compounds. Talc and asbestos are silicates of magnesium. Their properties are related to their silicate structures.

Dolomite, $CaCO_3 \cdot MgCO_3$, is a double carbonate of magnesium and calcium that is found throughout the United States and Europe. It is an excellent building stone and is used for lining steel furnaces. Pulverized dolomite neutralizes soil acids and also supplies magnesium for plant growth.

Elemental magnesium, shown in Figure 25-2, was first prepared by Davy in 1808. This same series of experiments resulted in the isolation of sodium, calcium, and similar active metals.

❑ 25.3 Extraction of magnesium

Most commercial magnesium is produced by electrolytic reduction of molten magnesium chloride. The Mg^{++} ions may be obtained from sea water, brine, or minerals. Sea water is the most economical source.

About three kilograms of magnesium are recovered from each metric ton of sea water processed. The water is first treated with lime made from oyster shells, which are cheap and readily

Table 25-2
IONIZATION ENERGIES OF GROUP II ATOMS

Element	Ionization energy		
	First	Second	Third
		(kcal/mole)	
Be	215	42̄0	3549
Mg	176	347	1848
Ca	141	274	1174
Sr	13<u>1</u>	254	1005(?)
Ba	120	231	850(?)
Ra	122	234	—

Beryllium and its compounds are extremely toxic.

Amphoteric: acts either as an acid or a base.
Polymeric: characterized by repeating structural units.

MAGNESIUM

The inhalation of asbestos fibers is a cause of lung scarring and lung cancer.

Figure 25-2. Feathery crystals shown here are composed of magnesium, the eighth most abundant element.

available. This treatment causes magnesium ions to precipitate as magnesium hydroxide. The reactions are shown by the following equations.

$$CaO(s) + H_2O(l) \rightarrow Ca(OH)_2(s)$$

$$Ca(OH)_2(s) \rightleftharpoons Ca^{++}(aq) + 2OH^-(aq) \qquad K_{sp} = 5.5 \times 10^{-6}$$

$$Mg^{++}(aq) + 2OH^-(aq) \rightleftharpoons Mg(OH)_2(s) \qquad K_{sp} = 1.5 \times 10^{-11}$$

The two values for K_{sp} show that $Mg(OH)_2$ is less soluble than $Ca(OH)_2$. The precipitation of $Mg(OH)_2$ lowers the concentration of OH^- ions in equilibrium with $Ca(OH)_2$, and more $Ca(OH)_2$ dissolves.

Magnesium hydroxide is separated from the water by filtration. The addition of hydrochloric acid converts the magnesium hydroxide to magnesium chloride.

$$Mg(OH)_2 + 2HCl \rightarrow MgCl_2 + 2H_2O$$

Calcium chloride and sodium chloride are added to increase the conductivity and lower the melting point of the magnesium chloride. Magnesium metal is then recovered from the fused $MgCl_2$ by electrolysis.

$$Mg^{++} + 2Cl^- \rightarrow Mg(l) + Cl_2(g)$$

Chlorine gas collected at the anode is used to produce the hydrochloric acid required in the process. The Ca^{++} and Na^+ ions have higher reduction (electrode) potentials than Mg^{++} ions. Thus they are not reduced under the electrolysis conditions used. A flow diagram for this magnesium extraction process is shown in Figure 25-3.

Figure 25-3. Diagram of a plant for the production of magnesium from sea water.

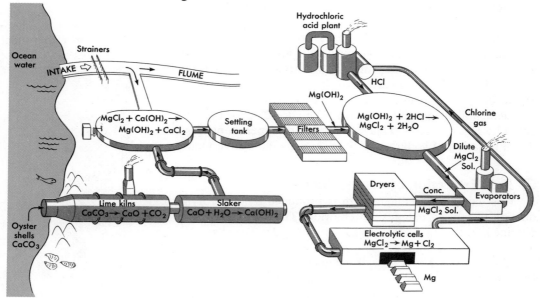

☐ 25.4 Properties of magnesium

Magnesium is a silver-white metal with a density of 1.74 g/cm^3. When heated it becomes ductile and malleable. Its tensile strength (resistance to being pulled apart) is not quite as great as that of aluminum.

Dry air does not affect magnesium. In moist air, however, a coating of basic magnesium carbonate forms on its surface. Because this coating is not porous, it protects the metal underneath from tarnishing. *A metal that forms a nonporous, nonscaling coat of tarnish is said to be a **self-protective metal.***

Aluminum and zinc are also self-protective metals; iron is not.

When heated in air to the kindling point, magnesium burns with an intensely hot flame and gives off a dazzling white light. See Figure 8-5. The combustion produces magnesium oxide, MgO, and magnesium nitride, Mg_3N_2. Once ignited, magnesium also burns in steam, in carbon dioxide, and in nitrogen. Magnesium is one of the few metals that combines directly with nitrogen. Boiling water reacts slowly with magnesium to form magnesium hydroxide and hydrogen. Common acids react with magnesium.

CAUTION: *looking directly at burning magnesium can seriously damage the eyes.*

☐ 25.5 Uses of magnesium

The brilliant white light of burning magnesium makes it useful for flares and fireworks. Magnesium forms light, strong alloys with aluminum. Examples are *magnalium* and *Dow metal.* Other alloying metals are lithium, thorium, zinc, and manganese. Magnesium alloys are used for making tools and fixtures, for the beams of chemical balances, and for auto and airplane parts.

Table 25-3
COMMON MAGNESIUM COMPOUNDS

Chemical name	Common name	Formula	Appearance	Uses
magnesium carbonate	(none)	$MgCO_3$	white, usually fluffy	for lining furnaces; in making the oxide
basic magnesium carbonate	magnesia alba	$Mg_4(OH)_2(CO_3)_3 \cdot 3H_2O$	soft, white powder	in tooth cleansers; for pipe coverings
magnesium chloride	(none)	$MgCl_2$	white, crystalline solid	with asbestos for stone flooring
magnesium hydroxide	milk of magnesia	$Mg(OH)_2$	white, milky suspension	as antacid; in laxatives
magnesium oxide	magnesia	MgO	white powder	as refractory; for lining furnaces
magnesium sulfate, heptahydrate	Epsom salts	$MgSO_4 \cdot 7H_2O$	white, crystalline solid	in laxatives, cathartics; in dye industry

CALCIUM

25.6 Preparation of calcium

Calcium ranks fifth in abundance by weight among the elements in the earth's crust, atmosphere, and surface waters. It is widely distributed in many rock and mineral forms. The best known of these mineral forms are the carbonate and the sulfate.

Since calcium occurs as combined Ca^{++} ions, the metal must be recovered by reduction. Electrolytic reduction involves fused calcium chloride.

$$Ca^{++} + 2Cl^- \rightarrow Ca + Cl_2(g)$$

Today chemical reduction is generally employed for recovering calcium. Calcium oxide is heated with aluminum in a vacuum retort.

$$3CaO + 2Al \rightarrow Al_2O_3 + 3Ca(g)$$

The reaction proceeds because the calcium metal is distilled off as a gas at the reaction temperature.

25.7 Properties of calcium

Metallic calcium is silver-white in color, but a freshly cut piece tarnishes to bluish-gray within a few hours. Calcium is somewhat harder than lead. The density of calcium is 1.55 g/cm^3. If a piece of calcium is added to water, it reacts with the water to slowly give off hydrogen gas.

$$Ca + 2H_2O \rightarrow Ca(OH)_2 + H_2(g)$$

The calcium hydroxide produced is only slightly soluble and coats the surface of the calcium. This coating protects the metal from rapid interaction with the water.

Calcium is a good reducing agent. It burns in oxygen with a bright, yellowish-red flame. It also unites directly with chlorine. Calcium salts yield a yellowish-red color in flame tests. See Figure 25-4.

Calcium is used in small amounts to reduce uranium tetrafluoride to uranium, and thorium dioxide to thorium.

$$UF_4 + 2Ca \rightarrow 2CaF_2 + U$$

$$ThO_2 + 2Ca \rightarrow 2CaO + Th$$

Calcium is an effective deoxidizer for iron, steel, and copper. Some alloy steels contain small quantities of calcium. Lead-calcium alloys are used for bearings in machines. Calcium is also used to harden lead for cables and storage-battery plates.

25.8 Calcium carbonate

Calcium carbonate, $CaCO_3$, is an abundant mineral found in many different forms.

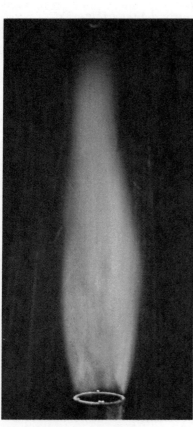

Figure 25-4. Calcium salts impart a yellowish-red color to the Bunsen flame. Sodium contamination often changes the color to orange-yellow. The flame color is greenish when viewed through cobalt-blue glass. The calcium flame color is masked by the yellowish-green flame of barium salts. A calcium flame test must be used with caution.

1. Limestone. This is the most common form of calcium carbonate. It was formed in past geologic ages by great pressures on layers of seashells. Limestone is found in layers as a *sedimentary rock.* Pure calcium carbonate is white or colorless when crystalline. Most deposits, however, are gray because of impurities.

Limestone is used for making glass, iron, and steel, and as a source of carbon dioxide. It is a building stone, and large quantities are used for building roads. Powdered or pulverized limestone is used to neutralize acid soils. Limestone is heated to produce calcium oxide, CaO, commonly called *lime.*

A mixture of limestone and clay is converted to *cement* by heating strongly in a rotary kiln. Some limestone deposits, called *natural cement,* contain clay and calcium carbonate naturally mixed in about the right proportions for making cement.

2. Calcite. The clear, crystalline form of calcium carbonate is known as calcite. See Figure 25-5. Transparent, colorless specimens are called *Iceland spar.*

3. Marble. This rock was originally limestone. Heat and pressure changed it into marble with a resulting increase in the size of the calcium carbonate crystals. Hence it is classed as a *metamorphic* (changed) *rock.* See Figure 25-6.

4. Shells. The shells of such animals as snails, clams, and oysters consist largely of calcium carbonate. In some places, large masses of such shells have become cemented together to form rock called *coquina* (koh-*kee*-nuh). It is used as a building stone. Tiny marine animals called *polyps* deposit limestone as they build *coral* reefs. *Chalk,* such as that of the chalk cliffs of England, consists of the microscopic shells of small marine animals. Blackboard "chalk" is made of claylike material mixed with calcium carbonate; it should not be confused with natural chalk.

5. Precipitated chalk. This form of calcium carbonate is made by the reaction of sodium carbonate with calcium chloride.

$$Na_2CO_3 + CaCl_2 \rightarrow CaCO_3(s) + 2NaCl$$

It is soft and finely divided, and thus forms a nongritty scouring powder suitable for toothpastes and tooth powders. Under the name of *whiting* it is used in paints to fill the pores in the wood. When it is ground with linseed oil it forms putty.

☐ 25.9 Hardness in water

Rainwater falling on the earth usually contains carbon dioxide in solution. As it soaks through the ground, it reaches deposits of limestone or dolomite. Some of the calcium carbonate and magnesium carbonate in these rocks reacts with

Figure 25-5. Calcite, a crystalline form of calcium carbonate.

Lime ranks second only to sulfuric acid in the amount produced in the United States. The 1979 production was about 17.6 million metric tons.

Figure 25-6. Marble is an excellent stone for the construction of buildings and monuments. Here it is shown being quarried in Vermont.

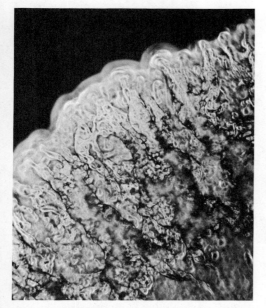

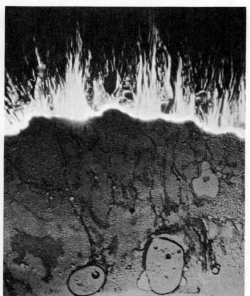

Figure 25-7. Photomicrographs of soap in the process of dissolving in hard water (top) and in soft water (bottom). In hard water the solution process is inhibited by a barrier of sticky soap curd; but in soft water, soap streamers extend into the water, forming a clear solution.

the CO_2 solution. This reaction produces the soluble hydrogen carbonates of these metals.

$$CaCO_3(s) + CO_2(aq) + H_2O(l) \rightarrow Ca^{++}(aq) + 2HCO_3^-(aq)$$

$$MgCO_3(s) + CO_2(aq) + H_2O(l) \rightarrow Mg^{++}(aq) + 2HCO_3^-(aq)$$

The ground water now contains Ca^{++}, Mg^{++}, and HCO_3^- ions in solution. It is said to be *"hard"* water. This term indicates that it is "hard" to get a lather when soap is added to the water. Water that lathers readily with soap is called *"soft"* water. The terms are not precise, but they are in common use. Deposits of iron and other heavy metals in the ground may also produce hard water.

Water hardness is of two types. *Temporary hardness* results from the presence of HCO_3^- ions along with the metal ions. *Permanent hardness* results when other negative ions (usually SO_4^{--}) more stable than the HCO_3^- ion are present along with the metal ions.

The main ingredient of ordinary soap is water-soluble sodium stearate, $NaC_{18}H_{35}O_2$. When soap is added to water containing Ca^{++} ions, the large $C_{18}H_{35}O_2^-$ ions react with the Ca^{++} ions. The reaction produces the insoluble stearate $Ca(C_{18}H_{35}O_2)_2$, which deposits as a gray scum.

$$Ca^{++} + 2C_{18}H_{35}O_2^- \rightarrow Ca(C_{18}H_{35}O_2)_2(s)$$

The metal ions in hard water continue to react with soap to form precipitates until all of the ions are removed. No lasting lather is produced up to this point. Soft water does not contain these ions and lathers easily when soap is added. See Figure 25-7.

◻ 25.10 Softening of hard water

Hard water is a nuisance in laundering. The sticky precipitate wastes soap and collects on the fibers of the garments being laundered. In bathing, the hard water does not lather freely, and the precipitate forms a scum on the bathtub. In steam boilers, temporary hard water containing HCO_3^- ions presents a still more serious problem. When this water is boiled, calcium carbonate collects as a hard scale inside the boiler and the steam pipes. It may form a thick crust, acting as a heat insulator and preventing efficient transfer of heat. Thus, for most purposes, hard water should be softened before it is used.

There are several practical methods of softening water. Generally, the nature of the hardness and the quantity of soft water required determine the best method.

1. Boiling (for temporary hardness). Hard water containing HCO_3^- ions can be softened by boiling. The metal ions precipitate as carbonates according to the following equation:

$$Ca^{++} + 2HCO_3^- \rightarrow CaCO_3(s) + H_2O + CO_2(g)$$

This reaction is reversible except for the fact that boiling drives off the CO_2.

2. Precipitation. When sodium carbonate, Na_2CO_3, is added to hard water, Ca^{++} and Mg^{++} ions precipitate as insoluble carbonates. The Na^+ ions added to the water cause no difficulties with soap.

$$Ca^{++} + CO_3^{--} \rightarrow CaCO_3(s)$$

$$Mg^{++} + CO_3^{--} \rightarrow MgCO_3(s)$$

The addition of a basic solution such as $NH_3(aq)$ or limewater to temporary hard water supplies OH^- ions. These ions neutralize the HCO_3^- ions and precipitate the "hard" metal ions as carbonates.

$$Ca^{++} + HCO_3^- + OH^- \rightarrow CaCO_3(s) + H_2O$$

$$Mg^{++} + HCO_3^- + OH^- \rightarrow MgCO_3(s) + H_2O$$

Other precipitating agents such as borax and sodium phosphate are sometimes used. Both produce basic solutions by hydrolysis, and the phosphate salts of calcium and magnesium are insoluble.

3. Ion exchange. Certain natural minerals called *zeolites* have porous, three-dimensional networks of silicate-aluminate groups. These networks are negatively charged. Mobile Na^+ ions are distributed throughout the porous network. If hard water is allowed to stand in contact with sodium zeolite, Na^+ ions are exchanged for the aqueous Ca^{++} and Mg^{++} ions. The process is an *ion exchange*. The zeolite is the *ion exchanger*.

$$Ca^{++}(aq) + 2Na \text{ zeolite} \rightleftarrows Ca(zeolite)_2 + 2Na^+(aq)$$

The reaction can be reversed and the Na zeolite regenerated by adding a concentrated sodium chloride solution to the $Ca(zeolite)_2$. This solution has a high concentration of Na^+ ions. The Ca^{++} ions are replaced by Na^+ ions according to the mass-action principle.

The law of mass action is explained in Section 20.13.

A synthetic zeolite known as *permutit* reacts more rapidly than natural zeolites. Permutit is used today in many household water softeners. Sodium chloride, the cheapest source of Na^+ ions, is used to renew the exchanger in these softeners.

Chemists have developed *ion-exchange resins* far superior to the zeolites. See Figure 25-8. One type of resin is called an *acid-exchange resin* or a *cation exchanger*. This type has large negatively charged organic units whose neutralizing ions in water are H_3O^+ ions. A second type of resin is the *base-exchange resin* or *anion exchanger*. These resins have large positively charged organic units whose neutralizing ions in water are OH^- ions.

Used together, the two types of ion-exchange resins can remove all positive and negative ions from water. The cation ex-

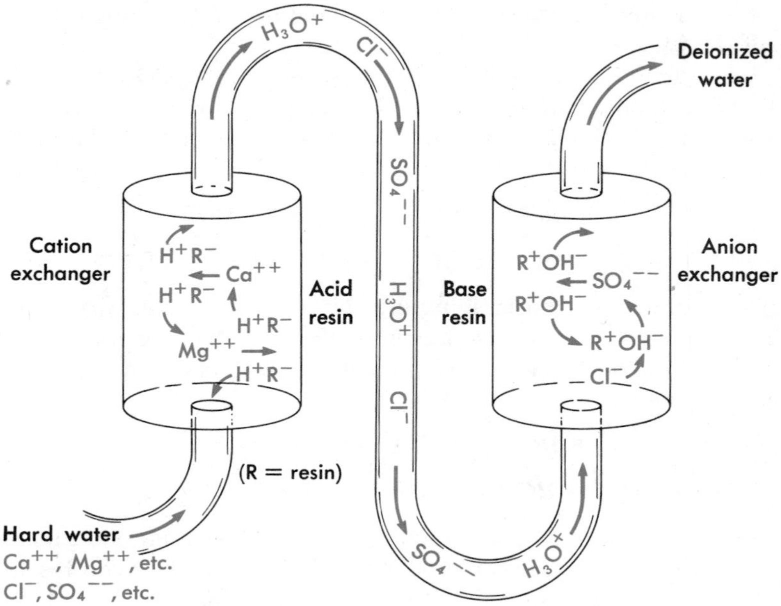

Figure 25-8. An ion-exchange system. All positive ions in the water are exchanged for hydronium ions in the acid resin. All negative ions are exchanged for hydroxide ions in the base resin. Water leaving the system is completely deionized.

changer removes metallic ions (cations) and replaces them with H_3O^+ ions. The water is then passed through the anion exchanger. Here, negative ions (anions) are removed and replaced by OH^- ions. The H_3O^+ and OH^- ions form water by neutralization.

Natural water or a water solution of salts treated by combinations of ion-exchange resins is made *ion-free*. (Only the small equilibrium quantities of H_3O^+ and OH^- ions remain.) This treated water is called *deionized* or *demineralized* water. Deionized water is now used in many processes that once required distilled water. Deionized water is as free of ions as the most carefully distilled water, although it may contain some dissolved carbon dioxide.

An acid-exchange resin can be renewed by running a strong acid through it. Similarly, a base-exchange resin can be renewed by using a basic solution.

Lime heated to incandescence gives off a brilliant white light— "limelight"—that once served as a theater spotlight.

☐ 25.11 Calcium oxide

Calcium oxide is a white, ionic solid commonly called *lime* or *quicklime*. It is *refractory* since it does not melt or vaporize below the temperature of the electric arc. It unites chemically with water to form calcium hydroxide.

$CaCO_3$: *limestone*
CaO: *lime or quicklime*
$Ca(OH)_2$: *slaked lime or hydrated lime*

$$CaO(s) + H_2O \rightarrow Ca(OH)_2(s) \quad \Delta H = -16 \text{ kcal}$$

During this process, called *slaking,* the mass swells and a large amount of heat is released. The reaction is strongly exothermic.

Because $Ca(OH)_2$ is prepared by this *slaking* process, its common name is *slaked lime.*

A lump of quicklime exposed to air gradually absorbs water. It swells, then cracks, and finally crumbles to a powder. It first forms calcium hydroxide, and then slowly unites with carbon dioxide from the air to form calcium carbonate. Thus a mixture of calcium hydroxide and calcium carbonate is formed. Such a mixture is valuable for treating acidic soils. However, lime that has been air slaked cannot be used to make mortar and plaster.

Calcium oxide is produced by heating calcium carbonate to a high temperature in a kiln, as shown in Figure 25-9.

$$CaCO_3(s) \rightarrow CaO(s) + CO_2(g)$$

A high concentration of carbon dioxide would drive the reaction in the reverse direction according to Le Chatelier's principle. Such an equilibrium is avoided by removing the carbon dioxide from the kiln as it forms.

*Historically, the thermal decomposition of calcium carbonate has been called **calcination**. The calcium carbonate is said to have been **calcined**.*

◻ 25.12 Calcium hydroxide

Calcium hydroxide, or *slaked lime,* is a white solid that is sparingly soluble in water. Its water solution, called *limewater,* has basic properties. A suspension of calcium hydroxide in water is known as milk of lime. Mixed with flour paste or glue, it makes whitewash.

Calcium hydroxide is the cheapest hydroxide. It is used to remove hair from hides before they are tanned or made into leather. It is useful for treating soils, for freeing ammonia from ammonium compounds, for softening temporary hard water, and for making mortar and plaster.

Lime mortar consists of slaked lime, sand, and water. Mortar of this type has been used for many centuries. The mortar first hardens as water evaporates. Crystals of $Ca(OH)_2$ form and cement the grains of sand together. On exposure to air, the mortar continues to get harder. The calcium hydroxide is slowly converted to the carbonate by action of atmospheric carbon dioxide.

$$Ca(OH)_2 + CO_2 \rightarrow CaCO_3 + H_2O$$

◻ 25.13 Calcium sulfate

Calcium sulfate occurs as the mineral *gypsum,* a dihydrate $CaSO_4 \cdot 2H_2O$. When gypsum is heated gently, it partially dehydrates to form a white powder known as *plaster of paris.* The equation is

$$2CaSO_4 \cdot 2H_2O(s) \rightarrow (CaSO_4)_2 \cdot H_2O(s) + 3H_2O(g)$$

gypsum   **plaster of paris**

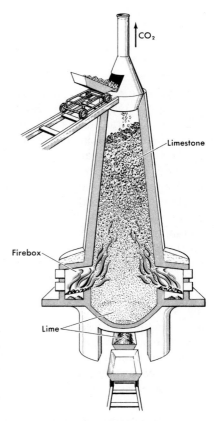

Figure 25-9. Calcination: An ancient process used by alchemists and still used today to convert limestone, $CaCO_3$, into lime, CaO.

The formula for plaster of paris, $(CaSO_4)_2 \cdot H_2O$, is equivalent to $CaSO_4 \cdot \frac{1}{2}H_2O$, as it is sometimes written.

When plaster of paris is mixed with water, it hydrates back to the gypsum structure. The reaction is the reverse of the equation given above.

$$(CaSO_4)_2 \cdot H_2O + 3H_2O \rightarrow 2CaSO_4 \cdot 2H_2O$$

A thin paste (or slurry) of plaster of paris and water sets quickly and expands slightly. It forms a solid mass of interlacing crystals of gypsum. Because of the slight expansion, it gives remarkably faithful reproductions when cast in molds. The plaster of paris slurries are suited for making wallboard and rocklath, surgical casts, pottery molds, statuary, and numerous other uses.

SUMMARY

The elements of Group II are the metals beryllium, magnesium, calcium, strontium, barium, and radium. They are known as the alkaline-earth metals and as the Calcium Family of elements. They are not found as the free elements in nature. The metals of Group II are recovered from their natural compounds.

The alkaline-earth metals are characterized by two outer-shell electrons added to the preceding noble-gas structure. Their ions have the electron configurations of the preceding noble gases. The metals are denser, harder, and have higher melting points than the corresponding members of the alkali metals of Group I. Bonding shows some covalency. The chemistry of the elements of Group II, like that of the Group I elements, is uncomplicated.

Magnesium is recovered mainly by electrolysis of its chloride. Sea water is the most economical source of magnesium. Magnesium is a light, self-protective metal. It is used structurally when alloyed with other metals and, because it burns with a brilliant white light, for flares and fireworks. Soluble magnesium compounds contribute to the "hardness" of water.

Calcium is a low density and relatively hard metal. It is a good reducing agent. It reacts with water slowly and burns in oxygen with a yellow-red flame. Calcium is widely distributed in the earth's crust as insoluble compounds, mainly as carbonates and sulfates. It is recovered by electrolytic reduction from its chloride and by chemical reduction with aluminum.

Ground water usually contains Ca^{++} ions contributed by soluble and slightly soluble calcium compounds. Water containing certain minerals in solution, mainly the hydrogen carbonates and sulfates of calcium and magnesium, is called hard water. The presence of these substances interferes with the use of water in laundering and in steam boilers and steam pipes. Water may be softened by the removal of the hardening agents. Hard water is softened by boiling, precipitation, and ion-exchange methods.

The oxide, hydroxide, carbonate, and sulfate of calcium are important industrial substances. Calcium oxide is produced by heating calcium carbonate. Calcium hydroxide is formed by reacting calcium oxide with water. Calcium sulfate is mined mainly as the mineral gypsum.

◀ VOCABULARY

alkaline-earth metals	Iceland spar	quicklime
calcination	ion exchange	refractory
calcite	lime	self-protective metal
cement	limestone	slaked lime
chalk	marble	slaking
deionized water	permanent hardness	soft water
dolomite	permutit	temporary hardness
gypsum	plaster of paris	zeolite
hard water	precipitated chalk	

◀ QUESTIONS

Group A

1. (a) Write the equation for the production of quicklime from limestone. (b) How is an equilibrium avoided in this process?
2. (a) What is dolomite? (b) For what purposes is it used?
3. Since magnesium is an active metal, why do objects made from it not corrode rapidly as does iron?
4. Compare the preparation of elemental calcium with that of elemental sodium.
5. What are the important uses of metallic calcium?
6. In what forms is calcium carbonate found in nature?
7. (a) What does the term *hard water* mean? (b) What does the term *soft water* mean? (c) What is the difference between temporary and permanent hardness of water?
8. What principle is employed to regenerate a zeolite water softener?
9. Distinguish (a) limestone; (b) quicklime; (c) slaked lime; (d) lime; (e) hydrated lime.
10. For what gas is limewater used as a test solution?
11. How could you demonstrate that a piece of coral is a carbonate?
12. Write an empirical equation to show the action of water containing dissolved carbon dioxide on limestone.
13. How is cement manufactured from clay and limestone?

Group B

14. Write three balanced equations to show the steps in the preparation of magnesium from sea water.
15. How do beryllium compounds differ from those of the other Group II elements?
16. Why are the members of the Calcium Family denser and harder than the corresponding members of the Sodium Family?
17. (a) Write the equation for the slaking of lime. (b) Give a reason for the reaction going to completion.
18. Give two reasons why the reaction of calcium with water is not as vigorous as that of potassium with water.
19. (a) What metallic ions cause water to be hard? (b) What negative ion causes temporary hardness? (c) What negative ion causes permanent hardness?
20. What type of chemical reaction occurs between soap and hard water?
21. Write an empirical equation to show the softening action of sodium carbonate on hard water containing (a) calcium sulfate; (b) magnesium hydrogen carbonate.
22. (a) How is plaster of paris made? (b) Why does it harden?
23. (a) What impurity may still remain in water that has been passed through both an acid exchange resin and a base exchange resin? (b) For what kind of solutions would such water be unsuited?

24. How can you account for the fact that temporary hard water, containing Ca^{++} ions, is softened by the addition of limewater, a solution containing Ca^{++} ions and OH^- ions?

◀ | PROBLEMS

Group A

1. How many kilograms of calcium oxide can be produced from 1.000 metric ton of limestone that contains 12.5% of impurities?
2. How much mass will 86.0 kg of gypsum lose when it is converted into plaster of paris?
3. Calculate the percentage of beryllium in beryl, $Be_3Al_2Si_6O_{18}$.
4. What quantity of magnesium can be prepared from a metric ton of magnesium oxide, MgO?
5. A cubic kilometer of sea water contains in solution enough minerals to form about 4.0×10^6 kg of magnesium chloride. How much metallic magnesium could be obtained from this volume of sea water?
6. How many liters of hydrogen at STP can be prepared by reacting 8.10 g of magnesium with excess dilute hydrochloric acid?

Group B

7. If dolomite is 95.0% a double carbonate of calcium and magnesium, together with 5.0% of impurities such as iron and silica, what is the percentage of magnesium in the sample? (Compute to 3 significant figures.)
8. How many kilograms of carbon dioxide can be obtained from a metric ton of oyster shells that are 81.0% calcium carbonate?
9. How many liters will the carbon dioxide produced in Problem 7 occupy at STP?
10. If the carbon dioxide of Problem 8 is measured at $72\overline{0}$ mm pressure and $2\overline{0}°C$, what volume does it occupy?
11. The thermal decomposition of a charge of limestone produced $50\overline{0} \ m^3$ of carbon dioxide when stored at 28 °C and $95\overline{0}$ mm pressure. How many moles of the gas was this?

The Transition Metals

For human beings long ago, survival was a constant struggle. They lived in caves, foraged for food in uncultivated forests, and hunted animals with primitive weapons made from stone. These Stone Age cave dwellers had little control over their environment. Tools to build habitations, cultivate land, and slaughter animals for food had to await the discovery of a material stronger and more durable than stone. About 5000 years ago an amazing discovery changed the lot of these early people. Copper, which exists in a free state with tin as an impurity, could be worked to form solid implements. This Bronze Age lasted more than 2000 years. Then another technological revolution occurred—the extraction of iron from ores. Here was a metal that had the malleability and the durability of copper, and far greater strength. Iron is still one of civilization's most important metals, and the Iron Age that started 3000 years ago still continues.

◻ 26.1 General properties

The periodic table on pages 96–97 has short periods (or series) through the third row of elements. The fourth and succeeding rows are long periods. Beginning with Period 4, ten subgroups of elements intervene between Group II and Group III. These elements occupy the *transition region* of the periodic table. They are called the *transition elements* because, with increasing atomic number, there is an increase in the number of electrons in the next-to-outermost shell. This inner building of electronic structure may be considered an interruption, between Group II and Group III, of the regular increase of outer-shell electrons from Group I to Group VIII across a period. See Figure 26-1.

The properties of the elements remain similar going down each main group. However, the properties change steadily from metallic to nonmetallic going horizontally across a short period from Group I to Group VII. In the transition region, horizontal similarities may be as great, or in some cases even greater, than similarities going down a subgroup.

All transition elements are metals. The metallic character is related to the presence of no more than one or two electrons in the outermost shells of their atoms. These metals are generally harder and more brittle than the Group I and Group II metals. Their melting points are higher. Mercury (at. no. 80) is a familiar exception. It is the only metal that is liquid at room temperature. The transition metals are good conductors of heat and electricity. Such conduction is characteristic of a metallic crystal lattice permeated by an electron gas.

In this chapter you will gain an understanding of:

- **the general unique properties of the transition elements**
- **the structural characteristics responsible for the unique nature of the transition elements**
- **the members of the Iron Family**
- **iron and steel production**
- **the members of the Copper Family**
- **the natural occurrence, general refining methods, and compounds of iron and copper**

Periodic table: periods are horizontal rows; groups are vertical columns.

In very hot weather, mercury may lose this distinction since gallium (at. no. 31) and cesium (at. no. 55) have melting points of 29.8 °C and 28.4 °C, respectively.

TRANSITION ELEMENTS

	II	Sc subgroup											III
3	24.305 **Mg** 12												26.9815 **Al** 13
4	40.08 **Ca** 20	44.9559 **Sc** 21	47.90 **Ti** 22	50.9414 **V** 23	51.996 **Cr** 24	54.9380 **Mn** 25	55.847 **Fe** 26	58.9332 **Co** 27	58.71 **Ni** 28	63.546 **Cu** 29	65.37 **Zn** 30		69.72 **Ga** 31
5	87.62 **Sr** 38	88.9059 **Y** 39	91.22 **Zr** 40	92.9064 **Nb** 41	95.94 **Mo** 42	98.9062 **Tc** 43	101.07 **Ru** 44	102.9055 **Rh** 45	106.4 **Pd** 46	107.868 **Ag** 47	112.40 **Cd** 48		114.82 **In** 49
6	137.34 **Ba** 56	Lanthanide Series / 174.97 **Lu** 71	178.49 **Hf** 72	180.9479 **Ta** 73	183.85 **W** 74	186.2 **Re** 75	190.2 **Os** 76	192.22 **Ir** 77	195.09 **Pt** 78	196.9665 **Au** 79	200.59 **Hg** 80		204.37 **Tl** 81
7	226.0254 **Ra** 88	Actinide Series / [257] **Lr** 103	[261] **Unq** 104	[260] **Unp** 105	[263] **Unh** 106	[261] **Uns** 107							

Figure 26-1. Transition metals are characterized by the buildup of the *d* sublevel in the next-to-outermost shell.

Figure 26-2. These potato-size nodules on the Pacific Ocean floor between Mexico and Hawaii contain nickel, copper, cobalt, and manganese. Preparations are being made for mining the nodules which are a new source of these strategic transition metals.

The chemical properties of transition elements are varied. Electrons of the next-to-outermost *d* sublevel as well as those of the outer shell may become involved in the formation of some compounds. Most transition metals exhibit variable oxidation states in forming compounds, and most of their compounds have color. They have a pronounced tendency to form complex ions. Many of their compounds are attracted into a magnetic field (a property called paramagnetism).

◻ 26.2 Transition subgroups

The electron configuration of each transition element is shown in Figure 26-1. Compare the electron configurations of the Group II metals with the corresponding metals of the first transition subgroup, the scandium (Sc) subgroup. What differences do you observe? Now compare the electron configurations across the first-row transition metals. Note the generally regular pattern of change in electron configuration with increasing atomic number. Notice also whether irregularities appear in the pattern.

The stepwise buildup of the electron configuration across the first-row transition metals results in the $3d$ sublevel being filled with 10 electrons. Following this $3d$ filling, the regular increase in $4p$ electrons occurs in Group III through Group VIII.

There are minor irregularities in the $3d$ electron buildup at Cr (at. no. 24) and at Cu (at. no. 29). The electron configuration for chromium is $\text{-----}3d^5 4s^1$ instead of $\text{-----}3d^4 4s^2$ as might have been predicted. That for copper is $\text{-----}3d^{10} 4s^1$ instead of the $\text{-----}3d^9 4s^2$ that might have been expected. These apparent irregularities are attributed to the extra stability associated with half-filled and completely filled sublevels.

In the fifth period following strontium ($-----4s^2 4p^6 5s^2$) there is a similar filling of the $4d$ sublevel before the buildup of the $5p$ sublevel occurs to complete the period. In the sixth period following barium ($-----4s^2 4p^6 4d^{10} 5s^2 5p^6 6s^2$) the filling of the $5d$ sublevel is interrupted by the buildup of the $4f$ sublevel. These two expansions greatly complicate this period. There are seven $4f$ orbitals that can accomodate 14 electrons. In the *lanthanide series* of elements, the number of $4f$ electrons increases with atomic number.

The stability of half-filled and completely filled sublevels is first mentioned in Section 4.7.

In the seventh period, the $6d$ sublevel filling is similarly interrupted by the buildup of the $5f$ sublevel characteristic of the *actinide series* of elements. The placement of lawrencium (at. no. 103) in the scandium subgroup marks the resumption of the $6d$ buildup. Unnilquadium, unnilpentium, unnilhexium, and unnilseptium in the titanium, vanadium, chromium, and manganese subgroups, respectively, indicate a continuation of this $6d$ buildup of electrons.

The lanthanide and actinide series of elements are described in Section 5.5.

The transition elements occupy the long periods in the periodic table. The choice of the first and last elements in the series depends somewhat on the definition used. Based on d and s electron configurations, the transition elements are considered to consist of the ten subgroups between Group II and Group III. The first-row transition elements are the most important and they are the most abundant. Their electron configurations are shown in Table 26-1.

◻ 26.3 Oxidation states

Variable oxidation states are common among the transition metals. Some form different compounds in which they exhibit several oxidation states. The energies of the outermost d and s electrons do not differ greatly. The energies to remove these electrons are relatively low.

Table 26-1
ELECTRON CONFIGURATIONS OF FIRST-ROW TRANSITION ELEMENTS

Name	Symbol	Atomic number	Number of electrons in sublevels						
			1s	2s	2p	3s	3p	3d	4s
scandium	Sc	21	2	2	6	2	6	1	2
titanium	Ti	22	2	2	6	2	6	2	2
vanadium	V	23	2	2	6	2	6	3	2
chromium	Cr	24	2	2	6	2	6	5	1
manganese	Mn	25	2	2	6	2	6	5	2
iron	Fe	26	2	2	6	2	6	6	2
cobalt	Co	27	2	2	6	2	6	7	2
nickel	Ni	28	2	2	6	2	6	8	2
copper	Cu	29	2	2	6	2	6	10	1
zinc	Zn	30	2	2	6	2	6	10	2

The d sublevel has five available orbitals that can hold ten electrons when all are filled. The s sublevel has one orbital and it can hold two electrons. Electrons occupy the d orbitals singly as long as unoccupied orbitals of similar energy exist. The s electrons and one or more d electrons can be used in bonding.

In the first-row transition metals, several $4s$ and $3d$ electrons may be transferred to or shared with other substances. Thus several oxidation states become possible. Remember that the maximum oxidation state is limited by the total number of $4s$ and $3d$ electrons present.

Table 26-2 gives the common oxidation states and $3d$ and $4s$ electron configurations of these metals. This table uses orbital notations introduced in Section 4.6. In these notations ___ represents an unoccupied orbital. The symbol _↑ represents an orbital occupied by one electron, and ↓↑ represents an orbital with an electron pair.

Observe that the maximum oxidation state increases to +7 for manganese and then decreases abruptly beyond manganese. The difficulty of forming the higher oxidation states increases toward the end of the row. This increase in difficulty is caused by the general increase in ionization energy with atomic number. The higher oxidation states generally involve covalent bonding.

Manganese atoms lose two $4s$ electrons to become Mn^{++} ions. Higher oxidation states involve one or more of the $3d$ electrons. In the permanganate ion, MnO_4^-, manganese is in the +7 oxidation state, covalently bonded with the oxygen atoms.

Table 26-2
OXIDATION STATES OF FIRST-ROW TRANSITION ELEMENTS

Element	Electron configuration $1s^2 2s^2 2p^6 3s^2 3p^6$	3d	4s	Common oxidation states
scandium	Each transition	↑ __ __ __ __	↓↑	+3
titanium	element has all	↑ ↑ __ __ __	↓↑	+2 +3 +4
vanadium	of these	↑ ↑ ↑ __ __	↓↑	+2 +3 +4 +5
chromium	sublevels filled	↑ ↑ ↑ ↑ ↑	↑	+2 +3 +6
manganese	in an argon	↑ ↑ ↑ ↑ ↑	↓↑	+2 +3 +4 +6 +7
iron	structure	↓↑ ↑ ↑ ↑ ↑	↓↑	+2 +3
cobalt		↓↑ ↓↑ ↑ ↑ ↑	↓↑	+2 +3
nickel		↓↑ ↓↑ ↓↑ ↑ ↑	↓↑	+2 +3
copper		↓↑ ↓↑ ↓↑ ↓↑ ↓↑	↑	+1 +2
zinc		↓↑ ↓↑ ↓↑ ↓↑ ↓↑	↓↑	+2

When the electron configuration includes both $3d$ and $4s$ valence electrons, the $3d$ electrons are lower in energy than the $4s$ electrons. Thus the first electron removed in an ionizing reaction is the one most loosely held, a $4s$ electron. This fact is illustrated by the step-by-step ionization of titanium. The ground-state configurations of the valence electrons are as follows:

$$
\begin{array}{ll}
\text{Ti} & 3d^2 4s^2 \\
\text{Ti}^+ & 3d^2 4s^1 \\
\text{Ti}^{++} & 3d^2 4s^0 \\
\text{Ti}^{+++} & 3d^1 \\
\text{Ti}^{++++} & 3d^0
\end{array}
$$

◻ 26.4 Color

A striking property of many compounds of transition metals is their color. Not all compounds formed with transition metals are colored. On the other hand, most colored inorganic compounds involve elements of the transition region of the periodic table. See Figure 26-3. The color of the compounds and their solutions may vary depending on what other ions or polyatomic groups are associated with the transition element. The colors of compounds of several first-row transition metals are listed in Table 26-3. In general, these colored compounds are thought to have some electrons that are easily excited by selectively absorbing part of the energy of white light.

The continuous spectrum of Figure 24-9 shows that white light is composed of red, orange, yellow, green, blue, and violet colors of light. If light energy of a discrete band of wavelengths corresponding to a color region is absorbed by a substance, the remaining light reflected or transmitted is no longer white. It is the *complement* of the color removed. The color of the substance that is seen is the complement of the color of light absorbed. *The energies of the wavelengths of white light that*

Complementary colors are two colors that yield white light when combined. Examples of complementary colors are blue—yellow, red—bluish-green, and green—magenta.

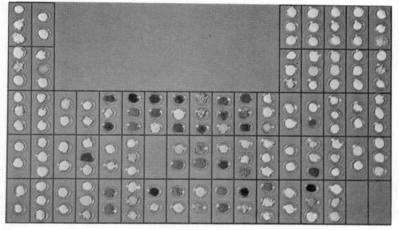

Figure 26-3. Most compounds of transition metals are colored. The color depends on the metal, its oxidation state, and the anion with which it is combined.

Table 26-3
COLORS OF COMPOUNDS OF TRANSITION METALS

Compound	Formula	Color
titanium(III) chloride	$TiCl_3$	violet
titanium(III) sulfate	$Ti_2(SO_4)_3$	green
titanium(IV) chloride	$TiCl_4$	yellow
vanadium(II) chloride	VCl_2	green
vanadium(II) sulfate, heptahydrate	$VSO_4 \cdot 7H_2O$	violet
vanadium(III) chloride	VCl_3	pink
vanadium(IV) chloride	VCl_4	violet
chromium(II) acetate	$Cr(C_2H_3O_2)_2$	red
chromium(II) sulfate, heptahydrate	$CrSO_4 \cdot 7H_2O$	blue
chromium(III) chloride	$CrCl_3$	violet
manganese(II) chloride	$MnCl_2$	pink
manganese(III) sulfate	$Mn_2(SO_4)_3$	green
manganese(IV) oxide	MnO_2	black
iron(II) chloride, dihydrate	$FeCl_2 \cdot 2H_2O$	green
iron(II) sulfate, heptahydrate	$FeSO_4 \cdot 7H_2O$	blue-green
iron(III) chloride, hexahydrate	$FeCl_3 \cdot 6H_2O$	brown-yellow
iron(III) sulfate	$Fe_2(SO_4)_3$	yellow
iron(III) thiocyanate	$Fe(SCN)_3$	red
cobalt(II) chloride, hexahydrate	$CoCl_2 \cdot 6H_2O$	red
cobalt(II) nitrate, hexahydrate	$Co(NO_3)_2 \cdot 6H_2O$	red
cobalt(II) sulfate, heptahydrate	$CoSO_4 \cdot 7H_2O$	pink
cobalt(III) sulfate	$Co_2(SO_4)_3$	blue-green
nickel(II) hydroxide	$Ni(OH)_2$	green
nickel(II) nitrate, hexahydrate	$Ni(NO_3)_2 \cdot 6H_2O$	green
nickel(II) sulfate	$NiSO_4$	yellow
copper(I) carbonate	Cu_2CO_3	yellow
copper(I) oxide	Cu_2O	red
copper(II) oxide	CuO	black
copper(II) nitrate, hexahydrate	$Cu(NO_3)_2 \cdot 6H_2O$	blue
copper(II) sulfate, pentahydrate	$CuSO_4 \cdot 5H_2O$	blue

In the $CuSO_4 \cdot 5H_2O$ crystal, four water molecules are close to the copper(II) ion. The fifth is more distant.

are absorbed giving these compounds color are the energies required to raise *d* electrons to higher energy states.

Copper(II) sulfate pentahydrate crystals are blue when viewed in white light. Their aqueous solutions are also blue. They are blue because energy of wavelengths corresponding to *yellow light* is absorbed. The light reflected (or transmitted) is *blue light,* the complement of yellow light. When these crystals are heated, the water of hydration is given up and the anhydrous salt is neither blue nor crystalline. It is a white powder. If water is added to the anhydrous powder, it turns blue. Since many sulfate compounds are colorless, it must be the *hydrated* copper(II) ion, $Cu(H_2O)_4^{++}$, that is blue.

☐ 26.5 The formation of complex ions

The NO_3^- ion, SO_4^{--} ion, and the NH_4^+ ion are examples of *polyatomic ions*. They are charged particles made up of more than a single atom. These familiar ions are covalent structures. Their net ionic charge is the algebraic sum of the oxidation numbers of all the atoms present. Because of their small size and their stability, they behave just like single-atom ions. They go through many chemical reactions unchanged.

Polyatomic ions are described in Section 6.23.

The name *complex ion* is ordinarily restricted to an ionic species composed of a central metal ion combined with a specific number of polar molecules or ions. The charge on the complex ion is the sum of the charge on the central ion and that of all the attached units. Complex ions vary in stability, but none is as stable as the common polyatomic ions mentioned above.

The most common complex ions are formed by ions of the transition metals with chemical species such as chloride ions (Cl^-), ammonia molecules (NH_3), water molecules (H_2O), and cyanide ions (CN^-). The transition cation is always the central ion upon which the complex is formed. The number of units covalently bonded to, or *coordinated* with, the central ion is its *coordination number* for that complex ion. The Fe^{++} ion in the $Fe(CN)_6^{----}$ complex shown in Figure 26-4 has a coordination number of 6.

The hydrated Cu^{++} ion, $Cu(H_2O)_4^{++}$, discussed in Section 26.4, is a complex ion. The Cu^{++} ion is coordinated with 4 molecules of water of crystallization. It is the ionic species that crystallizes from an aqueous sulfate solution as the compound $CuSO_4 \cdot 5H_2O$.

When an excess of concentrated ammonia-water solution is added to an aqueous solution of Cu^{++} ions (a $CuSO_4$ solution, for example), the light-blue color of the solution changes to a deep-blue color. The soluble $Cu(NH_3)_4^{++}$ complex has been formed.

$$Cu(H_2O)_4^{++} + 4NH_3\,(aq) \rightarrow Cu(NH_3)_4^{++} + 4H_2O$$

light blue   **deep blue**

Zinc and cadmium form similar complex ions with ammonia. Table 26-4 gives some typical complex ions formed by transition metals.

If the ammonia-water solution is added to a solution of silver nitrate, the complex $Ag(NH_3)_2^+$ ion is formed.

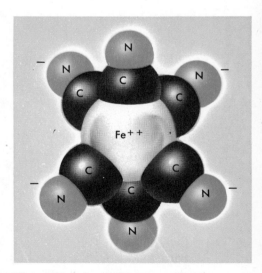

Figure 26-4. A possible space model of a complex ion, the hexacyanoferrate(II) ion, $Fe(CN)_6^{----}$. It is sometimes called the ferrocyanide ion.

Table 26-4
SOME COMMON COMPLEX IONS

Coordinating atom	Coordinating group	Complex ions	Color
N	H :N:H H	$Ag(NH_3)_2^+$ $Ni(NH_3)_4^{++}$ $Co(NH_3)_6^{+++}$	— blue blue
C	:C:::N:⁻	$Fe(CN)_6^{----}$ $Fe(CN)_6^{---}$	yellow red
S	:O: :S:S:O:⁻⁻ :O:	$Ag(S_2O_3)_2^{---}$	—
N	:S::C::N:⁻	$FeSCN^{++}$	red

Brackets are used in this expression simply to enclose the electron-dot formula and indicate that the +1 charge applies to the ion as a whole. They do not indicate a concentration expression.

$$Ag^+ + 2NH_3 \rightarrow Ag(NH_3)_2^+$$

$$Ag^+ + 2\,\begin{matrix}H\\:N:H\\H\end{matrix} \rightarrow \left[\begin{matrix}H & & H\\H:N: & Ag & :N:H\\H & & H\end{matrix}\right]^+$$

Because complex ions are unstable to some extent, the reaction is reversible. The more stable the complex ion, the more quickly equilibrium is established between the reactions involving the formation and dissociation of the complex ions. At equilibrium the equation is

$$Ag(NH_3)_2^+ \rightleftarrows Ag^+ + 2NH_3$$

Equilibrium constant: see Section 21.3.

The equilibrium constant has the usual form.

$$K = \frac{[Ag^+][NH_3]^2}{[Ag(NH_3)_2^+]} = 7 \times 10^{-8}$$

In cases of complex-ion equilibria, the equilibrium constant is called an *instability* constant. The *larger* the value of K, the more unstable is the complex ion.

When metallic ions in solution form complexes, they are, in effect, removed from the solution as simple ions. Thus the formation of complex ions increases the solubility of metallic ions. The solubility of a precipitate may also be increased if cations of the substance form complex ions. For example, the formation of chloride complexes may *increase* solubility where, by common ion effect, a *decrease* would be expected.

Common ion effect: see Section 21.6.

Consider the equilibrium of sparingly soluble AgCl.

$$AgCl(s) \rightleftarrows Ag^+(aq) + Cl^-(aq)$$

A small addition of Cl^- ions *does* shift the equilibrium to the left and lower the solubility as expected. However, if a large

Table 26-5
STABILITY OF COMPLEX IONS

Complex ion	Equilibrium reaction	K
$Ag(NH_3)_2^+$	$Ag(NH_3)_2^+ \rightleftharpoons Ag^+ + 2NH_3$	7×10^{-8}
$Co(NH_3)_6^{++}$	$Co(NH_3)_6^{++} \rightleftharpoons Co^{++} + 6NH_3$	1×10^{-5}
$Co(NH_3)_6^{+++}$	$Co(NH_3)_6^{+++} \rightleftharpoons Co^{+++} + 6NH_3$	2×10^{-34}
$Cu(NH_3)_4^{++}$	$Cu(NH_3)_4^{++} \rightleftharpoons Cu^{++} + 4NH_3$	3×10^{-13}
$Ag(CN)_2^-$	$Ag(CN)_2^- \rightleftharpoons Ag^+ + 2CN^-$	2×10^{-19}
$Au(CN)_2^-$	$Au(CN)_2^- \rightleftharpoons Au^+ + 2CN^-$	5×10^{-39}
$Cu(CN)_3^{--}$	$Cu(CN)_3^{--} \rightleftharpoons Cu^+ + 3CN^-$	1×10^{-35}
$Fe(CN)_6^{----}$	$Fe(CN)_6^{----} \rightleftharpoons Fe^{++} + 6CN^-$	1×10^{-35}
$Fe(CN)_6^{---}$	$Fe(CN)_6^{---} \rightleftharpoons Fe^{+++} + 6CN^-$	1×10^{-42}
$FeSCN^{++}$	$FeSCN^{++} \rightleftharpoons Fe^{+++} + SCN^-$	8×10^{-3}
$Ag(S_2O_3)_2^{---}$	$Ag(S_2O_3)_2^{---} \rightleftharpoons Ag^+ + 2S_2O_3^{--}$	6×10^{-14}

concentration of Cl^- ions is added, *the solid AgCl dissolves.* This apparent contradiction is explained by the formation of $AgCl_2^-$ complex ions.

The stability of complex ions is indicated by the small values of the equilibrium constants, *K*. See Table 26-5. The smaller the value of *K,* the more stable is the complex ion and the more effectively it holds the central metallic ion as part of the soluble complex.

◻ 26.6 Paramagnetism

Substances that are weakly attracted into a magnetic field are said to be paramagnetic. Paramagnetism among elements and their compounds indicates that there are unpaired electrons in the structure. Some transition metals have unpaired *d* electrons.

Manganese atoms, for example, have 5 unpaired 3*d* electrons as do Mn^{++} ions. Electron sharing in covalent complexes may reduce the number of unpaired electrons to the point where the substance is not paramagnetic. Most compounds of transition metals are paramagnetic in all but the highest oxidation states.

◻ 26.7 Transition metal similarities

The number of electrons in the outermost shell of the transition elements remains fairly constant. It never exceeds two electrons as the number of electrons in the *d* sublevel increases across a period. Similarities often appear in a horizontal sequence of transition elements as well as vertically through a subgroup. In some cases, horizontal similarity may exceed vertical similarity. The first five subgroups are those headed by Sc, Ti, V, Cr, and Mn. Generally, similarities among these elements are recognized within each subgroup. The 6th, 7th, and 8th subgroups are headed by Fe, Co, and Ni. Here, the similarities across each period are greater than those down each subgroup. Iron, cobalt, and nickel resemble each other more than do iron, ruthenium, and osmium, the members of the iron subgroup. The 9th and 10th subgroups are headed by Cu and Zn. Here again, the greatest similarity is within each subgroup.

THE IRON FAMILY

Family relationships in the 6th, 7th, and 8th subgroups of transition elements are horizontal rather than vertical, as in the other subgroups.

◻ 26.8 Members of the Iron Family

The Iron Family consists of the heavy metals *iron, cobalt,* and *nickel*. These metals are all in the fourth period. Each is the first member of a subgroup of transition metals that bears its name. The similarities between iron, cobalt, and nickel are greater than those within each of the three subgroups they head. The remaining six members of these three subgroups have properties similar to platinum. Thus they are considered to be members of the *Platinum Family*. They are called *noble metals* because they show little chemical activity. They are rare and expensive.

Iron is the most important member of the Iron Family. Alloys of iron, cobalt, and nickel are important structural metals. Some properties of the Iron Family are listed in Table 26-6.

The Iron Family is located in the middle of the transition elements. The next-to-outermost shell is incomplete. The $3d$ sublevels of iron, cobalt, and nickel contain only 6, 7, and 8 electrons, respectively, instead of the full number, 10. Each member exhibits the +2 and +3 oxidation states. The Fe^{++} ion is easily oxidized to the Fe^{+++} ion by air and other oxidizing agents. The +3 oxidation state occurs only rarely in cobalt and nickel. The electron configurations of iron, cobalt, and nickel sublevels are shown in Table 26-7. In this table paired and unpaired electrons of the $3d$ and $4s$ sublevels are represented by paired and unpaired dots.

The two $4s$ electrons are removed easily, as is usually the case with metals. This removal forms the Fe^{++}, Co^{++}, or Ni^{++}

Table 26-6
THE IRON FAMILY

Element	Atomic number	Atomic weight	Electron configuration	Oxidation numbers	Melting point (°C)	Boiling point (°C)	Density (g/cm³)
iron	26	55.847	2,8,14,2	+2, +3	1535	2750	7.87
cobalt	27	58.9332	2,8,15,2	+2, +3	1495	2870	8.9
nickel	28	58.70	2,8,16,2	+2, +3	1453	2732	8.90

ion. In the case of iron, one $3d$ electron is also easily removed since the five remaining $3d$ electrons make a half-filled sublevel. When two $4s$ and one $3d$ electrons are removed, the Fe^{+++} ion is formed. It becomes increasingly more difficult to remove a $3d$ electron from cobalt and nickel. This increasing difficulty is partly explained by the higher nuclear charges. Another factor is that neither $3d$ sublevel would be left at the filled or half-filled stage. Neither Co^{+++} nor Ni^{+++} ions are common. However, cobalt atoms in the +3 oxidation state occur in complexes.

All three metals of the Iron Family have a strong magnetic property. This property is commonly known as *ferromagnetism* because of the unusual extent to which it is possessed by iron. Cobalt is strongly magnetic, while nickel is the least magnetic of the three. The ferromagnetic nature of these metals is thought to be related to the similar spin orientations of their unpaired $3d$ electrons. Table 26-7 shows that atoms of iron have 4 unpaired $3d$ electrons, cobalt 3, and nickel 2.

Each spinning electron acts like a tiny magnet. Electron pairs are formed by two electrons spinning in opposite directions. The electron magnetisms of such a pair of electrons neutralize each other. In Iron Family metals, groups of atoms may be aligned and form small magnetized regions called *domains*. Ordinarily, magnetic domains within the metallic crystals point in random directions. In this way, they cancel one another so that the net magnetism is zero. A piece of iron becomes magnetized when an outside force aligns the domains in the same direction. Figure 26-5 illustrates the mechanism of electron spin for paired and unpaired electrons.

◻ 26.9 Occurrence of iron

Iron is the fourth element in abundance by mass in the earth's crust. Nearly 5% of the earth's crust is iron. It is the second most abundant metal, following only aluminum. Meteors are known to contain iron. This fact and the known magnetic nature of the earth itself suggest that the earth's core may consist mainly of iron.

Unfortunately, much of the iron in the crust of the earth cannot be removed profitably. Only minerals from which iron can be profitably recovered by practical methods are considered iron ores.

Taconite, presently the most abundant iron ore, has an iron content of roughly 25% to 50% in a chemically complex mixture. The main iron minerals present are hematite, Fe_2O_3, and magnetite, Fe_3O_4. The rest of the ore is rock. Modern blast furnaces for reducing iron ore to iron require ores containing well above 60% iron. Thus the raw ores must be concentrated by

Table 26-7
ELECTRON CONFIGURATIONS OF THE IRON FAMILY

Sublevel	1s	2s	2p	3s	3p	3d	4s
Maximum number of electrons	2	2	6	2	6	10	2
iron	2	2	6	2	6	⦙••••	⦙
cobalt	2	2	6	2	6	⦙⦙•••	⦙
nickel	2	2	6	2	6	⦙⦙⦙••	⦙

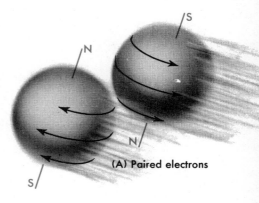

(A) Paired electrons

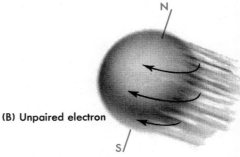

(B) Unpaired electron

Figure 26-5. Magnetism in matter stems basically from the spin of electrons.

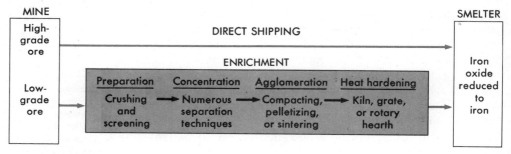

Figure 26-6. Enrichment of low-grade iron ores. Today nearly all iron ore mined in the United States is concentrated before shipment to the blast furnace.

removing much of the waste materials. This is done at the mines before the ores are transported to the blast furnaces.

Taconite ores are first crushed and pulverized. They are then concentrated by a variety of complex methods. The concentrated ores are hardened into pellets for shipment to the smelters. Ore concentrates containing 90% iron are produced by the chemical removal of oxygen during the pelletizing treatment. See Figure 26-6.

◻ 26.10 The blast furnace

Iron ore is converted to iron in a giant structure called a blast furnace. The charge placed in the blast furnace consists of iron ore concentrate, coke, and a flux (which causes mineral impurities in the ore to melt more readily). The proper proportions for the charge are calculated by analyzing the raw materials. Usually the flux is limestone, because silica or sand is the most common impurity in the iron ore. Some iron ores contain limestone as an impurity and, in such cases, the flux added is sand. See Figure 26-7. A blast of hot air, sometimes enriched with oxygen, is forced into the base of the furnace.

Iron oxide is reduced in the blast furnace to iron. The earthy impurities are removed as slag. Coke is required for the first function and limestone for the second. The products of the blast furnace are *pig iron, slag,* and *flue gas.*

The actual chemical changes that occur are complex and somewhat unclear. The coke is ignited by the blast of hot air, and some of it burns to form carbon dioxide.

$$C(s) + O_2(g) \rightarrow CO_2(g)$$

When the oxygen is blown in, the carbon dioxide comes in contact with other pieces of hot coke and is reduced to carbon monoxide.

$$CO_2(g) + C(s) \rightarrow 2CO(g)$$

The carbon monoxide thus formed is actually the reducing agent that reduces the iron oxide to metallic iron.

$$Fe_2O_3 + 3CO \rightarrow 2Fe(l) + 3CO_2(g)$$

This reduction probably occurs in steps as the temperature increases toward the bottom of the furnace. Possible steps are

$$Fe_2O_3 \rightarrow Fe_3O_4 \rightarrow FeO \rightarrow Fe$$

The white-hot liquid iron collects in the bottom of the furnace. Every four or five hours it is tapped off. It may be cast in molds as *pig iron* or converted directly to steel.

In the middle region of the furnace, the limestone decomposes to calcium oxide and carbon dioxide.

$$CaCO_3(s) \rightarrow CaO(s) + CO_2(g)$$

The calcium oxide combines with silica to form a calcium silicate slag. This slag melts more readily than silica.

$$CaO + SiO_2 \rightarrow CaSiO_3(l)$$

This glassy slag also collects at the bottom of the furnace. Since it has a much lower density than liquid iron, it floats on top of the iron. It prevents the reoxidation of the iron. The melted slag is tapped off every few hours. Usually it is thrown away.

□ 26.11 Steel production

The relatively high carbon content of iron recovered from the blast furnace makes it very hard and brittle. Two other impurities are phosphorus and sulfur. The phosphorus makes pig iron brittle at low temperatures. The sulfur makes it brittle at high temperatures.

The conversion of iron to steel *is essentially a purification process in which impurities are removed by oxidation.* This purification process is carried out in a furnace at a high temperature. Scrap steel that is being recycled is added to the charge of iron. Iron ore may be added to supply oxygen for oxidizing the impurities. Oxygen gas is blown in for very rapid oxidation. Limestone or lime is included in the charge for forming a slag with nongaseous oxides. Near the end of the process, selected alloying substances are added. By using different kinds and quantities of these alloys, the steel is given different desired properties.

The impurities in the pig iron are oxidized in the following way:

$$3C + Fe_2O_3 \rightarrow 3CO(g) + 2Fe$$

$$3Mn + Fe_2O_3 \rightarrow 3MnO + 2Fe$$

$$12P + 10Fe_2O_3 \rightarrow 3P_4O_{10} + 20Fe$$

$$3Si + 2Fe_2O_3 \rightarrow 3SiO_2 + 4Fe$$

$$3S + 2Fe_2O_3 \rightarrow 3SO_2(g) + 4Fe$$

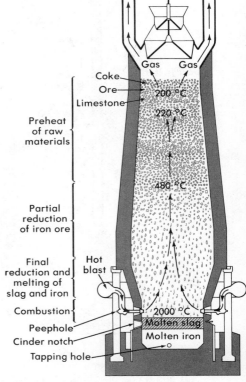

Figure 26-7. A sectional view of a blast furnace.

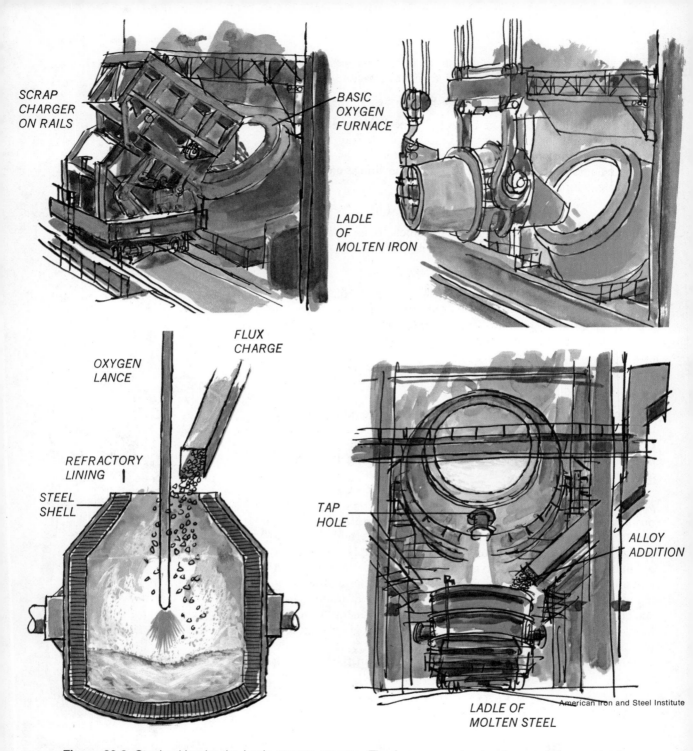

Figure 26-8. Steelmaking by the basic oxygen process. The furnace receives a charge of scrap steel (upper left) and a charge of molten iron from a blast furnace (upper right). Oxygen is blown into the furnace and flux is added (lower left). Molten steel is transferred to a ladle, and alloying substances are added according to precise specifications (lower right).

Carbon and sulfur escape as gases. The limestone flux decomposes as in the blast furnace.

$$CaCO_3 \rightarrow CaO + CO_2(g)$$

Calcium oxide and the oxides of the other impurities react to form slag.

$$P_4O_{10} + 6CaO \rightarrow 2Ca_3(PO_4)_2$$

$$SiO_2 + CaO \rightarrow CaSiO_3$$

$$MnO + SiO_2 \rightarrow MnSiO_3$$

These three reactions are between acidic nonmetallic oxides and basic metallic oxides.

◯ 26.12 Pure iron

Pure iron is a metal that is seldom seen. It is silver-white, soft, ductile, tough, and does not tarnish readily. It melts at 1535 °C. Commercial iron contains carbon and other impurities that alter its properties. Cast iron melts at about 1150 °C. All forms of iron corrode, or rust, in moist air, so it is not a self-protective metal. The rust that forms is brittle and scales off, exposing the metal underneath to further corrosion. Iron does not rust in dry air or in water that is free of dissolved oxygen.

Iron is only moderately active chemically. Even so, it corrodes more extensively than more active metals such as zinc and aluminum. These metals form oxide coatings that adhere to the metal surface and protect it from further corrosion. The rusting of iron is a complicated (and not completely understood) electrochemical process that involves water, air, and carbon dioxide.

Water containing CO_2 in solution is acidic. It reacts with iron to form Fe^{++} ions. The iron(II) ions are oxidized to the iron(III) state as hydrated Fe_2O_3 (rust) by oxygen. Iron is made rust-resistant in several ways: (1) by alloying it with chromium, copper, or nickel; (2) by treating it to form a coating of Fe_3O_4, which adheres and protects the surface; (3) by painting it, which protects the surface as long as the paint adheres and is not chipped or scratched; (4) by dip-coating it with a self-protective metal (galvanizing with zinc); (5) by plating it with nickel or chromium; and (6) by coating it with a material like porcelain.

Dilute acids generally react readily with iron. Strong hydroxides do not react with it. Concentrated nitric acid does not react with iron. In fact, dipping iron into concentrated nitric acid makes the iron *passive,* or *inactive,* with other chemicals. Concentrated sulfuric acid has little effect on iron.

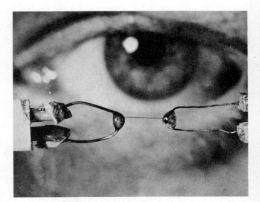

Figure 26-9. A tiny "whisker" of pure iron, free of the structural imperfections of the ordinary metal, provides scientists with a means of studying the nature of the enormous forces that bind atoms tightly together.

◯ 26.13 Three oxides of iron

Of the three oxides of iron, *iron(II) oxide,* FeO, is of little importance. It oxidizes rapidly when exposed to air to form *iron(III) oxide,* Fe_2O_3. This oxide is the important ore of iron. It is used as a cheap red paint pigment. It is also used for grinding and polishing glass lenses and mirrors. *Magnetic iron oxide,* Fe_3O_4, is an important ore. It is composed of Fe_2O_3 and FeO. Thus it may be considered to be iron(II, III) oxide, and its formula can be written $FeO \cdot Fe_2O_3$.

❑ 26.14 Reactions of the Fe^{++} ion

Hydrated iron(II) sulfate, $FeSO_4 \cdot 7H_2O$, is the most useful compound of iron in the +2 oxidation state. It is used as a reducing agent and in medicine for iron tonics. Iron(II) sulfate can be prepared by the action of dilute sulfuric acid on iron. The crystalline hydrate loses water of hydration when exposed to air and turns brown because of oxidation. Iron(II) sulfate in solution is gradually oxidized to the iron(III) state by dissolved oxygen. The brown precipitate of basic iron(III) sulfate that forms is evidence of this change:

$$4FeSO_4 + O_2 + 2H_2O \rightarrow 4Fe(OH)SO_4(s)$$

The Fe^{++} ions can be kept in the reduced state by making the solution acidic with sulfuric acid and adding pieces of iron. Hydrated iron(II) ammonium sulfate, $Fe(NH_4)_2(SO_4)_2 \cdot 6H_2O$, is a better source of Fe^{++} ions in the laboratory because it is stable in contact with air.

Iron(II) salts are readily oxidized to iron(III) salts by the corresponding acid and an oxidizing agent. In the case of the nitrate, nitric acid meets both requirements.

$$3Fe(NO_3)_2 + 4HNO_3 \rightarrow 3Fe(NO_3)_3 + NO(g) + 2H_2O$$

❑ 26.15 Reactions of the Fe^{+++} ion

A mordant is used to "fix" or lock a dye color into a fabric.

Deliquescence: the property of certain substances to take up water from the air. See Section 12.19.

Hydrated iron(III) chloride, $FeCl_3 \cdot 6H_2O$, is the most useful compound of iron in the +3 oxidation state. It is used as a mordant for dyeing cloth and as an oxidizing agent. The yellow crystalline hydrate is deliquescent. The hydrated Fe^{+++} ion, $Fe(H_2O)_6^{+++}$, is pale violet in color. This color usually is not seen, however, because of hydrolysis, which yields hydroxide complexes that are yellow-brown in color. The hydrolysis of Fe^{+++} ions in water solutions of its salts gives solutions that are acidic.

$$Fe^{+++} + 2H_2O \rightleftarrows FeOH^{++} + H_3O^+$$

$$FeOH^{++} + 2H_2O \rightleftarrows Fe(OH)_2^+ + H_3O^+$$

$$Fe(OH)_2^+ + 2H_2O \rightleftarrows Fe(OH)_3 + H_3O^+$$

The hydrolysis is extensive when it occurs in boiling water. A blood-red colloidal suspension of iron(III) hydroxide is formed.

This colloidal suspension can be produced by adding a few drops of $FeCl_3$ solution to a flask of boiling water.

Iron(III) ions are removed from solution by adding a solution containing hydroxide ions. A red-brown jelly-like precipitate of iron(III) hydroxide is formed.

$$Fe^{+++} + 3OH^- \rightarrow Fe(OH)_3(s)$$

By evaporating the water, red Fe_2O_3 remains.

◻ 26.16 Tests for iron ions

Potassium hexacyanoferrate(II), $K_4Fe(CN)_6$ (also called potassium ferrocyanide), is a light yellow crystalline salt. It contains the complex hexacyanoferrate(II) ion (ferrocyanide ion), $Fe(CN)_6^{----}$. The iron is in the +2 oxidation state. The hexacyanoferrate(II) ion forms when an excess of cyanide ions is added to a solution of an iron(II) salt.

$$6CN^- + Fe^{++} \rightarrow Fe(CN)_6^{----}$$

CAUTION: Solutions containing cyanide ions are deadly poisons and should never be handled by inexperienced chemistry students.

Suppose KCN is used as the source of CN^- ions and $FeCl_2$ as the source of Fe^{++} ions. The empirical equation is

$$6KCN + FeCl_2 \rightarrow K_4Fe(CN)_6 + 2KCl$$

The iron of the $Fe(CN)_6^{----}$ ion can be oxidized by chlorine to the +3 state. This reaction forms the hexacyanoferrate(III) ion (ferricyanide ion) $Fe(CN)_6^{---}$.

$$2Fe(CN)_6^{----} + Cl_2 \rightarrow 2Fe(CN)_6^{---} + 2Cl^-$$

(II) following hexacyanoferrate tells you it is the Fe^{++} ion in the complex. (III) tells you it is the Fe^{+++} ion.

As the iron is oxidized from the +2 oxidation state to the +3 state, the chlorine is reduced from the 0 state to the −1 state.

Using the potassium salt as the source of the $Fe(CN)_6^{----}$ ions, the empirical equation is

$$2K_4Fe(CN)_6 + Cl_2 \rightarrow 2K_3Fe(CN)_6 + 2KCl$$

$K_3Fe(CN)_6$, potassium hexacyanoferrate(III) (known also as potassium ferricyanide), is a dark red crystalline salt.

Intense colors are observed in most compounds that have an element present in *two different oxidation states*. When iron(II) ions and hexacyanoferrate(III) ions are mixed, and when iron(III) ions and hexacyanoferrate(II) ions are mixed, *the same intense blue substance is formed*.

$$Fe^{++} + K^+ + Fe(CN)_6^{---} + H_2O \rightarrow K\overset{+2}{Fe}\overset{+3}{Fe}(CN)_6 \cdot H_2O(s)$$

and

$$Fe^{+++} + K^+ + Fe(CN)_6^{----} + H_2O \rightarrow K\overset{+3}{Fe}\overset{+2}{Fe}(CN)_6 \cdot H_2O(s)$$

Before chemists learned that both blue hexacyanoferrate precipitates were the same substance, the one formed with Fe^{++} ions was called Turnbull's blue. That formed with Fe^{+++} ions was called Prussian blue.

In both reactions, the precipitate contains iron in the +2 and +3 oxidation states, and the same intense blue color is seen.

Iron(II) ions, Fe^{++}, and hexacyanoferrate(II) ions, $Fe(CN)_6^{----}$, form a white precipitate, $K_2FeFe(CN)_6$. Note that both Fe ions are in the same +2 oxidation state. This precipitate remains white if the oxidation of Fe^{++} ions is prevented. Of course, on exposure to air, it begins to turn blue. Iron(III) ions, Fe^{+++}, and hexacyanoferrate(III) ions, $Fe(CN)_6^{---}$, give a brown solution. Here, both Fe ions are in the same +3 oxidation state. The reactions given in the two preceding equations provide ways to detect the presence of iron in each of its two oxidation states.

Blueprints: The basis for the blueprinting process is a photochemical reaction that reduces Fe^{+++} ions to Fe^{++} ions, which react with hexacyanoferrate(III) ions to form the blue color in the paper. Blueprint paper is first treated with a solution of iron(III) ammonium citrate and potassium hexacyanoferrate(III) and allowed to dry in the dark. A drawing on tracing paper is laid over the blueprint paper and exposed to light. Where light strikes the paper, Fe^{+++} ions are reduced to Fe^{++} ions. The paper is dipped in water and the Fe^{++} ions react with the hexacyanoferrate(III) ions to form the blue color in the paper. Where drawing lines covered the paper, no reduction of Fe^{+++} ions occurs. This part of the paper rinses out white. Thus a blueprint has white lines on blue paper.

1. *Test for the Fe^{++} ion.* Suppose a few drops of $K_3Fe(CN)_6$ solution is added to a solution of iron(II) sulfate. The characteristic intense blue precipitate $KFeFe(CN)_6 \cdot H_2O$ forms. Two-thirds of the potassium ions and the sulfate ions are merely spectator ions. The net ionic reaction is

$$Fe^{++} + K^+ + Fe(CN)_6^{---} + H_2O \rightarrow KFeFe(CN)_6 \cdot H_2O(s)$$

The formation of a blue precipitate when $K_3Fe(CN)_6$ is added to an unknown solution serves to identify the Fe^{++} ion.

2. *Test for the Fe^{+++} ion.* Suppose a few drops of $K_4Fe(CN)_6$ solution is added to a solution of iron(III) chloride. The characteristic blue precipitate $KFeFe(CN)_6 \cdot H_2O$, is formed. The net reaction is

$$Fe^{+++} + K^+ + Fe(CN)_6^{----} + H_2O \rightarrow KFeFe(CN)_6 \cdot H_2O(s)$$

The formation of a blue precipitate when $K_4Fe(CN)_6$ is added to an unknown solution serves to identify the Fe^{+++} ion.

Potassium thiocyanate, KSCN, provides another good test for the Fe^{+++} ion. It is often used to confirm the $K_4Fe(CN)_6$ test. A blood-red solution results from the formation of the complex $FeSCN^{++}$ ion.

THE COPPER FAMILY

◻ 26.17 Members of the Copper Family

The Copper Family consists of *copper, silver,* and *gold,* the copper subgroup of transition metals. All three metals appear below hydrogen in the electrochemical series. They are not easily oxidized and often occur in nature in the free, or *native,* state. Because of their pleasing appearance, durability, and relative scarcity, these metals have been highly valued since the time of their discovery. All have been used in ornamental objects and coins throughout history.

All soluble compounds of copper, silver, and gold are very toxic.

The atoms of copper, silver, and gold have a single electron in their outermost energy levels. Thus they often form compounds in which they exhibit the +1 oxidation state. To this extent, they resemble the Group I metals of the Sodium Family.

Each metal of the Copper Family has 18 electrons in the next-to-outermost shell. The *d* electrons in this next-to-outermost

Table 26-8
THE COPPER FAMILY

Element	Atomic number	Atomic weight	Electron configuration	Oxidation numbers	Melting point (°C)	Boiling point (°C)	Density (g/cm^3)
copper	29	63.546	2,8,18,1	+1, +2	1083.4	2567	8.96
silver	47	107.868	2,8,18,18,1	+1	961.9	2212	10.5
gold	79	196.9665	2,8,18,32,18,1	+1, +3	1064.4	2807	19.3

shell have energies that differ only slightly from the energy of the outer s electron. Thus one or two of these d electrons can be removed with relative ease. For this reason, copper and gold often form compounds in which they exhibit the +2 and +3 oxidation states respectively. In the case of silver, the +2 oxidation state is reached only under extreme oxidizing conditions.

Copper, silver, and gold are very dense, ductile, and malleable. They are classed as heavy metals along with other transition metals in the central region of the periodic table. Some important properties of each metal are shown in Table 26-8.

◻ 26.18 Copper and its recovery

Copper, alloyed with tin in the form of bronze, has been in use for over 5000 years. Native copper deposits lie deep underground and are difficult to mine.

Sulfide ores of copper yield most of the supply of this metal. *Chalcocite,* Cu_2S, *chalcopyrite,* $CuFeS_2$, and *bornite,* Cu_3FeS_3, are the major sulfide ores. *Malachite,* $Cu_2(OH)_2CO_3$, and *azurite,* $Cu_3(OH)_2(CO_3)_2$, are basic carbonates of copper. Malachite is a rich green, and azurite is a deep blue. Besides serving as ores of copper, fine specimens of these minerals are sometimes polished for use as ornaments or in making jewelry.

The carbonate ores of copper are washed with dilute sulfuric acid, forming a solution of copper(II) sulfate. The copper is then recovered by electrolysis. High-grade carbonate ores are heated in air to convert them to copper(II) oxide. The oxide is then reduced with coke, yielding metallic copper.

The sulfide ores are usually low-grade and require concentrating before they can be refined profitably. The concentration is accomplished by *oil-flotation.* Earthy impurities are wetted by water and the ore is wetted by oil. Air is blown into the mixture to form a froth. The oil-wetted ore floats to the surface in the froth. This treatment changes the concentration of the ore from about 2% copper to as high as 30% copper. See Figure 26-10.

The concentrated ore is partially roasted to form a mixture of Cu_2S, FeS, FeO, and SiO_2. This mixture is known as *calcine.*

Figure 26-10. The oil-flotation (froth-flotation) process for concentrating copper ore. The particles of ore are carried to the surface by air bubbles in the froth.

The roasting process, using oxygen-enriched air, yields high quality sulfur dioxide. This gas is converted to sulfuric acid, as described in Section 29.13. Calcine is fused with limestone in a furnace. Part of the iron is removed as a silicate slag. The rest of the iron, together with the copper, forms a mixture of sulfides known as *matte*. Copper matte is processed in a reverberatory furnace, and the end product contains about 40% copper.

The melted matte is further refined in a converter supplied with oxygen-enriched air as the oxidizing agent. Sulfur from the sulfides, as well as impurities of arsenic and antimony, are removed as volatile oxides. Most of the iron is removed as slag. Some of the copper(I) sulfide is converted into copper(I) oxide.

Figure 26-11. A flow diagram of the copper refining process.

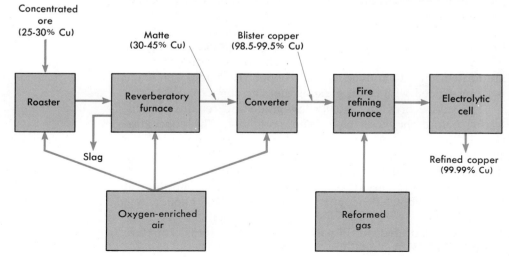

The copper(I) oxide then reacts with more copper(I) sulfide, forming metallic copper and sulfur dioxide. The following equations show the chemical reactions involved in this process.

$$2Cu_2S + 3O_2 \rightarrow 2Cu_2O + 2SO_2(g)$$
$$2Cu_2O + Cu_2S \rightarrow 6Cu + SO_2(g)$$

The molten copper is cast as *blister copper* of 98.5 to 99.5% purity. As the copper cools, dissolved gases escape and form blisters, hence the name. Impurities remaining are iron, silver, gold, and sometimes zinc. In the fourth step of the copper-refining process, blister copper is further purified in a fire-refining furnace. See Figure 26-11.

◻ 26.19 Electrolytic refining of copper

Unrefined copper contains fairly large amounts of silver and gold. Thus the cost of its refining is offset by the recovery of these precious metals. Copper is largely used for making electric conductors, and very small amounts of impurities greatly increase the electric resistance.

In electrolytic refining, shown in Figure 26-12, sheets of pure copper are used as the cathodes in electrolytic cells. Large plates of *impure* copper are used as the anodes. The electrolyte is a solution of copper(II) sulfate in sulfuric acid. A direct current at low voltage is used to operate the cell. During the electrolysis, copper and the other metals in the anode which are above copper in the electrochemical series are oxidized. They enter the solution as ions.

$$Cu \rightarrow Cu^{++} + 2e^-$$
$$Fe \rightarrow Fe^{++} + 2e^-$$
$$Zn \rightarrow Zn^{++} + 2e^-$$

At the low voltages used, the less active silver and gold are not oxidized and so do not go into solution. As the anode is used up, they fall to the bottom of the cell as a sludge and are recovered easily.

You might expect the various positive ions of the electrolyte to be reduced at the cathode. However, H_3O^+ ions, Fe^{++} ions, and Zn^{++} ions all require higher voltages than Cu^{++} ions for reduction. At the low potential maintained across the cell, only Cu^{++} ions are reduced at the cathode.

$$Cu^{++} + 2e^- \rightarrow Cu$$

Of all the metals present, only copper plates out on the cathode. Electrolytic copper is 99.99% pure.

◻ 26.20 Properties of copper

Copper is a soft, ductile, malleable, red metal with a density of 8.96 g/cm³. It is second to silver in electric conductivity.

Figure 26-12. Electrolytic refining of copper. In these large electrolytic cells, anodes of impure copper yield Cu^{++} ions in solution. These Cu^{++} ions are plated out on pure copper cathodes. Electrolytically refined copper is 99.99% pure.

Heated in air, copper forms a black coating of copper(II) oxide, CuO. Metallic copper and most copper compounds color a Bunsen flame green.

Copper forms copper(II) salts that dissociate in water to give blue solutions. The color is characteristic of the hydrated copper(II) ion, $Cu(H_2O)_4^{++}$. Adding an excess of ammonia to solutions containing this ion produces the deeper blue complex ion, $Cu(NH_3)_4^{++}$. Aqueous solutions of copper(II) salts are weakly acidic because of the mild hydrolysis of the Cu^{++} ion.

$$Cu(H_2O)_4^{++} + H_2O \rightarrow Cu(H_2O)_3OH^+ + H_3O^+$$

An excess of sulfur vapor forms a blue-black coating of copper(I) sulfide on hot copper. In moist air, copper tarnishes and forms a protective coating. This coating is a green basic carbonate, $Cu_2(OH)_2CO_3$. Sulfur dioxide in the air may also combine with copper. If so, a green basic sulfate, $Cu_4(OH)_6SO_4$, is produced. The green color seen on copper roofs is caused by the formation of these compounds.

Copper(II) compounds are much more common than copper(I) compounds. Copper(II) oxide is used to change alternating current to direct current. It is also used as an oxidizing agent in chemical laboratories.

Hydrated copper(II) sulfate, $CuSO_4 \cdot 5H_2O$, called *blue vitriol,* is an important copper compound. It is used to kill algae in reservoirs and to make certain pesticides. It is also used in electroplating and in preparing other copper compounds.

The activity series is explained in Section 8.8.

Because copper stands below hydrogen in the activity series, it does not replace hydrogen from acids. Thus it is not acted on by nonoxidizing acids such as hydrochloric and dilute sulfuric except very slowly when oxygen is present. The oxidizing acids, nitric and hot concentrated sulfuric, react vigorously with copper. Such reactions produce the corresponding copper(II) salts.

❑ 26.21 Tests for the Cu^{++} ion

A dilute solution of a copper(II) salt changes to a very deep blue color when an excess of ammonia is added. This color change is caused by the formation of complex $Cu(NH_3)_4^{++}$ ions.

$$Cu^{++} + 4NH_3 \rightarrow Cu(NH_3)_4^{++}$$

The addition of $K_4Fe(CN)_6$ to a solution containing Cu^{++} ions produces a red precipitate of $Cu_2Fe(CN)_6$. This precipitate is copper(II) hexacyanoferrate(II), also known as copper(II) ferrocyanide. If copper is present in a borax bead formed in an *oxidizing flame,* a clear blue color appears on cooling. The hot bead is green. A bead formed in a *reducing* flame is colorless while hot, and an opaque red when cool.

SUMMARY

The transition metals consist of ten subgroups interposed between Group II and Group III in the periodic table. They are in this position because they represent an interruption of the regular increase of outer-shell electrons from Group I to Group VIII in the long periods.

Chemical properties of transition metals are varied. Electrons of the next-to-outermost d sublevel as well as those of the outer shell may become involved in the formation of compounds. Most of the transition metals show different oxidation states in their reactions. They have strong tendencies to form complex ions. Many of their compounds are paramagnetic and are colored.

With minor apparent irregularities, the transition metals have two outer-shell electrons. In the first row of transition elements, chromium and copper have one $4s$ electron. The availability of $3d$ electrons tends to increase the number of oxidation states up to manganese in the middle of the row, after which the number of common oxidation states for each element decreases.

The color of the compounds of transition elements depends to some extent on the ions or polyatomic groups associated with the element. The colors result from the ease with which d electrons can be excited by absorption of discrete quantities of light energy.

Transition metals form many complex ions. A transition element cation is the central ion in the complex. Certain ionic or molecular species coordinate with the central ion to form the complex ion. The coordinating atom of the species must have unshared electron pairs that the central ion can share. Formation of complex ions in a solution has the effect of increasing the solubility of the metallic ions that form the complex.

The Iron Family consists of iron, cobalt, and nickel. These transition metals are ferromagnetic. All are present in nature in combined form. Purified iron is used as a construction metal in the form of steel. By alloying other metals with steel, a variety of structural characteristics can be obtained. The metals of the Iron Family are recovered from their ores by reduction methods.

Iron forms compounds in two oxidation states, $+2$ and $+3$. Iron(II) ions are easily oxidized to the iron(III) state. Iron(II) compounds are used as reducing agents. Iron(III) compounds are used as oxidizing agents. The iron(III) ion hydrolyzes in water solutions of its salts. Its hydroxide is very sparingly soluble and is precipitated by the addition of aqueous ammonia to solutions of iron(III) salts. Both the Fe^{++} ion and the Fe^{+++} ion can be identified by precipitation reactions with potassium hexacyanoferrate(III) and potassium hexacyanoferrate(II), respectively. The color of the intense blue precipitate results from iron being present in both the $+2$ and $+3$ oxidation states.

The Copper Family consists of copper, silver, and gold. All are found as the native metals in nature. Most copper used in commerce and industry is recovered from its sulfide ores by reduction and electrolytic refining. All soluble compounds of copper, silver, and gold are very toxic. The copper(II) ions can be identified by the formation of colored complex ions.

VOCABULARY

actinide series	hematite	pig iron
blast furnace	instability constant	slag
complex ion	lanthanide series	taconite
coordination number	mordant	transition elements
domains	noble metals	
ferromagnetism	paramagnetism	

◖ | **QUESTIONS**

Group A

1. What structural similarity determines the metallic character of transition elements?
2. Copper(II) sulfate crystals are blue. To what color does the light energy absorbed by the crystals correspond?
3. Chemically, what happens to iron (*a*) in the blast furnace; (*b*) during steel making?
4. List five points of similarity between copper, silver, and gold.
5. Why does the copper trim on roofs frequently acquire a green surface?
6. What is the oxidation number of manganese in (*a*) Mn; (*b*) MnO_2; (*c*) $MnSO_4 \cdot 4H_2O$; (*d*) $KMnO_4$; (*e*) $BaMnO_4$?

Group B

7. Why were some metals used in very early times, while many other metals were obtained only within the last century?
8. Distinguish between a polyatomic ion and a complex ion.
9. When potassium hexacyanoferrate(II) is added to a solution of iron(II) sulfate, a white precipitate forms that gradually turns blue. Explain the color change.
10. How can you detect an iron(II) and an iron(III) compound if both are present in the same solution?
11. Why does it usually pay to refine copper by electrolysis?

◖ | **PROBLEMS**

Group A

1. How much iron(II) chloride can be produced by adding 165 g of iron to an excess of hydrochloric acid?
2. How much iron(III) chloride can be prepared from the iron(II) chloride in Problem 1 if more hydrochloric acid is added and air is blown through the solution?
3. What is the percentage of iron in a sample of limonite, $2Fe_2O_3 \cdot 3H_2O$?
4. How many grams of silver nitrate can be obtained by adding 100 g of pure silver to an excess of nitric acid?
5. A sample of hematite ore contains Fe_2O_3 87.0%, silica 8.0%, moisture 4.0%, other impurities 1.0%. What is the percentage of iron in the ore?
6. What will be the loss in mass when 1.0×10^6 metric tons of the ore in Problem 5 is heated to 200 °C?

Group B

7. How much limestone will be needed to combine with the silica in 1.0×10^6 metric tons of the ore of Problem 5?
8. (*a*) How much carbon monoxide is required to reduce 1.0×10^6 metric tons of the ore of Problem 5? (*b*) How much coke must be supplied to meet this requirement? (Assume the coke to be 100% carbon.)
9. Iron(II) sulfate is oxidized to iron(III) sulfate in the presence of sulfuric acid using nitric acid as the oxidizing agent. Nitrogen monoxide and water are also formed. Write the balanced formula equation.
10. Silver reacts with dilute nitric acid to form silver nitrate, water, and nitrogen monoxide. Write the balanced formula equation.
11. Copper reacts with hot concentrated sulfuric acid to form copper(II) sulfate, sulfur dioxide, and water. Write the balanced equation.

Aluminum and the Metalloids

Aluminum is the most abundant metal in the earth's crust. Unlike iron or copper, however, it is hard to extract from its ore. It is believed that in 1825 the Danish chemist Hans Christian Oersted isolated aluminum in impure form. It wasn't until 1827, however, that the German chemist Friedrich Wöhler first isolated the pure metal. Unfortunately, his process could not be used on a commercial scale. The French chemist Henri Sainte-Claire Deville improved Wöhler's method, making the production of aluminum economically feasible. In spite of Deville's improvement, aluminum still cost $535 per pound, making it a more precious metal than gold. In fact, at the Paris exhibition of 1855, bars of aluminum were exhibited next to the crown jewels! In 1886, the American Charles Martin Hall developed a more practical method for its production. With his method, the price of aluminum fell to $2 per pound, eventually reaching 20¢ per pound.

⛉ 27.1 Nature of metalloids

Some elements are neither distinctly metallic nor distinctly nonmetallic. Their properties are intermediate between those of metals and nonmetals. As a group, these elements are called *metalloids* or *semimetals*. In the periodic table, they occupy a diagonal region from the upper center toward the lower right. See Figure 27-1.

The metalloids are the elements *boron, silicon, germanium, arsenic, antimony, tellurium,* and *polonium*. Although aluminum is not included in the metalloids, it is studied in this chapter because of its unique position in the periodic table relative to the metalloids.

Elemental aluminum is distinctly metallic and is recognized by the familiar properties of metals. But aluminum forms the negative aluminate ion, $Al(OH)_4^-$. Its hydroxide, $Al(OH)_3$, is amphoteric. The oxide of aluminum is ionic, yet the hydride is polymeric. As a metal, aluminum is so resistant to oxidation that it can be used as cooking ware on hot stove burners. Yet it is easily oxidized in sodium hydroxide solution to yield hydrogen and sodium aluminate. When considered collectively, these characteristics tend to place aluminum among the metalloids.

Boron, silicon, arsenic, and antimony are the typical metalloids. Table 27-1 lists some of their important properties, together with those of aluminum and the other metalloids.

Germanium is a moderately rare element. With the development of the transistor, germanium became important as a semiconductor material. It is chemically similar to silicon, the ele-

In this chapter you will gain an understanding of:

- **the nature of the seven elements known as metalloids**
- **the important properties, uses, and compounds of aluminum**
- **the natural occurrence and commercial preparation of aluminum**
- **the major properties, uses, and compounds of boron, silicon, arsenic, and antimony**

The amphoterism of aluminum hydroxide is discussed in detail in Section 15.9.

Polymeric: *Having repeating structural units.*

Semiconductor: *A substance with an electric conductivity between that of a metal and an insulator.*

METALS					NON METALS				VIII
									4.00260 ² **He** 2
				III	IV	V	VI	VII	
				10.81 ²₃ **B** 5	12.011 ²₄ **C** 6	14.0067 ²₅ **N** 7	15.9994 ²₆ **O** 8	18.9984 ²₇ **F** 9	20.179 ²₈ **Ne** 10
				26.9815 ²₈₃ **Al** 13	28.086 ²₈₄ **Si** 14	30.9738 ²₈₅ **P** 15	32.06 ²₈₆ **S** 16	35.453 ²₈₇ **Cl** 17	39.948 ²₈₈ **Ar** 18
58.9332 ²₈₁₅₂ **Co** 27	58.71 ²₈₁₆₂ **Ni** 28	63.546 ²₈₁₈₁ **Cu** 29	65.37 ²₈₁₈₂ **Zn** 30	69.72 ²₈₁₈₃ **Ga** 31	72.59 ²₈₁₈₄ **Ge** 32	74.9216 ²₈₁₈₅ **As** 33	78.96 ²₈₁₈₆ **Se** 34	79.904 ²₈₁₈₇ **Br** 35	83.8 ²₈₁₈₈ **Kr** 36
102.9055 ²₈₁₈₁₆₁ **Rh** 45	106.4 ²₈₁₈₁₈₀ **Pd** 46	107.868 ²₈₁₈₁₈₁ **Ag** 47	112.40 ²₈₁₈₁₈₂ **Cd** 48	114.82 ²₈₁₈₁₈₃ **In** 49	118.69 ²₈₁₈₁₈₄ **Sn** 50	121.75 ²₈₁₈₁₈₅ **Sb** 51	127.60 ²₈₁₈₁₈₆ **Te** 52	126.9045 ²₈₁₈₁₈₇ **I** 53	131.30 ²₈₁₈₁₈₈ **Xe** 54
192.22 ²₈₁₈₃₂₁₃₂ **Ir** 77	195.09 ²₈₁₈₃₂₁₇₁ **Pt** 78	196.9665 ²₈₁₈₃₂₁₈₁ **Au** 79	200.59 ²₈₁₈₃₂₁₈₂ **Hg** 80	204.37 ²₈₁₈₃₂₁₈₃ **Tl** 81	207.2 ²₈₁₈₃₂₁₈₄ **Pb** 82	208.9806 ²₈₁₈₃₂₁₈₅ **Bi** 83	[210] ²₈₁₈₃₂₁₈₆ **Po** 84	[211] ²₈₁₈₃₂₁₈₇ **At** 85	222 ²₈₁₈₃₂₁₈₈ **Rn** 86

Figure 27-1. The metalloids are the elements *boron, silicon, germanium, arsenic, antimony, tellurium,* and *polonium*. While *aluminum* is generally considered to be a metal, it does have some properties that relate it to the metalloids.

ment above it in Group IV. Germanium is more metallic than arsenic just to its right in Period Four. The major oxidation state of germanium is +4.

Tellurium is a member of Group VI in the periodic table. As expected, the metal-like characteristics of Group VI elements increase down the group. Tellurium is more metallic (or less nonmetallic) than selenium above it. It is less metallic (or more nonmetallic) than polonium below it. This gradation in properties down the group is illustrated by the change in odor of their hydrogen compounds. Hydrogen oxide (water) is odorless. Hydrogen sulfide has the offensive odor of rotten eggs.

Table 27-1
PROPERTIES OF ALUMINUM AND METALLOIDS

Element	Atomic number	Electron configuration	Oxidation states	Melting point (°C)	Boiling point (°C)	Density (g/cm³)	Atomic radius (Å)	First ionization energy (kcal/mole)
boron	5	2, 3	+3	2079	2550	2.34	0.82	191
aluminum	13	2, 8, 3	+3	660	2467	2.70	1.18	138
silicon	14	2, 8, 4	+2, +4, −4	1410	2355	2.33	1.11	188
germanium	32	2, 8, 18, 4	+2, +4, −4	937	2830	5.32	1.22	182
arsenic	33	2, 8, 18, 5	+3, +5, −3	sublimes		5.73	1.20	226
antimony	51	2, 8, 18, 18, 5	+3, +5, −3	631	1750	6.69	1.40	199
tellurium	52	2, 8, 18, 18, 6	+2, +4, +6, −2	450	990	6.24	1.36	208
polonium	84	2, 8, 18, 32, 18, 6	+4, +6	254	962	9.32	1.46	196

The odor of hydrogen selenide is even more offensive, and that of hydrogen telluride is the foulest of them all.

Although it can be amorphous, tellurium is more commonly a brittle, silvery, metal-like crystalline substance. It is classed as a semiconductor and its chemistry is typically metalloidal. It appears with oxygen in both tellurite (TeO_3^{--}) and tellurate (TeO_4^{--}) ions. In these ions, tellurium shows the +4 and +6 oxidation states, respectively. Tellurium combines covalently with oxygen and the halogens in which the +2, +4, and +6 oxidation states are observed. It forms tellurides (−2 oxidation state) with such elements as gold, hydrogen, and lead. In fact, tellurium is the only element combined with gold in nature.

Polonium is a radioactive element. It was discovered by Pierre and Marie Curie in 1898, just prior to their discovery of radium. Polonium is so rare in nature that little is known of its chemistry. It appears to be more metallic than tellurium.

Amorphous: Without form; non-crystalline.

⬚ 27.2 Aluminum as a light metal

Aluminum, atomic number 13, is the second member of Group III. This group is headed by boron and includes gallium, indium, and thallium. All are typically metallic except boron, which is classed as a metalloid. The chemistry of boron differs from that of aluminum and the other Group III elements mainly because of the small size of the boron atom. Its chemistry resembles that of silicon and germanium more than it does that of aluminum. Much of the chemistry of aluminum is similar to that of its corresponding Group II metal, magnesium.

Aluminum is a low-density metal; it is about one-third as dense as steel. The pure metal is used in chemical processes, in electronics, for forming jewelry, and as foil wrapping. Aluminum alloys are used in structural and industrial applications. Each alloying substance improves certain properties of the aluminum to which it is added. For example, approximately 1% manganese yields aluminum alloys that are 20% stronger and more resistant to corrosion than pure aluminum. The common

ALUMINUM

Except in the United States, aluminum is spelled aluminium and pronounced al-yuh-min-ee-um.

Figure 27-2. Aluminum-sheathed transit cars operating over the San Francisco Bay Area Rapid Transit System.

Figure 27-3. Bauxite being placed in storage at Pinjarra, on the southwestern coast of Australia.

Figure 27-4. Batteries of electrolytic cells used for the recovery of aluminum from aluminum oxide. In the foreground, molten aluminum is being poured into a transfer ladle.

alloying elements are copper, magnesium, manganese, silicon, and zinc. Other elements may be added for special effects.

Aluminum is the most abundant metal in the earth's crust. It is found in many clays, rocks, and minerals. Bauxite, a hydrated aluminum oxide ore, is the source of aluminum. Major deposits are located throughout the tropical and semitropical regions of the earth. Bauxite containing 40–60% aluminum oxide is required for present aluminum-recovery technology. Major foreign sources are Australia, Jamaica, Surinam, and Guyana. Bauxite is also mined in Georgia, Alabama, Tennessee, and Arkansas. Anhydrous aluminum oxide is called alumina.

27.3 Recovery of aluminum

Aluminum is extracted by electrolyzing anhydrous aluminum oxide (refined bauxite) dissolved in molten cryolite, Na_3AlF_6. The process requires a temperature slightly below 1000 °C.

In the electrolytic cell, an iron box lined with graphite serves as the cathode, graphite rods serve as the anode, and molten cryolite-aluminum oxide is the electrolyte. The cryolite is melted in the cell, and the aluminum oxide dissolves as it is added to the molten cryolite. The operating temperature of the cell is above the melting point of aluminum (660 °C). Thus the aluminum metal at the bottom of the cell is in the liquid phase and is easily drawn off. See Figure 27-4.

The electrode reactions are complex and are not understood completely. Aluminum is reduced at the cathode. The anode is gradually converted to carbon dioxide. This fact suggests that oxygen is formed at the anode by oxidation of the O^{--} ion. The following equations for the reaction mechanism may be overly simple. However, they serve to summarize the oxidation-reduction processes in the cell.

$$\text{cathode:} \qquad 4Al^{+++} + 12e^- \rightarrow 4Al$$

$$\text{anode:} \qquad\qquad 6O^{--} \rightarrow 3O_2 + 12e^-$$

$$3C + 3O_2 \rightarrow 3CO_2(g)$$

27.4 Properties of aluminum

Aluminum has a density of 2.70 g/cm³. It is ductile and malleable but is not as tenacious as brass, copper, or steel. Only silver, copper, and gold are better conductors of electricity. Aluminum can be welded, cast, or spun but can be soldered only by using a special solder.

Aluminum is a very active metal. The surface is always covered with a thin layer of aluminum oxide. This oxide layer is not affected by air or moisture, hence aluminum is a self-protective metal. At high temperatures, the metal combines vigorously with oxygen, releasing intense light and heat. Photoflash lamps contain aluminum foil or fine wire in an atmosphere of oxygen.

Aluminum is a very good reducing agent but is not as active as the Group I and Group II metals.

$$Al \rightarrow Al^{+++} + 3e^-$$

The Al^{+++} ion is quite small and carries a large positive charge. The ion hydrates vigorously in water solution and is usually written as the hydrated ion, $Al(H_2O)_6^{+++}$. Water solutions of aluminum salts are generally acidic because of the hydrolysis of $Al(H_2O)_6^{+++}$ ions.

$$Al(H_2O)_6^{+++} + H_2O \rightarrow Al(H_2O)_5OH^{++} + H_3O^+$$

Water molecules are amphoteric but are very weak proton donors or acceptors. Water molecules that hydrate the Al^{+++} ion, however, give up protons more readily. This increased activity results from the repulsion effect of the highly positive Al^{+++} ion. In the hydrolysis shown above, a water molecule does succeed in removing one proton from the $Al(H_2O)_6^{+++}$ ion.

Hydrochloric acid reacts with aluminum to form aluminum chloride and release hydrogen. The net ionic equation is

$$2Al(s) + 6H_3O^+ + 6H_2O \rightarrow 2Al(H_2O)_6^{+++} + 3H_2(g)$$

Nitric acid does not react readily with aluminum because of aluminum's protective oxide layer.

In basic solutions, aluminum forms aluminate ions, $Al(OH)_4^-$, and releases hydrogen.

$$2Al(s) + 2OH^- + 6H_2O \rightarrow 2Al(OH)_4^- + 3H_2(g)$$

If the base is sodium hydroxide, sodium aluminate, $NaAl(OH)_4$, is the soluble product and hydrogen is given up as a gas.

$$2Al(s) + 2NaOH + 6H_2O \rightarrow 2NaAl(OH)_4 + 3H_2(g)$$

The oxide surface coating protects aluminum under normal atmospheric conditions. It must be removed before the metal underneath can react with hydronium ions or with hydroxide ions. Hydroxide ions dissolve this oxide layer more readily than do hydronium ions. This explains why aluminum reacts more readily with hydroxides than with acids.

☐ 27.5 The thermite reaction

When a mixture of powdered aluminum and an oxidizing agent such as iron(III) oxide is ignited, the aluminum reduces the oxide to the free metal. This reduction is rapid and violent, and yields a tremendous amount of heat. The sudden release of

Ductile: Capable of being drawn into wire.
Malleable: Capable of being rolled into sheets.
Tenacious: Resists being pulled apart.

Figure 27-5. This top-charging aluminum-melting furnace receives a charge of 30,000 pounds of metal in less than 2 minutes.

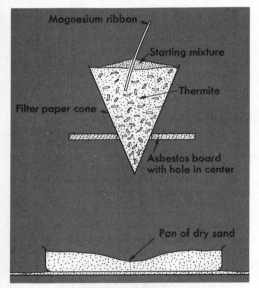

Figure 27-6. The thermite reaction. Dry sand protects the table. Note the brilliance of the molten iron.

Figure 27-7. Verneuil flame fusion furnace for synthetic sapphire.

this heat energy produces temperatures from 3000 to 3500 °C, enough to melt the iron. Such a reaction between aluminum and the oxide of a less active metal is called the *thermite reaction*. The mixture of powdered aluminum and iron(III) oxide is called *thermite*. See Figure 27-6.

The formation of aluminum oxide is strongly exothermic. The reaction releases 399 kilocalories of heat per mole of aluminum oxide formed. The heat of formation of iron(III) oxide is 196 kilocalories per mole. In the thermite reaction, the amount of heat released per mole of aluminum oxide formed equals the difference between these values. The net thermite reaction is considered to be the sum of these two separate reactions.

$$2Al + \tfrac{3}{2}O_2 \rightarrow Al_2O_3 \qquad \Delta H = -399 \text{ kcal}$$
$$Fe_2O_3 \rightarrow 2Fe + \tfrac{3}{2}O_2 \qquad \Delta H = +196 \text{ kcal}$$

$$2Al + Fe_2O_3 \rightarrow 2Fe + Al_2O_3 \qquad \Delta H = -203 \text{ kcal}$$

It is not practical to use aluminum to reduce cheaper metals. However, the thermite reaction is often used to produce small quantities of carbon-free metal. A more important use of this reaction is to reduce metallic oxides that are not readily reduced with carbon. Chromium, manganese, titanium, tungsten, and molybdenum can be recovered from their oxides by the thermite reaction. All of these metals are used in making alloy steels.

The very high temperature produced by the thermite reaction makes it useful in welding. Large steel parts, such as propeller shafts and rudder posts on a ship or the crankshafts of heavy machinery, are repaired by thermite welding.

☐ 27.6 Uses of aluminum oxide

Bauxite, the chief ore of aluminum, is an oxide. *Corundum* and *emery* are also natural oxides of this metal, and are used as abrasives. Emery is used in emery boards, emery paper, emery cloth, or emery grinding wheels.

Rubies and sapphires are aluminum oxide colored by traces of other metallic oxides. Synthetic rubies and sapphires are made by melting pure aluminum oxide in the flame of an oxy-hydrogen blowtorch. In making clear sapphires, no coloring matter is added. Synthetic rubies are colored by adding a very small amount of chromium. Synthetic sapphires are colored by titanium. Synthetic rubies and sapphires are used as gem stones in jewelry. Because of the hardness of Al_2O_3, these synthetic stones are also used as bearings (jewels) in watches and other precision instruments, and as dies for drawing wires.

Scientists are finding new ways to strengthen and stiffen structural materials. One important development involves monocrystalline strands or fibers of one substance embedded in and held in place by some other material. An aluminum rod containing very hard, strong sapphire "whiskers" is quite unlike ordinary soft, ductile aluminum. Such a structure is six times stronger than aluminum and twice as stiff. These *fiber composites* enable engineers to greatly improve the strength-to-weight ratio of structural materials. See Figure 27-9.

Alundum is an oxide of aluminum made by melting bauxite. It is used for making grinding wheels and other abrasives. It is also found in crucibles, funnels, tubing, and other pieces of laboratory equipment.

☐ 27.7 The alums

Alums are common compounds that usually contain aluminum. They have the type formula $M^+M^{+++}(SO_4)_2 \cdot 12H_2O$. The M^+ can be any one of several monopositive ions but is usually Na^+, K^+, or NH_4^+. The M^{+++} can be any one of a number of tripositive ions such as Al^{+++}, Cr^{+++}, Co^{+++}, Fe^{+++}, or Mn^{+++}. Potassium aluminum sulfate, $KAl(SO_4)_2 \cdot 12H_2O$, is the most common alum. You can see from this formula why alums are sometimes called double sulfates.

All alums have the same crystal structure. This crystal-structure requirement may explain why some monopositive and tripositive ions do not form alums. The alum crystals are hydrated structures in which six water molecules are coordinated to each metallic ion. This coordination number of six for both the monopositive and tripositive ions may restrict the kinds of metallic ions that can form alums.

Alums are used for water purification, as mordants, and in paper manufacture. $NaAl(SO_4)_2 \cdot 12H_2O$ is used as the acid compound in one type of baking powder.

☐ 27.8 Boron as a metalloid   METALLOIDS

The first member of a periodic group often has properties somewhat different from those of the rest of the group. This is true because the outer electrons of its atoms are shielded from the nucleus only by the K shell. The first member of Group III, boron, is a metalloid while all other Group III elements are metals. Boron also has the highest electronegativity of any element in Group III. Boron atoms are small, with an atomic radius of only 0.82 Å. Their valence electrons are quite tightly bound giving boron a relatively high ionization energy for a Group III element. The properties of boron indicate that it forms only covalent bonds with other atoms. At low temperatures boron is a poor conductor of electricity. As the temperature is raised, its electrons have more kinetic energy and its conductivity increases. This behavior is typical of a *semiconductor*.

Figure 27-8. Both synthetic and natural sapphires (top) and rubies (bottom) are composed of aluminum oxide, Al_2O_3. The blue color of a sapphire is due to titanium. The red color of a ruby is due to chromium.

Alums are hydrated double sulfates.

Figure 27-9. Cross section of a fiber composite magnified 245 times. The experimental composite shown here consists of sapphire whiskers in a silver matrix.

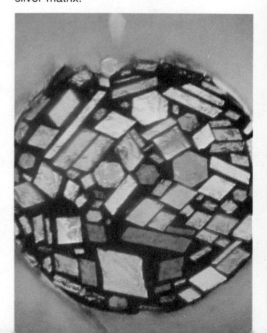

Figure 27-10. Boron, a metalloid, is best known as a constituent of borax.

27.9 Occurrence of boron

Boron is not found as the free element. It can be isolated in fairly pure form by reducing boron trichloride with hydrogen at a high temperature. Elemental boron is important in mono-crystalline fiber research. Boron filaments, embedded in and held in place by an epoxy plastic, form a very strong and stiff structural material.

Colemanite is a hydrated borate of calcium with the formula $Ca_2B_6O_{11} \cdot 5H_2O$. It is found in the desert regions of California and Nevada. Sodium tetraborate, $Na_2B_4O_7 \cdot 4H_2O$, is found as the mineral *kernite,* also in California. The salt brines of Searles Lake, California, yield most of the commercial supply of boron compounds.

27.10 Useful compounds of boron

Boron carbide, B_4C, known as *Norbide,* is an extremely hard abrasive. It is made by combining boron with carbon in an electric furnace. Boron nitride, BN, has a soft, slippery structure similar to graphite. Under very high pressure it acquires a tetrahedral structure similar to diamond. This form of boron nitride, called *Borazon,* has a hardness second only to diamond. It is used industrially for cutting, grinding, and polishing. Alloys of boron with iron or manganese are used to increase the hardness of steel.

Boric acid, H_3BO_3, can be prepared by adding sulfuric acid to a concentrated solution of sodium tetraborate in water.

$$B_4O_7^{--} + 2H_3O^+ \rightarrow H_2B_4O_7 + 2H_2O$$
$$H_2B_4O_7 + 5H_2O \rightarrow 4H_3BO_3$$
$$\overline{B_4O_7^{--} + 2H_3O^+ + 3H_2O \rightarrow 4H_3BO_3}$$

The acid is only moderately soluble and separates as colorless, lustrous scales. It is a weak acid and is used as a mild antiseptic.

Recall that an acid and an alcohol react to form an ester. Sulfuric acid catalyzes the reaction. Suppose a small quantity of methanol and a few drops of dilute sulfuric acid are added to a sample of boric acid. The solution is warmed and the methanol vapors ignited. The flame has green edges, as shown in Figure 27-11. The alcohol vapor contains the volatile ester $(CH_3)_3BO_3$, which is responsible for the green flame color.

$$3CH_3OH + H_3BO_3 \xrightarrow{H_2SO_4} (CH_3)_3BO_3(g) + 3H_2O$$

Figure 27-11. An alcohol flame has green edges when boric acid is present. This serves as a qualitative test for boric acid.

This green-flame test indicates the presence of boric acid, or more specifically, the borate ion.

Borax is sodium tetraborate, $Na_2B_4O_7 \cdot 10H_2O$. It is used alone and in washing powders as a water softener. Because it dissolves metallic oxides and leaves a clean metallic surface, it is also used in welding metals.

$$B_4O_7^{--} + 5O^{--} \rightarrow 4BO_3^{---}$$

The borates of certain metals are used in making glazes and enamels. Large amounts of boron compounds are used to make borosilicate glass.

◻ 27.11 Borax bead tests

Powdered borax held in a burner flame on a platinum wire loop swells and then fuses into a clear, glass-like bead. This bead can be used to identify certain metals. The bead is contaminated with a tiny speck of metal or metallic compound and heated again in the oxidizing flame. The metallic oxide formed fuses with the bead. Certain metals give characteristic transparent colors to the borax bead. Such colors serve to identify the metal involved. For example, cobalt colors the bead *blue;* chromium produces a *green* bead; and nickel yields a *brown* bead. Other metals that can be identified by means of the borax bead test are manganese, copper, and iron. The borax bead colors are shown in Figure 27-12.

◻ 27.12 Silicon as a metalloid

Silicon atoms have four valence electrons. Silicon crystallizes with a tetrahedral bond arrangement similar to that of carbon atoms in diamond. Atoms of silicon also have small atomic radii and tightly held electrons. Thus their ionization energy and electronegativity are fairly high. Silicon is a metalloid. It forms bonds with other elements that are essentially covalent. The electric conductivity of silicon is similar to that of boron; it, too, is a semiconductor. Unlike carbon, silicon forms only single bonds. It forms silicon-oxygen bonds more readily than silicon-silicon or silicon-hydrogen bonds. However, much of its chemistry is similar to that of carbon. Silicon has much the same role in mineral chemistry as carbon has in organic chemistry.

Boron and silicon atoms have roughly similar small radii. This similarity allows them to be substituted for one another in glass, even though boron is a member of Group III and silicon of Group IV.

Where relative size of atoms defines properties, elements in diagonal positions in the periodic table (as boron-silicon-arsenic) often have similar properties. In general, atom size decreases to the right from Groups I to VIII. It increases down each group. This balancing effect results in atoms of similar size along diagonals in the periodic table.

◻ 27.13 Silicones

Silicon resembles carbon in the ability of its atoms to form chains. Unlike carbon chains which are formed by carbon-carbon

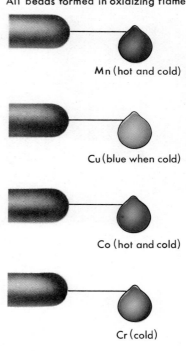

All beads formed in oxidizing flame

Mn (hot and cold)

Cu (blue when cold)

Co (hot and cold)

Cr (cold)

Ni (reddish when cold)

Fe (or brownish-red)

Figure 27-12. Borax bead tests for certain metals. Color is due to a minute trace of a certain metal.

Figure 27-13. Silicon, the second most abundant element. Its abundance is due to the wide distribution in nature of silicon dioxide and many different silicates.

bonds, silicon chains are usually formed by silicon-oxygen bonds. That is, silicon atoms are bound into chains by other atoms such as oxygen. A group of synthetic compounds called *silicones* has the silicon chain bound together with oxygen atoms. Hydrocarbon groups are attached to the silicon atoms. Thus the silicones are part organic and part inorganic. By using different hydrocarbon groups, a variety of silicones can be produced. One silicone chain has the structure

$$\begin{bmatrix} & H & & H & \\ H-&C&-H \quad H-&C&-H \\ -&Si&-O-&Si&-O- \\ H-&C&-H \quad H-&C&-H \\ & H & & H & \end{bmatrix}_x$$

The silicones are not greatly affected by heat. They have very good electric insulating properties and are water repellent. Water does not penetrate cloth treated with a silicone. Some silicones have the character of oils or greases and can be used as lubricants. Silicone varnishes are used to coat wires for the windings of electric motors. This insulation permits the electric motor to operate at high temperatures without developing short circuits. Silicones are used in automobile and furniture polishes.

CAUTION: *Although elemental arsenic is not as toxic as commonly assumed, its dusts and vapors and most of its compounds are extremely poisonous.*

CAUTION: *The soluble compounds of antimony are almost as toxic as those of arsenic.*

☐ 27.14 Properties and uses of arsenic

Metallic arsenic is a brittle, gray solid. Chemically, arsenic may act as a metal and form oxides and chlorides. It may also act as a nonmetal and form acids. When heated, arsenic sublimes and forms a yellow vapor, As_4, which has the odor of garlic. Metallic arsenic has few commercial uses except as a hardening agent in certain alloys. A trace of arsenic in lead used for making lead shot hardens the shot. Arsenic and its compounds are poisonous.

Figure 27-14. The bearings shown here are made of an "antifriction" alloy to help reduce friction produced when a shaft turns inside them.

☐ 27.15 Properties and uses of antimony

Antimony is a dense, brittle, silver-white metalloid with a bright metallic luster. It is less active than arsenic. When strongly heated in air, antimony forms a white oxide Sb_4O_6.

An alloy of lead and antimony is used to reduce friction between the surfaces of moving parts in machinery. Another alloy of lead and antimony is used for the plates in storage batteries. This alloy is stronger and more resistant to acids than lead alone. Tartar emetic, potassium antimonyl tartrate, $KSbOC_4H_4O_6$, is used as a mordant in the dyeing of cotton goods.

SUMMARY

Metalloids have properties intermediate between those of metals and nonmetals. They occupy a diagonal region of the periodic table from upper center toward lower right. Metalloids include boron, silicon, germanium, arsenic, antimony, tellurium, and polonium.

Aluminum is distinctly metallic in many of its properties. It is always covered with an oxide surface coating that protects it from corrosion by air and moisture. Aluminum is a self-protective metal. Certain properties tend to place aluminum among the metalloids. It forms negative aluminate ions and some covalent halides, and its hydroxide is amphoteric. Its oxide is ionic; its hydride polymeric.

Aluminum is recovered by electrolysis of the oxide dissolved in molten cryolite. It is a good reducing agent. Aluminum is a low-density structural metal when alloyed with selected elements. Powdered aluminum mixed with iron(III) oxide and ignited reduces the oxide to the free metal in a rapid, violent combustion reaction. This is the thermite reaction. The aluminum-oxygen bond is a very strong bond. Some natural or synthetic oxides of aluminum are very hard and are used as abrasives. Alums are double sulfates with the general formula $M^+M^{+++}(SO_4)_2 \cdot 12H_2O$. The most common alum is $KAl(SO_4)_2 \cdot 12H_2O$.

Boron has typical metalloidal properties. It is a semiconductor. The element can be recovered from its trichloride by reduction with hydrogen. Boron carbide and boron nitride are extremely hard abrasives. Borax, sodium tetraborate, is the most common boron compound. It is used as a cleaning agent and a welding flux. Boric acid is prepared by reacting borax with aqueous sulfuric acid. When present in an alcohol, boric acid imparts a green color to the alcohol flame. Borax bead tests are used to identify cobalt, chromium, nickel, manganese, copper, and iron.

Silicon forms strong bonds with oxygen. Silicon-oxygen lattice chains are similar to carbon-carbon chains. Much of the chemistry of the element silicon is similar to that of carbon. Silicon chains bound together with oxygen atoms and having hydrocarbon groups attached to the silicon atoms are called silicones. Some silicones have properties similar to organic oils and greases.

Arsenic and antimony are used in alloys. Arsenic is a hardening agent for lead. Antimony and lead form "antifriction" alloys and battery-plate alloys.

VOCABULARY

alumina	borax bead test	emery	metalloid
bauxite	corundum	fiber composite	semiconductor
borax	cryolite	Hall process	thermite reaction

QUESTIONS

Group A

1. In what materials does aluminum occur in nature?
2. What are the important physical properties of aluminum?
3. (*a*) What is the chemical composition of corundum and emery? (*b*) Write the formulas for these substances. (*c*) What is their important use?
4. Why must aluminum oxide be dissolved in molten cryolite before it can be decomposed by electricity?
5. Why are certain metallic oxides reduced with aluminum rather than with carbon?

6. Write the chemical formulas for four different alums.
7. What is the main source of boron compounds in the United States?
8. Why can borax be used to prepare metals for welding?
9. How does silicon rank in abundance among the elements?
10. Why must extreme care be used in handling arsenic and its compounds?

Group B

11. What reaction occurs when aluminum is placed in: (*a*) hydrochloric acid solution, (*b*) sodium hydroxide solution? (*c*) Why is there no reaction in neutral water?
12. Write equations to show the net anode and cathode reactions during the electrolysis of aluminum oxide.
13. Why is bauxite imported from the West Indies and South America when almost any clay bank in the United States contains aluminum?

14. What geographic conditions affect the location of plants for the production of aluminum from purified bauxite?
15. Describe the properties characteristic of metalloids such as boron and silicon in terms of (*a*) atomic radius; (*b*) ionization energy; (*c*) electronegativity; (*d*) type of bonds formed; (*e*) electric conductivity.
16. Explain the test for boric acid.
17. When a red crystalline compound was tested by means of a borax bead, the bead turned blue. What metal was probably present?
18. Borazon, a form of boron nitride, and diamond have similar crystal structures. Is there any relationship between this fact and the similarity of their hardness? Explain.
19. (*a*) What is the principal form of boric acid in water solution: molecular or ionic? (*b*) What evidence supports your answer?
20. (*a*) What is a silicone? (*b*) What are some of the important uses for silicones?
21. Why would you expect silicones to be water repellent?

◖ PROBLEMS

Group A

1. How much aluminum and how much iron(III) oxide must be used in a thermite mixture to produce 10.0 kg of iron for a welding job?
2. What is the percentage of aluminum in sodium alum which crystallizes with 12 molecules of water of hydration?
3. How many liters of hydrogen can be prepared by the reaction of 50.0 g of aluminum and 100 g of sodium hydroxide in solution?
4. Calculate the percentage of boron in colemanite, $Ca_2B_6O_{11} \cdot 5H_2O$.
5. How many grams of $SbCl_3$ can be prepared by the reaction of 10.0 g of antimony with chlorine?

Group B

6. A compound contains 96.2% arsenic and 3.85% hydrogen. Its vapor is found to have a density of 3.48 g/L. What is the molecular formula of the compound?

7. Boric acid, H_3BO_3, is produced when sulfuric acid is added to a water solution of borax, $Na_2B_4O_7$. How much boric acid can be prepared from 5.00 g of borax?
8. Tellurium (at. no. 52) appears before iodine (at. no. 53) in the periodic table, yet the atomic weight of tellurium is higher than that of iodine. Using the following data, show why this is so.

Isotope	Atomic mass	Distribution
Te-120	119.904 u	0.09%
Te-122	121.903 u	2.46%
Te-123	122.904 u	0.87%
Te-124	123.903 u	4.61%
Te-125	124.904 u	6.99%
Te-126	125.903 u	18.71%
Te-128	127.905 u	31.79%
Te-130	129.906 u	34.48%
I-127	126.904 u	100.00%

Nitrogen and Its Compounds

Elemental nitrogen is an inactive gas that accounts for most of the volume of our atmosphere. It serves to dilute the highly active oxygen, thus slowing such destructive oxidation processes as rusting and uncontrolled burning. This chemical inactivity, however, creates certain problems for living organisms. They need nitrogen to build tissue, yet are unable to take it directly from the atmosphere and incorporate it into organic protein molecules that make up the tissue. Specific microorganisms—nitrogen-fixing bacteria—can accomplish this, however. Residing in nodules found in the roots of plants known as legumes, the nitrogen-fixing bacteria reduce atmospheric nitrogen to ammonia, a form of nitrogen that can be utilized by growing plants. Animals and humans can, in turn, eat plants or other animals for their sources of nitrogen.

☐ 28.1 Occurrence of nitrogen

About four-fifths of the volume of the earth's atmosphere is elemental nitrogen. The earth is the only planet of the solar system where nitrogen is a significant component of the atmosphere. Its presence on earth is directly related to the action of bacteria during the nitrogen cycle.

Combined nitrogen is widely distributed on the earth. It is found in the proteins of both plants and animals. Natural deposits of potassium nitrate and sodium nitrate are used as raw materials for producing other nitrogen compounds.

☐ 28.2 Preparation of nitrogen

The commercial method for preparing nitrogen is fractional distillation of liquid air. Small amounts of liquid air were first produced in France in 1877. Today it is made in large amounts as a first step in separating the various gases of the atmosphere. The physical principles involved in liquefying gases were discussed in Section 12.7.

Liquid air resembles water in appearance. Under ordinary atmospheric pressure, liquid air boils at a temperature of about −190 °C. Because liquid air is mainly a mixture of liquid nitrogen and liquid oxygen, its boiling temperature is not constant. Liquid nitrogen boils at −195.8 °C, while liquid oxygen boils at −183.0 °C. The lower boiling point of the nitrogen causes it to separate in the first portions that evaporate. Fractional distillation of liquid air is also used for producing oxygen and the noble gases (except helium).

NITROGEN

In this chapter you will gain an understanding of:

- **the occurrence and preparation of nitrogen**
- **the physical and chemical properties of nitrogen**
- **natural and artificial methods of nitrogen fixation**
- **the preparation, properties, and uses of ammonia and nitric acid**

Liquefying a gas involves compressing the gas and removing the heat of compression. Then the cool, compressed gas is allowed to expand without absorbing external energy.

Nitrogen ranks fifth among chemicals in the quantity produced in the United States. Production in 1979 was nearly 14 million metric tons.

◻ 28.3 Physical properties of nitrogen

Nitrogen is a colorless, odorless, and tasteless gas. It is slightly less dense than air and only slightly soluble in water. Its density indicates that its molecules are diatomic, N_2. Nitrogen condenses to a colorless liquid at $-195.8\,°C$ and freezes to a white solid at $-209.9\,°C$.

◻ 28.4 Chemical properties of nitrogen

Nitrogen atoms have the electron configuration $1s^2 2s^2 2p^3$. Nitrogen atoms share $2p$ electrons to form nonpolar diatomic molecules having a triple covalent bond.

$$\overset{\circ}{\underset{\circ}{N}} \vdots\vdots \overset{\circ}{\underset{\circ}{N}}$$

This triple covalent bond is very strong. Even at 3000 °C, nitrogen molecules do not decompose measurably. The nitrogen molecule bond energy is very large, 225 kcal/mole. This explains why elemental nitrogen is rather inactive. It combines with other elements only with difficulty. Many nitrogen compounds have positive heats of formation.

The electron-dot symbol for a nitride ion is $\overset{\circ\circ}{\underset{\circ\circ}{N}}\!:^{---}$.

At a high temperature, nitrogen combines directly with such metals as magnesium, titanium, and aluminum. Nitrides are formed in these reactions.

Nitrogen does not burn in oxygen. However, when nitrogen and oxygen are passed through an electric arc, nitrogen monoxide, NO, is formed. Similarly, NO is formed when lightning passes through the air.

Oxides of nitrogen are also formed during the high-temperature and high-pressure combustion in automobile engines. When catalyzed by the sun's ultraviolet radiation, these oxides of nitrogen can react with unburned hydrocarbons from automobiles. In urban areas with poor natural air circulation, the result is a buildup of an irritating cloud of photochemical smog. Ozone and a variety of organic compounds are produced in such a smog.

By the use of a catalyst, nitrogen can be made to combine with hydrogen at a practical rate. Ammonia, NH_3, is formed in this reaction.

◻ 28.5 Uses of elemental nitrogen

An important use of pure nitrogen is in the commercial preparation of ammonia. Other uses of pure nitrogen are based upon its inactivity.

Substances burn rapidly in pure oxygen, but nitrogen does not support combustion. In the air, therefore, nitrogen serves as a diluting agent and lowers the rate of combustion. Its inactivity makes pure nitrogen useful in food processing, metallurgical operations, chemical production, and the manufacture of electronic devices. As a "blanket" atmosphere, it prevents unwanted oxidation in these processes. It is similarly used in the chemical, petroleum, and paint industries to prevent fires or explosions. Electric lamps are filled with a mixture of nitrogen and argon.

Liquid nitrogen is used for freezing and cooling foods to about − 100 °C for preservation during storage and transportation.

◻ 28.6 Nitrogen fixation

All living things contain nitrogen compounds. The nitrogen in these compounds is called *combined* or *fixed* nitrogen. *Any process that converts free nitrogen to nitrogen compounds is called nitrogen fixation.* Such processes are important because nitrogen compounds in the soil are necessary for plant growth. There are both *natural* and *artificial* methods of nitrogen fixation.

1. One natural method is to grow crops that restore nitrogen compounds to the soil. Most crops rapidly remove such compounds from the soil. On the other hand, certain plants called *legumes* actually restore large amounts of nitrogen compounds. These plants include beans and peas. They have small swellings or *nodules* on their roots. Organisms known as *nitrogen-fixing bacteria* grow in these nodules.

In alkaline soil, the nitrogen-fixing bacteria take free nitrogen from the air and convert it to nitrogen compounds. If these plants are plowed under or if their roots are left to decay, the soil is enriched by nitrogen compounds.

Certain blue-green algae have nitrogen-fixing ability, also.

2. Another natural method of nitrogen fixation occurs during electric storms. Lightning supplies energy which enables some of the nitrogen and oxygen of the air to combine. An oxide of nitrogen is formed. After a series of changes, nitrogen compounds are washed down into the soil in rain.

3. The most important *artificial method* of nitrogen fixation involves making ammonia from a mixture of nitrogen and hydrogen. This ammonia is then oxidized to nitric acid. The nitric acid, in turn, is converted to nitrates suitable for fertilizer.

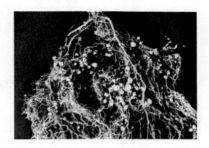

Figure 28-1. The nodules on these soybean roots are the result of infection by nitrogen-fixing bacteria.

◻ 28.7 Preparation of ammonia

1. By decomposing ammonium compounds. In the laboratory, ammonia is prepared by heating a mixture of a moderately strong hydroxide and an ammonium compound. Usually, calcium hydroxide and ammonium chloride are used.

$$Ca(OH)_2(s) + 2NH_4Cl(s) \rightarrow CaCl_2(s) + 2NH_3(g) + 2H_2O(g)$$

The mixture is heated in a test tube fitted with an L-shaped delivery tube, as shown in Figure 28-2. Ammonia is so soluble in water that it cannot be collected by water displacement. Instead, it is collected by downward displacement of air in an inverted

AMMONIA AND AMMONIUM COMPOUNDS

The density of ammonia is 0.77 g/L at STP; the density of air is 1.29 g/L at STP. Gases that are soluble in water and are less dense than air can be collected by downward displacement of air.

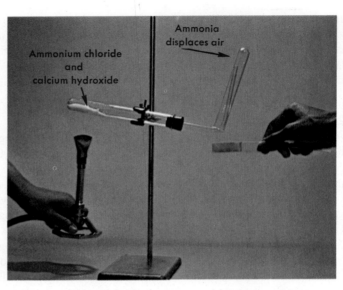

Ammonium chloride
and
calcium hydroxide

Ammonia
displaces air

Figure 28-2. When the mixture of ammonium chloride and calcium hydroxide in the test tube is heated, ammonia is given off. Ammonia is collected by downward displacement of air because it is less dense than air and very soluble in water.

The Haber process is described in Section 21.4.

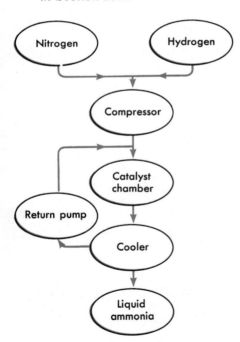

Figure 28-3. A flow diagram of the Haber process. Ammonia gas produced in the catalyst chamber is condensed into a liquid in the cooler. The uncombined nitrogen and hydrogen are recirculated through the catalyst chamber.

container. In what way would moist red litmus paper show when the test tube is full?

2. By destructive distillation of bituminous coal. When bituminous coal is heated in a closed container without air, ammonia is one of the gaseous products.

3. By the Haber process. Chemists long ago discovered that ammonia is formed when an electric spark passes through a mixture of nitrogen and hydrogen. However, the reaction is reversible:

$$N_2(g) + 3H_2(g) \rightleftarrows 2NH_3(g) + 22 \text{ kcal}$$

Only a very small percentage of ammonia is produced at equilibrium. The problem of increasing that percentage was solved in 1913 by Fritz Haber (1868–1934), a German chemist.

The reaction between nitrogen and hydrogen is exothermic. Higher temperatures increase the rate at which the molecules of nitrogen and hydrogen react. But, *higher temperatures shift the equilibrium toward the left.* On the other hand, four volumes of reactants produce only two volumes of products. Thus, *increased pressure shifts the equilibrium toward the right.* Haber used a catalyst to increase the speed of reaction. He used a temperature of about 600 °C and a pressure of about 200 atmospheres. These conditions resulted in a yield of about 8% ammonia.

Today, the yield from the Haber process has been raised to about 40% to 60%. This was done by using pressures as high as 1000 atmospheres, and an improved catalyst. This catalyst is a mixture of porous iron and the oxides of potassium and aluminum. Its use enables the reaction to proceed at a satisfactory rate at the lower temperature of 400°–550 °C. The pressures and temperatures used in different Haber-process plants vary widely.

The ammonia is produced in special chrome-vanadium steel converters designed to withstand the tremendous pressure. It is separated from the unreacted nitrogen and hydrogen by being dissolved in water, or by being cooled until it liquefies. The uncombined gases are returned to the converters and exposed again to the action of the catalyst.

The nitrogen used in the Haber process comes from the air; the hydrogen comes from the methane in natural gas. See Section 9.17(4).

Ammonia ranks third, behind sulfuric acid and lime, in the quantity produced in the United States. In 1979, production was over 16 million metric tons.

◻ 28.8 Physical properties of ammonia

Ammonia is a colorless gas with a characteristic, strong odor. It is less dense than air and is easily liquefied when cooled to the proper temperature. Liquid ammonia, which boils at $-33\,°C$ at atmospheric pressure, is sold in steel cylinders. The melting point of ammonia is $-78\,°C$.

An important property of ammonia is its great solubility in water. One liter of water at $20\,°C$ dissolves about 700 liters of ammonia. At $0\,°C$ about 1100 volumes of ammonia can be dissolved in one volume of water.

The electron-dot formula for ammonia is

$$\overset{\circ\circ}{\underset{\overset{\circ\circ}{H}}{H\!:\!N\!:\!H}}$$

The hydrogen atoms bond covalently to the nitrogen atom. In this bonding, the $1s$ hydrogen electrons occupy the half-filled $2p$ nitrogen orbitals. The hydrogen nuclei in ammonia molecules form an equilateral triangle 1.6 Å on a side. The nitrogen nucleus is 0.38 Å vertically above the midpoint of this triangle. This pyramid structure is evidence of sp^3 hybridization in the molecule. See Figure 6-12.

For a compound with such a simple molecular structure and low molecular weight, ammonia has a high boiling point and a very high melting point. In Chapter 12, you learned that water shows these properties to an even greater degree. The high melting and boiling points of both ammonia and water are explained as resulting from hydrogen bonds between their molecules in the solid and liquid phases. Ammonia molecules are polar because the three hydrogen atoms are not symmetrically bonded to the nitrogen atom. Hydrogen atoms from one ammonia molecule form hydrogen bonds with the nitrogen atom in adjacent ammonia molecules. The polar nature of both water and ammonia molecules is also believed to cause the high solubility of ammonia in water.

Ammonia's high heat of vaporization is also evidence of its hydrogen bonding. Much energy is required to break the hydrogen bonds between molecules and to separate the molecules when ammonia boils.

Liquid ammonia shows many of the solvent properties of water. Many salts dissolve and dissociate in liquid ammonia.

☐ 28.9 Chemical properties of ammonia

Gaseous ammonia does not support combustion. It does burn in air or oxygen.

$$4NH_3 + 3O_2 \rightarrow 2N_2 + 6H_2O$$

At ordinary temperatures ammonia is a stable compound. However, it decomposes into nitrogen and hydrogen at high temperatures. When ammonia is dissolved in water, most of the ammonia forms a simple solution. A very small part of the ammonia, however, reacts with water and ionizes.

The reaction of ammonia and water is described in Chapter 15. The structure of the ammonium ion is given in Section 6.23. Formation of complex ions containing ammonia is explained in Section 26.5.

☐ 28.10 Uses of ammonia and ammonium compounds

1. As fertilizers. Ammonia can be applied directly as a fertilizer. It is also used to make large quantities of urea, $(NH_2)_2CO$, and diammonium hydrogen phosphate, $(NH_4)_2HPO_4$, which are widely used fertilizers.

2. As a cleaning agent. Ammonia-water solution makes a good cleaning agent. It is weakly basic, emulsifies grease, and leaves no residue to be wiped up.

3. As a refrigerant. Ammonia is used as a refrigerant in frozen food production and storage plants.

4. For making other compounds. Great quantities of ammonia are oxidized to make nitric acid, as explained in Section 28.11. Ammonia is also used in producing nylon and one type of rayon, and as a catalyst in making several types of plastic. Ammonia is used to make sulfa drugs, vitamins, and drugs for treating the tropical disease malaria. It is also used as a neutralizing agent in the petroleum industry. In the rubber industry, it prevents the rubber in latex from separating out during shipment.

Figure 28-4. When used as a fertilizer, ammonia may be applied directly to the soil.

NITRIC ACID

☐ 28.11 Preparation of nitric acid

Two methods are commonly used to prepare this important acid.

1. From nitrates. Small amounts of nitric acid are prepared in the laboratory by heating a nitrate with concentrated sulfuric acid. The reaction is carried out in a glass-stoppered retort because nitric acid oxidizes rubber stoppers or rubber connectors.

$$NaNO_3(s) + H_2SO_4(aq) \rightarrow NaHSO_4(aq) + HNO_3(g)$$

The nitric acid vapor is condensed in the side arm of the retort and collected in the receiver. The reddish-brown gas nitrogen dioxide, NO_2, is produced because some of the HNO_3 formed does decompose. Nitrogen dioxide appears in the retort and contaminates the nitric acid.

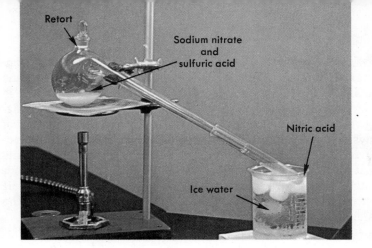

Retort

Sodium nitrate and sulfuric acid

Nitric acid

Ice water

Figure 28-5. Nitric acid may be prepared in the laboratory by the action of sulfuric acid on sodium nitrate. Some reddish-brown nitrogen dioxide is also formed because of decomposition of some nitric acid. It fills the retort and colors the nitric acid product. Pure nitric acid is colorless.

2. From ammonia. Wilhelm Ostwald (1853–1932), a German chemist, discovered how to oxidize ammonia to nitric acid with a catalyst. In the Ostwald process, a mixture of ammonia and air is heated to a temperature of 600 °C. It is then passed through a tube containing platinum gauze, which serves as the catalyst. On the surface of the platinum, the ammonia is oxidized to nitrogen monoxide, NO.

$$4NH_3 + 5O_2 \rightarrow 4NO + 6H_2O$$

This reaction is exothermic and raises the temperature of the mixture of gases to about 1000 °C. Then more air is mixed with colorless nitrogen monoxide to oxidize it to reddish-brown nitrogen dioxide, NO_2.

$$2NO + O_2 \rightarrow 2NO_2$$

The nitrogen dioxide is cooled and absorbed in water, forming nitric acid.

$$3NO_2(g) + H_2O(l) \rightarrow 2HNO_3(aq) + NO(g)$$

The nitrogen monoxide produced is recycled to oxidize it to nitrogen dioxide and absorb it in water.

Nitric acid ranks tenth in the amount of chemicals produced in the United States. In 1979, production was nearly 8 million metric tons.

☐ 28.12 Physical properties of nitric acid

Pure HNO_3 is a colorless liquid, about 1.5 times as dense as water. It fumes in moist air and boils at 86 °C. Pure HNO_3 is unstable. For this reason, commercial concentrated nitric acid is a 68% solution of HNO_3 in water. The solution boils at 120 °C.

☐ 28.13 Chemical properties of nitric acid

1. Stability. Concentrated nitric acid is not very stable. When boiled, or even when exposed to sunlight, it decomposes to some extent. Nitrogen dioxide, water, and oxygen are the decomposition products.

$$4HNO_3 \rightarrow 4NO_2 + 2H_2O + O_2$$

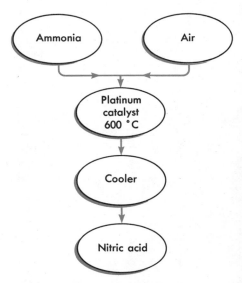

Ammonia   Air

Platinum catalyst 600 °C

Cooler

Nitric acid

Figure 28-6. Flow diagram of the Ostwald process for the oxidation of ammonia into nitric acid.

Figure 28-7. The reactions of concentrated nitric acid with copper and zinc. What is the reddish-brown gas? What salt is in solution in each beaker? The gaseous products are being drawn off to the right by an exhaust system not shown in the photograph. These reactions should be carried out in a hood or where there is similar provision for removing the product gases, because they are poisonous.

Figure 28-8. An explosion set off in the Gulf of Mexico helps in the search for oil. Shock waves from this explosion, reflected from different geological formations, are detected at different points using seismological instruments. Interpreting the graphs from these instruments reveals formations that could possibly contain oil.

2. Acid properties. *Dilute* nitric acid has the usual properties of acids. It reacts with metals, metallic oxides, and metallic hydroxides, forming salts known as *nitrates*.

3. As an oxidizing agent. Nitric acid is a powerful oxidizing agent. It can react as an oxidizing agent in a variety of ways. The concentration of the acid, the activity of the reducing agent mixed with it, and the reaction temperature determine what products are formed. Under ordinary conditions, moderately dilute nitric acid is reduced to nitrogen monoxide. If concentrated nitric acid is reduced, nitrogen dioxide is the product.

4. Action with metals. Nitric acid is such a vigorous oxidizing agent that hydrogen gas is *not* produced in significant amounts when the acid is added to common metals. *Very dilute nitric acid,* however, does react with the active metal magnesium to produce hydrogen and a nitrate.

In reactions with less active metals such as zinc and copper, the hydrogen appears in the water product. In these reactions, the nitrogen of the nitric acid is reduced. Copper reacts with cold, dilute nitric acid as shown by this equation:

$$3Cu(s) + 8HNO_3(aq) \rightarrow 3Cu(NO_3)_2(aq) + 2NO(g) + 4H_2O(l)$$

With concentrated nitric acid, copper reacts as follows:

$$Cu(s) + 4HNO_3(aq) \rightarrow Cu(NO_3)_2(aq) + 2NO_2(g) + 2H_2O(l)$$

Nitric acid does not react with gold or platinum because of the stability of these metals. Very concentrated nitric acid reacts with aluminum and iron extremely slowly. The reactions are probably slowed by the formation of semiprotective surface coatings on the metal.

☐ 28.14 Uses of nitric acid

1. For making fertilizers. About 75% of the nitric acid produced in the United States is used in the manufacture of fertilizers. Ammonium nitrate is the most important nitrate so used.

2. For making explosives. Many explosives are made directly or indirectly from nitric acid. The acid itself is not an explosive. However, some of its compounds form the most violent explosives known. Among these are nitroglycerin, smokeless powders, and TNT (trinitrotoluene).

3. For making dyes. Nitric acid reacts with several products obtained from coal tar to form *nitro compounds*. One of these coal tar products is benzene. Benzene reacts with nitric acid to form nitrobenzene, $C_6H_5NO_2$. (See Section 18.21.) Aniline, $C_6H_5NH_2$, is used in making many different dyes. It is made by reducing nitrobenzene with hydrogen.

4. For making plastics. Cotton consists mainly of cellulose, $(C_6H_{10}O_5)_n$. When treated with a mixture of nitric acid and sulfuric acid, cellulose forms nitrocellulose plastics. Celluloid, pyroxylins, and many other products are made from nitrocellulose plastics.

SUMMARY

About four-fifths by volume of the earth's atmosphere is free nitrogen. Nitrogen is obtained commercially from the air by fractional distillation. Nitrogen is colorless, odorless, tasteless, slightly less dense than air, and only slightly soluble in water. Elemental nitrogen is rather inactive. Because of this inactivity, nitrogen is used as a blanketing atmosphere to prevent unwanted oxidation. Nitrogen does not readily combine with other elements. The compounds it does form are usually unstable. Nitrogen does not burn, but nitrogen and oxygen do combine to form several oxides of nitrogen. Nitrogen and hydrogen combine to form ammonia under proper conditions. The conversion of free nitrogen to nitrogen compounds is called nitrogen fixation.

In the laboratory, ammonia is prepared by heating calcium hydroxide and an ammonium compound. Using the Haber process, ammonia is made industrially from nitrogen of the air and hydrogen prepared from natural gas. Ammonia is a colorless gas with a characteristic, strong odor. It is less dense than air, easily liquefied, and very soluble in water. Ammonium ions act like metallic ions; they combine with negative ions to form salts. Ammonia and ammonium compounds are used as fertilizers. Ammonia-water solution is a good cleaning agent. Ammonia is also used as a refrigerant and for making medicinal drugs such as sulfa drugs and vitamins.

Nitric acid is prepared in the laboratory by heating a mixture of sodium nitrate and concentrated sulfuric acid. Commercially, nitric acid is prepared by the catalytic oxidation of ammonia, using the Ostwald process. Nitric acid is a dense, colorless liquid that fumes in moist air. Pure nitric acid is not very stable. Concentrated nitric acid is a powerful oxidizing agent. Nitric acid reacts with metals, metallic oxides, and metallic hydroxides. Its salts are called nitrates. Nitric acid is used for making fertilizers, explosives, dyes, and plastics.

VOCABULARY

ammonia	legume	nitrogen-fixing bacteria
blanket atmosphere	nitrate	nodule
fixed nitrogen	nitride	Ostwald process
Haber process	nitrogen fixation	photochemical smog

QUESTIONS

Group A

1. (*a*) Where can you find elemental nitrogen in large quantities? (*b*) In what kinds of compounds does combined nitrogen occur naturally?

2. (*a*) Which has the higher boiling point, liquid nitrogen or liquid oxygen? (*b*) What practical use is made of this difference in boiling points?

3. What effects do the oxides of nitrogen pro-

duced by automobile engines have on the atmosphere?

4. What is meant by *nitrogen fixation?*

5. (*a*) What are two natural methods of nitrogen fixation? (*b*) Name an artificial method.

6. (*a*) What is the purpose of high pressure in the Haber process? (*b*) What is the function of the catalyst?

7. (*a*) Describe the shape of NH_3 molecules. (*b*) What type of bonding occurs in these molecules?

8. Give two reasons why ammonia-water solution makes an excellent window cleaner.

9. Why is a completely glass apparatus used for the laboratory preparation of nitric acid?

10. What condition must be met for the reaction between sodium nitrate and sulfuric acid to run to completion?

11. Write three equations to show the steps in the production of nitric acid from ammonia.

12. Why does concentrated nitric acid turn yellow in the laboratory?

Group B

13. (*a*) Why does compressing a gas raise its temperature? (*b*) Why does a gas become colder when it is allowed to expand?

14. What structural feature of nitrogen molecules accounts for the stability of this element?

15. Name three uses for nitrogen. For each use, give the related physical or chemical property of nitrogen that makes the use possible.

16. What must be the condition of the soil for nitrogen-fixing bacteria to be most effective?

17. Why might farmers alternate crops of corn and lima beans on one of their fields in successive years?

18. (*a*) Write the balanced equation for the reaction between calcium hydroxide and ammonium nitrate that produces ammonia. (*b*) Write the net ionic equation for this reaction. (*c*) How does the net ionic equation for this reaction compare with the net ionic equation for the reaction between calcium hydroxide and ammonium chloride? Between sodium hydroxide and ammonium sulfate?

19. Why is the boiling point of ammonia, $-33\,°C$, so much higher than the boiling point of methane, $-164\,°C$, when molecules of both have nearly the same molecular weight?

20. Why is ammonia so soluble in water, while methane is nearly insoluble in water?

21. What solvent and complexing properties does ammonia have?

22. Why can zinc be used with either dilute hydrochloric or sulfuric acid for producing hydrogen but not with dilute nitric acid?

23. The equation for the reaction of copper and dilute nitric acid indicates that colorless nitrogen monoxide gas is one of the products. Yet when this reaction is carried out in an evaporating dish, dense reddish-brown nitrogen dioxide gas flows over the rim of the dish. Explain.

24. What is the oxidation number of nitrogen in (*a*) NH_3, (*b*) N_2H_4, (*c*) N_2, (*d*) NO, (*e*) HNO_2, (*f*) NO_2, (*g*) HNO_3?

PROBLEMS

Group A

1. How many grams of ammonia can be produced by the reaction of calcium hydroxide and 15.0 g of ammonium chloride?

2. How many liters of nitrogen and hydrogen are required for the preparation of $20\overline{0}$ L of ammonia?

3. If 15 g of HNO_3 is needed for a laboratory experiment, what mass of sodium nitrate is required for its preparation?

Group B

4. What volume, in liters, of nitrogen at STP can be prepared from a mixture of $1\overline{0}$ g of NH_4Cl and $1\overline{0}$ g of $NaNO_2$?

5. How many grams of nitric acid can be prepared from 50.0 g of KNO_3 of 80.0% purity?

6. (*a*) What mass of copper(II) nitrate can be prepared from 254 g of copper by reaction with nitric acid? (*b*) How many liters of nitrogen monoxide at STP are also produced?

Sulfur and Its Compounds

Chemistry has always been an important ally of medicine in the battle against disease. The fifteenth-century alchemist and physician Paracelsus believed that life is a chemical process, and disease a biochemical disturbance. In the nineteenth century, the German chemist Paul Ehrlich pioneered the use of chemical agents to treat infectious diseases. His researches in chemotherapy, as he called his new science, yielded cures for a host of human diseases. In the twentieth century, the principles laid down by Ehrlich led to the discovery of an important class of chemotherapeutic substances, the sulfa drugs. These chemicals, easily synthesized in the laboratory, are derivatives of sulfonic acids. These acids are prepared by treating benzene and related compounds with sulfuric acid. The sulfa drugs are important weapons against infections.

◻ 29.1 Occurrence of sulfur

Sulfur is one of the elements known since ancient times. It occurs in nature as the free element or combined with other elements in sulfides and sulfates.

The United States is the greatest producer of sulfur. Huge deposits of nearly pure sulfur occur between 150 and 600 meters underground in Texas and Louisiana, near the Gulf of Mexico.

The Voyager mission has discovered at least eight active volcanoes on Jupiter's moon Io. The gas vented from these volcanoes is believed to contain sulfur. The colors of Io's surface can be explained by the colors of various forms of sulfur.

SULFUR

In this chapter you will gain an understanding of:

- **the occurrence and production of sulfur**
- **the chemical and physical properties of sulfur**
- **the allotropic forms of sulfur**
- **the uses of sulfur**
- **the important compounds of sulfur: sulfur dioxide, sulfurous acid, sulfuric acid**
- **acid rain**

Figure 29-1. A portion of the highly colored surface of Io, one of the moons of Jupiter. The photo shows the eruption of one of the volcanoes on Io. The gas from these volcanoes is believed to contain sulfur. The colors of Io's surface are similar to the colors of various forms of sulfur.

607

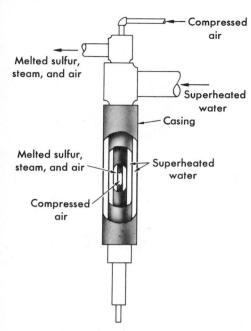

Figure 29-2. The system of concentric pipes used in the Frasch process of mining sulfur.

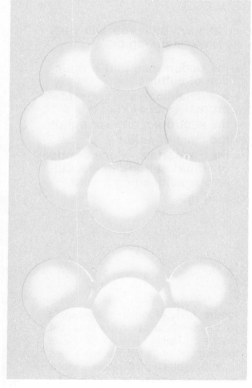

Figure 29-3. The structure of S_8 molecules of sulfur.

☐ 29.2 The production of sulfur

The sulfur beds in Texas and Louisiana are as much as 60 meters thick. Between the surface of the ground and the sulfur there is usually a layer of quicksand. This makes it difficult to sink a shaft and mine the sulfur by ordinary methods.

The American chemist Herman Frasch (1852–1914) developed a method for obtaining the sulfur without sinking a shaft. This method uses a complex system of pipes. Superheated water (170 °C, under pressure) is pumped into the sulfur deposit. The hot water melts the sulfur, which is then forced to the surface by compressed air. See Figure 29-2.

Elemental sulfur is also obtained from pyrite (FeS_2), coke oven gas, smelter gases, petroleum, and natural gas by various chemical processes.

In 1979, the total United States production of elemental sulfur was nearly 12 million metric tons.

☐ 29.3 Physical properties of sulfur

Common sulfur is a yellow, *odorless* solid. It is practically insoluble in water and is twice as dense as water. It dissolves readily in carbon disulfide and less readily in carbon tetrachloride.

Sulfur melts at a temperature of 112.8 °C, forming a pale yellow liquid that flows easily. When heated to a higher temperature, it becomes more *viscous* (thicker), instead of flowing more easily as liquids usually do. At a temperature above about 160 °C, melted sulfur becomes so thick that it hardly flows at all. As the temperature rises, the color changes from a light yellow to a reddish-brown, and then almost to black. Near its boiling point the liquid again flows freely. Sulfur boils at 445 °C. This unusual behavior is caused by the properties of different allotropes of liquid sulfur, allotropes formed at different temperatures.

☐ 29.4 Allotropes of sulfur

Sulfur exists in several different solid and liquid allotropic forms. These forms are produced by different arrangements of groups of sulfur atoms.

1. Rhombic sulfur. This form of solid sulfur is stable at ordinary temperatures. It consists of eight-membered, puckered rings of sulfur atoms. The sulfur atoms are connected in these rings by single covalent bonds. See Figure 29-3. Crystals of rhombic sulfur are prepared by dissolving sulfur in carbon disulfide and then allowing the solvent to evaporate slowly. The density of rhombic sulfur is 2.07 g/cm³.

2. Monoclinic sulfur. Sulfur can also be crystallized in the form of long needle-like monoclinic crystals. This allotropic form is prepared by first melting some sulfur in a crucible at as low a temperature as possible. Next the sulfur is allowed to cool slowly until a crust begins to form. The crust is broken and the remaining liquid sulfur is poured off. A mass of monoclinic crystals is then found lining the walls of the crucible. Heat energy must be added to produce this type of sulfur. When such crystals cool below 95 °C, they gradually change back into the rhombic form. In monoclinic sulfur, eight-membered rings of sulfur atoms are arranged in a monoclinic crystal pattern. The density of monoclinic sulfur is 1.96 g/cm^3.

3. *λ-sulfur. (Lambda-sulfur.)* This is the liquid allotropic form of sulfur produced at temperatures just above the melting point. It flows easily and has a straw-yellow color. It is believed to consist of eight-membered rings of sulfur atoms. The rounded shape of these S_8 molecules enables them to roll over one another easily, giving this form of sulfur its fluidity.

4. *μ-sulfur. (Mu-sulfur.)* If λ-sulfur is heated to about 160 °C, it darkens to a reddish and then almost black liquid. The melted sulfur becomes so viscous that it does not flow. It is thought that the heating gives enough energy to the sulfur atoms to break some of the eight-membered rings. When a ring of sulfur atoms breaks open, the sulfur atoms on either side of the break are each left with an unshared electron. These sulfur atoms form bonds with similar sulfur atoms from other open rings. In this way, long chains of sulfur atoms are formed. These chains are another allotropic form of sulfur, μ-sulfur. The dark color of μ-sulfur arises from the greater absorption of light by electrons from the broken ring structure. In μ-sulfur these electrons are free to migrate along the chain structure.

The high viscosity of μ-sulfur is explained by the tangling of the sulfur-atom chains. As the temperature is raised, however, these chains break up into smaller groups of atoms. The mass then flows more easily. The color becomes still darker because more free electrons, which absorb more light, are produced by the breaking of chains.

Sulfur vapor, produced when sulfur boils at 445 °C, also consists of S_8 molecules. If sulfur vapor is heated to a higher temperature, these molecules gradually dissociate into S_6 and then S_2 molecules. Monatomic molecules of sulfur are produced at very high temperatures.

5. *Amorphous sulfur.* Amorphous sulfur is a rubbery, plastic mass made by pouring boiling sulfur into cold water. It is dark brown or even black in color and is elastic like rubber. At the boiling point of sulfur, the long tangled chains of μ-sulfur have largely broken down, and the sulfur is fluid again. Eight-membered rings of sulfur atoms and chains are in equilibrium. The S_8 rings are evaporating. When this boiling mixture is suddenly cooled, the chains of μ-sulfur have no time to re-form into rings. Instead, amorphous sulfur is produced. A mass of amorphous sulfur soon loses its elasticity and becomes hard and brittle. For amorphous

Figure 29-4. Part of a chain of sulfur atoms as found in μ-sulfur (mu-sulfur).

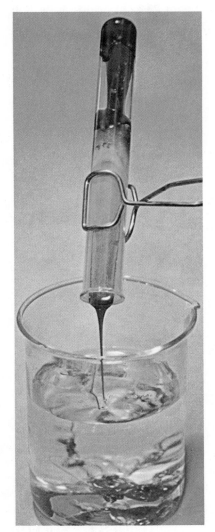

Figure 29-5. The sudden cooling of μ-sulfur produces the allotropic amorphous sulfur.

Figure 29-6. Elemental sulfur is a yellow nonmetallic solid. The photo shows sulfur being loaded into railroad cars.

sulfur, at room temperature, the successive changes into allotropic forms occur in reverse order; eventually the amorphous sulfur again becomes the S_8 arrangement of stable rhombic sulfur. Amorphous sulfur is insoluble in carbon disulfide.

29.5 Chemical properties of sulfur

At room temperature, sulfur is not very active chemically. When heated, sulfur combines with oxygen to produce sulfur dioxide.

$$S(s) + O_2(g) \rightarrow SO_2(g)$$

Traces of sulfur trioxide, SO_3, also form when sulfur burns in the air. Sulfur can be made to combine with nonmetals such as hydrogen, carbon, and chlorine. However, such compounds are formed with difficulty and are not very stable.

The formulas SO_3, SO_2, and H_2S indicate that sulfur can have oxidation numbers of +6 or +4 when combined with oxygen, and −2 when combined with hydrogen. Electron-dot formulas for these compounds are shown below.

sulfur trioxide   sulfur dioxide   hydrogen sulfide

The reaction between powdered zinc and powdered sulfur is shown in Figure 2-11.

The actual molecules of sulfur trioxide and sulfur dioxide are resonance hybrids of the possible structures given.

Sulfur combines directly with all metals except gold and platinum. Powdered zinc and sulfur combine vigorously. The heat produced when iron filings and sulfur unite causes the whole mass to glow red hot. Copper unites with the vapor of boiling sulfur to form copper(I) sulfide.

29.6 Uses of sulfur

Sulfur is used in making sulfur dioxide, carbon disulfide, sulfuric acid, and other sulfur compounds. Several million tons are used annually to make sulfuric acid. Matches, fireworks, and black gunpowder all contain either sulfur or sulfur compounds. Sulfur is used in the preparation of certain dyes, medicines, and fungicides. It is also used in the vulcanization of rubber. (See Section 18.26.) New uses for sulfur are in a sulfur concrete and a sulfur asphalt for road building.

OXIDES OF SULFUR

29.7 Occurrence of sulfur dioxide

Traces of sulfur dioxide get into the air from several sources. Sulfur dioxide occurs in some volcanic gases and in some mineral waters. Coal and fuel oil may contain sulfur as an impurity. As these fuels are burned, the sulfur burns to sulfur dioxide. Coal and fuel oil of low sulfur content produce less sulfur dioxide air pollution than similar fuels of high sulfur content.

The roasting of sulfide ores converts the sulfur in the ore to sulfur dioxide. In modern smelting plants, this sulfur dioxide is converted to sulfuric acid.

◱ 29.8 Preparation of sulfur dioxide

1. By burning sulfur. The simplest way to prepare sulfur dioxide is to burn sulfur in air or in pure oxygen.

$$S(s) + O_2(g) \rightarrow SO_2(g)$$

2. By roasting sulfides. Huge quantities of sulfur dioxide are produced by roasting sulfide ores. The roasting of zinc sulfide ore is typical.

$$2ZnS(s) + 3O_2(g) \rightarrow 2ZnO(s) + 2SO_2(g)$$

Sulfur dioxide is a by-product in this operation.

3. By the reduction of sulfuric acid. In one laboratory method of preparing this gas, copper is heated with concentrated sulfuric acid. See Figure 29-7.

$$Cu(s) + 2H_2SO_4(aq) \rightarrow CuSO_4(aq) + 2H_2O(l) + SO_2(g)$$

4. By the decomposition of sulfites. In this second laboratory method, sulfur dioxide is formed by the action of a strong acid on a sulfite.

$$Na_2SO_3(aq) + H_2SO_4(aq) \rightarrow Na_2SO_4(aq) + H_2O(l) + SO_2(g)$$

Sulfurous acid, H_2SO_3, is first formed. It then decomposes into water and sulfur dioxide. See Figure 29-8.

◱ 29.9 Physical properties of sulfur dioxide

Pure sulfur dioxide is a colorless gas with a suffocating, choking odor. It is more than twice as dense as air and is very soluble in water. It is one of the easiest gases to liquefy, becoming liquid at room temperature under a pressure of about three atmospheres.

◱ 29.10 Chemical properties of sulfur dioxide

1. It is an acid anhydride. Sulfur dioxide is the anhydride of sulfurous acid. As it dissolves in water, it also reacts with the water.

$$SO_2(aq) + H_2O(l) \rightleftarrows H_2SO_3(aq)$$

This reaction partly accounts for the high solubility of sulfur dioxide in water. Sulfurous acid is a weak acid. It turns litmus paper red, neutralizes hydroxides, and forms hydrogen sulfites

Copper and hot, concentrated sulfuric acid

Sulfur dioxide

Figure 29-7. Sulfur dioxide can be prepared in the laboratory by reducing hot, concentrated sulfuric acid with copper. The gas is collected by upward displacement of air. This preparation should be performed in a hood to prevent the escape of sulfur dioxide with its suffocating, choking odor.

The conditions for liquefying gases are described in Sections 12.7 and 12.8.

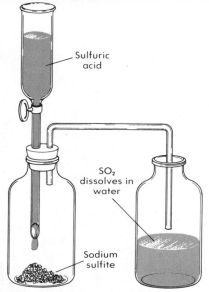

Figure 29-8. An acid added to a sulfite forms unstable sulfurous acid, which decomposes into sulfur dioxide and water. Here the sulfur dioxide is being passed into a wide-mouth bottle partly filled with water. The sulfur dioxide will dissolve in the water to form sulfurous acid. This preparation should also be performed in a hood.

Figure 29-9. A dual alkali scrubbing system used to remove sulfur dioxide from flue gases at a coal-burning electric generating station.

and sulfites. If exposed to the air, a solution of sulfurous acid reacts slowly with oxygen to form sulfuric acid.

2. It is a stable gas. Sulfur dioxide does not burn. With a suitable catalyst and at a high temperature, it can be oxidized to sulfur trioxide.

$$2SO_2(g) + O_2(g) \rightleftarrows 2SO_3(g)$$

29.11 Uses for sulfur dioxide and sulfurous acid

1. For making sulfuric acid. In the chemical industry, great quantities of sulfur dioxide are oxidized to sulfur trioxide. The sulfur trioxide is then combined with water, forming sulfuric acid. (See Section 29.13.)

2. As a preservative. Dried fruits such as apricots and prunes are treated with sulfur dioxide, which acts as a preservative.

3. For bleaching. Sulfurous acid does not harm the fibers of wool, silk, straw, or paper. Thus, it can be used to bleach these materials. It is believed that sulfurous acid converts the colored compounds in these materials to colorless sulfites.

4. In preparing paper pulp. Sulfurous acid reacts with limestone to form calcium hydrogen sulfite, $Ca(HSO_3)_2$. Wood chips are heated in calcium hydrogen sulfite solution as a first step in paper-making. The hot solution dissolves the lignin, which binds the cellulose fibers of wood together. The cellulose fibers are left unchanged and are processed to form paper.

29.12 Acid rain

Sulfur dioxide is produced when sulfur-containing coal is burned or when sulfide ores are smelted. The waste gases of newer industrial plants are treated to remove sulfur dioxide. But millions of metric tons still enters the atmosphere annually. Sulfur dioxide reacts with oxygen and water vapor in the air to form sulfuric acid.

Oxides of nitrogen, principally nitrogen monoxide, NO, and nitrogen dioxide, NO_2, get into the air as combustion products of coal and automobile engines (as described in Section 28.4). Nitrogen monoxide reacts with oxygen in the air to form nitrogen dioxide. Nitrogen dioxide reacts with water vapor in the air to form nitric acid.

Oxide and acid pollutants of both sulfur and nitrogen can be carried many miles through the atmosphere by the prevailing winds.

The pH of normal rainwater is 5.6. This slight acidity is caused by dissolved carbon dioxide. Carbon dioxide reacts with water to form hydronium ions and hydrogen carbonate ions, as explained in Section 17.18. Sulfuric acid and nitric acid are both very soluble in water and readily dissolve in falling raindrops. The pH of such rainwater ranges from 4.5 to 4.0, but in extreme cases can be as low as 2.4. Rainwater having a pH below 5.6 is called *acid rain*.

Acid rain may fall many miles away from the sources of sulfur dioxide and oxides of nitrogen. Where it falls, acid rain may be harmful to plant and animal life. More needs to be learned about the effects of acid rain and about methods to minimize the release of sulfur dioxide and oxides of nitrogen into the atmosphere.

☐ 29.13 Preparation of sulfuric acid

Most of the sulfuric acid produced in the United States today is made by the contact process. In this process, sulfur dioxide is prepared by burning sulfur or by roasting iron pyrite, FeS_2. Impurities that might combine with and ruin the catalyst used in the process are removed from the sulfur dioxide gas. The purified sulfur dioxide is mixed with air and passed through heated iron pipes. These pipes contain the catalyst, usually divanadium pentoxide, V_2O_5. This close "contact" of the sulfur dioxide and the catalyst gives the *contact process* its name. Sulfur dioxide and oxygen of the air are both adsorbed on the surface of the catalyst. There they react to form sulfur trioxide. See Figure 29-10.

The sulfur trioxide is then dissolved in approximately 98% sulfuric acid. Sulfur trioxide combines readily and smoothly with sulfuric acid, forming pyrosulfuric acid, $H_2S_2O_7$.

$$SO_3(g) + H_2SO_4(l) \rightarrow H_2S_2O_7(l)$$

When diluted with water, pyrosulfuric acid yields sulfuric acid.

$$H_2S_2O_7(l) + H_2O(l) \rightarrow 2H_2SO_4(l)$$

Very pure, highly concentrated sulfuric acid is produced by the contact process.

In terms of tonnage, sulfuric acid ranks first among the substances produced by the United States chemical industry. In 1979, about 38 million metric tons was prepared.

☐ 29.14 Physical properties of sulfuric acid

Concentrated sulfuric acid is a dense, oily, colorless liquid. It contains about 2% water, has a density of about 1.84 g/mL, and a boiling point of 338 °C.

When sulfuric acid is added to water, a large amount of heat is released as the hydrates $H_2SO_4 \cdot H_2O$ and $H_2SO_4 \cdot 2H_2O$ are formed.

CAUTION: *Never add water to sulfuric acid.*

☐ 29.15 Chemical properties of sulfuric acid

1. Its acid properties. Sulfuric acid is a diprotic acid. It ionizes in dilute water solution in two stages:

$$H_2SO_4 + H_2O \rightleftarrows H_3O^+ + HSO_4^-$$

$$HSO_4^- + H_2O \rightleftarrows H_3O^+ + SO_4^{--} \qquad K_i = 1.26 \times 10^{-2}$$

SULFURIC ACID

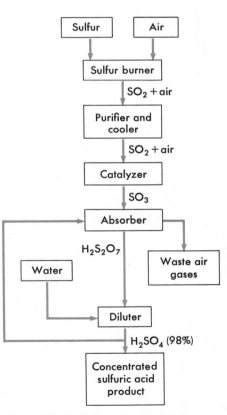

Figure 29-10. A flow diagram of the contact process for manufacturing sulfuric acid.

At 25 °C, 0.1-M H_2SO_4 is completely ionized in the first stage and about 10% ionized in the second stage. Sulfuric acid reacts with hydroxides to form hydrogen sulfates and sulfates. It reacts with metals and with the oxides of metals. Dilute sulfuric acid is more highly ionized than cold, concentrated sulfuric acid. Thus the dilute acid reacts more vigorously than the cold, concentrated acid with metals above hydrogen in the oxidizing and reducing agents series. See Table 22-3 for this series.

2. Its oxidizing properties. Hot, concentrated sulfuric acid is a vigorous oxidizing agent. The sulfur is reduced from the $+6$ oxidation state to the $+4$ or -2 oxidation state. The extent of the reduction depends on the strength of the acid and on the reducing agent used.

3. Its dehydrating properties. The strong attraction of sulfuric acid for water makes it a very good *dehydrating* agent. Gases that do not react with sulfuric acid can be dried by bubbling them through the concentrated acid. Sulfuric acid is such an active dehydrating agent that it takes hydrogen and oxygen *directly and in the proportion found in water* from certain substances. For example, it does so with cellulose, $(C_6H_{10}O_5)_n$, and sucrose, $C_{12}H_{22}O_{11}$, leaving the carbon uncombined. The equation for this process with sucrose is

The dehydration of formic acid by sulfuric acid to prepare carbon monoxide is described in Section 17.21.

$$C_{12}H_{22}O_{11} + 11H_2SO_4 \rightarrow 12C + 11H_2SO_4 \cdot H_2O$$

In some commercial chemical processes, water is formed as a by-product. The production of nitroglycerin, $C_3H_5(NO_3)_3$, is such a process.

$$C_3H_5(OH)_3 + 3HNO_3 \rightarrow C_3H_5(NO_3)_3 + 3H_2O$$

The sulfuric acid acts as a dehydrating agent. It absorbs the water as fast as it is formed and maintains the reaction rate.
CAUTION: *Sulfuric acid burns the flesh severely.* The burns are the result of its dehydrating action on the skin. Handling sulfuric acid requires constant care to prevent its contact with the skin.

◻ 29.16 Uses of sulfuric acid

Calcium phosphate, $Ca_3(PO_4)_2$, is found in great quantities especially in Florida and Tennessee. It is treated with sulfuric acid (about 4 million metric tons/year) to make it more soluble. The soluble form is used as *superphosphate* fertilizer.

Sulfuric acid is also used in making phosphoric and other acids, various sulfates, and many chemicals.

The iron and steel industries consume large quantities of sulfuric acid. The acid removes oxides from the surface of iron or steel before the metal is plated or coated with an enamel.

In petroleum refining, sulfuric acid is used to remove certain organic impurities. The electrolyte in lead storage batteries is dilute sulfuric acid.

Sulfuric acid serves as a dehydrating agent in the production of smokeless powder and nitroglycerin. It is used in making photographic film, nitrocellulose plastics, and rayon. It is useful in producing paints and pigments, cellophane, and thousands of other commercial articles.

◖ SUMMARY

Sulfur occurs in nature as the free element or combined with other elements in sulfides and sulfates. The Frasch process is used to mine sulfur in Texas and Louisiana. Elemental sulfur is also obtained from pyrite and from the purification of coke oven gas, smelter gases, petroleum, and natural gas.

Ordinary sulfur is a yellow, odorless solid that is practically insoluble in water. It is soluble in carbon disulfide and in carbon tetrachloride. Sulfur exists in several allotropic forms. The solid allotropes are rhombic, monoclinic, and amorphous sulfur. The liquid allotropes are lambda- and mu-sulfur. Sulfur is not very active chemically at room temperature. When heated, sulfur combines with oxygen to form sulfur dioxide. Zinc, iron, and copper unite with sulfur at elevated temperatures to form sulfides. Sulfur is used for making sulfur dioxide, carbon disulfide, sulfuric acid, and other sulfur compounds.

Sulfur dioxide is produced by (1) burning sulfur, (2) roasting sulfides, (3) the reduction of sulfuric acid, and (4) the decomposition of sulfites. It is a dense, suffocating gas that is easily liquefied and extremely soluble in water. Sulfur dioxide is the anhydride of sulfurous acid. It does not burn and is a fairly stable compound. With a suitable catalyst, sulfur dioxide can be oxidized to sulfur trioxide.

Sulfur dioxide is used for making sulfuric acid and sulfites. It is also used for bleaching, as a preservative, and in preparing paper pulp.

Acid rain is rain with a pH below 5.6. Oxides of sulfur and nitrogen react with oxygen and water vapor in the air to form sulfuric acid and nitric acid, the chief pollutants in acid rain.

Sulfuric acid is made from sulfur dioxide, oxygen, and water by the contact process. It is a dense, oily, colorless liquid that is soluble in water in all proportions. In dilute form, it acts as an acid. When hot and concentrated, it is a vigorous oxidizing agent. It is also a good dehydrating agent. Sulfuric acid is one of the most important chemicals used in industry. Some of its uses are (1) in making fertilizer, (2) in making phosphoric acid, (3) in cleaning metals, (4) in petroleum refining, (5) as the electrolyte in lead storage batteries, and (6) in producing explosives.

◖ VOCABULARY

acid rain	dehydrating agent	monoclinic sulfur	rhombic sulfur
amorphous sulfur	Frasch process	mu-sulfur	superphosphate
contact process	lambda-sulfur	pyrite	viscous

◖ QUESTIONS

Group A

1. Where are sulfur deposits located in the United States?
2. (*a*) What is the function of the superheated water in the Frasch process? (*b*) the function of the compressed air? (*c*) Why is this process used instead of more common mining methods?
3. (*a*) What is the odor of sulfur? (*b*) of sulfur dioxide?

4. A pupil prepared some nearly black amorphous sulfur in the laboratory. When it was examined the following week, it had become brittle and much lighter in color. Explain.
5. What are the uses of elemental sulfur?
6. Sulfur dioxide may be found as an impurity in the air. From what sources does it come?
7. Write balanced formula equations for (a) a commercial preparation of sulfur dioxide; (b) a laboratory preparation of sulfur dioxide.
8. (a) What method of gas collection is used in a laboratory preparation of sulfur dioxide? (b) What properties of sulfur dioxide determine this choice?
9. What is the principal use for sulfur dioxide?
10. Write balanced chemical equations to show the formation from sulfurous acid and sodium hydroxide of (a) sodium hydrogen sulfite; (b) sodium sulfite.
11. (a) What is the pH of normal rainwater? (b) Why is the pH not 7.0?
12. Why is the contact process for producing sulfuric acid so named?
13. What is the proper method of diluting sulfuric acid?
14. Why are large quantities of sulfuric acid used in the iron and steel industries?
15. Why is a mixture of nitric acid and sulfuric acid used in making nitroglycerin?

Group B

16. (a) What is the molecular formula for rhombic sulfur? (b) Why do you suppose this molecular formula is not usually used in formula equations?
17. Explain the changes in color and fluidity of sulfur between its melting point and boiling point.
18. Is the change from rhombic sulfur to monoclinic sulfur exothermic or endothermic? Explain.
19. Draw electron-dot formulas to show the resonance structure of sulfur dioxide.
20. Is sulfur dioxide easy or difficult to liquefy? Explain.
21. Why is sulfur dioxide so soluble in water?
22. Explain how the sulfuric acid in acid rain is formed.
23. Balance the following oxidation-reduction equations:
    (a) $Hg + H_2SO_4 \rightarrow HgSO_4 + SO_2(g) + H_2O$
    (b) $Cu_2S + O_2 \rightarrow Cu_2O + SO_2(g)$
24. Give two reasons why boiling concentrated sulfuric acid burns the flesh so badly.

◖ PROBLEMS

Group A

1. How many kilograms of sulfur dioxide can be produced by burning 1.0 kg of pure sulfur?
2. What is the empirical formula for a sulfide containing 86.6% lead?
3. What is the percentage composition of H_2SO_4?
4. How many grams of sodium sulfite are needed to produce 1.00 L of sulfur dioxide at STP by reaction with sulfuric acid?
5. A lead smelter processes 5 0̄0 metric tons of zinc sulfide, ZnS, each day. If no sulfur dioxide is lost, how many kilograms of sulfuric acid could be made in the plant daily?

Group B

6. How many kilograms of sulfuric acid can be prepared from 5.00 kg of sulfur that is 99.5% pure?
7. How many liters of sulfur dioxide at 25 °C and 74 0̄ mm pressure can be produced by roasting 12 0̄0 kg of iron pyrite, FeS_2?
8. (a) If 14 0̄ kg of scrap iron is added to a large vat of dilute sulfuric acid, how many kilograms of iron(II) sulfate can be produced? (b) How many kilograms of 95% sulfuric acid are required?
9. How many liters of sulfur dioxide at STP can be prepared from a mixture of 10 0̄ g of copper and 10 0̄ g of H_2SO_4?
10. For barium sulfate, $K_{sp} = 1.5 \times 10^{-9}$. If a barium chloride solution is 0.01 M, what is the smallest sulfate ion concentration that can be detected by precipitation?

The Halogen Family

The halogenated hydrocarbons play important roles in modern society. Dichlorodifluoromethane, a Freon compound used as a refrigerant, has made the once-inconvenient processes of preserving, storing, and transporting food as easy as going to the kitchen refrigerator. DDT, another halogenated hydrocarbon, is a potent insecticide that has provided farmers with a powerful weapon against plant-destroying insects. Without the plasticizer PCB, life would be dull. Plastics made with it are used in tapes, phonograph records, athletic equipment, and thousands of other recreational products. These marvels of chemical ingenuity have also created many problems. It is believed that Freon depletes the layer of atmospheric ozone that shields us from cosmic radiation. DDT and PCB have been found to adversely affect living things. These unfortunate effects have prompted chemists to evaluate the products of chemical research in terms of their effect on the environment.

☐ 30.1 The Halogen Family: Group VII of the Periodic Table

The members of the Halogen Family are the colorful, active elements fluorine, chlorine, bromine, iodine, and astatine. Figure 30-1 shows samples of the first four of these elements. Table 30-1 gives some data about them.

The atoms of each halogen have seven electrons in the outer shell. The addition of one electron to a *halogen* atom converts it to a *halide* ion having an outer octet of electrons. Using a chlorine atom as an example,

$$:\ddot{\underset{.}{Cl}}: + e^- \rightarrow :\ddot{\underset{..}{Cl}}:^-$$

The halogens are all active elements that have high electronegativities. They are very rarely found free in nature. In the elemental state they exist as covalent, diatomic molecules.

Fluorine has the smallest atoms in the Halogen Family. It has a strong attraction for electrons. Fluorine is both the most highly electronegative element and the most active nonmetal. Because of these properties, fluorine cannot be prepared from its compounds by chemical reduction. It must be prepared by electrolysis.

The other halogens, with increasingly larger atoms, are less electronegative than fluorine. As a result, the smaller, lighter halogens can replace and oxidize the larger, heavier halogens from their compounds. Astatine is a synthetic radioactive halogen.

In this chapter you will gain an understanding of:

- the electron configurations of the members of the halogen family
- the regular change in properties of the halogen family: ionization energy, electron affinity, electronegativity
- the preparation, properties, and uses of fluorine, chlorine, bromine, and iodine
- the properties and uses of the major halogen compounds

Reactions involving the replacement of halogens are described in Section 8.6(4).

Figure 30-1. The halogens are colorful elements. Fluorine is a pale-yellow gas; chlorine, a greenish-yellow gas; bromine, a reddish-brown liquid; iodine, a bluish-black crystalline solid.

Table 30-1 clearly shows the regular change in properties that occurs in this family. This change in properties proceeds from the smallest and lightest atom to the largest and heaviest one. You should refer to Figures 5-7, 5-10, and 6-14 while studying Table 30-1. These figures provide ionization energy, electron affinity, and electronegativity data for members of the Halogen Family.

Each of the halogens combines with hydrogen. The great electronegativity difference between hydrogen and fluorine explains why hydrogen fluoride molecules are so polar that they associate by hydrogen bonding. The remaining hydrogen halides have smaller electronegativity differences and do not show this property. All hydrogen halides are colorless gases that are highly ionized in water solution. Hydrofluoric acid is a weak acid because hydronium ions are strongly hydrogen bonded to fluoride ions. The other binary halogen acids are highly dissociated, strong acids.

Each of the halogens forms ionic salts with metals. Hence the name *halogen,* which means "salt producer."

FLUORINE

❐ 30.2 Preparation and properties of fluorine

Fluorine is prepared by electrolyzing a mixture of potassium fluoride and hydrogen fluoride. A steel and Monel metal electrolytic cell with a carbon anode is used. The fluoride coating that forms on these metals protects them from further reaction.

Fluorine is the most active nonmetallic element. It unites with hydrogen explosively, even in the dark. It forms compounds with all elements except helium, neon, and argon. There are no known positive oxidation states of fluorine. It forms salts known as *fluorides.* Fluorine reacts with gold and platinum slowly. Special carbon steel containers are used to transport fluorine. These containers become coated with iron fluoride, which resists further action.

❐ 30.3 Usefulness of fluorine compounds

The mineral fluorspar, CaF_2, is used in preparing most fluorine compounds. Sodium fluoride is used as a poison for destroying roaches, rats, and other pests. A trace of sodium fluoride, or the less expensive sodium silicofluoride, is added to drinking water in many areas to help prevent tooth decay. For this reason, fluorides have also been added to some toothpastes.

One of the Freons, dichlorodifluoromethane, CCl_2F_2, is used as a refrigerant. It is odorless, nonflammable, and nontoxic. In producing aluminum, melted cryolite, $AlF_3 \cdot 3NaF$, is used as a solvent for aluminum oxide. Uranium is changed to uranium

Table 30-1
THE HALOGEN FAMILY

Element	Atomic number	Atomic weight	Electron configuration	Principal oxidation number	Melting point (°C)	Boiling point (°C)	Color	Density, 0 °C	Atomic radius (Å)	Ionic radius (Å)
fluorine	9	18.998403	2,7	−1	−219.6	−188.1	pale-yellow gas	1.696 g/L	0.68	1.33
chlorine	17	35.453	2,8,7	−1	−101.0	−34.6	greenish-yellow gas	3.214 g/L	0.99	1.81
bromine	35	79.904	2,8,18,7	−1	−7.2	58.78	reddish-brown liquid	3.12 g/mL	1.14	1.96
iodine	53	126.9045	2,8,18,18,7	−1	113.5	184.35	bluish-black crystals	4.93 g/mL	1.33	2.20
astatine	85	210	2,8,18,32,18,7	−1	302	337			1.45	

hexafluoride gas, UF_6, in the process for separating the uranium isotopes.

Fluorine combines with the noble gases krypton, xenon, and radon. Two fluorides of krypton, KrF_2 and KrF_4, are prepared by passing electricity through krypton-fluorine mixtures. This process is carried out at the temperature of liquid nitrogen. At room temperature the krypton fluorides are not stable and decompose quickly.

Three fluorides of xenon, XeF_2, XeF_4, and XeF_6, have been made. All are white solids at ordinary temperatures. XeF_6 is the most highly reactive. Each of the three compounds reacts with hydrogen to produce elemental xenon and hydrogen fluoride. With water, XeF_2 produces xenon, oxygen, and hydrogen fluoride. The other two fluorides react with water to yield xenon trioxide, XeO_3, a colorless, highly explosive solid.

Hydrofluoric acid, HF, is used as a catalyst in producing high-octane gasoline. It is also used in making synthetic cryolite for aluminum production. For many years hydrofluoric acid has been used for etching glass. Glassware is given a frosty appearance by exposing it to hydrogen fluoride fumes.

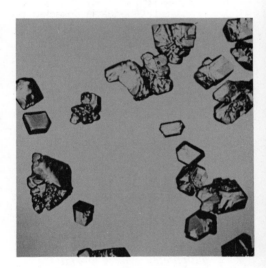

Figure 30-2. Crystals of xenon tetra-fluoride.

◻ 30.4 Wide occurrence of compounds

Chlorine is rarely found uncombined in nature. Elemental chlorine is found in small amounts in some volcanic gases. Chlorides of sodium, potassium, and magnesium are fairly abundant. Common table salt, sodium chloride, is a widely distributed compound. It is found in sea water, in salt brines underground, and in rock salt deposits. Sodium chloride is the commercial source of chlorine.

CHLORINE

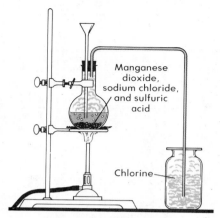

Figure 30-3. One method of preparing chlorine in the laboratory is by heating a mixture of manganese dioxide, sodium chloride, and sulfuric acid. Chlorine is collected by upward displacement of air. The preparation should be performed in a hood.

☐ 30.5 Preparation of chlorine

The element chlorine was first isolated in 1774 by Carl Wilhelm Scheele, the codiscoverer of oxygen. The preparation of elemental chlorine involves the oxidation of chloride ions. Strong oxidizing agents are required.

1. By the electrolysis of sodium chloride. Chlorine is most often prepared by the electrolysis of sodium chloride in water solution. The concentration of the solution is such that hydrogen from the water is released at the cathode, and chlorine is set free at the anode. The hydrogen and chlorine gases are kept separate from each other and from the solution by asbestos partitions. The sodium and hydroxide ions remaining in the solution are recovered as sodium hydroxide.

$$2NaCl(aq) + 2H_2O(l) \xrightarrow{\text{(electricity)}} 2NaOH(aq) + H_2(g) + Cl_2(g)$$

2. By the oxidation of hydrogen chloride. This method involves heating a mixture of manganese dioxide and concentrated hydrochloric acid. The manganese oxidizes half of the chloride ions in the reacting HCl to chlorine atoms. Manganese is reduced during the reaction from the +4 oxidation state to the +2 state.

$$MnO_2(s) + 4HCl(aq) \rightarrow MnCl_2(aq) + 2H_2O(l) + Cl_2(g)$$

This is the method used by Scheele in first preparing chlorine. It is a useful laboratory preparation.

An alternate process involves heating a mixture of manganese dioxide, sodium chloride, and sulfuric acid.

$$2NaCl(s) + 2H_2SO_4(aq) + MnO_2(s) \rightarrow Na_2SO_4(aq) + MnSO_4(aq) + 2H_2O(l) + Cl_2(g)$$

In 1979 the commercial production of chlorine in the United States amounted to about 11 million metric tons. Chlorine ranked eighth among chemicals in terms of tonnage produced.

3. By the action of hydrochloric acid on calcium hypochlorite. Hydrochloric acid added drop by drop to calcium hypochlorite powder releases chlorine and forms calcium chloride and water.

$$4HCl(aq) + Ca(ClO)_2(s) \rightarrow CaCl_2(aq) + 2Cl_2(g) + 2H_2O(l)$$

☐ 30.6 Physical properties of chlorine

At room temperature, chlorine is a greenish-yellow gas with a disagreeable, suffocating odor. It is about 2.5 times as dense as air. It is moderately soluble in water, forming a pale greenish-yellow solution. Chlorine is easily liquefied and is usually marketed in steel cylinders.

When inhaled in small quantities, chlorine affects the mucous membranes of the nose and throat. If inhaled in larger quantities, chlorine is so poisonous that it may cause death.

☐ 30.7 Chemical properties of chlorine

The outer shell of a chlorine atom contains seven electrons. There are many reactions by which chlorine atoms can acquire an additional electron and complete the octet.

1. Action with metals. All metals react with chlorine directly. For example, when powdered antimony is sprinkled into a jar of moist chlorine, the two elements combine spontaneously, emitting a shower of sparks. Antimony trichloride is formed. See Figure 22-1.

$$2Sb(s) + 3Cl_2(g) \rightarrow 2SbCl_3(s)$$

In a similar manner, hot metallic sodium burns in chlorine to form sodium chloride. See Figure 6-2. Chlorine combines directly with such metals as copper, iron, zinc, and arsenic, if they are heated slightly.

2. Action with hydrogen. If hydrogen and chlorine are mixed in the dark, no reaction occurs. But such a mixture explodes violently if it is heated or exposed to sunlight. The heat or sunlight provides the activation energy. A jet of hydrogen that is burning in air will continue to burn if it is inserted into a bottle of chlorine.

$$H_2(g) + Cl_2(g) \rightarrow 2HCl(g)$$

The burning of hydrogen in chlorine is an example of combustion without the presence of oxygen.

Chlorine does not support the combustion of wood or paper. A paraffin candle, however, continues to burn in chlorine with a smoky flame. In this reaction the hydrogen of the paraffin combines with the chlorine, forming hydrogen chloride. The carbon is left uncombined.

3. Action with water. A freshly prepared solution of chlorine in water has a greenish-yellow color. If the solution stands in sunlight for a few days, both the color and the strong chlorine odor will disappear. The chlorine combines with the water to form hypochlorous acid and hydrochloric acid. Hypochlorous acid is unstable and decomposes into hydrochloric acid and oxygen.

$$2H_2O(l) + 2Cl_2(g) \rightarrow 2HClO(aq) + 2HCl(aq)$$
$$\searrow$$
$$2HCl(aq) + O_2(g)$$

The instability of hypochlorous acid makes chlorine water a good oxidizing agent.

30.8 Uses of chlorine

1. For bleaching. Bleaching solution is usually a solution of sodium hypochlorite. It is made by electrolyzing sodium chloride solution. The released chlorine is allowed to react with the sodium hydroxide that is produced at the same time. Sodium hypochlorite is also formed in a reaction between chlorine and sodium carbonate.

CAUTION: Chlorine destroys silk or wool fibers. *Never use commercial bleaches containing hypochlorites on silk or wool.*

Figure 30-4. Chlorine has such a great attraction for hydrogen that it can take hydrogen from some of its compounds. A paraffin candle will burn in chlorine. The hydrogen of the paraffin combines with the chlorine to form hydrogen chloride. The carbon is left uncombined as the smoke.

Figure 30-5. Chlorine is added to the water in swimming pools to maintain the bacterial content at a safe level.

2. As a disinfectant. Since moist chlorine is a good oxidizing agent, it destroys bacteria. Large quantities of chlorinated lime, $Ca(ClO)Cl$, are used as a disinfectant.

In city water systems, billions of gallons of water are treated with chlorine to kill disease-producing bacteria. The water in swimming pools is usually treated with chlorine. As part of the sewage purification process, chlorine is sometimes used to kill bacteria in sewage.

3. For making compounds. Because chlorine combines directly with many substances, it is used to produce a variety of compounds. Among these are aluminum chloride, Al_2Cl_6, used as a catalyst; carbon tetrachloride, CCl_4, a solvent; 1,1,2-trichloroethene, $CHCl{=}CCl_2$, a cleaning agent; and polyvinyl chloride, the polymer of vinyl chloride, $CH_2{=}CHCl$, a plastic.

◻ 30.9 Preparation of hydrogen chloride

In the laboratory, hydrogen chloride can be prepared by treating sodium chloride with concentrated sulfuric acid.

$$NaCl(s) + H_2SO_4(l) \rightarrow NaHSO_4(s) + HCl(g)$$

This same reaction, carried out at a higher temperature, is used commercially. Under this condition and if more NaCl is used, a second molecule of HCl can be produced per molecule of H_2SO_4.

$$2NaCl(s) + H_2SO_4(l) \rightarrow Na_2SO_4(s) + 2HCl(g)$$

Another commercial preparation involves the direct union of hydrogen and chlorine. Both elements are obtained by the electrolysis of concentrated sodium chloride solution. (See Section 30.5.)

By far the most important commercial source of hydrogen chloride is as a by-product of chlorination processes. Some of these processes are the chlorination of hydrocarbons described in Sections 18.12 and 18.21.

Hydrogen chloride dissolved in pure water is sold under the name of hydrochloric acid.

◻ 30.10 Physical properties of hydrogen chloride

Hydrogen chloride is a colorless gas with a sharp, penetrating odor. It is denser than air and extremely soluble in water. One volume of water at 0 °C dissolves more than 500 volumes of hydrogen chloride at standard pressure. Hydrogen chloride makes a fog with moist air. It is so soluble that it condenses water vapor from the air into tiny drops of hydrochloric acid.

◻ 30.11 Chemical properties of hydrogen chloride

Hydrogen chloride is a stable compound that does not burn. Some vigorous oxidizing agents react with it to form water and

Figure 30-6. The solutions used for cleaning buildings usually contain hydrochloric acid.

chlorine. The water solution of hydrogen chloride is a strong acid known as *hydrochloric acid*. Concentrated hydrochloric acid contains about 38% hydrogen chloride by weight and is about 1.2 times as dense as water. Hydrochloric acid reacts with metals above hydrogen in the activity series and with the oxides of metals. It neutralizes hydroxides, forming salts and water.

◻ 30.12 Uses of hydrochloric acid

Hydrochloric acid is used in preparing certain chlorides and in cleaning metals. This cleaning involves removing oxides and other forms of tarnish.

Some hydrochloric acid is essential in the process of digestion. The concentration of hydrochloric acid in gastric juice is 0.16 M.

◻ 30.13 Bromine from bromides   **BROMINE**

In the laboratory, bromine can be prepared by using manganese dioxide, sulfuric acid, and sodium bromide.

$$2NaBr(s) + MnO_2(s) + 2H_2SO_4(aq) \rightarrow Na_2SO_4(aq) + MnSO_4(aq) + 2H_2O(l) + Br_2(g)$$

This method is similar to the preparation of chlorine.

The commercial production of bromine from salt-well brines depends on the ability of chlorine to displace bromide ions from solution. Chlorine displaces bromide ions because it is more highly electronegative than bromine.

$$2Br^-(aq) + Cl_2(g) \rightarrow 2Cl^-(aq) + Br_2(l)$$

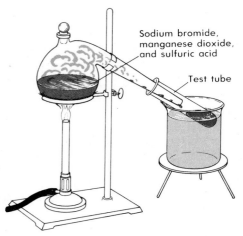

Figure 30-7. Bromine can be prepared in the laboratory by heating a mixture of sodium bromide, manganese dioxide, and sulfuric acid in a glass-stoppered retort. This preparation should be performed in a hood.

☐ 30.14 Physical properties of bromine

Bromine is a dark-red liquid that is about three times as dense as water. It evaporates readily, forming a vapor that burns the eyes and throat and has a very disagreeable odor. Bromine is moderately soluble in water. The reddish-brown water solution used in the laboratory is known as bromine water. Bromine dissolves readily in carbon tetrachloride, carbon disulfide, and water solutions of bromides.

CAUTION: *Use great care in handling bromine.* It burns the flesh and forms wounds that heal slowly.

☐ 30.15 Chemical properties of bromine

Bromine unites directly with hydrogen to form hydrogen bromide. It combines with most metals to form bromides. When it is moist, bromine is a good bleaching agent. Its water solution is a strong oxidizing agent that forms hydrobromic acid and oxygen in sunlight.

☐ 30.16 Uses of bromine compounds

Complex bromine-containing organic compounds are added to polyurethane and polystyrene plastics to make them flame retardant. Methyl bromide, CH_3Br, is used by farmers as a soil fumigant. Improved crop yields result from such treatment. Ethylene bromide, $C_2H_4Br_2$, increases the efficiency of lead tetraethyl in antiknock gasoline. Ethylene bromide is also used to control insects in grain and in the soil.

Silver bromide, AgBr, is a yellowish solid. It is highly photosensitive (sensitive to light rays) and is widely used in making photographic film. The bromides of sodium and potassium are

Figure 30-8. Hydrogen burns in an atmosphere of bromine vapor. Hydrogen bromide is formed.

used in medicine as sedatives. Such medicines should not be used unless prescribed by a physician. Certain bromine compounds may be used as disinfectants.

☐ 30.17 Preparation of iodine

The laboratory preparation of iodine is similar to that of chlorine and bromine. An iodide is heated with manganese dioxide and sulfuric acid.

$$2NaI(s) + MnO_2(s) + 2H_2SO_4(aq) \rightarrow Na_2SO_4(aq) + MnSO_4(aq) + 2H_2O(l) + I_2(g)$$

The iodine is driven off as a vapor. It can be condensed as a solid on the walls of a cold dish or beaker.

☐ 30.18 Physical properties of iodine

Iodine is a steel-gray solid. When heated it sublimes (vaporizes without melting) and produces a violet-colored vapor. The odor of this vapor is irritating, resembling that of chlorine.

Iodine is very slightly soluble in water. It is much more soluble in water solutions of sodium or potassium iodide. With these solutions it forms complex I_3^- ions. It dissolves readily in alcohol, forming a dark-brown solution. It is very soluble in carbon disulfide and carbon tetrachloride, giving a rich purple color.

☐ 30.19 Chemical properties of iodine

Iodine is active chemically, though less so than either bromine or chlorine. It combines with metals to form iodides. It can also form compounds with all nonmetals except sulfur, selenium, and the noble gases. Iodine reacts with organic compounds just as chlorine and bromine do. But since the carbon-iodine bond is not strong, many of the compounds formed decompose readily.

☐ 30.20 Uses of iodine

Iodine is most useful as a disinfectant. Iodine complexed (loosely bonded) with certain organic compounds is used as an antiseptic on the skin. Detergents with which iodine is complexed make good combination cleaning-and-sanitizing agents. Iodine and some iodine compounds are used as catalysts in certain organic reactions.

☐ 30.21 Uses of iodides

Silver iodide is a light-sensitive compound used in photographic film. Potassium iodide is added to table salt to provide the iodine necessary for proper nutrition.

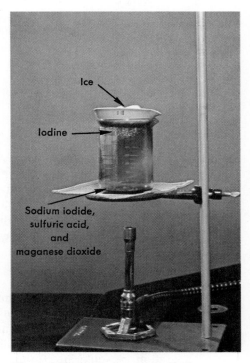

Figure 30-9. Iodine is prepared in the laboratory by heating sodium iodide and manganese dioxide with sulfuric acid.

◀ SUMMARY

The Halogen Family consists of the highly electronegative elements fluorine, chlorine, bromine, iodine, and astatine. The atoms of each halogen have seven electrons in the outermost shell. Very rarely found free in nature, the elements exist as covalent, diatomic molecules.

Fluorine is prepared by the electrolysis of a mixture of potassium fluoride and hydrogen fluoride. The other three common halogens are prepared in the laboratory by oxidizing their binary acids with manganese dioxide. Commercially, chlorine is made by the electrolysis of sodium chloride solution.

Hydrogen chloride is prepared by treating a salt of the acid with sulfuric acid. Each of the hydrogen halides is a colorless gas that is ionized in water solution.

Fluorine compounds are used (1) as refrigerants, (2) to help prevent tooth decay, (3) in aluminum production, (4) for separating uranium isotopes, (5) in gasoline production, and (6) for etching glass. Chlorine is used for bleaching, disinfecting, and making chlorine-containing compounds. Bromine compounds are used (1) to make plastics flame retardant, (2) in agriculture, (3) in antiknock gasoline, (4) as disinfectants, (5) in medicine, and (6) in photography. Iodine is used as a disinfectant and in synthesizing organic compounds. Iodides are used in photography and as a nutritional supplement.

◀ VOCABULARY

bromide	halide	hydrochloric acid
fluoride	halogen	iodide

◀ QUESTIONS

Group A

1. Why are the halogens very rarely found in nature as free elements?
2. List the halogens in order of increasing activity.
3. What does the term *halogen* mean?
4. What kind of container must be used for fluorine?
5. What are the most important uses of hydrofluoric acid?
6. (*a*) What compound is the commercial source of chlorine? (*b*) For what other element is this compound the commercial source?
7. Write the equation for the laboratory preparation of chlorine from (*a*) manganese dioxide and hydrochloric acid; (*b*) manganese dioxide, sodium chloride, and sulfuric acid. (*c*) Assign oxidation numbers in both equations and tell which element is oxidized and which element is reduced. (*d*) How do these reactions compare?
8. Describe the effects of chlorine on the body.
9. (*a*) List the physical and chemical properties of hydrogen chloride that must be considered in choosing a method of collecting this gas in the laboratory. (*b*) Which method of collection would you choose for a gas with this combination of properties?
10. (*a*) Write the ionic equation for the reaction involved in extracting bromine from salt-well brines. (*b*) What type of reaction is this?
11. List the important physical properties of bromine.
12. Write an equation using electron-dot symbols for the formation of an iodide ion from an iodine atom.

13. Write balanced formula equations for the following:
    (a) zinc + chlorine →
    (b) calcium + fluorine →
    (c) nickel + bromine →
    (d) silver + iodine →

Group B

14. If a reaction occurs, complete and balance the following ionic equations.
    (a) $Br^- + F_2 \rightarrow$ (d) $Cl^- + I_2 \rightarrow$
    (b) $I^- + Br_2 \rightarrow$ (e) $Cl^- + F_2 \rightarrow$
    (c) $F^- + Br_2 \rightarrow$

15. Fluorine does not exhibit any positive oxidation state. Why?

16. Water reacts with xenon difluoride and yields xenon, oxygen, and hydrogen fluoride. (a) Write an equation for this reaction. (b) Assign oxidation numbers to each element and balance the equation by a method used to balance oxidation-reduction equations.

17. What properties does dichlorodifluoromethane have that make it useful as a refrigerant?

18. Why must the hydrogen, chlorine, and sodium hydroxide produced by the electrolysis of aqueous sodium chloride be kept separated from each other?

19. (a) For which does chlorine have greater attraction, carbon or hydrogen? (b) What experimental evidence can you give to support your answer?

20. (a) Why is freshly prepared chlorine water greenish-yellow in color? (b) Why does it become colorless after standing in sunlight?

21. Compare the colors of (a) solid iodine; (b) iodine in alcohol; (c) iodine in carbon tetrachloride; (d) iodine vapor.

22. Hydrogen forms binary compounds with each of the four common halogens. (a) Write the formulas you would expect for these compounds. (b) From electronegativity differences, compare the ionic characters of the bonds in each of these compounds. (c) Write equations for the reactions you would expect each to have with water.

23. The chemical reactions between water molecules and molecules of the hydrogen halides are reversible. (a) Qualitatively, at equilibrium what are the relative concentrations of the particles involved? (b) What does this indicate about the relative stability of the hydrogen halide molecules compared with the stability of the ions that can be formed from them?

24. Why are sodium chloride and calcium chloride ionic salts, while aluminum chloride is molecular?

◖ PROBLEMS

Group A

1. What mass of sodium hydroxide is formed during the production of $71\bar{0}$ kg of chlorine by the electrolysis of sodium chloride?

2. Bromine (10.0 g) is needed for an experiment. How many grams of sodium bromide are required to produce this bromine?

3. Chlorine reacts with calcium hydroxide to produce bleaching powder, Ca(ClO)Cl, and water. (a) What mass of calcium hydroxide is required for making $25\bar{0}$ g of bleaching powder? (b) What mass of chlorine is also required?

4. How many grams of zinc chloride can be produced from 11.2 L of chlorine at STP?

Group B

5. What is the percentage of bromine in ethylene bromide, $C_2H_4Br_2$?

6. How many liters of chlorine at STP can be obtained from 468 g of sodium chloride by electrolysis?

7. A laboratory experiment requires five $25\bar{0}$-mL bottles of chlorine, measured at 27 °C and $75\bar{0}$ mm pressure. What volume of 38% hydrochloric acid (density 1.20 g/mL) and what mass of manganese dioxide will be required?

8. How many grams of hydrogen chloride can be obtained when $60\bar{0}$ g of 95% sulfuric acid reacts with $50\bar{0}$ g of sodium chloride?

crystals

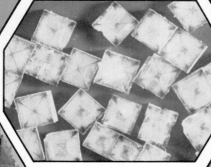

**NaCl
CUBIC CRYSTALS**

**KNO₃
ORTHORHOMBIC
CRYSTALS**

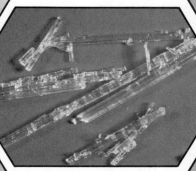

**NiSO₄·6H₂O
TETRAGONAL CRYSTALS**

**oxalic acid dihydrate
MONOCLINIC CRYSTALS**

**Na₃PO₄·12H₂O
HEXAGONAL CRYSTALS**

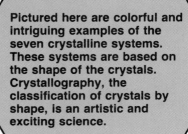

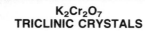

**K₂Cr₂O₇
TRICLINIC CRYSTALS**

Pictured here are colorful and intriguing examples of the seven crystalline systems. These systems are based on the shape of the crystals. Crystallography, the classification of crystals by shape, is an artistic and exciting science.

**NaNO₃
TRIGONAL CRYSTALS**

Radioactivity

Life in Poland had been difficult for the young woman; yet at last, here in Paris, her dream of studying chemistry was soon to be realized. Beloved homeland, family, friends — all that she cherished remained behind. She knew she must face the future alone; science would be her only companion. Hard work and almost unsurmountable challenges awaited her. Thirsting for knowledge, she spent more hours studying than sleeping. Here indeed was a rare human being, one who caught the eye of the young scientist Pierre Curie. At last, Marie Sklodowska had found one who could share her love for knowledge, her hope for humanity. Polonium, radium, radioactivity — legacies of the Curies' laboratory — ushered in a new age of science. When Pierre met with an untimely death, Marie pressed on. Life was short, and what remained of it would be dedicated to the memory of Pierre and their great love, science.

◻ 31.1 Discovery of radioactivity

In 1896 the French scientist Henri Becquerel (bek-*rel*) (1852–1908) was studying the properties of certain minerals. He was particularly interested in their ability to *fluoresce* (give off visible light after being exposed to sunlight). Among these minerals was a sample of uranium ore. By accident Becquerel found that uranium ore gives off invisible rays. He discovered that these rays penetrate the lightproof covering of a photographic plate and affect the film as if it had been exposed to light rays directly. Substances that give off such invisible rays are *radioactive,* and the property is called *radioactivity.* **Radioactivity** *is the spontaneous breakdown of an unstable atomic nucleus with the release of particles and rays.*

◻ 31.2 Discovery of radium

Becquerel was very interested in the source of radioactivity. At his suggestion, Pierre (1859–1906) and Marie (1867–1934) Curie began to investigate the properties of uranium and its ores. They soon learned that uranium and uranium compounds are mildly radioactive. They also discovered that one uranium ore, pitchblende, has four times the amount of radioactivity expected on the basis of its uranium content.

In 1898 the Curies discovered two new radioactive metallic elements in pitchblende. These elements, *polonium* and *radium,* accounted for the high radioactivity of pitchblende. Radium is more than 1,000,000 times as radioactive as the same mass of uranium.

NATURAL RADIOACTIVITY

In this chapter you will gain an understanding of:

- **the discovery and nature of radioactivity**
- **radioactive decay and half-life**
- **the three kinds of particles and rays given off by radioactive elements**
- **transmutations and writing nuclear equations**
- **stability of a nucleus: mass defect and binding energy**
- **artificial radioactivity: nuclear disintegrations, fission, and fusion**
- **the design of a nuclear reactor**
- **the difference between natural and artificial radioactivity**

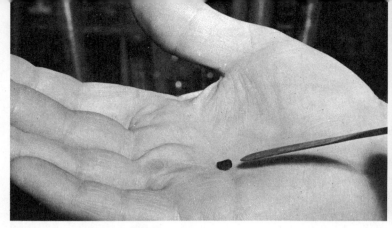

Figure 31-1. (Left) A fragment of metallic uranium, one of the radioactive elements. (Right) A photograph produced when radiation from the same fragment of uranium penetrated the light-tight wrappings of a photographic plate.

A nuclide is a variety of atom distinguished by the number of protons and number of neutrons in its nucleus. In the expression radium-226, recall that 226 is the mass number of the nuclide. See Section 3.7.

Figure 31-2. The activity of a radioactive material may be measured by the speed with which it discharges a goldleaf electroscope like this one. The material to be tested is placed in the hinged drawer at the bottom.

Radium is always found in uranium ores. However, it never occurs in such ores in a greater proportion than 1 part of radium to 3×10^6 parts of uranium. The reason for this proportion will be explained in Section 31.7. The production of radium from uranium ore is a long, difficult, and costly procedure. Radium is usually marketed as radium bromide rather than as elemental radium.

☐ 31.3 Properties of radium

Radium is the element of highest atomic weight in Group II of the periodic table. Its physical properties are listed in Table 25-1. It is the least electronegative and thus the most metallic member of its group. Radium has chemical properties similar to those of barium.

Radium is important because of its radioactivity. Radium-226 is a naturally occurring radioactive nuclide. Because of its radioactivity, radium-226 and its compounds have several unusual properties. These properties, also observed in other radioactive elements, include the following:

1. They affect the light-sensitive emulsion on a photographic film. Photographic film can be wrapped in heavy black paper and stored in the dark. This will protect it from ordinary light. However, radiations from radioactive elements penetrate the wrapping. They affect the film in the same way that light does when the film is exposed. When the film is developed, a black spot shows up on the negative where the invisible radiation struck it. The rays from radioactive elements penetrate paper, wood, flesh, and *thin* sheets of metal.

2. They produce an electric charge in the surrounding air. The radiation from radioactive elements ionizes the molecules of the gases in the air surrounding it. These ionized molecules conduct electric charges away from the knob of a charged electroscope, thus discharging it. The activity of a radium compound can be measured by the rate at which it discharges an electroscope. Similarly, the radiation given off by radioactive elements ionizes the low pressure gas in the tube of a Geiger counter. Electricity thus passes through the tube for an instant. The passage of electricity is registered as a "click" in a set of earphones.

3. They produce fluorescence with certain other compounds. A small quantity of radium bromide added to zinc sulfide causes the zinc sulfide to glow. Since the glow is visible in the dark, the mixture is used in making luminous paint.

4. Their radiations have special physiological effects. The radiation from radium can destroy the germinating power of seed. It can kill bacteria or animals. People who work with radium may be severely burned by the rays it emits. Such burns heal slowly and can be fatal. However, controlled radiations from radioactive materials are used in the treatment of cancer and certain skin diseases.

5. They undergo radioactive decay. The atoms of all radioactive elements steadily decay into simpler atoms as they release radiation. For example, one-half of any number of radium-226 atoms decays into simpler atoms in 1620 years. One-half of what remains, or one-fourth of the original atoms, decays in the next 1620 years. One-half of what is left, or one-eighth of the original atoms, decays in the next 1620 years, and so on. This period of 1620 years is called the *half-life of radium-226.* **Half-life is the** *length of time during which half of a given number of atoms of a radioactive nuclide decays.* Each radioactive nuclide has its characteristic half-life.

The half-life of a nuclide varies slightly depending on its chemical form. For example, beryllium-7 decays at very slightly different rates when it is elemental, in BeO, in HCl(aq) solution as Be^{++}, or in solid $Be_2P_2O_7$. The decay rate is also affected by large changes in the environment. Some of these changes are very low temperature, high pressure, or large variations in a surrounding electric field. Somewhat larger alteration of the half-life of certain nuclides has been found when the decaying nucleus and its valence electrons interact.

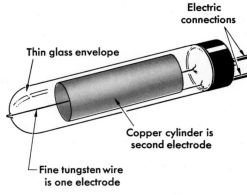

Electric connections

Thin glass envelope

Copper cylinder is second electrode

Fine tungsten wire is one electrode

Figure 31-3. A diagram showing the construction of a Geiger-Müller counter tube. Radiation passing through the tube ionizes the gas it contains and enables current to flow.

PRACTICE PROBLEMS

1. How many years will be needed for the decay of 15/16 of a given amount of radium-226?   *ans.* 6480 years
2. The half-life of radon-222 is 3.823 days. After what time will only one-fourth of a given amount of radon remain? *ans.* 7.646 days
3. The half-life of polonium-210 is 138.4 days. What fraction remains after 415.2 days?   *ans.* 1/8

◻ 31.4 Other natural radioactive elements

The radioactive elements known to Becquerel were uranium and thorium. The Curies discovered two more, polonium and radium. Since that time, many other natural radioactive nuclides

Table 31-1
REPRESENTATIVE NATURAL RADIOACTIVE NUCLIDES
WITH ATOMIC NUMBERS UP TO 83

Nuclide	Abundance in natural element	Half-life	Nuclide	Abundance in natural element	Half-life
	(%)	(years)		(%)	(years)
$^{40}_{19}K$	0.0118	1.3×10^9	$^{130}_{52}Te$	34.49	8×10^{20}
$^{48}_{20}Ca$	0.185	$> 10^{18}$	$^{180}_{74}W$	0.135	$> 1.1 \times 10^{15}$
$^{64}_{30}Zn$	48.89	$> 8 \times 10^{15}$	$^{182}_{74}W$	26.4	$> 2 \times 10^{17}$
$^{70}_{30}Zn$	0.62	$> 10^{15}$	$^{183}_{74}W$	14.4	$> 1.1 \times 10^{17}$
$^{87}_{37}Rb$	27.85	4.8×10^{10}	$^{186}_{74}W$	28.4	$> 6 \times 10^{15}$
$^{113}_{48}Cd$	12.26	$> 1.3 \times 10^{15}$	$^{190}_{78}Pt$	0.0127	6.9×10^{11}
$^{116}_{48}Cd$	7.58	$> 10^{17}$	$^{192}_{78}Pt$	0.78	10^{15}
$^{124}_{50}Sn$	5.98	$> 2 \times 10^{17}$	$^{198}_{78}Pt$	7.19	$> 10^{15}$
$^{123}_{51}Sb$	42.75	$> 1.3 \times 10^{16}$	$^{196}_{80}Hg$	0.146	$> 1 \times 10^{14}$
$^{123}_{52}Te$	0.87	1.2×10^{13}	$^{209}_{83}Bi$	100	$> 2 \times 10^{18}$

Figure 31-4. The variation in the amount of radon in soil gases near geologic faults helps in predicting earthquakes. The monitoring station shown in the photo measures and records the amount of radon and on signal transmits these data to a central laboratory where they are analyzed.

Electrons are described in Section 3.4.

Electromagnetic radiation is explained in Section 4.2.

have been identified. Some of these are listed in Table 31-1. All nuclides of the elements beyond bismuth (at. no. 83) in the periodic table are radioactive. However, only polonium (at. no. 84), radon (at. no. 86), radium (at. no. 88), actinium (at. no. 89), thorium (at. no. 90), protactinium (at. no. 91), and uranium (at. no. 92) have any natural radioactive nuclides. The remainder of the elements beyond bismuth have only radioactive nuclides that have been artificially produced.

One important natural radioactive nuclide is the noble gas radon-222. Radon-222 is given off when radium atoms decay. It is collected in tubes and used for the treatment of disease. Variations in the amount of radon in soil gases near geologic faults help in predicting earthquakes.

⬭ 31.5 Nature of the radiation

The radiation given off by such radioactive elements as uranium, thorium, and radium is complex. It consists of three different kinds of particles and rays.

1. The α (alpha) particles are helium nuclei. Their mass is nearly four times that of a protium atom. They have a +2 charge and move at speeds that are approximately one-tenth the speed of light. Because of their relatively low speed, they have low penetrating ability. A thin sheet of aluminum foil or a sheet of paper stops them. However, they burn flesh and ionize air easily.

2. The β (beta) particles are electrons. They travel at speeds close to the speed of light, with penetrating ability about 100 times greater than that of alpha particles.

3. The γ (gamma) rays are high-energy electromagnetic waves. They are the same kind of radiation as visible light, but are of much shorter wavelength and higher frequency. Gamma rays are produced when nuclear particles undergo transitions in nuclear energy levels. They are the most penetrating of the radiations given off by radioactive elements. Alpha and beta particles are seldom, if ever, given off simultaneously from the same nucleus. Gamma rays, however, are often produced along with either alpha or beta particles.

Figure 31-5 shows the effect of a powerful magnetic field on the complex radiation given off by a small particle of radioactive material. The field is perpendicular to the plane of the paper. The heavy alpha particles are slightly deflected in one direction. The lighter beta particles are deflected more sharply in the opposite direction. The gamma rays, being uncharged, are not affected by the magnet.

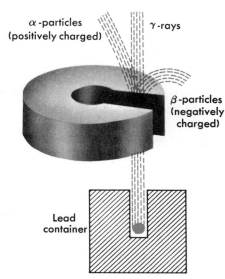

Figure 31-5. The effect of a magnet on the different types of radiations. The north pole of the magnet is toward the reader, and the south pole is away from the reader.

☐ 31.6 Decay of atoms of radioactive elements

Radioactive nuclides decay spontaneously, yielding energy. A long series of experiments has shown that this energy results from the decay of nuclei of radium-226 and other radioactive nuclides. Alpha and beta particles are products of such nuclear decay. Certain heavy nuclei break down spontaneously into simpler and lighter nuclei, releasing enormous quantities of energy.

At first it was believed that radioactive nuclides did not lose mass and would give off energy forever. However, more careful investigation proved that radioactive materials do lose mass slowly. The presence of electrons and helium nuclei among the radiations is evidence for the loss of mass.

☐ 31.7 A series of related radioactive nuclides

All naturally occurring radioactive nuclides with atomic numbers greater than 83 belong to one of three series of related nuclides. The heaviest nuclide of each series is called the *parent* nuclide. The parent nuclides are uranium-238, uranium-235, and thorium-232. The decay series of uranium-238 contains radium-226 and is traced in the following example. The various nuclear changes are charted in Figure 31-6.

The nucleus of a uranium-238 atom contains 92 protons (the atomic number of uranium is 92). It has a mass number (number of protons + number of neutrons) of 238. As this nucleus decays, it emits an alpha particle, which becomes an atom of helium when its positive charge is neutralized. An alpha particle has a mass number of 4. Since it contains two protons, it has an atomic number of 2. The remainder of the uranium nucleus thus has an atomic number of 90 and a mass number of 234. This nuclide is an isotope of thorium. See the left portion of Figure 31-7. A *transmutation reaction* has taken place. *A **transmutation** is a*

A physical change is one in which certain physical properties of a substance change, yet its identifying properties remain unchanged.

A chemical change is one in which different substances with new properties are formed by a rearrangement of atoms.

A nuclear change is one in which new substances are formed by changes in the identity of atoms.

See Sections 2.11, 2.12, and 2.15.

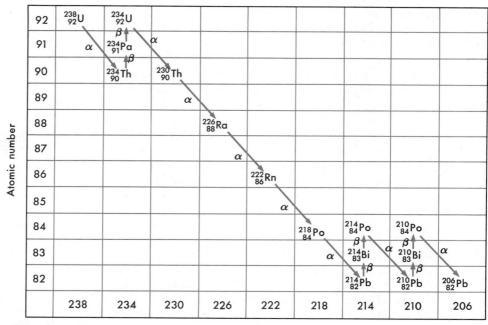

Figure 31-6. The parent nuclide of the uranium decay series is $^{238}_{92}$U. The final nuclide of the series is $^{206}_{82}$Pb.

change in the identity of a nucleus because of a change in the number of its protons. The *nuclear equation* for this *transmutation reaction* can be written as

$$^{238}_{92}\text{U} \rightarrow {}^{234}_{90}\text{Th} + {}^{4}_{2}\text{He}$$

Since the above equation is a nuclear equation, only nuclei are represented. The superscript is the mass number. The subscript is the atomic number. Alpha particles are represented as helium nuclei, $^{4}_{2}$He. The total of the mass numbers on the left side of the equation must equal the total of the mass numbers on the right side of the equation. The total of the atomic numbers on the left must equal the total of the atomic numbers on the right.

Figure 31-7. This diagram shows successive alpha and beta particle emissions in the decay of $^{238}_{92}$U.

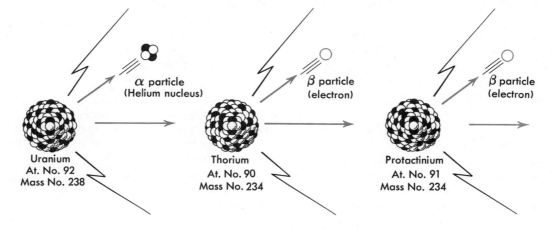

The half-life of $^{234}_{90}$Th is about 24 days. It decays by giving off beta particles. The loss of a beta particle from a nucleus increases the number of positive charges in the nucleus (the atomic number) by one. The beta particle is believed to be formed by the change of a neutron into a proton and beta particle (electron). Since the mass of the lost beta particle is so small that it may be neglected, the mass number of the resulting nuclide stays the same. See the right portion of Figure 31-7.

$$^{234}_{90}\text{Th} \rightarrow {}^{234}_{91}\text{Pa} + {}^{0}_{-1}\text{e}$$

The symbol $^{0}_{-1}$e represents an electron with an atomic number of -1 and a mass number of 0. $^{234}_{91}$Pa is an isotope of protactinium. This nuclide decays by releasing beta particles to produce $^{234}_{92}$U.

$$^{234}_{91}\text{Pa} \rightarrow {}^{234}_{92}\text{U} + {}^{0}_{-1}\text{e}$$

The $^{234}_{92}$U nuclide decays by giving off alpha particles.

$$^{234}_{92}\text{U} \rightarrow {}^{230}_{90}\text{Th} + {}^{4}_{2}\text{He}$$

The resulting isotope of thorium also emits alpha particles, forming radium-226.

$$^{230}_{90}\text{Th} \rightarrow {}^{226}_{88}\text{Ra} + {}^{4}_{2}\text{He}$$

Now you can see why ores of uranium contain radium. Radium is one of the products of the decay of uranium atoms. The half-lives of $^{238}_{92}$U and $^{226}_{88}$Ra determine the proportion of uranium atoms to radium atoms in uranium ores.

The decay of $^{226}_{88}$Ra proceeds according to the chart shown in Figure 31-6. The $^{226}_{88}$Ra nuclide decays by giving off alpha particles, forming radon-222. The nuclear equation is

$$^{226}_{88}\text{Ra} \rightarrow {}^{222}_{86}\text{Rn} + {}^{4}_{2}\text{He}$$

The $^{222}_{86}$Rn nuclei are unstable and have a half-life of about four days. They decay by giving off alpha particles.

$$^{222}_{86}\text{Rn} \rightarrow {}^{218}_{84}\text{Po} + {}^{4}_{2}\text{He}$$

The remaining atomic number and mass number changes shown on the decay chart are also explained in terms of the particles given off. When it loses alpha particles, $^{210}_{84}$Po forms $^{206}_{82}$Pb. This is a stable, nonradioactive isotope of lead. Thus a series of spontaneous transmutations begins with $^{238}_{92}$U, passes through $^{226}_{88}$Ra, and ends with the formation of stable $^{206}_{82}$Pb.

PRACTICE PROBLEMS

Complete the following nuclear equations:

1. $^{218}_{84}$Po $\rightarrow \cdots + {}^{4}_{2}$He

2. $^{214}_{82}$Pb $\rightarrow {}^{214}_{83}$Bi $+ \cdots$

3. $^{214}_{83}$Bi $\rightarrow \cdots + \cdots$

4. $^{214}_{84}$Po $\rightarrow \cdots + \cdots$

Figure 31-8. A portion of the west coast of Greenland. These rocks are among the oldest on earth. Radio-active-dating measurements show that the rocks in the right foreground crystallized about 3.75 billion years ago. The strip of light-colored rocks to the left of the photo is about 2.6 billion years old.

☐ 31.8 Applications of natural radioactivity

The age of any mineral containing radioactive substances can be estimated with a fair degree of accuracy. Such an estimate is based on the fact that radioactive substances decay at known rates and the assumption that these rates have not changed during the existence of the mineral. The mineral is analyzed to determine the amount of long-lived parent nuclide and the amounts of shorter-lived *daughter* nuclides in the sample. Then, by calculation, scientists can determine how long it must have taken for these amounts of daughter nuclides to be produced. This time is assumed to be the age of the mineral. By this method, the oldest known minerals on earth have been estimated to be about 3.7 billion years old. Dust from sites of moon landings has been found to be about 4.6 billion years old. The ages of moon rocks range from 3.2 to 4.6 billion years.

The age of more recent potassium-containing minerals, 50 thousand to 50 million years old, is determined quite accurately by the proportion of potassium to argon they contain. Some nuclei of $^{40}_{19}K$ decay by capturing an orbital electron to form $^{40}_{18}Ar$. So, over a period of time, the proportion of argon to potassium in the mineral increases and is used to establish the mineral's age.

Some carbon atoms involved in the oxygen–carbon dioxide cycle of living plants and animals are radioactive. Radioactive $^{14}_{6}C$ is continuously being produced from $^{14}_{7}N$ atoms in the atmosphere. This change is brought about by the action of *cosmic rays*. (Cosmic rays are protons and other nuclei of very high energy. These particles come to the earth from outer space.) When living things die, the oxygen–carbon dioxide cycle ceases to continue in them. They no longer replace carbon atoms in their cells with other carbon atoms. Thus, the level of radioactivity produced by the radioactive carbon in a given amount of nonliving material slowly diminishes.

Carbon from a wooden beam taken from the tomb of an Egyptian pharaoh yields about half the radiation of carbon in living trees. The half-life of a $^{14}_{6}C$ atom is about 5730 years. Thus the age of dead wood with half the radioactivity of living wood is about 5730 years. Objects from wood up to about 30,000 years old have been dated by this method. The use of $^{14}_{6}C$ dating has been applied to the study of bone proteins. This technique dates bone material up to about 50,000 years old.

ARTIFICIAL RADIOACTIVITY

The atomic mass scale based on carbon-12 is described in Section 3.13.

☐ 31.9 Stability of a nucleus

On the atomic mass scale the isotope of carbon with six protons and six neutrons in its nucleus is defined as having an *atomic mass* of exactly 12 u. On this scale, a $^{4}_{2}He$ nucleus has a mass of 4.0015 u. The mass of a proton is 1.0073 u, and the mass of a neutron is 1.0087 u. A $^{4}_{2}He$ nucleus contains two protons and two neutrons. Thus you might expect its mass to be the combined mass of these four particles, 4.0320 *u.* [2(1.0073 *u*) + 2(1.0087 *u*) = 4.0320 *u.*] Note, however, that there is a *difference* of 0.0305 *u* between the measured mass, 4.0015 *u,* and the calculated mass, 4.0320 *u,* of a $^4_2$He nucleus. This difference in mass is called the *nuclear mass defect. The **nuclear mass defect** is the difference between the mass of a nucleus and the sum of the masses of its constituent particles.* The mass defect, converted into energy units by using Einstein's equation, $E = mc^2$, is the energy released when a nucleus is formed from the particles that compose it. This energy is generally referred to as the *binding energy. The **nuclear binding energy** is the energy released when a nucleus is formed from its constituent particles.* This energy must be supplied to a nucleus to separate it into its constituent particles.

Calculations of binding energies of the atoms of the elements show that the lightest and the heaviest elements have the smallest binding energies per nuclear particle. Elements having intermediate atomic weights have the greatest binding energies per nuclear particle. See Figure 31-9. The elements with the greatest binding energies per nuclear particle are those with the most stable nuclei. Therefore the nuclei of the lightest and heaviest elements are less stable than the nuclei of elements having intermediate atomic weights.

The stability of atomic nuclei is affected by the ratio of the neutrons to protons that compose them. *Among atoms having*

Einstein's mass-energy equation is explained in Section 1.11.

Figure 31-9. This graph shows the relationship between binding energy per nuclear particle and mass number.

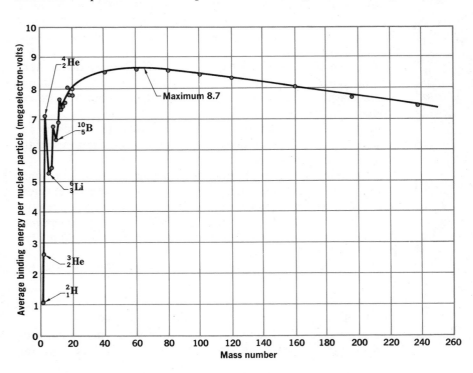

low atomic numbers, the most stable nuclei are those whose neutron-to-proton ratio is 1:1. Nuclei with a greater number of neutrons than protons have lower binding energies and are less stable. Many properties of nuclear particles indicate that energy levels exist *within* the atomic nucleus. In nuclei with an equal number of neutrons and protons, the particles apparently occupy the lowest energy levels in the nucleus. In this way, they give it stability. However, in low-atomic-number nuclei that contain an excess of neutrons over protons, some of the neutrons seem to occupy higher energy levels. This reduces the binding energy and consequently lowers the stability of the nucleus.

As the atomic number increases, the most stable nuclei have a neutron-to-proton ratio increasingly greater than 1:1. For example, $^{127}_{53}I$ with a $\frac{\text{neutron}}{\text{proton}}$ ratio of $\frac{74}{53}$ (about 1.40:1) is stable. On the other hand, $^{126}_{53}I \left(\frac{73}{53}\right)$, $^{128}_{53}I \left(\frac{75}{53}\right)$, and all other isotopes of iodine are radioactive. The stable end product of the uranium decay series is $^{206}_{82}Pb$. It has a $\frac{\text{neutron}}{\text{proton}}$ ratio of $\frac{124}{82}$ (about 1.51:1).

The stability of a nucleus *also* depends on the even-odd relationship of the number of protons and neutrons. Most stable nuclei, 157 of them, have even numbers of both protons and neutrons. There are 52 stable nuclei having an even number of protons and an odd number of neutrons; 50 stable nuclei have an odd number of protons and an even number of neutrons. Only five stable nuclei having odd numbers of both protons and neutons are known.

Because of the difference in stability of different nuclei, there are four types of nuclear reactions. In each type a small amount of the mass of the reactants is converted into energy, forming products of greater stability.

1. A nucleus undergoes *radioactive decay*. The nucleus releases an alpha or beta particle and gamma rays, forming a slightly lighter, more stable nucleus.

2. A nucleus is bombarded with alpha particles, protons, deuterons (deuterium nuclei, ^2_1H), neutrons, or other particles. The now unstable nucleus emits a proton or a neutron and becomes more stable. This process is called *nuclear disintegration*.

3. A very heavy nucleus splits to form medium-weight nuclei. This process is known as *fission*.

4. Light-weight nuclei combine to form heavier, more stable nuclei. This process is known as *fusion*.

Figure 31-10. Radioactive materials are handled by remote control in specially designed and shielded "cells."

❏ 31.10 Stable nuclei from radioactive decay

The release of an alpha particle from a radioactive nucleus such as $^{238}_{92}U$ decreases the mass of the nucleus. The resulting

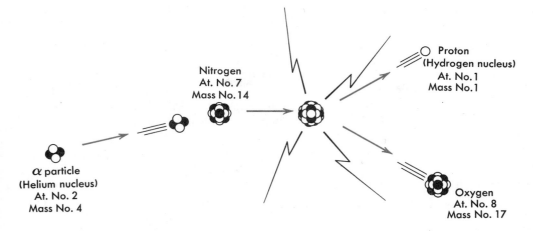

Nitrogen
At. No. 7
Mass No. 14

Proton
(Hydrogen nucleus)
At. No. 1
Mass No. 1

α particle
(Helium nucleus)
At. No. 2
Mass No. 4

Oxygen
At. No. 8
Mass No. 17

lighter nucleus has higher binding energy per nuclear particle. The release of an alpha particle decreases the number of protons and neutrons in a nucleus *equally and also by an even number*.

Beta particles are released when neutrons change into protons, as during the decay of $^{234}_{90}$Th. This change lowers the neutron-to-proton ratio toward the value found for stable nuclei of the same mass number. Both alpha-particle release and beta-particle release yield a product nucleus that is more stable than the original nucleus. Refer once again to Section 31.7 and Figure 31-6.

Figure 31-11. This diagram shows the historic nuclear disintegration performed by Rutherford.

☐ 31.11 The first artificial nuclear disintegration

After scientists discovered how uranium and radium undergo natural decay and transmutation, they worked to produce artificial transmutations. They had to find a way to add protons to a nucleus of an atom of an element, converting it to the nucleus of an atom of a different element. In 1919, Rutherford produced the first artificial nuclear disintegration. His method involved bombarding nitrogen with alpha particles from radium. He obtained protons (hydrogen nuclei) and a stable isotope of oxygen. See Figure 31-11. This nuclear disintegration is represented by the following equation:

$$^{14}_{7}N + ^{4}_{2}He \rightarrow ^{17}_{8}O + ^{1}_{1}H$$

☐ 31.12 Proofs of Einstein's equation

In 1932, the two English scientists J. D. Cockcroft (1897–1967) and E. T. S. Walton (b. 1903) experimentally proved Einstein's equation, $E = mc^2$. They bombarded lithium with high-speed protons. Alpha particles and an enormous amount of energy were produced.

$$^{7}_{3}Li + ^{1}_{1}H \rightarrow ^{4}_{2}He + ^{4}_{2}He + \text{energy}$$

There is a loss of matter in this reaction. One lithium nucleus (mass 7.0144 u) was hit by a proton (mass 1.0073 u). These particles formed two alpha particles (helium nuclei) each having a mass of 4.0015 u. Calculation shows that there is a loss of 0.0187 u. (7.0144 u + 1.0073 u) − 2(4.0015 u). Cockcroft and Walton found that the energy released very nearly equaled that predicted by Einstein for such a loss in mass. Additional experiments have further supported Einstein's equation.

31.13 Neutron emission in some nuclear disintegrations

Neutrons are described in Section 3.5.

You have already learned that neutrons were discovered by Chadwick in 1932. He first detected them in an experiment that involved bombarding beryllium with alpha particles.

$$_{4}^{9}\text{Be} + _{2}^{4}\text{He} \rightarrow _{6}^{12}\text{C} + _{0}^{1}\text{n}$$

The symbol for a neutron is $_{0}^{1}\text{n}$. This symbol indicates a particle with zero atomic number (no protons) and a mass number of 1. The reaction described above proved that neutrons were a second type of particle in the nuclei of atoms.

31.14 The cyclotron and other particle accelerators

Radium was used as a natural source of alpha particles in many early experiments. However, radium is not very efficient in producing nuclear changes. As a result, scientists sought more effective ways of producing high-energy particles for bombarding nuclei. This search resulted in the development of many large electric devices for accelerating charged particles.

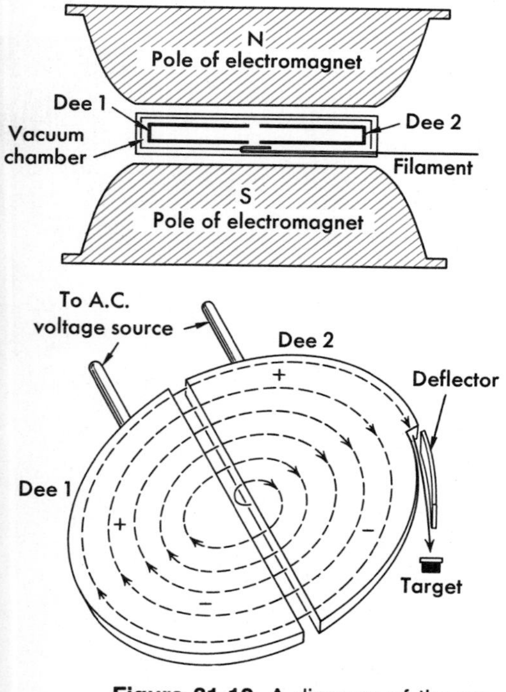

The *cyclotron* was invented by E. O. Lawrence (1901–1958) of the University of California. It consists of a cylindrical box placed between the poles of a huge electromagnet. Air is pumped out of the box until a high vacuum is produced. The "bullets" used to bombard nuclei are usually protons (protium nuclei) or deuterons (deuterium nuclei). They enter the cylindrical box through its center.

Inside the box are two hollow, D-shaped electrodes called *dees*. These dees are connected through an oscillator to a source of very high voltage. When the cyclotron is in operation, the oscillator reverses the electric charge on the dees very rapidly. The combined effects of the high-voltage alternating potential and the electromagnetic field cause the protons or deuterons inside to move in a spiral course. They move faster and faster as they near the outside of the box, gaining more and more energy. When they reach the outer rim of the box, they are deflected toward the target. The energy of particles accelerated in a simple cyclotron can reach 15,000,000 electron-volts. This is the energy an electron would have if it were accelerated across a potential difference of 1.5×10^7 volts. By studying the fragments of

Figure 31-12. A diagram of the cyclotron used to produce "atomic bullets" of very high energy.

atoms formed by bombardment, scientists have learned a great deal about atomic structure. They have also discovered much about the products formed when atoms disintegrate.

Other machines for bombarding atomic nuclei are the *synchrotron,* the *betatron,* and the *linear accelerator.* The synchrotron works much like the cyclotron. By varying both the oscillating voltage and the magnetic field, particles are accelerated in a narrow circular path rather than in a spiral. A synchrotron can give an energy of more than 500 billion electron-volts to the protons it accelerates. The betatron accelerates electrons rather than positively charged particles. The accelerated electrons can be used as "bullets" for bombardment or for production of high-energy X rays. In the linear accelerator the particles travel in a straight line. They are accelerated by passage through many stages of potential difference.

☐ 31.15 Neutrons as "bullets"

Before the discovery of neutrons in 1932, alpha particles and protons were used to study atomic nuclei. But alpha particles and protons are charged particles. It requires great quantities of energy to "fire" these charged "bullets" into a nucleus. Their positive charge causes them to be repelled by the positive nuclear charge. The various kinds of particle accelerators were developed to give charged "bullets" enough energy to overcome this repelling force.

When accelerated positive particles strike a target material, usually lithium or beryllium, neutrons are produced. Neutrons have no charge. Thus there is no repelling force, and they can easily penetrate the nucleus of an atom. Some fast neutrons may go through an atom without causing any change in it. Other fast neutrons may cause nuclear disintegration. Slow neutrons, on the other hand, are sometimes trapped by a nucleus. This nucleus then becomes unstable and may break apart. Fast neutrons are slowed down by passage through materials composed of elements of low atomic weight. Examples are deuterium oxide or graphite.

☐ 31.16 Artificial elements from neutron bombardment

The $^{238}_{92}U$ nuclide is the most plentiful isotope of uranium. When hit by slow neutrons, a $^{238}_{92}U$ nucleus may capture a neutron. This capture produces the nucleus of an atom of an unstable isotope of uranium, $^{239}_{92}U$. This nucleus emits a beta particle and, in so doing, becomes the nucleus of an atom of an artificial radioactive element, neptunium. Neptunium has atomic number 93. The nuclide formed has the symbol $^{239}_{93}Np$.

$$^{238}_{92}U + ^{1}_{0}n \rightarrow ^{239}_{92}U$$

$$^{239}_{92}U \rightarrow ^{239}_{93}Np + ^{0}_{-1}e$$

Figure 31-13. A portion of the tunnel containing the proton synchrotron at the Fermi National Accelerator Laboratory near Chicago. The tunnel has a circumference of 6.3 km.

Figure 31-14. The heavy-ion linear accelerator at the Lawrence Berkeley Laboratory used to synthesize element 106.

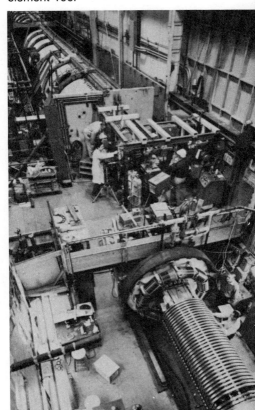

Table 31-2
REACTIONS FOR THE FIRST PREPARATION
OF TRANSURANIUM ELEMENTS

Atomic number	Name	Symbol	Nuclear reaction
93	neptunium	Np	$^{238}_{92}\text{U} + ^{1}_{0}\text{n} \rightarrow ^{239}_{93}\text{Np} + ^{0}_{-1}\text{e}$
94	plutonium	Pu	$^{238}_{92}\text{U} + ^{2}_{1}\text{H} \rightarrow ^{238}_{93}\text{Np} + 2^{1}_{0}\text{n}$
			$^{238}_{93}\text{Np} \rightarrow ^{238}_{94}\text{Pu} + ^{0}_{-1}\text{e}$
95	americium	Am	$^{239}_{94}\text{Pu} + 2^{1}_{0}\text{n} \rightarrow ^{241}_{95}\text{Am} + ^{0}_{-1}\text{e}$
96	curium	Cm	$^{239}_{94}\text{Pu} + ^{4}_{2}\text{He} \rightarrow ^{242}_{96}\text{Cm} + ^{1}_{0}\text{n}$
97	berkelium	Bk	$^{241}_{95}\text{Am} + ^{4}_{2}\text{He} \rightarrow ^{243}_{97}\text{Bk} + 2^{1}_{0}\text{n}$
98	californium	Cf	$^{242}_{96}\text{Cm} + ^{4}_{2}\text{He} \rightarrow ^{245}_{98}\text{Cf} + ^{1}_{0}\text{n}$
99	einsteinium	Es	$^{238}_{92}\text{U} + 15^{1}_{0}\text{n} \rightarrow ^{253}_{99}\text{Es} + 7^{0}_{-1}\text{e}$
100	fermium	Fm	$^{238}_{92}\text{U} + 17^{1}_{0}\text{n} \rightarrow ^{255}_{100}\text{Fm} + 8^{0}_{-1}\text{e}$
101	mendelevium	Md	$^{253}_{99}\text{Es} + ^{4}_{2}\text{He} \rightarrow ^{256}_{101}\text{Md} + ^{1}_{0}\text{n}$
102	nobelium	No	$^{246}_{96}\text{Cm} + ^{12}_{6}\text{C} \rightarrow ^{254}_{102}\text{No} + 4^{1}_{0}\text{n}$
103	lawrencium	Lr	$^{252}_{98}\text{Cf} + ^{10}_{5}\text{B} \rightarrow ^{258}_{103}\text{Lr} + 4^{1}_{0}\text{n}$
104	unnilquadium (USSR)	Unq	$^{242}_{94}\text{Pu} + ^{22}_{10}\text{Ne} \rightarrow ^{260}_{104}\text{Unq} + 4^{1}_{0}\text{n}$
104	unnilquadium (US)	Unq	$^{249}_{98}\text{Cf} + ^{12}_{6}\text{C} \rightarrow ^{257}_{104}\text{Unq} + 4^{1}_{0}\text{n}$
105	unnilpentium (US)	Unp	$^{249}_{98}\text{Cf} + ^{15}_{7}\text{N} \rightarrow ^{260}_{105}\text{Unp} + 4^{1}_{0}\text{n}$
106	unnilhexium (US)	Unh	$^{249}_{98}\text{Cf} + ^{18}_{8}\text{O} \rightarrow ^{263}_{106}\text{Unh} + 4^{1}_{0}\text{n}$
107	unnilseptium (USSR)	Uns	$^{209}_{83}\text{Bi} + ^{54}_{24}\text{Cr} \rightarrow ^{261}_{107}\text{Uns} + 2^{1}_{0}\text{n}$

Neptunium is itself an unstable element. The nucleus of a neptunium atom gives off a beta particle. This change produces the nucleus of an atom of still another artificial element, plutonium, atomic number 94. This nuclide has the symbol $^{239}_{94}\text{Pu}$.

$$^{239}_{93}\text{Np} \rightarrow ^{239}_{94}\text{Pu} + ^{0}_{-1}\text{e}$$

Neptunium and plutonium were the first artificial *transuranium* elements. **Transuranium elements** are those with more than 92 protons in their nuclei. As this is written, 15 artificially prepared transuranium elements have been reported. In addition to neptunium and plutonium, there are americium, curium, berkelium, californium, einsteinium, fermium, mendelevium, nobelium, and lawrencium. Elements 104, 105, 106, and 107 have only systematic names. All of these elements are prepared by bombarding the nuclei of uranium or more complex atoms with neutrons, alpha particles, or other "nuclear bullets." See Table 31-2.

Systematic names for elements with atomic numbers over 100 are explained in Section 2.4.

◻ 31.17 Artificial radioactive atoms

In 1934, Madame Curie's daughter Irène (1897–1956) and her husband Frédéric Joliot (1900–1958) discovered that stable atoms can be made radioactive by artificial means. This occurs when they are bombarded with deuterons or neutrons. Radioactive isotopes of all the elements have been prepared. For example, radioactive $^{60}_{27}Co$ can be produced from natural nonradioactive $^{59}_{27}Co$ by slow-neutron bombardment. The nuclear equation is

$$^{59}_{27}Co + ^{1}_{0}n \rightarrow ^{60}_{27}Co$$

Radiation from $^{60}_{27}Co$ consists of beta particles and gamma rays.

Radioactive $^{32}_{15}P$ is prepared by bombardment of $^{32}_{16}S$ with slow neutrons.

$$^{32}_{16}S + ^{1}_{0}n \rightarrow ^{32}_{15}P + ^{1}_{1}H$$

The radiation from $^{32}_{15}P$ consists of only beta particles.

Radioactive phosphorus, radioactive cobalt, and some other radioactive elements are used to treat certain forms of cancer. Radioactive drugs are used for diagnostic purposes and for test purposes on blood and tissue samples. Many radioactive isotopes are used as *tracers*. By using them, scientists can determine the course of chemical reactions, the cleaning ability of detergents, the wearing ability of various products, the efficiency of fertilizers, the flow of fluids through pipelines, and the movement of sand along sea coasts. Many new radioactive isotopes are made by slow-neutron bombardment in the nuclear reactor at Oak Ridge, Tennessee.

☐ 31.18 Fission of uranium

The element uranium exists as three naturally occurring isotopes: $^{238}_{92}U$, $^{235}_{92}U$, and $^{234}_{92}U$. Most uranium is the nuclide $^{238}_{92}U$. Only 0.7% of natural uranium is $^{235}_{92}U$. The nuclide $^{234}_{92}U$ occurs in only the slightest traces. You have learned that transuranium elements can be produced when $^{238}_{92}U$ is bombarded with slow neutrons. However, when $^{235}_{92}U$ is bombarded with slow neutrons, each atom may capture one of the neutrons. This extra neutron in the nucleus makes it very unstable. Instead of giving off an alpha or beta particle, as in other radioactive changes, the nucleus splits into medium-weight parts. Neutrons are usually produced during this *fission*. There is a small loss of mass, which appears as a great amount of energy. One equation for the fission of $^{235}_{92}U$ is

$$^{235}_{92}U + ^{1}_{0}n \rightarrow ^{138}_{56}Ba + ^{95}_{36}Kr + 3^{1}_{0}n + \text{energy}$$

The atomic mass of $^{235}_{92}U$ is slightly greater than 235 u. The atomic masses of the unstable barium and krypton isotopes are slightly less than 138 u and 95 u, respectively. Thus the masses of the reactants and the masses of the products are not equal. Instead, about 0.2 u of mass is converted to energy for each uranium atom undergoing fission. Plutonium, made from $^{238}_{92}U$, also undergoes fission to produce more neutrons when bombarded with slow neutrons.

Uranium atoms exist in very small amounts in many minerals. In the time since their formation, some $^{238}_{92}U$ atoms have

The slow-neutron fission of $^{235}_{92}U$ yields products having atomic numbers from 30 to 65 and mass numbers from 72 to 161. See Figure 31-15. Fission into two equal fragments is not the most probable. The highest yield is of particles with mass numbers 95 and 138.

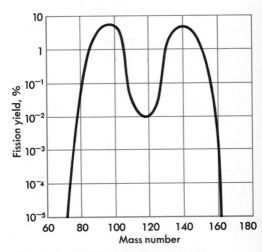

Figure 31-15. This graph shows the yield of various nuclides that are produced by the slow-neutron fission of uranium-235. The products vary in mass number from 72 to 161. The most probable products have mass numbers of 95 and 138. Observe the low probability of fission products of nearly equal mass numbers.

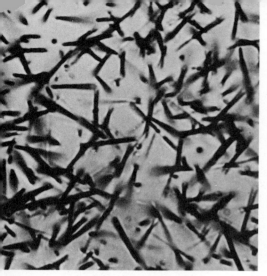

Figure 31-16. The tracks shown in the photo were caused by the spontaneous fission of uranium-238 atoms. The tracks were enlarged by etching so they would be visible through a light microscope. The tracks are magnified over three thousand times. The crystalline material in which they appear here is zircon.

Most $^{238}_{92}U$ atoms decay by emitting an alpha particle as described in Section 31.7. But about one out of every 2 million $^{238}_{92}U$ atoms undergoes spontaneous fission.

undergone spontaneous fission. These fissions have left tracks in certain mineral crystals and in glassy materials. These tracks can be made visible under a microscope by etching. The number of tracks in a given area and the amount of $^{238}_{92}U$ in the specimen are used to determine the age of the crystal or the time since a glassy material was last heated to a high temperature. This method, called fission-track dating, can establish the age of materials from a few decades old to as old as the solar system.

❑ 31.19 Nuclear chain reaction

A *chain reaction is one in which the material or energy that starts the reaction is also one of the products.* The fissions of $^{235}_{92}U$ and $^{239}_{94}Pu$ can produce chain reactions. One neutron causes the fission of one $^{235}_{92}U$ nucleus. Two or three neutrons given off when this fission occurs can cause the fission of other $^{235}_{92}U$ nuclei. Again neutrons are emitted. These can cause the fission of still other $^{235}_{92}U$ nuclei. This is a chain reaction. It continues until all the $^{235}_{92}U$ atoms have split or until the neutrons fail to strike $^{235}_{92}U$ nuclei. This is what happens in an uncontrolled chain reaction such as the explosion of a nuclear warhead.

❑ 31.20 Action in a nuclear reactor

A *nuclear reactor is a device in which the controlled fission of radioactive material produces new radioactive substances and energy.* One of the earliest nuclear reactors was built at Oak Ridge, Tennessee, in 1943. This reactor uses natural uranium. It has a lattice-type structure with blocks of graphite forming the framework. Spaced between the blocks of graphite are rods of uranium, encased in aluminum cans for protection. *Control rods* of neutron-absorbing boron steel are inserted into the lat-

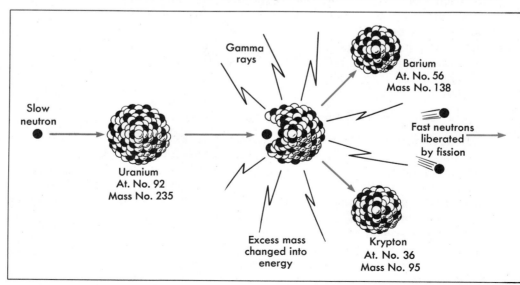

tice to limit the number of free neutrons. The reactor is air-cooled.

The rods of uranium or uranium oxide are the *nuclear fuel* for the reactor. The energy released in the reactor comes from changes in the uranium nuclei. Graphite is said to be the *moderator* because it slows down the fast neutrons produced by fission. By doing so, it makes them more readily captured by a nucleus and thus more effective for producing additional nuclear changes. The mass of uranium in such a reactor is important. Enough uranium must be present to provide the number of neutrons needed to sustain a chain reaction. This quantity of uranium is called the **critical mass**.

Two types of reactions occur in the fuel in such a reactor. Neutrons cause $^{235}_{92}U$ nuclei to undergo fission. The fast neutrons from this fission are slowed down as they pass through the graphite. Some strike other $^{235}_{92}U$ nuclei and continue the chain reaction. Other neutrons strike $^{238}_{92}U$ nuclei, starting the changes that finally produce plutonium. Great quantities of heat energy are released. For this reason the reactor must be cooled continuously by blowing air through tubes in the lattice. The rate of the reaction is controlled by the insertion or removal of the neutron-absorbing control rods. This type of reactor is now used to produce radioactive isotopes.

In nuclear power plants, the reactor is the source of heat energy. Pressurized water is both the moderator and the coolant. The heat from the reactor absorbed by the pressurized water is used to produce steam. This steam turns the turbines, which drive the electric generators. Present problems with nuclear power plant development include questions about location, environmental requirements, and safety of operation. Procurement and enrichment of uranium, as well as methods and policies

Figure 31-17. Neutrons from fission of a $^{235}_{92}U$ nucleus, when slowed down by a carbon moderator, can cause fission in a second $^{235}_{92}U$ nucleus. This process makes a chain reaction possible.

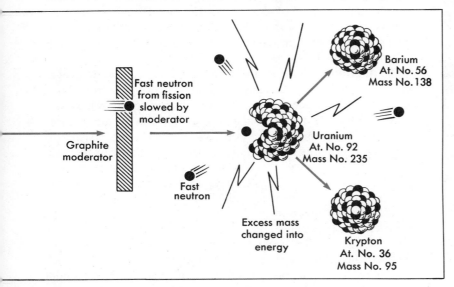

Graphite moderator

Fast neutron from fission slowed by moderator

Fast neutron

Uranium At. No. 92 Mass No. 235

Barium At. No. 56 Mass No. 138

Krypton At. No. 36 Mass No. 95

Excess mass changed into energy

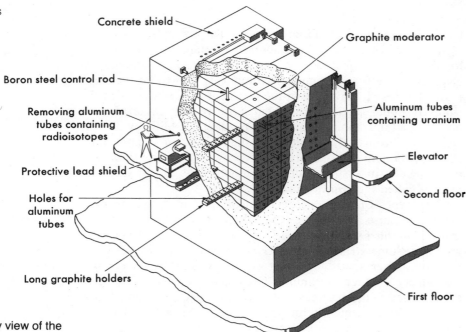

Figure 31-18. A cutaway view of the Oak Ridge reactor.

for storing or reprocessing used nuclear reactor fuel, are also being studied.

◻ 31.21 Fusion reactions

Nuclear stability can be increased by combining light-weight nuclei into heavier nuclei. This process is defined as *fusion*.

Fusion reactions are the source of the sun's energy. It is believed that there are two series of such reactions going on in the sun. One series occurs at the very hot center of the sun, while the other takes place in the cooler outer portion of the sun. These two reactions proceed by different pathways. However, their net effect is the combination of four hydrogen nuclei into a helium nucleus. A loss of mass occurs and a tremendous amount of energy is released.

The thermonuclear bomb, sometimes called the hydrogen bomb, or H-bomb, produces energy by a fusion reaction. More energy is released per gram of fuel in a fusion reaction than in a fission reaction. For this reason, the H-bomb is much more destructive than the atomic bomb, a fission bomb. Also, the quantities of reacting materials in a fusion reaction can be made much larger. In theory, there is no limit to the amount of reactants that can be used. Fusion reactions are not chain reactions and thus do not require a critical mass of reacting materials.

One possible reaction in a hydrogen bomb involves the formation of alpha particles and tremendous energy from a specific lithium hydride. This special compound may be formed from lithium-6 and deuterium and have the formula $^6_3\text{Li}^2_1\text{H}$. Such a fusion reaction can be started only by placing $^6_3\text{Li}^2_1\text{H}$ under

Figure 31-19. The Princeton Large Torus shown in the photograph is capable of producing a temperature of 60,000,000 °C. Devices like this are used by scientists in their attempts to produce controlled nuclear fusion.

extremely high temperature and pressure. These conditions are created by using an atomic bomb to set off the hydrogen bomb.

Current research indicates that fusion reactions may be controlled. Scientists are attempting to find ways to confine the nuclear fuel, usually ionized deuterium and tritium, and at the same time make it hot enough and dense enough for fusion to occur. Experiments using high-powered laser light or beams of electrons as ways to start the fusion reaction are being conducted. Such reactions may some day produce useful energy that can be converted to electricity.

◀ SUMMARY

Radioactivity is the spontaneous breakdown of an unstable atomic nucleus with the release of particles and rays.

Radium was discovered by Pierre and Marie Curie in 1898. It is a very radioactive element always found in uranium ores. Radium resembles barium in its chemical properties. Radioactive nuclides and their compounds have several unusual properties: (1) they affect the light-sensitive emulsion on a photographic film, (2) they produce an electric charge in the surrounding air, (3) they produce fluorescence with certain other compounds, (4) their radiations have special physiological effects, (5) they undergo radioactive decay. The half-life of a radioactive nuclide is the length of time that it takes for half of a given number of atoms of the nuclide to decay.

The radiation given off by radioactive elements consists of three different kinds of particles and rays: (1) alpha particles, which are helium nuclei; (2) beta particles, which are electrons; and (3) gamma rays, which are high-energy X rays. The emission of these particles from the nuclei of radioactive nuclides causes the nuclides to decay into simpler ones.

All naturally occurring radioactive nuclides with atomic numbers greater than 83 belong to one of three series of related nuclides. Uranium-238 is the parent element of the radioactive series that contains radium. A transmutation is a change in the identity of a nucleus because of a change in the number of its protons.

The age of certain minerals and of carbon-containing materials can be estimated by the amounts of radioactive nuclides they contain.

The difference between the sum of the masses of the separate particles making up a nucleus and the actual mass of a nucleus is the nuclear mass defect. The mass defect, converted into energy units, is the energy released when a nucleus is formed from the particles that compose it. This energy is known as the binding energy. The lightest and heaviest elements have the smallest binding energies per nuclear particle and the least stable nuclei. Elements having intermediate atomic weights have the greatest binding energies per nuclear particle and the most stable nuclei. The ratio of neutrons to protons and the even-odd nature of the number of neutrons and protons in a nucleus are also related to its stability.

There are four types of reactions that nuclei undergo to become more stable: (1) radioactive decay, (2) nuclear disintegration, (3) fission, and (4) fusion.

The cyclotron is an electromagnetic device for accelerating protons and deuterons in a spiral path. Other particle accelerators are the synchrotron, the betatron, and the linear accelerator.

When bombarded by slow neutrons, a $^{238}_{92}U$ nucleus may capture a neutron and ultimately be transformed into $^{239}_{94}Pu$. Stable atoms may be made artificially radioactive by bombardment with deuterons or neutrons. Artificial radioactive nuclides are used in medicine and in research.

When $^{235}_{92}U$ is bombarded with slow neutrons, it undergoes fission. Fission is the splitting of a very heavy nucleus into medium-weight parts. A chain reaction is one in which the material or energy that starts the reaction is also one of the products.

A nuclear reactor is a device in which the controlled fission of radioactive material produces new radioactive substances and heat energy, which may be used to generate electricity.

A fusion reaction is one in which light-weight nuclei are combined into heavier nuclei. Fusion reactions produce the sun's heat and light.

◖ VOCABULARY

alpha particle	cyclotron	half-life	nuclear reactor
beta particle	daughter nuclide	linear accelerator	parent nuclide
betatron	deuteron	moderator	radioactive decay
chain reaction	fission	nuclear binding energy	radioactivity
control rods	fluoresce	nuclear disintegration	synchrotron
cosmic ray	fusion	nuclear equation	transmutation
critical mass	gamma ray	nuclear mass defect	transuranium element

◖ QUESTIONS

Group A

1. (*a*) Who discovered radioactivity? (*b*) How was the discovery made?
2. What evidence led Marie and Pierre Curie to suspect that there were radioactive elements other than uranium in pitchblende?
3. How does the radioactivity of radium compare with that of uranium?
4. What practical use is made of the fluorescence produced in zinc sulfide by a radium compound?
5. What is meant by the *half-life* of a radioactive nuclide?
6. From what part of a radioactive nuclide do the alpha or beta particles come?
7. What change in identity and mass number occurs when a radioactive nuclide gives off an alpha particle?
8. What change in identity and mass number occurs when a radioactive nuclide gives off a beta particle?
9. How is the age of a radioactive mineral estimated?
10. Name the four types of nuclear reactions that produce more stable nuclei.
11. In what ways does natural radioactive decay produce more stable nuclei?
12. How were neutrons first detected as nuclear particles?
13. Why are neutrons more effective particles for bombarding atomic nuclei than protons or alpha particles?
14. What may happen to a neutron that is fired at the nucleus of an atom?
15. For what purposes are radioactive isotopes used?
16. (*a*) What are the naturally occurring isotopes of uranium? (*b*) What is their relative abundance?
17. (*a*) What is fission? (*b*) How is it produced in $^{235}_{92}U$?
18. What is meant by the *critical mass* of a reactor?
19. Why must a nuclear reactor be continually cooled?
20. What reaction produces the sun's energy?

Group B

21. Why is radium studied separately rather than with the other elements of Group II?
22. Why can the radiation from a radioactive material affect photographic film, even though the film is well wrapped in black paper?

23. How does a radioactive material affect the rate of discharge of an electroscope?
24. (*a*) What conditions cause variations in the decay rate of a radioactive material? (*b*) Are these variations slight, moderate, or great?
25. Where are most of the radioactive nuclides located in the periodic table?
26. Make a chart that compares the following properties of alpha particles and beta particles: identity, mass number, charge, speed, and penetrating ability.
27. What are gamma rays?
28. Write the nuclear equation for the release of an alpha particle by $^{226}_{88}Ra$.
29. Write the nuclear equation for the release of a beta particle by $^{214}_{82}Pb$.
30. Write nuclear equations for successive releases of an alpha particle and a beta particle from $^{214}_{84}Po$.
31. (*a*) Which kinds of elements have the smallest binding energy per nuclear particle? (*b*) Which kind has the greatest binding energy per nuclear particle? (*c*) How does the binding energy per nuclear particle affect the stability of a nucleus?
32. What factors affect the stability of a nucleus?
33. How does each type of nuclear reaction produce more stable nuclei?
34. (*a*) Who produced the first artificial nuclear disintegration? (*b*) Write the equation for this reaction.
35. How was Einstein's equation for the relationship between matter and energy, $E = mc^2$, proved to be correct?
36. (*a*) Describe the path of the accelerated particles in a cyclotron. (*b*) What causes them to take this path?
37. Explain the changes occurring in the nucleus by which $^{239}_{94}Pu$ is produced from $^{238}_{92}U$.
38. (*a*) How are artificially radioactive isotopes prepared? (*b*) Write a nuclear equation to show the preparation of such a nuclide. (*c*) What use is made of the nuclide whose preparation you have shown in this nuclear equation?
39. (*a*) Describe a chain reaction. (*b*) How does the fission of $^{235}_{92}U$ produce a chain reaction?
40. How is a uranium-graphite reactor constructed?

◖ PROBLEMS

Group A

1. The half-life of thorium-227 is 18.2 days. How many days are required for three-fourths of a given amount to decay?
2. The half-life of $^{234}_{91}Pa$ is 6.75 hours. How much of a given amount remains after 20.25 hours?
3. After 4860 years, how much of an original 0.250 g of $^{226}_{88}Ra$ remains?
4. The atomic mass of a ^7_3Li nucleus is 7.01436 *u*. Calculate the nuclear mass defect. The atomic masses of nuclear particles are given in Section 3.13.
5. Calculate the nuclear mass defect of $^{20}_{10}Ne$ if its nucleus has an atomic mass of 19.98695 *u*.

Group B

6. The half-life of $^{222}_{86}Rn$ is 3.823 days. What was the original mass of $^{222}_{86}Rn$ if 0.0500 g remains after 7.646 days?
7. The half-life of $^{239}_{94}Pu$ is 24,390 years. Of an original mass of 100 g, approximately how much remains after 10^5 years?
8. The relative abundance of uranium-238 and radium-226 in uranium ores is proportional to their respective half-lives. The half-life of uranium-238 is 4.51×10^9 years while that of radium-226 is 1.62×10^3 years. What is the proportion of radium atoms to uranium atoms in a uranium ore sample.
9. Calculate the nuclear mass defect per nuclear particle for ^7_3Li using the answer to Problem 4. Convert the mass in *u* to binding energy in megaelectron-volts by using the relationship 1 *u* = 931 megaelectron-volts.
10. Calculate the binding energy per nuclear particle of $^{238}_{92}U$, if the atomic mass of its nucleus is 238.0003 *u*.

Appendix

Table 1

METRIC SYSTEM PREFIXES

Factor	Prefix	Symbol	Factor	Prefix	Symbol
10^{12}	tera	T	10^{-1}	deci	d
10^{9}	giga	G	10^{-2}	centi	c
10^{6}	mega	M	10^{-3}	milli	m
10^{3}	kilo	k	10^{-6}	micro	μ (mu)
10^{2}	hecto	h	10^{-9}	nano	n
10^{1}	deka	da	10^{-12}	pico	p

Table 2

ISOTOPES OF SOME ELEMENTS

(Naturally occurring nonradioactive isotopes are given in bold type. Naturally occurring radioactive isotopes are boldface italics in color. All other radioactive isotopes are in italics. Naturally occurring isotopes are listed in order of their abundance. All other isotopes are listed in order of length of half-life.)

Element	Mass numbers of isotopes
H	**1, 2,** *3*
He	**4, 3,** *6, 8*
Li	**7, 6,** *8, 9*
Be	**9,** *10, 7, 11, 6*
B	**11, 10,** *8*
C	**12, 13,** *14, 11, 10, 15, 16, 9*
N	**14, 15,** *13, 16, 17, 18*
O	**16, 18, 17,** *15, 14, 19, 20*
F	**19,** *18, 17, 20, 21, 22*
Ne	**20, 22, 21,** *24, 23, 19, 18, 17*
Na	**23,** *22, 24, 25, 21, 26, 20*
Mg	**24, 26, 25,** *28, 27, 23, 20, 21*
Al	**27,** *26, 29, 28, 25, 30, 24*
Si	**28, 29, 30,** *32, 31, 27, 26, 25*
P	**31,** *33, 32, 30, 34, 29, 28*
S	**32, 34, 33, 36,** *35, 38, 37, 31, 30, 29*
Cl	**35, 37,** *36, 39, 38, 40, 33, 34, 32*
Ar	**40, 36, 38,** *39, 42, 37, 41, 35, 33*
K	**39, 41,** *40, 43, 42, 44, 45, 38, 47, 37*
Ca	**40, 44, 42,** *48,* **43, 46,** *41, 45, 47, 49, 50, 39, 38, 37*
Cr	**52, 53, 50, 54,** *51, 48, 49, 56, 55, 46*
Fe	**56, 54, 57, 58,** *60, 55, 59, 52, 53, 61*
Ni	**58, 60, 62, 61, 64,** *59, 63, 56, 66, 57, 65, 67*
Cu	**63, 65,** *67, 64, 61, 60, 62, 58, 66, 59, 68, 57*
Zn	*64,* **66, 68, 67,** *70, 65, 72, 62, 69, 63, 71, 60, 61*
Br	**79, 81,** *77, 82, 76, 83, 75, 74, 84, 80, 78, 85, 87, 86, 88, 89, 90*
Sr	**88, 86, 87, 84,** *90, 85, 89, 82, 91, 83, 92, 80, 81, 93, 94, 95*
Ag	**107, 109,** *105, 111, 113, 112, 104, 103, 106, 115, 102, 116, 108, 117, 110, 114*
Sn	**120, 118, 116, 119, 117,** *124,* **122, 112, 114, 115,** *126, 123, 113, 125, 121, 110, 127, 128, 111, 109, 108, 129, 131, 130, 132*
I	**127,** *129, 125, 126, 131, 124, 133, 123, 130, 135, 132, 121, 120, 134, 128, 119, 118, 117, 122, 136, 137, 138, 139*

Table 2

Element	Mass numbers of isotopes
Ba	**138, 137, 136, 135, 134, 130, 132,** *133, 140, 131, 128, 129, 126, 139, 141, 142, 127, 125, 123, 143*
W	**184,** *186, 182, 183, 180,* 181, *185, 188, 178, 187, 176, 177, 179, 175, 174, 173, 189*
Pt	**195, 194, 196,** *198, 192, 190, 193, 188, 191, 197, 200, 189, 186, 187, 185, 199, 184, 183, 182, 201, 181, 180, 179, 178, 177, 176, 175, 174*
Pb	**208, 206, 207, 204,** *205, 202, 210, 203, 200, 212, 201, 209, 198, 199, 197, 196, 211, 214, 195, 194, 213*
Bi	*209, 208, 207, 205, 206, 210, 203, 204, 201, 202, 212, 213, 200, 199, 214, 197, 215, 211, 198*
Rn	*222, 211, 210, 224, 223, 209, 221, 212, 208, 207, 206, 205, 204, 220, 203, 202, 219*
Ra	*226, 228, 225, 223, 224, 230, 227, 213, 222, 221*
U	*238, 235, 236, 234, 233, 232, 230, 237, 231, 240, 229, 239, 228, 227*
Np	*237, 236, 235, 234, 239, 238, 236, 240, 231, 233, 241, 232, 230, 229*
Pu	*244, 242, 239, 240, 238, 241, 236, 237, 246, 245, 234, 243, 232, 235, 233*
Am	*243, 241, 240, 242, 239, 244, 245, 238, 237, 246, 247*
Cm	*247, 248, 250, 245, 246, 243, 244, 242, 241, 240, 239, 238, 249*
Bk	*247, 249, 245, 246, 248, 243, 244, 250, 251*
Cf	*251, 249, 250, 252, 248, 254, 253, 246, 247, 245, 244, 243, 242*
Es	*254, 252, 255, 253, 251, 250, 249, 248, 246, 247, 245*
Fm	*257, 253, 252, 255, 251, 254, 256, 250, 249, 248, 247, 245, 246, 258*
Md	*258, 257, 256, 255, 254, 252, 251, 250, 249, 248*
No	*259, 255, 253, 254, 257, 256, 252, 251, 258*
Lr	*260, 256, 255, 254, 259, 258, 257, 253*
Unq	*261, 257, 259, 260, 258*
Unp	*263, 262, 261, 260*
Unh	*263?*
Uns	*261?*

Table 3

PHYSICAL CONSTANTS

Quantity	Symbol	Value
atomic mass unit	u	$1.6605655 \times 10^{-24}$ g
Avogadro number	N_A	6.022045×10^{23}/mole
electron rest mass	m_e	9.10953×10^{-28} g
mechanical equivalent of heat	J	4.1868 j/cal
molar gas constant	R	8.20568×10^{-2} L atm/mole °K
molar volume of ideal gas at STP	V_m	22.4136 L/mole
neutron rest mass	m_n	1.674954×10^{-24} g
normal boiling point of water	T_b	373.15 °K = 100.0 °C
normal freezing point of water	T_f	273.15 °K = 0.00 °C
Planck's constant	h	6.626176×10^{-34} j s
proton rest mass	m_p	1.672649×10^{-24} g
speed of light in vacuum	c	2.99792458×10^8 m/s
temperature of triple point of water		273.16 °K = 0.01 °C

Table 4

THE ELEMENTS, THEIR SYMBOLS, ATOMIC NUMBERS, AND ATOMIC WEIGHTS

The more common elements are printed in color.

Name of element	Symbol	Atomic number	Atomic weight	Name of element	Symbol	Atomic number	Atomic weight
actinium	Ac	89	227.0278	molybdenum	Mo	42	95.94
aluminum	Al	13	26.98154	neodymium	Nd	60	144.24
americium	Am	95	[243]	neon	Ne	10	20.179
antimony	Sb	51	121.75	neptunium	Np	93	237.0482
argon	Ar	18	39.948	nickel	Ni	28	58.70
arsenic	As	33	74.9216	niobium	Nb	41	92.9064
astatine	At	85	[210]	nitrogen	N	7	14.0067
barium	Ba	56	137.33	nobelium	No	102	[259]
berkelium	Bk	97	[247]	osmium	Os	76	190.2
beryllium	Be	4	9.01218	oxygen	O	8	15.9994
bismuth	Bi	83	208.9804	palladium	Pd	46	106.4
boron	B	5	10.81	phosphorus	P	15	30.97376
bromine	Br	35	79.904	platinum	Pt	78	195.09
cadmium	Cd	48	112.41	plutonium	Pu	94	[244]
calcium	Ca	20	40.08	polonium	Po	84	[209]
californium	Cf	98	[251]	potassium	K	19	39.0983
carbon	C	6	12.011	praseodymium	Pr	59	140.9077
cerium	Ce	58	140.12	promethium	Pm	61	[145]
cesium	Cs	55	132.9054	protactinium	Pa	91	231.0359
chlorine	Cl	17	35.453	radium	Ra	88	226.0254
chromium	Cr	24	51.996	radon	Rn	86	[222]
cobalt	Co	27	58.9332	rhenium	Re	75	186.207
copper	Cu	29	63.546	rhodium	Rh	45	102.9055
curium	Cm	96	[247]	rubidium	Rb	37	85.4678
dysprosium	Dy	66	162.50	ruthenium	Ru	44	101.07
einsteinium	Es	99	[254]	samarium	Sm	62	150.4
erbium	Er	68	167.26	scandium	Sc	21	44.9559
europium	Eu	63	151.96	selenium	Se	34	78.96
fermium	Fm	100	[257]	silicon	Si	14	28.0855
fluorine	F	9	18.998403	silver	Ag	47	107.868
francium	Fr	87	[223]	sodium	Na	11	22.98977
gadolinium	Gd	64	157.25	strontium	Sr	38	87.62
gallium	Ga	31	69.72	sulfur	S	16	32.06
germanium	Ge	32	72.59	tantalum	Ta	73	180.9479
gold	Au	79	196.9665	technetium	Tc	43	[98]
hafnium	Hf	72	178.49	tellurium	Te	52	127.60
helium	He	2	4.00260	terbium	Tb	65	158.9254
holmium	Ho	67	164.9304	thallium	Tl	81	204.37
hydrogen	H	1	1.0079	thorium	Th	90	232.0381
indium	In	49	114.82	thulium	Tm	69	168.9342
iodine	I	53	126.9045	tin	Sn	50	118.69
iridium	Ir	77	192.22	titanium	Ti	22	47.90
iron	Fe	26	55.847	tungsten	W	74	183.85
krypton	Kr	36	83.80	unnilhexium	Unh	106	[263?]
lanthanum	La	57	138.9055	unnilpentium	Unp	105	[263]
lawrencium	Lr	103	[260]	unnilquadium	Unq	104	[261]
lead	Pb	82	207.2	unnilseptium	Uns	107	[261?]
lithium	Li	3	6.941	uranium	U	92	238.029
lutetium	Lu	71	174.967	vanadium	V	23	50.9415
magnesium	Mg	12	24.305	xenon	Xe	54	131.30
manganese	Mn	25	54.9380	ytterbium	Yb	70	173.04
mendelevium	Md	101	[258]	yttrium	Y	39	88.9059
mercury	Hg	80	200.59	zinc	Zn	30	65.38
				zirconium	Zr	40	91.22

A value given in brackets denotes the mass number of the isotope of longest known half-life. The atomic weights most of these elements are believed to have an error no greater than ±1 in the last digit given.

Table 5

COMMON ELEMENTS

Name	Symbol	Approx. at. wt.	Common ox. nos.	Name	Symbol	Approx. at. wt.	Common ox. nos.
aluminum	Al	27.0	+3	magnesium	Mg	24.3	+2
antimony	Sb	121.8	+3,+5	manganese	Mn	54.9	+2,+4,+7
arsenic	As	74.9	+3,+5	mercury	Hg	200.6	+1,+2
barium	Ba	137.3	+2	nickel	Ni	58.7	+2
bismuth	Bi	209.0	+3	nitrogen	N	14.0	−3,+3,+5
bromine	Br	79.9	−1,+5	oxygen	O	16.0	−2
calcium	Ca	40.1	+2	phosphorus	P	31.0	+3,+5
carbon	C	12.0	+2,+4	platinum	Pt	195.1	+2,+4
chlorine	Cl	35.5	−1,+5,+7	potassium	K	39.1	+1
chromium	Cr	52.0	+2,+3,+6	silicon	Si	28.1	+4
cobalt	Co	58.9	+2,+3	silver	Ag	107.9	+1
copper	Cu	63.5	+1,+2	sodium	Na	23.0	+1
fluorine	F	19.0	−1	strontium	Sr	87.6	+2
gold	Au	197.0	+1,+3	sulfur	S	32.1	−2,+4,+6
hydrogen	H	1.0	−1,+1	tin	Sn	118.7	+2,+4
iodine	I	126.9	−1,+5	titanium	Ti	47.9	+3,+4
iron	Fe	55.8	+2,+3	tungsten	W	183.8	+6
lead	Pb	207.2	+2,+4	zinc	Zn	65.4	+2

Table 6

COMMON IONS AND THEIR CHARGES

Name	Symbol	Charge	Name	Symbol	Charge
aluminum	Al^{+++}	+3	lead(II)	Pb^{++}	+2
ammonium	NH_4^+	+1	magnesium	Mg^{++}	+2
barium	Ba^{++}	+2	mercury(I)	Hg_2^{++}	+2
calcium	Ca^{++}	+2	mercury(II)	Hg^{++}	+2
chromium(III)	Cr^{+++}	+3	nickel(II)	Ni^{++}	+2
cobalt(II)	Co^{++}	+2	potassium	K^+	+1
copper(I)	Cu^+	+1	silver	Ag^+	+1
copper(II)	Cu^{++}	+2	sodium	Na^+	+1
hydronium	H_3O^+	+1	tin(II)	Sn^{++}	+2
iron(II)	Fe^{++}	+2	tin(IV)	Sn^{++++}	+4
iron(III)	Fe^{+++}	+3	zinc	Zn^{++}	+2
acetate	$C_2H_3O_2^-$	−1	hydrogen sulfate	HSO_4^-	−1
bromide	Br^-	−1	hydroxide	OH^-	−1
carbonate	CO_3^{--}	−2	hypochlorite	ClO^-	−1
chlorate	ClO_3^-	−1	iodide	I^-	−1
chloride	Cl^-	−1	nitrate	NO_3^-	−1
chlorite	ClO_2^-	−1	nitrite	NO_2^-	−1
chromate	CrO_4^{--}	−2	oxide	O^{--}	−2
cyanide	CN^-	−1	perchlorate	ClO_4^-	−1
dichromate	$Cr_2O_7^{--}$	−2	permanganate	MnO_4^-	−1
fluoride	F^-	−1	peroxide	O_2^{--}	−2
hexacyanoferrate(II)	$Fe(CN)_6^{----}$	−4	phosphate	PO_4^{---}	−3
hexacyanoferrate(III)	$Fe(CN)_6^{---}$	−3	sulfate	SO_4^{--}	−2
hydride	H^-	−1	sulfide	S^{--}	−2
hydrogen carbonate	HCO_3^-	−1	sulfite	SO_3^{--}	−2

Table 7

ELECTRON ARRANGEMENT OF THE ELEMENTS

Shells		K	L		M			N				O				P				Q
Sublevels		1s	2s	2p	3s	3p	3d	4s	4p	4d	4f	5s	5p	5d	5f	6s	6p	6d	6f	7s
1	hydrogen	1																		
2	helium	2																		
3	lithium	2	1																	
4	beryllium	2	2																	
5	boron	2	2	1																
6	carbon	2	2	2																
7	nitrogen	2	2	3																
8	oxygen	2	2	4																
9	fluorine	2	2	5																
10	neon	2	2	6																
11	sodium	2	2	6	1															
12	magnesium	2	2	6	2															
13	aluminum	2	2	6	2	1														
14	silicon	2	2	6	2	2														
15	phosphorus	2	2	6	2	3														
16	sulfur	2	2	6	2	4														
17	chlorine	2	2	6	2	5														
18	argon	2	2	6	2	6														
19	potassium	2	2	6	2	6		1												
20	calcium	2	2	6	2	6		2												
21	scandium	2	2	6	2	6	1	2												
22	titanium	2	2	6	2	6	2	2												
23	vanadium	2	2	6	2	6	3	2												
24	chromium	2	2	6	2	6	5	1												
25	manganese	2	2	6	2	6	5	2												
26	iron	2	2	6	2	6	6	2												
27	cobalt	2	2	6	2	6	7	2												
28	nickel	2	2	6	2	6	8	2												
29	copper	2	2	6	2	6	10	1												
30	zinc	2	2	6	2	6	10	2												
31	gallium	2	2	6	2	6	10	2	1											
32	germanium	2	2	6	2	6	10	2	2											
33	arsenic	2	2	6	2	6	10	2	3											
34	selenium	2	2	6	2	6	10	2	4											
35	bromine	2	2	6	2	6	10	2	5											
36	krypton	2	2	6	2	6	10	2	6											
37	rubidium	2	2	6	2	6	10	2	6			1								
38	strontium	2	2	6	2	6	10	2	6			2								
39	yttrium	2	2	6	2	6	10	2	6	1		2								
40	zirconium	2	2	6	2	6	10	2	6	2		2								
41	niobium	2	2	6	2	6	10	2	6	4		1								
42	molybdenum	2	2	6	2	6	10	2	6	5		1								
43	technetium	2	2	6	2	6	10	2	6	5		2								
44	ruthenium	2	2	6	2	6	10	2	6	7		1								
45	rhodium	2	2	6	2	6	10	2	6	8		1								
46	palladium	2	2	6	2	6	10	2	6	10										
47	silver	2	2	6	2	6	10	2	6	10		1								
48	cadmium	2	2	6	2	6	10	2	6	10		2								
49	indium	2	2	6	2	6	10	2	6	10		2	1							
50	tin	2	2	6	2	6	10	2	6	10		2	2							
51	antimony	2	2	6	2	6	10	2	6	10		2	3							
52	tellurium	2	2	6	2	6	10	2	6	10		2	4							

Table 7

	Shells	K	L		M			N				O				P				Q
	Sublevels	1s	2s	2p	3s	3p	3d	4s	4p	4d	4f	5s	5p	5d	5f	6s	6p	6d	6f	7s
53	iodine	2	2	6	2	6	10	2	6	10		2	5							
54	xenon	2	2	6	2	6	10	2	6	10		2	6							
55	cesium	2	2	6	2	6	10	2	6	10		2	6			1				
56	barium	2	2	6	2	6	10	2	6	10		2	6			2				
57	lanthanum	2	2	6	2	6	10	2	6	10		2	6	1		2				
58	cerium	2	2	6	2	6	10	2	6	10	1	2	6	1		2				
59	praseodymium	2	2	6	2	6	10	2	6	10	3	2	6			2				
60	neodymium	2	2	6	2	6	10	2	6	10	4	2	6			2				
61	promethium	2	2	6	2	6	10	2	6	10	5	2	6			2				
62	samarium	2	2	6	2	6	10	2	6	10	6	2	6			2				
63	europium	2	2	6	2	6	10	2	6	10	7	2	6			2				
64	gadolinium	2	2	6	2	6	10	2	6	10	7	2	6	1		2				
65	terbium	2	2	6	2	6	10	2	6	10	9	2	6			2				
66	dysprosium	2	2	6	2	6	10	2	6	10	10	2	6			2				
67	holmium	2	2	6	2	6	10	2	6	10	11	2	6			2				
68	erbium	2	2	6	2	6	10	2	6	10	12	2	6			2				
69	thulium	2	2	6	2	6	10	2	6	10	13	2	6			2				
70	ytterbium	2	2	6	2	6	10	2	6	10	14	2	6			2				
71	lutetium	2	2	6	2	6	10	2	6	10	14	2	6	1		2				
72	hafnium	2	2	6	2	6	10	2	6	10	14	2	6	2		2				
73	tantalum	2	2	6	2	6	10	2	6	10	14	2	6	3		2				
74	tungsten	2	2	6	2	6	10	2	6	10	14	2	6	4		2				
75	rhenium	2	2	6	2	6	10	2	6	10	14	2	6	5		2				
76	osmium	2	2	6	2	6	10	2	6	10	14	2	6	6		2				
77	iridium	2	2	6	2	6	10	2	6	10	14	2	6	7		2				
78	platinum	2	2	6	2	6	10	2	6	10	14	2	6	9		1				
79	gold	2	2	6	2	6	10	2	6	10	14	2	6	10		1				
80	mercury	2	2	6	2	6	10	2	6	10	14	2	6	10		2				
81	thallium	2	2	6	2	6	10	2	6	10	14	2	6	10		2	1			
82	lead	2	2	6	2	6	10	2	6	10	14	2	6	10		2	2			
83	bismuth	2	2	6	2	6	10	2	6	10	14	2	6	10		2	3			
84	polonium	2	2	6	2	6	10	2	6	10	14	2	6	10		2	4			
85	astatine	2	2	6	2	6	10	2	6	10	14	2	6	10		2	5			
86	radon	2	2	6	2	6	10	2	6	10	14	2	6	10		2	6			
87	francium	2	2	6	2	6	10	2	6	10	14	2	6	10		2	6			1
88	radium	2	2	6	2	6	10	2	6	10	14	2	6	10		2	6			2
89	actinium	2	2	6	2	6	10	2	6	10	14	2	6	10		2	6	1		2
90	thorium	2	2	6	2	6	10	2	6	10	14	2	6	10		2	6	2		2
91	protactinium	2	2	6	2	6	10	2	6	10	14	2	6	10	2	2	6	1		2
92	uranium	2	2	6	2	6	10	2	6	10	14	2	6	10	3	2	6	1		2
93	neptunium	2	2	6	2	6	10	2	6	10	14	2	6	10	4	2	6	1		2
94	plutonium	2	2	6	2	6	10	2	6	10	14	2	6	10	6	2	6			2
95	americium	2	2	6	2	6	10	2	6	10	14	2	6	10	7	2	6			2
96	curium	2	2	6	2	6	10	2	6	10	14	2	6	10	7	2	6	1		2
97	berkelium	2	2	6	2	6	10	2	6	10	14	2	6	10	8	2	6	1		2
98	californium	2	2	6	2	6	10	2	6	10	14	2	6	10	10	2	6			2
99	einsteinium	2	2	6	2	6	10	2	6	10	14	2	6	10	11	2	6			2
100	fermium	2	2	6	2	6	10	2	6	10	14	2	6	10	12	2	6			2
101	mendelevium	2	2	6	2	6	10	2	6	10	14	2	6	10	13	2	6			2
102	nobelium	2	2	6	2	6	10	2	6	10	14	2	6	10	14	2	6			2
103	lawrencium	2	2	6	2	6	10	2	6	10	14	2	6	10	14	2	6	1		2
104	unnilquadium	2	2	6	2	6	10	2	6	10	14	2	6	10	14	2	6	2		2?
105	unnilpentium	2	2	6	2	6	10	2	6	10	14	2	6	10	14	2	6	3		2?
106	unnilhexium	2	2	6	2	6	10	2	6	10	14	2	6	10	14	2	6	4		2?
107	unnilseptium	2	2	6	2	6	10	2	6	10	14	2	6	10	14	2	6	5		2?

Table 8

WATER-VAPOR PRESSURE

Temperature (°C)	Pressure (mm Hg)	Temperature (°C)	Pressure (mm Hg)	Temperature (°C)	Pressure (mm Hg)
0.0	4.6	19.5	17.0	27.0	26.7
5.0	6.5	20.0	17.5	28.0	28.3
10.0	9.2	20.5	18.1	29.0	30.0
12.5	10.9	21.0	18.6	30.0	31.8
15.0	12.8	21.5	19.2	35.0	42.2
15.5	13.2	22.0	19.8	40.0	55.3
16.0	13.6	22.5	20.4	50.0	92.5
16.5	14.1	23.0	21.1	60.0	149.4
17.0	14.5	23.5	21.7	70.0	233.7
17.5	15.0	24.0	22.4	80.0	355.1
18.0	15.5	24.5	23.1	90.0	525.8
18.5	16.0	25.0	23.8	95.0	633.9
19.0	16.5	26.0	25.2	100.0	760.0

Table 9

DENSITY OF GASES AT STP

Gas	Density (g/L)	Gas	Density (g/L)
air, dry	1.2929	hydrogen	0.0899
ammonia	0.771	hydrogen chloride	1.639
carbon dioxide	1.977	hydrogen sulfide	1.539
carbon monoxide	1.250	methane	0.716
chlorine	3.214	nitrogen	1.251
dinitrogen monoxide	1.977	nitrogen monoxide	1.340
ethyne (acetylene)	1.171	oxygen	1.429
helium	0.1785	sulfur dioxide	2.927

Table 10

DENSITY OF WATER

Temperature (°C)	Density (g/mL)	Temperature (°C)	Density (g/mL)
0	0.99987	15	0.99913
1	0.99993	20	0.99823
2	0.99997	25	0.99707
3	0.99999	30	0.99567
4	1.00000	40	0.99224
5	0.99999	50	0.98807
6	0.99997	60	0.98324
7	0.99993	70	0.97781
8	0.99988	80	0.97183
9	0.99981	90	0.96534
10	0.99973	100	0.95838

Table 11

SOLUBILITY OF GASES IN WATER

Volume of gas (reduced to STP) that can be dissolved in 1 volume of water at the temperature (°C) indicated.

Gas	0°	10°	20°	60°
air	0.02918	0.02284	0.01868	0.01216
ammonia	1130	870	680	200
carbon dioxide	1.713	1.194	0.878	0.359
carbon monoxide	0.03537	0.02816	0.02319	0.01488
chlorine	4.54	3.148	2.299	1.023
hydrogen	0.02148	0.01955	0.01819	0.01600
hydrogen chloride	512	475	442	339
hydrogen sulfide	4.670	3.399	2.582	1.190
nitrogen	0.02354	0.01861	0.01545	0.01023
nitrogen dioxide	0.07381	0.05709	0.04706	0.02954
oxygen	0.04889	0.03802	0.03102	0.01946
sulfur dioxide	79.789	56.647	39.374	—

Table 12

SOLUBILITY CHART

S = soluble in water. A = soluble in acids, insoluble in water. P = partially soluble in water, soluble in dilute acids. I = insoluble in dilute acids and in water. a = slightly soluble in acids, insoluble in water. d = decomposes in water.

	acetate	bromide	carbonate	chlorate	chloride	chromate	hydroxide	iodide	nitrate	oxide	phosphate	silicate	sulfate	sulfide
aluminum	S	S	—	S	S	—	A	S	S	a	A	I	S	d
ammonium	S	S	S	S	S	S	—	S	S	—	S	—	S	S
barium	S	S	P	S	S	A	S	S	S	S	A	S	a	d
calcium	S	S	P	S	S	S	S	S	S	P	P	P	P	P
copper(II)	S	S	—	S	S	—	A	—	S	A	A	A	S	A
hydrogen	S	S	—	S	S	—	—	S	S	—	S	I	S	S
iron(II)	S	S	P	S	S	—	A	S	S	A	A	—	S	A
iron(III)	S	S	—	S	S	A	A	S	S	A	P	—	P	d
lead(II)	S	S	A	S	S	A	P	P	S	P	A	A	P	A
magnesium	S	S	P	S	S	S	A	S	S	A	P	A	S	d
manganese(II)	S	S	P	S	S	—	A	S	S	A	P	I	S	A
mercury(I)	P	A	A	S	a	P	—	A	S	A	A	—	P	I
mercury(II)	S	S	—	S	S	P	A	P	S	P	A	—	d	I
potassium	S	S	S	S	S	S	S	S	S	S	S	S	S	S
silver	P	a	A	S	a	P	—	I	S	P	A	—	P	A
sodium	S	S	S	S	S	S	S	S	S	S	S	S	S	S
strontium	S	S	P	S	S	P	S	S	S	S	A	A	P	S
tin(II)	d	S	—	S	S	A	A	S	d	A	A	—	S	A
tin(IV)	S	S	—	—	S	S	P	d	—	A	—	—	S	A
zinc	S	S	P	S	S	P	A	S	S	P	A	A	S	A

Table 13

SOLUBILITY OF COMPOUNDS

Solubilities are given in grams of anhydrous solute that can be dissolved in 100 g of water at the temperature (°C) indicated.

Compound	Formula	0°	20°	60°	100°
aluminum sulfate	$Al_2(SO_4)_3$	31.2	36.4	59.2	89.0
ammonium chloride	NH_4Cl	29.4	37.2	55.3	77.3
ammonium nitrate	NH_4NO_3	118	192	421	871
ammonium sulfate	$(NH_4)_2SO_4$	70.6	75.4	88	103
barium carbonate	$BaCO_3$	$0.0016^{8°}$	$0.0022^{18°}$	—	0.0065
barium chloride	$BaCl_2$	31.2	35.8	46.2	59.4
barium hydroxide	$Ba(OH)_2$	1.67	3.89	20.94	$101.40^{80°}$
barium nitrate	$Ba(NO_3)_2$	4.95	9.02	20.4	34.4
barium sulfate	$BaSO_4$	0.000115	0.00024	—	0.000413
cadmium sulfate	$CdSO_4$	75.4	76.6	81.8	60.8
calcium acetate	$Ca(C_2H_3O_2)_2$	37.4	34.7	32.7	29.7
calcium carbonate	$CaCO_3$	—	0.0012	—	0.002
calcium fluoride	CaF_2	$0.0016^{18°}$	$0.0017^{25°}$	—	—
calcium hydrogen carbonate	$Ca(HCO_3)_2$	16.15	16.60	17.50	18.40
calcium hydroxide	$Ca(OH)_2$	0.189	0.173	0.121	0.076
calcium sulfate	$CaSO_4$	0.176	$0.209^{30°}$	0.205	0.162
cerium sulfate	$Ce_2(SO_4)_3$	21.4	9.84	3.87	—
cesium nitrate	$CsNO_3$	9.33	23.0	83.8	197
copper(II) chloride	$CuCl_2$	68.6	73.0	96.5	120
copper(II) sulfate	$CuSO_4$	23.1	32.0	61.8	114
lead(II) chloride	$PbCl_2$	0.67	1.00	1.94	3.20
lead(II) nitrate	$Pb(NO_3)_2$	37.5	54.3	91.6	133
lithium chloride	$LiCl$	69.2	83	98.4	128
lithium sulfate	Li_2SO_4	36.1	34.8	32.6	29.9
magnesium hydroxide	$Mg(OH)_2$	—	$0.0009^{18°}$	—	—
magnesium sulfate	$MgSO_4$	22.0	33.7	54.6	68.3
mercury(I) chloride	Hg_2Cl_2	0.00014	0.0002	$0.0007^{40°}$	—
mercury(II) chloride	$HgCl_2$	3.63	6.57	16.3	61.3
potassium aluminum sulfate	$KAl(SO_4)_2$	3.00	5.90	24.8	109
potassium bromide	KBr	53.6	65.3	85.5	104
potassium chlorate	$KClO_3$	3.3	7.3	23.8	56.3
potassium chloride	KCl	28.0	34.2	45.8	56.3
potassium chromate	K_2CrO_4	56.3	63.7	70.1	75.6
potassium iodide	KI	128	144	176	206
potassium nitrate	KNO_3	13.9	31.6	106	245
potassium permanganate	$KMnO_4$	2.83	6.34	22.1	—
potassium sulfate	K_2SO_4	7.4	11.1	18.2	24.1
silver acetate	$AgC_2H_3O_2$	0.73	1.05	1.93	$2.59^{80°}$
silver chloride	$AgCl$	0.00007	0.000194	$0.0005^{50°}$	0.002
silver nitrate	$AgNO_3$	122	216	440	733
sodium acetate	$NaC_2H_3O_2$	36.2	46.4	139	170.15
sodium chlorate	$NaClO_3$	79.6	95.9	137	204
sodium chloride	$NaCl$	35.7	35.9	37.1	39.2
sodium nitrate	$NaNO_3$	73.0	87.6	122	180
sucrose	$C_{12}H_{22}O_{11}$	179.2	203.9	287.3	487.2
ytterbium sulfate	$Yb_2(SO_4)_3$	44.2	$22.2^{30°}$	10.4	4.7

Table 14

HEAT OF FORMATION

ΔH_f is heat of formation of the given substance from its elements. All values of ΔH_f are expressed as kcal/mole at 25 °C. Negative values of ΔH_f indicate exothermic reactions. s = solid, l = liquid, g = gas.

Substance	Phase	ΔH_f	Substance	Phase	ΔH_f
aluminum oxide	s	−400.4	lead(II) nitrate	s	−108.0
ammonia	g	−11.02	lead(II) sulfate	s	−219.87
ammonium chloride	s	−75.15	lithium chloride	s	−97.58
ammonium sulfate	s	−282.23	lithium nitrate	s	−115.1
barium chloride	s	−205.1	lithium sulfate	s	−342.83
barium nitrate	s	−237.11	magnesium chloride	s	−153.35
barium sulfate	s	−352.1	magnesium oxide	s	−143.8
benzene	g	+19.82	magnesium sulfate	s	−307.1
benzene	l	+11.71	manganese(IV) oxide	s	−124.29
calcium carbonate	s	−288.46	manganese(II) sulfate	s	−254.60
calcium chloride	s	−190.2	mercury(I) chloride	s	−63.39
calcium hydroxide	s	−235.7	mercury(II) chloride	s	−53.6
calcium nitrate	s	−224.28	mercury(II) fulminate	s	+64
calcium oxide	s	−151.80	mercury(II) nitrate	s	−93.8
calcium sulfate	s	−342.76	mercury(II) oxide	s	−21.71
carbon (diamond)	s	+0.45	methane	g	−17.89
carbon (graphite)	s	0.00	nitrogen dioxide	g	+7.93
carbon dioxide	g	−94.05	nitrogen monoxide	g	+21.57
carbon disulfide	g	+27.98	dinitrogen monoxide	g	+19.61
carbon disulfide	l	+21.44	dinitrogen pentoxide	g	+2.70
carbon monoxide	g	−26.42	dinitrogen pentoxide	s	−10.0
carbon tetrachloride	g	−25.5	dinitrogen tetroxide	g	+2.19
copper(II) nitrate	s	−72.4	oxygen (O_2)	g	0.00
copper(II) oxide	s	−37.6	ozone (O_3)	g	+34.1
copper(II) sulfate	s	−184.36	diphosphorus pentoxide	s	−713.2
copper(I) sulfide	s	−19.0	potassium bromide	s	−93.73
copper(II) sulfide	s	−12.7	potassium chloride	s	−104.18
ethane	g	−20.24	potassium hydroxide	s	−101.78
ethyne (acetylene)	g	+54.19	potassium iodide	s	−78.31
hydrogen (H_2)	g	0.00	potassium nitrate	s	−117.76
hydrogen bromide	g	−8.71	potassium sulfate	s	−342.66
hydrogen chloride	g	−22.06	silicon dioxide (quartz)	s	−217.72
hydrogen fluoride	g	−64.80	silver acetate	s	−95.3
hydrogen iodide	g	+6.33	silver chloride	s	−30.37
hydrogen oxide (water)	g	−57.72	silver nitrate	s	−29.73
hydrogen oxide (water)	l	−68.15	silver sulfide	s	−7.79
hydrogen peroxide	g	−32.5	sodium bromide	s	−86.38
hydrogen peroxide	l	−44.88	sodium chloride	s	−98.23
hydrogen sulfide	g	−4.82	sodium hydroxide	s	−101.99
iodine (I_2)	s	0.00	sodium nitrate	s	−111.54
iodine (I_2)	g	+14.92	sodium sulfate	s	−330.90
iron(III) chloride	s	−95.48	sulfur dioxide	g	−70.94
iron(III) oxide	s	−197.0	sulfur trioxide	g	−94.58
iron (II, III) oxide	s	−267.3	tin(IV) chloride	l	−122.2
iron(II) sulfate	s	−221.9	zinc nitrate	s	−115.6
iron(II) sulfide	s	−23.9	zinc oxide	s	−83.24
lead(II) oxide	s	−52.12	zinc sulfate	s	−234.9
lead(IV) oxide	s	−65.6	zinc sulfide	s	−49.23

Table 15

HEAT OF COMBUSTION

ΔH_c = heat of combustion of the given substance. All values of ΔH_c are expressed as kcal/mole of substance oxidized to $H_2O(l)$ and/or $CO_2(g)$ at constant pressure and 25 °C. s = solid, l = liquid, g = gas.

Substance	Formula	Phase	ΔH_c
hydrogen	H_2	g	−68.32
graphite	C	s	−94.05
carbon monoxide	CO	g	−67.64
methane	CH_4	g	−212.79
ethane	C_2H_6	g	−372.81
propane	C_3H_8	g	−530.57
butane	C_4H_{10}	g	−687.98
pentane	C_5H_{12}	g	−845.16
hexane	C_6H_{14}	l	−995.01
heptane	C_7H_{16}	l	−1149.9
octane	C_8H_{18}	l	−1302.7
ethene (ethylene)	C_2H_4	g	−337.23
propene (propylene)	C_3H_6	g	−490.2
ethyne (acetylene)	C_2H_2	g	−310.61
benzene	C_6H_6	l	−780.96
toluene	C_7H_8	l	−934.2
naphthalene	$C_{10}H_8$	s	−1231.8
anthracene	$C_{14}H_{10}$	s	−1712.0
methanol	CH_3OH	l	−173.64
ethanol	C_2H_5OH	l	−326.68
ether	$(C_2H_5)_2O$	l	−657.52
formaldehyde	CH_2O	g	−136.42
glucose	$C_6H_{12}O_6$	s	−669.94
sucrose	$C_{12}H_{22}O_{11}$	s	−1348.2

Table 16

PROPERTIES OF COMMON ELEMENTS

Name	Form/color at room temperature	Density (g/cm³)	Melting point (°C)	Boiling point (°C)	Common oxidation numbers
aluminum	silv metal	2.70	660.4	2467	+3
antimony	silv metal	6.69	630.7	1750	+3, +5
argon	colorless gas	1.784*	−189.2	−185.7	0
arsenic	gray metal	5.73	817 (28 atm)	613 (sublimes)	+3, +5
barium	silv metal	3.5	725	1640	+2
beryllium	gray metal	1.85	1280	2970	+2
bismuth	silv metal	9.75	271.3	1560	+3
boron	blk solid	2.34	2079	2550 (sublimes)	+3
bromine	red-br liquid	3.12	−7.2	58.8	−1, +5
calcium	silv metal	1.55	839	1484	+2
carbon	diamond	3.51	3700	4200	+2, +4
	graphite	2.26	3620 (sublimes)	4200	
chlorine	grn-yel gas	3.214*	−101.0	−34.6	−1, +5, +7
chromium	silv metal	7.19	1860	2672	+2, +3, +6
cobalt	silv metal	8.9	1495	2870	+2, +3
copper	red metal	8.96	1083.4	2567	+1, +2
fluorine	yel gas	1.696*	−219.6	−188.1	−1
germanium	gray metalloid	5.32	937.4	2830	+4
gold	yel metal	19.3	1064.4	2807	+1, +3
helium	colorless gas	0.1785*	−272.2 (26 atm)	−268.9	0
hydrogen	colorless gas	0.08988*	−259.1	−252.9	−1, +1
iodine	bl-blk solid	4.93	113.5	184.4	−1, +5
iron	silv metal	7.87	1535	2750	+2, +3
lead	silv metal	11.4	327.5	1740	+2, +4
lithium	silv metal	0.534	180.5	1347	+1
magnesium	silv metal	1.74	649	1090	+2
manganese	silv metal	7.3	1244	1962	+2, +4, +7
mercury	silv liquid	13.5	−38.8	356.6	+1, +2
neon	colorless gas	0.8999*	−248.7	−246.0	0
nickel	silv metal	8.90	1453	2732	+2
nitrogen	colorless gas	1.251*	−209.9	−195.8	−3, +3, +5
oxygen	colorless gas	1.429*	−218.4	−183.0	−2
phosphorus	yel solid	1.82	44.1	280	+3, +5
platinum	silv metal	21.4	1772	3800	+2, +4
plutonium	silv metal	19.8	641	3232	+3, +4, +5, +6
potassium	silv metal	0.862	63.6	774	+1
radium	silv metal	5(?)	700	1140	+2
radon	colorless gas	9.73*	−71	−61.8	0
silicon	gray solid	2.33	1410	2355	+4
silver	silv metal	10.5	961.9	2212	+1
sodium	silv metal	0.971	97.8	882.9	+1
strontium	silv metal	2.54	769	1384	+2
sulfur	yel solid	2.07	112.8	444.7	−2, +4, +6
tin	silv metal	7.31	232.0	2270	+2, +4
titanium	silv metal	4.54	1660	3287	+3, +4
tungsten	gray metal	19.3	3410	5660	+6
uranium	silv metal	19.0	1132	3818	+4, +6
xenon	colorless gas	5.89*	−111.9	−107	0
zinc	silv metal	7.13	419.6	907	+2

*Densities of gases are given in grams/liter.

Table 17

FOUR-PLACE LOGARITHMS OF NUMBERS

n	0	1	2	3	4	5	6	7	8	9
10	0000	0043	0086	0128	0170	0212	0253	0294	0334	0374
11	0414	0453	0492	0531	0569	0607	0645	0682	0719	0755
12	0792	0828	0864	0899	0934	0969	1004	1038	1072	1106
13	1139	1173	1206	1239	1271	1303	1335	1367	1399	1430
14	1461	1492	1523	1553	1584	1614	1644	1673	1703	1732
15	1761	1790	1818	1847	1875	1903	1931	1959	1987	2014
16	2041	2068	2095	2122	2148	2175	2201	2227	2253	2279
17	2304	2330	2355	2380	2405	2430	2455	2480	2504	2529
18	2553	2577	2601	2625	2648	2672	2695	2718	2742	2765
19	2788	2810	2833	2856	2878	2900	2923	2945	2967	2989
20	3010	3032	3054	3075	3096	3118	3139	3160	3181	3201
21	3222	3243	3263	3284	3304	3324	3345	3365	3385	3404
22	3424	3444	3464	3483	3502	3522	3541	3560	3579	3598
23	3617	3636	3655	3674	3692	3711	3729	3747	3766	3784
24	3802	3820	3838	3856	3874	3892	3909	3927	3945	3962
25	3979	3997	4014	4031	4048	4065	4082	4099	4116	4133
26	4150	4166	4183	4200	4216	4232	4249	4265	4281	4298
27	4314	4330	4346	4362	4378	4393	4409	4425	4440	4456
28	4472	4487	4502	4518	4533	4548	4564	4579	4594	4609
29	4624	4639	4654	4669	4683	4698	4713	4728	4742	4757
30	4771	4786	4800	4814	4829	4843	4857	4871	4886	4900
31	4914	4928	4942	4955	4969	4983	4997	5011	5024	5038
32	5051	5065	5079	5092	5105	5119	5132	5145	5159	5172
33	5185	5198	5211	5224	5237	5250	5263	5276	5289	5302
34	5315	5328	5340	5353	5366	5378	5391	5403	5416	5428
35	5441	5453	5465	5478	5490	5502	5514	5527	5539	5551
36	5563	5575	5587	5599	5611	5623	5635	5647	5658	5670
37	5682	5694	5705	5717	5729	5740	5752	5763	5775	5786
38	5798	5809	5821	5832	5843	5855	5866	5877	5888	5899
39	5911	5922	5933	5944	5955	5966	5977	5988	5999	6010
40	6021	6031	6042	6053	6064	6075	6085	6096	6107	6117
41	6128	6138	6149	6160	6170	6180	6191	6201	6212	6222
42	6232	6243	6253	6263	6274	6284	6294	6304	6314	6325
43	6335	6345	6355	6365	6375	6385	6395	6405	6415	6425
44	6435	6444	6454	6464	6474	6484	6493	6503	6513	6522
45	6532	6542	6551	6561	6571	6580	6590	6599	6609	6618
46	6628	6637	6646	6656	6665	6675	6684	6693	6702	6712
47	6721	6730	6739	6749	6758	6767	6776	6785	6794	6803
48	6812	6821	6830	6839	6848	6857	6866	6875	6884	6893
49	6902	6911	6920	6928	6937	6946	6955	6964	6972	6981
50	6990	6998	7007	7016	7024	7033	7042	7050	7059	7067
51	7076	7084	7093	7101	7110	7118	7126	7135	7143	7152
52	7160	7168	7177	7185	7193	7202	7210	7218	7226	7235
53	7243	7251	7259	7267	7275	7284	7292	7300	7308	7316
54	7324	7332	7340	7348	7356	7364	7372	7380	7388	7396

Table 17

FOUR-PLACE LOGARITHMS OF NUMBERS (cont'd)

n	0	1	2	3	4	5	6	7	8	9
55	7404	7412	7419	7427	7435	7443	7451	7459	7466	7474
56	7482	7490	7497	7505	7513	7520	7528	7536	7543	7551
57	7559	7566	7574	7582	7589	7597	7604	7612	7619	7627
58	7634	7642	7649	7657	7664	7672	7679	7686	7694	7701
59	7709	7716	7723	7731	7738	7745	7752	7760	7767	7774
60	7782	7789	7796	7803	7810	7818	7825	7832	7839	7846
61	7853	7860	7868	7875	7882	7889	7896	7903	7910	7917
62	7924	7931	7938	7945	7952	7959	7966	7973	7980	7987
63	7993	8000	8007	8014	8021	8028	8035	8041	8048	8055
64	8062	8069	8075	8082	8089	8096	8102	8109	8116	8122
65	8129	8136	8142	8149	8156	8162	8169	8176	8182	8189
66	8195	8202	8209	8215	8222	8228	8235	8241	8248	8254
67	8261	8267	8274	8280	8287	8293	8299	8306	8312	8319
68	8325	8331	8338	8344	8351	8357	8363	8370	8376	8382
69	8388	8395	8401	8407	8414	8420	8426	8432	8439	8445
70	8451	8457	8463	8470	8476	8482	8488	8494	8500	8506
71	8513	8519	8525	8531	8537	8543	8549	8555	8561	8567
72	8573	8579	8585	8591	8597	8603	8609	8615	8621	8627
73	8633	8639	8645	8651	8657	8663	8669	8675	8681	8686
74	8692	8698	8704	8710	8716	8722	8727	8733	8739	8745
75	8751	8756	8762	8768	8774	8779	8785	8791	8797	8802
76	8808	8814	8820	8825	8831	8837	8842	8848	8854	8859
77	8865	8871	8876	8882	8887	8893	8899	8904	8910	8915
78	8921	8927	8932	8938	8943	8949	8954	8960	8965	8971
79	8976	8982	8987	8993	8998	9004	9009	9015	9020	9025
80	9031	9036	9042	9047	9053	9058	9063	9069	9074	9079
81	9085	9090	9096	9101	9106	9112	9117	9122	9128	9133
82	9138	9143	9149	9154	9159	9165	9170	9175	9180	9186
83	9191	9196	9201	9206	9212	9217	9222	9227	9232	9238
84	9243	9248	9253	9258	9263	9269	9274	9279	9284	9289
85	9294	9299	9304	9309	9315	9320	9325	9330	9335	9340
86	9345	9350	9355	9360	9365	9370	9375	9380	9385	9390
87	9395	9400	9405	9410	9415	9420	9425	9430	9435	9440
88	9445	9450	9455	9460	9465	9469	9474	9479	9484	9489
89	9494	9499	9504	9509	9513	9518	9523	9528	9533	9538
90	9542	9547	9552	9557	9562	9566	9571	9576	9581	9586
91	9590	9595	9600	9605	9609	9614	9619	9624	9628	9633
92	9638	9643	9647	9652	9657	9661	9666	9671	9675	9680
93	9685	9689	9694	9699	9703	9708	9713	9717	9722	9727
94	9731	9736	9741	9745	9750	9754	9759	9763	9768	9773
95	9777	9782	9786	9791	9795	9800	9805	9809	9814	9818
96	9823	9827	9832	9836	9841	9845	9850	9854	9859	9863
97	9868	9872	9877	9881	9886	9890	9894	9899	9903	9908
98	9912	9917	9921	9926	9930	9934	9939	9943	9948	9952
99	9956	9961	9965	9969	9974	9978	9983	9987	9991	9996

Glossary

absolute zero The lowest possible temperature, 0 °K or −273.15 °C.

accuracy The nearness of a measurement to its accepted value.

acid (1) A substance that increases the hydronium-ion concentration of its aqueous solution. (2) A proton donor. (3) An electron-pair acceptor.

acid anhydride An oxide that reacts with water to form an acid, or that is formed by the removal of water from an acid.

acid rain Rainwater having a pH below 5.6.

actinide series Rare-earth elements of the seventh period following radium, in which the transitional inner building of the $6d$ sublevel is interrupted by the inner building of the $5f$ sublevel.

activated complex The transitional structure resulting from an effective collision of reactant particles.

activation energy Energy required to transform reactants into an activated complex.

activity series A table of metals or nonmetals arranged in order of descending activities.

addition A reaction in which atoms are added to an unsaturated organic molecule.

adsorption The concentration of a gas, liquid, or solid on the surface of a liquid or solid with which it is in contact.

alcohol A compound containing a hydrocarbon group and one or more —OH (hydroxyl) groups.

aldehyde A compound that has a hydrocarbon group and one or more —C (formyl) groups.

alkadiene A straight- or branched-chain hydrocarbon with two double covalent bonds between carbon atoms in each molecule.

alkali metal An element of Group I of the periodic table.

alkaline-earth metal An element of Group II of the periodic table.

alkane A straight- or branched-chain hydrocarbon in which the carbon atoms are connected by only single covalent bonds; a member of the paraffin series.

alkene A straight- or branched-chain hydrocarbon in which two carbon atoms in each molecule are connected by a double covalent bond; a member of the olefin series.

alkylation The combining of simple hydrocarbons with unsaturated hydrocarbons by heat in the presence of a catalyst.

alkyl group A group derived from an alkane by the loss of a hydrogen atom; frequently symbolized by R—.

alkyl halide An alkane in which a halogen atom is substituted for a hydrogen atom.

alkyne A straight- or branched-chain hydrocarbon in which two carbon atoms in each molecule are connected by a triple covalent bond; a member of the acetylene series.

allotrope One of the two or more different forms of an element in the same physical phase.

allotropy The existence of an element in two or more forms in the same physical phase.

alloy A material composed of two or more metals.

alpha particle A helium nucleus emitted from the nucleus of a radioactive element.

alum A double salt of the type $M^+M^{+++} (SO_4)_2 \cdot 12H_2O$, $KAl(SO_4)_2 \cdot 12H_2O$ being the most common.

amorphous Having neither definite form nor structure.

amphoteric Capable of acting as either an acid or a base.

amyl group The C_5H_{11}— group.

analysis The separation of a material into its component parts to determine the composition.

angstrom A unit of linear measure; 1×10^{-8} cm.

anhydrous Without water of crystallization.

anion An ion attracted to the anode of an electrolytic cell; a negative ion.

anion hydrolysis Hydrolysis reaction in which an anion base accepts a proton from a water molecule, increasing the OH^- ion concentration of the solution.

anode A positively charged, or electron-poor, electrode.

antifriction alloy An alloy that reduces friction.

aqueous In water; watery.

aqueous acid A water solution having acid properties due to the nature of the solute present.

aqueous base A water solution having basic properties due to the nature of the solute present.

aqueous solution A solution in which water is the solvent.

aromatic hydrocarbon A hydrocarbon having a resonance structure sometimes represented by alternating single and double covalent bonds in six-membered carbon rings.

atom The smallest unit of an element that can exist either alone or in combination with atoms of the same or different elements.

atomic mass The mass of an atom expressed in atomic mass units.

atomic mass unit A unit of mass that is exactly $\frac{1}{12}$ the mass of a carbon-12 atom; $1.6605655 \times 10^{-24}$ g.

atomic number The number of protons in the nucleus of an atom.

atomic theory A theory that includes information about the structure and properties of atoms, the kinds of compounds they form, and the properties of these compounds. It also includes information about the mass, volume, and energy relationships in reactions between atoms.

atomic weight   The ratio of the gram-atomic weight of an element to $1/12$ the mass in grams of one mole of carbon-12 atoms.

autooxidation   Self-oxidizing and reducing. Redox process in which the substance acts both as the oxidizing agent and reducing agent.

Avogadro number   The number of carbon-12 atoms in exactly 12 grams of this nuclide; 6.022045×10^{23}.

baking soda   Sodium hydrogen carbonate, $NaHCO_3$.

barometer   An instrument for measuring atmospheric pressure.

base   (1) A substance that increases the hydroxide-ion concentration of its aqueous solution. (2) A proton acceptor. (3) An electron-pair donor.

basic anhydride   An oxide that reacts with water to form a solution containing OH^- ions.

bauxite   A hydrated aluminum oxide ore.

beta particle   An electron emitted from the nucleus of a radioactive element.

betatron   A device for accelerating electrons.

binary compound   A compound consisting of only two elements.

binding energy   The energy released when a nucleus is formed from its constituent particles.

biomass   The collective term for living materials (or matter derived from living things) that could be used to provide energy.

blast furnace   A tall, cylindrical chamber in which iron oxide is reduced using coke, limestone, and a blast of hot air.

bleaching   The operation by which color is partially or wholly removed from a colored material.

blister copper   Crude copper as refined in a converter.

blue vitriol   Hydrated copper(II) sulfate, $CuSO_4 \cdot 5H_2O$.

boiling point   The temperature at which the equilibrium vapor pressure of a liquid is equal to the prevailing atmospheric pressure.

bond energy   The energy required to break chemical bonds in order to form neutral atoms.

borax   Sodium tetraborate, $Na_2B_4O_7 \cdot 10H_2O$.

borax-bead test   An identification test for certain metals whose oxides impart characteristic colors to borax beads when fused with them.

borazon   A crystalline form of boron nitride, BN, having about the same hardness as diamond.

bright-line spectrum   A spectrum consisting of a series of bright lines that have frequencies characteristic of the atoms present.

brine   A concentrated saltwater solution, containing principally sodium chloride.

buffer   A substance that, when added to a solution, causes a resistance to any change in pH.

buffered solution   A solution containing a relatively high concentration of a buffer salt that tends to maintain a constant pH.

calcine   A partially roasted copper ore.

calorie   A unit of heat; the heat required to raise the temperature of one gram of water through one Celsius degree.

calorimeter   An apparatus for measuring heat of reaction.

carbonyl group   The $\diagdown\!C\!=\!O$ group.

carboxyl group   The $-C\!\diagup^{\displaystyle O}_{\diagdown O-H}$ group.

catalyst   A substance or combination of substances that accelerates a chemical reaction without itself being used up.

catalytic agent   See *catalyst.*

catalytic cracking   The breaking-up of large molecules into smaller ones by using a catalyst at high temperature.

cathode   A negatively charged, or electron-rich, electrode.

cation   An ion attracted to the cathode of an electrolytic cell; a positive ion.

cation hydrolysis   Hydrolysis reaction in which a cation acid donates a proton to a water molecule, increasing the H_3O^+ ion concentration of the solution.

caustic   (1) Capable of converting some types of animal and vegetable matter into soluble materials by chemical action. (2) A substance with such properties.

Celsius temperature   Temperature on the Celsius scale, which has two fixed points, the freezing point and the steam point of water, as $0°$ and $100°$.

cement   A material made from limestone and clay which, after mixing with water, sets to a hard mass.

centi-   Metric prefix meaning 0.01.

centigrade scale   The Celsius temperature scale.

chain reaction   A reaction in which the material or energy that starts the reaction is also one of the products.

chemical bond   The linkage between atoms produced by the transfer or sharing of electrons.

chemical change   A change in which new substances with new properties are formed.

chemical equilibrium   The state of balance attained in a reversible chemical action in which the rates of the opposing reactions are exactly equal.

chemical equilibrium law   See *equilibrium constant.*

chemical equivalent   See *equivalent.*

chemical formula   A shorthand method of representing the composition of a substance by using chemical symbols and numerical subscripts.

chemical kinetics   The branch of chemistry that deals with reaction rates and reaction mechanisms.

chemical properties   Those properties that pertain to the behavior of a material in changes in which its identity is altered.

chemical symbol   Either a single capital letter or a capital letter and a small letter used together that serves as an abbreviation for (1) an element; (2) an atom of an element; (3) a mole of atoms of an element.

chemistry   The science dealing with the structure and composition of substances, the changes in composition, and the mechanisms by which these changes occur.

coalesce To join together; to collect into a whole.

coalescence The act of coalescing.

colligative property A property of a system that is determined by the number of particles present in the system, but that is independent of the nature of the particles themselves.

colloidal state A state of subdivision of matter ranging between the dimensions of ordinary molecules and microscopic particles.

colloidal suspension A two-phase system having dispersed particles suspended in a dispersing medium.

combining weight The weight of any element that combines with a fixed weight of a particular element—oxygen, for example.

combustion Any chemical action that occurs so rapidly that both noticeable heat and light are produced.

common-ion effect The decrease in ionization of a weak electrolyte by the addition of a salt having an ion common to the solution of the electrolyte.

complementary colors Two colors that, when combined, yield white light.

complex ion An ionic species composed of a central metal ion combined with a specific number of polar molecules or ions.

composition reaction A chemical reaction in which two or more substances combine to form a more complex substance.

compound A substance that can be decomposed into two or more simpler substances by ordinary chemical means.

concentrated Containing a relatively large amount of solute.

condensation The process of converting a gas into a liquid or solid.

condensation temperature The lowest temperature at which a substance can exist as a gas at atmospheric pressure.

conjugate acid The species formed when a base acquires a proton.

conjugate base The species that remains after an acid has donated a proton.

constant A magnitude that does not change in value.

control rod A rod of neutron-absorbing material used to regulate the reaction in a nuclear reactor.

coordination number The number of molecules or ions covalently bonded to (coordinated with) a central ion.

cosmic ray A proton or other nucleus of very high energy coming to the earth from outer space.

covalent bonding Bonding in which atoms share electrons.

covalent molecular crystal A crystal consisting of molecules arranged in a systematic order.

covalent network crystal A crystal consisting of an array of atoms that share electrons with their neighboring atoms to form a giant, compact, interlocking structure.

cracking A process of breaking up complex organic molecules by the action of heat and usually a catalyst.

critical mass The amount of radioactive material required to sustain a chain reaction.

critical pressure The pressure required to liquefy a gas at its critical temperature.

critical temperature The highest temperature at which it is possible to liquefy a gas with any amount of pressure.

critical volume The volume occupied by one mole of a gas at its critical temperature and critical pressure.

cryolite Sodium aluminum fluoride, Na_3AlF_6.

crystal A homogeneous portion of a substance bounded by plane surfaces making definite angles with each other, giving a regular geometric form.

crystal lattice The pattern of points that describes the arrangement of particles in a crystal structure.

crystalline Consisting of or made of crystals.

cubic A crystalline system in which the three axes are at right angles and are of equal length.

cyclotron An electromagnetic device for accelerating protons or deuterons in a spiral path.

daughter nuclide A nuclide that is the product of the radioactive decay of a given nuclide.

decomposition reaction A chemical reaction in which one substance breaks down to form two or more simpler substances.

dehydrating agent A substance that removes water from a material.

dehydration The removal of oxygen and hydrogen atoms in the form of water from a substance.

deliquescence The property of certain substances to take up water from the air to form a solution.

denatured alcohol Ethanol to which poisonous materials have been added so it is unfit for drinking.

density The mass per unit volume of a material.

destructive distillation The process of decomposing materials by heating them in a closed container without access to air or oxygen.

detergent A substance that removes dirt.

deuterium The isotope of hydrogen having one proton and one neutron in the nucleus; hydrogen-2.

deuteron The nucleus of deuterium, consisting of one proton and one neutron.

diatomic Consisting of two atoms.

diffusion The process of spreading out spontaneously to occupy a space uniformly; the intermingling of the particles of substances.

dilute Containing a relatively small amount of solute.

dimer A compound formed by two simpler molecules or radicals.

dimeric Capable of forming twofold polymers.

dipole A polar molecule, one region of which is positive and the other region negative.

dipole-dipole attraction A type of van der Waals force that is the attraction between the oppositely charged portions of neighboring polar molecules.

diprotic Pertaining to an acid capable of donating two protons per molecule.

dispersion interaction A type of van der Waals force dependent on the number of electrons in the interacting molecules and the tightness with which they are held.

dissociation The separation of the ions from the crystals of an ionic compound during the solution process.

distillation   The process of evaporation followed by condensation of the vapors in a separate vessel.

domain   Small magnetized regions formed by groups of properly aligned atoms of ferromagnetic substances.

ductile   Capable of being drawn into a wire.

effervescence   The rapid evolution of a gas from a liquid in which it is dissolved.

efflorescence   The property of hydrated crystals to lose water of crystallization when exposed to the air.

elastic collision   A collision in which there is no net loss of energy.

electrochemical   Pertaining to spontaneous oxidation-reduction reactions used as a source of electric energy.

electrochemical cell   A system of electrodes and electrolyte by which a spontaneous oxidation-reduction reaction can be used as a source of electric current.

electrochemical reaction   A spontaneous oxidation-reduction reaction in which chemical energy can be transformed into electric energy.

electrode   A conductor used to establish electric contact with a nonmetallic part of a circuit.

electrode potential   The potential difference between an electrode and its solution in a half-reaction.

electrolysis   (1) The separation of a compound into simpler substances by an electric current. (2) The process by which an electric current is used to drive an oxidation-reduction reaction.

electrolyte   A substance whose water solution conducts an electric current.

electrolytic   Pertaining to driven oxidation-reduction reactions that utilize electric energy from an external source.

electrolytic cell   A system of electrodes and electrolyte by which an electric current can be used to drive an oxidation-reduction reaction.

electrolytic reaction   A driven oxidation-reduction reaction in which electric energy can be transformed into chemical energy.

electromagnetic radiation   A form of energy, such as light, X rays, or radio waves, that travels through space as waves at the rate of 3.00×10^8 m/s.

electron   A negatively charged particle found in an atom. It has $\frac{1}{1837}$ of the mass of the simplest type of hydrogen atom.

electron affinity   The energy change that occurs when an electron is acquired by a neutral atom.

electron cloud   The part of an atom outside the nucleus in which the electrons may most probably be found.

electron configuration   The arrangement of electrons in an atom that is in its ground state.

electronegativity   The property of an atom of attracting the shared electrons that form a bond between it and another atom.

electron pair   Two electrons of opposite spin in the same space orbital.

electron-volt   The energy required to move an electron across a potential difference of one volt.

electroplating   An electrolytic process by which a metal is deposited on a surface.

electroscope   A device for determining the presence of electric charge.

element   A substance that cannot be further decomposed by ordinary chemical means; a substance in which all the atoms have the same number of protons.

empirical formula   A chemical formula that denotes the constituent elements of a substance and the simplest whole-number ratio of atoms of each.

endothermic   Pertaining to a process that occurs with the absorption of energy.

end point   The point reached in a titration process at which the reaction is just complete.

energy   The capacity for doing work.

energy level   A region about the nucleus of an atom in which electrons move. A shell.

enthalpy   The heat content of a system at constant pressure.

enthalpy change   A measure of the quantity of heat exchanged by a system and its surroundings (at constant pressure).

entropy   That property which describes the disorder of a system.

enzyme   A catalyst produced by living cells.

equilibrium   A dynamic state in which two opposing processes take place at the same time and at the same rate.

equilibrium constant   The ratio of the product of the concentrations of the substances produced at equilibrium to the product of the concentrations of reactants, each concentration raised to that power which is the coefficient of the substance in the chemical equation.

equilibrium vapor pressure   The pressure exerted by a vapor in equilibrium with its liquid.

equivalence point   The theoretical end point in a titration process. That point reached in a titration process at which equivalent quantities of reactants are present.

equivalent   (1) The mass in grams of a reactant that contains, replaces, or reacts with (directly or indirectly) the Avogadro number of hydrogen atoms. (2) The mass in grams of a reactant that acquires or supplies the Avogadro number of electrons.

ester   A compound formed by the reaction between an acid and an alcohol.

esterification   The process of producing an ester by the reaction of an acid with an alcohol.

ether   An organic oxide.

eudiometer   A gas-measuring tube.

evaporation   The escape of molecules from the surface of liquids and solids.

excited atom   An atom that has absorbed a photon.

exothermic   Pertaining to a process that occurs with the liberation of energy.

external phase   The dispersing medium of a colloidal suspension.

fat   An ester of glycerol and long-carbon-chain acids.

fermentation   A chemical change produced by the action of an enzyme.

ferromagnetism The property of certain metals whereby they are strongly attracted by a magnet.

filtration The process of removing suspended material from a liquid by allowing the liquid to pass through a porous material such as filter paper or a layer of sand.

fission The breakup of a very heavy nucleus into medium-weight nuclei.

flame test A test to determine the identity of an element in a compound by the color the compound imparts to a flame.

fluoresce To give off visible light after exposure to sunlight.

flux A material used to promote the melting of minerals.

formula A shorthand method of representing the composition of substances by using chemical symbols and numerical subscripts.

formula equation A concise, symbolized statement of a chemical change.

formula weight The sum of the atomic weights of all the atoms represented in the chemical formula.

formyl group The $-C\overset{\displaystyle O}{\underset{\displaystyle H}{<}}$ group.

fractional distillation The separation of the components of a mixture that have different boiling points by carefully controlled vaporization.

free energy The function of the state of a reaction system that assesses the tendencies toward lowest energy and highest entropy at a given temperature.

free-energy change The net driving force of a reaction system.

freezing The process of converting a liquid into a solid.

fuel A material that is burned to provide heat.

fungicide A chemical material that kills non-green, microscopic plants known as fungi.

fuse To melt. To change to the liquid phase by heating.

fusion The combination of light-weight nuclei to form heavier, more stable nuclei.

galvanize To coat iron or steel with zinc.

gamma ray A high-energy electromagnetic wave emitted from the nucleus of a radioactive element.

gas The phase of matter characterized by neither a definite volume nor a definite shape.

gas constant The value of the quotient pV/nT; 0.082057 L atm/mole °K.

gasohol A mixture of 10% ethanol and 90% unleaded gasoline.

Geiger counter A device for determining the presence of radiation from radioactive materials.

generator In chemistry, the vessel in which a reaction occurs to produce a desired gaseous product.

gram A metric unit of mass equal to one-thousandth of the standard kilogram.

gram-atomic weight The mass in grams of one mole of naturally occurring atoms of an element.

gram-equivalent weight See *equivalent*.

gram-formula weight (1) The mass of a substance in grams equal to its formula weight. (2) The mass of one mole of a substance.

gram-molecular weight (1) The mass of a molecular substance in grams equal to its molecular weight. (2) The mass of one mole of molecules of the substance.

ground state The most stable state of an atom.

group A vertical column of elements in the periodic table.

half-cell The portion of a voltaic cell consisting of an electrode immersed in a solution of its ions.

half-life The length of time during which half of a given number of atoms of a radioactive nuclide decays.

half-reaction The reaction at an electrode in a half-cell of a voltaic cell.

halide (1) A binary compound of a halogen with a less electronegative element or group of elements. (2) Fluoride, chloride, bromide, iodide, or astatide.

halogen The name given to the family of elements having seven valence electrons.

hard water Water containing ions such as calcium or magnesium that form precipitates with soap.

heat energy The energy transferred between two systems that is associated exclusively with the difference in temperature between the two systems.

heat of combustion The heat of reaction released by the complete combustion of one mole of a substance.

heat of formation The heat released or absorbed in a composition reaction.

heat of reaction The quantity of heat evolved or absorbed during a chemical reaction.

heat of solution The difference between the heat content of a solution and the heat contents of its components.

heterogeneous Having parts with different properties.

heterogeneous catalyst A catalyst introduced into a reaction system in a different phase from that of the reactants.

heterogeneous reaction A reaction system in which reactants and products are present in different phases.

hexagonal A crystalline system in which three equilateral axes intersect at angles of 60° and with a vertical axis of variable length at right angles to the equilateral axes.

homogeneous Having similar properties throughout.

homogeneous catalyst A catalyst introduced into a reaction system in the same phase as all reactants and products.

homogeneous reaction A reaction system in which all reactants and products are in the same phase.

homologous series A series of similar compounds in which adjacent members differ by a constant unit.

hybridization The combining of two or more orbitals of nearly the same energy into new orbitals of equal energy.

hydrate A crystallized substance that contains water of crystallization.

hydrated ion An ion of a solute to which molecules of water are attached.

hydration (1) The attachment of water molecules to particles of the solute. (2) The solvation process in which water is the solvent. (3) The addition of hydrogen and oxygen atoms to a substance in the proportion in which they occur in water.

hydride A compound consisting of hydrogen and one other less electronegative element.

hydrocarbon   A compound containing hydrogen and carbon.

hydrogenation   The chemical addition of hydrogen to a material.

hydrogen bond   A weak chemical bond between a hydrogen atom in one polar molecule and a very electronegative atom in a second polar molecule.

hydrolysis   An acid-base reaction between water and ions of a dissolved salt.

hydrolysis constant   The equilibrium constant of a reversible reaction between an ion of a dissolved salt and water.

hydronium ion   A hydrated proton; the H_3O^+ ion.

hygroscopic   Absorbing and retaining moisture from the atmosphere.

hypothesis   A possible or tentative explanation.

ideal gas   An imaginary gas whose behavior is described by the gas laws.

immiscible   Not capable of being mixed.

indicator   A substance that changes in color on the passage from acidity to alkalinity, or the reverse.

inertia   Resistance of matter to change in position or motion.

inhibitor   A substance that hinders catalytic action.

inorganic   Pertaining to materials that are not hydrocarbons or their derivatives.

insoluble   (1) Not soluble. (2) So sparingly soluble as to be considered not soluble in the usual sense.

internal phase   The dispersed particles of a colloidal suspension.

ion   An atom or group of atoms that has a net positive or negative charge resulting from unequal numbers of positively charged protons and negatively charged electrons.

ion-exchange resin   A resin that can exchange hydronium ions for positive ions, or one that can exchange hydroxide ions for negative ions.

ionic bonding.   Bonding in which one or more electrons are transferred from one atom to another.

ionic crystal   A crystal consisting of ions arranged in a regular pattern.

ionic equilibrium   The state of balance attained in a reversible ionization action between un-ionized molecules in solution and their hydrated ions.

ionic reaction   A chemical reaction in which ions in solution combine to form a product that leaves the reaction environment.

ionization   The formation of ions from polar solute molecules by the action of the solvent.

ionization constant   The equilibrium constant of a reversible reaction by which ions are produced from molecules.

ionization energy   The energy required to remove an electron from an atom.

isomer   One of two or more compounds having the same molecular formula but different structures.

isotope   One of two or more forms of atoms with the same atomic number but different atomic masses.

Kelvin temperature   Temperature on the Kelvin scale, which is numerically 273° higher than that on the Celsius scale.

kernel   The portion of an atom excluding the valence electrons.

ketone   An organic compound that contains the $\diagdown C = O$ (carbonyl) group.

kiln   A furnace used for producing quicklime, making glass, baking pottery, etc.

kilo-   Metric prefix meaning 1000.

kilocalorie   The quantity of heat required to raise the temperature of one kilogram of water through one Celsius degree.

kinetic energy   Energy of motion.

kinetic theory   A theory that explains the properties of gases, liquids, and solids in terms of the forces between the particles of matter and the energy these particles possess.

knocking   A pounding sound produced in automobile engines when the mixture of gasoline vapor and air does not burn at a uniform rate.

lanthanide series   Rare-earth elements of the sixth period following barium, in which the transitional inner building of the $5d$ sublevel is interrupted by the inner building of the $4f$ sublevel.

law   A generalization that describes behavior in nature.

leavening agent   A substance that releases carbon dioxide in a dough or batter.

lime   Calcium oxide, CaO. Also called quicklime.

limewater   A water solution of calcium hydroxide.

linear accelerator   A particle accelerator in which the particles travel in a straight line through many stages of potential difference.

liquid   The phase of matter characterized by a definite volume but an indefinite shape.

liter   One cubic decimeter.

litmus   A dye extracted from lichens used as an acid-base indicator.

lye   A commercial grade of either sodium hydroxide or potassium hydroxide.

magnetic quantum number   The quantum number that indicates the position of the orbital about the three axes in space.

malleable   Capable of being shaped by hammering or rolling.

mass   The quantity of matter that a body possesses; a measure of the inertia of a body.

mass action equation   See *equilibrium constant*.

mass defect   See *nuclear mass defect*.

mass number   (1) The whole number closest to the atomic mass of an atom. (2) The sum of the number of protons and neutrons in the nucleus of an atom.

matte   A partially refined copper ore consisting of a mixture of the sulfides of iron and copper.

matter   Anything that occupies space and has mass.

melting   The process of converting a solid into a liquid.

melting point   The temperature at which a solid changes to a liquid.

metal   One of a class of elements that show a luster, are good conductors of heat and electricity, and are electropositive.

metallic crystal A crystal lattice consisting of positive ions surrounded by a cloud of valence electrons.

metalloid An element having certain properties characteristic of a metal, but which is generally classed as a nonmetal.

metamorphic Pertains to rocks that have undergone a change in form due to heat or pressure.

meter The metric unit of length.

metric system A decimal system of measurement.

milli- Metric prefix meaning 0.001.

miscible Capable of being mixed.

mixture A material composed of two or more substances, each of which retains its own characteristic properties.

moderator A material that slows down neutrons.

molal boiling-point constant The boiling-point elevation of a solvent in a 1-molal solution of a nonvolatile, molecular solute in the solvent.

molal freezing-point constant The freezing-point depression of a solvent in a 1-molal solution of a molecular solute in the solvent.

molality The concentration of a solution expressed in moles of solute per 1000 grams of solvent.

molal solution A solution containing one mole of solute per 1000 grams of solvent.

molar heat of formation The heat of reaction released or absorbed when one mole of a compound is formed from its elements.

molar heat of fusion The heat energy required to melt one mole of solid at its melting point.

molar heat of vaporization See *standard molar heat of vaporization.*

molarity The concentration of a solution expressed in moles of solute per liter of solution.

molar solution A solution containing one mole of solute per liter of solution.

molar volume The volume in liters of one mole of a gas at STP; taken as 22.4 liters for ordinary gases, 22.414 liters for the ideal gas.

mole The amount of substance containing the Avogadro number of any kind of chemical unit. In practice, the gram-atomic weight of an element represented as monatomic; the gram-molecular weight of a molecular substance; the gram-formula weight of a nonmolecular substance; and the gram-ionic weight of an ion.

molecular crystal See *covalent molecular crystal.*

molecular formula A chemical formula that denotes the constituent elements of a molecular substance and the number of atoms of each element composing one molecule.

molecular weight The formula weight of a molecular substance.

molecule The smallest chemical unit of a substance that is capable of stable independent existence.

monatomic Consisting of one atom.

monoclinic A crystalline system in which there are three unequal axes, with one oblique intersection.

monomer A simple molecule, or single unit, of a polymer.

monoprotic Pertaining to an acid capable of donating one proton per molecule.

mordant A substance that, by combining with a dye, produces a fast color in a textile fiber.

mortar A mixture of slaked lime, sand, and water that sets to a hard mass.

natural gas A mixture of hydrocarbon gases and vapors found in porous formations in the earth's crust.

neutralization The reaction between hydronium ions and hydroxide ions to form water.

neutron A neutral particle found in the nucleus of an atom. It has about the same mass as a proton.

nitride A compound of nitrogen and a less electronegative element.

nitrogen fixation A process of converting elemental nitrogen into nitrogen compounds.

noble metal A metal that shows little chemical activity, especially toward oxygen.

nodule A knoblike swelling on the roots of plants called legumes in which nitrogen-fixing bacteria grow.

nonelectrolyte A substance whose water solution does not conduct an electric current appreciably.

nonmetal One of a class of elements that are usually poor conductors of heat and electricity and are electronegative.

nonpolar covalent bond A covalent bond in which there is an equal attraction for the shared electrons and a resulting balanced distribution of charge.

nonpolar molecule A molecule with all nonpolar bonds or with uniformly spaced, like polar bonds that has a uniform exterior electron distribution.

normality The concentration of a solution expressed in equivalents of solute per liter of solution.

normal solution A solution containing one equivalent of solute per liter of solution.

nuclear change Formation of a new substance through changes in the identity of the atoms involved.

nuclear disintegration The emission of a proton or neutron from a nucleus as a result of bombarding the nucleus with alpha particles, protons, deuterons, neutrons, etc.

nuclear equation An equation representing changes in the nuclei of atoms.

nuclear mass defect The difference between the mass of a nucleus and the sum of the masses of its constituent particles.

nuclear reactor A device in which the controlled fission of radioactive material produces new radioactive substances and energy.

nucleus The positively charged, dense central part of an atom.

nuclide A variety of atom as determined by the number of protons and number of neutrons in its nucleus.

octane rating A number indicating how a gasoline behaves with regard to knocking when compared with a test fuel given an arbitrary rating of 100.

octet An outer shell of an atom having *s* and *p* orbitals filled with eight electrons.

orbital See *space orbital.*

orbital quantum number The quantum number that indicates the shape of an orbital.

ore A mineral containing an element that can be extracted profitably.

organic Pertaining to carbon compounds, particularly hydrocarbons and their derivatives.

organic chemistry The study of carbon compounds.

orthorhombic A crystalline system in which there are three unequal axes at right angles.

oxidation A chemical reaction in which an element attains a more positive oxidation state.

oxidation number A signed number, assigned to an element according to a set of rules, that designates its oxidation state.

oxidation-reduction reaction Any chemical process in which there is a simultaneous attainment of a more positive oxidation state by one element and a more negative oxidation state by an associated element.

oxidation state See *oxidation number*.

oxide A compound consisting of oxygen and usually one other element in which oxygen has an oxidation number of -2.

oxidizing agent The substance that is reduced in an oxidation-reduction reaction.

oxyacid An acid containing hydrogen, oxygen, and a third element.

oxygen–carbon dioxide cycle The combination of photosynthesis and the various natural and artificial methods of producing atmospheric carbon dioxide.

ozone An allotropic form of oxygen containing three atoms per molecule.

paramagnetism The property of a substance whereby it is weakly attracted into a magnetic field.

parameter Any of a set of measurements whose values characterize behavior or performance.

parent nuclide The heaviest, most complex, naturally occurring nuclide in a decay series of radioactive elements.

partial pressure The pressure each gas of a gaseous mixture would exert if it alone were present.

period A horizontal row of elements in the periodic table.

periodic table A tabular arrangement of the chemical elements based on their atomic structure.

permanent hardness Hardness in water caused by the sulfates of calcium or magnesium, which can be removed by precipitation or ion-exchange methods.

permutit A synthetic zeolite, used in softening water.

petroleum A liquid mixture of hydrocarbons obtained from beneath the surface of the ground.

pH Hydronium ion index; the common logarithm of the reciprocal of the hydronium-ion concentration.

phenyl group The C_6H_5— group.

phlogiston theory An obsolete theory that explained combustion as being due to the loss of a substance called phlogiston.

photon A quantum (unit) of electromagnetic radiation energy.

photosynthesis The process by which plants produce carbohydrates and oxygen with the aid of sunlight, using carbon dioxide and water as the raw materials and chlorophyll as the catalyst.

physical change A change in which the identifying properties of a substance remain unchanged.

physical equilibrium A dynamic state in which two opposing physical changes occur at equal rates in the same system.

physical properties Those properties that can be determined without causing a change in the identity of a material.

pig iron Iron recovered from a blast furnace.

plaster of paris A form of calcium sulfate, $(CaSO_4)_2 \cdot H_2O$, produced by partially dehydrating gypsum.

plastic A natural or synthetic material that can be shaped while soft into a required form and then hardened to produce a durable finished article.

polar covalent bond A covalent bond in which there is an unequal attraction for the shared electrons and a resulting unbalanced distribution of charge.

polar molecule A molecule containing one or more nonuniformly arranged polar covalent bonds and having a nonuniform exterior electron distribution.

polyatomic ion A charged group of covalently bonded atoms.

polymer A compound formed by two or more simpler molecules or radicals with repeating structural units.

polymeric Capable of forming a polymer.

potential energy Energy of position.

precipitate (1) A substance, usually a solid, that separates from a solution as a result of some physical or chemical change. (2) To produce such a substance.

precipitation The separation of a solid from a solution.

precision The agreement between the numerical values of two or more measurements made in the same way; the reproducibility of measured data.

pressure Force per unit area.

principal quantum number The quantum number that indicates the most probable distance of an orbital from the nucleus of an atom.

product An element or compound resulting from a chemical reaction.

promoter A substance that increases the activity of a catalyst when introduced in trace quantities.

protium The isotope of hydrogen having one proton and no neutrons in the nucleus; hydrogen-1.

protolysis Proton-transfer reactions.

proton A positively charged particle found in the nucleus of an atom. It has $^{1836}/_{1837}$ of the mass of the simplest type of hydrogen atom.

proton acceptor A base according to the Brønsted system.

proton donor An acid according to the Brønsted system.

pure substance See *substance*.

quantum numbers The numbers that describe the distance from the nucleus, the shape, and the position with respect to the three axes in space of an orbital, as well as the direction of spin of the electron(s) in each orbital.

quicklime Calcium oxide, CaO; also called lime.

radioactive Having the property of radioactivity.

radioactive decay A radioactive change in which a nucleus emits a particle and rays, forming a slightly lighter, more stable nucleus.

radioactive tracer A radioactive element introduced in small quantities to determine the behavior of chemically similar nonradioactive atoms in various physical or chemical changes.

radioactivity The spontaneous breakdown of an unstable atomic nucleus with the release of particles and rays.

rare-earth element An element that usually differs in electronic configuration from that of next lower or higher atomic number only in the number of f electrons in the second-from-outside shell.

rate-determining step The slowest of a sequence of steps along a reaction pathway.

rate law An equation that relates the reaction rate and concentrations of reactants.

reactant An element or compound entering into a chemical reaction.

reaction mechanism The pathway of a chemical reaction; the sequence of steps by which a reaction occurs.

reaction pathway See *reaction mechanism*.

reaction rate A measure of the amount of reactants converted to products per unit of time.

redox Pertaining to oxidation-reduction reactions.

reducing agent The substance that is oxidized in an oxidation-reduction reaction.

reduction A chemical reaction in which an element attains a more negative oxidation state.

replacement reaction A chemical reaction in which one substance is displaced from its compound by another substance.

resonance The bonding situation in substances whose bond properties cannot be satisfactorily represented by any single formula using the electron-dot notation system and keeping the octet rule.

resonance hybrid A substance whose properties show that its structure is intermediate between several electron-dot structures.

respiration The process by which a plant or animal absorbs oxygen and gives off products of oxidation in the tissues, especially carbon dioxide.

reversible reaction A chemical reaction in which the products re-form the original reactants under suitable conditions.

rhombic See *orthorhombic*.

roasting Heating in the presence of air.

salt A compound composed of the positive ions of an aqueous base and the negative ions of an aqueous acid.

saponification The process of making a soap by hydrolysis of a fat with a strong hydroxide.

saturated (1) Pertaining to a solution in which the concentration of solute is the maximum possible under existing conditions. (2) Pertaining to an organic compound that has only single covalent bonds between carbon atoms.

saturated solution A solution in which the dissolved and undissolved solutes are in equilibrium.

sedimentary Pertains to rocks formed from sediment that has been deposited in layers.

self-protective metal A metal that forms a nonporous, nonscaling coat of tarnish.

semiconductor A substance with an electric conductivity between that of a metal and an insulator.

shell A region about the nucleus of an atom in which electrons move. An energy level.

significant figures The digits in a measurement that represent the number of units counted with reasonable assurance.

silicone One of a group of compounds containing a chain of alternate silicon and oxygen atoms, with hydrocarbon groups attached to the silicon atoms.

simplest formula See *empirical formula*.

slag An easily melted product of the reaction between the flux and the impurities of an ore.

slaked lime Calcium hydroxide, $Ca(OH)_2$; also called hydrated lime.

slaking The addition of water to lime, CaO, to produce hydrated (slaked) lime, $Ca(OH)_2$.

soda ash Anhydrous sodium carbonate, Na_2CO_3.

soft water (1) Water that lathers readily with soap. (2) Water that is free of hardening agents, or from which these agents have been removed.

solid The phase of matter characterized by a definite shape.

solubility The amount of a solute dissolved in a given amount of solvent at equilibrium, under specified conditions.

solubility-product constant The product of the molar concentrations of the ions of a sparingly soluble substance in a saturated solution, each concentration raised to the appropriate power.

soluble Capable of being dissolved.

solute The dissolved substance in a solution.

solution A homogeneous mixture of two or more substances, the composition of which may be varied within definite limits.

solution equilibrium The physical state attained in which the opposing processes of dissolving and crystallizing of a solute occur at equal rates.

solvation The clustering of solvent particles about the particles of solute.

solvent The dissolving medium in a solution.

space orbital A highly probable location about a nucleus in which an electron may be found.

spectator ion An ion in a reaction system that takes no part in the chemical action.

spectroscope An optical instrument consisting of a collimator tube, a glass prism, and a telescope, used for producing and viewing spectra.

spectrum The pattern of colors formed by passing light through a prism.

spin quantum number The quantum number that indicates the direction of spin of an electron.

stable compound A compound that is not decomposed easily.

standard boiling point The temperature at which the equilibrium vapor pressure of a liquid is equal to the standard atmospheric pressure, 760 mm of mercury.

standard molar heat of vaporization The heat energy required to vaporize one mole of liquid at its standard boiling point.

standard pressure The pressure exerted by a column of mercury exactly 760 mm high at 0 °C.

standard solution A solution that contains a definite concentration of solute which is known precisely.

standard temperature 0 °Celsius.

stoichiometry Pertaining to the numerical relationships of elements and compounds and the mathematical proportions of reactants and products in chemical reactions.

STP The abbreviation for "standard temperature and pressure."

structural formula A formula that indicates the kind, number, arrangement, and valence bonds of the atoms in a molecule.

sublimation The change of phase from a solid to a vapor.

sublime To pass from the solid to the gaseous phase without liquefying.

subscript A number written below and to the side of a symbol. If at the left, it represents the atomic number; if at the right, it represents the number of atoms of the element.

substance A homogeneous material consisting of one particular kind of matter.

substitution A reaction in which one or more atoms are substituted for hydrogen atoms in a hydrocarbon.

substitution product A compound in which various atoms or groups have been substituted for one or more atoms.

superheated water Water heated under pressure to a temperature above its normal boiling point.

supersaturated Pertaining to a solution that contains an amount of solute in excess of that normally possible under existing conditions.

superscript A number written above and to the side of a symbol. If at the left, it represents the mass number of the nuclide represented by the symbol.

suspension See *colloidal suspension.*

symbol See *chemical symbol.*

synchrotron A particle accelerator in which particles move in a circular path due to the varying of the oscillating voltage and the magnetic field.

synthetic Artificial.

taconite A low-grade iron ore consisting of Fe_2O_3, Fe_3O_4, and rock.

tartar emetic Potassium antimonyl tartrate, $KSbOC_4H_4O_6$.

temperature A measure of the ability of a system to transfer heat to, or acquire heat from, other systems.

temporary hardness Hardness in water caused by the presence of hydrogen carbonates of calcium or magnesium, which can be removed by boiling.

tensile strength The resistance of a material to being pulled apart.

tetragonal A crystalline system in which the three axes are at right angles, but only the two lateral axes are equal.

theory A plausible explanation of a natural phenomenon in terms of a simple model that has familiar properties.

thermal cracking The breaking-up of large molecules into smaller ones by the use of high temperature.

thermal equilibrium The condition in which all objects in an isolated system are at the same temperature.

thermite reaction The reaction by which a metal is prepared from its oxide by reduction with aluminum.

titration The process by which the capacity of a solution of unknown concentration to combine with one of known concentration is measured.

transition Pertaining to subgroups of elements characterized by the belated filling of the next-to-outermost energy level of the atoms.

transition element An element that usually differs in electronic configuration from that of the next lower or higher atomic number only in the number of d electrons in the next-to-outermost energy level.

transition interval The pH range over which the color change of an indicator occurs.

transmutation reaction A reaction in which the nucleus of an atom undergoes a change in the number of its protons and, consequently, in its identity.

transuranium element An element with atomic number higher than uranium, atomic number 92.

triclinic A crystalline system in which there are three unequal axes and three unequal oblique intersections.

trigonal A crystalline system in which there are three equal axes and three equal oblique intersections.

triple point of water The single temperature and pressure condition at which water exists in all three phases at equilibrium.

triprotic Pertaining to an acid capable of donating three protons per molecule.

tritium The isotope of hydrogen having one proton and two neutrons in the nucleus; hydrogen-3.

unit cell The smallest portion of the crystal lattice that exhibits the pattern of the lattice structure.

unsaturated Pertaining to an organic compound with one or more double or triple covalent bonds between carbon atoms in each molecule.

unstable compound A compound that is decomposed easily.

valence electron One of the electrons in an incomplete outer shell of an atom.

van der Waals forces Forces of attraction between molecules.

vapor A gas at a temperature below its critical temperature.

vapor pressure Pressure due to the vapor of confined liquids and solids.

vinyl group The $CH_2{=}CH{-}$ group.

volatile Easily vaporized.

voltaic cell An electrochemical cell arranged to deliver an electric current to an external circuit.

vulcanization The heating of rubber with other materials to improve its properties.

washing soda Hydrated sodium carbonate, $Na_2CO_3 \cdot 10H_2O$.

water gas A fuel gas containing mainly CO and H_2 made by blowing a blast of steam through a bed of red-hot coke.

water of crystallization Water that has united with some compounds as they crystallize from solution.

water of hydration See *water of crystallization*.

water softener A chemical substance that removes hardness from water.

weight The measure of the earth's gravitational attraction for a body.

word equation A brief statement that identifies the reactants entering into a chemical reaction and the products formed.

X rays Electromagnetic radiations of high frequency and short wavelength.

zeolite A natural mineral, sodium silico-aluminate, used to soften water.

Index

Chemical reaction(s) (continued)
457; replacement, 173–174; reversible, 174, 461–462; salt-producing, 335–337; spontaneous, 53–54; tendencies in, 53–54; *see also* individual entries for these chemical reactions

Chemical solution(s), 269–270; buffered, 477; concentration of, 283–284 (table), 285; concentration and equilibrium, 468–469; conductivity of, 295–297; definition of, 269; equilibrium, 274–275, 462–464; expressing concentration of, 346 (table); heats of, 282 (table), 283; as homogeneous mixtures, 40; liquids in liquids, 279; molality of, 283–284 (table), 285; molar, 341–342; normal, 346–348; pH of, 350–352; reactions in, 52; saturated, 275; supersaturated, 278; types of, 271 (table), 272

Chemical symbols, 45 (table), 46

Chemical technicians, 4

Chemistry, careers in, 4; definition of, 3; history of, 2, 4–5; measurement in, 13–25; modern era of, 4–5; organization of, 3; as science, 3–4; study of, 1–3; uses of, 1–2

Chemists, 4

Chloride ion, 111; formation of, 304

Chlorine, as disinfectant, 622; oxidation state of, 114; oxyacids of, 322, 323; preparation of, 620; properties of, 620–621; reaction with hydrogen, 223, 225; in replacement reaction, 170, 174; structure and properties of, 525; uses of, 621–622; *see also* Period Three Elements

Chlorine atom, 111–112

Chlorine bleach, 621

Chlorine compounds, 619

Chlorine molecule, 120

Chlorophyll, 382

Cider vinegar, 426

Coal(s), analysis of representative, 374 (table); as carbon source, 369–370; as energy source, 375, 411; formation of, 373–375; and peat compared, 374 (table); types of, 374–375

Cobalt, properties of, 570–571

Cockcroft, J. D., and lithium bombardment, 639–640

Coke, 370; petroleum, 378; preparation and properties of, 375–376

Colemanite, 592

Colligative property, definition of, 287

Collision theory, 447–448; *see also* Kinetic theory

Colloid(s), definition of, 270

Colloidal suspensions, 269

Color(s), complementary, 565; of transition metal compounds, 565–566 (table), 567

Combined oxygen, 184

Combining volumes of gases, law of, 223–224

Combining weight, definition of, 89

Combustion, heat of, 436 (table), 437–440

Common ion effect, 473–474

Complex ions, common, 568 (table); formation of, 567–569; stability of, 569 (table)

Complementary colors, 565

Composition reactions, 168

Compounds, *see* Chemical compounds

Concentration, and freezing point of sodium chloride solution, 310 (table); and equilibrium system change, 468–469; of solutions, 283, 284 (table) 285

Condensation process, 245–246

Condensation temperatures, definition of, 206; table, 207

Conductivity, of solutions, 295–297

Conjugate acid(s), 331–334; definition of, 332

Conjugate base, definition of, 331

Conservation of atoms, law of, 162

Conservation of electrons, 498

Conservation of energy, 12–13

Conservation of matter, law of, 12–13

Contact process, 613

Continuous spectrum, 542

Copper, compounds of, 582; electrolytic refining of, 581; properties of, 578–579, 581–582; reaction with nitric acid, 604; recovery of, 579–581; in replacement reaction, 169–170, 173, 174–175; *see also* Copper Family of Elements

Copper Family of Elements, 578–579 (table)

Copper ions, test for, 581–582

Copper ores, processing of, 579–581

Copper(II) sulfate pentahydrate crystals, 566–567

Coquina, 553

Core, of earth, 46–47

Corundum, 590

Cosmic rays, 636

Covalent bonding, in chlorine molecule, 119–120; definition of, 110; in hydrogen molecule, 118–119; in hydrogen peroxide molecule, 121, 123; in molecules containing hydrogen, 123–124; in nitrogen molecule, 120–121; nonpolar, 127; in oxygen molecule, 120; polar, 127; of unlike atoms, 121–122; in water molecule, 122–123

Covalent compounds, ionization of, 302–305

Covalent molecular crystals, 257

Covalent network crystals, 256

Cracking, definition of, 402–403

Critical mass, definition of, 645

Critical pressure, definition of, 250 (table)

Critical temperature, definition of, 250 (table); and molecular attraction, 250–251

Critical volume, definition of, 250

Crust, of earth, 46 (table), 47

Crystal(s), atoms in, 254; binding forces in, 255–257; covalent molecular, 257; covalent network, 256; ionic 255–256, 299; metallic, 256–257; nature of, 254–255; structures, 254–257; *see also* individual crystals

Crystal lattice, definition of, 254

Crystalline solids, 252; *see also* Crystal(s)

Crystallization, water of, 261–262

Crystallography, 254

Crystalloids, definition of, 270

Cube, volume formula for, 17

Cubic unit, body-centered, 533

Curie, Irene, and artificial radioactive atoms, 642

Curie, Marie Sklodowska, and discovery of radium, 5; and radioactive elements, 629

Curie, Pierre, and radioactive elements, 629

Curium, 42

Cyclotron, 640–641

Law of combining volumes of gases, 223–224
Law of conservation of atoms, 162
Law of conservation of matter and energy, 13
Law of definite composition, 48–49, 147
Law of mass action, 457
Law of multiple proportions, 148–149
Law of partial pressures, 217
Lawrence, E. O., 42; and cyclotron, 640–641
Lawrencium, 42
Lead storage battery, 512–514
Lead(II) acetate, ion-charge formula for, 141
Lead(II) oxide, formation of, 171
Lead(II) sulfate, ion-charge formula for, 140
Leavening agents, carbon dioxide production by, 383
Le Chatelier, Henri Louis, and equilibrium, 247–248
Le Chatelier's principle, 247–248, 468, 469
Length, definition of, 17
Lewis, G. N., acid-base system, 325–326
Light energy, in chemical reaction, 52
Lignite, 374–375
Lime, 553, 556
Limestone, 553, 556
Limewater, 557
Linear accelerator, 641
Liquid(s), boiling of, 248–249; description of, 9, 10; equilibrium vapor pressure of, 246; evaporation of, 243, 245–246; gases in, 277–278; kinetic theory description of, 244–245; in liquids, 279; physical equilibrium of, 245–246; properties of, 243–245; solids in, 278–279; temperature ranges of, 245 (table)
Liquid air, 597; oxygen preparation from, 187
Liquid gas(es), formation of, 249–250
Liquid hydrogen, 196
Liquid solution, 271
Liquid-phase temperature ranges of representative substances, 245 (table)
Liter, definition of, 16
Lithium atom, 65–66

M

M shell, 66, 94
Magnesium, occurrence and production of, 549–550; properties of, 524, 547, 548, 551; structure of, 524; uses of, 550, 551; see also Period Three Elements
Magnesium atom, 116; energy level transitions, 102–103
Magnesium bromide, formation of, 114–116
Magnesium compounds, 551 (table)
Magnesium hydroxide, ion-charge formula, 140; preparation and properties of, 530
Magnesium ion, 114
Magnesium oxide, formation of, 169; preparation and properties of, 528
Magnetic iron oxide, 576
Magnetic quantum number, 80
Magnetism, see Ferromagnetism
Malachite, 579
Malleability, definition of, 534, 589

Manganese dioxide, reaction with hydrochloric acid, 500–504
Mantle, of earth, 46–47
Marble, 553
Mass, definition of, 7, 8; measurement of, 8; and weight, 7–8
Mass action, law of, 457
Mass number, see Atomic mass number
Mass spectrograph, 66
Mass–gas volume problems, 232, 237
Mass–mass problems, mole method of solving, 177–179
Matte, 580
Matter, change of phase, 53–54; chemical change in, 50–53; classes of, 39–40; concept of, 7; conservation of, 12–13; conversion to energy, 12–13; definition of, 7; density of, 8–9; heterogeneous and homogeneous, 39–41; mass and weight, 7–8; particles of, 59; phases of, 9–10, 50–54; physical change in, 50; properties of, 10–11; thermal properties of 19–20; see also Atom(s); Element(s); Substances
Measurement, accuracy in, 22; deviation in, 22 (table), 23; of dimensions, 17–18; errors in, 22; of fluids, 16; of heat, 19–20; of kinetic energy, 20; metric system of, 13–16; of pH, 365–366; of physical quantity, 17–18; precision of, 22; of proportions, 34–35; significant figures in, 23–25; of speed, 20; of temperature, 19; uncertainty in, 21–22; of weight, 8
Mechanical energy, 11
Medical treatment, oxygen use in, 190
Melting, 252–253; definition of, 252
Melting points of representative substances, 256 (table)
Mendeleev, Dmitri, and periodic table, 90–91
Mendelevium, 42
Mercury, as metallic element, 44; displacement of in gas collection, 214–216
Mercury(II) oxide, decomposition of, 169; in reversible reaction, 461–462
Metal(s), acid reactions with, 320–321, 335; chlorine reaction with, 621; hydrogen reaction with, 198; hydroxides of, 330–331; ions of, 137–139; noble, 570; oxygen reactions with, 188–189; properties of, 44; in replacement reactions, 173; self-protective, 551; transition, 561–582; water reactions with, 260
Metallic aluminum, recovery of, 495–496
Metallic carbonates, decomposition of, 171–172
Metallic chlorates, decomposition of, 172
Metallic crystals, 256–257
Metallic glasses, 253–254
Metallic hydroxides, decomposition of, 172; formation of, 173; solubility of, 328–329 (table); and negative ions, 486
Metallic oxide, acid reaction with, 335–336; nonmetallic oxide reaction with, 337; water reaction with, 260–261
Metallic sodium, combustion of, 493–494, 495
Metalloid(s), 44; nature of, 585; in periodic table, 98; properties of, 586 (table); see also individual metalloids
Methane, 401; molecular formula for, 157; oxidation of, 406
Methane molecule, 124, 125, 399
Methanol, preparation, properties, and uses of, 420

Methyl group, 400
Metric equivalents, 15 (table)
Metric prefixes, 14 (table)
Metric system, 13–16
Metric–English equivalents, 15 (table), 16
Meyer, Lothar, and periodic table, 91
Mineral acids, 314
Miscible substances, definition of, 272
Mixtures, 40–41, 47–48; compared with compounds, 47–48 (table); definition of, 41; examples of, 49; *see also* individual mixtures
Molal boiling-point constant, 288 (table); definition of, 290
Molal freezing-point constant, 288 (table); definition of, 287
Molality, concentration of solutions in, 284 (table); definition of, 283
Molality of solution, definition of, 342
Molar heat of formation, definition of, 434–435
Molar heat of fusion, definition of, 252
Molar heat of vaporization, 249
Molar solutions, 341–342; titration with, 360–361
Molar volume, definition of, 228; of gases, 228–230
Molar-volume method, 230–232
Molasses, in carbon dioxide production, 379; fermentation of, 379
Mole, 69–70; concept of, 149–153 (table); definition of, 69; and mass relationships, 151 (table); and mass–mass problems, 177–178; relationships between reactants and products, 176–177
Molecular attraction, and critical temperature, 250–251
Molecular formula(s), 143–144, 226–227; definition of, 119, 143; determination of, 157–158
Molecular weight, definition of, 144; of gases, 230–232; of solutes, 290–292
Molecule(s), of active gaseous elements, 225–228; definition of, 118; diatomic, 132; gas, 204–206; kinetic energy of, 206; noble gas, 228; polarity of, 129–130; size, 126; *see also* Covalent bonds; individual molecules
Monatomic ions, 138–139
Monatomic molecules, of noble gases, 228
Monoclinic sulfur, 608–609
Monomers, 404–405; definition of, 406
Monosilane, preparation and properties of, 530
Morley, Edward W., and empirical formula for water, 152–155
Moseley, Henry Gwyn-Jeffreys, and X rays, 91–92
Multiple proportions, law of, 148–149
Mu-sulfur, 609

N _____

Naphthalene, 409
Naphthalene molecule, 407
Natural cement, 553
Natural elements, 41
Natural gas, in carbon dioxide production, 379; description of, 395; processing of, 395
N-butane molecule, 400
Neoprene, 412–413

Neptunium, 42, 641–642
Neutralization reaction, and acids, 319–320; *see also* individual reactions; Titration
Neutron(s), definition of, 63
Neutron bombardment, 641–642
Neutron emissions, in nuclear disintegrations, 640
Newlands, John A. R., and atomic weight, 90
Nickel, properties of, 570–571
Nitrate ion, 131, 132
Nitration, 408
Nitric acid, 314, 315; as oxidizing agent, 604; preparation of, 602–603; properties of, 603–604; reactions with copper and zinc, 604; uses of, 604–605
Nitride ion, 598
Nitro compounds, 604
Nitrocellulose plastics, 605
Nitrogen, occurrence of, 597; oxides of, 598; preparation of, 597; properties of, 598; reaction with hydrogen, 224; uses of, 598–599
Nitrogen Family of Elements, 95; *see also* individual elements
Nitrogen fixation, definition of, 599
Nitrogen molecule, 120–121
Nitrogen-fixing bacteria, 599
Nitrogen–oxygen series of binary compounds, 142 (table)
Nobelium, 42
Noble gas(es), 44, 132; molecules of, 228; in periodic table, 91, 93
Noble metals, 570
Nodules, 562
Nonelectrolytes, 295–296; definition of, 270; *see also* Electrolytes
Nonmetallic oxide, reaction with base, 336; reaction with metallic oxide, 337; reaction with water, 261
Nonmetals, hydrogen reaction with, 197–198; oxygen reaction with, 188; properties of, 44
Nonpolar (pure) covalent bond, definition of, 127
Nonpolar molecule, 129–130
Norbide, 592
Normal solutions, 346–348; titration with, 362–363
Normality of solution, definition of, 346
N-pentane molecule, 400
Nuclear binding energy, definition of, 637
Nuclear chain reaction, 644–646
Nuclear change, definition of, 53
Nuclear chemistry, 3
Nuclear disintegration, definition of, 638; *see also* Nuclear transformation
Nuclear energy, 11
Nuclear fission, as energy source, 411
Nuclear fission reactions, 646–647
Nuclear forces, 63
Nuclear mass defect, definition of, 637
Nuclear power plants, 645–646
Nuclear reactor(s), definition of, 644; Oak Ridge, 644–646
Nuclear transformations, neutron emissions in, 640; *see also* Nuclear disintegration; Half-life
Nucleus, *see* Atomic nucleus

Nuclide(s), definition of, 64; molar quantities of, 70 (table); naturally occurring, 67 (table); radioactive, 630–632 (table), 633–635

O

Observation, in science, 6
Octane, isomers of, 392–393
Octane molecule, 392
Oil(s), and fats, 428
Oil shale, as energy souce, 411
Oil-flotation process, 579–581
Oil-in-vinegar emulsions, 271
Olefin series, *see* Alkene series
Orbital notation, 80
Orbital quantum number, 79
Organic acids, 314
Organic chemistry, 3, 369
Organic compounds, behavior of, 394–395; and inorganic compounds compared, 394–395; structural formulas for, 392–394; *see also* Carbon compounds
Organic structural formula, determination of, 393–394
Ostwald, Wilhelm, and nitric acid production, 603
Ostwald process, 603
Oxidation, of alcohols, 423; definition of, 114; and reduction, 113–114
Oxidation number, 494–497; definition of, 113; rules for assigning, 133, 494 (table)
Oxidation-number method of balancing redox equations, 498–502
Oxidation process, 493–494; definition of, 493
Oxidation state of atom, 497; of Period Three Elements, 527; of transition metals, 563–564 (table), 565
Oxidation-reduction equations, balancing of, 498–504
Oxidation-reduction reaction, 495–505; definition of, 495; *see also* Electrochemical reactions
Oxidation-reduction terminology, 505 (table)
Oxides, decompositions of, 172; definition of, 188; iron, 575–576; of metals, acid reactions with, 321; nitrogen, 598; of nonmetals, hydroxide reactions with, 327–328; of Period Three Elements, 527 (table), 528–529; *see also* Metallic oxide; Nonmetallic oxide
Oxidizing agent(s), 504–505 (table), 506; chemical equivalents of, 506–507; definition of, 114
Oxyacids, 321–324; names of, 322 (table)
Oxygen, density of, 204; discovery of, 184–185; free and combined, 183–184; molar volume of, 229; occurrence of, 183–184; and ozone compared, 191–192 (table); in ozone preparation, 191; preparation of in laboratory, 166, 185–187; properties of, 187 (table), 188–189, 192 (table); reaction with hydrogen, 223–224, 225; reaction with metals and nonmetals, 188–189; test for, 189; uses of, 189–190
Oxygen Family of Elements, 95; *see also* individual elements
Oxygen molecule, 120, 192; electron-dot formula for, 187
Oxygen-carbon dioxide cycle, 382
Ozone, in atmosphere, 418–419; occurrence of, 191, and oxy-

gen compared, 191–192 (table); preparation of, 191; properties of, 192–193 (table); uses of, 193
Ozone generator, 191
Ozone molecule, 192

P

Paraffin series, *see* Alkane series
Paramagnetism, definition of, 569
Parent nuclides, 633
Partial pressures, law of, 217
Particle accelerators, 640–641
Peat, 373–374
Pentanes, 400
Period, definition of, 92; in periodic table, 93–94, 95–98
Period Three Elements, atomic structure and related properties of, 526 (table); appearance of, 523; binary compounds of, 529 (table), 530–531; electron configurations of, 526–527; ionization energies of, 526; oxidation states of, 527; oxides of, 527 (table), 528–529; physical properties of, 524 (table), 525–526; structure of, 524–526; *see also* individual elements
Periodic law, 92
Periodic Table of Atomic Radii, 98
Periodic Table of Elements, 90–98; transition region of, 561; value of, 106
Periodic Table of Electron Affinities, 104
Periodic Table of Electronegativities, 128
Periodic Table of Ionization Energies, 100
Permanganate ion, reduction of, 496
Permutit, 555
Petroleum, 395; alkene production from, 402–403; refining of, 396; substitutes for, 410–411
Petroleum coke, 378
Petroleum refinery, 397
pH, calculation of, 352–355; of common materials, 352 (table); measurement of, 365–366
pH of solution, 350–352; definition of, 351
pH meter, 365
pH scale, 354
Phase(s) of matter, 9–10; change in 53–54, 252–253
Phase symbols, in an equation, 165
Phenyl group, 407
Phlogiston, 183
Phlogiston theory, 4–5
Phosphate ion, 131
Phosphine, preparation and properties of, 530–531
Phosphoric acid, 314; preparation and properties of, 528–529
Phosphorous, structure and properties of, 525; *see also* Period Three Elements
Phosphorous molecule, 525
Photon(s), definition of, 76
Photosynthesis, 52; definition of, 382
Physical change, definition of, 50
Physical chemistry, 3, 442
Physical equilibrium, 462–463; definition of, 245

Physical model, 6
Physical quantity, measurement of, 17–18
Physical properties, definition of, 11
Physics, 442
Pig iron, 572–573
Pipe still, 396, 397
Planck's constant, 76
Plaster of paris, 557–558
Platinum Family of Elements, 570; *see also* individual elements
Plutonium, 42, 642
Polar covalent bond, definition of, 127
Polar molecule, 129–130
Pollutants, in acid rain, 612–613
Polonium, 585, 587, 629
Polyatomic ions, 131–132, 140, 567
Polyethylene, 404
Polymer, 405–406; definition of, 406
Polymeric, definition of, 549
Polymerization, 404
Potassium, flame test for, 541; preparation and properties of, 540–541; reaction of with water, 535
Potassium chlorate, oxygen preparation from, 172, 186–187
Potassium chloride, decomposition of, 169
Potassium compounds, 541–542 (table)
Potassium-argon dating, 636
Potential energy, 11
Precipitate, formation of, 52, 473; *see also* Precipitation
Precipitated chalk, 553
Precipitation, 301–302; calculation of, 487–489; of hard water, 555
Precision, definition of, 22
Pressure, critical, 250; and equilibrium system changes, 469–470; and gas temperature, 204, 206, 208; and solubility, 275–277
Priestley, Joseph, and oxygen preparation, 184–185
Primary standard, 359
Principal quantum number, 79
Principles, scientific, 5–6; definition of, 5
Product(s), of chemical reactions, 161; and reactants, mole relationships, 176–177
Propane, as fuel, 250
Propane molecule, 399
Proportions, measurement of, 34–35
Propyl group, 401
Protium, 64; physical properties of, 199–200 (table)
Protolysis reaction, 331–334
Proton(s), definition of, 63
Proton-transfer reaction, 331–334
Proust, Louis, and definite composition, 48–49
Pure water, 296

Q

Quantum numbers, 78–80; definition of, 78; relationships in atomic structure, 79 (table)
Quicklime, 379

R

Radial automobile tire, 412
Radiant energy, 11
Radiation, electromagnetic, 76; nature of, 632–633
Radioactive atoms, artificial, 642–643
Radioactive dating, 636
Radioactive decay, 631, 633; stable nuclei from, 638–639
Radioactive elements, properties of, 630–631; *see also* individual radioactive elements
Radioactive materials, handling of, 638
Radioactive nuclides, 630–632 (table); related, 633–635
Radioactivity, applications of, 636; definition of, 629; discovery of, 629
Radium, 629–630; properties of, 630–631
Radon-22, 632
Ramsay, Sir William, and noble gases, 91
Rare-earth elements, 95–96
Reactants, definition of, 161; and products, mole relationships, 176–177
Reaction(s), *see* Chemical reactions
Reaction heat, and bond energy, 440–441
Reaction mechanism, 445–447; definition of, 431
Reaction pathway, 445–447
Reagent bottle label, 347
Real gas(es), behavior of, 218–219, 239–240
Redox reaction, *see* Oxidation-reduction reaction
Reducing agents, 504–505 (table), 506; chemical equivalents of, 506–507; definition of, 114; hydrogen as, 199
Reducing atmosphere, 199
Reduction, definition of, 114
Reduction process, 494–495; definition of, 493
Refrigerant; ammonia as, 602; carbon dioxide as, 383
Replacement reaction, 169; kinds of, 174–175
Resonance, 130–131; definition of, 130
Resonance hybrid bond, 407
Respiration, preparation of carbon dioxide by, 380
Reversible chemical reaction, 174, 461–462; *see also* individual reactions
Rhombic sulfur, 608
Rocket propulsion, liquid oxygen in, 190
Rounding off result of a computation, 28 (table)
Rubber, nature of, 412; processing of, 412; synthetic, 412–413
Rutherford, Ernest, and artificial nuclear disintegration, 639; and atomic nucleus, 61–62

S

STP (standard temperature and pressure), correction for, 236–237
Safety matches, 528
Salt, *see* Sodium chloride
Salt(s), chemical equivalents of, 346; definition of, 335; double, 337; formation of, 335–337; hydrolysis of, 478–479; naming of, 337–338 (table); nature of, 334–337; nomenclature, 337 (table); solubility of, 335 (table)
Salt deposit, cross section, 541

Saponification, definition of, 428

Saturated hydrocarbons, 398

Saturated solution, definition of, 275

Scheele, Karl Wilhelm, and oxygen preparation, 184

Scientific method, 5–7, definition of, 5

Scientific notation, 26–27 (table)

Scientists, 3

Sea water, magnesium production from, 550; freezing point of, 286

Self-ionization, of water, 348–350

Self-protective metal, 551

Semiconductor(s), silicon as, 44

Series, definition of, 92

Sewage treatment, 190

Significant figures, 23–25; definition of, 23; operations with, 27–29

Silicon, 585; as metalloid, 593; structure and properties of, 525; *see also* Period Three Elements

Silicon dioxide, preparation and properties of, 528

Silicones, 593

Silver, properties of, 578–579

Silver chloride, formation of, 170–171; solubility product constant, 482–483

Slag, 572–573

Slaked lime, 556–557

Slaking process, 556–557

Soap, manufacture of, 428

Soda ash, 539

Sodium, flame test for, 537; occurrence of, 535; preparation of, 535–536; properties and uses of, 536–537; reaction with alcohol, 423; structure of, 524; *see also* Period Three Elements

Sodium atom, 111–112; energy-level transitions, 102–103

Sodium carbonate, percentage composition, 146–147; production of, 538–539

Sodium chloride, electrolysis of, 620; formation of, 111, 493–494, 495; ion-charge formula for, 139; properties of, 537

Sodium chloride crystal, 299; dissociation of, 299–300

Sodium chloride solutions, electrolysis of, 510–511; relation between concentration and freezing point, 310 (table)

Sodium compounds, 540 (table)

Sodium Family of Elements, 94; chemical activity of, 534–535; as reducing agents, 504–505; structure and properties of, 533–534 (table); *see also* individual elements

Sodium fluoride, 618

Sodium hydrogen carbonate, preparation of, 539

Sodium hydroxide, preparation and properties of, 529–530; production of, 537–538

Sodium ion, 111

Sodium oxide, preparation and properties of, 528

Sodium peroxide, in oxygen preparation, 185

Solid solution, 271

Solids, amorphous, 252, 253–254; crystalline, 252; description of, 9, 10; dissolving of, 279–282; kinetic theory description of, 252; phase change in, 252–253; properties of, 251–252; solubility in liquids, 278–279

Solubility, definition of, 275; of metallic hydroxides, 328 (table), 329; pressure influence on, 275–277; of salts, 335

(table); and temperature, 277–279

Solubility curves, 278–279

Solubility product, 482–484

Solubility product constant, calculation of, 484–486; definition of, 483; at 25°, 485 (table)

Solute(s), definition of, 269; electrolytes as, 297; ionic, freezing-point depressions, 308 (table); masses, 275; molecular weights, 290–292

Solution(s), *see* Chemical solution(s)

Solution equilibrium, 274–275; definition of, 275

Solvation, definition of, 281

Solvay process, 538–539

Solvent(s), boiling points, 307–309; boiling-point elevation of, 288 (table), 289–290; definition of, 269, 370; freezing-point depression of, 285–289, 307–308 (table), 309; molecular models of, 272; selectivity of, 272–273; vapor pressure of, 286

Soot, 377–378

Space orbital, 78

Specific properties, definition of, 10

Spectator ions, 302

Spectroscope, 542

Spectroscopy, 542–544

Spectrum(a), atomic, 76–78; bright-line, 77; *see also* Spectroscopy

Speed, formula for, 20; measurement of, 29–30; of wave motion, 76

Spin quantum number, 80

Spontaneous chemical reaction, 53–54

Stable compound, definition of, 260

Standard meter, definition of, 15

Standard pressure, definition of, 209

Standard temperature, definition of, 209; and pressure (STP), correction for, 236–237

Stas, Jean Servais, and atomic weight, 89; and definite composition, 48–49

Steel, production of, 573–575

Stirring, diffusion of solids by, 279–280

Stock system of naming salts, 337

Stoichiometry, definition of, 176

Structural formula, definition of, 119, 392–393; for organic compounds, 392–394

Styrene, 409

Styrene butadiene rubber (SBR), 413

Subbituminous coal, 375

Sublimation, definition of, 253

Substance(s), definition of, 41

Substitution products, definition of, 401

Sugar, as compound, 41; decomposition of, 41

Sugar solution, 40, 269, 274–275, 278

Sulfate ion, 131

Sulfation, of alcohols, 423

Sulfonation, 408

Sulfur, allotropes of, 608–610; chemical properties of, 610; as nonmetallic element, 44; occurrence of, 607; physical properties of, 525, 608; production of, 608; structure of, 525; uses of, 610; *see also* Period Three Elements

Sulfur dioxide, critical temperature of, 251; formula for, 610;

in, 258; properties of, 10, 257–258, 264 (table); purification of, 190, 193; reaction, with metallic oxides, 260–261, with metals, 260, with nonmetallic oxides, 261; softening of, 554–556; test for, 262; triple point of, 211; volume-mass relations, 16 (table)

Water of crystallization, 261–262

Water dipole, 272

Water displacement, in gas collection, 216–218, 236–237

Water gas, 196, 384; formation of, 440–445

Water molecule, 121, 122–123, 126, 132–133, 272; formation of, 358–359; structure and properties of, 258–260

Water vapor, formation of, 223, 225; molecular formula for, 226–227

Water-purification process, 167

Wave mechanics, concept of atom, 78

Wave motion, speed of, 76

Weak acid, ionization constant, 474–477

Weight, definition of, 8; and mass, 7–8, *see also* Atomic weight

Word equations, 161–162

Work, formula for, 11

Picture Credits

Chapter 21: p. **461**—United Feature Syndicate.

Chapter 22: p. **508**—From the CHEM Study Film: *Electric Interactions*.

Chapter 23: p. **524**—Fred Maroon; p. **525**—© 1980 Alan Benoit; p. **526**—Grumman Corp.; p. **528**—top, Courtesy W. R. Grace & Co.; bottom, Diamond International Corporation; p. **529**—Freeport Minerals.

Chapter 24: p. **535**—T. P. Schmitter; p. **537**—bottom, B. M. Shaub.

Chapter 25: pp. **548-9**—B. M. Shaub; p. **553**—top, Lee Boltin; bottom, G. R. Roberts; p. **554**—The Permutit Co.

Chapter 26: p. **562**—Kennecott Copper Corp.; p. **565**—From the CHEM Study Film: *Vanadium, Transition Element;* p. **574**—American Iron and Steel Institute; p. **575**—Westinghouse; p. **580**—Kennecott Copper Corp.; p. **581**—Courtesy of ASARCO, Incorporated.

Chapter 27: p. **588**—top, David Moore/Black Star; bottom, Anaconda; p. **589**—Kaiser Aluminum and Chemical Corp.; p. **590**—bottom, Union Carbide; p. **591**—center, John Cubitto; bottom, Space Sciences Laboratories, General Electric Co.; p. **592**—top and p. **594**—top, B. M. Shaub; bottom, Clevite Corporation.

Chapter 28: p. **599**—Professor Winston J. Brill; p. **604**—top, From the CHEM Study Film: *Nitric Acid;* bottom, Fritz Henle/Photo Researchers.

Chapter 29: p. **607**—NASA; p. **610**—© Arthur d'Arazien; p. **612**—Central Illinois Public Service Company.

Chapter 30: p. **619**—Argonne National Laboratory; p. **622**—Lizabeth Corlett/DPI; p. **623**—Courtesy Mike Kupperman, Surface Cleaning Corp.; p. **624**—bottom, From the CHEM Study Film: *Bromine—Element from the Sea.*

Photo Essay: p. **628**—All HRW Photos by E. R. Degginger.

Chapter 31: p. **630**—top right, Mark Schupack; top left, Matt Grimaldi; bottom, Sargent Welch Scientific Company; p. **632**—W. K. Kellogg Radiation Laboratory, California Institute of Technology; p. **636**—Dr. Stephen Moorbath; p. **638**—ERDA, Oakridge, Tennessee; p. **641**—top, Fermi National Accelerator Laboratory; bottom, Lawrence Berkeley Laboratory, University of California, Berkeley; p. **644**—Dr. J. D. Macdougall, Scripps Institution of Oceanography, University of California, San Diego; p. **646**—Princeton Plasma Physics Laboratory.